Lester

~~30301~~

ORGANIC SYNTHESIS

NOT RETURNABLE – SOLD AS IS

Volume 1

OPEN-CHAIN SATURATED COMPOUNDS

by

VARTKES MIGRDICHIAN

Senior Research Chemist, American Cyanamid Company

REINHOLD PUBLISHING CORPORATION
NEW YORK
CHAPMAN & HALL, LTD., LONDON

Library of Congress Catalog Card Number 57-6095

REINHOLD PUBLISHING CORPORATION

Publishers of Chemical Engineering Catalog, Chemical Materials Catalog, "Automatic Control," "Materials & Methods"; Advertising Management of the American Chemical Society.

Printed in U.S.A.

PREFACE

The task of presenting the art of chemistry, its methods, processes and techniques, has been performed with eminent distinction by capable hands in excellent treatises almost from the beginning of the science, and initiates of this branch of knowledge owe much to the self-sacrificing labors of these men. Emphasis has, however, almost always been placed in these works on techniques and on processes of fundamental nature, though detailed treatments of outstanding value of certain specialized subjects have been offered in some of them. Texts dealing with special aspects of chemical synthesis are not lacking, and reviews of progress appear regularly both in the strictly synthetic field and in fields in which synthesis plays a prominent role. The searching chemist can supplement the knowledge obtained from these texts with that to be found in fine reviews available in such periodicals as the *Chemical Reviews, Quarterly Reviews,* etc. With such rich sources on hand the chemist, it may be assumed, should have no difficulty in getting at facts, until one fully grasps the magnitude of the task involved. One can indeed become well acquainted with any given branch of chemistry with the aid of the existing literature, but often only at the cost of an immense and prolonged effort, and only a few achieve mastery even in a limited field.

In view of this situation many a chemist has, no doubt, keenly felt the lack of a comprehensive work dealing adequately with the entire subject of organic synthesis. It was with the hope of satisfying this need that I undertook the preparation of the present work—with no illusions about the magnitude and difficulties of the task, which would have been beyond the capabilities of one individual were it not for the host of general treatises, special monographs and general reviews already alluded to. I wish to acknowledge, with due gratitude to the authors of these works, my indebtedness to these sources. While these sources have been the mainstays in the task, in many cases original articles have been consulted for supplementary information.

Meeting the requirements of the serious organic chemical research worker has been the primary objective, but the problems faced by those who at one time or another may have occasion to undertake organic synthetic work of some magnitude have not been lost sight of, and it is hoped that the book will adequately meet the needs of all engaged in organic synthesis. Completeness has been set as a goal, and I have tried to satisfy the justified expectation that all newer developments receive due attention.

Thanks are due to Mrs. Alice Booth who graciously typed nearly the entire manuscript, and to Dr. R.B. Booth, and many others, who kindly proofread the manuscript. Thanks are due also to the American Cyanamid Company authorities for their generous attitude toward the publication of this work. I wish, finally, to express my appreciation of the efforts of the Reinhold Publishing Corporation for assuring the generally excellent workmanship displayed in publishing the book.

Greenwich, Connecticut V. Migrdichian
January, 1957

ORGANIZATION AND SCOPE OF THE BOOK

The arrangement of the subject matter of this work will be evident on inspection of the table of contents. The system adopted approximates that usually followed in organic chemistry texts and offers the advantages of compactness of presentation, adequate flexibility and logical sequence. General principles and basic facts have received special attention because of their indisputable importance, and exceptions to these rules have been pointed out. General methods of preparation have been fully described, and where a general procedure was lacking, descriptions of representative special methods have been given. Specific examples of synthesis have been cited if the importance of the particular compound warranted, or when the method presented a deviation from the *general* procedure.

Important reactions are discussed in detail and every effort has been made to make their treatment complete in all essentials. The effect of structural variations on the course of a reaction has been pointed out, and any exceptional behavior has been indicated. Known side reactions have been discussed because of their bearing on the course of the principal reaction. Basic processes of halogenation, nitration, etc., have received extensive and complete treatment.

The location of certain of the subjects calls for comment. When a reaction gives rise to compounds of one class only, there will be general agreement that it should be treated in connection with that class of compounds. Such a clear-cut basis of choice does not exist with, for example, the Friedel-Crafts reaction, or the Grignard reaction. In such cases the author has chosen to treat the reaction in connection with the class of compounds which is the most essential component of the reaction.

The relative space allotted to a given subject has been determined by the volume of essential information available. It is fair to assume that the extent of such information in the chemical literature is an indication both of the importance of the subject and of the apparent interest it has attracted. Anticipation of a subject not yet discussed, which is ever a matter of annoyance to the reader, could not always be avoided despite the good intentions of the author; for this he will beg the reader's forbearance.

References to original articles have been selected with the object of enabling the reader to secure the details of matters discussed and to make possible the acquisition of a good grounding in the subject under consideration. References to related subjects have been included with the latter objective in view. Outstanding reviews of the subject matter discussed have been cited.

Many a reaction presents considerable industrial interest. Discussions relating to industrial applications, however, lie beyond the scope of the present treatise, and only the briefest mention could be made of some of the more important industrial developments having their basis in certain reactions. Theoretical developments of the last few decades have had a great impact in the field of chemical synthesis, and their importance cannot be overestimated. However, theoretical discussions are beyond the scope of this work. Reaction mechanisms receive mention only when well-nigh complete agreement exists on their essential correctness.

The index assumes particular importance in a book of this character, in which of necessity a given subject receives repeated mention in various connections. A complete index is invaluable as a means for locating descriptions of general procedures, methods of preparation of specific compounds, or references to the preparation of compounds. Efforts have not, therefore, been spared to make the index complete in every respect.

The scope of the present two volumes encompasses all reactions excepting the majority of those leading to the formation of heterocyclic bodies. The compilation of a third volume to deal with the latter is contemplated.

The few abbreviations employed in the text are those in general usage and commonly understood. *Temperatures given throughout the book are in degrees centigrade.*

ABBREVIATIONS OF NAMES OF PERIODICALS

Abhandl. braunschweig Wiss. Ges.	Abhandlungen der braunschweigischen Wissenschaftlichen Gesellschaft
Acta Chem. Scand.	Acta Chemica Scandinavica
Acta Chim. Acad. Sci. Hung.	Acta Chimica Academiae Scientiarum Hungaricae
Am. Chem. J.	American Chemical Journal
Am. J. Pharm.	American Journal of Pharmacy and the Sciences Supporting Public Health
Am. J. Sci.	American Journal of Science
Anales asoc. quím. argentina	Anales de la asociación química argentina
Anales fís. y quím. (Madrid)	Anales de física y química (Madrid); formerly Anales de la sociedad española de física y química
Anales real soc. españ. fís. y quim (Madrid)	Anales de la real sociedad española de física y quimica (Madrid)
Angew. Chem.	Angewandte Chemie
Ann.	Liebigs Annalen der Chemie
Ann. Acad. Sci. Fennicae	Annales Academiae Scientiarum Fennicae
(No abbreviation)	Annales de l'institut Agronomique de Moscou
Ann. chim.	Annales de chimie (Paris)
Ann. chim. applicata	Annali di chimica applicata
Ann. chim. phys.	Annales de chimie et de physique
Ann. phys.	Annales de physique
Ann. Reports on Progress Chem. (Chem. Soc. London)	Annual Reports on the Progress of Chemistry (Chemical Society of London)
Ann. Rev. Biochem.	Annual Review of Biochemistry
Ann. sci. univ. Jassy	Annales scientifiques de l'université de Jassy
Ann. univ. Lyon	Annales de l'université de Lyon

Anz. Akad. Wiss. Wien	Anzeiger der Akademie der Wissenschaften in Wien
Arch. Pharm.	Archiv der Pharmazie und Berichte der deutschen pharmazeutischen Gesellschaft
Arch. sci. phys. et nat.	Archives des sciences physiques et naturelles (Archives des sciences (Geneva))
Arhiv. Hem. i Farm.	Arhiv za Hemiju i Farmaciju (Arhiv za Hemiju i Technologiju)
Arkiv Kemi Mineral. Geol.	Arkiv för Kemi, Mineralogi och Geologi; since 1949 Arkiv för Kemi
Atti accad. Lincei	Atti della reale accademia dei Lincei
Atti accad. nazl. Lincei, Classe sci. fis. mat. e nat.	Atti della accademia nazionale dei Lincei Rendiconti, Classe di scienze fisiche matematiche e naturali
Atti accad. sci. Torino	Atti della accademia delle scienze di Torino
Atti accad. sci. Torino, Classe sci. fis. mat. e nat.	Atti della reale accademia delle scienze di Torino, Classe di scienze fisiche matematiche e naturali
Australian J. Sci.	Australian Journal of Science, The
Ber.	Berichte der deutschen chemischen Gesellschaft; changed with Vol. 80, No. 1 (Jan., 1947) to Chemische Berichte
Ber. deut. pharm. Ges.	Berichte der deutschen pharmazeutischen Gesellschaft
Ber. Schimmel & Co. Akt.-Ges.	Bericht der Schimmel & Co. Aktien-Gesellschaft über ätherische Oele, Riechstoffe, usw.
Biochem. J.	Biochemical Journal, The (London)
Biochem. Z.	Biochemische Zeitschrift
Biochim. et Biophys. Acta	Biochimica et Biophysica Acta (Amsterdam)
Brennstoff-Chem.	Brennstoff-Chemie
Brit. Ass. Advance Sci. Rep.	British Association for the Advancement of Science, Report
Brit. Med. J.	The British Medical Journal
Bull. Acad. roy. Belg.	Bulletin de la classe des sciences, Académie royale de Belgique
Bull. acad. sci. Russ.	Bulletin de l'académie des sciences de Russie
Bull. Chem. Soc. Japan	Bulletin of the Chemical Society of Japan

Bul. Chim. Soc. Chim. România	Buletinul de Chimie Pură şi Aplicată Societatea de Chimie din România
Bull. acad. sci. URSS	Bulletin de l'académie des sciences de l'URSS
Bull. classe sci. Acad. Roy. Belg.	Bulletin de la classe des sciences, Académie royale de Belgique
(no abbreviation)	Bulletin of the Chemical Society
Bull. intern. acad. polon.	Bulletin international de l'académie polonaise des sciences et des lettres
Bull. soc. chim.	Bulletin de la société chimique de France
Bull. soc. chim. Belg.	Bulletin de la société chimique de Belgique
Bull. soc. chim. biol.	Bulletin de la société de chimie biologique
Bull. soc. ind. Mulhouse	Bulletin de la société industrielle de Mulhouse
Bull. soc. nat. Moscou	Bulletin de la société des naturalistes de Moscou
Bur. Standards J. Research	Bureau of Standards Journal of Research; changed with Vol. 13, No. 1 (July, 1934) to Journal of Research of the National Bureau of Standards
Can. Chem. J.	Canadian Chemical Journal; changed with vol. 5, Jan. 1921, to Canadian Chemistry and Metallurgy
Can. J. Research	Canadian Journal of Research
Chem. Eng. News	Chemical and Engineering News
Chem. Eng. Progr.	Chemical Engineering Progress
(no abbreviation)	Chemische Zeitschrift
Chem. Ind. (Düsseldorf)	Chemische Industrie (Düsseldorf)
(no abbreviation)	Chemistry & Industry; formerly a part of Journal of the Society of Chemical Industry; issued as a separate journal beginning Jan., 1937
Chem. Listy	Chemické Listy (Ústřední) výzkumu a technickéko rozvoje (Ústřední ústav chemický)
Chem. Met. Eng.	Chemical and Metallurgical Engineering
Chem. News	Chemical News and Journal of Industrial Science, The
Chem. Obzor	Chemický Obzor

Chem. Products	Chemical Products and Chemical News
Chem. Revs.	Chemical Reviews
Chem. Trade J.	Chemical Trade Journal and Chemical Engineer
Chem. Weekblad	Chemisch Weekblad
Chem. Zentr.	Chemisches Zentralblatt
Chem. Ztg.	Chemiker-Zeitung mit dem Sonderteil, Die Chemische Praxis, und der Beilage, Chemische-technische Übersicht
(no abbreviation)	Chimie & Industrie (Paris)
Collection Czech Chem. Communs.	Collection of Czech Chemical Communications; suspended with Vol. 11, No. 12 (1939), resumed publication in 1947 with title Collection Czechoslov. Chem. Commun. (Collection of Czechoslovak Chemical Communications)
Color Trade J.	Color Trade Journal
Compt. rend.	Comptes rendus Hebdomadaires des séances de l'académie des sciences
Compt. rend. acad. sci. URSS	Comptes rendus de l'académie des sciences de l'U.R.S.S.
Compt. rend. trav. lab. Carlsberg, Sér. chim.	Comptes rendus des travaux du laboratoire Carlsberg, Série chimique
Contrib. Inst. Chem. Nat. Acad. Peiping	Contributions from the Institute of Chemistry, National Academy of Peiping
Dansk Tids. Farm.	Dansk Tidsskrift for Farmaci
Deut. med. Wochschr.	Deutsche medizinische Wochenschrift
(no abbreviation)	Die Chemie
(no abbreviation)	Experientia
(no abbreviation)	Fette u. Seifen
Fortsch. chem. Forsch.	Fortschritte der chemischen Forschung
Fortsch. Chem. org. Naturstoffe	Fortschritte der Chemie organischer Naturstoffe
Fortsch. Chem. Phys. u. phys. Chem.	Fortschritte der Chemie, Physik und physikalischen Chemie
Gazz. chim. ital.	Gazzetta chimica italiana
Ges. Abhandl. Kenntnis Kohle	Gesammelte Abhandlungen zur Kenntnis der Kohle
Giorn. chim. ind. appl.	Giornale di chimica industriale ed applicata
Helv. Chim. Acta	Helvetica Chimica Acta

Ind. Chemist	Industrial Chemist and Chemical Manufacturer, The
Ind. chim. belge	Industrie chimique belge
Ind. Eng. Chem.	Industrial and Engineering Chemistry
Ind. Eng. Chem. Anal. Ed.	Industrial and Engineering Chemistry, Analytical Edition
Iowa State Coll. J. Sci.	Iowa State College Journal of Science
Jahresb.	Jahresbericht über die Fortschritte der Chemie (Liebig-Kopps)
Jahresber. Pharm.	Jahresbericht der Pharmazie
J. Am. Chem. Soc.	Journal of the American Chemical Society
J. Am. Pharm. Assoc.	Journal of the American Pharmaceutical Association
J. Applied Chem. U.S.S.R.	Journal of Applied Chemistry (U.S.S.R.)
J. Biol. Chem.	The Journal of Biological Chemistry
J. Chem. Ind. (U.S.S.R.)	Journal of Chemical Industry (U.S.S.R.); same as Zhur. Khim. Prom. (Zhurnal Khimicheskoi Promyshlennosti)
J. Chem. Soc.	Journal of the Chemical Society (London)
J. Chem. Soc. Japan	Journal of the Chemical Society of Japan
J. Chinese Chem. Soc.	Journal of the Chinese Chemical Society
J. Gasbeleucht.	Journal für Gasbeleuchtung und verwandte Beleuchtungsarten sowie für Wasserversorgung; discontinued under this name in 1920; followed by Das Gas- und Wasserfach
J. Gen. Chem. U.S.S.R.	Journal of General Chemistry (U.S.S.R.); now Zhur. Obshcheĭ Khim. (Zhurnal Obshcheĭ Khimii)
J. Indian Chem. Soc.	Journal of Indian Chemical Society
J. Indian Inst. Sci.	Journal of Indian Institute of Science, A and B
J. Inst. Petroleum	Journal of the Institute of Petroleum
J. Org. Chem.	Journal of Organic Chemistry, The
J. pharm. chim.	Journal de pharmacie et de chimie
J. Pharm. Soc. Japan	Journal of the Pharmaceutical Society of Japan
J. Phys. Chem.	Journal of Physical Chemistry, The
J. Physiol. Chem.	Journal of Physiological Chemistry

J. prakt. Chem.	Journal für praktische Chemie
J. Proc. Roy. Soc. N.S. Wales	Journal and Proceedings of the Royal Society of New South Wales
J. Russ. Phys.-Chem. Soc.	Journal of the Russian Physical-Chemical Society
J. Soc. Chem. Ind. London	Journal of the Society of Chemical Industry (London)
J. Soc. Dyers Colourists	Journal of the Society of Dyers and Colourists, The
J. Soc. Org. Synth. Chem. Japan	Journal of the Society of Organic Synthetic Chemistry, Japan
J. Tenn. Acad. Sci.	Journal of the Tennessee Academy of Science
J. Tex. Inst.	Journal of the Textile Institute, The
J. Univ. Bombay	Journal of the University of Bombay
Khim. Farm. Prom.	Khimiko-Farmatsevticheskaya Promyshlennost
Kolloidchem. Beih.	Kolloidchemische Beihefte
Kolloid-Z.	Kolloid-Zeitschrift
Konink. Akad. Wetenschap Amsterdam	Koninklijke Akademie van Wetenschappen te Amsterdam
Mem. Coll. Sci. Univ. Kyoto	Memoirs of the College of Science, University of Kyoto
Mem. Proc. Manchester Lit. Phil. Soc.	Memoirs and Proceedings of the Manchester Literary and Philosophical Society (Manchester Memoirs)
Mem. reale accad. nazl. Lincei, Classe sci. fis. mat. e nat.	Memorie della reale accademia nazionale dei Lincei, Classe di scienze, fisiche, matematiche e naturali
Monatsh.	Monatschefte für Chemie und verwandte Teile anderer Wissenschaffen
Nachr. Ges. Wiss. Göttingen	Nachrichten der Gesellschaft der Wissenschaften zu Göttingen (1923)
Nachr. kgl. Ges. Wiss. Göttingen	Nachrichten von der königlichen Gesellschaft der Wissenschaften zu Göttingen
Naturaliste can.	Naturaliste canadien, Le
(no abbreviation)	Nature
Naturwiss.	Naturwissenschaften
Norske Forh.	Det Kongelige Norske Videnskabers Selskabs, Forhandlinger
Notiz. chim. ind.	Notiziario chimico-industriale; name changed with Vol. 4, No. 1 (Jan., 1929) to L'Industria chimica

(no abbreviation)	Oil & Soap; name changed with Vol. 24, No. 1 (Jan., 1947) to Journal of the American Oil Chemists' Society
Oil Gas J.	Oil and Gas Journal, The
Perfumery Essent. Oil Record	Perfumery and Essential Oil Record, The
Pharm. Ztg.	Pharmazeutische Zeitung
(no abbreviation)	Pharmazie, Die
Phil. Mag.	Philosophical Magazine, The
Praktika Akad. Athenon	Praktika tes Akademias Athenon
Proc. Acad. Sci. Amsterdam	Proceedings of the Royal Academy of Sciences of Amsterdam
Proc. Am. Petroleum Inst.	Proceedings of the Annual Meeting American Petroleum Institute
Proc. Imp. Acad. (Tokyo)	Proceedings of the Imperial Academy (Tokyo)
Proc. Indian Acad. Sci.	Proceedings of the Indian Academy of Science
Proc. Iowa Acad. Sci.	Proceedings of the Iowa Academy of Science
Proc. Japan. Acad.	Proceedings of the Japan Academy; formerly Proceedings of the Imperial Academy
Proc. Nat. Acad. Sci. U.S.	Proceedings of the National Academy of Sciences of the United States of America
Proc. Physiol. Soc. Phila.	Proceedings of the Physiological Society of Philadelphia; published in American Journal of the Medical Sciences.
Proc. Roy. Irish Acad.	Proceedings of the Royal Irish Academy
Proc. Roy. Soc. (London)	Proceedings of the Royal Society (London)
Proc. Soc. Exp. Biol. Med.	Proceedings of the Society for Experimental Biology and Medicine
Quart. J. Indian. Chem. Soc.	Quarterly Journal of the Indian Chemical Society
Quart. Revs. (London)	Quarterly Reviews of the Chemical Society, London
Rec. trav. chim.	Recueil des travaux chimiques des Pays-Bas
Refiner Natural Gasoline M.	Refiner and Natural Gasoline Manufacturer

Rend. accad. Lincei	Rendiconti della reale accademia nazionale dei Lincei
Rend. accad. sci. fis. mat. e nat. reale Napoli	Rendiconti dell'accademia di scienze fisiche, matematiche e naturali della società reale di Napoli
Rev. gén. mat. color.	Revue générale des matières colorantes
Ricerca sci.	Ricerca scientifica ed il progresso tecnico nell'economia nazionale, La
Riechstoff Ind. u. Kosmetik	Riechstoff Industrie und Kosmetik
Roczniki Chem.	Roczniki Chemii
(no abbreviation)	Science
Science Reports, Tôhoku Imp. Univ.	Science Reports of the Tôhoku Imperial University
Science Rep. Tokyo Bunrika Daigaku	Science Reports of the Tokyo Bunrika Daigaku (Tokyo University of Literature and Science)
Sci. Papers Inst. Phys. Chem. Res. (Tokyo)	Scientific Papers of the Institute of Physical and Chemical Research (Tokyo)
Sci. Records Leningrad. Univ.	Scientific Records of the Leningrad University
Sitzber. kgl. preuss. Akad. Wiss.	Sitzungsberichte der königlichen preussischen Akademie der Wissenschaften
Svensk Kem. Tid.	Svensk Kemisk Tidskrift
Tech. Rep. Tôhoku Imp. Univ.	The Technology Reports of the Tôhoku University
Trans. Am. Electrochem. Soc.	Transactions of the American Electrochemical Society
Trans. Faraday Soc.	Transactions of the Faraday Society
Trans. Roy. Soc. Can.	Transactions of the Royal Society of Canada
Trans. State Institute (U.S.S.R.)	Transactions of the State Institute of Applied Chemistry (U.S.S.R.)
Umschau	Die Umschau
Univ. Kansas Sci. Bull.	University of Kansas Science Bulletin
Uspekhi Khim.	Uspekhi Khimii
(no abbreviation)	Vitamins and Hormones
Z. anal. Chem.	Zeitschrift für analytische Chemie
Z. angew. Chem.	Zeitschrift für angewandte Chemie
Z. anorg. allgem. Chem.	Zeitschrift für anorganische und allgemeine Chemie

(no abbreviation)	Zeitschrift für Chemie
Z. Elektrochem.	Zeitschrift für Elektrochemie und angewandte physikalische Chemie
Z. Farben-Ind.	Zeitshrift für Farben-Industrie
Z. ges. Schiess- u. Sprengstoffw.	Zeitschrift für das gesamte Schiess- und Sprengstoffwesen mit der Sonderabteilung Gasschutz
Zhur. Obshcheĭ Khim.	Zhurnal Obshcheĭ Khimii (Journal of General Chemistry)
Z. Krist.	Zeitschrift für Kristallographie
Z. Naturforsch.	Zeitschrift für Naturforschung
Z. physik. Chem.	Zeitschrift für physikalische Chemie
Z. physiol. Chem.	Zeitschrift für physiologische Chemie (Hoppe-Seyler's)
Z. Untersuch. Lebensm.	Zeitschrift für Untersuchung der Lebensmittel
Z. Ver. deut. Zücker-Ind.	Zeitschrift des Vereines der deutschen Zücker-Industrie
Z. wiss. Phot.	Zeitschrift für wissenschaftliche Photographie, Photophysik und Photochemie

CONTENTS

Part I
OPEN-CHAIN COMPOUNDS

Section 1
SATURATED COMPOUNDS

Chapter 1
HYDROCARBONS, ALCOHOLS, INORGANIC ESTERS AND CARBOHYDRATES

Chapter 3
ALIPHATIC CARBONYL COMPOUNDS: FORMATION

Chapter 4
REACTIONS INVOLVING CARBONYL COMPOUNDS: Part 1

Chapter 11
ALIPHATIC HALOGEN COMPOUNDS

Chapter 12
GRIGNARD REACTION

Chapter 14
ALIPHATIC NITRO AND NITROSO COMPOUNDS, SULFONIC AND SULFINIC ACIDS, AND RELATED COMPOUNDS

Chapter 15
ORGANO METALLIC COMPOUNDS

ERRATA

Page 11, line 21: *for* alcoxide *read* alkoxide
Page 22, line 19: *for* cohol *read* composition
Page 26, side heading and lines 17 and 19: *for* selenoles *read* selenols
Page 53, line 24: *for* quire *read* quite
Page 59, line 22: *for* galatonic *read* galactonic
Page 79, line 7: *for* 1-clycerol *read* 1-glycerol
Page 85, line 10: *for* bulyrates *read* butyrates
Page 87, line 18: *for* velicity *read* velocity
Page 108, line 7: *for* lenic *read* linic
Page 109, line 23: *for* dimerized *read* dimerizes
Page 120, line 23: *for* caid *read* acid
Page 128, line 1: *for* acid *read* acids
Page 201, line 8: *for* monixide *read* monoxide; 4th equation: *for* $2CH = C(OC_2H_5)_2$ *read* $2CH_2 = C(OC_2H_5)_2$
Page 202, line 2: *for* minearl *read* mineral; line 23: *for* accompanies with *read* accompanied by
Page 212, line 21: *for* acetyl- *read* acetylenic
Page 220, line 25: *for* *p*-nitrostlibene *read* *p*-nitrostilbene
Page 225, line 23: *for* sulvent *read* solvent
Page 236, line 18: *for* pisition *read* position
Page 248, line 2: *for* Monochloracetone *read* Monochloroacetone
Page 269, line 15: *for* caralytically *read* catalytically
Page 291, line 19: *for* phosphomolyodic *read* phosphomolybdic
Page 293, line 12: *for* substitutes *read* substituents
Page 300, line 23: *for* Tye *read* The; line 31: *for* α-Bromoacetic *read* α-Bromoacetoacetic
Page 301, line 16: *for* Hall-Volhard *read* Hell-Volhard
Page 317, line 3 under "Acid": *for* Chloracetic *read* Chloroacetic
Page 360, line 36: *for* Atropic acid *read* Atropic acid chloride
Page 368, line 7: *for* amide *read* imide; line 17: *for* acids *read* acid esters
Page 392, line 19: *for* amides *read* imides
Page 394, line 3: *for* hydrazines *read* hydrazides
Page 420, line 10: *for* cyanhydrin *read* cyanohydrin
Page 431, line 12: *for* end product of diaminotriazine, *read* end product, diaminotriazine,
Page 438, line 1: *for* action *read* reaction
Page 443, line 4: *for* ehereal *read* ethereal
Page 445, line 20: *for* ester *read* esters
Page 454, line 6: *for* hydroxyurea *read* hydroxyisourea
Page 474, line 17: *for* Beckann *read* Beckmann
Page 482, line 4: *for* $(C_3H_7)_2NH.NNO_2$ *read* $(C_3H_7)_2NH.HNO_2$
Page 483, last line: *for* mjxture *read* mixture
Page 502, line 16: *for* acid *read* acids
Page 515, line 25: *for* prolylene *read* propylene
Page 519, line 18: *for* of *read* with

Page 521, line 26: *for* Mercurous *read* Mercuric
Page 522, line 23: *for* compound *read* compounds
Page 523, line 24: *for* Tetrafluoreethylene *read* Tetrafluoroethylene;
line 26: *for* tetrafluroethylene *read* tetrafluoroethylene
Page 526, line 14: *for* methy *read* methyl; line 15: *for n*-octy *read n*-octyl;
line 15: delete "de-" at end of line
Page 527, second formula: *for* CH_2 = CHCH Br *read* CH_2 = $CHCH_2Br$
Page 530, line 10: *for* is *read* are
Page 531, 4th line from bottom: Insert "atom" at end of line
Page 571, line 7: *for* Benzalphthalenes *read* Benzalphthalanes
Page 580, line 7: *for* acids *read* acid
Page 606, line 6: *for* gives *read* give
Page 628, 6th line from bottom: *for* alkylnaphthalene *read* alkylnaphthalenes
Page 632, line 17: *for* 3,6,7-tetramethyanthracene *read* 3,6,7-tetramethylanthracene
Page 633, line 24: *for* Trimethylphenyl *read* Trichloromethylphenyl
Page 652, line 19: *for* aminophenyl-4′-dimethylamino-1-naphthoyl *read* aminophenyl-4′-dimethylamino-1-naphtho
Page 653, line 6: *for* depends *read* depend
Page 690, line 26: *for* carbonyl *read* carboxyl
Page 691, line 25: *for* nitrate *read* nitrite
Page 706, line 20: *for* spretrographic *read* spectrographic
Page 707, line 16: *for* sulfuric *read* sulfonic; line 17: *for* acid *read* acids
Page 711, line 4: *for* monomitrobenzylsulfonic *read* mononitrobenzylsulfonic
Page 712, line 17: *for* molachite *read* malachite
Page 789, line 5: *for* tetrahalides *read* trihalides
Page 795, line 28: *for* Quarternary *read* Quaternary
Page 797, line 32: *for* compound *read* compounds
Page 803, 2nd line from bottom: *for* ari *read* air
Page 822, line 17: delete "in" at end of line

PART I

OPEN-CHAIN COMPOUNDS

SECTION 1. SATURATED COMPOUNDS

CHAPTER 1

HYDROCARBONS, ALCOHOLS, INORGANIC ESTERS AND CARBOHYDRATES

HYDROCARBONS

Organic compounds may be considered as derivatives of hydrocarbons, and may, in general, be converted to these hydrocarbons. Alkyl iodides, RI, may be converted to the hydrocarbons, RH, by reduction with the zinc-copper couple.[1] Reduction may also be accomplished with zinc dust and acetic acid with fair yields. The lower alkyl iodides may be reduced simply by heating with zinc dust. Magnesium amalgam and aluminum-mercury couple may also be used for the purpose.[2] The use of the aluminum-mercury couple is of wide applicability.

Hydrocarbons may be prepared from alcohols by converting these to iodides and subsequently reducing the latter, or by dehydrating the alcohol and hydrogenating the resulting olefin. This method may be used in conjunction with the reaction of organomagnesium halides with carbonyl compounds, leading to the formation of carbinols.[70] Many branched chain hydrocarbons have been prepared by a combination of these methods.

Another method of conversion of alcohols to hydrocarbons is to transform the alcohol directly to an olefin by dehydration, and subsequently to reduce the olefin. This method also has been used in conjunction with the reaction of organo magnesium halides with carbonyl compounds or with esters.[71]

Aldehydes and ketones[72] may be reduced to hydrocarbons by the zinc-mercury couple and hydrochloric acid *(Clemmensen reduction)*. A further method of reduction of the carbonyl group is offered by the *Wolff-Kishner reaction*, which consists in heating the hydrazone or semicarbazone of the carbonyl compound at 180 to 200° with sodium ethoxide and alcohol. Reduction of ketones may also be accomplished by converting the ketone to the corresponding dichloride with phosphorus pentachloride and reducing this.[3]

Acids may be converted to the corresponding hydrocarbons by heating at 200-250° with red phosphorus and concentrated hydriodic acid. The reaction proceeds particularly well with acids of higher molecular weight.

Würtz's reaction offers a method for bringing about the union of two hydrocarbon radicals. The same purpose can be achieved through the interaction of a *Grignard reagent* with an organic halide.[66] The reaction proceeds particularly well with radicals containing six or more carbon atoms. The reaction of *zinc alkyls* with alkyl chlorides or ketone chlorides, $RCCl_2R$, also gives hydrocarbons.

Kolbe's electrosynthesis, which is based on the electrolysis of solutions of alkali metal salts of aliphatic acids, offers another method for the synthesis of hydrocarbons.[3] A typical example is the formation of ethane through the electrolysis of a concentrated aqueous solution of sodium acetate:

$$2CH_3COONa \rightarrow 2Na^+ + 2CH_3COO^-$$
$$2CH_3COO^- \rightarrow C_2H_6 + 2CO_2$$

Small quantities of other products, such as hydrogen, ethylene and methanol are also formed. Homologs of acetic acid yield an olefin, an ester and an alcohol, in addition to the expected paraffin. The formation of these various products may be explained by assuming the combination of discharged anions, or by postulating a process of oxidation, as follows:[4]

$$2RCO_2^- \rightarrow RCOOR + CO_2$$
$$RCO_2^- - + OH^- \rightarrow ROH + CO_2$$
$$2RCOOH + O \rightarrow RCOOR + CO_2 + H_2O$$
$$RCOOH + O \rightarrow ROH + CO_2$$

Potassium valerate yields *n*-octane, *n*-butylvalerate, butylene and hydrogen. Potassium caproate gives principally *n*-decane with small quantities of amyl alcohol, amyl caproate and amylene. Trichloroacetic acid gives trichloromethyl trichloroacetate as the principal product.[5] Dibasic acids yield principally unsaturated hydrocarbons, sodium succinate giving ethylene, and sodium maleate, acetylene.

Aliphatic hydrocarbons are noted for their comparative stability. Lee observed that in a series of straight chain carbon compounds the fifth, tenth and fifteenth members exhibit maxima or minima in many physical and chemical properties. The rule holds presumably for hydrocarbons as well as for compounds with various functional groups.[7]

Saturated open chain hydrocarbons are inert toward cold concentrated or fuming sulfuric acid. Substitution products result from the prolonged action of hot concentrated sulfuric acid. Hydrocarbons with branched chains are more susceptible to attack. Normal hydrocarbons are less readily attacked by chlorosulfonic acid[434] or nitric acid,[435] than are branched chain hydrocarbons. Tertiary paraffins are oxidized by fuming nitric acid to fatty acids, and carbon dioxide. Nitro compounds are also formed during the reaction. Normal paraffins are resistant to the action of cold neutral, alkaline, or acid permanganate and cold chromic acid. Oxidation proceeds slowly on heating.

Halogenation of Hydrocarbons

Aliphatic hydrocarbons may be *chlorinated* in the cold in diffuse daylight. Catalysts are not required, although the presence of moisture is of advantage in the case of the more volatile hydrocarbons.[8] Cyclohexane is more readily chlorinated than *n*-hexane. In chlorinating the latter, the halogen replaces the hydrogen of a CH_2 group rather than combining with a terminal carbon[9], although, according to Straus, primary monochlorides are formed when the reaction is carried out under reduced pressure and above the boiling temperature of the hydrocarbon.[10]

Monohalogenated aliphatic hydrocarbons, subjected to further chlorination, give a dichloro compound in which the halogen atoms are attached to two adjacent carbon atoms. A third chlorine atom tends to attach itself to a carbon atom bearing a halogen, and this holds true also of a fourth and other succeeding chlorine atoms. Groups $CHCl_2$, if present in the molecule, are converted to CCl_3 on further chlorination. Chloroform reacts vigorously with chlorine at 5-10° forming carbon tetrachloride. It is generally possible to replace all hydrogen atoms with chlorine, at least in lower hydrocarbons, by vigorous chlorination.

Mereshkowsky has formulated the following rules in regard to halogenation of hydrocarbons:

1. If the number of carbon atoms in the hydrocarbon is *n*, then, at temperatures below 100°, *n*-1 halogen atoms will attach themselves to carbon iaoms bearing a halogen.

2. If *n*-1 atoms in the hydrocarbon already carry halogen atoms, a further halogen will attach itself partly to the halogen-free carbon atom, and partly to that carbon atom to which the greater number of halogens is attached. Further substitution generally occurs on carbon atoms with the greatest number of hydrogen atoms.

3. The direction of substitution varies depending upon the nature of the catalyst, if one is employed.

Chlorination of hydrocarbons may be accelerated by heat. A marked increase in the rate of halogenation is observed with methane at 250°. This hydrocarbon reacts readily with chlorine at 230° in the presence of antimony trichloride, giving methyl chloride, methylene dichloride and chloroform.[74] Methane has also been chlorinated in the presence of partially reduced copper, using nitrogen as a diluent to avoid a violent reaction.[75] Ethane is more readily chlorinated than methane. Isopentane is halogenated more readily than normal hydrocarbons.

A mixture in equal proportions of ethane and chlorine, led over active carbon heated to 100-300°, yields equal amounts of mono- and 1,1-dichloroethane, with small proportions of more highly chlorinated products. Good yields of methyl chloride have been obtained by passing a mixture of 1 part chlorine and 1 part methane with 70 parts of moist nitrogen over a specially prepared cuprous chloride catalyst containing some cupric chloride. Carbon tetrachloride has been obtained in 90% yield by passing a mixture of methane and chlorine in approximately theroetical proportions over a heated cupric chloride catalyst.

Ethyl chloride, CH_3CH_2Cl, subjected to the action of chlorine in sunlight gives principally ethylidene chloride, CH_3CHCl_2, and a little ethylene dichloride, $ClCH_2CH_2Cl$. On continued chlorination in the presence of light, ethylidene chloride gives methyl chloroform, CH_3CCl_3, and vinyl trichloride, $ClCH_2CHCl_2$; further chlorination gives $ClCH_2CCl_3$, Cl_2CHCCl_3, and CL_3CCCl_3.[76]

1,2-Dichloropropane, chlorinated in the presence of sulfur chloride, sulfuryl chloride, or sulfur dioxide, gives trichlorohydrin, $ClCH_2CHClCH_2Cl$.

The use of iodine, sulfur chloride, or red phosphorus as catalysts causes excessive production of polychlorides. High yields of monohalo compounds are obtained with certain insoluble, non-volatile metallic chlorides, but these cause the transformation of primary halides to secondary or tertiary halides.

In the direct chlorination of aliphatic hydrocarbons with the halogen there is danger of ignition and explosive reaction. These dangers are avoided in commercial practice by proper dilution of the reaction mixture, or by passing the mixture of the hydrocarbon and chlorine through the heated reaction zone at a high velocity.

In the monochlorination of pentane,[77] the hydrocarbon is pumped at 75 lb pressure, through a heater at 85°, and led through a venturi throat into the stream of gaseous chlorine which is heated to 50° and under 60 lb pressure. The velocity of the hydrocarbon vapors is maintained at this point at 60 miles per hour; the reaction temperature is held at 250 to 350°. The concentration of chlorine in the reaction mixture is held at about 6% in order to minimize as much as possible the formation of dichloropentane. Reaction is quantitative, and a high yield of the monochloro compound is obtained. *n*-Pentane yields about equal amounts of primary and secondary chloropentanes; isopentane gives 85% of primary isoamyl chloride and 15% of tertiary amyl chloride.

Hydrocarbons may be chlorinated by use of certain chlorinating agents. Methane, for example, may be converted to chloroform in 50% yield at 350° with *sulfuryl chloride* in the presence of a small amount of carbon, the latter regulating the decomposition of the chloride.[78] *Antimony pentachloride* may also be used for the purpose of chlorinating hydrocarbons. The hydrocarbon vapors are led through a column packed with quartz impregnated with cuprous chloride, and heated at 300°, while the pentachloride is allowed to run down the column. The antimony trichloride emerging from the column may be reconverted to the pentachloride by treatment with chlorine. High molecular aliphatic compounds may be chlorinated with antimony pentachloride by use of iodine as a catalyst. Since *phosphorus pentachloride* dissociates to a considerable extent at moderately high temperatures, it acts as a vigorous chlorinating agent when heated with organic bodies. The compound is dissociated to the extent of 41.7% at 182°, and 97.3% at 300°. *Hydrochloric acid* may act as a chlorinating agent at high temperatures in the presence of oxygen (Deacon Process). Thus, methane is chlorinated when it is mixed with hydrogen chloride and air, and is passed through a tube containing pumice impregnated with cupric chloride and heated at 400°. The proportion of methane and hydrogen chloride should be 2 to 1 by volume. Chlorination is complete if the tube is sufficiently long.[79]

Petroleum hydrocarbons may be chlorinated with gaseous chlorine. In this reaction a protracted induction period is observed, during which the halogen simply dissolves in the liquid.

Chloroform and tetrachloroethylene are formed when a mixture of carbon monoxide and hydrogen chloride under pressure is passed over a nickel oxide, aluminum oxide, or copper oxide catalyst at 230-240°:[81]

$$2CO + 6HCl \rightarrow 2HCCl_3 + 2H_2O$$
$$2CO + 4HCl \rightarrow Cl_2C{=}CCl_2 + 2H_2O$$

Carbon tetrachloride is prepared commercially by the action of chlorine on carbon disulfide in the presence of a little iron. The reaction is carried out in two steps. In the first, carbon tetrachloride and sulfur monochloride are formed which are separated by distillation. The sulfur monochloride is subsequently caused to react with additional carbon disulfide to form carbon tetrachloride:

$$CS_2 + 3Cl_2 \rightarrow CCl_4 + S_2Cl_2$$
$$CS_2 + 2S_2Cl_2 \rightarrow CCl_4 + 4S$$

Bromination of paraffin hydrocarbons proceeds less readily than chlorination. Pentanes may be brominated under the influence of intense illumination. Other paraffins react when gently warmed and illuminated. In the presence of metallic iron or iron bromides, the halogen combines with succeeding carbon atoms in the hydrocarbon chain, and thus it is possible to prepare 1,2-dibromopropane from propyl bromide.[12]

Methane and ethane may be brominated by passing a mixture of the hydrocarbon with bromine over a catalyst heated at 400-450°. Bromination may be carried out under ordinary or higher pressure. Propyl bromide, $CH_3CH_2CH_2Br$, is readily converted to propylene bromide, $CH_3CHBrCH_2Br$, by the action of bromine in the presence of iron wire.

Carbon tetrabromide has been obtained by heating carbon disulfide in a sealed tube at 150° for 48 hours with bromine containing a little iodine, and distilling the product with an excess of caustic.[80]

Unsaturated compounds may be brominated by use of N-bromoacetamide without affecting the multiple bonds. Tetramethylethylene can, thus, be converted to bromomethyltetramethylethylene, $(CH_3)_2C{=}C(CH_3)CH_2Br$, by the action of this reagent.

Iodine does not generally displace hydrogen atoms in a hydrocarbon. Substitution may take place, however, if iodine is made to react with the hydrocarbon in the presence of iodic acid or mercuric oxide:

$$5C_3H_8 + 2I_2 + HIO_3 \rightarrow 5C_3H_7I + 3H_2O$$
$$2C_3H_8 + 2I_2 + HgO \rightarrow 2C_3H_7I + H_2O + HgI_2$$

A general method for the iodination of organic compounds consists in treating the substance in ethereal or benzene solution with a suspension of silver perchlorate and elemental iodine. The reaction proceeds at a low temperature. With alkylaromatic compounds nuclear substitution takes place in the dark, and side-chain substitution occurs in direct sunlight. The perchloric acid formed in the reaction is neutralized with the oxides or carbonates of magnesium or calcium.

Iodinated paraffins result when certain chlorinated or brominated hydrocarbons are treated with sodium iodide. The reaction, which usually proceeds rapidly at room temperature, is best carried out in acetone, an excellent solvent for sodium iodide.[13]

Fluorination of Aliphatic Hydrocarbons

The reaction of undiluted fluorine with hydrocarbons proceeds with violence, and direct fluorination with the element can only be successfully carried out when the halogen is diluted with nitrogen.

Hydrocarbons may be converted to their fully fluorinated derivatives by passing the mixture of the hydrocarbon with fluorine diluted with nitrogen through a tube packed with a catalyst consisting of silver-plated copper turnings and heated at 200-300°.[85] Before fluorination is begun in a reactor previously used for the same purpose, the reactor should be thoroughly purged with fluorine at the reaction temperature in order to destroy any polymeric body that may be present in the catalyst.

Under optimum conditions the yield of fluorocarbons decreases with increase in the molecular weight of the hydrocarbon.

Fluorides of certain metals in their highest valency state, such as CoF_3, AgF_2, CeF_4, have been used successfully for the fluorination of hydrocarbons. The reaction proceeds far less violently than with elemental fluorine, and is less sensitive to temperature fluctuations. The reaction of hydrocarbons with cobalt trifluoride is still so vigorous that it is necessary to dilute the vapors of the hydrocarbons with nitrogen in order to moderate the reaction.[86]

Cobalt trifluoride is prepared *in situ* in the reaction tube from cobalt chloride, $CoCl_2$, by passing hydrogen fluoride over the compound heated at 400-450°, and treating the resulting cobalt difluoride with fluorine at 250°. After removal of the excess fluorine by a stream of nitrogen, the hydrocarbon, diluted with nitrogen, is admitted. The products are condensed, freed of hydrogen fluoride and separated by fractional distillation. The cobalt trifluoride is regenerated by treating the cobalt difluoride in the reaction tube with fluorine at 250°.

The yield of fluorocarbon tends to decrease with increase in molecular weight of the hydrocarbon. Yields of up to 88% have been recorded.

Fluorides of cerium and manganese, CeF_4 and MnF_3, are more satisfactory than cobalt trifluoride for the fluorination of high boiling hydrocarbons and the preparation of fluoro lubricants.[87]

Many fluoro compounds have been prepared by reaction with antimony trifluoride in the presence of bromine.

Fluorocarbons may be prepared from other halogenated hydrocarbons by replacement of the halogens with fluorine. In some instances replacement of other halogens with fluorine may be effected by reaction with hydrogen fluoride. A CCl_3 group activated by an aromatic residue as in benzotrichloride, $C_6H_5CCl_3$, may be converted to CF_3 by reaction with hydrogen fluoride. Replacement by reaction with hydrogen fluoride may be brought about in many cases when the reaction is carried out under high pressure. As a rule, replacement of chlorine in an aliphatic hydrocarbon with fluorine under normal working conditions requires the use of catalysts, such as antimony pentachloride, antimony dichlorotrifluoride, halogen fluorides, etc. The more vigorous reagents antimony pentafluoride, bromine trifluoride and iodine pentafluoride are employed for the most resistant compounds. Dichlorodifluoromethane, for example, is prepared through the reaction of carbon tetrachloride with hydrogen fluoride in the presence of antimony pentachloride:

$$CCl_4 + 2HF \xrightarrow{SbCl_5} CCl_2F_2 + 2HCl$$

The desired product is obtained in good yield by removing it from the reaction zone as it is formed.

Halogens in an isolated group such as those in CH_3CCl_3, and $CH_3CCl_2CH_3$, are smoothly replaced with fluorine; the group CCl_3 seems to be generally resistant to substitution, especially when it is adjacent to a halogenated group.

ALCOHOLS

Alcohols result when inorganic esters are saponified, or hydrolyzed. Many alkyl halides may be hydrolyzed by heating with water under pressure. Alkyl iodides may be readily converted to alcohols by treatment with moist silver oxide or by heating with an aqueous suspension of lead oxide. Benzylglycolic aldehyde, $C_6H_5CH_2CH(OH)CHO$, has been obtained by refluxing the corresponding halo compound with an aqueous suspension of barium carbonate.[82] Alcohols may be prepared indirectly from halides through the saponification of acetic esters obtained from the halides and silver acetate. Many alcohols with various functional groups have been prepared by this method.[83] Alcohols have been prepared similarly *via* the formates. The structure of alcohols obtained *via* the acetate may differ from that obtained *via* the formate.[84] Glycols are usually prepared *via* the acetate.

Halohydrins resulting from the interaction of polyhydric alcohols and halogen acids may be reduced to alcohols, hydrogen atoms replacing the halogens. Isopropyl alcohol may be prepared by this method from glycerine via glycerine dichlorohydrin. Polyhydric alcohols may be reduced directly by treatment with iodine and phosphorus, yielding an iodo compound which may be converted to an alcohol. Isopropyl and isobutyl alcohols may be obtained by this method from glycerine and erythritol respectively.

Primary amines are converted to alcohols by treatment with nitrous acid. The higher primary amines yield secondary alcohols by this method through molecular rearrangement.[14]

Primary alcohols result when aldehydes, acid chlorides or anhydrides are reduced with sulfuric acid and sodium amalgam, sodium, iron or zinc dust.[15] The reduction of ketones results in general in the formation of secondary alcohols, together with pinacones. Esters may be reduced to the corresponding alcohols by the combined use of sodium or sodamide and an alcohol.

Alcohols by Reduction of Esters and Carbonyl Compounds

Sodium Reduction of Esters

The sodium reduction of esters,[16], originated by *Bouveault and Blanc,* which consists in the treatment of the compound to be reduced in solution in an alcohol with metallic sodium, was wasteful of the reagent in its original form. A modification of the procedure developed by Hansley makes full use of the reducing efficiency of the metal. The reduction may be assumed to proceed in the stages indicated below:

$$RCOOC_2H_5 + 2Na \rightarrow R\overset{\overset{\displaystyle ONa}{|}}{\underset{\underset{\displaystyle Na}{|}}{C}}OC_2H_5$$

$$\underset{\displaystyle Na}{\overset{\displaystyle ONa}{RCOC_2H_5}} + C_2H_5OH \rightarrow \overset{\displaystyle ONa}{RCHOC_2H_5} + C_2H_5ONa$$

$$\overset{\displaystyle ONa}{RCHOC_2H_5} \rightarrow RCHO + C_2H_5ONa$$

$$RCHO + 2Na \rightarrow \overset{\displaystyle ONa}{RCHNa}$$

$$\overset{\displaystyle ONa}{RCHNa} + C_2H_5OH \rightarrow RCH_2ONa + C_2H_5ONa$$

Hydrolysis of the final sodium alcoholate mixture leads to the formation of the alcohol and sodium hydroxide.

The procedure consists essentially in introducing the alcohol only as rapidly as it is utilized in the reaction, allowing no appreciable excess of alcohol to be present at any time. It is important also to select an alcohol of medium or low reactivity, such as a secondary or tertiary alcohol or an aliphatic alcohol of high molecular weight. Methylhexalin, mixed hexahydroresorcinols, or methyl isobutyl carbinol may be used to advantage for the purpose.

Two moles of alcohol and four atoms of sodium are required theoretically for the reduction of one mole of ester, but it is desirable to use a 5% excess of both the alcohol and sodium.

The general procedure is to add the mixture of ester and alcohol to molten sodium covered with a small amount of an inert solvent such as toluene or xylene. It is of the utmost importance to keep the mixture in a fluid condition throughout the entire period of the reaction. This can be accomplished in part by the addition of the proper quantity of an inert solvent, and in part by an adjustment of the temperature at which the reaction is carried out. It is important also to keep the mass well agitated during the reaction.

The alcohol ester mixture can be added quite rapidly. One pound of beef tallow can thus be reduced completely within 60 to 90 minutes in a 3-liter flask.

The final hydrolysis of the resulting alcoholates is accomplished by pouring the reaction product into the required quantity of water. The reverse procedure may cause the setting of the product to a gel.

Yields are in general quite high. To obtain the best yields, the reducing alcohol, the solvent and reaction temperature must be properly selected. Glycerides are reduced more readily than methyl esters, though castor oil is not reduced well by this method, while methyl ricinoleate can be reduced quite readily.

Care must be exercised to avoid accidentally spilling the reaction mixture or blowing it into the air, since the finely divided sodium will ignite spontaneously at temperatures much over 100°.

Optically active esters in which the activity is due to asymmetry of the α-carbon atom are racemized by the Bouveault-Blanc hydrogenation procedure.[88] The optically active alcohols may be prepared by the addition of small pieces of sodium to a mixture of the ethereal solution of the ester and aqueous sodium acetate maintained at 0° and well agitated; the liquid is kept slightly acidic by the periodic addition of acetic acid (*Prins' method*).[89]

Sodium reduction does not, in general, affect multiple bonds. Certain conjugated systems are, however, partially reduced; thus, one of the double bonds in eleostearic esters (tung oil) is reduced. Double bonds in abietates and in menhaden oil are not affected. The method is not applicable to formic esters and to aromatic acids in which the carbonyl group is attached to the nucleus. Esters of a-hydroxy acids are poorly reduced. Esters of aliphatic dibasic acids are reduced to glycols.

When alcohols of very low reactivity are employed in the sodium reduction of esters, acyloin condensation[17] may take place. The reaction presumably proceeds according to the scheme:

$$\underset{\underset{Na}{|}}{\overset{\overset{ONa}{|}}{RCOC_2H_5}} + RCOOC_2H_5 \rightarrow \underset{\underset{OC_2H_5}{|}}{\overset{\overset{ONa}{|}}{RC}} - \underset{\underset{OC_2H_5}{|}}{\overset{\overset{ONa}{|}}{CR}}$$

$$\rightarrow RCOCOR + 2C_2H_5ONa$$

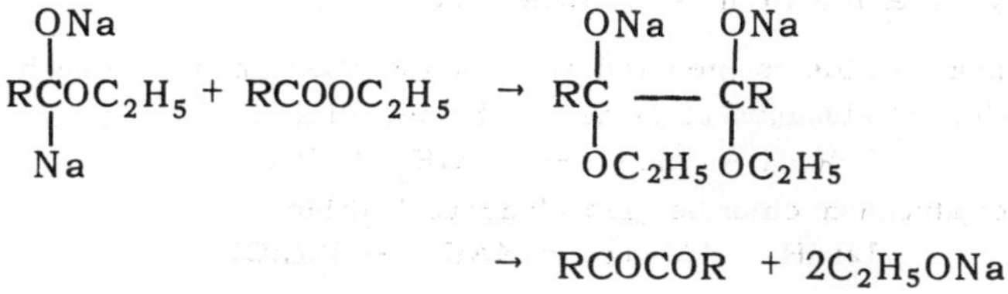

$$RCOCOR + 2Na \rightarrow RC(ONa)=C(ONa)R$$

Hydrolysis of the sodio acyloin yields the acyloin:

$$RC(ONa)=C(ONa)R + 2H_2O \rightarrow RCOCH(OH)R + 2NaOH$$

Sodium hydride, NaH, may be employed for the reduction of esters to alcohols with improved yields. Glycerides of aliphatic acids may be effectively reduced to alcohols by this reagent.

Reduction of Esters, etc., with Lithium Aluminum Hydride

Esters are reduced to alcohols by lithium aluminum hydride.[90] Carboxylic acids are also reduced smoothly to alcohols by this reagent.[91] The reaction probably proceeds in the following manner:

$$4RCOOH + 3LiAlH_4 \rightarrow LiAl(OCH_2R)_4 + 2LiAlO_2 + 4H_2$$

hydrolysis of the metallic alcoxide yields the alcohol. The hydroxyl group in hydroxy acids also takes part in the reaction:

$$2RCH(OH)COOH + 2LiAlH_4 \rightarrow LiAl\begin{bmatrix}OCHR\\|\\OCH_2\end{bmatrix}_2 + LiAlO_2 + 4H_2$$

The *procedure* is to add an ethereal solution of the acid to a mixture of the reagent with ether, under reflux, at such a rate that the liquid boils gently. The mixture is allowed to stand for 15 minutes after the introduction of all of the acid, and is then diluted with water and is treated with 10% sulfuric acid or sodium hydroxide of the same concentration. The alcohol remains in solution in the ether layer and is recovered by removing the solvent by evaporation. The yields range between 80 and 97%.

The halogen in α-halo acids is not replaced with hydrogen, and the reaction thus offers a convenient method for the preparation of α-halo alcohols. Free hydroxyl and amino groups do not interfere in the reaction. Olefinic acids are generally reduced without affecting the unsaturated bonds.[92] Ethylenic linkages adjacent to a phenyl group on one side and a reducible group on the other are hydrogenated, however. The double bond in cinnamic acid, for example, is reduced. The method has been used successfully for the conversion of heterecyclic carboxylic acids to the corresponding carbinols.[93]

Thiol esters are reduced by lithium aluminum hydride to alcohols, although less satisfactory results are obtained with this reagent than with Raney nickel.[94]

Lactones are smoothly reduced to diols by lithium aluminum hydride. Pentane-1, 4-diol is obtained from α-valerolactone.

Lithium aluminum hydride is prepared through the reaction of lithium hydride with a molecular equivalent of aluminum chloride in ethereal solution:[95]

$$4LiH + AlCl_3 \rightarrow LiAlH_4 + 3LiCl$$

Larger amounts of aluminum chloride give aluminum hydride:

$$12LiH + 4AlCl_3 \rightarrow 4AlH_3 + 12LiCl$$

Catalytic Reduction of Esters to Alcohols

Esters may be catalytically reduced to alcohols by use of the more active Raney nickel catalyst at temperatures below 100°. α-Hydroxy and α-amino esters have been reduced by use of this catalyst at 25 to 50°.

A highly reactive form of nickel is obtained by digesting the Raney nickel-aluminum alloy at 50° with 25% aqueous caustic by adding the alloy to the solution in small portions. Washing must be effected with great care, in the complete absence of air, until the wash water reacts neutral. Counter current washing in an upright glass tower, with water running upward at such a rate that the catalyst remains in suspension is a most effective method. At the end of the washing process, the water surrounding the catalyst is displaced with 95% alcohol, then finally with absolute alcohol, and the finished catalyst is preserved under alcohol, preferably at 0°.[96] A somewhat more active catalyst is obtained if the digestion and washing are performed in an atmosphere of hydrogen under slight pressure.

Esters have been successfully reduced to alcohols catalytically under pressure using *copper chromite* and other catalysts.[97] A number of higher aliphatic alcohols are produced commercially by such methods.

The copper chromite catalyst may be prepared by heating to ignition a mixture of ammonium chromate, copper and barium nitrate.[98] The lactam linkage in carbethoxypyrrolidines and carbethoxypiperidones is not affected in the catalytic hydrogenation of the ester group.[99] Optically active esters in which the activity is due to asymmetry of the α-carbon atom are racemized by catalytic hydrogenation. Malonates, β-keto esters and β-hydroxy esters have been reduced to 1,3-diols, using high ratios of copper chromite catalyst to ester at 160-180°.

Reduction of Carbonyl Compounds to Alcohols

Ketones are readily reduced to alcohols by the Bouveault-Blanc method.[18] The procedure has been applied successfully to the preparation of alcohols from methyl alkyl, aryl alkyl and cyclic ketones.[19] With aldehydes a sodium addition compound (sodium "ketal") is first formed, and this, on reaction with a molecule of alcohol, gives the sodium alcoholate:

$$RCHO + 2\,Na \rightarrow RCH(Na)ONa$$

$$RCH(Na)ONa + C_2H_5OH \rightarrow RCH_2ONa + C_2H_5ONa$$

The alcohol is obtained on decomposing the sodium compound with water. The method is not uniformly successful with aldehydes.

Heptaldehyde has been reduced successfully to the corresponding alcohol by adding the aldehyde mixed with acetic acid and toluene to finely subdivided sodium suspended in toluene.

Lithium aluminum hydride serves satisfactorily for the reduction of aldehydes and ketones to alcohols. The reaction may be carried out at ordinary temperature in ethereal solution. The method is of special value for the reduction of unsaturated carbonyl compounds, since double bonds remain unaffected in most cases.[100] The method gives satisfactory results also in cases where catalytic reduction would cause secondary reactions; it may be used for the reduction of hindered ketones, such as acetylenic ketones and 9-aroyl anthracenes. The method has been used for the conversion of steroid ketones to the corresponding alcohols.[101] The selective reduction of halo ketones to halohydrins has also been brought about by use of lithium aluminum hydride.

The less reactive *sodium* or *lithium borohydrides* may often be used to advantage for the reduction of enol acetates; cholesterone enol acetate and 7-dehydrocholesterone enol acetate have been converted to the corresponding alcohols by these reagents. Aldonic lactones have been converted by sodium borohydride to aldoses and glycitols. Benzylthienol, ethylene hemithioketal and acetal groups are unaffected by lithium aluminum hydride. Benzyloxy groups are also generally unaffected.

An active zinc-copper couple has been used for the reduction of unsaturated aldehydes to dienols.[102] Dipropenyl glycol,

$$CH_3CH{=}CHCH(OH)CH(OH)CH{=}CHCH_3,$$

has been obtained, for example, from crotonaldehyde.

Aldehydes may be reduced to alcohols by treatment with formaldehyde and alkali.[103] Furfuryl alcohol has been obtained in 90% yield from furfural by this method.

Reduction of Addition Compounds of Formaldehyde and Ethylene[104]

Ethylenic compounds of the type ArCR = CR'R" combine with formaldehyde in the presence of acids forming cyclic acetals:

$$ArCR=CR'R'' + CH_2O + H_2O \rightarrow ArCRCR'R''CH_2OH$$
$$OH$$

$$\xrightarrow{CH_2O} ArCR-CR'R''-CH_2$$
$$O - CH_2 - O$$

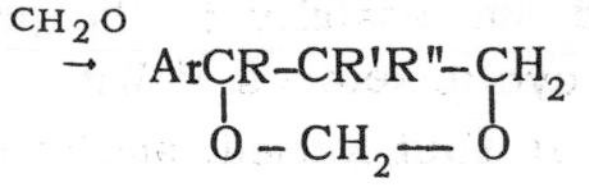

These compounds are converted to monohydric alcohols when subjected to the Bouveault-Blanc reduction:

$$ArCR-CR'R''CH_2 \xrightarrow{H_2} ArCHR - CR'R''CH_2OH$$
$$O - CH_2 - O$$

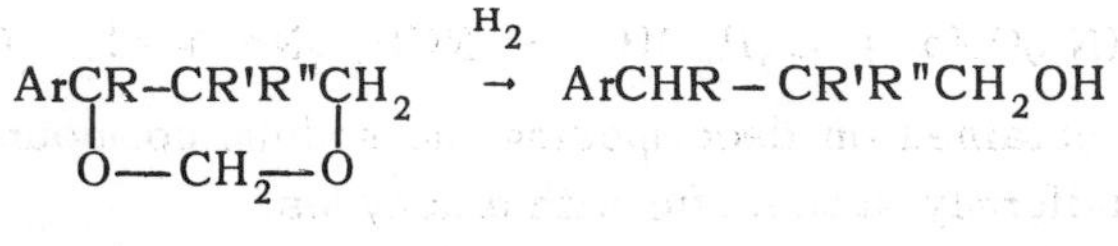

Meerwein–Ponndorff–Verley–Reduction of Carbonyl Compounds[23]

An excellent method for the conversion of ketones and aldehydes to alcohols has been developed independently by Meerwein, Ponndorff and Verley, which consists in heating the carbonyl compound with aluminum isopropoxide in benzene or toluene solution. Acetone, which is a product of the reaction, is then distilled off, and an excess of dilute sulfuric acid is added to the residue to obtain the free alcohol. The reaction proceeds according to the following scheme:

$$RCOR' + Al \left[OCH(CH_3)_2 \right]_3 \rightarrow \left[RCH(R') O \right]_3 Al + CH_3COCH_3$$

The time required for reduction varies, depending on the type of carbonyl compound. Aldehydes are in general more readily reduced than ketones; quinone and cyclohexanone are reduced completely in a few minutes, while the reduction of camphor requires twelve hours or longer. The absence of acetone in the last portions of the distillate, which can be determined by testing with 2,4-dinitrophenylhydrazine, indicates the end of the reaction.

The proper choice of a solvent is often of importance for the success of the reaction. Thus, 4-ketotetrahydrochrysene can be readily reduced in toluene but not in isopropyl alcohol; 1-menthene-4-one-3 can be reduced in isobutyl alcohol, though reduction does not proceed in isopropyl alcohol. The boiling point of the solvent is often a determining factor in the success or failure of the reaction. The yield of alcohol is generally good, ranging between 80 and 100%.

Side reactions are of significance only in special cases. Dehydration of the alcohol formed in the reaction to an olefin[24], shifting of a multiple bond[25], the formation of the ether of the alcohol[26], lactone formation from γ-ketoesters, and alcohol exchange during the reduction of some ketoesters[27] are some of the side reactions observed. The reduction of the esters of hydroxy ketones usually results in the cleavage of the acid group, with the formation of a glycol, though ether and acetal linkages are not affected. α-Bromoacetophenone gives the corresponding bromohydrin in 85% yield, but α-bromopropiophenone gives a large proportion of benzyl methyl carbinol with a moderate yield of bromohydrin. α-Bro-

moisobutyrophenone, $C_6H_5COCBr(CH_3)_2$, gives a mixture of isomeric carbinols[28], apparently as a result of the isomerization of the oxide

$$C_6H_5CHCH\,(CH_3)_2$$
$$\diagdown\!\diagup$$
$$O$$

which may be assumed to be the first product of the reaction, and the subsequent reduction of the carbonyl compounds formed. When the reduction is carried out at 33° benzalbromoacetone, $C_6H_5CH{=}C(CH_3)CH_2Br$, is obtained as the principal product together with small quantities of its allylic isomers. 9,9-Dimethylanthrone-10, reduced in xylene solution, is converted in large measure into the corresponding hydrocarbon.

Other groups susceptible to reduction are usually unaffected by aluminum isopropoxide. Double bonds, carboxylic esters, nitro groups and compounds containing reactive halogen, with some exceptions, are not reduced. Furthermore, pinacol formation has never been reported.

In compounds containing two carbonyl groups, one carbonyl can be selectively reduced providing the other is protected by conversion to acetal, or by pinacol formation, or finally by conversion to an enol ester, if the carbonyl group is capable of enolization.

In the reduction of an optically active ketone, the reaction results in the appearance of an additional asymmetric center. Two diastereoisomers are, therefore, possible and in many cases both isomers are formed in comparable quantities.[26]

An excess of the reagent may be used to advantage except with aromatic aldehydes. In reducing ketones the use of a 100 to 200% excess of the reagent is to be recommended.

Unsatisfactory results are obtained with hydroxyaldehydes and aminoaldehydes. Phenolic aldehydes are not reduced.

Alkoxymagnesium chlorides, alkOMgCl, may be employed in the reaction instead of aluminum alkoxides. These compounds are prepared by the action of alocholic magnesium chloride on magnesium alkoxides or simply by heating metallic magnesium with absolute alcohol containing the theoretical quantity of hydrogen chloride.

Alcohols are obtained from carbonyl compounds by the Reformatsky reaction, a subject which has been treated in Chapter 4.

The reaction of *Grignard compounds*, RMgX, with carbonyl compounds, R′COR″, results in the formation of addition products R′C(R″)(R)OMgX which on decomposition with water yield alcohols R′C(R″)(R)OH. Organic oxides and esters reacting with Grignard reagents also yield addition products which on treatment with water give alcohols. Butlerow carried out a similar synthesis with zinc alkyls and acid chlorides.

Butlerow's Synthesis of Tertiary Alcohols[29]

An acid chloride reacting with two molecular equivalents of a zinc alkyl gives a complex which is decomposed with water to an alkane, zinc hydroxide and an alcohol. The reaction proceeds in two stages, as follows:

$$RCOCl + ZnR'_2 \rightarrow R-\underset{\underset{Cl}{|}}{\overset{\overset{R'}{|}}{C}}-OZnR'$$

$$\underset{\underset{Cl}{|}}{\overset{\overset{R'}{|}}{RC}}OZnR' + ZnR'_2 \rightarrow R-\underset{\underset{R'}{|}}{\overset{\overset{R'}{|}}{C}}_2OZnR' + ClZnR''$$

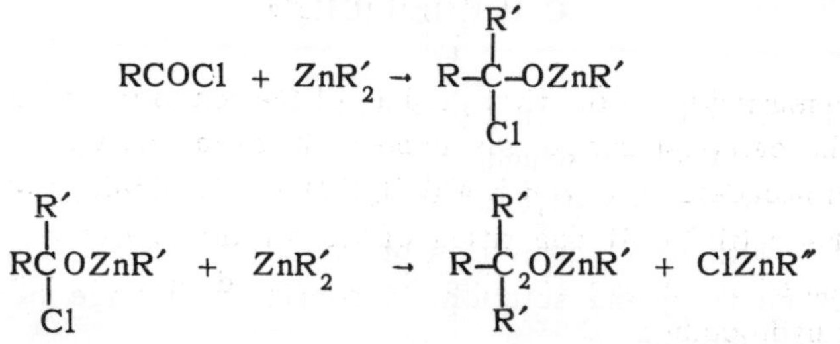

and it is possible to carry out each step separately. Two different radicals may be introduced in the molecule of the final alcohol by using different zinc alkyls in each step. While zinc methyl and zinc ethyl yield tertiary alcohols, a secondary alcohol results with cleavage of propylene when zinc propyl is used in the reaction.

Alcohols result from olefinic bodies when these are oxidized under the proper conditions. The subject has been dealt with in Chapter 17. The Oxido function present in 1,2-oxides may be transformed to an alcoholic function by various reactions discussed in Chapter 5 in the section dealing with ethylene oxides.

Behavior and Reactions of Alcohols

Reaction of Alcohols with Alkali Metals

Alcohols, ROH, react with alkali metals to form alcoholates of the metal ROM. The reaction proceeds very readily with the lower primary alcohols; it may be conveniently carried out in toluene solution using equivalent amounts of alcohol and metal, when the alcoholate may be isolated practically free of alcohol.

The higher secondary and tertiary alcohols react slowly. The potassium derivatives of these alcohols may be prepared readily through the reaction of finely subdivided potassium with a toluene solution of the alcohol. Even such compounds as cholesterol and ergosterol yield potassium derivatives by this method.[30]

In concentrated solutions of alkali metal hydroxides in alcohol a portion of the metal is present as the alcoholate in equilibrium with the hydroxide. Water reacts with alkali metal alcoholates forming the hydroxide of the metal and regenerating the alcohol.

Formation of Urethanes and Thiourethanes

Alcohols react with isocyanates to form urethanes:

$$RNCO + HOR' \rightarrow RNHCOOR'$$

The reaction appears to be applicable to hydroxy compounds generally.[31] With isothiocyanates alcohols similarly yield thiourethanes.[32]

Action of Halogens

Halogens cause oxidation of alcohols to halo derivatives of aldehydes. Ethanol is converted by chlorine to a mixture of chloral and chloral hydrate, halogenation taking place more readily in the presence of iron. *n*-Butyl alcohol, chlorinated in the presence of iron at 10°, is converted to the dibutyl acetal of a monochlorobutyraldehyde, $C_4H_7Cl(OC_4H_9)_2$, while at 40-80°, the dibutyl acetal of a dichlorobutyraldehyde, $C_4H_7Cl_2(OC_4H_9)_2$, is obtained.

INORGANIC ESTERS

Alkyl Halides

Hydrogen halides react with alcohols to give alkyl halides, the reaction conforming in type to the process of esterification:

$$ROH + HX \rightarrow RX + H_2O$$

An equilibrium condition is attained where the ester and water formed coexist with some unreacted alcohol and acid. The behavior of halogen acids differs from that of organic acids in that the reaction with the former takes place most readily with tertiary alcohols and least readily with primary alcohols, while the reverse holds true with organic acids. Thus, tertiary bromides are formed by the reaction of tertiary alcohols with 48% hydrobromic acid in the cold; secondary alcohols react readily when warmed, while reaction with primary alcohols proceeds slowly even in the warm.[34] The replacement of the hydroxyl group with halogens takes place most readily with hydriodic acid and least readily with hydrochloric acid. The reaction proceeds slowly with the anhydrous alcohol, the presence of a limited amount of water causing an acceleration of the rate. The presence of water beyond a limiting concentration causes a reversal of the reaction and is therefore undesirable. The undesirable effect of the water formed in the reaction may be eliminated by use of a dehydrating agent, such as anhydrous zinc chloride.

Halides by Use of Hydrogen Halides

Good yields of chlorides are obtained with some alcohols when they are made to react with hydrogen chloride in the absence of dehydrating agents. The reaction of hydrogen chloride with some alcohols proceeds so readily that it is sufficient to pass gaseous hydrogen chloride through the alcohol at room temperature to obtain the chloride. This is the case, for example, with benzyl and tertiary butyl alcohols.[105] Trimethylphenylethyl alcohol, $(CH_3)_3C_6H_2CH(CH_3)OH$, in alcoholic solution, treated at 0° with hydrogen chloride, is converted to the corresponding chloride.[106] Alcohols of the type $ROCH_2C(OH)R_2$ give excellent yields of the corresponding chloride by reaction with 38% hydrochloric acid.[35] β-Dihydroxydiethyl sulfide, $S(CH_2CH_2OH)_2$, gives the dichloride quantitatively with concentrated hydrochloric acid at 60°.[107] Glycerine monochlorohydrin is obtained in 75% yield on heating a mixture of glycerine with aqueous hydrochloric acid of sp. g. 1.185 in a sealed tube at 120° for fifteen hours.

The reaction of alcohols with hydrogen bromide proceeds with greater ease than with hydrogen chloride. Pinacone is converted to tetramethylethylene dibromide by reaction with hydrobromic acid; piperonyl bromide is formed similarly from piperonyl alcohol. The hydroxyl group in allyl alcohol may be replaced with bromine by treatment with hydrobromic acid, without affecting the double bond:

$$CH_2{=}CHCH_2OH + HBr \rightarrow CH_2{=}CHCH_2Br + H_2O$$

The reaction may be carried out by saturating the cooled alcohol with gaseous hydrogen bromide and heating under reflux for several hours until the reaction is complete. Alternatively, the alcohol may be added dropwise to a mixture of 50% sulfuric acid and potassium bromide.

It has been found of advantage, in some cases, to generate the hydrogen bromide required for the reaction by the interaction of bromine with naphthalene. Three gram molecules of the alcohol are mixed with 35 grams of naphthalene, the mixture is heated to boiling under reflux and 500-550 grams of bromine added gradually. Methyl, ethyl, propyl, and isopropyl bromides have been prepared by this method in 75 to 85% yield. Isobutyl bromide is obtained in only 50% yield; a considerable amount of dibromoisobutane, $(CH_3)_2CBrCH_2Br$, is formed simultaneously in the reaction.[108]

The reaction of hydrobromic acid with certain tertiary alcohols in acetic acid solution at 40-50° results in the formation of ethylenic hydrocarbons, and involves the migration of a methyl group in the molecule.[109]

The most convenient, and perhaps the most satisfactory method of preparation of ethyl bromide is by the reaction of ethyl ether with hydrogen bromide.

All alcohols react with *hydriodic acid* forming alkyl iodides. Higher alcohols, and secondary and tertiary alcohols react with special ease.[110] Gaseous hydrogen iodide or fuming liquid hydriodic acid may be employed in the reaction. *n*-Octyl iodide has been prepared by conducting gaseous hydriodic acid into the heated alcohol.[111] Similarly *tert*-butyl iodide is formed when trimethylcarbinol is saturated with gaseous hydriodic acid.[112]

In the reaction of hydriodic acid with polyhydric alcohols only one hydroxyl group is replaced with iodine, the remaining hydroxyl groups are replaced with hydrogen, or they are removed with the formation of ethylenic bonds.[113] The end product of the reaction of glycerine with hydriodic acid is isopropyl iodide:[114]

$$HOCH_2CH(OH)CH_2OH + 5HI \rightarrow CH_3CHICH_3 + 3H_2O + 2I_2$$

Erythrite gives secondary butyl iodide.[115] Glyceric acid, $HOCH_2CH(OH)COOH$, gives β-iodopropionic acid. Mannite yields *sec*-hexyl iodide.[116] This generalization does not hold with respect to polyhydric compounds in which hydroxymethyl groups are attached to an aromatic nucleus; for example, 1,2-hydroxymethylbenzine gives 1,2-iodomethylbenzene:[117]

$$\text{(cyclohexane)} \begin{array}{c} CH_2OH \\ CH_2OH \end{array} + 2HI \rightarrow \text{(cyclohexane)} \begin{array}{c} CH_2I \\ CH_2I \end{array} + 2H_2O$$

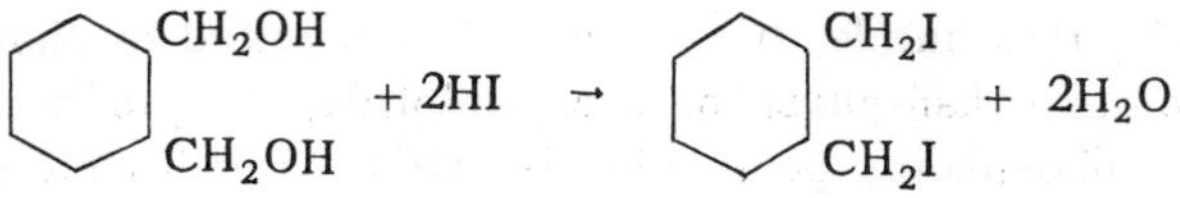

The hydroxyl group in hydroxy acids may be replaced with iodine by reaction with hydriodic acid, and it is possible to prepare the monoiodides of the acids by heating the hydroxy acids at 50-70° with a solution of hydriodic acid in glacial acetic acid.

The reaction of alcohols with *hydrogen fluoride* proceeds less readily than with other hydrogen halides. Ethyl fluoride may be obtained in 36% yield by heating a mixture of four molecular proportions of anhydrous hydrogen fluoride with one of ethanol at 190° in a sealed tube.[118] The reaction may be accelerated by use of catalysts.[119]

Chlorides by Reaction of Hydrogen Chloride with Alcohols in the Presence of Zinc Chloride

The reaction of hydrogen chloride with alcohols, which often proceeds incompletely because of the occurrence of the reverse reaction caused by the water formed, may be forced to completion by use of zinc chloride.[120]

The *procedure* is as follows: Two molecular proportions of zinc chloride are dissolved in two molecular equivalents of concentrated hydrochloric acid, and one molecular equivalent of alcohol is added. The mixture is boiled under reflux for one hour, and is then distilled, collecting only the high boiling portion. This is boiled under reflux with an equal volume of concentrated sulfuric acid, whereupon the chloride is obtained generally in 60 to 82% yield.

Alternatively, one part of fused zinc chloride is added to one and a half to two parts of alcohol, and gaseous hydrogen chloride is passed through the mixture kept at boiling temperature under reflux. Alkyl chlorides have been prepared successfully by this method from methyl, ethyl, n- and siopropyl, n- and sec-butyl, isoamyl, cetyl, β-phenylethyl, and m- and p-nitrobenzyl alcohols.

The use of zinc chloride in connection with higher alcohols leads to the formation of unsaturated compounds; these react with hydrogen chloride, usually yielding chlorides isomeric with those obtained by direct replacement of the hydroxyl group. Higher alkyl halides and tarry matter are also formed when such alcohols are heated with hydrogen chloride in the presence of zinc chloride. The expected alkyl halides may be prepared from these alcohols in good yield by heating with an excess of hydrochloric acid.[36] Normal ester formation may be brought about also in such cases, by use of glaubers salts, a mild dehydrating agent.

Replacement of Hydroxyl Groups with Halogens by Use of Halides of Phosphorous and other Halides

An alcoholic hydroxyl group may be replaced with a halogen by treatment with phosphorous halides. Alkyl chlorides may be obtained by the reaction of alcohols with phosphorus pentachloride. The reaction takes place less readily with phosphorous trichloride; this halide, furthermore, is converted to phosphorous acid, which is less volatile than phosphorus oxychloride, the product resulting from the reaction with phosphorus pentachloride. Better results are obtained when zinc chloride is used in conjunction with phosphorus trichloride.[37]

Phosphorus tri- and *pentabromides* have been used for the replacement of alcoholic hydroxyl groups with bromine. Propargyl bromide has been obtained in 80% yield through the reaction of phosphorus tribromide with propargyl alcohol:

$$3CH{\equiv}CCH_2OH + PBr_3 \rightarrow 3CH{\equiv}CCH_2Br + P(OH)_3$$

The method is useful in cases where, as with furfur alcohol, the use of hydrobromic acid would cause the polymerization of the compound. Furfuryl bromide has been obtained from furfur alcohol in 70% yield by this method. Diethyl tartrate has been converted to diethyl bromomalate, $C_2H_5OCOCHBrCH(OH)COOC_2H_5$, by reaction with phosphorus tribromide. Morphine has been converted to its bromide similarly.

Replacement of hydroxyl groups with iodine may be brought about by use of *phosphorus triiodide*. Again, the method is useful in cases where the use of acid would cause undesirable effects. α-Furfuryl iodide has been prepared in 40% yield by treating α-furfuryl alcohol in ethereal solution with phosphorus triiodide.[121]

A mixture of the halogen and phosphorus may be used effectively for the replacement of a hydroxyl group with a halogen atom. In effect, the preferred method of preparation of alkyl bromides is to heat the appropriate alcohol with a mixture of bromine and phosphorus.[122]

Alkyl iodides are obtained very readily by treating an alcohol with iodine and red phosphorus.[123]

The procedure is as follows: One-fourth of the alcohol to be used in the reaction is poured on phosphorus placed in a flask and the mixture is heated until the phosphorus melts. A portion of the iodine is dissolved in the remainder of the alcohol and the solution is added slowly with stirring to the heated mixture of alcohol and phosphorus; the remainder of iodine is then added, and heating and stirring is continued. In preparing ethyl iodide, the iodine may be introduced in solution in a little ethyl iodide.[124] Solid alcohols are melted with the phosphorus and the iodine is then added.[125]

When polyhydric alcohols are subjected to the reaction, one secondary hydroxyl group is replaced with iodine and the others are replaced with hydrogen, or are removed with the formation of ethylenic bonds. For example, on heating glycerine with phosphorus and iodine, in the presence of a little water, isopropyl iodide, CH_3CHICH_3, is formed.[114] In the complete absence of water, monoiodopropylene is obtained as the principal product. Monoiodohexane may be prepared by the same treatment from mannite.

Phosphorus oxychloride is useful in cases where it is desired to replace with chlorine alcoholic hydroxyl groups in compounds containing free carboxyl groups, since it does not affect acidic hydroxyl groups. Diphenylchoroacetic acid may thus be prepared readily by heating equal quantities of benzilic acid and phosphorus oxychloride.

Sulfur monochloride, S_2Cl_2, has been employed to a limited extent for the replacement of alcoholic hydroxyl groups with chlorine. It has been used, for example, for the preparation of glycerine dichlorohydrin from glycerine:[126]

$$HOCH_2CH(OH)CH_2OH + 2S_2Cl_2 \rightarrow ClCH_2CH(OH)CH_2Cl + 2HCl + SO_2 + 3S$$

Thionyl chloride, $SOCl_2$, gives good yields of chlorides with normal primary alcohols, but poor yields with secondary alcohols, and is of no value for the preparation of chlorides from tertiary alcohols.[38 127] Best results are obtained with the lower primary and secondary alcohols when a tertiary base such as pyridine, dimethyl or diethylamine is added to the reaction mixture to remove the hydrogen chloride formed.[38] The higher alcohols give better results when thionyl chloride is used alone or diluted with benzene.[40]

The tendency of anhydrous *beryllium fluoride* to form an oxyfluoride can be utilized to effect the exchange of an alcoholic hydroxyl group with fluorine. The reaction is carried out in an excess of hydrogen fluoride:

$$RCH_2OH + 2BeF_2 \rightarrow RCH_2F + BeOBeF_2 + HF$$

It may be carried out also in the presence of the sodium fluoride-hydrogen fluoride complex, $NaHF_2$, in which case Na_2BF_4, as well as the oxyfluoride are formed.

Halides by Exchange Reactions

Certain alkyl halides may be prepared successfully by an exchange reaction. Thus, alkyl iodides may be obtained from alkyl chlorides or bromides by reaction with sodium or potassium iodide. A rapid reaction often takes place when a 15% acetone solution of sodium iodide is mixed with chloro or bromo compounds, with precipitation of sodium chloride or sodium bromide.

Iodoethylalcohol, ICH_2CH_2OH, has been prepared by heating on a water bath for 24 hours a thin slurry of 25 grams of sodium iodide with 25 cc of ethylene chlorohydrin.[128] *Monoiodoacetone* has been obtained in theoretical yield by allowing monochloro-acetone to react with an aqueous-alcoholic solution of potassium iodide for 48 hours.[129] *Benzoyl-2-iodoamylamine* has been made in 80% yield through the reaction of potassium iodide with the corresponding chloro compound.[130] γ-Iodopropylphthalimide is formed on heating under reflux for one hour the corresponding bromo compound with a solution of potassium iodide in 90% alcohol.[131]

The reverse process of replacement of an iodine atom in an iodinated compound with chlorine has also been recorded: iodoform, heated in a sealed tube at 150° in ethereal solution with mercuric chloride is converted to dichloroiodomethane, $HCICl_2$.[132]

The iodine atom in ethyl iodide may be replaced with fluorine by reaction with silver fluoride.[133]

Sulfuric Esters, $(RO)_2SO_2$

Neutral alkyl sulfates result when sulfuryl chloride or alkyl chlorosulfonates react with alcohols or sodium alcoholates.[41] The reaction of fuming sulfuric acid with alcohols at a moderate temperature also leads to the formation of neutral esters, together with small amounts of other products.[42]

Acid esters are obtained when concentrated sulfuric acid is made to react with alcohols. The reaction is accompanied with evolution of heat, although it does not proceed to completion.

A convenient procedure for the preparation of the acid esters is to dissolve the alcohol in a small quantity of sulfuric acid and to add fuming sulfuric acid gradually to the cooled solution. A substantially complete conversion of the alcohol to ester is brought about in this manner. The excess of sulfuric acid is removed by the addition of barium carbonate and the filtered solution is evaporated to crystallization. The acid ester may be freed by treating the barium salt thus obtained with the calculated amount of sulfuric acid.[43]

Acid sulfuric esters may be prepared from secondary and tertiary alcohols by carefully mixing the well-cooled alcohol and sulfuric acid.[44]

Acid sulfuric esters also result when olefin hydrocarbons react with sulfuric acid. The reaction takes place particularly well in the presence of metal catalysts.[45]

Acid sulfuric esters are viscous liquids which cannot be distilled without decohol.

Chlorosulfonic Esters, $ROSO_2Cl$

Chlorosulfonic esters are formed when sulfuryl chloride reacts with one molecule of alcohol.[46]

$$C_2H_5OH + SO_2Cl_2 \rightarrow C_2H_5OSO_2Cl + HCl$$

Chlorosulfonic esters result also when acid sulfuric esters are treated with phosphorus pentachloride, as well as through the interaction of olefins with chlorosulfonic acid, and of sulfur dioxide with hypochlorous ester, C_2H_5OCl.

Water decomposes chlorosulfonic esters slowly, while alcohol reacts rapidly forming acid esters, together with ethyl chloride.

Sulfurous Esters

Salts of acid esters of sulfurous acid are obtained when sulfur dioxide is passed through an alcoholic solution of alkali metal alcoholates; or when sulfur dioxide and gaseous ammonia are led through absolute alcohol.[47] These esters are unstable in contrast with the isomeric sulfonic acids.

Neutral sulfurous esters are obtained when thionyl chloride, $SOCl_2$, or sulfur monochloride are made to react with alcohols:[48]

$$2C_2H_5OH + SOCl_2 \rightarrow (C_2H_5O)_2SO + 2HCl$$

$$3C_2O_5OH + S_2Cl_2 \rightarrow (C_2H_5O)_2SO + C_2H_5SH + 2HCl$$

The neutral alkyl sulfites are insoluble in water and are saponified with difficulty with aqueous caustic.

Hypochlorous and *perchloric esters* result when the free acids react with alcohols. They are explosive compounds with a strong unpleasant odor.[49]

Nitric Esters, Etc.

Nitric esters are prepared from alcohols and nitric acid.[50] Partial oxidation of the alcohol may take place simultaneously with the formation of nitrous acid. This is destroyed by the addition of urea, since, if allowed to accumulate, it may initiate the decomposition of the ester, which may proceed with *explosive violence.*

Nitric acid reacts rather vigorously with trimethyl carbinol, $(CH_3)_3COH$, giving nitrobutylene.[134] Dimethyl ethyl carbinol similar gives nitroamylene.[135]

Nitroglycerine, nitroglycol, nitromannitol, etc., have been prepared by the action of a mixture of sulfuric and nitric acids on the corresponding polyhydric alcohols.[136]

Ethyl nitrate is reduced with tin and hydrochloric acid to hydroxylamine. Reacting with hydroxylamine in the presence of sodium ethoxide, the ester gives the sodium salt of nitrohydroxamic acid, HONO = NOH.

Nitrous esters are also formed through the interaction of nitrous acid and alcohols, the reaction proceeding even with dilute aqueous solutions of the acid.[51] Nitrosyl chloride reacts with alcohols in pyridine solution to form nitrous esters.[52] The reaction of silver nitrate with alkyl iodides gives nitrous esters together with the higher boiling nitroparaffins.[53]

Esters of *phosphoric*[54], *phosphorous*[55] and *thiophosphoric*[56] *acids* may be prepared from the chlorides of these acids $POCl_3$, PCl_3 and $PSCl_3$, and alcohols or sodium alcoholates. Phosphorus trichloride gives the neutral esters, $P(OR)_3$, with sodium alcoholates, while with alcohols the dialkyl esters of asymmetric phosphorous acid, $HPO(OR)_2$, are obtained. The former are isomerized with alkyl iodides to alkylphosphonic esters, $RPO(OR)_2$.

Boric, arsenious and *silicic acid* esters may be obtained similarly from the halides BCl_3, $AsBr_3$, and $SiCl_4$. Alkyl arsenites may also be prepared by boiling arsenious oxide with alcohol in the presence of copper sulfate.

Ortho-silicoformic esters, $HSi(OR)_3$, are obtained from silicoform, $HSiCl_3$ by reaction with alcohol. These esters give silane, SiH_4, on heating with sodium.[57]

MERCAPTANS

A general method of preparation of mercaptans, RSH, consists in the replacement of halogens or other acid groups with the sulfhydryl group by reaction with potassium or sodium acid sulfide:[134]

$$C_2H_5Cl + KSH \rightarrow C_2H_5SH + KCl$$

In preparing mercaptans by this method from many of the lower aliphatic halides it is necessary to heat the mixture of halide and alkali sulfide under pressure. The necessity of heating under pressure is avoided by employing the alkali metal salts of aliphatic acid sulfates, $ROSO_2OK$. The sulfuric ester required for the reaction need not be isolated in the pure form and may be readily prepared as follows:

The alcohol is added slowly in a thin stream and with stirring to a mixture in equal parts of fuming and concentrated sulfuric acid. The liquid is next cooled and made slightly alkaline with sodium hydroxide. It is then concentrated by boiling, cooled and filtered from the solid sodium sulfate. For the purpose of preparing the mercaptan, the crude ester thus obtained is heated with a large excess of concentrated potassium acid sulfide solution, which is prepared by saturating a 33% aqueous solution of potassium hydroxide with hydrogen sulfide.

Aliphatic esters may also be successfully employed in the reaction although when the esters are of low molecular weight, heating under pressure becomes necessary. The reaction is illustrated by the following:

$$CH_3COOC_2H_5 + KSH \xrightarrow{140^\circ} CH_3COOK + C_2H_5SH$$

A satisfactory method for the preparation of aliphatic dithiols is based on the reaction of the corresponding halides with ammonium dithiocarbamate and the subsequent decomposition of the resulting dithiocarbamate with an alkali:[59]

$$2NH_2CSSHNH_3 + Br(CH_2)_n Br \quad NH_2CSS(CH_2)_nSCSNH_2 + 2NH_4Br$$

$$NH_2CSS(CH_2)_nSCSNH_2 + 2KOH \quad HS(CH_2)_nSH + 2NH_2CSOK$$

Aminothiols may be prepared from bromoalkyl phthalimides by reaction with an alkali hydrosulfide followed by saponification of the resulting mercapto alkylimide with alkali:

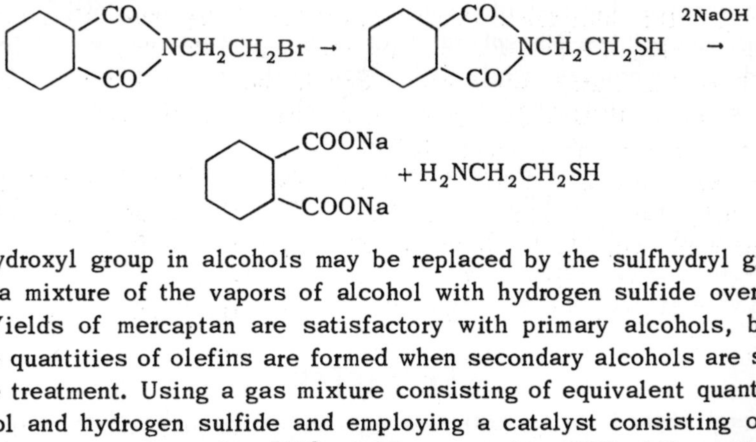

The hydroxyl group in alcohols may be replaced by the sulfhydryl group by passing a mixture of the vapors of alcohol with hydrogen sulfide over heated *thoria*. Yields of mercaptan are satisfactory with primary alcohols, but considerable quantities of olefins are formed when secondary alcohols are subjected to the treatment. Using a gas mixture consisting of equivalent quantities of of alcohol and hydrogen sulfide and employing a catalyst consisting of thoria supported on pumice heated to 380°, yields approaching 50% of theoretical have been obtained with various aliphatic primary alcohols.[60]

Alcoholic hydroxyl groups may be replaced by the sulfhydryl group by reaction with bromine and phosphorus in the presence of sodium sulfate.[58] Replacement of the alcoholic hydroxyl groups by the sulfhydryl group does not, in general, take place by the action of phosphorus pentasulfide.

Aromatic halo compounds can be converted to thiophenols by heating with an alkali hydrosulfide in the presence of copper powder. The reaction proceeds with varying degrees of ease, depending upon the character of the halo compound. Thiophenols are obtained by distilling the alkali salts of aromatic sulfonic acids with an alkali hydrosulfide. Thiophenol may be prepared by this method from potassium benzenesulfonate.[61]

Replacement of the diazo group in aromatic diazo chlorides with the xanthate group proceeds normally and well, yielding an aromatic xanthic ester:

$$C_2H_5OCSSK + ClN_2C_6H_5 \rightarrow C_2H_5OCSSC_6H_5 + KCl + N_2$$

A thiophenol results when the ester is decomposed with alkali. This offers the basis for a satisfactory method of preparation of thiophenols from aromatic amines.[62]

Mercaptans may be prepared by the reduction of disulfides with alkali sulfides[63] or a mixture of alkali sulfide and sodium hydroxide:[64]

$$4RSSR + 2Na_2S + 6NaOH \rightarrow 8RSNa + Na_2S_2O_3 + 3H_2O$$

Yields of 50 to 60% of theoretical have been reported by investigators who employed the latter method. A mixture of dextrose and sodium hydroxide has also been employed as a reducing agent for the conversion of disulfides to mercaptans.[65] This method has given satisfactory results with disulfides that resisted the action of other reducing agents.

Thiophenols are obtained through the reduction of aromatic sulfuryl chlorides with zinc and sulfuric acid, or with tin and hydrochloric acid. This is an excellent method that generally gives satisfactory results.[66]

Other methods of preparation of mercaptans are the following:[138] Saponification of isothioureas with sodium hydroxide;[139] reduction of higher alkyl thiocyanates with zinc and hydrochloric acid;[140] catalytic addition of hydrogen sulfide at a terminal olefinic bond in the presence of peroxides or metallic chlorides, resulting in the formation of primary mercaptans.[141]

Alkyl isothioureas, $RSC(=NH)NH_2$, are formed by the interaction of alkyl bromides and thioureas.[73]

Reaction of Mercaptans

Mercaptans give metal derivatives more readily than alcohols; thus, they react readily with aqueous solutions of alkalies to form alkali mercaptides, which may also be obtained through the reaction of mercaptans with alkali metals in an inert solvent. Reacting with metallic oxides and hydroxides, mercaptans yield the mercaptides of the metals. These are only slightly decomposed in cold water, but are completely hydrolyzed by boiling water. Mercaptans react with the chlorides of gold and of the metals of the platinum group with the liberation of hydrochloric acid and the formation of the mercaptide of the metal.

Metallic mercaptides, with the exception of mercury mercaptide, are decomposed on heating to the sulfides of the metal and of the hydrocarbon radical:

$$(RS)_2Pb \rightarrow (R)_2S + PbS$$

Mercuric mercaptide decomposes to metallic mercury and an organic disulfide:

$$(RS)_2Hg \rightarrow RSSR + Hg$$

Ester formation proceeds less readily with mercaptans than with alcohols.[67]

Thio ethers result when mercaptans are made to react with alkyl halides, sulfates or aryl sulfonates.

Mercaptans react with the carbonyl group of aldehydes and ketones forming thioacetals (mercaptals):

$$RR'CO + 2HSR'' \rightarrow RR'C(SR'')_2 + H_2O$$

Zinc chloride or hydrogen chloride are used as condensing agents.[68] Mercapto acids, such as thioglycollic acid or thiolactic acid react with aldehydes without the use of a condensing agent. Thus, benzaldehyde mixed with thioglycollic acid gives the compound $C_6H_5CH(SCH_2COOH)_2$; the reaction is complete within a few minutes. Formaldehyde in 40% aqueous solution reacts with thioglycollic with equal ease. In contrast to acetals, mecaptals are unaffected by acids; they are also unaffected bv alkalies, but are converted to disulfones on oxidation.

Oxidizing agents such as ferric chloride, bromine and iodine convert mercaptans to disulfides:

$$2RSH + O \rightarrow RSSR + H_2O$$

Vigorous oxidation of mercaptans results in the formation of sulfonic acids. Hot nitric acid is a suitable reagent for the oxidation of aliphatic mercaptans, but its use in the aromatic series should be avoided, since nitration of the nucleus and other reactions may take place. Benzyl mercaptan yields benzoic acid on oxidation.

Selenoles.[69]

Selenoles, RSeH, result when alkali hydroselenides are heated with alkali metal salts of monoalkyl sulfates or with alkyl halides:

$$NaSeH + ROSO_2ONa \rightarrow RSeH + Na_2SO_4$$

Sodium selenoles result through the reaction of metallic sodium with dialkyl selenides:

$$C_6H_5SeSeC_6H_5 + Na \rightarrow 2C_6H_5SeNa$$

Alkyl selenides may also be prepared directly from elemental selenium by the action of Grignard reagents:

$$Se + RMgX \rightarrow RSeMgX \xrightarrow{HCl} RSeH + ClMgX$$

CARBOHYDRATES[142]

Carbohydrates are polyhydric alcohols containing, as a rule, an aldehydic or ketonic group, the former in the form of an internal cyclic half acetal. In the typical simple carbohydrates, i.e. the monosaccharides, such as glucose, dextrose, etc., hydroxyl groups are attached to all carbon atoms in the molecule, with the exception of the carbonyl carbon atom in ketoses. Carbohydrates play an important role in nature, and many of the known compounds of this class have been isolated from plants and plant products. Many are commercial articles of importance and a large number of the individual compounds are conveniently obtained from natural sources. The total synthesis of these compounds generally presents only an academic interest for this reason. In theory, the simple carbohydrates are obtainable by a series of aldol condensations from formaldehyde and, indeed, heating this compound under pressure with dilute magnesia or other condensing agents results in the formation of some carbohydrates, along with numerous other products.[143] The formation in this reaction of a ketohexose, for example, may be assumed to proceed by the following steps:[144]

$$3CH_2O \rightarrow HOCH_2COCH_2OH \text{ and } HOCH_2CH(OH)CHO$$

$$HOCH_2COCH_2OH + HOCH_2CH(OH)CHO$$

$$\rightarrow HOCH_2COCH(OH)CH(OH)CH(OH)CH_2OH$$

Hexitols have been synthesized starting with acrolein, which was converted to divinylglycol by condensation in the presence of zinc, copper, and acetic acid; oxidation with silver chlorate containing a little osmic acid resulted then in the formation of a mixture of hexahydric alcohols:[145]

$$2CH_2{=}CHCHO \rightarrow CH_2{=}CHCH(OH)CH(OH)CH{=}CH_2$$

$$\rightarrow HOCH_2CH(OH)CH(OH)CH(OH)CH(OH)CH_2OH$$

The individual components of the mixture were allitol and d,l-mannitol.

Hexitols and other polyhydric alcohols of a similar type have been obtained also through the reaction of certain chloro aldehydes with acetylenic Grignard reagents, and the successive conversion of the product to expoxide, polyhydroxy acetylene, polyhydroxy ethylene, and finally oxidation of this to hexitols with silver chlorate containing some osmic acid.[146] A mixture of allitol and dulcitol has been obtained in this way from the reaction product of two molecular equivalents of chloroacetaldehyde with one of acetylenedimagnesium dibromide:

$$2ClCH_2CHO \xrightarrow{BrMgC\equiv CMgBr} ClCH_2CH(OH)C{\equiv}CCH(OH)CH_2Cl$$

$$\xrightarrow{KOH} \overset{O}{CH_2{-}CH}C{\equiv}C\overset{O}{CH{-}CH_2} \xrightarrow{H_2O} HOCH_2CH(OH)C{\equiv}CCH(OH)CH_2OH$$

$$\xrightarrow{H_2} HOCH_2CH(OH)CH{=}CHCH(OH)CH_2OH$$

$$\rightarrow HOCH_2CH(OH)CH(OH)CH(OH)CH(OH)CH_2OH$$

Pentitols have been prepared from the reaction product of one molecular equivalent of α, β-dichloropropionaldehyde with one of acetylenemagnesium bromide. This was converted to an acetylenic chloroepoxide and then to a chloro dihydro alcohol. Treatment of the latter with a mixture of acetic anhydride and silver acetate gave the acetylated trihydroxy acetylene, which was reduced to the corresponding ethylenic body, and the latter gave a mixture of pentitols on oxidation with silver chlorate and osmic acid, followed by hydrolysis of the resulting acetylated compound:

$$ClCH_2CHClCHO \xrightarrow{CH\equiv CMgBr} ClCH_2CHClCH(OH)C{\equiv}CH$$

$$\xrightarrow{KOH} ClCH_2\overset{O}{CH{-}CH}C{\equiv}CH \xrightarrow{H_2O} ClCH_2CH(OH)CH(OH)C{\equiv}CH$$

$$\xrightarrow{Ac_2O + AgOAc} AcOCH_2CH(OAc)CH(OAc)C{\equiv}CH$$

$$\xrightarrow{H_2} \mathrm{AcOCH_2CH(OAc)CH(OAc)CH{=}CH_2}$$

$$\xrightarrow[\mathrm{OsO_4}]{\mathrm{AgClO_3}} \mathrm{AcOCH_2CH(OAc)CH(OAc)CH(OH)CH_2OH}$$

$$\rightarrow \mathrm{HOCH_2CH(OH)CH(OH)CH(OH)CH_2OH}$$

Ribitol and *d,l*-arabitol have been identified as constituents of the product. The reduction of the acetylenic compound was carried out by use of Bourgel's catalyst,[147] which consists of colloidal palladium dispersed in starch solution.

Methods Employed for Lengthening the Carbohydrate Chain

Lengthening of the carbon chain of a simple aldose may be accomplished by reacting the sugar aldehyde with hydrocyanic acid, hydrolyzing the cyanohydrin formed to the corresponding acid, and reducing the lactone of the acid with sodium amalgam:[148]

$$\mathrm{HOCH_2(CHOH)_4CHO} + \mathrm{HCN} \rightarrow \mathrm{HOCH_2(CHOH)_4CH(OH)CN}$$

$$\rightarrow \mathrm{HOCH_2(CHOH)_4CH(OH)COOH} \rightarrow \mathrm{HOCH_2(CHOH)_2\overline{CH(CHOH)_2CO.O}}$$

$$\xrightarrow{H_2} \mathrm{HOCH_2(CHOH)_5CHO}$$

The acid is converted to the lactone by concentrating its aqueous solution to a syrup on the water bath. This is diluted with nine parts of water, the solution is cooled to the freezing point, and sulfuric acid is added in small amounts at a time, followed by sodium amalgam, which is also added in small portions at a time. Reduction proceeds rapidly as the solution is shaken, with complete utilization of the hydrogen generated. The liquid is maintained in an acid condition during the reaction. Reduction is complete after the addition of eight parts by weight of sodium amalgam to one of syrup. Dicarboxylic acids may also be reduced to the corresponding aldoses by this method.[149] The carbohydrate is obtained as a mixture of epimeric forms.

The Grignard reaction has been used for the synthesis of sugars with an increased number of carbon atoms in the chain.[150] Still another method employed to the same end is to cause a fully acetylated sugar acid chloride to react with diazomethane:

$$\underset{\mathrm{AcO}}{\mathrm{H_2C}}-\underset{\mathrm{OAc}}{\mathrm{CH}}-\underset{\mathrm{OAc}}{\mathrm{CH}}-\underset{\mathrm{OAc}}{\mathrm{CHCOCl}} + \mathrm{CH_2N_2} \rightarrow \underset{\mathrm{AcO}}{\mathrm{H_2C}}-\underset{\mathrm{OAc}}{\mathrm{CH}}-\underset{\mathrm{OAc}}{\mathrm{CH}}-\underset{\mathrm{OAc}}{\mathrm{CH}}-\mathrm{COCHN_2}$$

The diazo group in the reaction product is replaced with a hydroxyl group by refluxing with a solution of cupric acetate in acetic acid. Deacetylation is effected by treatment with barium hydroxide solution.

The Nef Reaction

The Nef reaction offers a further method making possible lengthening of the chain of a carbohydrate. When 2,4-benzylidene-1-xylopyranose and the benzylidene derivatives of other aldoses are treated with a mixture of nitromethane and methanolic sodium methoxide, addition of the nitromethane at the aldehyde group takes place: [151]

$$
\begin{array}{ccc}
\text{CHO} & & \text{CH(OH)CH}_2\text{NO}_2 \\
| & & | \\
\text{O}-\text{CH} & & \text{O}-\text{C} \\
/\quad | & & /\quad | \\
\text{C}_6\text{H}_5\text{CH}\quad \text{HCOH} & \xrightarrow{\text{CH}_3\text{NO}_2} & \text{C}_6\text{H}_5\text{CH}\quad \text{HCOH} \\
\backslash\quad | & & \backslash\quad | \\
\text{O}-\text{CH} & & \text{O}-\text{CH} \\
| & & | \\
\text{HOCH} & & \text{HOCH} \\
| & & | \\
\text{CH}_2\text{OH} & & \text{CH}_2\text{OH}
\end{array}
$$

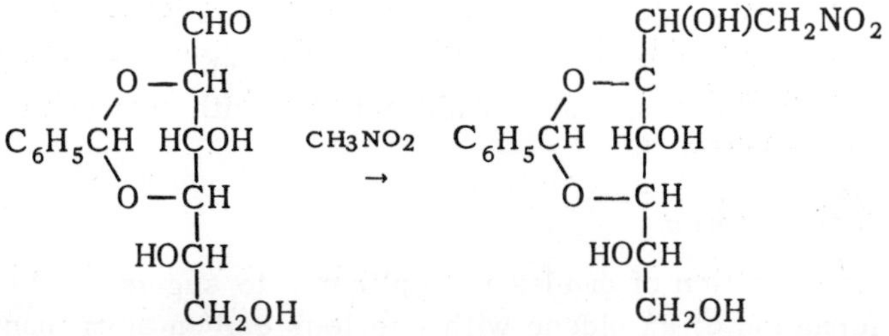

Removal of the benzylidene group is accomplished by acid hydrolysis, and the conversion of the nitromethyl group CH_2NO_2 to aldehyde is brought about by treating the sodio derivative of the nitro sugar with 60% sulfuric acid.

A ketose with two additional carbon atoms is obtained by using 2-nitroethanol instead of nitromethane in the Nef reaction. Thus, a mixture of d-glucoheptulose and d-mannoheptulose has been obtained from arabinose. [152]

Degradative Methods

Degradative methods making possible the removal of one carbon atom from the molecule of a carbohydrate, have played an important role in the development of the chemistry of carbohydrates.

Zemplén's Method [153]

The cyanohydrin method of forming sugars with one more carbon atom may be reversed, and carbohydrates with one less carbon atom may be obtained from the aldoses. The aldonic nitriles are obtained in the acetylated form from the sugars by reaction with hydroxylamine followed by treatment with a mixture of acetic anhydride and sodium acetate: [154]

$$
\overset{\lceil\quad\text{O}\quad\rceil}{\text{HOCH}_2\text{CH(CHOH)}_3\,\text{CHOH}} + \text{H}_2\text{NOH} \rightarrow \overset{\lceil\quad\text{O}\quad\rceil}{\text{HOCH}_2\text{CH(CHOH)}_3\text{CH.NHOH}}
$$

$$
\underset{\xrightarrow{\quad\quad}}{\overset{\text{Ac}_2\text{O} + \text{CH}_3\text{COONa}}{}} \quad \text{AcOCH(CHOAc)CH}_2\text{CH}=\text{NOAc} \rightarrow \text{AcOCH}_2\text{(CHOAc)CN}
$$

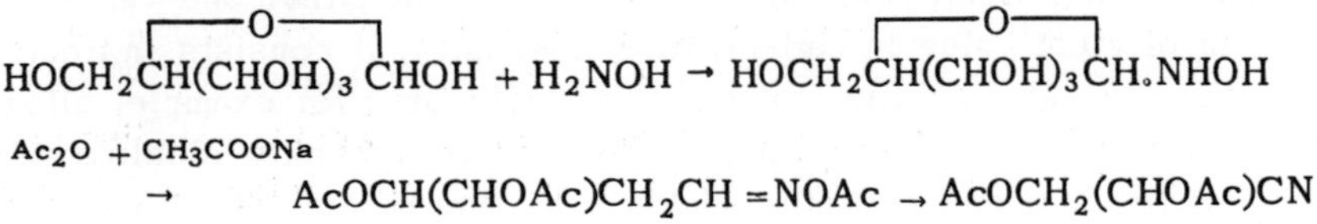

Treatment of the acetylated nitrile with sodium methoxide in chloroform solution results in the removal of the acetyl groups and the cleavage of the nitrile group, with the formation of an aldose:

$$
\begin{array}{c}
-\text{CH CN} + \text{NaOCH}_3 \rightarrow -\text{CHO} + \text{CH}_3\text{OAc} + \text{NaCN} \\
| \\
\text{OAc}
\end{array}
$$

The same result may be achieved also by use of ammoniacal silver oxide solution,[155] although this method is not quite as satisfactory as treatment with sodium methoxide.

Ruff's Method [156]

This is a modification of Fenton's reaction[157] and consists in causing bromine to react at room temperature with the calcium salt of the sugar acid in the presence of calcium carbonate. The reaction leads to the formation of the next lower aldose. This is probably the most used of all methods of degradation of carbohydrates. The oxidation may be carried out also with hydrogen peroxide in the presence of ferric ions.

Other Methods of Degradation

The *Hofmann degradation* of amides is applicable to sugars.[158] The reaction results in the formation of an aldose with one less carbon atom than the sugar amide:

$$HOCH_2(CHOH)_4CONH_2 \quad \xrightarrow{\text{NaOCl + NaOH}} \quad HOCH_2(CHOH)_3CHO$$

The amide is prepared from the corresponding aldose by oxidation to acid, conversion of the acid to lactone and treatment of the lactone with ammonia:

$$\overset{\overbrace{\qquad O \qquad}}{HOCH_2CH(CHOH)_3CHO} \quad \xrightarrow{O_2} \quad HOCH_2(CHOH)_4COOH \rightarrow$$

$$\overset{\overbrace{\qquad O \qquad}}{HOCH_2CHOHCH(CHOH)_2CO} \quad \xrightarrow{NH_3} \quad HOCH_2(CHOH)_4CONH_2$$

Ozonation of glucals results in the formation of an aldose with one less carbon atom than the glucals:[159]

$$\overset{\overbrace{\qquad\qquad O \qquad\qquad}}{CH_3CH(CHOAc)_2CH=CH} \quad \xrightarrow{O_3} \quad CH_3(CHOH)_3CHO$$

Glucals are obtained in the form of their acetyl derivatives by treating acetylated bromoaldoses with zinc dust and acetic acid.

The Lobry de Bruyn-van Ekenstein Transformation

A method of isomerization of sugars originated by de Bruyn and van Ekenstein has proven of great value in carbohydrate chemistry; it consists in treating the sugar with a weakly alkaline solution.[160] *d*-Glucose, for example, allowed to stand for a sufficiently long period in the cold in a weakly alkaline solution, such as baryta water or lime water, yields a mixture containing 64.5% *d*-glucose, 31% *d*-fructose, 2.5% of *d*-mannose. The principal transformation in this instance, namely that from *d*-glucose to *d*-fructose, may be depicted as follows:

$$
\begin{array}{c}
\overset{\displaystyle OH\ OH\ H\quad OH\ O\quad OH}{\underset{\displaystyle H\qquad\quad OH\ H\quad H}{\rceil\!-C-\!C-\!C-\!C-\!C-\!CH_2}} \rightarrow
\overset{\displaystyle OH\ O\quad H\quad OH\ OH\ OH}{\underset{\displaystyle\qquad\quad OH\ H\quad H}{H_2C-\!C-\!C-\!C-\!C-\!CH_2}}
\end{array}
$$

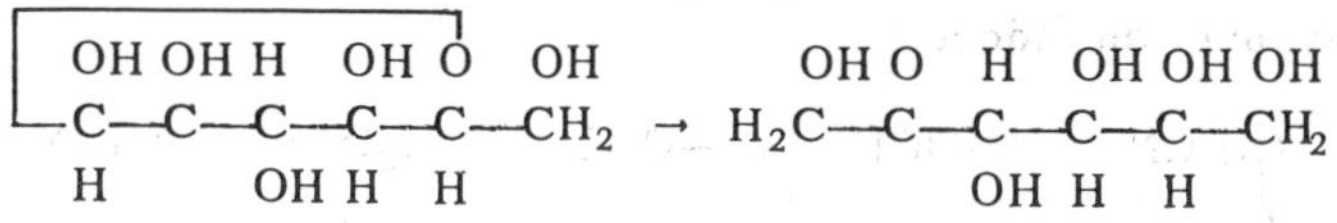

The composition of the final solution in any particular instance depends on the concentration and nature of the base used. The transformation is not a simple reversible reaction. 2-Methyl sugars do not yield ketoses by this treatment, since a methyl group does not migrate as readily as a hydrogen atom, while 3-methyl-d-glucose may be converted to 3-methyl-d-fructose in 32% yield by treatment with lime water. The de Bruyn-van Ekenstein transformation may involve a spatial rearrangement of hydroxyl groups around the carbon atoms. The transformation may be brought about also by heating the solution of the sugar with quinoline or pyridine.[161] The method has been employed for the preparation of ketoses from aldoses, as well as for bringing about the transformation of aldoses and ketoses to their epimers.

Conversion of Aldoses to Ketoses and Vice Versa

One of the changes observed in the de Bruyn-van Ekenstein rearrangement is the formation of a ketose from an aldose. Other methods are also available for bringing about this transformation. When an aldose is converted to the corresponding osazone and this is then reduced with zinc dust and acetic acid, the amine of a ketose is formed:

$$\overset{O}{\overset{|}{\underset{|}{\begin{array}{c} CHOH \\ CHOH \end{array}}}} \rightarrow \begin{array}{c} CH=NNHC_6H_5 \\ C = NNHC_6H_5 \end{array} \rightarrow \begin{array}{c} CH_2NH_2 \\ CO \end{array}$$

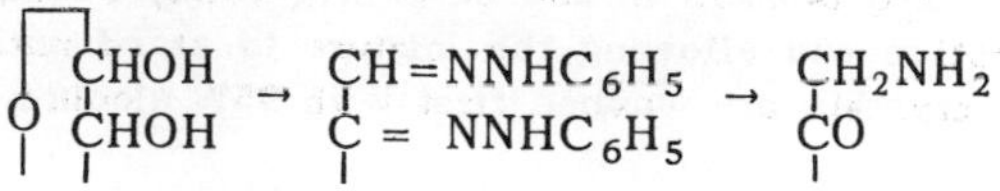

The amine may be converted to the corresponding ketose by treatment with nitrous acid. The osazone may be converted to the ketose by another route, namely by first converting it to the corresponding osone, and reducing this under carefully controlled conditions:

$$\begin{array}{c} CH=NNHC_6H_5 \\ C=NNHCH \end{array} \rightarrow \begin{array}{c} CHO \\ CO \end{array} \rightarrow \begin{array}{c} CH_2OH \\ CO \end{array}$$

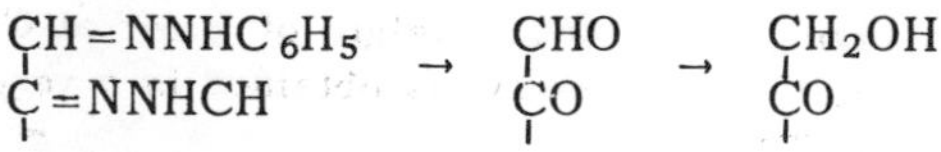

Ketoses may be converted to aldoses by reduction to the sugar alcohol, oxidation of this to the aldonic acid, conversion of the acid to lactone, and finally reduction to the aldose. In this way a pair of epimeric aldoses are obtained.

N-Aryl-d-glucosamines undergo transformation to N-aryl-1-amino-1-desoxy-d-fructose. This is known as the *Amadory rearrangement*. N-p-Totyl-d-glucosamine gives N-p-tolylamino-1-desoxy-d-fructose:

$$\begin{array}{c} CH_3C_6H_4NHCH \\ HCOH \\ HOCH \quad O \\ HCOH \\ HC \\ CH_2OH \end{array} \rightarrow \begin{array}{c} H_2CNHC_6H_4CH_3 \\ HOC \\ HOCH \quad O \\ HCOH \\ HC \\ CH_2OH \end{array}$$

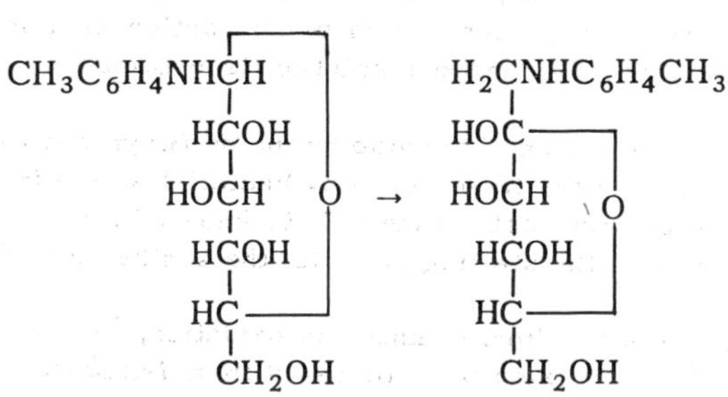

The position of the oxygen bridge in these compounds has not been established with certainty.

Preparation of Some of the Simpler Sugars

Glucose is prepared commercially by the hydrolysis of starch with hydrochloric acid under pressure. The aqueous suspension of starch is added to boiling hydrochloric acid and heating is then continued under a pressure of 1 to 2 atm, until hydrolysis is complete. Glucose may be prepared in the laboratory by adding 250 gm of finely pulverized sugar, in portions and with good agitation, to a mixture of 750 cc alcohol and 30 cc of hydrochloric acid of density 1.19, and 30 cc of water, and heating at 50°. On cooling glucose separates as a thick syrup, which crystallizes within a few days when seeded with a few crystals of glucose.[162] Grape sugar, which is an article of commerce, consists in the main of *d*-clucose. *d*-Glucose may be obtained in the pure form from this in the following manner: The sugar is dissolved in ten times its weight of water, the solution is acidified slightly with phosphoric acid, decolorized with charcoal, filtered and evaporated down to a thin syrup. The syrup is diluted with an equal volume of glacial acetic acid, then the liquid is seeded with a few crystals of glucose and allowed to stand. The crystals of glucose are filtered, dried, and recrystallized from absolute alcohol. The product is anhydrous, and consists of a mixture of the α- and β-forms of *d*-glucose.

α-d-Glucose may be obtained from the purified mixture of the α- and β-forms by dissolving 500 gm of the mixed isomers in 250 cc of hot water, adding 1000 cc of glacial acetic acid to the solution and allowing the mixture to stand until crystallization is complete. The filtered crystals are washed first with 95% alcohol, then with absolute alcohol and dried.[163]

β-d-Glucose is obtained by crystallizing the purified mixture of the α- and β-isomers from hot concentrated acetic acid. Five hundred grams of the mixed isomers are dissolved in 50 cc of water by first heating on the water-bath then on a free flame. The temperature of the solution is brought down to 100°, 600 cc of acetic acid heated to 100° are added and the mixture is stirred. Crystallization proceeds when a few crystals of β-glucose are added to the cooled solution. The crystals consist largely of β-*d*-glucose. They are further purified by dissolving in an equal weight of water at 0°, rapidly filtering, and adding five parts of alcohol. The compound is obtained in a very pure form by a repetition of this operation.[164]

l-Glucose has been obtained through the reduction of *l*-gluconic acid lactone with sodium amalgam.[165] The acid is obtained by hydrolysis of the cyanohydrin resulting from the addition of hydrocyanic acid to *l*-arabinose.

d-Fructose has been prepared through the hydrolysis of inulin with very dilute acid.[166] It is prepared industrially from invert sugar.[167]

d-Galactose results on hydrolyzing milk sugar; also by reducing *d*-galactonic acid lactone,[168] and by the de Bruyn-van Ekenstein rearrangement of *d*-tulose or *d*-sorbose.[169] *l-Galactose* is obtained by reducing *l*-galactonic acid lactone.[170]

Maltose is made commercially from starch by the action of diastatic ferment in the presence of dead yeast.[171] The enzyme solution is obtained by extracting malt with water.[172]

d-Sorbose has been prepared from *d*-glucose by the de Bruyn-van Ekenstein transformation.[173] *l*-Sorbose is made on the large scale by bacterial action from *d*-sorbite.[174] The latter is prepared from mountain ash berries. It is known in commerce under the name "Sinon". *l*-Sorbose serves as the starting point for the synthesis of the important vitamin *ascorbic acid*.

d-Mannose has been obtained from mannite by oxidation,[175] and from *d*-manonic acid lactone by reduction.[176] It has also been prepared from *d*-glucose and *d*-fructose by the de Bruyn-van Ekenstein transformation.[177] *l-Mannose* has been made from *d*-gluconic acid lactone by reduction with sodium amalgam.

Structure of Carbohydrates; Dependence Between Optical Rotation and Configuration.[178]

The presence of asymmetric carbons in carbohydrates accounts for the existence of many isomeric carbohydrates with the same empirical formula. With a carbohydrate possessing *n* asymmetric carbon atoms, the number of stereoisomers possible is 2^n. The configuration of the isomerides is shown by the Fischer projection formula. In this, it is assumed that the chain of hypothetical tetrahedra representing the carbon atoms is aligned vertically. The edges of the tetrahedra forming a line of junction of the carbon atoms above and below are assumed to lie in the plane of the paper, while the edges representing a line of junction of the hydrogen atom and hydroxyl group are assumed to lie above the paper. The vertical edges lying

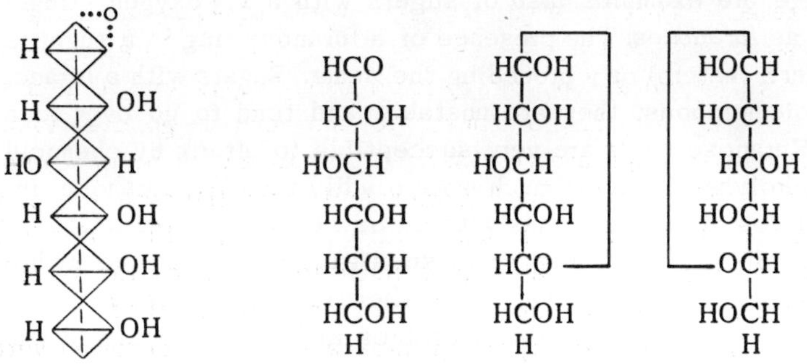

I II III IV

in the plane of the paper are shown in broken lines in (I), the horizontal edges, lying above the plane of the paper in solid lines. Diagram (I) represents the configuration of the aldehydic form of *d*-glucose; (II) represents the corresponding Fischer projection.

The space arrangement of pairs of all the possible stereoisomers of an aldose or ketose are in the relation of object to image; (III) and (IV) represent one such pair, *d*-glucopyranose and *l*-glucopyranose, respectively. Such pairs are designated as epimers. The hydroxyl group attached to the next to the last carbon atom is at the right in the Fischer projection in the *d*-epimer, at the left in the *l*-epimer.

A distinction is made in the designation of sugars that differ only by the configuration of the "reducing" carbon: the α- designation is attached to those of the *dextro* or *levo* rotating sugars which show the greatest rotation, and the β-designation to those showing the least rotation. In the Fischer projection of glucopyranose, the "reducing" hydroxyl group is to the right in the α-form, and to the left in the β-isomer. We will present the Fischer projection formula in a horizontal position in order to save space. The carbon atom 1 is at the left in this presentation, with positions above the carbon chain corresponding to positions to the right in the normal, vertical presentation; positions below the chain corresponding to positions to the left. The configurations of a- and β-d-gluco-pyranose in this presentation are as follows:

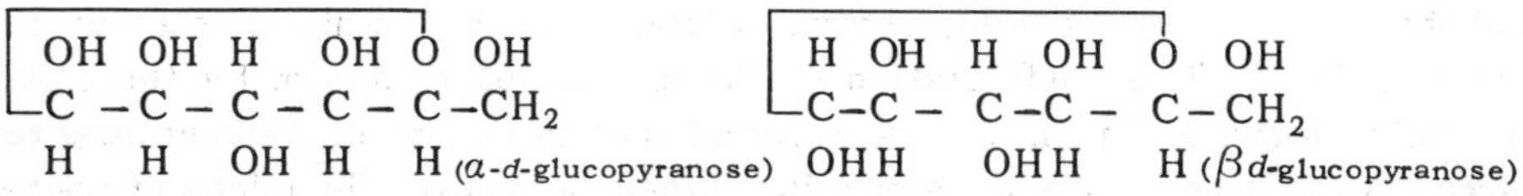

$$
\begin{array}{cccccc}
\text{OH} & \text{OH} & \text{H} & \text{OH} & \text{O} & \text{OH} \\
\text{C} & -\text{C} & -\text{C} & -\text{C} & -\text{C} & -\text{CH}_2 \\
\text{H} & \text{H} & \text{OH} & \text{H} & \text{H} & \\
\end{array}
\qquad (a\text{-}d\text{-glucopyranose})
$$

$$
\begin{array}{cccccc}
\text{H} & \text{OH} & \text{H} & \text{OH} & \text{O} & \text{OH} \\
\text{C} & -\text{C} & -\text{C} & -\text{C} & -\text{C} & -\text{CH}_2 \\
\text{OH} & \text{H} & \text{OH} & \text{H} & \text{H} & \\
\end{array}
\qquad (\beta\,d\text{-glucopyranose})
$$

In the a-isomer, 1- and 2-hydroxyl groups are in *cis* position, in the β-isomer in *trans* position.

An oxygen bridge is normally present in aldohexoses, spanning the carbon atoms 1 and 5. Sugars with this type of oxygen bridge are designated as *pyranoses*. There are examples also of sugars with a 1,4-oxygen bridge; these are designated as *furanoses*. The presence of a furanose ring in a sugar is indicated by the letter *h* (hetero) or γ preceding the name. Sugars with a furanose ring are termed alloiomorphous; they are unstable and tend to go over to a pyranose structure. Furanose rings are very susceptible to attack by chemical reagents; they are hydrolyzed by acids much more readily than the pyranose ring.

In derivatives of carbohydrates with an oxygen bridge, the latter is fixed only when the "reducing" carbon atom is substituted, or when the hydroxyl groups which would serve for the formation of other rings are blocked.

Carbohydrates containing oxygen bridges are usually endowed with a strong optical rotatory power.[102]

Many regularities have been observed in the optical rotatory power of various classes of compounds. Rules have been evolved relating the rotatory power with structure. These rules have played an important role in the determination of the configuration of carbohydrates.

Hudson's Lactone Rule[179]

This rule states that γ-lactones of hydroxy acids are dextrorotatory when the carbon atom 4 is of *dextro* configuration. In other words, the rotation sign tends to be positive when lactone ring formation engages a hydroxyl group to the right of Fischer's projection formula. The rotation is in the reverse direction if C-4 is of *levo* configuration. This rule depends upon the fact that C-4 in these ring compounds contributes most to the rotatory power of the molecule.[180] A parallel significance should be attached to the placing of the ring to the right or to the left in the free sugars or their glucosides. The rule does not always hold.

Similar regularities have been observed with respect to aldoses. Here the carbon atoms C-1 and C-5 forming part of the pyranose ring exert the greatest influence on molecular rotation.[181]

Hudson's Amide Rule

According to this rule the 2-carbon atom in α-hydroxy acids has the *dextro* configuration if the amide of the acid in aqueous solution is dextrorotatory.[182] Inversely, the configuration at C-2 is *levo* if the amide is levorotatory. Freudenberg modified this rule somewhat and stated it as follows: When conversion of an α-hydroxy acid to its amide causes a shift in the rotation to the right, then the acid belongs to the *dextro* series and vice versa. The rule holds in the case of aldonic acids, although it breaks down in the case of mandelic acid. A similar rule holds with respect to phenylhydrazide of acids.

Freudenberg's Rule of Shifting of Optical Rotation [183]

This rule may be stated as follows: Analogous compounds show variations in their optical rotation in the same direction when identical or comparable substituents are introduced in their molecules, without bringing about deep-seated chemical changes. Stated in simpler terms, identical changes in analogously constituted compounds cause changes in the same direction in the optical rotation. This general rule includes Hudson's amide rule as a special case.

Tschugaeff's Rule[184]

According to this rule, chemical changes brought about at a distance from a center of asymmetry cause only a slight change in the optical rotatory power of a compound.

Principle of Optical Superposition

The optical rotation due to single centers of asymmetry in a compound is independent of the effect of other centers of asymmetry. The optical rotatory power of a compound is, therefore, the sum of the individual rotatory powers due to each center of asymmetry present in the molecule.

Hudson derived two rules from this principle:[185]

1. Differences in molecular rotation are nearly constant with aldoses belonging to the same ring type.

2. The sum of the molecular rotations of the α- and β-forms remain nearly constant when the sugar molecule is modified by a change on carbon 1, without changing its ring type.

Bertrand's Rule[186]

The organism *A. xylinum* is capable of oxidizing two secondary hydroxyl groups adjacent to a primary alcohol group only if the secondary hydroxyl groups are in *cis* position.

Orientation of the Oxygen Bridge

When in a mixture of α- and β-forms, these isomers are present in equal amounts, then the configuration of C-5 is the determining factor in the optical rotation. If such a mixture rotates to the right (+), the oxygen bridge lies to the right in the projection formula, and *vice versa*. Thus, the structures of *d*-glucose ($\alpha = +66°$) and of β-*d*-galaheptose ($\alpha = -48.5°$) are as follows:

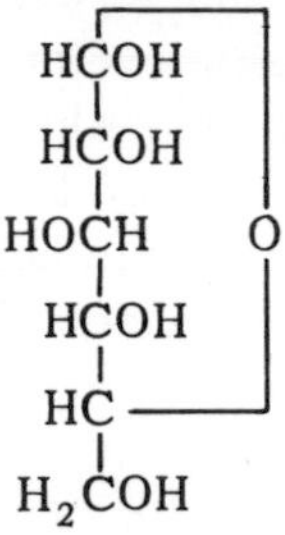

d-glucose

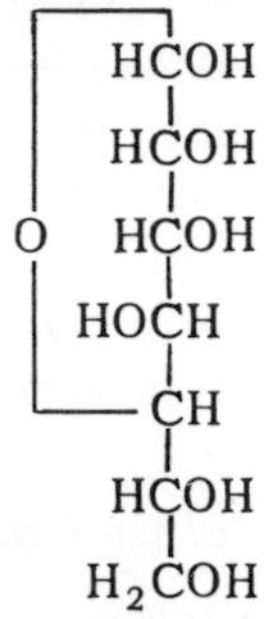

β-*d*-galaheptose

Ethers of Carbohydrates

The various hydroxyl groups in a carbohydrate are not equivalent in reactivity. The 1-hydroxyl group in pyranoses forming part of the reducing group shows especially marked differences from the other hydroxyl groups. This hydroxyl group reacts readily with alcohols in the presence of acids to form ethers. These ethers, which are termed *glucosides,* show distinctive characteristics.

Glucoside formation with aliphatic alcohols may be effected by heating a solution of the sugar in the alcohol at 100° in an autoclave in the presence of about 0.25% of hydrogen chloride. Completion of the reaction with methyl alcohol requires about 50 hours' heating.[187] The α- and β-isomers of the pyranoside as well as the furanosides are formed in the reaction. Furanosides are formed almost exclusively when the reaction is carried out in the cold,[188] but the pyranosides are formed predominantly at higher temperatures. Isolation of the various isomers has been effected by utilizing differences in their solubilities. α-Methyl glucoside, for example, has been separated from the β-isomer by taking advantage of the lesser solubility of the α-isomer in methanol. The γ-methyl glocuside has been isolated by utilizing its solubility in ethyl acetate.

Glucoside formation with alcohols may be brought about by heating the carbohydrate under reflux with the alcohol containing a little hydrochloric acid, but the reaction proceeds quite slowly.[189] *d*-Xylose, which has a free aldehyde group in its molecule, reacts in the cold with methyl alcohol containing a little hydrochloric acid, giving a mixture of methyl glucosides of α- and β-furanoses.[190]

Glucosidic alkyl groups are readily removable by treatment with acids, while alkyloxy groups in other positions in the molecule show the characteristics of true ethers and are not removable by this treatment, and are, furthermore, resistant to the action of alkalies. α-Methyl glucosides of the simple carbohydrates may be distilled without decomposition under reduced pressure.

Complete Etherification of Carbohydrates

The complete etherification of carbohydrates may be brought about by various methods.

Howorth's Method

Direct methylation of carbohydrates has been effected by reaction with dimethyl sulfate and sodium hydroxide.[191] This procedure has been originated by Howorth. If the sugar is of the reducing type, then the glucoside is first prepared as follows:

The sugar is dissolved in the least possible amount of water, by heating if necessary, and a little more than one molecular equivalent of dimethyl sulfate and a molecular equivalent of 30% caustic are added dropwise and with good stirring to the solution cooled to 30°. The temperature should not be allowed to rise above 30° during the reaction.

After the completion of the glucosidation, complete etherification is effected in the following manner:

The temperature of the solution is raised to 70°, and three times the theoretically required quantity of dimethyl sulfate and an equivalent quantity of caustic are added at such a rate that the solution always remains slightly alkaline. This operation generally requires an hour or longer. After the addition of all of the methylating agent, the mixture is heated at 100° in order to destroy the excess dimethyl sulfate, care being taken not to allow the liquid to become acidic in reaction. The mass is finally cooled, and the methylated sugar is isolated by extraction with chloroform.[192]

With non-reducing sugars, methylation is carried out directly at 70° in the manner described. With some carbohydrates it is necessary to repeat the methylating operation a number of times in order to attain complete methylation. In many cases, however, methylation fails to proceed beyond a certain point, because as methylation proceeds, the product becomes less and less soluble in hot water. With cane sugar, for example, methylation proceeds only to the point of formation of the heptamethyl derivative.[193] In such cases, the partially methylated sugars may be further methylated by the Purdie-Irvine method, although even this method fails to bring about complete methylation in some cases.

The nearly complete conversion of *cellulose* to a trimethylate has been accomplished with dimethyl sulfate and sodium hydroxide at 20°.[194] A permethylated product has been prepared by repeated methylation at higher temperatures. These products may be readily purified and have been obtained in a crystalline form from solutions in mixtures of chloroform and alcohol, or benzene and alcohol. *Ethylation* of cellulose has been effected similarly with diethyl sulfate and caustic. The products have been successfully crystallized.[195] Methyl cellulose has also been prepared from acetyl cellulose by a saponification process.[196]

Starch may be converted to a trimethyl derivative only after a large number of repetitions of the methylating process with dimethyl sulfate and caustic. Usually twenty-four repetitions of the treatment are required.[197] Acetylated starch in acetone solution may be converted to the trimethylated derivative after six repetitions of the operation of methylation with dimethyl sulfate and caustic.

Purdie and Irvine's Method

Chronologically, this is the first method worked out for the methylation of sugars. Methylation is effected by the simultaneous action of methyl iodide and silver oxide.[198]

The reaction is carried out in the beginning in methyl alcoholic solution; partially methylated products are then formed, which precipitate out. These are brought into solution by the addition of methyl iodide, and the operation is completed by the addition of silver oxide.

The method is not directly applicable to reducing sugars, since the carbonyl group in these is oxidized by silver oxide. Glucosides of these sugars, on the other hand, are successfully methylated by this method. Fully methylated glucoses have been prepared by this method from methyl glucosides.

Freudenberg and Hixon's Method

This method is based on the ability of certain sugar derivatives to yield sodio compounds when their solutions in ether, benzene or other indifferent solvents are treated with metallic sodium. The sodio compound reacts with methyl iodide to form the methylated derivative.[199] The methylated derivative of diacetone glucose has been prepared by this method.

Methylation of dimethylmercapto glucose first by dimethyl sulfate and caustic, then by Freudenberg's method yields the fully methylated derivative. On treating this with mercuric chloride, pentamethyl glucose is obtained.[200] This compound represents the first example of a *true sugar aldehyde.* It is noteworthy that the compound gives the corresponding dimethyl acetal by reaction with methyl alcohol with extreme ease.

Diazomethane has been used in some cases as a methylating agent for sugars.[201]

Trityl Ethers of Carbohydrates

Trityl chloride, $(C_6H_5)_3CCl$, reacts with carbohydrates in the presence of pyridine to form the monotrityl ether of the sugar:[202]

$$\begin{array}{c} \overline{\text{OH OH H   OH O}} \quad \text{OH} \\ \text{—C—C—C—C—C—CH}_2 + (C_6H_5)_3CCl + C_5H_5N \quad \rightarrow \\ \text{H   H   OH H   H} \end{array}$$

$$\begin{array}{c} \overline{\text{OH OH H   OH O}} \quad \text{OC}(C_6H_5)_3 \\ \text{—C—C—C—C—C—CH} \qquad \qquad + C_6H_5NHCl \\ \text{H   H   OH H   H} \end{array}$$

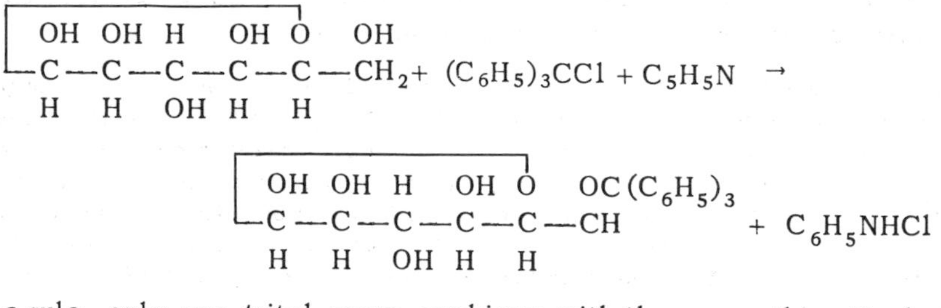

As a rule, only one trityl group combines with the sugar; this attaches itself to the oxygen of the primary hydroxyl group, although the preparation of di- and tri-trityl ethers has been reported.[203] As an example the preparation of the trityl ether of d-fructose has been described below.[204]

To a cooled solution of 36 gm of anhydrous glucose in 180 cc of absolute pyridine are added 58 gm of triphenyl chloromethane and the mixture is allowed to stand one to two days at room temperature. A small amount of an addition compound of tritylcarbinol and hydrogen chloride which precipitates out is filtered, and water is gradually added with good stirring to the filtrate cooled to 0° until a turbidity just appears. The mixture is placed in ice for a half hour and is then poured in a thin stream into 1¾ lit ice water with agitation. The light yellow syrup which settles out is washed repeatedly with water, and is reduced into droplets and dissolved in 200 cc of methanol. On cooling the solution to 0° about 2 gm of triphenylmethylcarbinol first precipitates out and is removed by filtration; then trityl-a-d-glucose separates in 36% yield. The compound crystallizes from alcohol with some alcohol of crystallization.

Trityl ethers are difficultly soluble in water, often crystallize well, and are relatively stable toward alkalies. They are decomposed, however, when treated with halogen acids.

Tritylation plays an important role in sugar chemistry, as it makes possible the protection of the primary hydroxyl group in sugars. A carbohydrate acetylated at all but the primary hydroxyl group may be obtained, for example, by acetylating a trityl ether of a carbohydrate, and subsequently removing the trityl group by treatment with hydrochloric acid. Tritylation makes possible the determination of the number of primary hydroxyl groups present in the molecule of a complex sugar.[205]

Preparation of Glucosides from Halogenoses, Acetates, etc.

Glucosides may be prepared from l-halo compounds of aldoses, the so-called halogenoses, by various procedures. These methods are important since they make possible the preparation of complex glucosides of the type of natural glucosides.

In the *Königs-Knorr procedure*[206] an acetobromo sugar is made to react with the alcohol in the presence of silver carbonate. The product obtained from a-acetobromo sugar is an acetyl β-glucoside. β-Acetohalogenoses give a mixture of isomers in which the a-glucoside largely predominates.[207] The free glucoside is obtained by removal of the acetyl group by saponification. This method serves well in difficult cases, as for example, for the preparation of the glucosides of disaccharides. This procedure presents the advantage that the reaction may be carried out in the cold in neutral solution, and the acetylated products are water-insoluble and crystallize well.

Certain halogenoses, such as those of d-mannose, d-ribose, and maltose, when treated with methanol and silver carbonate, and subsequently hydrolyzed, give 1,2-a-methoxyethylidene compounds of the type

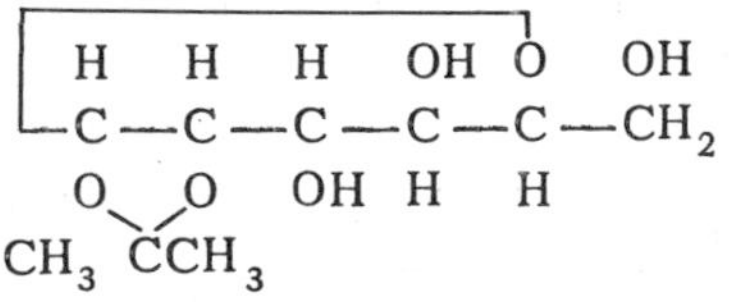

$$\left[\begin{array}{c} \text{H} \quad \text{H} \quad \text{H} \quad \text{OH} \quad \text{O} \quad \text{OH} \\ \text{C} - \text{C} - \text{C} - \text{C} - \text{C} - \text{CH}_2 \\ \text{O} \quad \text{O} \quad \text{OH} \quad \text{H} \quad \text{H} \\ \text{CH}_3 \quad \text{CCH}_3 \end{array}\right]^{208}$$

a-Acetobromoglucose apparently undergoes molecular rearrangement when subjected to this reaction and is converted to β-acetobromoglucose.[209]

Schlubach and Schröter's method consists in treating β-halogenoses in solution in pyridine or acetonitrile with alcohol and silver nitrate.[210] a-Glucosides are obtained by this procedure in very pure form.

Zemplén's procedure consists in boiling a-halogenoses with the alcohol in benzene solution in the presence of mercuric acetate. a-Glucosides result exclusively by this treatment when 100% excess of alcohol is used, and β-gluco-sides are obtained when more than 400% excess of alcohol is used.[211] Oligosac-charides, i.e., polysaccharides with two to six hexose units, with α-glucosidic bonding may be prepared by this method.[212] β-Glucosides are obtained when mercuric cyanide is used in the reaction.[213]

Phenol glucosides have been obtained by the reaction of acetobromoglucose with alkali metal derivatives of alcohols and phenols.[214] α-Halogenoses yield β-glucosides; β-halogenoses also give β-glucosides with potassium methylate and ethylate, but alkali metal phenolates and β-halogenoses yield a mixture consisting of two thirds α- and one third β-phenol glucosides. By carrying out the condensation of hydroxy compounds and acetobromo sugars in the presence of organic bases, such as quinoline, a mixture of α- and β-glucosides are ob-tained which are separable by fractional crystallization.[215]

Helferich's method serves for the preparation of aromatic glucosides. A sugar pentaacetate is heated with the phenol in the presence of a catalyst, such as zinc chloride or p-toluenesulfonic acid:[216]

$$\underset{\text{AcOCH}_2\text{CH(CHOAc)}_3\overset{\lceil\text{——O——}\rceil}{\text{CHOAc}}}{} + \text{HOC}_6\text{H}_5$$

$$\rightarrow \quad \text{AcOCH}_2\text{CH(CHOAc)}_3\overset{\lceil\text{——O——}\rceil}{\text{CHOC}_6\text{H}_5} + \text{AcOH}$$

Zemplén obtained glucosides through the reaction of sugar acetates with a chloroform solution of the alcohol in the presence of anhydrous ferric chloride, in the complete absence of moisture.[217] Mixtures of isomeric glucosides are obtained in which the α-isomer predominates. The method is not of general ap-plicability.

Glucosides have been obtained from certain sugar anhydrides by reaction with primary and secondary alcohols and phenols. Triacetyl-d-glucosan (1,2) yields β-glucosides with alcohols and α-glucosides with phenols.[218] α-Methyl gluco-sides are formed on heating α-glucosan and α-galactosan with methanol under pressure.[219]

Glucosides are formed from *glucals* by the combined action of alcohols and perbenzoic acid. α-Methyl-d-mannoside is obtained, for example, from d-glucal and methanol:[220]

$$\underset{\substack{\text{H}\quad\text{H}\quad\text{OH H}\quad\text{H}}}{\overset{\lceil\text{——O——}\rceil}{\underset{\text{OH}}{\text{H}_2\text{C——C——C——C——C}=\text{C}}}} \quad \overset{\text{CH}_3\text{OH} + \text{C}_6\text{H}_5\text{COOOH}}{\rightarrow} \quad \underset{\substack{\text{H}\quad\text{H}\quad\text{OH OH OCH}_3}}{\overset{\lceil\text{——O——}\rceil}{\underset{\text{OH}}{\text{H}_2\text{C——C——C——C——C}}}}$$

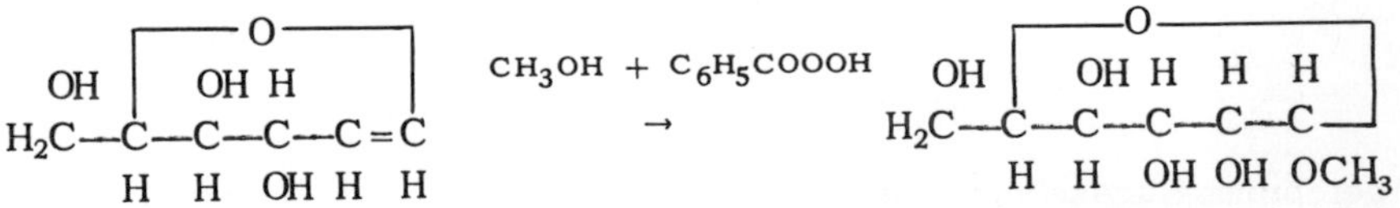

1,2-Anhydrides are probably formed as intermediates in this reaction.

Mercaptals are converted to methyl glucosides when boiled with a solution of two molecular equivalents of mercuric chloride in methanol:[221]

$$\underset{\substack{\text{| }\\+\text{ CH}_3\text{OH}}}{\text{HC(SCH}_2\text{C}_6\text{H}_5)_2} \overset{\text{HgCl}_2}{\underset{}{\rightarrow}} \quad \underset{\text{| }\quad\text{|}}{\overset{\text{SCH}_2\text{C}_6\text{H}_5}{\text{HC}——\text{O}}} \quad \rightarrow \underset{\text{| }\quad\text{|}}{\overset{\text{OCH}_3}{\text{HC}——\text{O}}}$$

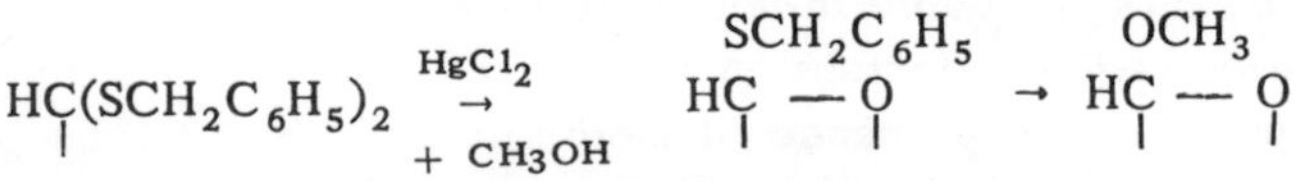

The above methods may be employed with satisfactory results for the preparation of simple as well as complex glucosides.

The natural glucoside *coniferin* has been prepared synthetically by condensing acetobromoglucose with the potassium derivative of 4-hydroxy-3-methoxycinnamaldehyde, and removing the acetyl groups from the product of reaction by hydrolysis.[222] *Indican* has been synthesized in the following manner: Methyl-3-hydroxyindole-2-carboxylate was made to react with acetobromoglucose in acetone solution in the presence of potassium hydroxide and the product was deacetylated by hydrolysis to 3-hydroxyindole-2-carboxylic acid β-glucoside. This was decarboxylated by heating with a mixture of acetic acid and sodium acetate, and the resulting acetylated product was deacetylated with methanolic ammonia to indican.[223] Two glucosides of alizarin have been prepared in an attempt at the synthesis of ruberythoic acid, but the compounds were both found to differ from the natural glucoside.[224]

Glucosides do not reduce Fehling's solution and are stable toward alkalies. Natural glucosides undergo reductive cleavage under the action of specific enzymes. This property has been employed for the characterization of natural glucosides.[225] A β-glucosidase present in emulsin causes the cleavage of β-*d*-glucosides,[226] while α-glucosidase which is a constituent of yeast, causes the cleavage of α-*d*-glucosides, but is without action on β-glucosides.[227]

Synthesis of Di- and Polysaccharides

Di- and polysaccharides may be regarded as special types of glucosides, in which carbohydrates are combined glucosidically with aldoses. Their synthesis may, therefore, be effected by the methods employed for the preparation of glucosides.

The combination of hexoses to disaccharides has been brought about by simply heating a mixture of the carbohydrates.[228] *Maltose* has been prepared, for example, by heating a mixture of equal amounts of α- and β-glucose at 160° under vacuum. Similarly, *lactose* has been obtained by heating a mixture of β-glucose and β-galactose with zinc chloride for 30 minutes at 150° under 15 mm pressure.

The coupling of two molecules of glucose to a disaccharide has been accomplished under the influence of concentrated hydrochloric acid.[229]

Disaccharides have been obtained by simply shaking a solution of the acetylated monosaccharides in which a definite hydroxyl group is free, with phosphorus pentoxide. Examples of appropriate solvents are benzene and chloroform. The claim has been made that *sucrose* has been synthesized by this method from tetraacetyl-γ-fructose and tetraacetylglucose,[230] but this claim does not appear to have been substantiated.

Purdie and Irvine's procedure has been employed for the preparation of disaccharides. Thus, acetobromogalactose has been made to react with 1,2,3,4-tetraacetylglucose in the presence of silver oxide to obtain glucose-β-galactoside octaacetate.[231]

$$
\begin{array}{cccccc}
\text{OAc} & \text{OAc} & \text{OAc} & \text{OAc} & \text{H} & \text{OH} \\
\text{C} - \text{C} - \text{C} - \text{C} - \text{C} - \text{CH}_2 \\
\text{H} & \text{H} & \text{H} & \text{H} & \text{O}
\end{array}
\quad + \quad
\begin{array}{cccccc}
\text{Br} & \text{OAc} & \text{OAc} & \text{OAc} & \text{H} & \text{OAc} \\
\text{C} - \text{C} - \text{C} - \text{C} - \text{C} - \text{CH}_2 \\
\text{H} & \text{H} & \text{H} & \text{H} & \text{O}
\end{array}
$$

$$
\rightarrow
\begin{array}{cccccc}
\text{OAc} & \text{OAc} & \text{OAc} & \text{OAc} & \text{H} & \text{O} \\
\text{C} - \text{C} - \text{C} - \text{C} - \text{C-CH}_2 \\
\text{H} & \text{H} & \text{H} & & \text{O}
\end{array}
\begin{array}{cccccc}
\text{OAc} & \text{OAc} & \text{OAc} & \text{H} & \text{OAc} \\
\text{C} - \text{C} - \text{C} - \text{C} - \text{C} - \text{CH}_2 \\
\text{H} & \text{H} & \text{H} & \text{H} & \text{O}
\end{array}
$$

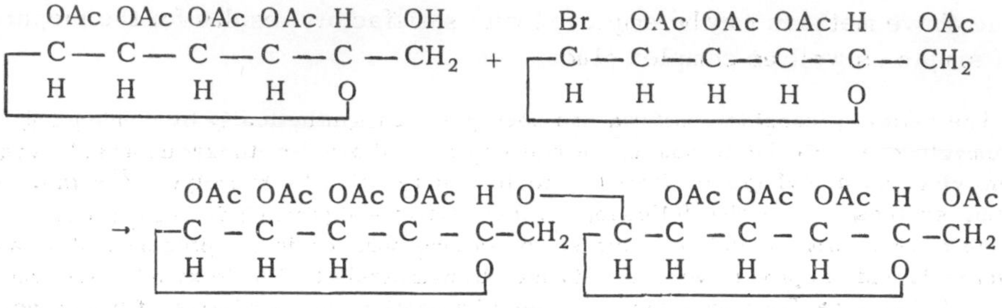

The naturally occurring disaccharides primeverose, gentibiose[232], and melibiose[233] have been prepared by this method. A crystalline disaccharide of the trehalose type, *isotrehalose*, has been obtained through the action of silver carbonate in aqueous suspension on acetobromoglucose.[234]

2,3,4-Tribenzoylglucosyl fluoride has been condensed with acetobromoglucose in the presence of silver oxide. The acetyl groups may be removed from the product by treatment with alcoholic ammonia to form gentibiosyl fluoride, and this gives gentibiose when boiled in aqueous solution with calcium carbonate.

Diacetoneglucose, which has a free hydroxyl at 3-position, could not be made to react with acetobromoglucose. Diacetonegalactose, on the other hand, has been successfully converted to di- and trisaccharides by reaction with acetobromosugars.[235] Removal of the acetone groups from the resulting compounds by the action of dilute acids takes place more readily than cleavage of the sugar groups and it is therefore possible to prepare the free di- and trisaccharides from the acetone compounds.[236] Sugar derivatives with a free hydroxyl group which fail to react with the acetobromosugars can be converted to disaccharides through the reaction of their sodio derivatives with acetobromosugars.[237]

Zemplén's mercuric acetate method for the preparation of glucosides is also of value for the synthesis of disaccharides.

The presence of a furanose group in disaccharides can be demonstrated by Helferich's "diene" method, which utilizes the property of furanoses with a double bond at the 5,6-position, e.g.,

$$
\begin{array}{ccccc}
 & \text{OH} & \text{O} & \text{H} & \text{OH} & \text{H} \\
\text{CH}_2 = \text{C} - \text{C} - \text{C} - \text{C} - \text{C} \\
 & \text{H} & \text{OH} & \text{H} & & \text{OR}
\end{array}
$$

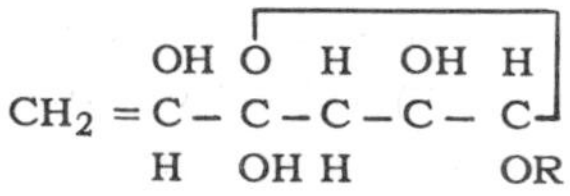

to reduce Fehling's solution. Pyranose derivatives do not possess this property.[238]

Disaccharides in the pure form are capable of crystallizing well. Reducing disaccharides behave in the same manner as monodisaccharides; they yield aldonic acids by oxidation and alcohols and glucals by reduction.

Chemical methods for the determination of the *molecular weight* of polysaccharides are available. In the polysaccharide, the two *end groups* differ in nature from each other and from other groups in the chain. In an aldohexose chain the end groups may be as shown below

$$
\begin{array}{c}
\text{H} \\
\text{HOCO} \boxed{} \\
\text{HCOH} \\
\text{HOCH} \\
\text{HC} \boxed{} \\
\text{HCO} \boxed{} \\
\text{CH}_2\text{OH}
\end{array}
\quad \text{and} \quad
\begin{array}{c}
\text{H} \\
-\text{C} \boxed{} \\
\text{HCOH} \\
\text{HOCH} \\
\text{HCOH} \\
\text{CO} \boxed{} \\
\text{CH}_2\text{OH}
\end{array}
$$

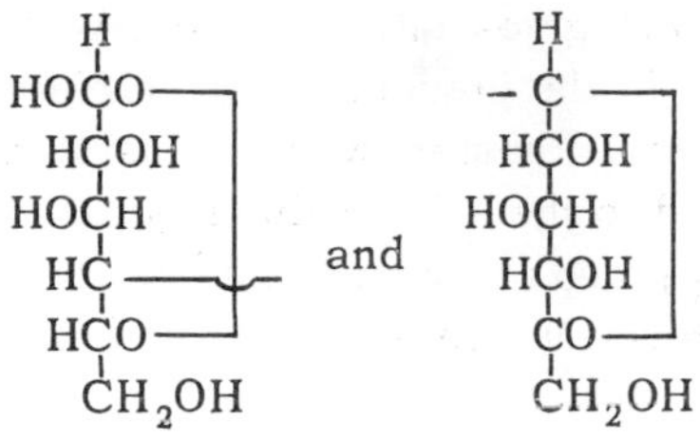

The proportion of the glucosidic group in the unit, i.e., the end group shown at the left, to the whole molecule may be determined by the hypoiodite method.[239] The proportion of the other end group to the whole molecule may also be determined. This is done by complete methylation followed by hydrolytic cleavage of the glucosidic methyl group. All groups in the polysaccharide then yield trimethyl ethers, except the end group shown at the right, which gives a tetramethyl ether. A determination of the total methoxyl makes possible the calculation of the proportion the end group bears to the whole molecule, and from this the molecular weight of the polysaccharide may be calculated.[240]

Acetals and Ketals of Carbohydrates

In common with other alcoholic bodies, carbohydrates are capable of reacting with aldehydes and ketones in the presence of acids to form acetals and ketals. As with other polyhydric alcohols, the usual type of compounds formed are cyclic, the carbonyl group reacting with two hydroxyl groups in the molecule of the carbohydrate:

$$
\begin{array}{c}
\overline{\text{O} \quad \text{H}} \\
\text{HC} - \text{C} - \\
\text{OH OH}
\end{array}
+ \text{OC} \!\!\begin{array}{c} \nearrow \text{R} \\ \searrow \text{R}' \end{array}
\rightarrow
\begin{array}{c}
\overline{\text{O} \quad \text{H}} \\
\text{HC} - \text{C} - \\
\text{O} \quad \text{O} \\
\searrow \text{C} \swarrow \\
\text{R} \quad \text{R}'
\end{array}
$$

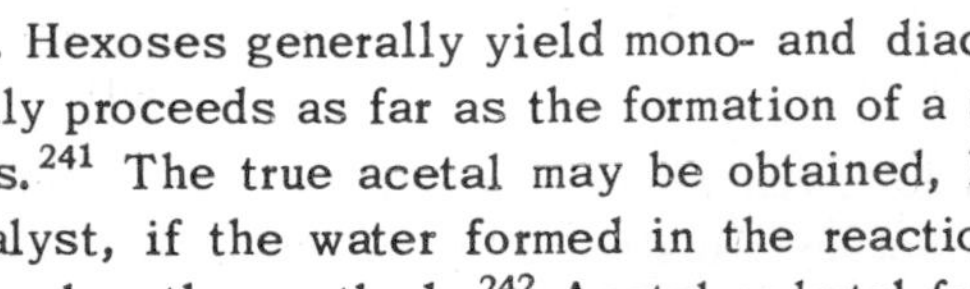

With aldehydes and with unsymmetrical ketones, three isomeric acetals or ketals, d, l, and dl, are formed because of the introduction of a new asymmetric carbon atom into the molecule. Hexoses generally yield mono- and diacetals and ketals.

The reaction generally proceeds as far as the formation of a semiacetal in the absence of a catalysts.[241] The true acetal may be obtained, however, even in the absence of a catalyst, if the water formed in the reaction is removed by azeotropic distillation or by other methods.[242] Acetal or ketal formation proceeds readily in the presence of mineral acids, zinc chloride and anhydrous copper sulfate.[243] The reaction proceeds well also in the presence of phosphorus pentoxide and other dehydration agents, though not as readily as in the presence of concentrated mineral acids.[244] In many cases the use of zinc chloride rather than acids is preferred because of the difficulty experienced in purifying the product when acids are used as catalysts.[245]

The type of product obtained may vary according to the catalyst employed. 1,6-Dibenzoyldulcitol gives the 2,3:4,5-dibenzylidene derivative, for example, when it is made to react with benzaldehyde in the presence of hydrogen chloride at room temperature, but gives an isomeric dibenzylidene derivative when the reaction is carried out in the presence of zinc chloride and at ordinary temperature. When this isomer is heated with behzaldehyde in the presence of zinc chloride, it is converted to the 2,3:4,5-dibenzylidene derivative.[246] The presence of chlorine or a nitro group as substituents in the nucleus of an aromatic aldehyde facilitates the reaction, while methyl and methoxy groups hinder the reaction.

The configuration of the carbohydrate molecule determines to a large extent the course of its reaction with carbonyl compounds. The structure of the carbonyl compound also exerts an important influence on the type of compound formed. It has been observed that in the reaction of glycerol with substituted acetaldehydes, electrophilic substituents, such as chlorine, and high temperatures favor the formation of five-membered or β-rings, and electrophobic groups favor the formation of six-membered or γ-rings.[247] A close scrutiny of experimental results led Hudson and Hann to formulate certain general rules which make possible the prediction of the course of reaction in any particular instance with some degree of certainly.

A β-*cis* combination is favored over a β-*trans* combination, a β-ring formation over a γ-ring. A γ-*trans* combination is favored over a γ-*cis* combination. An α-ring may appear where the formation of a β-ring is not permissible. The order of precedence appears to be as follows: β-*cis* ring, α-ring, β-*trans* or γ-*trans* ring. In methylideneation, a β-*trans* ring takes precedence over γ-*trans* ring formation. The last two rules may fail to hold if one or both of the carbon atoms carrying the hydroxyl groups concerned in the reaction are part of a ring system.

With some carbohydrates reaction with carbonyl compounds is accompanied by a change of the oxygen bridge from a pyranose to a furanose type. Glucose, for example, reacting with two molecules of acetone, yields diacetoneglucofuranose:

$$\begin{array}{ccccccc} & \overline{OH} & OH & H & OH & O & OH \\ & | & | & | & | & | & | \\ & C & - & C & - & C & - & C & - & C & - & CH_2 \\ & | & | & | & | & & \\ & H & H & OH & H & & \end{array} \rightarrow \begin{array}{ccccccc} & C(CH_3)_2 & & C(CH_3)_2 \\ & / \backslash & & / \backslash \\ & O & O & H & O & O & O \\ & | & | & | & | & | & | \\ & C & - & C & - & C & - & C & - & C & - & CH_2 \\ & | & | & | & & \\ & H & H & OH & & \end{array}$$

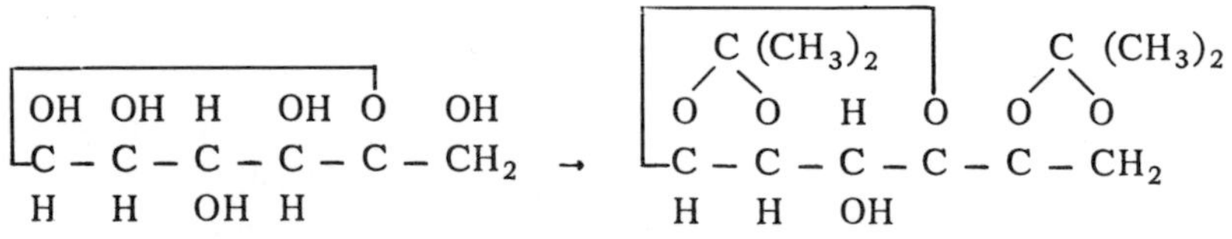

The *procedures* followed when using hydrochloric acid, sulfuric acid, or zinc chloride as a catalyst are illustrated by the examples given below.

Preparation of Diacetoneglucose[248] —Use of Sulfuric Acid

Sixty-five grams of finely ground and sifted glucose are suspended in 1.8 lit of commercial acetone, 55 cc of sulfuric acid are added and the mixture is shaken until all but 5 gm of the glucose disappears; this requires from 4 to 5 hours. The solution is filtered and anhydrous calcium carbonate is added to the filtrate gradually and with shaking until the color becomes a light yellow. Generally 150 to 200 gm of carbonate are required. The filtered solution is evaporated to dryness under vacuum, the residue is dissolved in the smallest possible amount of ether, the solution is filtered and petroleum ether is added gradually with cooling, whereupon diacetoneglucose precipitates out. For complete purification the compound may be crystallized from petroleum ether, sulfur dioxide, methanol, or aqueous methanol.

Tin chloride increases the solubility of *d*-glucose in acetone. Acetaldehyde acts as a catalyst in the reaction.

Monoacetoneglucose is prepared from diacetoneglucose in the following manner:[249] Fifty grams of diacetoneglucose are dissolved by shaking at 50° in 800 cc of water containing 0.4 gm hydrogen chloride, and the solution is held at 50° for 1½ to 2 hours, or until its rotating power in a 1 cm tube decreases to 0.8 to 0.2. The solution is then shaken with silver carbonate to eliminate the hydrogen chloride. The solution is evaporated to dryness under vacuum by heating in a bath at 50°, the solid is taken up with boiling ethyl acetate, and the solution is filtered and cooled to crystallization. The liquid sets to an almost gelatinous mass. This is filtered and the solid is pressed and dried. The yield is 80% of the diacetoneglucose used. The compound is purified by repeated crystallization from ethyl acetate.

Preparation of Diacetonemannose[250]—Use of Hydrochloric Acid

Mannose is shaken with fifteen times its weight of acetone containing 1% hydrochloric acid until all the sugar dissolves. This requires ten to twelve hours. The free hydrogen chloride is then eliminated by treatment with lead carbonate, and the filtered solution is concentrated under vacuum. The diacetone compound crystallizes out in clusters of needles; it is filtered and recrystallized from twelve parts of petroleum ether. The yield is 84 to 90% of theory.

Preparation of Diacetonegalactose[251]—Use of Zinc Chloride

Five grams of pulverized galactose are boiled under reflux with a solution of 30 gm zinc chloride in 200 cc acetone. The sugar dissolves within half an hour. The solution is filtered and allowed to stand overnight. The acetone is then evaporated off under vacuum at 30°, 140 cc of concentrated sodium hydroxide are added to the residue and the mass is shaken with ether. The liquid is then filtered, the ether layer is removed and the aqueous layer is extracted twice with ether. The extracts and the original ether layer are combined, dried, and the ether is removed by evaporation. The residue is finally distilled under a vacuum of 0.8 mm. Yield 2.0 gm.

4,6-Benzylidene-*d*-glucose is formed through the reaction of benzaldehyde with glucose under the action of zinc chloride.[252] 1,2-Monoacetoneglucose gives a 3,5-benzylidene derivative with benzaldehyde, if condensation is carried out rapidly, but a 5,6-derivative on long heating.[253]

Fructose reacting with acetone in the presence of hydrogen chloride gives five different acetone fructoses, two diacetone fructoses, two monoacetonefructoses corresponding to these, and another, the 2,5-derivative obtained only in the form of syrup. 1,2:4,5-Diisopropylidene-*d*-fructose has been obtained in 55% yield by shaking *d*-fructose with acetone in the presence of zinc chloride.[254] A satisfactory method for the preparation of β-diisopropylidene-*d*-fructose consists in shaking cane sugar with acetone, zinc chloride, phosphoric oxide, and phosphoric acid.[255] Acetonation of *l-sorbose* results in the formation of 1,2- and 2,3-monoisopropylidene and the 2,3:4,6-diisopropylidene derivatives.[256] A triethylidene-*d*-sorbitol has been obtained from *d-sorbitol*, paraldehyde and hydrochloric acid.[257] *Mannitol* gives 1,2:5,6-diisopropylidene-*d*-mannitol with acetone in the presence of cupric sulfate, but 1,2:3,4:5,6-triisopropylidene-*d*-mannitol in 75% yield in the presence of concentrated sulfuric acid.[258] With boric acid and concentrated sulfuric acid, the triisopropylidene is formed, together with the 4,5-boric ester of 1,2-isopropylidene mannitol.[259] The latter yields the 1,2-diisopropylidene derivative by alcoholysis. Acidic hydrolysis of the triketal affords 1,2:3,4-diisopropylidene-mannitol and 3,4-isopropylidenemannitol.[260] A trimethylene-*d*-mannitol has been obtained by warming the hexitol with 40% formaldehyde in the presence of concentrated sulfuric acid.[261] *Rhamnose* forms only a monoacetone derivative; this is obtained very readily by shaking the carbohydrate with acetone containing 0.2% hydrogen chloride.[262] *Erythritol* gives a diisopropylidene derivative when shaken with acetone containing 1% hydrogen chloride.[263] If the reaction is carried out with acetone containing 25% water, a monoisopropylideneerythritol is formed.[264] Diisopropylidenearabinose has been prepared from *arabinose* and acetone containing a little hydrochloric acid in solution.[265] *Dulcitol* yields only the diisopropylidene and dibenzylidene derivatives with acetone and benzaldehyde.

The best method of determination of isopropylidene groups in sugars is a modified iodoform reaction of Messinger.[266]

Resistance of Alkylidene and Arylidene Derivatives of Carbohydrates to Chemical Reagents

The alkylidene and arylidene derivatives of carbohydrates show marked resistance to certain chemical reagents; on the other hand, their removal may be accomplished by acid hydrolysis under comparatively mild conditions. These facts together with the ready formation of acetals or ketals of many carbohydrates under mild conditions give these compounds special importance in the chemistry of carbohydrates. The introduction and removal of alkylidene and arylidene groups may often be effected without affecting the configuration at asymmetric centers. These groups are resistant to many of the more common reagents used in carbohydrate chemistry and do not readily migrate. Acetals and ketals of carbohydrates may be exposed to processes such as acylation, sulfonation, methylation, benzoylation, and tritylation under the usual mild conditions without affecting the alkylidene or arylidene groups in any way. Two anomalies should be pointed out, however. The benzylidene residue in 3,5-benzylidene-6-chloro-6-desoxy-1,4-anhydro-*d*-sorbitol, while stable toward cold sodium methoxide, may be removed by steam distillation.[267] The benzoylation of 2,3:5,6-diisopropylidene-*d,l*-galacitol may be ascribed to the migration of the ketal group.[268] It would appear, therefore, that although the treatment of an acetal or ketal with a basic reagent is not likely to cause structural rearrangements, the possibility that such changes may occur cannot be ignored.

Acetals and ketals are stable toward oxidizing agents. Periodates and lead tetraacetate are the most used among such agents in structural studies in the carbohydrate field. The former are used in aqueous solution, the latter generally in organic solvents.

It has already been pointed out that alkylidene and arylidene groups in acetals and ketals of carbohydrates, while resistant to the action of alkalies, may be removed by the action of dilute acids. When hot hydrochloric acid is employed, hydrolysis is virtually complete in most cases in the course of one hour. In general, the ease of removal of the two groups in diacetals and diketals varies considerably. Thus, the 5,6-isopropylidene group in 1,2:5,6-diisopropylideneglucose is removed forty times as rapidly as the 1,2-group. This fact makes possible the easy preparation of monoacetals or -ketals from the di- compounds. Acetals of formaldehyde appears to be more resistant to hydrolysis than those of higher aliphatic aldehydes.

The α- and γ-*trans*-rings in benzylidene, ethylidene, and methylidene acetals are more readily hydrolyzed than β-rings, and the β-ring more readily than β-*cis* rings. In isopropylidene and cyclohexylidene ketals, the α-ring is hydrolyzed more readily than the α-*trans* ring.

A mixture of acetic anhydride, acetic acid, and 1-2% sulfuric acid at 0° ruptures preferentially any methylene bridge which spans a primary and a secondary position, i.e., α- and β-rings, giving the acetic ester of the primary hydroxyl and the acetoxymethyl ether of the secondary hydroxyl. The reaction is not specific, however, for α- and β-rings, as it has been found that prolonged acetolysis of 1,3:2,5:4,6-trimethylene mannitol at 20° furnishes hexaacetylmannitol.[269] Benzylidene acetals are much less resistant to acetolysis than methylene acetals, and all rings are ruptured.[270]

Mercaptals of Carbohydrates

Aldoses react with a variety of thiols in the presence of acids to form mercaptals:[271]

$$\underset{\substack{| \\ H \quad\ \ H \quad\ OH \ \ H \quad\ H}}{H_2C - \overset{\substack{OH}}{C} - \overset{\substack{O}}{C} - \overset{\substack{OH}}{C} - \overset{\substack{H}}{C} - \overset{\substack{OH \ \ OH}}{C} -} + 2HSC_2H_5 \rightarrow$$

$$\underset{\substack{| \\ H \quad H \quad OH \ \ H \quad\ H}}{H_2C - \overset{\substack{OH}}{C} - \overset{\substack{OH}}{C} - \overset{\substack{OH}}{C} - \overset{\substack{H}}{C} - \overset{\substack{OH \ \ SC_2H_5}}{C}SC_2H_5} + H_2O$$

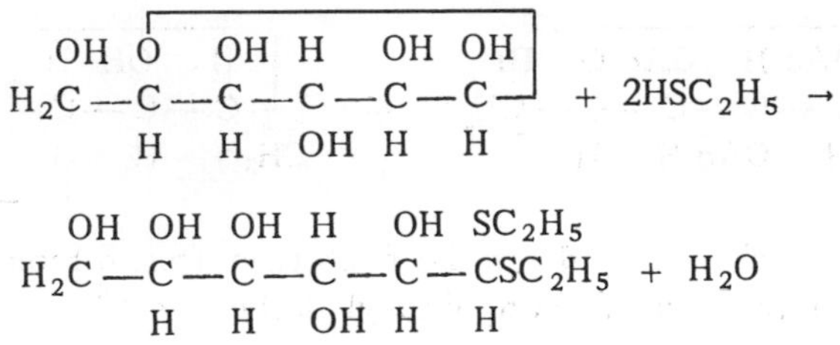

Benzoates of carbohydrates of the open chain and of the furanose type react with mercaptans to form mercaptals, the former with loss of a benzoyl group. The pyranose type fails to react unless the carbonyl group is free.[272]

Ketoses do not react directly with mercaptans. Certain derivatives of ketoses are capable of reacting with mercaptans, however, to form mercaptals. Thus, keto-*d*-fructose pentabenzoate reacts with ethyl mercaptan normally to form a mercaptal.[273] The pentaacetate also reacts to form a mercaptal, and this may be deacetylated with methanolic ammonia or with barium methoxide to *d*-fructose diethyl mercaptal.[274]

Because of the resistance of the mercaptal grouping to various chemical agents, mercapto groups may be used for protecting the aldehyde group in aldoses. The hydroxy groups in mercaptals may be methylated, for example, without affecting the mercaptal group. The mercaptal groups may be readily removed by treatment with mercuric chloride. Removal may be effected also by treating the solution of the mercaptal in acetone first with cadmium carbonate, then with a solution of mercuric chloride in acetone.[275]

Sugar Anhydrides

Sugar anhydrides are internal ethers or oxides. They are formed through the elimination of water from a molecule of the carbohydrate. Anhydrides may be obtained by simply heating the carbohydrate under vacuum.[276] Glucosan is obtained in this way from a-d-glucose, and levulosan from fructose. Anhydrides are formed also by the action of acids on carbohydrates.[277] The use of concentrated acids and long periods of reaction are necessary for obtaining good yields of the anhydrides. Anhydrous hydrogen halides under pressure have proven especially effective agents for bringing about anhydride formation.

Inorganic sugar esters in which the reducing group is protected by esterification or otherwise, have been converted to anhydrides by saponification. In the resulting anhydrides the reducing group remains intact. 6-Bromo- and 6-toluenesulfonic derivatives are especially susceptible to anhydridization by this method. In many instances 3,6-anhydrides are formed.[278] For successful anhydridization it is important that carbon atom 5 should not carry a hydroxyl group, and that a free hydroxyl group be available on carbon atom 3 on the same side of the sugar ring as the side chain C-6. A 3,6-anhydro glucose has been obtained, for example, by the action of baryta water on the methyl glucoside of 2,3,4-triacetylglucose-6-bromohydrin:

$$
\begin{array}{ccccccc}
\text{H} & \text{OAc} & \text{H} & \text{OAc} & \text{O} & \text{Br} \\
\text{C} & \text{C} & \text{C} & \text{C} & \text{C} & \text{CH}_2 \\
\text{CH}_3\text{O} & \text{H} & \text{OAc} & \text{H} & \text{H}
\end{array}
\quad\rightarrow\quad
\begin{array}{ccccccc}
\text{H} & \text{OH} & \text{H} & \text{OH} & \text{O} \\
\text{C} & \text{C} & \text{C} & \text{C} & \text{C} & \text{CH}_2 \\
\text{CH}_3\text{O} & \text{H} & \text{O} & \text{H} & \text{H}
\end{array}
$$

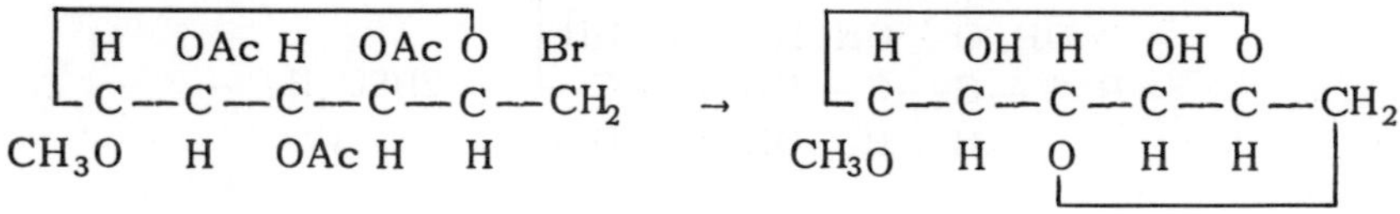

A 5,6-anhydride was obtained for the first time from 6-bromoisopropylidene-d-glucose and from the corresponding 6-tosyl derivative.[279]

Levoglucosan has been obtained by the action of boiling baryta water on the naturally occurring glucosides picein, salicin, and coniferin.[280] Anhydrides have also been obtained by the action of hot baryta water on phenyl-β-d-glucosides.[281]

Unsaturated anhydro glucoses have been made by the action of silver sulfate or silver fluoride on 6-halohydrins.[282] The reaction proceeds successfully only in anhydrous media.

Karrer converted the acetohalo sugars to quaternary trimethylamino glucosides by reaction with trimethylamine. Upon treatment of the halide of the amine with caustic, the amino group was removed and an anhydride was obtained:[283]

$$
\begin{array}{cccccc}
\text{Br} & \text{OAc} & \text{OAc} & \text{OAc} & \text{H} & \text{OH} \\
\text{C} & \text{C} & \text{C} & \text{C} & \text{C} & \text{CH}_2 \\
\text{H} & \text{H} & \text{H} & \text{H} & \text{O}
\end{array}
+(CH_3)_3N \rightarrow
\begin{array}{cccccc}
\text{Br}(\text{CH}_3)_3\text{N} & \text{OAc} & \text{OAc} & \text{OAc} & \text{H} & \text{OAc} \\
\text{C} & \text{C} & \text{C} & \text{C} & \text{C} & \text{CH}_2 \\
\text{H} & \text{H} & \text{H} & \text{H} & \text{O}
\end{array}
$$

$$
\xrightarrow{\text{NaOH}}
\begin{array}{cccccc}
& \text{OH} & \text{OH} & \text{OH} & \text{H} & \text{O} \\
\text{C} & \text{C} & \text{C} & \text{C} & \text{C} & \text{CH}_2 \\
\text{H} & \text{H} & \text{H} & \text{H} & \text{O}
\end{array}
$$

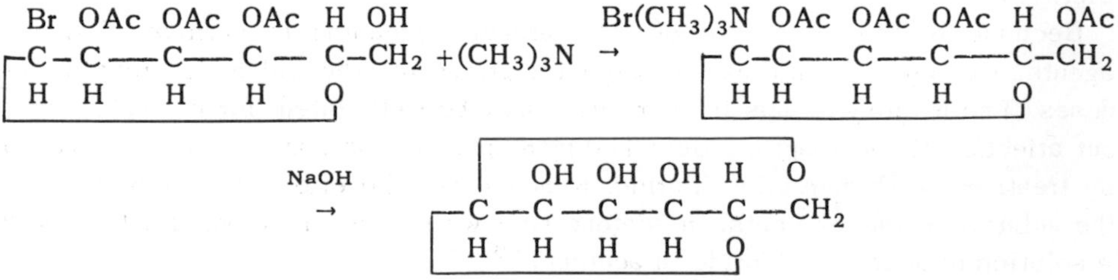

This method has given the 1,6-anhydride in all cases to which it has been applied.

Sugar anhydrides have been obtained by treating amino sugars with nitrous acid.[284] 1,4-Anhydrosorbitol has been obtained from glucamine by this method:

$$\underset{\substack{\\ \text{H} \quad\;\; \text{OH} \;\; \text{H}}}{\overset{\text{NH}_2\;\text{OH} \;\; \text{H} \quad\; \text{OH} \;\; \text{OH} \;\; \text{OH}}{\text{H}_2\text{C}-\text{C}-\text{C}-\text{C}-\text{C}-\text{CH}_2}} \overset{\text{HNO}_2}{\rightarrow} \underset{\substack{\\ \text{H} \quad \text{OH} \;\; \text{H} \quad\; \text{H}}}{\overset{\overline{\text{O} \quad\; \text{OH} \;\; \text{H} \;\;\Big|} \quad\; \text{OH} \;\; \text{OH}}{\text{H}_2\text{C}-\text{C}-\text{C}-\text{C}-\text{C}-\text{CH}_2}}$$

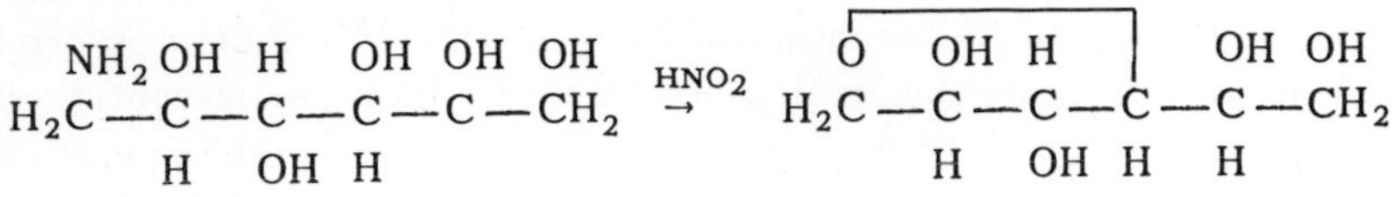

Chitose has been obtained from d-glucosamine by the same method.

Anhydrides have been prepared through the hydrogenation of acetobromo-sugars.[285] 1,5-Anhydropentitols and hexitols have been obtained by desulfurizing thioglycopyranosides with Raney nickel.[286]

A cellobiose anhydride has been obtained through acetolysis of cellulose with a mixture of glacial acetic acid and hydrogen bromide, followed by exchange of the glucosidically bound bromine atom for an acetyl group and fractionation of the product.[287]

Anhydrides of carbohydrates show a strong tendency toward polymerization. Polymerization is favored by heat and catalysts, such as zinc chloride.[288] The type of polymer formed may depend on the pressure under which the polymerization is carried out. It is believed that certain anhydrides show a tendency toward molecular association by secondary valencies.

Monomeric anhydrides are, as a rule, readily soluble in water, methanol, ethanol and pyridine. They are almost insoluble in ether, acetone, and chloroform. Dimolecular anhydrides are insoluble in ethanol and soluble in methanol, but solubility in the latter solvent decreases with increasing molecular weight.

Ethylene oxide type of anhydrides undergo ring cleavage when treated with acids or alkalies, while the normal hydrofuranol is resistant to the action of these reagents. Glucosans, even those with five membered rings, are stable to alkalies but are readily hydrolyzed by acids. Ring fissure in this case is attended by a Walden inversion at carbon atom 1.[289]

Some monomeric anhydrides are hydrolyzed to the corresponding monosaccharides on contact with water. These anhydrides are of the ethylene oxide type; they reduce Fehling's solution, give the acetate of the corresponding sugar when acetylated, and readily add hydrogen chloride to form the chlorides of the sugars. The 2,5-anhydro ring shows a remarkable stability. It has not been possible to break this ring by treatment with acids.[290] Dimolecular anhydrides are resistant to the action of acids.

Esters of Carbohydrates

Acetylated sugars are best prepared by the action of acetic anhydride on the carbohydrate in the presence of pyridine or of catalysts such as sodium acetate, zinc chloride, or sulfuric acid.[291] Acetylation in the presence of pyridine, which may be carried out at low temperatures, may be employed in connection with sensitive sugar derivatives. The isomeric α- and β-glucose pentaacetates have been prepared by this method from α- and β-glucose. The use of catalysts usually leads to the formation of only one isomer, sodium acetate and sulfuric acid giving the β-acetate, zinc chloride at high temperatures giving the α-isomer. Zinc chloride causes no configurational change in the cold.[292] Acetylation with acetyl chloride leads to the formation of the α-acetate.[433] α-Acetates are usually prepared from the β-isomer by boiling a solution of the latter in acetic anhydride containing a little zinc chloride. An equilibrium mixture of the α- and β-isomers is formed, from which the two isomers may be separated by making use of their differences in solubility in certain solvents.

β-*n*-*d*-Glucose pentaacetate has been prepared by heating on a water bath with agitation a mixture of *d*-glucose with acetic anhydride and sodium acetate for 2 to 3 hours.[293] After the completion of the reaction the mixture was poured in ice water, the product was allowed to remain in contact with water for several hours, in order to destroy the excess of acetic anhydride, and the pentaacetate was then purified by crystallization from alcohol.

When 1,2-isopropylidene glucose is treated with one molecule of acetic anhydride, the 6-hydroxyl group is esterified in preference to the others.

Other acylation reactions are carried out by methods similar to these employed for acetylation.[294] A general method for the esterification of the free hydroxyl groups in partially substituted sugars consists in treating them with the chloride of the appropriate acid in the presence of pyridine or quinoline.[295]

α-n-Pentabenzoyl-d-glucose has been obtained by treating α-*d*-glucose in chloroform solution with benzoyl chloride and quinoline or pyridine at low temperatures.[296]

Fructose 1,2:4,5-dicarbonate has been obtained by conducting phosgene into a solution of fructose in pyridine.[297] The compound is a fructopyranose.

Hesperonal, or sucrose monophosphate, is obtained by adding a mixture of sugar solution and lime to a solution of phosphorus oxychloride in chloroform.[298] Phosphatase causes cleavage of the compound to sucrose and phosphoric acid.

Sugar acetates may be hydrolyzed to the original sugars by treatment with acids or alkalies. A very satisfactory procedure originated by Zemplén[299] consists in adding a methyl alcoholic solution of sodium methylate to the chloroform solution of the sugar acetate. An addition compound of the acetylated sugar with sodium methylate precipitates out, which, on treatment with water, yields the free sugar. As an illustration of Zemplén's procedure the hydrolysis of cellobiose octaacetate is described below.[300]

Four hundred grams of octaacetylcellobiose are dissolved in one liter chloroform, the solution is strongly cooled in a freezing mixture, and a sodium methoxide solution prepared from 20 gm metallic sodium and 1 lit absolute methanol, similarly cooled, is added with stirring and continued cooling. The sodium methoxide addition compound separates within five minutes in a gelatinous form. One liter of ice water is now added in small portions with agitation. A small sample of the chloroform layer is withdrawn and evaporated to dryness; lack of a residue indicates that the operation has been properly conducted. Forty to fifty cubic centimeters of acetic acid are now added and the mass is shaken; the chloroform layer is withdrawn, and the aqueous layer is evaporated down under vacuum to a thick syrup. This is poured into a liter of warm absolute alcohol with good stirring, whereupon well-formed colorless crystals of cellobiose separate. The whole is allowed to stand overnight; the crystals are then filtered off, washed with a little absolute alcohol, and dried at 40-50°. Yield 180-185 grams.

A series of sugar nitrates have been prepared from glucosan, including 2,3,4-trimethylglucose-1,6-dinitrate.[301] This has been converted to the corresponding methyl glucoside mononitrate, triacetylglucose dinitrate and tetraacetylglucose mononitrate.

Cellulose[302] may be acetylated with acetic anhydride in the presence of sulfuric acid[303] or zinc chloride.[304] Sulfur dioxide containing traces of chlorine also acts as a catalyst and gives good results, especially in the acetylation of starch.[305] Acetylation of cellulose proceeds most rapidly when sulfuric acid is used as a catalyst. Sulfuric acid brings about some degree of acetolytic degradation of cellulose, however, and also combines with cellulose. A more satisfactory product is obtained when zinc chloride is used as a catalyst and the reaction is carried out at 10-20°. Under these conditions very little cleavage of the cellulose molecule takes place. The fully acetylated product, containing 62.5% acetyl, is designated as the primary acetyl cellulose. Secondary, or acetone-soluble acetyl cellulose ("Cellit") differs markedly from the primary product. It is prepared from the primary product by partial deacetylation under the action of dilute acids.[306] The acetyl content varies between 50 and 57.6%. Triacetylcellulose from various sources have been crystallized successfully from dilute tetrachloroethane solution.[307]

Wholly dried cotton cellulose does not react with anhydrous acetyl chloride, but reaction proceeds slowly at 17-20° in the presence of 4-5% moisture, giving a 92% yield of the triacetate within four days.

The acetylation of starch succeeds only if the material is subjected to the proper pretreatment. The simplest method is to make a thin paste in water by warming, and to precipitate the starch from the warm paste by the addition of alcohol. The precipitate is washed several times with alcohol, and finally with ether in order to eliminate all traces of water. Starch, acetylated in the cold with acetic anhydride in the presence of concentrated sulfuric acid, gives a di- and trihexosan acetate. Acetates of starch have been prepared also by use of other catalysts.[308]

Cellulose nitrates with the maximum nitrogen content have been prepared by nitrating cellulose with mixtures of nitric and phosphoric acids, or a mixture consisting of 50 parts 99.9% nitric acid, 25 parts glacial acetic acid and 27 parts acetic anhydride.[309] Nitrocellulose is stabilized by a boiling process with alcohol or water. Stabilization depends on the removal of various unstable impurities. Nitrocellulose may be denitrated with alcoholic sodium ethylate, or with ammonium salt of alkali sulfhydrate.[310]

Cellulose xanthate is made by the action of carbon disulfide on alkali cellulose.[311] Evidence indicates that to every two $C_6H_{10}O_5$ unit in the molecule of the xanthate there are present one CS_2 group and one atom of sodium.[312]

The structural unit containing the xanthate group is represented as

$$
\begin{array}{cccccccc}
 & \text{OCSNa} & \text{H} & \text{O} & & & \text{OH} \\
\text{---C} & \text{---C} & \text{------} & \text{C} & \text{---C} & \text{---C} & \text{---CH}_2 \\
\text{H} & \text{H} & & \text{OH} & \text{H} & \text{H} &
\end{array}
$$

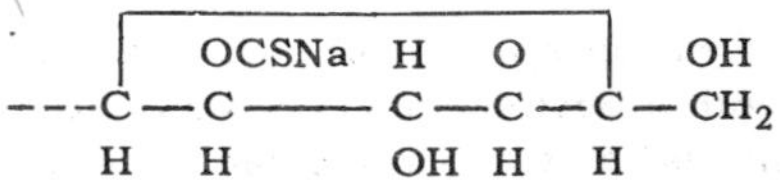

It is assumed that every glucosidic unit is not accessible to the reagent, and that only certain groups at the surface of the fibres react with the disulfide. The formation of definite compounds of the type $(C_6H_{10}O)_2MOH$ between cellulose and alkali hydroxides is now regarded as definitely established.[313]

Inulin may be acetylated by the action of acetic anhydride and pyridine at 20 to 60° to a hexaacetate in 80% yield. The product is apparently a hexaacetyldifructose anhydride.[314] On boiling inulin acetate in chloroform solution in the presence of traces of benzenesulfonic acid, it is converted to inulan.[315] Heating should not be continued too long.

Halogen Derivatives of Carbohydrates

The hydroxyl groups in carbohydrates are replaceable with halogens. As with alkoxy compounds of carbohydrates, a halogen atom in the 1 or the reducing position in aldoses differs in its behavior toward chemical agents from those in the remaining positions. Halo derivatives of aldoses with the halogen in 1-position will be referred to as *halogenoses*, those with the halogen in other positions as *halohydrins*.

The hydroxyl groups in carbohydrates may be replaced with halogen atoms by reaction with hydrogen halides, but reaction with free carbohydrates results in the formation of mixtures of halo compounds.

Acetylated 1-halo derivatives of aldoses are prepared from the fully acetylated carbohydrates. The bromides are formed from the latter by the action of a mixture of hydrogen bromide and acetic acid,[316] while the chlorides are obtained by reaction with phosphorus pentachloride or titanium tetrachloride. In these reactions, an acetyl group is replaced with a halogen atom. Replacement of the 1-acetyl group with a halogen atom may be brought about by heating the acetylated sugar with liquid hydrogen halide in a bomb. The reaction time should not be unduely prolonged, since otherwise, side reactions take place to an appreciable extent.

Halogenoses, like the free carbohydrates, exist in the α- and β-forms. The β-isomers are less stable and undergo rapid transformation to the α-form in most solvents. This transformation is accelerated in many cases by silver nitrate.

a-Acetobromoglucose may be prepared from β-*d*-glucose pentaacetate by reaction with a solution of hydrogen bromide in acetic acid:[317]

$$
\begin{array}{l}
\overline{\text{H}\quad\text{OAc}\ \text{H}\quad\text{OAc}\ \text{O}\quad\text{OAc}} \\
\text{C}-\text{C}-\text{C}-\text{C}-\text{C}-\text{CH}_2 + \text{HBr} \\
\text{OAc}\ \text{H}\quad\text{OAc}\ \text{H}\quad\text{H}
\end{array}
\rightarrow
\begin{array}{l}
\overline{\text{Br}\quad\text{OAc}\ \text{H}\quad\text{OAc}\ \text{O}\quad\text{OAc}} \\
\text{C}-\text{C}-\text{C}-\text{C}-\text{C}-\text{CH}_2 + \text{AcOH} \\
\text{H}\quad\text{H}\quad\text{OAc}\ \text{H}\quad\text{H}
\end{array}
$$

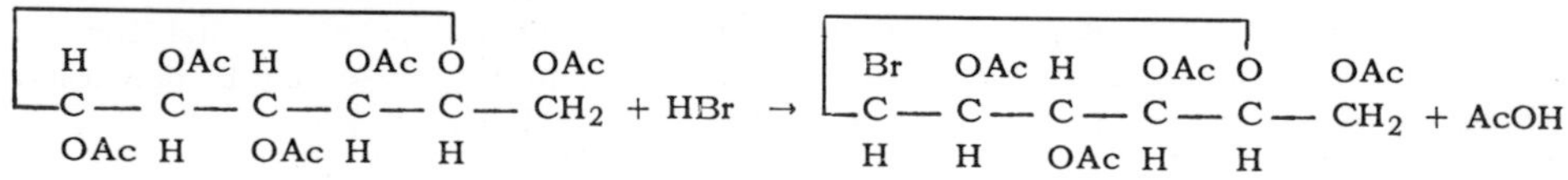

The reaction is complete within two to three hours at room temperature. The bromo compound is isolated by dilution with chloroform and pouring the mixture in water. The product is purified by crystallization from ether. *a-Acetochloroglucose* has been prepared by the action of phosphorus pentachloride and aluminum chloride on β-pentaacetyl-*d*-glucose in chloroform solution.[318]

A crystalline *tetraacetyl-d-fructopyranosyl bromide* has been obtained through the reaction of hydrogen bromide with *d*-fructopyranose pentaacetate or tetraacetate. The compound is highly reactive and unstable, decomposing even on storage at room temperature.[319] A crystalline *tetraacetyl-β-d-fructopyranosyl fluoride* results when *d*-fructopyranose pentaacetate or tetraacetate is treated for a brief period with liquid hydrogen fluoride. Prolonged treatment with hydrogen fluoride gives *3,4,5-triacetyl-β-d-fructopyranosyl fluoride*.[320]

A reactive aceto chloromaltose is formed by the action of ethereal hydrogen chloride on octaacetylmaltose.[321] This compound apparently exists in the tautomeric form

$$
\begin{array}{l}
\overline{\text{Cl}\ \text{C}\ \text{CH}_3} \\
\text{O}\quad\text{O}\quad\ \text{H}\quad\text{OAc}\ \text{O}\quad\text{OAc} \\
\text{C}-\text{C}-\text{C}-\text{C}-\text{C}-\text{CH}_2 \\
\text{H}\quad\text{H}\quad\text{OH}\ \text{H}\quad\text{H}
\end{array}
$$

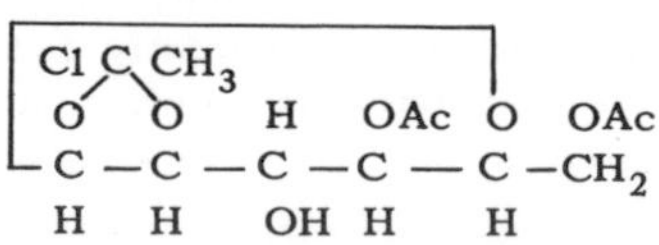

Shaken in benzene solution with silver acetate, the compound is converted to an isomeric acetyl maltose. The chlorine atom in the compound may be replaced with a methoxy group by treatment with methanol and silver carbonate.[322] When this compound is saponified, only three acetyl groups are removed, and 1,2-[*α*-methoxyethylidene]-*d*-mannose is formed.[323] Halogenoses of *l*-rhamnose and *l*-lyxose and other sugars which have an acetyl group at carbon atom 2 also exist in such tautomeric form and behave in a similar manner. It is claimed that acetobromoglucose as well as acetobromo derivatives of xyclose, cellobiose, and lactose, but not of maltose, may be obtained directly from the free carbohydrate by the action of a mixture of hydrogen bromide and acetic acid.[324]

Acetolysis of polysaccharides with an acetyl halide is another method employed for the preparation of acetyl halogenoses.

β-Acetochloroglucose has been obtained from acetobromoglucose by treatment with a suspension of active silver chloride in ether.[325]

α-Acetofluoroglucose has been obtained from *β*-*d*-glucose pentaacetate by the action of liquid hydrogen fluoride.[326] The *β*-isomer has been made by the interaction of *α*-acetobromoglucose and silver fluoride in acetone solution.[327] The compound gradually isomerizes to the *α*-form in solution.

Acetochlorodisaccharides may be prepared by the Skraup-Kremann method,[328] i.e. by the action of phosphorus pentachloride and aluminum chloride on the fully acetylated disaccharide. It is important, for the success of the reaction, that the aluminum chloride be prepared by the Stockhausen and Gattermann method.[329]

Halogenoses are generally rather unstable at ordinary temperature. The halogenose of glucose can be kept unchanged in an ice chest for a few weeks.

The halogen in 1-position in aldoses is quire reactive. *α*-Acetochloroglucose reacts much more vigorously with many reagents than the *β*-isomer. Acetohalogenoses of simple hexoses give the corresponding pentaacetates by reaction with silver acetate. The methyl, phenyl, and *β*-naphthyl glucosides are obtained by reaction with methanol, phenol, and *β*-naphthol. The halogen atom may be replaced with a hydroxyl group by treating the halogenose in acetone solution with silver carbonate and a little water.

Acethohalogenoses with a *cis* configuration at C 1 and C 2 react with tertiary bases to form quaternary ammonium salts.[330]

Halohydrins are formed from halogenoses by the prolonged action of liquefied hydrogen halides. The second halogen enters the 6-position. By the continued reaction of hydrobromic acid with acetobromoglucoses, dibromoglucoses result which have formed important starting materials for the preparation of anhydroglucoses. The first synthetic methyl pentose, *d*-isorhamnose, has been prepared by way of a dibromosugar. The bromine atom in 1-position in acetodibromoglucose shows the same reactivity as that in acetobromoglucose, while the halogen in 6-position is more strongly bound.

The 6-iodohydrin of diisopropylidene galactose has been converted to the corresponding unsaturated methylene derivative by removal of the elements of hydrogen iodide by heating at 130° with sodium methoxide:[331]

$$\begin{array}{c} \underset{C(CH_3)_2}{\diagup\diagdown} \\ O \quad O \quad H \quad H \quad O \quad I \\ \underset{H \quad H \quad O \quad O \quad H}{\overline{C-C-C-C-C-CH_2}} \\ \underset{C(CH_3)_2}{\diagdown\diagup} \end{array} \rightarrow \begin{array}{c} \underset{C(CH_3)_2}{\diagup\diagdown} \\ O \quad O \quad H \quad H \quad O \\ \underset{H \quad H \quad O \quad O}{\overline{C-C-C-C-C=CH_2}} \\ \underset{C(CH_3)_2}{\diagdown\diagup} \end{array}$$

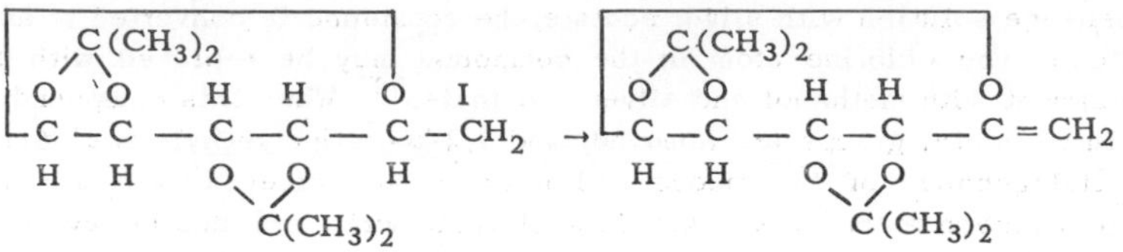

The compound has been converted to the corresponding methyl pentoside by hydrogenation in the presence of palladium.

Similarly, the 6-iodohydrin of the methyl glucoside of tribenzoyl galactose has been converted to the corresponding unsaturated methylene derivative by removal of the elements of hydrogen iodide by treatment wilt silver fluoride and absolute pyridine.[332]

Dehydrobromination and deacetylation of triacetylmethylglucoside-6-bromohydrin have been effected by treatment in an indifferent solvent with a weak base, such as diethylamine or pyridine.

Thio Sugars

l-Thioglucose has been prepared through the reaction of acetobromoglucose with potassium disulfide, deacetylation of the resulti.ig acetoglucose disulfide, and subsequent reduction with sodium amalgam:[333]

$$2AcOCH_2\overset{\displaystyle\overline{\quad O \quad}}{CH(CHOAc)_3CHBr} \;\xrightarrow{K_2S_2}\; AcOCH_2\overset{\displaystyle\overline{\quad O \quad}}{CH(CHOAc)_3CHSS}\overset{\displaystyle\overline{\quad O \quad}}{CH(CHOH)_3CHCH_2OH}$$

$$\rightarrow CH_3OCH_2\overset{\displaystyle\overline{\quad O \quad}}{CH(CHOH)_3CHSS}\overset{\displaystyle\overline{\quad O \quad}}{CH(CHOH)_3CHCH_2OH} \;\xrightarrow[\text{H}_2\text{O}]{Na}\; 2\,HOCH_2\overset{\displaystyle\overline{\quad O \quad}}{CH(CHOH)_3CHSH}$$

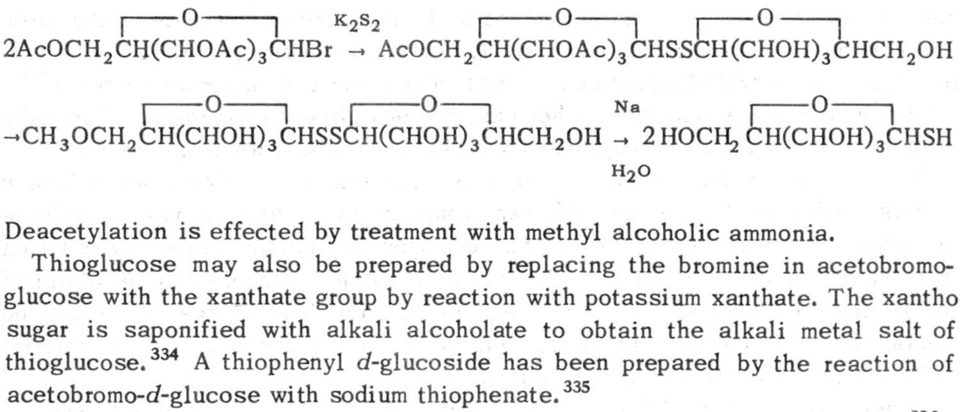

Deacetylation is effected by treatment with methyl alcoholic ammonia.

Thioglucose may also be prepared by replacing the bromine in acetobromoglucose with the xanthate group by reaction with potassium xanthate. The xantho sugar is saponified with alkali alcoholate to obtain the alkali metal salt of thioglucose.[334] A thiophenyl *d*-glucoside has been prepared by the reaction of acetobromo-*d*-glucose with sodium thiophenate.[335]

Thio compounds of cellobiose, galactose, digalactose have been prepared.[336]

The silver salt of various isothioureas, reacting with acetobromoglucose, yield the isothiourea derivatives of the acetylated glucose.[337] It has not been possible to deacetylate these compounds without affecting the thio group. Acetylglucose derivatives of N-Allyl,-benzyl, and -naphthylthiourethanes have been prepared by this method.[338] The acetylglucose derivative of the o-phenyl ester of thiocarbanilic acid has also been prepared.[339]

An isothiocyano derivative of glucose has been obtained through the reaction of acetobromo-*d*-glucose with silver thiocyanate.[340]

The free hydroxyl group in 3-position in diacetone glucose has been replaced with a thiol group by the following series of transformations: conversion to a xanthogeno group, esterification to the methylxanto group, isomerization, and finally hydrolysis with ammonia:[341]

$$\begin{array}{ccccc} \text{H} & \text{CS}_2 & \text{H} & \text{CH}_3\text{I} & \text{H} \\ -\text{C}- & \rightarrow & -\text{C} & \rightarrow & -\text{C} & \overset{\text{heat}}{\rightarrow} \\ \text{OH} & \text{NaOH} & \text{OCSSNa} & & \text{OCSSCH}_3 \end{array}$$

$$\begin{array}{ccc} \text{H} & \text{NH}_3 & \text{H} \\ -\text{C}- & \rightarrow & -\text{C}- \\ \text{SCOSCH}_3 & & \text{SH} \end{array}$$

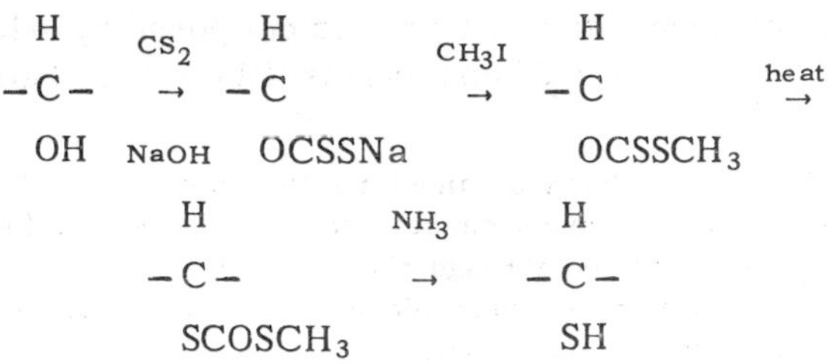

Tschugaeff's method of preparation of unsaturated compounds was found to be inapplicable to carbohydrates.

Acetates or benzoates of certain carbohydrates, heated with ethylmercaptan in the presence of zinc chloride or hydrogen chloride, give mercaptides through the replacement of a free hydroxyl group with the mercapto group.[342] Replacement may be accompanied by the migration of acyl groups. 2-Thioethyl-*d*-glucose has been obtained by this method. 2-Mercapto derivatives result from the reaction of fully acetylated pyranoses with a mercaptan in the presence of zinc chloride:[343]

$$\text{AcOCH}_2-\underset{\overset{|}{\text{OAc}}}{\text{C}} - \underset{\text{OAc}}{\overset{\text{H}}{\text{C}}} - \underset{\text{H}}{\overset{\text{OAc}}{\text{C}}} - \underset{\text{H}}{\overset{\text{OAc}}{\text{C}}} - \overset{\text{O}}{\text{CH}_2} \quad \overset{\text{C}_2\text{H}_5\text{SH}}{\underset{\text{ZnCl}_2}{\rightarrow}}$$

$$\text{AcOCH}_2\underset{\overset{|}{\text{SC}_2\text{H}_5}}{\text{C}} \underline{\quad\quad} \underset{\text{OAc}}{\overset{\text{H}}{\text{C}}} - \underset{\text{H}}{\overset{\text{OAc}}{\text{C}}} - \underset{\text{H}}{\overset{\text{OAc}}{\text{C}}} - \overset{\text{O}}{\text{CH}_2}$$

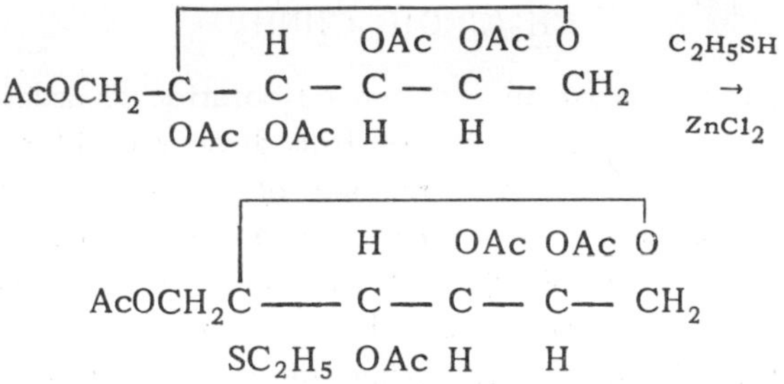

1-Mercaptides of aldoses are obtained from the corresponding mercaptals by removal of one mercapto group by the action of aqueous mercuric chloride:[344]

$$\text{HOCH(CHOH)}_4\text{CH(SC}_2\text{H}_5)_2 \overset{\text{HgCl}_2}{\rightarrow} \text{HOCH}_2\overset{\text{O}}{\overline{\text{CH(CHOH)}_3\text{CHSC}_2\text{H}_5}}$$

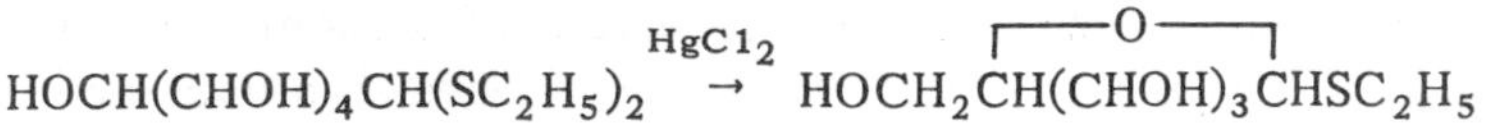

This reaction yields the *a*-isomer, while the original Fischer method gives the *β*-form of the mercaptide.

The 6-tosyl derivatives of xylose and glucose, heated with potassium ethylmercaptide, give the 6-mercaptides of the carbohydrates by replacement of the tosyl group.[345]

The thiocyano residue has been introduced in 6-position in carbohydrates by reaction of their tosyl derivatives with potassium thiocyanate.[346] Tosyl esters of secondary hydroxyl groups fail to react either with alkali thyocyanates or with alkali metal mercaptides.

Di(glucosyl-6)-sulfide has been prepared by treatment of 6-bromo-*β*-*d*-glucoside triacetate with potassium hydrogen sulfide followed by deacetylation and hydrolysis.[347] Acetobromoglucose, reacting with potassium disulfide, K_2S_2, in alcoholic solution, gives acetodiglucosyl disulfide:[348]

$$\text{AcOCH}_2\overline{\text{CH(CHOAc)}_3\text{CHS}}.\overline{\text{SCH(CHOAc)}_3\text{CHCH}_2\text{OAc}}$$

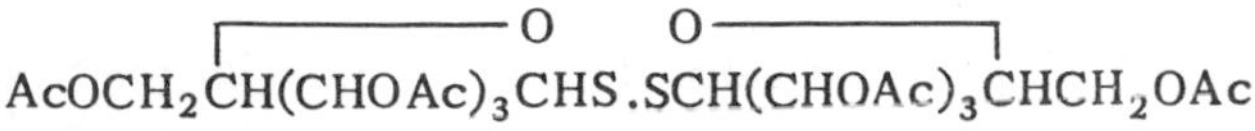

1-Thioglucose has been obtained from this compound by reductive cleavage.[349] A wide variety of other sugar sulfides and disulfides have been synthesized.[350]

Seleno Sugars

Seleno isotrehalose has been obtained by the interaction of hydrogen selenide and acetobromoglucose, and subsequent deacetylation of the acetoselenide formed.[351] Seleno derivatives have been obtained through the reaction of methyl-6-bromo-*d*-glucoside triacetate with potassium hydrogen selenide and potassium selenide.[352] In these derivatives the selenium is attached to a non-carbonyl carbon.

Amino Sugars

Some amino sugars are formed directly by the action of mathanolic ammonia on the free sugar.[353] The amino compound generally precipitates out as the reaction proceeds; this is not true, however, of amino arabinose, which is very soluble in methanol.[354] Glucosidic amines are formed, in general, when *d*-glucose is heated with an amine in alcoholic solution, but when the mixture of an amine with *d*-glucose is melted, Schiff bases are formed. *d*-Lyxosylamine,

$$\begin{array}{l} \quad\ulcorner\text{------------}\text{O} \\ \text{CH}_2(\text{CHOH})_3\text{CHNH}_2 \end{array}$$

results on dissolving *d*-lyxose in a saturated solution of ammonia in methyl alcohol. An aminohexose has been obtained from diisopropylidene galactose by the action of liquid ammonia followed by removal of the isopropylidene groups.[355]

Amino sugars are also formed through the interaction of ammonia with halo sugars. Dulcitolamine, $C_6H_{13}O_5NH_2$, for example, results when a halohydrin of dulcitol is heated at 100° with alcoholic ammonia.[356] 6-Amino-*d*-glucose has been obtained from triacetylmethylglucoside-6-bromohydrin and ammonia.[357] Methyl epiglucosamine results through the action of ammonia on methyl glucoside bromohydrin or chlorohydrin at 100°.

Amino sugars may be obtained by the action of ammonia on aryl sulfonic esters of sugars.[358] Hydrazine reacts with greater ease than ammonia. 6-Aminodiacetone galactose is formed readily from diacetone galactose sulfonic ester and ammonia. In this case, a secondary amino compound of the structure R_2NH is also formed, R representing a diacetone galactose residue. Diacetone galactose toluenesulfonic ester also gives both a primary and an asymmetrical secondary hydrazine compound.[359] The diacetone compound of 3-amino glucose results from diacetone 3-*p*-toluenesulfo-*d*-glucose by reaction with ammonia at 170°.[360] Similarly monoacetone-6-amino-*d*-glucose is obtained from monoacetone-6-*p*-toluenesulfo-*d*-glucose and methanolic ammonia.[361]

2-Amino sugars have been prepared from 2,3-anhydro sugars by heating with methanolic ammonia. The 2-amino derivative of *d*-altrose has been obtained, for example, from methyl 4-6-dimethyl-2,3-anhydro-β-*d*-mannopyranoside by heating with methyl alcoholic ammonia under pressure.[362] A small amount of amino-*d*-glucose is also formed in the reaction.

Amino sugars may be prepared from aldoses by the addition of ammonia to the aldehyde group, and converting the resulting product to an amino nitrile by reaction with hydrocyanic acid. Hydrolysis of the nitrile to the corresponding acid, conversion of the acid to lactone, and finally reduction of the lactone yields an amino sugar with one more carbon atom than the original aldose.[363] Conversion of the acid to lactone is brought about by heating with an absolute alcoholic solution of hydrogen chloride; reduction to the amino sugar is effected with sodium amalgam.

Two epimeric bodies are formed by the addition of hydrocyanic acid to pentoside ammonias.[364] The separation of these epimers is achieved by fractional crystallization. Epimers of some hexosamines may be separated by taking advantage of differences in their behavior toward benzaldehyde, one yielding a dibenzylidene derivative, the other a lactone. Dextro-*d*-xylohexosamine, for example, gives a dibenzylidene ester with benzaldehyde, while its epimer forms a monobenzylidene lactone.

2-Aminoheptose acid has been prepared by the addition of hydrogen cyanide to galactoseamine and hydrolysis of the nitrile formed.[365] Two pairs of stereoisomeric 3-aminoheptonic acids have been obtained from the two naturally occurring 2-hexoseamines by the addition of hydrocyanic acid and hydrolysis.[366]

The amino group in amino sugars may be alkylated by treatment with an alkyl iodide and silver oxide. Triacetyl-N-dimethyl-β-methylglucosamine has been obtained, for example, from acetobromoglucosamine hydrobromide by treatment first with methanol, then with methyl iodide and silver oxide.[367]

Methylation of free amino sugars is complicated by the presence of the basic group. Treatment with dimethyl sulfate under the usual conditions causes the breakdown of the molecule. Acetylation of the amino group affords adequate protection, and methylation may be carried out under the normal alkaline conditions.

Peptide-like compounds have been prepared from glucosamine hydrochloride by reaction with α-halo fatty acid halides, followed by treatment with ammonia:[368]

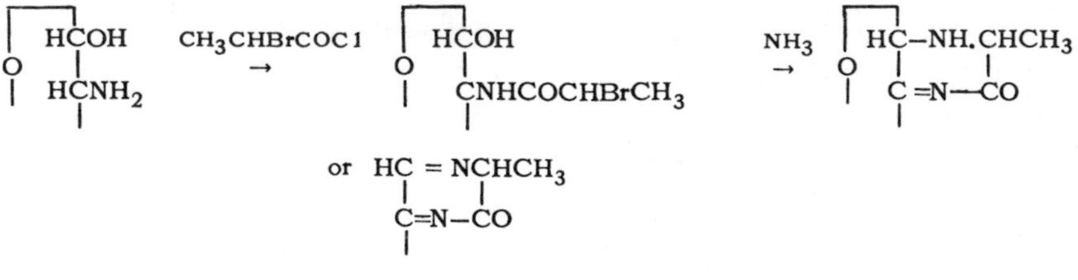

$$\begin{array}{ccccc}
\overset{\lceil}{|}\ \text{HCOH} & & \overset{\lceil}{|}\ \text{HCOH} & & \text{NH}_3\ \overset{\lceil}{|}\ \text{HC—NH.CHCH}_3 \\
\text{O}\ | & \text{CH}_3\text{CHBrCOCl} & \text{O}\ | & \rightarrow & \text{O}\ | \\
|\ \text{HCNH}_2 & \rightarrow & |\ \text{CNHCOCHBrCH}_3 & & |\ \text{C}=\text{N—CO} \\
| & & | & & |
\end{array}$$

$$\text{or}\ \ \text{HC} = \text{NCHCH}_3$$
$$| \quad\quad |$$
$$\text{C=N—CO}$$
$$|$$

Peptide-like compounds may be obtained also from the reaction of amino acids with benzoylated acid azides. For example, hippuryl-N-glucosamine results from glucosamine hydrochloride and hippuric azide in 2-normal sodium hydroxide:[369]

$$\begin{array}{ccc}
\text{HCOH} \quad \overset{\lceil}{|} & & \text{HCOH}\quad\overset{\lceil}{|} \\
| \quad\quad \text{O} + \text{C}_6\text{H}_5\text{CONHCH}_2\text{CON}_3 \rightarrow & & |\quad\quad\text{O} \quad\quad + \text{HN}_3 \\
\text{HCNH}_2 \quad | & & \text{HCNH}\ | \\
| & & |\ | \\
& & \text{COCH}_2\text{NHCOC}_6\text{H}_5
\end{array}$$

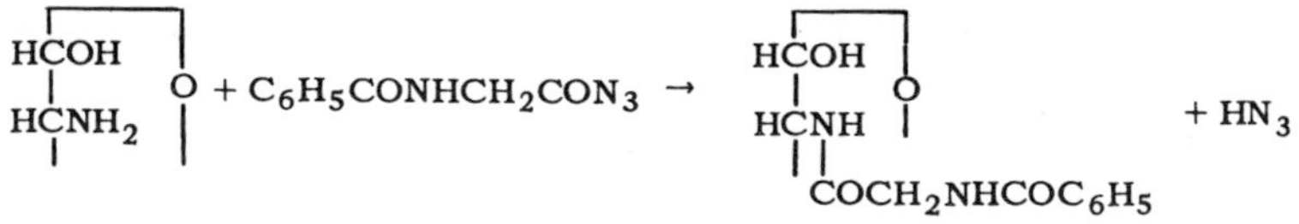

Another method involves the condensation of *d*-glusosamine with α-azido acid chlorides and the catalytic hydrogenation of the resulting compound:[370]

$$\begin{array}{c} \text{HCOH} \\ | \quad \text{O} \\ \text{HCNH}_2 \end{array} \quad \xrightarrow{\overset{N_3}{CH_3\dot{C}HCOC1}} \quad \begin{array}{c} \text{HCOH} \\ | \quad \text{O} \\ \text{HCNH} \\ \quad \underset{\text{COCHCH}_3}{\overset{N_3}{|}} \end{array} \quad \xrightarrow{H_2} \quad \begin{array}{c} \text{HCOH} \\ | \quad \text{O} \\ \text{HCNH} \\ \quad \underset{\text{COCHCH}_3}{\overset{NH_2}{|}} \end{array}$$

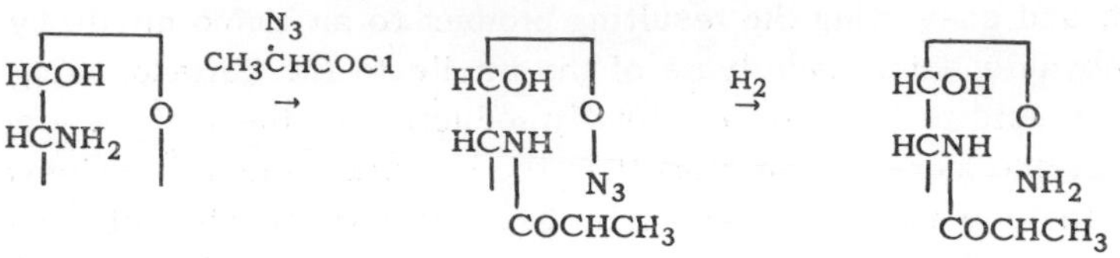

Glucopeptides have been obtained in a crystalline form by condensing tetraacetyl-*d*-glucosamine with carbobenzoxyamino acid chlorides, e.g., $C_6H_5CH_2OCONHCH_2COC1$, removing the acetyl groups by saponification, then causing the cleavage of the carbobenzoxy group by catalytic reduction in acid solution.[371]

The presence of an amino group in 2-position in a carbohydrate apparently does not interfere with the ability of the carbohydrate to condense with benzaldehyde.[372]

Hydrazones and Osazones of Carbohydrates

Carbohydrates react with a hydrazine to form a hydrazone. When the reaction is carried out at an elevated temperature and an excess of hydrazine is used, a carbinol group is oxidized to a carbonyl group, and this reacts with a second molecule of hydrazine to form an osazone:

$$\begin{array}{c} \text{O}- \\ \text{HCOH} \\ | \\ \text{HCOH} \\ | \end{array} \quad \xrightarrow{H_2NNHR} \quad \begin{array}{c} \text{O}- \\ \text{HCNHNHR} \\ | \\ \text{HCOH} \\ | \end{array} \quad \xrightarrow{H_2NNHR} \quad NH_3 + RNH_2 \quad \begin{array}{c} \text{O}- \\ \text{HCNHNHR} \\ | \\ \text{CO} \\ | \end{array}$$

$$\xrightarrow{H_2NNHR} \quad \begin{array}{c} \text{O}- \\ \text{HCNHNHR} \\ | \\ \text{C:NNHR} \\ | \end{array} \quad \text{or} \quad \begin{array}{c} \text{HC}=\text{NNHR} \\ | \\ \text{C}=\text{NNHR} \\ | \end{array}$$

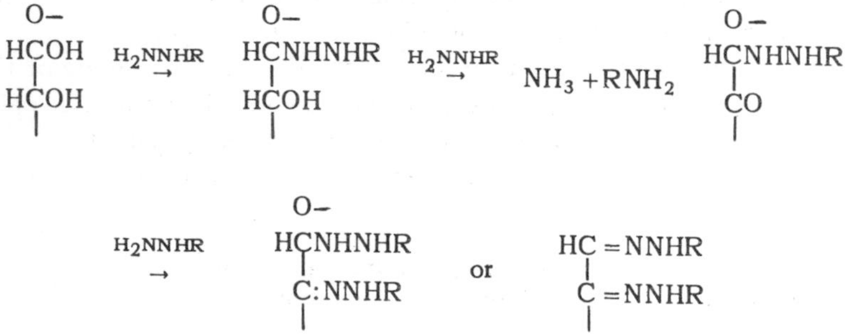

In aldoses, the 2-carbinol group, and in ketoses the 1-carbinol group undergoes oxidation to a carbonyl group. For this reason the same osazone is obtained from glucose, fructose and mannose. Ketoses yield osazones more readily and in better yield than aldoses.

Diphenylhydrazine has proved to be a satisfactory reagent for the preparation of most *sugar hydrazones*. The reaction is carried out by dissolving equal amounts of the hydrazine and sugar in the least amount of 90% alcohol and heating the solution on the water bath for 10 minutes. The hydrazone crystallizes out of solution in the course of a few days.[373] Benzylphenylhydrazine and *p*-nitrophenylhydrazine have also been employed for the preparation of aldose hydrazones. The most suitable substituted hydrazine for any particular aldose must be determined by trial.

The general procedure in preparing phenyl osazones of carbohydrates is as follows:

One part by weight of the carbohydrate, 2 parts of phenylhydrazine hydrochloride and 3 parts of crystalline sodium acetate are dissolved in 20 parts of water, and the solution is heated for one to one and a half hours on a boiling water bath. It may be necessary to continue heating for a longer period in some cases, especially when dealing with impure sugar solutions. In the latter case osazones occasionally separate as oils. If the oil eventually sets to a solid, it is ground to a powder and is washed with benzene to eliminate any coloring matter present, and the osazone is purified by crystallization.[374]

Glucose osazone is obtained as a light yellow solid after crystallization from hot dilute alcohol. It crystallizes in needles, is difficultly soluble in water and absolute alcohol, hardly soluble in acetone, and fairly soluble in hot dilute alcohol.

The solubility of osazones of polysaccharides increases with increase in the chain length of the sugar molecules, so that the osazones of hexoses, for example, cannot be isolated as solids because of their excessive solubility.

Osazones are much less soluble in water than hydrazones, and crystallize better; for this reason osazones serve better for the isolation and identification of sugars.

Benzaldehyde is generally used for the liberation of aldoses from their hydrazones. Formaldehyde is more satisfactory for the recovery of aldoses from substituted hydrazones.[375]

Osazones may be decomposed by the action of concentrated hydrochloric acid or of benzaldehyde. The reaction results in the formation of an osone:[376]

$$\begin{matrix} HC=NNHC_6H_5 \\ | \\ C=NNHC_6H_5 \\ | \end{matrix} + 2C_6H_5CHO \rightarrow \begin{matrix} HCO \\ | \\ CO \\ | \end{matrix} \text{ or } \begin{matrix} HCOH \\ | \\ CO \\ | \end{matrix} O + 2C_6H_5CHNNHC_6H_5$$

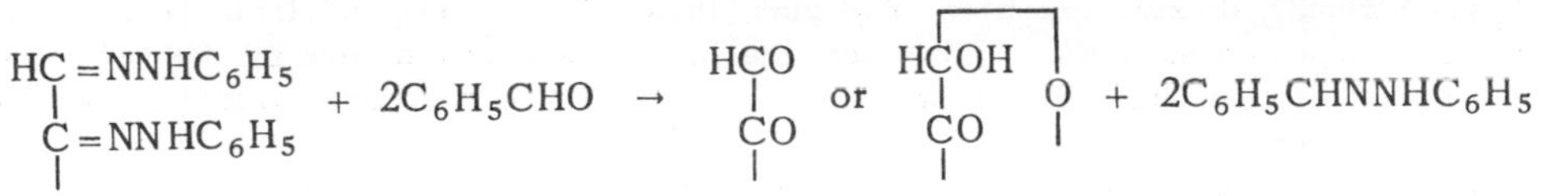

Oxidation of Carbohydrates

On mild oxidation of aldoses the aldehyde group is first attacked and is converted to a carboxylic group. The resulting products are termed *aldonic acids*. Examples of such acids are gluconic, mannonic, and galatonic acids. Chlorine was formerly used as the oxidizing agent, but bromine is more frequently employed at present.[377] Nitric acid and iodine have also been employed for the purpose.[378] Oxidation with iodine is carried out by treating the aldose with iodine and barium hydroxide solution:

$$2RCHO + 3Ba(OH)_2 + 2I_2 \rightarrow (RCOO)_2Ba + 2BaI_2 + 4H_2O$$

The procedure followed in oxidizing sugars with bromine may be illustrated by the preparation of *gluconic acid:*

Fifty grams of grape sugar are dissolved in 300 cc water, 100 gm bromine are added and the mixture is maintained at room temperature for three days with occasional shaking. The mixture is next boiled vigorously in an open dish with good stirring. The recovery of the acid is a rather tedious process and is effected as follows: The solution is diluted to about 500 cc, cooled to room temperature and is treated with an excess of white lead; the solution is filtered, treated with hydrogen sulfide and once more filtered and boiled ½ hour with calcium carbonate. The solution is again filtered, concentrated to 120 cc, cooled, and seeded with a few crystals of calcium gluconate. The salt which crystallizes out on standing is filtered, decolorized with animal charcoal, and purified by crystallization from hot water.

The oxidation of glucose with iodine in basic solution is carried out as follows:

Nine grams of glucose are dissolved in 670 cc of 0.3*N* iodine in aqueous barium iodide solution, and a liter of 0.4*N* barium hydroxide solution is added at a constant rate in the course of three minutes. The mixture is allowed to stand for 15 minutes and is then acidified with a solution of 18.5 cc concentrated sulfuric acid in 150 cc of water. Finally 150 gm lead bicarbonate are added rapidly with stirring. The acid may be isolated in the form of the pure calcium salt in the following manner: Sulfuric acid and silver nitrate are added to the liquid with stirring, the solution is filtered and treated with sulfur dioxide and boiled with calcium carbonate and animal charcoal. The filtered solution is concentrated to a syrup and is poured into methanol. The precipitate of calcium gluconate is finally purified by crystallization from water.

Aldonic acids may be freed from their calcium salts by treatment with oxalic acid. Aldonic acids in the free state tend to form lactones; for this reason, they are usually converted to the difficultly soluble salts, or hydrazides.[379] The phenylhydrazides of aldonic acids are formed readily when to a moderately concentrated, say 10%, solution of the acid or its lactone, an excess of phenylhydrazine and a volume of 50% acetic acid equal to that of the solution are added, and the mixture is heated on the water bath for ½ to 2 hours. The barium salt of the acid is obtained from the hydrazide by heating it to boiling for ½ hour with a thirty-fold quantity of baryta solution containing 100 gm barium hydroxide per liter. The phenylhydrazine is removed from the reaction mixture by repeated extraction with ether, the barium is removed from the heated solution by precipitation with sulfuric acid, the liquid is filtered and evaporated to dryness to isolate the acid or lactone.

Diphenylhexitol has been obtained by the reaction of phenylmagnesium bromide with *d*-galactonic lactone tetraacetate in ethereal solution.[380]

More vigorous oxidation of monosaccharides as well as of aldonic acids results in the formation of dicarboxylic acids. Saccharic acid is obtained, for example, from glucose or aldonic acid, mannosaccharic acid from mannose or mannonic acid, and mucic acid from galactose or milk sugar. These acids have played an important role in the determination of the structure of carbohydrates. The formation of saccharic acid from a natural product may be considered as proof of the presence of glucose or a glucose group, since no other naturally occurring monosaccharide yields this acid by oxidation.

d-Gluconic acid results by the electrolytic oxidation of *d*-glucose in the presence of calcium carbonate and a little bromide.[381] The γ-lactone of *d*-gluconic acid is formed when solutions of the free acid are evaporated;[382] the δ-lactone is formed when the solutions of the acid are rapidly evaporated under vacuum.[383]

5-Ketogluconic acid, or 1-sorburonic acid, is obtained from *d*-glucose or *d*-gluconic acid by oxidation with nitric acid.[384]

The oxidation of *d*-glucoson with bromine water results in the formation of *2-keto-d-gluconic acid:*[385]

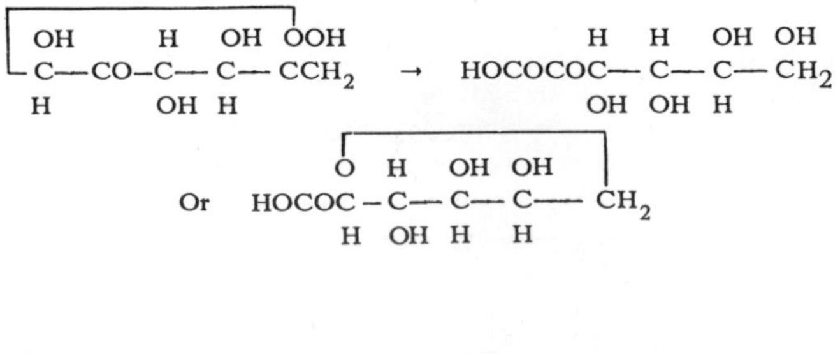
OH H OH OOH
C—CO—C—C—CCH2
H OH H
HOCOCOC—C—C—CH2
H H OH OH
OH OH H
Or
O H OH OH
HOCOC—C—C—C—CH2
H OH H H

d-Glucoson is obtained by treating *d*-glucosazone with concentrated hydrochloric acid;[376] it is also formed when *d*-fructose is oxidized at 100° with selenious acid.[386]

l-Mannuric acid is formed through the careful oxidation of *l*-mannonic lactone with nitric acid.[387] *l-Mannosaccharic acid* is obtained by energetic oxidation of *l*-mannonic lactone with nitric acid:[388]

$$\begin{array}{c} \text{OH OH H H \quad OH} \\ \text{CO—C —C —C–C —CH}_2 \\ \overline{\text{H \quad H \quad O \;\; OH}} \end{array} \rightarrow \begin{array}{c} \text{OH OH H \quad H} \\ \text{HOCOC —C —C —C— COOH} \\ \text{H \quad H \quad OH OH} \end{array}$$

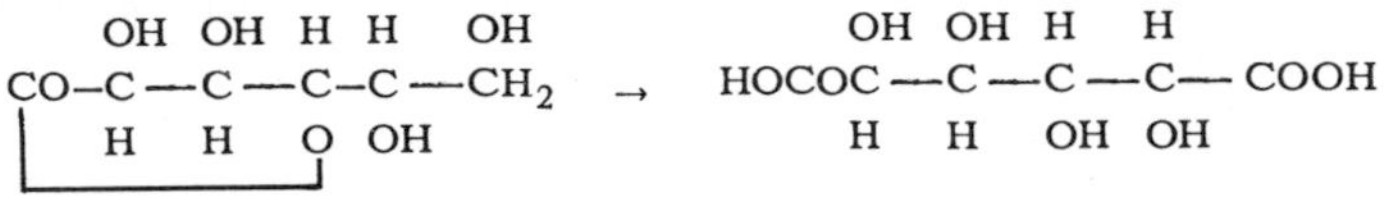

Ascorbic acid has been prepared by oxidizing 2,3:4,6-diisopropylidene-*l*-sorbose to the corresponding keto-*l*-gluconic acid derivative and hydrolyzing this to 2-keto-*l*-gluconic acid.[389] Isomerization produces ascorbic acid identical with the natural vitamin.

The free sugar acids gradually lose a molecule of water to form lactones. Formation of δ-lactones takes place very rapidly, while γ-lactones form very slowly. It is possible to determine the type of lactone formed by determining the rate of disappearance of the acid, and measuring the mutarotational velocities.

The acetal and ketal groups in aldehyde or ketone condensation products of carbohydrates are resistant to oxidizing agents; free carbinol groups in these compounds, on the other hand, are attacked by many oxidizing agents. Those of the glycol-splitting type, particularly lead tetraacetate and periodates, have been employed with fruitful results for the elucidation of the structure of the acetals and ketals of polyhydric alcohols. Lead tetraacetate is employed in organic solvents to treat acetals insoluble in water;[390] periodates are used in aqueous solution for treating acetals that are soluble in water. One mole of periodate is consumed by each α-glycol group, two moles are used up by three contiguous hydroxyl groups, and three moles by four adjacent hydroxyl groups. An α-glycol group which is composed of one primary and one secondary alcohol group yields one mole of formaldehyde. A secondary alcohol group situated in the center of a triol is converted to a mole of formic acid. Considerable information may be gained, therefore, concerning the structure of acetals and ketals of polyhydric alcohols by determining the amount of oxidant consumed and the amounts of formic acid and formaldehyde produced in the periodic acid oxidation of these compounds. When oxidation with glycol-splitting reagents is carried out in acid solution, the implications of the results should be accepted with some reserve, because of the possibility of removal or migration of acetal groups under the action of acids. Alkaline permanganate and chromium trioxide in glacial acetic acid have also been employed for the oxidation of acetals or ketals of carbohydrates, without affecting the alkylidene residues in the molecule.[391]

Diacetone-2-ketogluconic acid is obtained in the form of the potassium salt by oxidizing β-diacetonefructose with alkaline permanganate.[392]

d-Glucuronic acid, an aldehydic body, may be obtained from acetone benzylidene-glucose by oxidation with alkaline permanganate, hydrogenation of the resulting product in the presence of palladium, and finally heating the acetone-*d*-glucuronic acid formed with dilute acid.[393]

Amino acids derived from carbohydrates are oxidized by sodium benzenesulfonchloramide (Chloramine T) to the next lower aldehyde, when one molecular equivalent of the reagent is employed, and to the next lower nitrile by two molecular equivalents.[394]

The two naturally occurring amino hexoses are oxidized to glucoseamino acid and chondrosamino acid. Oxidation is best carried out with yellow mercuric oxide.[395] These acids are isomerized to their epimers when heated in aqueous pyridine.[396]

2-Desoxyaldonic acid is formed from triacetylhexose-2-halohydrin by treatment with lead oxide:[397]

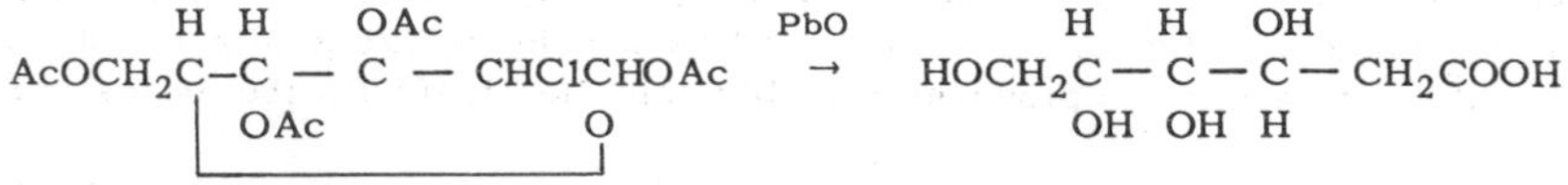
H H OAc
AcOCH2C—C — C — CHClCHOAc
OAc
O
PbO
H H OH
HOCH2C — C — C — CH2COOH
OH OH H

In this reaction, a disproportionation occurs at carbon atoms 1 and 2 simultaneously with removal of the acetyl groups and the halogen.

2-Desoxy-2-arabonic acid is formed on treating 2-chloro 2-desoxy-3,4-diacetylpentose with lead oxide:[434]

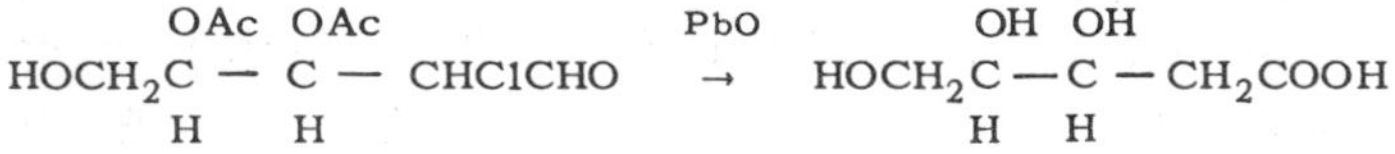
OAc OAc
HOCH2C — C — CHClCHO
H H
PbO
OH OH
HOCH2C — C — CH2COOH
H H

Reduction of Carbohydrates and Their Derivatives

Aldoses and ketoses may be reduced to the corresponding alcohols with sodium amalgam, and by various other methods of reduction. As an example of the procedure, the reduction of glucose to sorbitol with sodium amalgam is described below:[398]

A solution of 30 gm of pure glucose in 300 cc of water is shaken with six to seven 100-gm portions of 2½% sodium amalgam, neutralizing the solution every 15 minutes by the addition of dilute sulfuric acid, and fresh portions of the amalgam being added only after the exhaustion of the amalgam already added. The temperature is not allowed to rise above 50° in the course of the reduction. The operation requires ten to twelve hours. At the end of the reaction, the solution is separated from the mercury, concentrated to 120 cc, and is poured into one liter of hot absolute alcohol. The liquid is filtered, concentrated to a syrup, poured into 80 cc of 50% sulfuric acid, then 30 gm of benzaldehyde are added, the solution is well shaken and allowed to stand 24 hours at ordinary temperature with frequent shaking. The reaction mixture is then diluted with water and the dibenzalsorbitol which precipitates out is filtered, washed thoroughly first with water, then with ether, and finally with water again. The sorbitol is liberated from the dibenzal-compound by boiling for 40 minutes with five parts of 5% sulfuric acid under reflux. The sulfuric acid is then removed by adding aqueous barium hydroxide in slight excess, and the benzaldehyde is removed by repeated extraction with ether. Carbon dioxide is next passed through the solution to precipitate out the barium, the liquid is filtered, concentrated to a syrup, and poured with stirring into 90% alcohol. The precipitated sorbitol is filtered, washed, and purified by crystallization from hot 90% alcohol.

d-Glucose gives *d*-sorbitol on reduction with sodium. Reduction of *d*-glucose may be effected also with aluminum amalgam, or with calcium;[399] also with hydrogen in the presence of palladium, platinum, or nickel catalyst.[400] *l-Glucose* is converted to *l*-sorbitol by reduction with sodium amalgam.[401] *d-Fructose* has been converted to a mixture of *d*-sorbitol and *d*-mannitol by catalytic reduction.[402] Dulcitol results through the reduction of *d*- and *l-galactose* with sodium amalgam,[403] or with aluminum amalgam and ammonia.[404] Reduction of *d-sorbose* with sodium amalgam, or catalytically with Raney nickel, gives a mixture of *l*-iditol and *d*-glucitol.[405] *d-Mannose* gives *d*-mannitol, and *l-mannose* yields *l*-mannitol on reduction with sodium amalgam.[406] Similarly, *l*-arabinol is obtained from *l*-arabinose,[407] xylitol from *xylose*,[408] and rhamnitol from *rhamnose*.[409]

Sugar alcohols react with benzaldehyde in the presence of strong acids to form benzal derivatives.[410] Mannitol combines with three molecular proportions of the aldehyde, sorbitol with two molecular equivalents, and α-glucoheptitol with one. The benzal derivatives of various sugar alcohols undergo hydrolytic cleavage with varying ease.

Acetals or ketals of sugars may often be reduced without affecting the acetal or ketal groups. 2,4-Benzylidenexylitol and 2,4:3,5-dimethylene-*l*-xylitol have been prepared, for example, by the catalytic reduction of the corresponding sugar derivatives in the presence of Raney nickel under neutral conditions.[411] Keto-*l*-sorbose pentaacetate, reduced catalytically under low pressure in the presence of platinum, yields two alcohols, which, on subsequent acetylation, are converted to hexaacetyl-*d*-glucitol and hexaacetyl-*l*-iditol,[412]

$$
\begin{array}{c}
\text{H}\quad\text{H}\quad\text{OAc}\;\text{H} \\
\text{AcOCH}_2\text{C}-\text{C}-\text{C}-\text{C}-\text{CH}_2\text{OAc} \\
\text{OAC}\;\text{OAc}\;\text{H}\quad\text{OAc}
\end{array}
\quad\text{and}\quad
\begin{array}{c}
\text{OAc}\;\text{H}\quad\text{OAc}\;\text{H} \\
\text{AcOCH}_2\text{C}-\text{C}-\text{C}-\text{C}-\text{CH}_2\text{OAc} \\
\text{H}\quad\text{OAc}\;\text{H}\quad\text{OAc}
\end{array}
$$

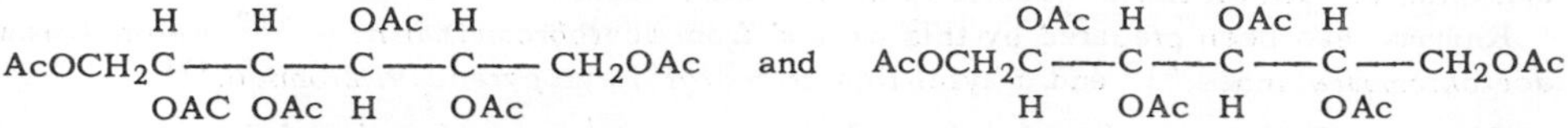

6-Halo derivatives of certain hexoses have been reduced to derivatives of methylpentoses. 6-Iododiisopropylidene galactose in ethereal solution has been reduced with sodium and water to isopropylidenerhodeose, and from this the free methylpentose has been obtained by treatment with dilute sulfuric acid:[413]

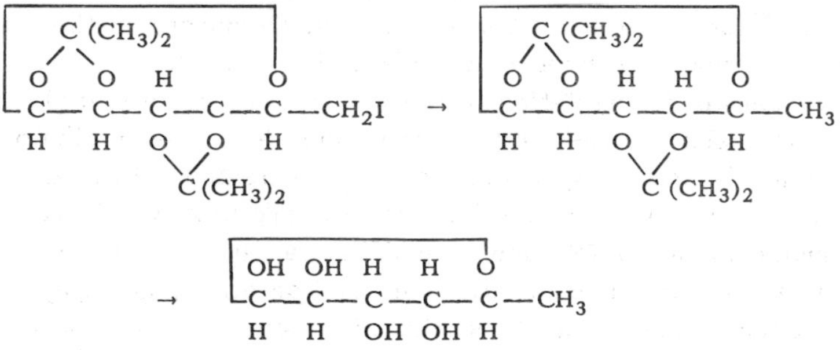

The methyl glucoside of triacetyl *d*-glucose-6-bromohydrin has been reduced with zinc dust and acetic acid to β-methyl-*d*-epirhamnoside, and from this epirhamnose has been obtained by saponification:[414]

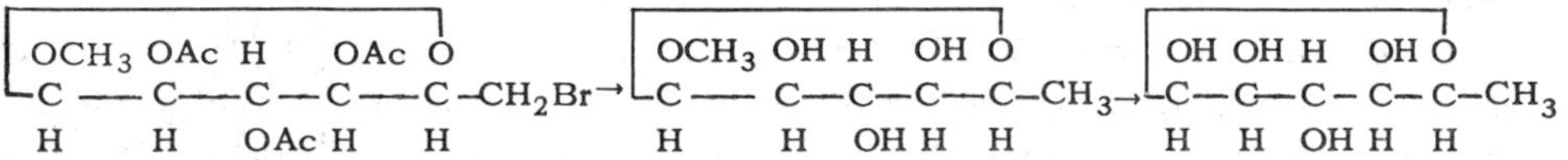

Similarly, triacetyl-β-methyl-*d*-galactoside-6-bromohydrin has been reduced with hydrogen in the presence of palladium to triacetyl-β-methyl-*d*-fucoside, and from this *d-fucose* has been obtained by hydrolysis.[415]

Glucals

Acetylated α-bromo aldoses treated with zinc dust and acetic acid at room temperature are converted to acetylated glucals:[416]

$$\overline{\underset{\substack{\text{H} \quad \text{H} \quad \text{OAc} \quad \text{H} \quad \text{H}}}{\underset{\text{C}-\text{C}-\text{C}-\text{C}-\text{CCH}_2\text{OAc}}{\text{Br} \quad \text{OAc} \quad \text{H} \quad \quad \text{OAc} \quad \text{O}}}} \quad \underset{\text{AcOH}}{\overset{\text{Zn}}{\rightarrow}} \quad \overline{\underset{\substack{\text{H} \quad \text{H} \quad \text{OAc} \quad \text{H}}}{\underset{\text{C}=\text{C}-\text{C}-\text{C}-\text{CCH}_2\text{OH}}{\text{H} \quad \quad \text{OAc} \quad \text{O}}}}$$

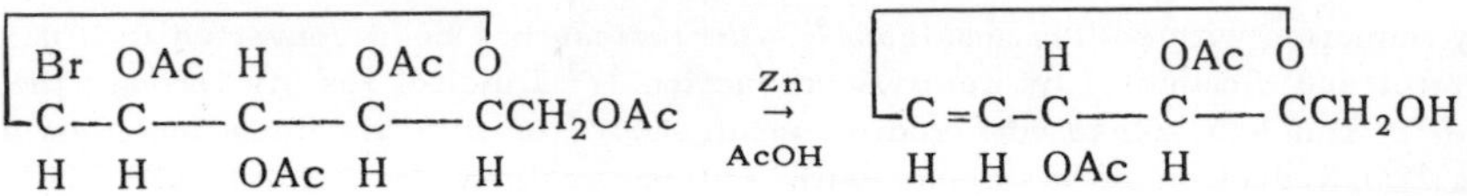

The reaction proceeds smoothly, and no instances of its failure have been recorded. Platinum chloride and copper salts act as catalysts in the reaction. As an example of the procedure the preparation of glucal is described below:

A mixture of 10 gm of acetobromoglucose, 100 cc of 50% acetic acid, and 20 gm zinc dust is shaken vigorously for 1½ hours at room temperature. The liquid is next filtered and evaporated down under 10 to 20 mm pressure until crystals of zinc salts appear; it is then diluted with 100 cc water. The oily layer is taken up with ether, the ethereal solution is washed successively with aqueous sodium bicarbonate and water, and the ether is finally evaporated. Acetylglucal is thus obtained in the form of a colorless viscous liquid, which crystallizes rapidly when seeded with a few crystals of acetylglucal. It may be purified by crystallization from absolute alcohol. The free glucal is obtained from the acetylated compound by removal of the acetyl groups by treatment with alkalies or with baryta water. Deacetylation may be effected also with methanolic ammonia, or with alcoholic caustic or sodium alkoxides.[417]

Rhamnal has been prepared by this method from *acetobromorhamnose*,[418] arabinal from *acetobromoarabinose*,[419] and *d*-xylal from *triacetyl-d-xylopyranosyl bromide*.[420]

Glucals of monosaccharides have been prepared from glucals of disaccharides by cleavage of the monosaccharide groups with an appropriate carbohydrase. A number of disaccharides have been prepared from the acetobromo derivatives of disaccharides. Thus, cellobial,[421] maltal,[422] melibial,[423] and lactal[424] have been obtained from the corresponding acetobromobioses.

The double bond in glucals behaves in many respects in the manner of reactive olefinic bonds. *Hydrogen bromide* adds to the double bond of triacetyl glucal with partial deacetylation of the compound. Triacetyl-*d*-glucal adds two atoms of halogens to yield crystalline dihalides. These dihalo derivatives yield the same 2-desoxy-*d*-galactonic acid when treated with lead oxide.[425] The halogen on carbon atom 1 of the dihalides is very reactive; it may be replaced with an amino group by reaction with ammonia, an acetoxy group by reaction with silver acetate in glacial acetic acid, and an alkoxy group by reaction with sodium alkoxides. Treatment of the dihalides with silver carbonate or oxide in the presence of methanolic ammonia results in the replacement of the halogen with a methoxy group. Water adds very readily to the double bond in glucals in the presence of sulfuric acid to yield desoxy sugars.[426] The reaction offers an excellent method for the preparation of 2-desoxyaldoses.

When glucals are treated with *perbenzoic acid*, oxygen adds at the double bond, and an epoxide is formed. The epoxide reacts with water to yield a mixture of epimeric aldoses.[427] When the hydroxyl at carbon atom 3 is substituted, a *trans* configuration for the new hydroxyl at carbon 2 is favored; when the third hydroxyl is free, the *cis* configuration is favored. The epoxide reacts with methanol to form the epimeric methyl glucosides. β-1-Benzoyl-3,4,6-triacetyl-6-glucals by the reaction of triacetyl-*d*-glucal and perbenzoic acid.[428] Treatment of triacetyl-*d*-glucal with ozone results in the formation of 1,3,5-triacetyl-*d*-arabinose,

$$\begin{array}{c} \quad\quad\quad\quad OH \quad Ac \quad H \\ AcOCH_2C - C - C - CHO \\ \quad\quad\quad\quad H \quad\ H \quad OAc \end{array}$$

Hydrogenation of glucals leads to the formation of dihydro compounds, which are 1,5-anhydrides of 2-hydroxy hexitols, pentitols, etc. Epoxides of glucals have been reduced successfully with lithium aluminum hydride without affecting other sensitive groups, such as benzylidene, in the molecule.[429]

The methylene group in methyl and ethyl 2-desoxyglucosides of pyranose and furanose type greatly increase the lability of the glucosidic linkage, particularly if the compound has a furanose structure.[430] The methylene group apparently activates carbon atoms 1, 3, and 6.[431]

Pseudoglucals

When a triacetyl glucal is boiled with water, an acetyl group is removed, and the compound is isomerized to a *diacetylpseudoglucal*.[432]

$$AcOCH_2\overline{CHCH(OAc)CH(OAc)CH{=}CH\text{—}O} \rightarrow AcOCH_2\overline{CHCH(OAc)CH{=}CHCHOH\text{—}O}$$

Monoacetylpseudoglucals undergo further deacetylation, and isomerization to *isoglucals:*

$$HOCH_2\overline{CHCH(OAc)CH{=}CHCHOH\text{—}O} \rightarrow H_2\overline{CCH(OH)CH(OH)CHCOCH_3\text{—}O}$$

Protoglucals may be obtained from diacetylpseudoglucals if the hydroxyl group attached to carbon 4 or 6 is free or is not substituted in too stable manner:

$$AcOCH_2\overline{CHCH(OAc)CH{=}CHCHOH\text{—}O} \rightarrow H_2\overline{CCH(OH)CH_2C{=}CHCHO\text{—}O}$$

Triacetyl-*d*-glucal is very rapidly resinified by acids to a dark amorphous body.

Acetylpseudoglucals may be hydrogenated by use of palladium black or platinum black to acetyl-2,3-didesoxyaldoses, and 2,3-desoxysugars may be obtained from the latter by deacetylation. The pyranose ring is retained in this reduction. More vigorous hydrogenation by use of a suitable catalyst, for example, Wieland's platinum black, brings about the reduction of the aldehyde group to carbinol.

References

1. Gladstone and Tribe, *J. Chem. Soc.*, **45,** 154 (1884).
2. Meunier, *Compt. rend.*, **134,** 473 (1902); Wislicenus, *J. prakt. Chem.*, (2), **54,** 18 (1896).
3. Kraft, *Ber.*, **15,** 1687, 1711 (1882); **19,** 2218 (1886).
4. Kolbe, *Ann.*, **69,** 279 (1849); Peterson, *Z. Elektrochem.*, **12,** 141 (1884); Kempf and Kolbe, *J. prakt. Chem.*, (2), **4,** 46 (1871); Hofer and Moest, *Z. Elektrochem.*, **10,** 833, (1904).
5. Crum Brown and Walker, *Ann.*, **261,** 101 (1891). Cf. Gibson, *J. Chem. Soc.*, **127,** 475 (1925).
6. Elbs and Kratz, *J. prakt. Chem.*, (2), **55,** 502 (1897).
7. Lee, *Trans. Faraday Soc.*, **23,** 79 (1927); Lee and van Rysselberge, *J. Phys. Chem.*, **33,** 1543 (1929); Fulton and Lee, *J. Chem. Soc.*, **1930,** 1057.

8. Aschan, *C.A.* **1919**, 2868; Meyer and Müller, *Ber.*, **24**, 4249 (1891).
9. Michael, *Ber.*, **39**, 2138 (1906).
10. *German Patent*, 267, 204.
11. Crossley and Renouf, *J. Chem. Soc.*, **91**, 81 (1907).
12. v. Meyer and Müller, *J. prakt. Chem.*, (2), **46**, 171 (1892).
13. Finkelstein, *Ber.*, **43**, 1528 (1910).
14. Freund and Schonfeld, *Ber.*, **24**, 3350 (1891); Eschert and Freund, *ibid.*, **26**, 2490 (1893).
15. Kraft, *ibid.*, **16**, 1715 (1883).
16. Bouveault and Blanc, *Compt. rend.*, **136**, 1678 (1903); **137**, 60, 328 (1903); *Bull. soc. chim.*, (3), **31**, 666, 1203 (1904); *French patent* 338, 895 (1903); *U.S. patent* 868, 252 (1907); Prins, *Rec. trav. chim.*, **42**, 1050 (1923); Adam and Dyer, *J. Chem. Soc.*, **127**, 70 (1925); Blatt, *"Organic Syntheses"*, vol. 2, p. 154 (1943); Chuit, *Helv. Chim. Acta*, **9**, 264 (1926); Franke and Kienberger, *Monatsh.*, **33**, 1189 (1912); Marvel and Tanenbaum, *J. Am. Chem. Soc.*, **44**, 2645 (1922); Meyer and Reed, *ibid.*, **44**, 2645 (1922); Hansley, *Ind. Eng. Chem.*, **39**, 55 (1947).
17. Hansley, *J. Am. Chem. Soc.*, **57**, 2303 (1935).
18. Blatt, *"Organic Syntheses"*, vol. 2, p. 317 (1943); Wiemann, *Compt. rend.*, **212**, 764 (1941).
19. Pickard and Kenyon, *J. Chem. Soc.*, **99**, 58 (1911); **103**, 1943 (1913); Klages and Allendorff, *Ber.*, **31**, 1003 (1898); **35**, 2245 (1902).
20. Lieben and Rossi, *Ann.*, **159**, 70 (1871); Lieben and Janeck, *ibid.*, **187**, 135 (1877); Rossi, *ibid.*, **133**, 180 (1865).
21. Levene and Taylor, *J. Biol. Chem.*, **35**, 281 (1918).
22. Weizmann and Gerard, *J. Chem. Soc.*, **117**, 324 (1920).
23. Meerwein and Schmidt, *Ann.*, **444**, 221 (1925); Ponndorf, *Z. angew. Chem.*, **39**, 138 (1926); Verley, *Bull. soc. chim.*, *(4)*, **37**, 537, 871 (1925); **41**, 788 (1927); Reichstein, *et al.*, *Helv. Chim. Acta*, **15**, 261 (1932); Linstead, *Ann. Reports on Progress Chem. (Chem. Soc. London)* **34**, 228 (1937); Bersin, *Angew. Chem.*, **53**, 266 (1940); Adams, *"Organic Reactions"*, vol. 2, p. 178 (1944).
24. Grubb and Read, *J. Chem. Soc.*, **1934**, 242; Short and Read, *ibid.*, **1939**, 1306; Doeuvre and Perret, *Bull. soc. chim.*, (5), **2**, 298 (1935); Bachmann and Struve, *J. Org. Chem.*, **4**, 461 (1939).
25. Heilbron, *et al.*, *J. Chem. Soc.*, **1938**, 869; Windaus and Buchholz, *Ber.*, **71**, 576 (1938); **72**, 597 (1939); Windaus and Kaufmann, *Ann.*, **542**, 218 (1939).
26. Lund, *Ber.*, **70**, 1520 (1937).
27. Schenk, *J. prakt. Chem.*, (2), **134**, 215 (1932).
28. Stevens *et al*, *J. Am. Chem. Soc.*, **62**, 1424, 3264 (1940).
29. Butlerow, *Zeifschrift fur chemie*, **1864**, 385; **1865**, 614; Pawlow, *Ann.*, **188**, 104 (1877); Markownikow, *Ber.*, **16**, 2284 (1883); Grigorowitsch and Pawlow, *Ber.*, **24**, R667 (1891).
30. Dose and Doran, *J. Chem. Soc.*, **1929**, 2246; Heilbron and Simpson, *ibid.*, **1932**, 270.
31. Gumpert, *J. prakt. Chem.*, (2), **31**, 119 (1885); **32**, 279 (1886); Bloch, *Bull. soc. chim.*, (3), **31**, 49 (1904).
32. Orndorff and Richmond, *Am. Chem. J.*, **22**, 458 (1899); Fromm, *Ber.*, **42**, 1957 (1904).
33. Oppenauer, *Rec. trav. chim.*, **56**, 137 (1937). Cf. Bersin, *Angew. Chem.*, **53**, 266 (1940); *Newer Methods of Preparative Organic Chemistry*, Interscience Publ. 1948, p. 143-158. *Mechanism:* Verley, *Bull. soc. chim.*, (4), **37**, 537 (1925); Pondorff, *Angew. Chem.*, **39**, 138 (1926); Meerwein *et al.*, *Ann.*, **444**, 221 (1925); *J. prakt. Chem.*, (2), **147**, 211 (1936); Davies and Hodgson, *J. Soc. Chem. Ind.*, **62**, 109 (1943); Woodward *et al.*, *J. Am. Chem. Soc.*, **67**, 1425 (1945); Jackman and Mills, *Nature*, **164**, 789 (1949); Lutz and Gillespie, *J. Am. Chem. Soc.*, **72**, 345 (1950); Doering and Young, *ibid.*, **72**, 631 (1950).
34. Kamm and Marvel, *J. Am. Chem. Soc.*, **42**, 299 (1920).
35. Paloma, *Ann. Acad. Sci. Fennicae*, **10A**, No. 17, 1 (1917); *C.A.*, **13**, **1919**, 2863.
36. Norris *et al.*, *J. Am. Chem. Soc.*, **38**, 1071 (1916); **42**, 2093 (1920); *German patent* 280, 740.
37. Clark and Straight, *Trans. Roy. Soc. Can.*, **23**, 77 (1929); Dehn and Davis, *J. Am. Chem. Soc.*, **29**, 1328 (1907).
38. McKenzie and Clough, *J. Chem. Soc.*, **103**, 698 (1913); McKenzie and Thorpe, *J. Biol. Chem.*, **62**, 551 (1924).
39) Darzens, *Compt. rend.*, **152**, 1314, 1601 (1911); *Chem. Ztg.*, **35**, 634 (1911); Helferich, *Ber.*, **54**, 1082 (1921).
40. Clark and Streight, *Trans. Roy. Soc. Can.*, **23**, 77 (1929).
41. Bushong, *Am. Chem. J.*, **30**, 212 (1903).
42. *German patent*, 113, 239 (1900).
43. Merck, *German patent* 77, 278 (1893); *Ber.*, **28**, R31 (1895).
44. Krüger, *Ber.*, **26**, 1203 (1893); Mamontoff, *J. Russ. Phys.-Chem. Soc.*, **29**, 230.
45. Damiens, *Brit. patent*, 152, 495 (1919).
46. Bushong, *Am. Chem. J.*, **30**, 212 (1903); Wilcox, *ibid.*, **32**, 446 (1904).
47. Ahrens and Stapler, *Ber.*, **38**, 1298 (1905); Goldberg and Zimmermann, *angew. Chem.*, **15**, 898 (1902).

48. Arbusow, *J. Russ. Phys.-Chem. Soc.*, **41**, 447 (1909).
49. Sandmeyer, *Ber.*, **18**, 1767 (1885); **19**, 857 (1886); Chattaway and Beckeberg, *J. Chem. Soc.*, **123**, 2999 (1923).
50. Bouveault and Wahl, *Compt. rend.*, **136**, 1563 (1903); Lachmann, *J. Am. Chem. Soc.*, **43**, 2084 (1921).
51. Baeyer and Villiger, *Ber.*, **34**, 755 (1901).
52. Pschorr and Stöhrer, *ibid.*, **35**, 4393 (1902).
53. Bewald, *J. Russ. Phys.-Chem. Soc.*, (I), **1892**, p. 125.
54. Cavalier, *Ann. chim. phys.*, (7), **18**, 449 (1899); Bailly, *Compt. rend.*, **168**, 560 (1919).
55. Milobedzki and Sachnowski, *Chemik Polski*, **15**, 34 (1917).
56. Emmett and Jones, *J. Chem. Soc.*, **99**, 713 (1911); Pischtschimuka, *J. Russ. Phys.-Chem. Soc.*, **44**, 1406 (1912); Autenrieth and Meyer, *Ber.*, **58**, 840 (1925).
57. Taurke, *Ber.*, **38**, 1661 (1905).
58. Mereshkowski, *J. Russ. Phys.-Chem. Soc.*, **46**, 1082 (1914).
59. Braun, *Ber.*, **42**, 4568 (1909), Cf. Braun, *ibid.*, **35**, 3368 (1902).
60. Kramer and Reid, *J. Am. Chem. Soc.*, **43**, 880 (1921).
61. Stadler, *Ber.*, **17**, 2080 (1880).
62. Leuckhardt, *J. prakt. Chem.*, (2), **41**, 184 (1890).
63. Schiller and Otto, *Ber.*, **9**, 1637 (1876).
64. Otto and Rössing, *ibid.*, **19**, 3129 (1886); Cleve, *ibid.*, **21**, 1099 (1888); Ekbom, *ibid.*, **35**, 654 (1902).
65. Class, *Ber.*, **45**, 2424 (1912).
66. Gebauer and Fulnegg, *J. Am. Chem. Soc.*, **49**, 1386 (1927).
67. Reid *et al.*, *Am. Chem. J.*, **43**, 489 (1910); *J. Am. Chem. Soc.*, **37**, 1934 (1915); **38**, 2746 (1916); **39**, 1930 (1917).
68. Baumann, *Ber.*, **18**, 884 (1885); **19**, 2803 (1886).
69. Krausse and Grosse, *Die Chemie der metallorganischen Verbindungen*, (1937). p. 667.
69a. Egloff et al, *Chem. Revs.*, **8**, 1 (1931).
70. Clarke, *J. Am. Chem. Soc.*, **31**, 107, 558, 585 (1909); **34**, 54, 60, 674, 680 (1912); **37**, 2536 (1915); Chonin, *J. Russ. Phys.-Chem. Soc.*, **41**, 327 (1909; Chavanne *et al.*, *Compt. rend.*, **168**, 1324 (1919); *Bull. soc. chim.*, **31**, 98 (1922); **33**, 366 (1924); de Draf, *ibid.*, **34**, 427 (1925); Edgar *et al.*, *J. Am. Chem. Soc.*, **51**, 1483 (1929) Staudinger and Kern, *Ber.*, **66**, 373 (1933); Suida and Planckh, *ibid.*, **66**, 1446 (1933); Backer and Strating, *ibid.*, **55**, 905 (1936); *Rec. trav. chim.*, **59**, 929 (1940).
71. Whitmore *et al.*, *J. Am. Chem. Soc.*, **64**, 1360, 1801 (1942); Lunshoff *et al. Rec. trav. chim.*, **66**, 348 (1947); Boord *et al.*, *Ind. Eng. Chem.*, **41**, 609 (1949).
72. Sherk *et al.*, *J. Am. Chem. Soc.*, **67**, 2239 (1945).
73. Lennartz, *Ber.*, **75**, 837, 838 (1942).
74. Martin, *U.S. patent* 1, 801, 873 (1931).
75. Boswell and McLaughlin, *Can. J. Research*, **1**, 240 (1929). *Cf. U.S. patent* 1, 889, 157 (1932).
76. D'Ans and Kautzsch, *J. prakt. Chem.*, (2) **80**, 308 (1909).
77. Groggins, *Unit Processes in Organic Synthesis*, pp. 190, 204 (1938); *U.S. patent* 1, 741, 393 (1929); 1, 831, 474 (1931); 1, 835, 202 (1931).
78. *U.S. patent*, 1, 765, 601 (1930).
79 . *U.S. patent*, 1, 654, 821 (1928); *German patent* 486, 952 (1929).
80. Bolas and Groves, *Ber.*, **3**, 508 (1870).
81. Thurm, *U.S. patent* 1, 590, 265.
82. Danilow and Venus-Danilowa, *Ber.*, **63B**, 2769 (1930); Witzemann, *J. Am. Chem. Soc.*, **39**, 109 (1917).
83. Carroll, *J. Chem. Soc.*, **1940**, 1267; Levene and Walti, *Org. Syntheses*, Col. 1, vol. II, 5 (1943); Auwers *et al.*, *Ann.*, **526**, 143 (1936); Hartmann Rahrs, *Org. Syntheses*, **24**, 81 (1944); Synerholm, *J. Am. Chem. Soc.*, **69**, 2581 (1947); Reid *et al.*, *J. Org. Chem.*, **15**, 579 (1950).
84. Auwers *et al,*, *Ann.*, **526**, 143 (1936).
85. Cady *et al.*, *Ind. Eng. Chem.*, **39**, 290 (1947).
86. Fowler *et al.*, *ibid.*, **39**, 292 (1947).
87. Fowler *et al.*, *ibid.*, **39**, 343 (1947); Irwin *et al.*, *ibid.*, **39**, 350 (1947).
88. Bawden and Adkins, *J. Am. Chem. Soc.*, **56**, 689 (1934).
89. Prins, *Rec. trav. chim.*, **42**, 1050 (1923).
90. Stoll *et al.*, *Helv. Chim. Acta*, **32**, 1947 (1949); Dürst *et al.*, *ibid.*, **32**, 46 (1949); Newman and Whitehouse, *J. Am. Chem. Soc.*, **71**, 3664 (1949); Specter *et al.*, *ibid.*, **71**, 57 (1949).
91. Nystrom and Brown, *J. Am. Chem. Soc.*, **69**, 2548 (1947).
92. Ligthelm *et al.*, *J. Chem. Soc.*, **1950**, 3187; Goering *et al.*, *J. Am. Chem. Soc.*, **70**, 3315 (1948).
93. Brehm, *J. Am. Chem. Soc.*, **71**, 3541 (1949); Blicke and Sheetz, *ibid.*, **71**, 2856 (1949); Sherman and Amstutz, *ibid.*, **72**, 2198 (1950).
94. Prelog *et al.*, *Helv. Chim. Acta*, **29**, 360, 684 (1946); McIntosh *et al.*, *J. Am. Chem. Soc.*, **70**, 1907, 2955 (1948); Heer and Mescher, *Helv. Chim. Acta*, **30**, 777 (1947); Erlenmeyer *et al.*, *ibid.*, **31**, 65, 571 (1948).

95. Finholt *et al.*, *J. Am. Chem. Soc.*, **69**, 1199 (1947).
96. Palvic and Adkins, *Ibid.*, **69**, 1471 (1946).
97. Adkins *et al.*, *ibid.*, **53**, 1091, 1095 (1931); **54**, 1138, 1145 (1932); **56**, 2425 (1934); Schrauth *et al.*, *Ber.*, **64**, 1314 (1931); Schmidt, *ibid.*, **64**, 2051 (1931); Adkins, *Reactions of Hydrogen*, University of Wisconsin (1937).
98. *Organic Syntheses*, Col 1, vol. II, 142 (1943); *U.S. patent* 1,746,782; 1,964,000.
99. Sauer and Adkins, *J. Am. Chem. Soc.*, **60**, 402 (1938).
100. Nystrom and Brown, *ibid.*, **69**, 1197 (1947); Inhoffen, *Ann.*, **565**, 35 (1949); Arens and van Dorp. *Rec. trav. chim.*, **68**, 604 (1949); Slabey and Wise, *J. Am. Chem. Soc.*, **71**, 3252 (1949); Volkenburg *et al.*, *ibid.*, **71**, 3595 (1949).
101. Fieser *et al.*, *J. Am. Chem. Soc.*, **71**, 2226 (1949); McKennis and Gaffney, *J. Biol. Chem.*, **175**, 217 (1948); Meyster and Miescher, *Helv. Chim. Acta*, **32**, 1758 (1949); Rosenkranz *et al.*, *J. Am. Chem. Soc.*, **71**, 3689 (1949). Cf. Levin *et al.*, *ibid.*, **71**, 2958 (1949); Witkop, *ibid.*, **70**, 3712 (1948); Uhle, *ibid.*, **71**, 761 (1949); Adams *et al.*, *ibid.*, **71**, 1624 (1949); Roberts and Sauer, *ibid.*, **71**, 3925 (1949).
102. Young *et al.*, *J. Am. Chem. Soc.*, **58**, 2274 (1930); Urion, *Ann. chim.*, (11) **1**, 39, 67 (1934); Wiemann, *ibid.* (11) **5**, 287 (1936).
103. Berkenheim and Dankova, *J. Gen. Chem. (U.S.S.R.)* **9**, 924 (1939).
104. Prins, *Chem. Weekblad*, **14**, 932 (1917); **16**, 1072, 1510 (1919); Fourneau *et al.*, *Bull. soc. chim.*, **47**, 858 (1930).
105. Cannizzaro, *Ann.* **88**, 130 (1853); Schramm, *Monatsh.* **9**, 619 (1888).
106. Klages and Allendorff. *Ber.*, **31**, 1006 (1898).
107. Clarke, *J. Chem. Soc.*, **101**, 1583 (1913); Gomberg, *J. Am. Chem. Soc.*, **41**, 1415 (1919).
108. Taboury, *Bull. soc. chim.*, (4) **9-10**, 124 (1911).
109. Ramert, *Compt. rend.*, **179**, 634 (1924).
110. Glaser, *Ann.*, **147**, 95 (1868); Freund and Schonfeld, *Ber.*, **24**, 3354 (1891).
111. Mőslinger, *Ann.*, **185**, 55 (1877).
112. Butlerow, *ibid.*, **144**, 5 (1867).
113. Markownikoff, *Ann.*, **138**, 364 (1866); Erlenmeyer, *ibid.*, **139**, 224 (1866); Zeisel and Fanto, *Fiedl.*, **42**, 551 (1903).
114. Erlenmeyer, *Ann.*, **126**, 305 (1863).
115. Luynes, *Compt. rend.*, **59**, 81 (1864).
116. Michael and Hartman, *Ber.*, **40**, 142 (1907).
117. Leser, *ibid.*, **17**, 1826 (1884).
118. Meslans, *Ann. chim.*, **7**, 94 (1896); *Compt. rend.*, **115**, 1080 (1892); **117**, 853 (1894).
119. Scherer, *Angew. Chem.*, **52**, 457 (1939).
120. Groves, *Ann.*, **174**, 372 (1874).
121. Zanetti, *J. Am. Chem. Soc.*, **49**, 1061 (1927).
122. Steinkopf and Frommel, *Ber.*, **38**, 1865 (1905).
123. Reith and Beilstein, *Ann.*, **126**, 251 (1863). *Cf.* Adams and Voorhees, *J. Am. Chem. Soc.*, **41**, 789 (1919); Bogert and Slocum, *ibid.*, **46**, 763 (1924).
124. Hofmann, *Ann.*, **115**, 273 (1860).
125. Fridau, *ibid.*, **83**, 9 (1852); Becker, *ibid.*, **102**, 209 (1857).
126. Carius, *Ann.*, **122**, 73 (1862); Claus, *ibid.*, **168**, 43 (1873); Rössing, *Ber.*, **19**, 64 (1886); Morley, *ibid.*, **13**, 222 (1880).
127. Ross and Bibbins, *Ind. Eng. Chem.*, **31**, 255 (1939).
128. Demuth and Meyer, *Ann.*, **256**, 28 (1890).
129. Scholl, *Ber.*, **29**, 1558 (1896).
130. Braun and Steindorff, *ibid.*, **38**, 174 (1905).
131. Fränkel, *ibid.*, **30**, 2506 (1897).
132. Schlagdenhaufen, *Jehresb.* **1856**, 576.
133. Moissan, *Compt. rend.*, **107**, 260, 1155 (1888).
134. Haitinger, *Wiener Anz.* **1877**, 77; *Chem. Zentr.* **1877**, 642.
135. Haitinger, *Wiener Anz.* **1881**, 96; *Monatsh.*, **2**, 286 (1881); *Chem. Zentr.*, **1881**, 308, 403; *Ann.*, **193**, 366 (1878).
136. Champion and Pellet, *Bull. soc. chim.*, (2) **24**, 448 (1876); Lea, *Chem. Zent.*, **1870**, 79; Schrimpff, *Chem. Zentr.*, **1919** IV, 697.
137. Hoffmann and Reid, *J. Am. Chem. Soc.*, **45**, 1831 (1923); Barkenbus *et al.*, *Monatsh.*, **49**, 2552 (1927) Swallen and Boord, *J. Am. Chem. Soc.*, **52**, 655 (1930); Ellis and Reid, *ibid.*, **54**, 1674 (1932); Collin *et al.*, *J. Soc. Chem. Ind.*, **52**, 272 T (1933); Karjala and McElvain, *J. Am. Chem. Soc.*, **55**, 2969 (1933); Hull and Reid, *ibid.*, **65**, 1466 (1943); Gilman and Gainer, *Monatsh.*, **67**, 1846 (1945); Thirtle, *J. Am. Chem. Soc.*, **68**, 342 (1946); Hromatka and Engel, *Monatsh.*, **78**, 32 (1948); Kharasch and Williams; *J. Am. Chem. Soc.*, **72**, 1843 (1950).
138. Lennartz, *Angew. Chem.*, **59**, 54 (1947).
139. Urguhart *et al.*, *Org. Syntheses*, **21**, 36 (1941).
140. Lennartz, *Ber.*, **75**, 833 (1942).

141. Hoeffelmann and Berkenbosch, *German patent* 740, 247 (1940).

142. Lipman, *Die Chemie der Zuckerarten*, 3rd ed., Braunschweig, 1904; Armstrong, *The Simple Carbohydrates and the Glucosides*, 4th ed., London, 1924; Pringsheim-Leibowitz, *Zuckerchemie*, Leipzig, 1925, *Die Polysaccharide*, Leipzig, 1925; *The Chemistry of monosaccharides, and Polysaccharides*, New York, 1925, Cramer, *Les Sucres et leurs Dérivés*, Paris, 1927; Pringsheim, *Die Polysaccharide*, 3rd ed.; Karrer, *Polymere Kohlenhydrate*, Leipzig, 1925; Fischer, *Untersuchungen über Kohlenhydrate und Fermente*, vol. 1, 1884-1908, Berlin, 1909; vol. 2, 1908-1919, Berlin 1922; Zemplén and Nord, "*Handbuch der biochemisçhen Arbeitsmethoden*" of Abderhalden, pt. 1, Vol. 5; Grafe, Zemplén, Newberg and Bewald, *Biochemischen Handlexikon* and *Supplement;* Oppenheime-Pincuss, *Die Methodik der Fermente*, Leipzig, 1929; *Rapport sur les hydrates de carbon-conference de L'Union Internationale de Chimie*, 1930; Howorth, *The Constitution of Sugars*, London, 1932; Bell, *Introduction to Carbohydrate Biochemistry*, University Tutorial Press, London, 1940; Pigman and Goepp, Jr., *Chemistry of the Carbohydrates*, Academic Press, Inc., New York, 1948; Houben-Weyl, *Die Methoden der organischen Chemie*, vol. 3, 1930; Tollens and Elsner, *Kurzes Handuch der Kohlenhydrate*, 1935; Pigman and Wolfran, *Advances in Carbohydrate Chemistry*, Academic Press, Inc., New York.

143. Butlerow, *Compt. rend.*, **53**, 145 (1861); *Ann.*, **120**, 295 (1861); Fischer *et al.*, *Ber.*, **20**, 1093, 2566, 3384 (1887); **21**, 989, 2634 (1888); **22**, 106, 359 (1889); **23**, 2125 (1890); **25**, 2549 (1892); Low, *J. prakt. Chem.*, (2) **33**, 321 (1886); *Chem. Zentr.*, **21**,231, 242 (1897); *Ber.*, **39**, 1592 (1906); **22**, 475 (1889); Tollens, *ibid.*, **15**, 1629 (1882); Wehmer and Tollens, *Ann.*, **243**, 334 (1888); Grimaux, *Bull, soc. chim.*, (2) **45**, 481 (1886); (2) **49**, 251 (1888); *Compt. rend.*, **104**, 1276 (1887); Fenton, *J. Chem. Soc.*, **67**, 779 (1895); **71**, 375 (1897); Jackson, *ibid.*, **77**, 129 (1900); Neuberg, *Z. physiol. Chem.*, **31**, 570 (1901); *Ber.*, **35**, 2632 (1902); Euler, *ibid.*, **39**, 45 (1906); Schmitz, *ibid.*, **46**, 2327 (1913); Kuster and Schoder, *Z. physiol. Chem.*, **141**, 110 (1924); Schmalfuss and Kalle, *Ber.*, **57**, 2101 (1924); *Biochem. Z.*, **185**, 70 (1927); Karrer and Krauss, *Helv. Chim. Acta*, **14**, 820 (1931). *Concerning photosynthesis of sugars see* Barton and Wright, *Recent Advances in Plant Physiology*, London, 1930, p. 143 ff.; Stiles, *Photosynthesis*, London, 1925; Spoehr, *Photosynthesis*, New York 1926.

144. Kiliani, *Ber.*, **19**, 767 (1886).

145. Lespieau and Wiemann, *Bull. soc. chim.*, (4) **53**, 1102 (1933); *Compt. rend.*, **194**, 1946 (1932); Wiemann, *Ann. chim.*, (11) **5**, 267 (1936).

146. Lespieau, *Bull. soc. chim.*, (4) **43**, 204 (1928).

147. Bourguel, *ibid.*, (4) **45**, 1067 (1929).

148. Fischer, *Ber.*, **22**, 2204 (1889); **23**, 370, 930 (1890); **24**, 2683 (1891); Fischer and Piloty, *ibid.*, **23**, 3107, 3827 (1890); Kiliani, *ibid.*, **19**, 3033 (1886); **21**, 916 (1888); **64**, 2018 (1931); Haworth and Peat, *J. Chem. Soc.*, **1929**, 350.

149. Fischer and Piloty, *Ber.*, **24**, 522 (1891).

150. Paal *et al.*, *ibid.*, **39**, 1361, 2823, 2827 (1906); **44**, 3543 (1911); **49**, 1583 (1916); Ohle and Dambergis, *Ann.*, **481**, 255 (1930).

151. Nef, *Ann.*, **280**, 263 (1894); Sowden and Fischer, *J. Am. Chem. Soc.*, **67**, 1713 (1945); **66**, 1312 (1944). *Cf.* Sowden *et al.*, *J. Am. Chem. Soc.*, **69**, 1048, 1963 (1947); **71**, 1897 (1949); **72**, 3325 (1950); **73**, 4662, 5496 (1951); *J. Biol. Chem.*, **180**, 55 (1949); Overend *et al.*, *J. Chem. Soc.*, **1949**, 1358.

152. Sowden, *J. Am. Chem. Soc.*, **72**, 3325 (1950).

153. Zemplén, *Ber.*, **59**, 1254 (1926); Zemplén and Kiss, *ibid.*, **60**, 165 (1927).

154. Wohl, *Ber.*, **26**, 730 (1893); Ruff, *ibid.*, **32**, 3672 (1899); Wolfrom and Thompson, *J. Am. Chem. Soc.*, **53**, 622 (1931).

155. Wohl, *l.c.*

156. Ruff, *Ber.*, **31**, 1573 (1898); **35**, 2360 (1902). *Cf.* Hockett and Hudson, *J. Am. Chem. Soc.*, **56**, 1632 (1934).

157. Fenton, *Proc. Chem. Soc.*, **9**, 113 (1893).

158. Weerman, *Rec. trav. chim.*, **37**, 16 (1917).

159. Micheel, *Ber.*, **63**, 347 (1930).

160. Lobry de Bruyn, *Rec. trav. chim.*, **14**, 150 (1895); de Bruyn and van Eckenstein, *ibid.*, **14**, 195 (1895); **16**, 257, 262, 274 (1897); **19**, 1, (1900); Nef, *Ann.*, **357**, 294 (1903); Wohl and Neuberg, *Ber.*, **33**, 3099 (1900); Austin *et al.*, *J. Am. Chem. Soc.*, **54**, 1933 (1932); Wolfrom and Lewis, *ibid.*, **50**, 837 (1928); Gätzi and Reichstein, *Helv. Chim. Acta*, **21**, 456 (1938).

161. Fischer *et al.*, *Ber.*, **60**, 479 (1927); Danilow *et al.*, *ibid.*, **63**, 2269 (1930).

162. Soxhlet, *J. prakt. Chem.*, (2) **21**, 244 (1880).

163. Hudson and Dale, *J. Am. Chem. Soc.*, **39**, 322 (1917).

164. Hudson and Dale, *l.c. Cf.* Levene, *J. Biol. Chem.*, **57**, 329 (1923); Behrend, *Ann.*, **353**, 106 (1907).

165. Fischer, *Ber.*, **23**, 2618 (1890); **24**, 2683 (1891).

166. Daniel, *German patent* 313, 986 (1916); Schering-Kahlbaum, *German patent* 507, 612 (1926).

167. Harding, *J. Am. Chem. Soc.*, **44**, 1765 (1922).

168. Fischer, *Ber.*, **23**, 935 (1890).

169. de Bruyn and van Ekenstein, *Rec. trav. chim.*, **16**, 266 (1897); **19**, 10 (1900).
170. Fischer and Hertz, *Ber.*, **25**, 1247 (1892).
171. Pringsheim *et al.*, *ibid.*, **56**, 1762 (1922); *Biochem. Z.*, **142**, 108 (1923); **148**, 336 (1924).
172. v. Euler and Svanberg, *Z. physiol. Chem.*, **112**, 193 (1921).
173. *Cf.* Wolfrom *et al.*, *J. Am. Chem. Soc.*, **66**, 204 (1944).
174. Bertrand, *Bull. soc. chim.*, (3) **15**, 627 (1896); *Ann. chim. phys.*, (8) **3**, 230 (1904); Schlubach and Vorwerk, *Ber.*, **66**, 1251 (1933); Vorwerk, *Dissert.*, Hamburg (1933).
175. Fischer and Hirschberger, *Ber.*, **22**, 365 (1889); Fenton and Jackson, *J. Am. Chem. Soc.*, **75**, 9 (1899).
176. Fischer, *Ber.*, **22**, 2204 (1889).
177. van Ekenstein, *Rec. trav. chim.*, **14**, 203 (1895).
178. Ley, *Polarisation und chemische Konstitution*, in *Handbuck der Physik*, vol. XX, Berlin, 1928; Kuhn and Freudenberg, *Drehung der Polarisationseben des Lichtes*, in *Hand- und Jahrbuch der chemischen Physik*, vol. 8, p. 111, Leipzig 1932.
179. Hudson, *J. Am. Chem. Soc.*, **32**, 338 (1910); **33**, 405 (1911).
180. Freudenberg and Kuhn, *Ber.*, **64**, 703 (1931).
181. Drew and Haworth, *J. Chem. Soc.*, **1926** 2303.
182. Hudson, *J. Am. Chem. Soc.*, **31**, 66 (1909); **37**, 1264 (1915); **38**, 1566, 1867 (1916); **39**, 462 (1917); **40**, 813 (1918); **41**, 1141 (1919); van Marle, *Rec. trav. chim.*, **39**, 549 (1920); van Wijk, *ibid.*, **40**, 221 (1921); Hudson, *Bur. Standards J. Research*, **1926**, Nr. 533, pp. 241-379.
183. Freudenberg, *Ber.*, **66**, 177 (1933).
184. Tschugaeff, *ibid.*, **31**, 1777 (1898).
185. Hudson, *Bur. Standards J. Research*, **1926**, Nr. 533, pp. 241-379.
186. Bertrand, *Ann. chim. phys.*, (8) **3**, 181 (1904); Hudson *et al.*, *J. Am. Chem. Soc.*, **60**, 1201 (1938).
187. Fischer, *Ber.*, **26**, 2400 (1893); **27**, 2985 (1894); **28**, 1145, 1151 (1895); Patterson and Robertson, *J. Chem. Soc.*, **1929**, 300; Levene *et al.*, *J. Biol. Chem.*, **95**, 699 (1932).
188. Fischer, *Ber.*, **47**, 1980 (1914).
189. Fischer, *Ber.*, **47**, 1980 (1914); Bourquelot, *Ann. chim.*, (9) **3**, 298 (1915); Hudson, *J. Am. Chem. Soc.*, **47**, 265 (1925); Phelps and Hudson, *ibid.*, **48**, 503 (1926); Patterson and Robertson, *J. Chem. Soc.*, **1929**, 300. *Cf.* Helferich and Schäfer, *Organic Syntheses*, **1**, 356 (1932); Voss, *Ann.*, **485**, 283 (1931).
190. Haworth and Westgarth, *J. Chem. Soc.*, **1926**, 880.
191. Haworth, *ibid.*, **107**, 8 (1915); Haworth and Leitch, *ibid.*, **113**, 188 (1918).
192. Haworth and Leitch, *ibid.*, **113**, 194 (1918).
193. Haworth, *ibid.*, **107**, 8 (1915).
194. Urban, *Cellulosechemie*, **7**, 73 (1926). *Cf.* Hess *et al.*, *Ann.*, **466**, 80 (1928); **442**, 54 (1926); **450**, 29 (1926).
195. Hess and Müller, *Ann.*, **455**, 205 (1927); **466**, 94 (1928).
196. Hess and Weltzien, *ibid.*, **435**, 81 (1923); **442**, 54 (1925); Hess and Pichlmayr, *ibid.*, **450**, 31, 35 (1926).
197. Irvine *et al.*, *J. Chem. Soc.*, **125**, 942, 1502 (1924); **1926**, 1502. *Cf.* Karrer, *Helv. Chim. Acta*, **3**, 620, (1920).
198. Irvine *et al.*, *J. Chem. Soc.*, **83**, 1021, 1025 (1903); **85**, 1049 (1904); **87**, 903 (1905); **95**, 1223 (1909); **107**, 524 (1918); *Biochem. Z.*, **22**, 357 (1909); Purdie and Pitkeathly, *J. Chem. Soc.*, **75**, 157 (1899); Purdie and Bridgett, *ibid.*, **83**, 1037 (1903).
199. Freudenberg and Hixon, *Ber.*, **56**, 2119 (1923); Levene and Meyer, *J. Biol. Chem.*, **70**, 343 (1926); **74**, 701 (1927).
200. Levene and Lowry, *J. Chem. Soc.*, **1926**, 720.
201. Schmidt and Zentner, *Monatsh.*, **49**, 111 (1928).
202. Helferich *et al.*, *Ann.*, **440**, 1 (1924); **447**, 19 (1926); *Ber.*, **57**, 587 (1924); **58**, 872 (1925); *Angew. Chem.*, **41**, 871 (1928). *Cf.* Hockett and Hudson, *J. Am. Chem. Soc.*, **53**, 4456 (1931); Oldham and Rutherford, *ibid.*, **54**, 366 (1932).
203. Zeile and Kruckenberg, *Ber.*, **75**, 1127 (1942). *Cf.* Helferich and Bredereck, *Ann.*, **465**, 166 (1928).
204. Helferich *et al.*, *Ber.*, **58**, 872 (1925).
205. Josephson, *Ann.*, **472**, 230 (1929).
206. Königs and Knorr, *Sitz. bayer. Acad. Wiss.*, **30**, 103 (1900); Brigl and Keppler, *Ber.*, **59**, 1588 (1926). *Cf.* Hickinbottom, *J. Chem. Soc.*, **1930**, 1676.
207. Königs and Knorr, *Ber.*, **34**, 974 (1901).
208. Fischer *et al.*, **53**, 2362 (1920); Dale, *J. Am. Chem. Soc.*, **46**, 1046 (1924); Levene and Wolfrom, *J. Biol. Chem.*, **78**, 525 (1928).
209. Hudson, *J. Am. Chem. Soc.*, **46**, 462 (1924); Hudson and Phelps, *ibid.*, **46**, 2591 (1924).
210. Schlubach and Schröter, *Ber.*, **61**, 1216 (1928); Hickinbottom, *J. Chem. Soc.*, **1929**, 1676.
211. Zemplén *et al.*, *Ber.*, **63**, 368, 2720 (1930).
212. Zemplén *et al.*, *ibid.*, **64**, 744 ,1545, 1852 (1931).
213. Zemplén and Gerecs, *ibid.*, **63**, 2720 (1930).

214. Michael, *Ber.*, **12**, 2260 (1879); *Am. Chem. J.*, **1**, 367 (1879); *Compt. rend.*, **89**, 355 (1879); Fischer and Armstrong, *Ber.*, **34**, 2885 (1901); Hickinbottom, *J. Chem. Soc.*, **1930**, 1338.
215. Fischer and v. Mechel, *Ber.*, **49**, 2813 (1916); Fischer and Bergmann, *ibid.*, **50**, 711 (1917).
216. Helferich and Schmitz-Hillebrecht, *Ber.*, **66**, 378 (1933).
217. Zemplen, *Ber.*, **62**, 988 (1929); Zemplén and Csürös, *ibid.*, **64**, 993 (1931).
218. Hickinbottom, *J. Chem. Soc.*, **1928**, 3140.
219. Vogel, *Ber.*, **66**, 1670 (1933).
220. Bergmann and Schotte, *ibid.*, **54**, 1564 (1921).
221. Pacsu, *ibid.*, **58**, 509, 1455 (1925); Pacsu and Ticharich, *ibid.*, **62**, 3008 (1929).
222. Pauly and Feuerstein, *Ber.*, **60**, 1031 (1927).
223. Robertson, *J. Chem. Soc.*, **1927**, 1937.
224. Glaser and Kuhler, *Ber.*, **60**, 1349 (1927).
225. Fischer, *ibid.*, **27**, 2992 (1894); Bourquelot, *J. pharm. Chim.*, (6) **23**, 369 (1906); (7) **2**, 241 (1910).
226. Willstätter *et al.*, *Z. physiol. Chem.*, **129**, 33 (1923).
227. Willstätter *et al.*, *Z. physiol. Chem.*, **134**, 224 (1924).
228. Pictet and Vogel, *Compt. rend.*, **184**, 1512 (1927); **185**, 332 (1927); *Helv. Chim. Acta*, **10**, 280 (1927). *Cf.* Irvine and Oldham, *J. Chem. Soc.*, **127**, 2903 (1925).
229. Fischer, *Ber.*, **23**, 3687 (1890).
230. Pictet and Vogel, *Compt. rend.*, **186**, 724 (1928); *Helv. Chim. Acta*, **11**, 436 (1928).
231. *Cf.* Freudenberg *et al.*, *Ber.*, **60**, 238 (1927).
232. Helferich and Klein, *Ann.*, **450**, 219 (1926).
233. Helferich and Bredereck, *ibid.*, **465**, 166 (1928).
234. Fischer and Delbrück, *Ber.*, **42**, 2776 (1909).
235. Freudenberg *et al.*, *ibid.*, **60**, 238 (1927).
236. Freudenberg *et al.*, *ibid.*, **61**, 1743 (1928).
237. Fischer and Armstrong, *ibid.*, **35**, 3144 (1902).
238. Helferich and Himmen, *ibid.*, **61**, 1827 (1928); Müller, *ibid.*, **65**, 1051 (1932).
239. Bergmann and Machemer, *Ber.*, **63**, 316, 2304 (1930). *Cf.* Hess *et al.*, *ibid.*, **63**, 1922 (1930); Klages, *Ann.*, **509**, 172 (1934).
240. Haworth *et al.*, *J. Chem. Soc.*, **1932**, 2270; *Trans. Faraday Soc.*, **29**, 14 (1933); *Nature*, **129**, 365 (1932); Hirst *et al.*, *J. Chem. Soc.*, **1932**, 2375.
241. Meldrum and Vad, *J. Indian Chem. Soc.*, **13**, 118 (1936).
242. Hoover, *U.S. patent*, 1,934,309 (1933).
243. Fischer *et al.*, *Ber.*, **49**, 93 (1916); **60**, 485 (1927); Ohle, *Biochem. Z.*, **131**, 611 (1922); Svanberg and Sjöberg, *Ber.*, **56**, 863 (1923).
244. Pette, *Rec. trav. chim.*, **53**, 967 (1934).
245. Fischer and Taube, *Ber.*, **60**, 485 (1927).
246. Hudson *et al.*, *J. Am. Chem. Soc.*, **64**, 136, 137 (1942).
247. Trister and Hibbert, *Can. J. Research*, **14B**, 415 (1936).
248. Freudenberg *et al.*, *Ber.*, **59**, 100, 107 (1926); **61**, 1735 (1928). *Cf.* Fischer and Rund, *ibid.*, **49**, 93 (1916); Freudenberg and Ivers, *ibid.*, **55**, 929 (1922); Svanberg and Sjöberg, *ibid.*, **56**, 863 (1923); Levene and Meyer, *J. Biol. Chem.*, **48**, 233 (1921); **57**, 317 (1923); Ohle, *Ber.*, **57**, 1566 (1924); Freudenberg and Smeykal, *ibid.*, **59**, 100 (1926); **61**, 1741 (1928).
249. Fischer, *Ber.*, **28**, 2496 (1895); Fischer and Rund, *ibid.*, **49**, 93 (1916); Freudenberg *et al.*, *ibid.*, **61**, 1735 (1928); Ohle and Dickhäuser, *ibid.*, **58**, 2593 (1925); Coles *et al.*, *J. Am. Chem. Soc.*, **51**, 519 (1929).
250. Freudenberg and Hixon, *Ber.*, **56**, 2119 (1923).
251. Fischer and Taube, *ibid.*, **60**, 485 (1927). *Cf.* Freudenberg *et al.*, *ibid.*, **58**, 294 (1925); **59**, 100 (1926).
252. Zervas, *Ber.*, **64**, 2289 (1931).
253. Brigl and Gruner, *ibid.*, **65**, 1428 (1932); Zervas and Sessler, *ibid.*, **66**, 1326 (1933); Levene *et al.*, *ibid.*, **66**, 384 (1933); *J. Biol. Chem.*, **53**, 431 (1922); **57**, 319 (1923).
254. Fischer and Taube, *Ber.*, **60**, 485 (1927). *Cf.* Glen *et al.*, *J. Chem. Soc.*, **1951**, 2568; Ohle and Koller, *Ber.*, **57**, 1566 (1924).
255. Glen *et al.*, *J. Chem. Soc.*, **1951**, 2568.
256. Reichstein and Grüssner, *Helv. Chim. Acta*, **17**, 311 (1934); Ohle, *Ber.*, **71**, 562 (1938).
257. Appel, *J. Chem. Soc.*, **1935**, 425.
258. v. Vorgha, *Ber.*, **66**, 1394 (1933); Wiggins, *J. Chem. Soc.*, **1946**, 13; Baer and Fischer, *J. Am. Chem. Soc.*, **61**, 761 (1939); Baer, *ibid.*, **67**, 338 (1945). *Cf.* Fischer, *Ber.*, **27**, 1524 (1894); Irvine and Paterson, *J. Chem. Soc.*, **105**, 898 (1914).
259. Brigl and Gruner, *Ber.*, **67**, 1969 (1934).
260. Irvine *et al.*, *J. Chem. Soc.*, **105**, 898 (1914); Fischer *et al.*, *Helv. Chim. Acta*, **17**, 1574 (1934); *J. Biol. Chem.*, **145**, 61, (1942); Brigl and Gruner, *l.c.*; Wiggins, *J. Chem. Soc.*, **1946**, 13.
261. Hudson *et al.*, *J. Am. Chem. Soc.*, **65**, 67 (1943).
262. Fischer, *Ber.*, **28**, 1145 (1895).

263. Speier, *ibid.*, **28**, 2531 (1895).
264. Fischer and Rund, *ibid.*, **49**, 88 (1916).
265. Fischer, *ibid.*, **28**, 1145 (1895). *Cf.* Ohle, *ibid.*, **60**, 810 (1927).
266. Elsner, *Ber.*, **61**, 2364 (1932).
267. Montgomery and Wiggins, *J. Chem. Soc.*, **1948**, 237.
268. Hudson *et al.*, *J. Am. Chem. Soc.*, **61**, 2432 (1939); Fischer and Bergmann, *Ber.*, **49**, 289 (1916).
269. Hudson,*et al.*, *J. Am. Chem. Soc.*, **66**, 1898 (1947).
270. Hudson *et al.*, *ibid.*, **64**, 132, 136, 137, 1614 (1942); Haworth *et all*, *J. Chem. Soc.*, **1944**, 155.
271. Fischer, *Ber.*, **27**, 673 (1894).
272. Brigl and Schinle, *ibid.*, **65**, 1890 (1932); **66**, 325 (1933).
273. Brigl and Schinle, *ibid.*, **66**, 325 (1933).
274. Wolfrom and Thompson, *J. Am. Chem. Soc.*, **56**, 880 (1934); Pacsu, *ibid.*, **61**, 1671 (1939).
275. Wolfrom, *ibid.*, **51**, 2188 (1929).
276. Pictet *et al.*, *Comp. rend.*, **171**, 243 (1920); *Helv. Chim. Acta*, **3**, 645 (1920); **4**, 613 (1921); **5**, 444 (1922); **6**, 129 (1923); **7**, 295 (1924); **11**, 898 (1928); Karrer, *ibid.*, **3**, 258 (1920).
277. Richtmeyer and Hudson, *J. Am. Chem. Soc.*, **61**, 214 (1939); **62**, 961 (1940); Levene and Meyer, *J. Biol. Chem.*, **55**, 221 (1922).
278. Fischer and Zach, *Ber.*, **45**, 456, 2058 (1912); Valentin, *Collection Czech. Chem. Commun.*, **8**, 35 (1936); Ohle *et al.*, *Ber.*, **61B**, 1211 (1928); **63B**, 2905 (1930); Haworth *et al.*, *J. Chem. Soc.*, **1940**, 620; Gardner and Purves, *J. Am. Chem. Soc.*, **65**, 444 (1943); Rao and Smith, *J. Chem. Soc.*, **1944**, 229; Percival and Soutar, *ibid.*, **1940**, 1475; Duff and Percival, *ibid.*, **1941**, 830; Gladding and Purves, *J. Am. Chem. Soc.*, **66**, 76, 153 (1944).
279. Freudenberg *et al.*, *Ber.*, **61B**, 1751 (1928); Ohle and Vargha, *ibid.*, **62B**, 2435 (1929). *Cf.* Brigl, *Z. physiol. Chem.*, **121**, 245 (1922).
280. Tanret, *Compt. rend.*, **119**, 158 (1894).
281. Hudson *et al.*, *J. Am. Chem. Soc.*, **64**, 1483 (1942); **65**, 3, 1848 (1943).
282. Helferich and Himmen, *Ber.*, **61**, 1825 (1928).
283. Karrer and Smirnoff, *Helv. Chim. Acta*, **4**, 817 (1922). *Cf.* Michael and Heso, *Ber.*, **60**, 1898 (1927); Michael, *ibid.*, **62B**, 687 (1929); Zemplén *et al.*, *ibid.*, **73B**, 575 (1940).
284. Levene and Sobotka, *J. Biol. Chem.* **71**, 181 (1926); Ohle and Erlbach, *Ber.*, **62B**, 2758 (1929); Bashford and Wiggins, *J. Chem. Soc.*, **1945**, 299; *Nature*, **165**, 566 (1950); Duff and Percival, *J. Chem. Soc.*, **1947**, 1675; Duff, *ibid.*, **1949**, 1597; Percival, *Quart. Revs.*, **4**, 369 (1949).
285. Ness *et al.*, *J. Am. Chem. Soc.*, **72**, 4547 (1950); **73**, 3742 (1951).
286. Fletcher and Richtmeyer, *Advances in Carbohydrate Chemistry*, **5**, 1 (1950).
287. Bergmann and Knehe, *Ann.*, **445**, 1 (1925).
288. Pictet *et al.*, *Helv. Chim. Acta*, **1**, 87 (1918); **2**, 698 (1919); **3**, 640 (1920); **4**, 788 (1921); **5**, 876 (1922). *Cf.* Zemplén and Gerees, *Ber.*, **64B**, 1545 (1931).
289. Freudenberg and Braun, *Ann.*, **460**, 288 (1928).
290. Levene, *J. Biol. Chem.*, **59**, 135 (1924).
291. Liebermann and Hörnmann, *Ber.*, **11**, 1618 (1878); Franchimont, *ibid.*, **12**, 2059 (1879); **14**, 1290 (1881); Erwig and Königs, *ibid.*, **22**, 1464, 2207 (1889); Behrend and Roth, *Ann.*, **331**, 361 (1904).
292. Hudson and Dale, *J. Am. Chem. Soc.*, **37**, 1264 (1915).
293. Tanret, *Bull. soc. chim.*, (3) **13**, 261 (1895); Fischer, *Ber.*, **49**, 584 (1916).
294. Fischer, *et al.*, *Ber.*, **45**, 915 (1912); **46**, 4029 (1913); **51**, 1760 (1918); Zemplén and László, *ibid.*, **48**, 915, 921 (1915); Odén, *Arkiv. Kenn*, **6**, Nr. 18 (1918); *Chem. Zentr.*, **1918** II, 1034; Hess and Messmer, *Ber.*, **54**, 499 (1921).
295. Fischer and Freudenberg, *Ber.*, **45**, 915, 2709 (1912); Fischer, *ibid.*, **47**, 3193 (1914); Zemplén and László, *ibid.*, **48**, 916 (1915); Hess and Messmer, *ibid.*, **54**, 499 (1921); Neuberg and Liebermann, *Biochem. Z.* **121**, 326 (1921); Ohle, *ibid.*, **131**, 601 (1922); Helferich *et al.*, *Ber.*, **54**, 1082 (1921); *Z. physiol. Chem.*, **128**, 146 (1923); Levene and Meyer *J. Biol. Chem.*, **48**, 233 (1921).
296. Fischer and Freudenberg, *Ber.*, **45**, 2724 (1912); Levene and Meyer, *J. Biol. Chem.*, **76**, 513 (1928).
297. Howorth and Porter, *J. Chem. Soc.*, **1930**, 151.
298. Neuberg and Pollak, *Biochem. Z.*, **26**, 514 (1910); Neuberg, *Z. Ver. deut. Zucker-Ind.*, 1926, 463 *(Zeit des Verein der Deut. Zucker-Ind.)*.
299. Zemplén, *Ber.*, **59**, 1254 (1926).
300. Hess, *Die Chemie der Cellulose und ihre Begleiter*, Leipzig (1928); Heuser, *Lehrbuch der Cellulosechemie*, 3rd ed., Berlin, 1927; A.W., *The Chemistry of Cellulose and Wood*, New York, 1926; Dorée, *The Methods of Cellulose Chemistry*, London, 1933; Pringsheim, *Die Polysaccharide*, 3rd ed., Berlin, 1931.
301. Oldham, *J. Chem. Soc.*, **127**, 2840 (1925).
302. Zemplén, *Ber.*, **59**, 1254 (1926).

303. Kruger, *Zelluloseazetate*, Dresden-Leipzig, 1933; Kausch, *Handbuch der Acetylcellulosen*, Munich, 1933.
304. Ost, *Angew. Chem.*, **32**, 66, 76, 82 (1919).
305. Barnett, *J. Soc. Chem. Ind., London*, **40**, 8T (1921).
306. Hess *et al.*, *Ann.*, **444**, 266 (1925); Ost, *Angew. Chem.*, **32**, 66, 76, 82 (1919). *Cf.* Elödt and Schrodt, *Angew. Chem.*, **44**, 933 (1931).
307. Hess and Schultze, *Angew. Chem.*, **37**, 999 (1924); Koll, *Beih.*, **23**, 93 (1926); Hess, *N.w.*, **13**, 1003 (1925).
308. Barnett, *J. Soc. Chem. Ind., London*, **40**, 8T (1921); Bermann and Knehe, *Ann.*, **452**, 141 (1927); Haworth *et al.*, *J. Chem. Soc.*, **1928**, 2681.
309. Berl and Rueff, *Ber.*, **63**, 3212 (1930); *Cellulosechemie*, **12**, 53 (1931); Bouchonnet *et al.*, *Compt. rend.*, **197**, 63 (1933).
310. Lunge and Weintraub, *Angew. Chem.*, **12**, 473 (1899); Rassow and Dörr, *J. prakt. Chem.*, (2) **108**, 163 (1924).
311. Cross *et al.*, *German patent* 70,999.
312. Lieser, *Ann.*, **470**, 110 (1929).
313. Dehnart and König, *Cellulosechemie*, **6**, 1 (1925); *Brit. Abst.*, **1925**, 369. *Cf.* Heuser and Bartunek, *Cellulosechemie*, **6**, 19 (1925); Collins, *J. Textile Inst.*, **16**, 123T (1925); Katz, *Cellulosechemie*, **6**, 35 (1925); Katz and Mark, *Z. Elektrochem.*, **31**, 105 (1925); Herzog, *Cellulosechemie*, **6**, 39 (1925).
314. Pringsheim and Aronowsky, *Ber.*, **54**, 1281 (1921). *Cf.* Bergmann and Knehe, *Ann.*, **449**, 302 (1926); Bergmann, *Ber.*, **59**, 2079 (1926).
315. Pringsheim and Reilly, *Ber.*, **61**, 2018 (1928); Pringsheim and Fellner, *Ann.*, **462**, 231 (1928).
316. Levene and Raymond, *J. Biol. Chem.*, **99**, 247 (1931).
317. Fischer, *Ber.*, **44**, 1898 (1911); **49**, 584 (1916); Brauns, *J. Am. Chem. Soc.*, **47**, 1280 (1925); Freudenberg *et al.*, *Ber.*, **60**, 238 (1927).
318. Skraup and Kremann, *Monatsh.*, **22**, 375 (1901); v. Arlt, *ibid.*, **22**, 144 (1901).
319. Brauns, *J. Am. Chem. Soc.*, **45**, 2381 (1923). *Cf.* Brauns, *ibid.*, **42**, 1846 (1920); Ohle *et al.*, *Ber.*, **62**, 833 (1929).
320. Brauns *et al.*, *Bur. Standards J. Research*, **6**, 449 (1931).
321. Freudenberg *et al.*, *Ber.*, **55**, 941 (1922); **58**, 666 (1925); **61**, 1740 (1928); **63**, 1969 (1930).
322. Dale, *J. Am. Chem. Soc.*, **46**, 1046 (1924).
323. Bott *et al.*, *J. Chem. Soc.*, **1930**, 1395, 2653.
324. Dale, *J. Am. Chem. Soc.*, **38**, 2187 (1916).
325. Schlubach *et al.*, *Ber.*, **59**, 840 (1926); **61**, 287 (1928).
326. Brauns, *J. Am. Chem. Soc.*, **45**, 833 (1923).
327. Helferich and Gootz, *Ber.*, **62**, 2505 (1929).
328. Skraup and Kremann, *Monatsh.*, **22**, 375 (1901). *Cf.* Hudson and Kunz, *J. Am. Chem. Soc.*, **47**, 2052 (1925); **48**, 1978 (1926).
329. Stockhausen and Gattermann, *Ber.*, **25**, 3521 (1892).
330. Micheel, *Ber.*, **63**, 386 (1930); Micheel and Micheel, *ibid.*, **65**, 253 (1932).
331. Freudenberg and Raschig, *Ber.*, **62**, 373 (1929).
332. Müller, *ibid.*, **64**, 1820 (1931).
333. Wrede, *ibid.*, **52**, 1756 (1919); *Z. physiol. Chem.*, **119**, 46 (1922).
334. Schneider *et al.*, *Ber.*, **61**, 1244 (1928).
335. Fischer and Delbrück, *ibid.*, **42**, 1476 (1909). *Cf.* Karrer *et al.*, *Helv. Chim. Acta*, **4**, 130 (1921); Purves, *J. Am. Chem. Soc.*, **51**, 3619, 3631 (1929).
336. Wrede and Hettche, *Z. physiol. Chem.*, **172**, 169 (1927); Schneider and Beuther, *Ber.*, **52**, 2135 (1919).
337. Schneider and Eisfeld, *Ber.*, **61**, 1260 (1938).
338. Schneider *et al.*, *ibid.*, **47**, 1258 (1914).
339. Schneider and Wrede, *ibid.*, **47**, 2038 (1914).
340. Fischer *et al.*, *Ber.*, **47**, 1378 (1914); **53**, 873 (1920); Johnson *et al.*, *J. Am. Chem. Soc.*, **55**, 395 (1933); **60**, 1916 (1938); Müller and Wilhelms, *Ber.*, **74**, 698 (1941); Wilhelms and Magyar, *Biol. Kutató Intézet Munkai*, **13**, 525 (1941).
341. Freudenberg and Wolf, *Ber.*, **60**, 232 (1927).
342. Brigl and Schinle, *ibid.*, **65**, 1890 (1932); **66**, 325 (1933).
343. Wolfrom and Thompson, *J. Am. Chem. Soc.*, **56**, 880, 1804 (1934).
344. Schneider *et al.*, *Ber.*, **49**, 2054 (1916); **51**, 220 (1918).
345. Raymond, *J. Biol. Chem.*, **107**, 85 (1934).
346. Müller and Wilhelms, *Ber.*, **74**, 698 (1941).
347. Wrede, *Z. physiol. Chem.*, **115**, 284 (1921).
348. Wrede, *Ber.*, **52**, 1756 (1919).
349. Wrede, *Z. physiol. Chem.*, **119**, 46 (1922). *Cf.* Schneider *et al.*, *Ber.*, **61**, 1244 (1928); Wrede and Hettche, *Z. physiol. Chem.*, **177**, 298 (1928).
350. Schneider *et al.*, *Ber.*, **50**, 793 (1917); **52**, 2135 (1919); **62**, 1384 (1929); Wrede *et al.*, *ibid.*,

52, 1756 (1919); *Z. physiol. Chem.*, **108**, 115 (1919); **112**, 1 (1920); **148**, 65 (1925); **172**, 169 (1927); Hudson *et al.*, *J. Am. Chem. Soc.*, **65**, 1477 (1943).
351. Schneider and Wrede, *Ber.*, **50**, 793 (1917).
352. Wrede, *Z. physiol. Chem.*, **115**, 284 (1921). *Concerning pharmacology of selnium compounds of carbohydrates*, see Wrede, *Deut. med. Wochschr.*, **50**, 1611 (1925); **51**, 148 (1925).
353. de Bruyn *et al.*, *Rec. trav. chim.*, **12**, 286 (1893); **14**, 98, 134 (1895); Irvine *et al.*, *J. Chem. Soc.*, **103**, 241 (1913); Levene and LaForge, *J. Biol. Chem.*, **22**, 333 (1915); **24**, 62 (1916); **36**, 80 (1918).
354. de Bruyn and Lent, *Rec. trav. chim.*, **14**, 145 (1895).
355. Freudenberg and Doser, *Ber.*, **58B**, 294 (1925).
356. Bouchardat, *Ann. chim. phys.*, (4) **27**, 145, 168 (1872).
357. Fischer and Zach, *Ber.*, **44**, 132 (1911).
358. Freudenberg *et al.*, *ibid.*, **55**, 3233 (1922); **56**, 1243 (1923); **58**, 294 (1925); **59**, 100, 714 (1926).
359. Freudenberg and Doser , *Ber.*, **58**, 294 (1925).
360. Freudenberg *et al.*, *ibid.*, **59**, 714 (1926).
361. Ohle and v. Varga, *ibid.*, **61**, 1203 (1928); **62**, 2425 (1929).
362. *Cf.* Irvine and Earl, *J. Chem. Soc.*, **121**, 2370, 2376 (1922); Haworth *et al.*, *ibid.*, **1939**, 271; Cutler and Peat, *ibid.*, **1939**, 782; James *et al.*, *ibid.*, **1946**, 625.
363. Fischer and Leuchs, *Ber.*, **35**, 3801 (1902). *Cf.* Levene, *Biochem. Z.*, **124**, 37 (1921).
364. Levene and LaForge, *J. Biol. Chem.*, **22**, 331 (1915); Levene, *ibid.*, **26**, 155 (1916); Voloček and Lukes, *Collection Czech. Chem. Commun.*, **7**, 424 (1935). *Cf.* Levene, *Hexosamines and Mucoproteins*, Longmans, Green and Co., 1925.
365. Fischer and Leuchs, *Ber.*, **35**, 3801 (1902).
366. Neuberg, *ibid.*, **35**, 4009 (1902); Neuberg and Wolf, *ibid.*, **36**, 618 (1903); Levene, *Biochem. Z.*, **124**, 78 (1921).
367. Irvine and Hynd, *J. Chem. Soc.*, **101**, 1128 (1912); **105**, 698 (1914).
358. Weizmann and Hopwood, *Proc. Roy. Soc.* (London) A **88**, 455 (1913); *Chem. Zentr.*, **1913** II, 1207; Bertho *et al.*, *Ann.*, **485**, 127 (1931).
369. Bertho *et al.*, *l.c.*
370. Bertho *et al.*, *l.c.; Ann.*, **498**, 50 (1932); **495**, 113 (1932).
371. Bergmann and Zervas, *Ber.*, **65**, 1201 (1932).
372. Wiggins, *J. Chem. Soc.*, **1947**, 18.
373. *Cf.* Jacobi, *Ann.*, **272**, 170 (1892); Rehrend *et al.*, *ibid.*, **353**, 106 (1907); **362**, 78 (1908); **377**, 189 (1910); Frèrejacque, *Compt. rend.*, **180**, 1210 (1915).
374. Fischer, *Ber.*, **17**, 579 (1884); **41**, 73 (1908); Knecht and Thompson, *J. Chem. Soc.*, **125**, 222 (1924).
375. Herzfeld, *Ber.*, **28**, 442 (1895); Ruff and Ollendorf, *ibid.*, **32**, 3234 (1899).
376. Fischer, *Ber.*, **21**, 2631 (1888); **22**, 88 (1889).
377. Hlasiwetz and Habermann, *Ann.*, **144**, 123 (1870); Fischer, *Anleitung zur Darstellung organischer Präparate*, 9th ed., p. 83.
378. Kiliani, *Ber.*, **54**, 456 (1921); **55**, 75 (1922); Goebel, *J. Biol. Chem.*, **72**, 801, 809 (1927). *Cf. Zückerchemie*, p. 37.
379. Schnelle and Tollens, *Ann.*, **271**, 81 (1892); Fischer and Passmore, *Ber.*, **22**, 2728 (1889); Fischer and Hirschberger, *ibid.*, **22**, 3218 (1889); Heffer, *ibid.*, **22**, 1049 (1889).
380. Paal and Weidenkaff, *Ber.*, **39**, 2830 (1906).
381. Isbell and Frush, *Bur. Standards J. Research*, **6**, 1145 (1931); **11**, 649 (1933).
382. Hedenburg, *J. Am. Chem. Soc.*, **37**, 345 (1915); Fischer, *Ber.*, **23**, 2625 (1890).
383. Haworth and Nicholson, *J. Chem. Soc.*, **1926**, 1899; Pryde, *ibid.*, **123**, 1808 (1923).
384. Kiliani, *Ber.*, **55**, 75, 2817 (1922).
385. Neuberg and Kitasato, *Biochem. Z.*, **183**, 485 (1927).
386. Dixon and Harrison, *Biochem. J.*, **26**, 1954 (1933).
387. Kiliani, *Ber.*, **55**, 2817 (1922); **56**, 2016 (1923).
388. Kiliani, *ibid.*, **20**, 341 (1887); **21**, 1422 (1888); **22**, 524 (1889); **54**, 456 (1921); **61**, 1155 (1928); **58**, 2344 (1925); Fischer, *Ber.*, **27**, 3227 (1894); **24**, 539 (1891).
389. Reichstein and Grussner, *Helv. Chim. Acta*, **17**, 311 (1934); Maroyama, *Sci. Papers Inst. Phys. Chem. Research (Tokyo)*, **27**, 56 (1935). *Cf.* Smith, *Advances in Carbohydrate Chemistry*, **2**, 79 (1946).
390. Baer *et al.*, *J. Am. Chem. Soc.*, **61**, 2607 (1939).
391. Haworth and Wiggins, *J. Chem. Soc.*, **1944**, 58; Mann and Hudson, *J. Am. Chem. Soc.*, **66**, 1909 (1944); Sullivan, *ibid.*, **67**, 837 (1945); Heyms and Stein, *Ann.*, **558**, 194 (1947).
392. Ohle and Wolter, *Ber.*, **63**, 843 (1930).
393. Zervas and Sessler, *ibid.*, **66**, 1326 (1933).
394. Dakin, *Biochem. J. (London)* **11**, 79 (1917).
395. Pringsheim and Rushmann, *Ber.*, **48**, 680 (1915).
396. Levene, *Biochem. Z.*, **124**, 37 (1921).
397. Danilov and Gakhokidze, *J. Gen. Chem. (U.S.S.R.)* **6**, 704 (1936); *C.A.*, **30**, 633 (1936).
398. Fischer, *Anleitung zur Darstellung organischer Präparate*, p. 53.

399. Meunier, *Compt. rend.*, **111**, 49 (1890); Fischer, *Ber.*, **23**, 2133, 3684 (1890); Neuberg and Marx, *Biochem. Z.*, **3**, 539 (1907); Nanji and Paton, *J. Chem. Soc.*, **125**, 2474 (1924).
400. Cake, *J. Am. Chem. Soc.*, **44**, 859 (1922); Ipatiew, *Bull. soc. chim.*, (4) **14**, 552 (1913); *Ber.*, **45**, 3218 (1912).
401. Fischer and Stahel, *Ber.*, **24**, 528 (1891); Lobry de Bruyn and van Ekenstein, *Rec. trav. chim.*, **19**, 7 (1900).
402. Pacsu and Rich, *J. Am. Chem. Soc.*, **55**, 3018 (1933).
403. Fischer and Hertz, *Ber.*, **25**, 1247 (1892); Crossley, *ibid.*, **25**, 2564 (1892); Riiber *et al.*, *ibid.*, **58**, 737, 964 (1925).
404. Nanji and Paton, *J. Chem. Soc.*, **125**, 2474 (1924).
405. de Bruyn and van Ekenstein, *Rec. trav. chim.*, **19**, 1 (1900); Hann and Hudson, *J. Am. Chem. Soc.*, **67**, 602 (1945); Flexner, *U.S. patent* 2,421,416 (1947).
406. Fischer and Hirschberger, *Ber.*, **21**, 1808 (1888); Fischer, *ibid.*, **23**, 370 (1890); **24**, 2683 (1891).
407. Scheibler, *Ber.*, **17**, 1732 (1884); Kiliani, *ibid.*, **20**, 1233 (1887).
408. Fischer and Stahel, *ibid.*, **24**, 538 (1891); Bertrand, *Bull. soc. chim.*, (3) **5**, 556, 740 (1891).
409. Fischer and Tafel, *Ber.*, **21**, 1658 (1888); Fischer and Piloty, *ibid.*, **23**, 3102 (1890).
410. *Cf.* Fischer, *ibid.*, **27**, 1524 (1894).
411. Baer and Fischer, *J. Biol. Chem.*, **128**, 463 (1939); Hudson *et al.*, *J. Am. Chem. Soc.*, **65**, 2215 (1943); **68**, 1769 (1946). *Cf.* Schmidt and Nieswandt, *Ber.*, **82**, 1 (1949); Sowden, *J. Am. Chem. Soc.*, **71**, 1897 (1949); **72**, 808 (1950).
412. Cramer and Pacsu, *J. Am. Chem. Soc.*, **59**, 1467 (1937).
413. Freudenberg and Raschig, *Ber.*, **60**, 1633 (1927).
414. Fischer and Zach, *ibid.*, **45**, 3761 (1912); Votoček, *Collection Czech. Chem. Commun.*, **1**, 234 (1929); Votoček and Rác, *ibid.*, **1**, 239 (1929).
415. Schlubach and Wagenitz, *Ber.*, **65**, 304 (1932).
416. Fischer *et al.*, *ibid.*, **47**, 196 (1914); **53**, 509 (1920); Levene and Raymond, *J. Biol. Chem.*, **90**, 247 (1931).
417. Overend *et al.*, *J. Chem. Soc.*, **1949**, 2841.
418. Bergmann and Schotte, *Ber.*, **54**, 1569 (1921). *Cf.* Fischer *et al.*, *ibid.*, **47**, 2047, 2057 (1914); **53**, 509 (1920).
419. Gehrke and Aichner, *Ber.*, **60**, 918 (1927).
420. Gehrke and Obst, *ibid.*, **64**, 1724 (1931); Levene and Mori, *J. Biol. Chem.*, **83**, 803 (1929). *Cf. also* Gehrke and Aichner, *Ber.*, **60**, 918 (1927); Fletcher and Hudson, *J. Am. Chem. Soc.*, **72**, 3684 (1949); Meisenheimer and Jung, *Ber.*, **60**, 1462 (1927); Deriaz *et al.*, *J. Chem. Soc.*, **1949**, 1879; Iselin and Reichstein, *Helv. Chim. Acta*, **1**, 159 (1945); Elderfield, *Advances in Carbohydrate Chemistry*, **1**, 159 (1945).
421. Fischer and Fodor, *Ber.*, **47**, 2058 (1914); Bergmann and Schotte, *ibid.*, **54**, 1570 (1921).
422. Bergmann and Kögel, *Ann.*, **434**, 100 (1923); Fischer and Kögel, *ibid.*, **436**, 219 (1924); Haworth *et al.*, *J. Chem. Soc.*, **1934**, 302.
423. Levene and Jorpes, *J. Biol. Chem.*, **86**, 403 (1930).
424. Fischer and Curme, *Ber.*, **47**, 2049 (1914); Bergmann *et al.*, *Ann.*, **434**, 86 (1923); Haworth *et al.*, *J. Chem. Soc.*, **1930**, 2644.
425. Gakhokidze, *J. Gen. Chem. (U.S.S.R.)* **10**, 497 (1940); *Chem. Zentr.*, **1940 II**, 2026.
426. Bergmann *et al.*, *Ber.*, **55**, 158 (1922). *Cf.* Overend *et al.*, *J. Chem. Soc.*, **1949**, 2841.
427. Bergmann and Schotte, *Ber.*, **54**, 440 (1921).
428. Tanaka, *Bull. Chem. Soc. Japan*, **5**, 214 (1930). *Chem. Zentr.*, **1930 II**, 2765.
429. Prins, *J. Am. Chem. Soc.*, **70**, 3955 (1948).
430. Overend *et al.*, *J. Chem. Soc.*, **1951**, 974, 994, 1480; **1949**, 2840; **1950**, 1433; Bolliger, *Helv. Chim. Acta*, **34**, 989 (1951).
431. Foster *et al.*, *J. Chem. Soc.*, **1951**, 980, 987.
432. Bergmann and Schotte, *Ann.*, **434**, 99 (1923).
433. Helferich and Rauch, *Ber.*, **59**, 2655 (1926).
434. Young, *J. Chem. Soc.*, **75**, 172 (1899).
435. Francis and Young, *ibid.*, **73**, 928 (1898); Markownikoff, *Ber.*, **32**, 1441 (1899); *J. prakt. Chem.*, (2) **59**, 556 (1899). *Cf.* Worstall, *Am. Chem. J.* **20**, 202, 665 (1898); **21**, 219 (1899).

CHAPTER 2

ETHERS AND RELATED COMPOUNDS

ETHERS

Methods of Preparation

Ethers derived from the lower aliphatic alcohols are usually prepared by heating a mixture of the alcohol and sulfuric acid. In this reaction an acid alkyl sulfate is first formed and reacts with the alcohol on continued heating to form the ether:

$$C_2H_5OH + H_2SO_4 \rightarrow C_2H_5OSO_2OH + H_2O$$

$$C_2H_5OSO_2OH + C_2H_5OH \rightarrow C_2H_5OC_2H_5 + H_2SO_4$$

Diethyl ether is prepared, for example, by the gradual addition of a mixture of sulfuric acid and ethyl alcohol to a flask, while the temperature is maintained at 140°. The reaction proceeds at a lower temperature if 5 – 10% anhydrous aluminum sulfate is added to the mixture.[1]

In the preparation of diisoamyl ether, the purification of the product was accomplished by converting the unreacted alcohol to the borate and recovering the ether by distillation.[77]

Sulfones and sulfonic acids are formed as a byproduct of the reaction.

It is possible to prepare mixed as well as simple ethers by this method. Mixed ethers are obtained by first preparing the acid alkyl sulfate with one alcohol and heating this with the other alcohol.

Mixed ethers may also be prepared by heating the mixture of alcohols with aqueous sulfuric acid, although the yields are not always good, and the simple ethers are formed simultaneously in varying proportions. Good yields of mixed ethers are obtained when mixtures of isobutyl alcohol with other alcohols are thus treated;[2] on the other hand a mixture of isopropyl alcohol with ethyl alcohol gives a poor yield of the mixed ether.[3]

When the method is applied to higher alcohols, unsaturated compounds are formed together with the ethers. Olefin formation is reduced to a minimum by using a small proportion of sulfuric acid. The ether formed is separated from the olefin by fractional distillation.

Ether formation proceeds the more readily the greater the number of carbon chains attached to the carbinol group. The effect of aromatic groups is more pronounced than that of open chain groups, and it is possible to prepare the ethers of triphenylcarbinol and benzhydrol by simply dissolving these compounds in the alcohol containing a trace of acid, the ethers being isolated by crystallization.

Sulfuric acid may be replaced by arylsulfonic acids or even their esters.[4] Other polybasic acids such as phosphoric and arsenic acids may also be used. Methionic acid, $CH_2(SO_3H)_2$, is an effective catalyst for the preparation of ethers. This compound is especially useful for the preparation of higher ethers.[78]

While with aliphatic alcohols ether formation by use of hydrogen chloride usually requires heating at 170°, in special cases the reaction takes place readily at a comparatively low temperature. Thus, methyl and ethyl ethers of benzoin are readily obtained by heating at 40° a solution of benzoin in alcohol saturated with hydrogen chloride. Glucosides may be prepared by this method from monosaccharides.[5]

The cyclic ether dioxan, $\overline{O\ CH_2CH_2O\ CH_2CH_2}$, results as the principal product when ethylene glycol is distilled with 4% concentrated sulfuric acid.

Dialkyl sulfates and esters of methionic acid react with alcohols to give ethers.[6] The reaction proceeds, in fact, more readily than the reaction of acid alkyl sulfates with alcohols.[7] The method has been employed for the preparation of methylated sugars.

Unsaturated ethers, $RCH=CHCH_2OCH_3$, have been prepared from the corresponding alcohols and dimethyl sulfate in the presence of sodium amide. Acetylenic ethers have been made similarly from acetylenic alcohols.

Ethers are obtained in good yield when alcohols are dehydrated by passing their vapors over anhydrous alumina heated at 180-195°.[8]

Triphenylmethyl ethers result when triphenylmethyl chloride reacts with alcohols in pyridine solution.[9] Reaction takes place preferentially with the primary alcohols, and use has been made of this fact in preparing hydroxy acylated sugars, by acylating the triphenylmethyl ether of the sugar and subsequently removing the triphenylmethyl group.

Compounds containing the groupings $=NC-OH$, such as cotarnine, berbinol, and the simple additive compounds of formaldehyde with primary and secondary aliphatic amines are readily converted to ethers by treatment with an alcohol.[10]

Acetals react with alkly magnesium halides on long heating, to form ethers:[11]

$$(CH_3)_2C(OC_2H_5)_2 + BrMgC_4H_9 \rightarrow (CH_3)_2C(C_4H_9)OC_2H_5 + BrMgOC_2H_5$$

α-Chloroethers are formed by reacting acyl chlorides with acetals

$$RCH(OR)_2 + CH_3COCl \rightarrow RCHClOR' + CH_3COOR'$$

acetals of both aliphatic and aromatic aldehydes undergo the reaction.

Williamson's Reaction

A general method for the preparation of ethers consists in the reaction of alkali metal alcoholates with alkyl halides:[12]

$$RONa + R'X \rightarrow ROR' + NaX.$$

The method is applicable to the preparation of phenol ethers. Aromatic halides are in general comparatively unreactive, and the reaction between such halides and an alkali alcoholate proceeds with difficulty. Reaction takes place most readily with alkyl iodides. Cholesteryl chloride does not react with alkali metal alcoholates, but reacts with magnesium alcoholates to form cholesteryl ether.[79]

Direct reaction between a hydroxy group and an alkyl iodide may be brought about in the presence of silver oxide, which serves to eliminate the hydriodic acid from the sphere of reaction almost as soon as it forms.[13] The method succeeds particularly well with sugars but has also been applied to the preparation of ethers of α-hydroxy acids. In order to prevent the oxidation of the aldehyde groups in sugars under the action of silver oxide, it is necessary to convert aldoses to glucosides. All of the hydroxyl groups present in the sugar can be alkylated by this method. This reaction is of importance, since it serves to reveal the point of attachment between the component molecules of the polysaccharides.[14] In this connection it may be pointed out that the reaction of alkyl iodides with silver oxide leads to the formation of ethers:

$$2C_2H_5I + Ag_2O \rightarrow (C_2H_5)_2O + 2AI$$

Special Methods

Vinyl ethyl ether, $CH_2{:}CHOC_2H_5$, may be prepared by conducting acetylene into a mixture of sulfuric acid and alcohol cooled to 0°[15], or preferably, into an alcoholic solution of an alkali metal hydroxide at 80-250° at atmospheric pressure.[16] This ether may also be prepared by heating chloroacetal, $ClCH_2CH(OC_2H_5)_2$, with sodium, or acetal with phosphorus pentoxide and quinoline.[17]

1,2-Dichlorovinyl ethyl ether, $ClCH{:}CClOC_2H_5$, results when sodium ethoxide is made to react with trichloroethylene.[18]

2,2-Dichlorovinyl ethyl ether, $Cl_2C{:}CHOC_2H_5$, is obtained through the action of zinc dust on ethyl tetrachlorethyl ether.[19] The compound readily combines with oxygen to give ethoxychloroacetyl chloride, $C_2H_5OCHClCOCl$.

Isopropenyl ethyl ether, $CH_2{=}C(CH_3)OC_2H_5$, is obtained from propylene bromide and alcoholic potassium hydroxide; also from ethoxycrotonic acid by decarboxylation.[20] Homologous β-alkylhydroxycrotonic acids also give the corresponding alkoxyethylene ethers, $R'CH{=}CROC_2H_5$, by decarboxylation. These ethers are decomposed into a ketone and an alcohol when heated with dilute acids.[21]

Monochloromethyl ethers result through the reaction of alcohols with formaldehyde and hydrochloric acid.[80]

$$RCH_2OH + H_2CO + HCl \rightarrow RCH_2OCH_2Cl + H_2O$$

The alcohol is saturated with hydrogen chloride, and is mixed with formaldehyde, also saturated with hydrogen chloride. Trioxymethylene or paraldehyde may be used in the reaction in place of the formaldehyde.[81]

α-Hydroxy-3-chloropropanol ethers have been obtained by the acid catalyzed reaction of aliphatic alcohols and 1,2-epoxy-3-chloropropane.[108]

$$H_2\overset{\overbrace{\quad O \quad}}{C{-}CH}CH_2Cl + ROH \rightarrow ROCH_2CH(OH)CH_2Cl$$

The chlorohydroxy ether gives the epoxy ether, $ROCH_2\overline{CHCH_2O}$, when treated with caustic.

While ethers of the type of vinyl ether are stable, the corresponding alcohols rapidly undergo internal rearrangement to a saturated aldehyde or ketone.

Pyruvic aldehyde diacetals undergo molecular rearrangement when heated above 100°, forming the ether of a lactate.[22]

$$CH_3COCH(OR)_2 \rightarrow CH_3CH(OR)COOR$$

The transformation is accelerated by acids.

Phenolic ethers $ROCH_2CH_2OH$ have been prepared by the condensation of phenols with ethylene sulfite or ethylene carbonate.[82]

α-Chimyl and -buty ethers of glycerol have been synthesized from isopropylidene 1-clycerol by treating the sodio derivative of this compound with n-hexadecyl and octadecyl iodide:[109]

$$HOCH_2\overline{CHCH_2OC(CH_3)_2O} \xrightarrow[RI]{NaC_{10}H_7;} ROCH_2\overline{CHCH_2OC(CH_3)_2O}$$

$$\xrightarrow{H_2O} ROCH_2CH(OH)CH_2OH$$

The synthesis of the oleyl alcohol ether has been accomplished through the reaction of oleyl alcohol with the toluenesulfonic ester of isopropylidene glycerol, followed by hydrolysis with 80% acetic acid.[110]

$$CH_3C_6H_4SO_2OCH_2\overline{CHCH_2OC(CH_3)_2O} \xrightarrow[alcohol]{oleyl} \text{Oleyl-}OCH_2\overline{CHCH_2OC(CH_3)_2O}$$

$$\xrightarrow{H_2O} CH_3(CH_2)_7CH = CH(CH_2)_8OCH_2CH(OH)CH_2OH.$$

Peroxides

Alkyl peroxides, ROOR, have been prepared through the reaction of alkyl sulfates with hydrogen peroxide in alkaline solution. They may form also from many types of compounds by simply shaking with hydrogen peroxide. The concentration of hydrogen peroxide employed is usually 8-10%. The temperature during the reaction should not exceed 30°. The peroxides generally precipitate out of the reaction mixture.

Chemical Characteristics of Ethers

Cleavage of Alkyl Ethers

The oxygen linkage in dialkyl ethers is, in general, unaffected by alkalies, ammonia and amines; alkali metals are also without action. Dialkyl ethers are not appreciably acted upon by dilute acids, but cleavage occurs when they are heated with concentrated acids, especially hydriodic acid:

$$ROR + HI \rightarrow RI + ROH$$

$$ROH + HI \rightarrow RI + H_2O$$

The lower aliphatic ethers dissolve in concentrated sulfuric acid forming acid alkyl sulfates, from which the alcohol may be recovered by distilling with water. Alkyl ethers can be decomposed also by heating with aluminum chloride or with a suspension of aluminum bromide in benzene.[23] Cleavage may also be brought about by heating the ether with the chloride of aniline or *p*-toluidine.[24] The treatment of an aliphatic ether with an acid chloride in the presence of zinc chloride or aluminum chloride results in the breakdown of the ether with the formation of an ester:[25]

$$C_2H_5OC_2H_5 + RCOCl \quad \rightarrow \quad RCOOC_2H_5 + C_2H_5Cl$$

Ethers of the type of alkoxy triphenylmethane decompose on heating into triarylmethane and an aldehyde:

$$(C_6H_5)_3COC_2H_5 \quad \rightarrow \quad (C_6H_5)_3CH + CH_3CHO$$

Diethyl ether, treated at $-20°$ or below with one equivalent of chlorine, gives chloroethyl ether in 42% yield. Further chlorination at this temperature leads to α,α-dichlorodiethyl ether in 57% yield, the second chlorine atom entering a new α-position in preference to an α-position already substituted by a halogen.

Oxonium Compounds

Ethers have the ability to combine with acids to give salt-like compounds. This property, while most marked in certain cyclic ethers, is possessed even by the simplest ethers. The oxygen apparently assumes a tetravalent condition, and plays a role similar to that of nitrogen in ammonium compounds; for this reason these compounds are termed oxonium compounds. Their structure may be represented by the general formula

$$(R)_2 \quad O\!\!\begin{array}{c} \diagup X \\ \diagdown H \end{array} \quad ,$$

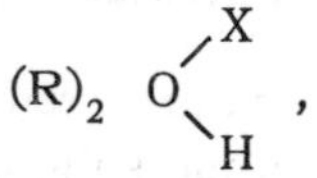

X standing for an acid radical.

In some instances the ether and acid are not combined in simple molecular proportions; moreover many metallic salts show the ability to combine with ethers. These facts make it appear possible that coordination compounds are involved, and that combination between ethers and acids or salts takes place through residual valencies. On the basis of this assumption the abnormal oxonium compounds may be represented as

$$\left[\begin{array}{c} R_2O \\ \quad \diagdown \!\! H \\ R_2O \diagup \end{array} \right] X \quad \text{or} \quad \left[(R_2O)_3 \!\!=\!\!=\!\! H \right] X.$$

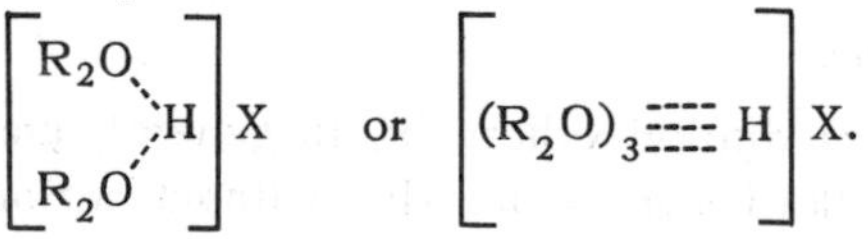

ALKYLENE OXIDES

Methods of Preparation

Formation from Unsaturated Compounds

The internal ethers or oxides constitute the important class of oxygen heterocycles, to be considered in the appropriate section. 1,2-Epoxides, or alkylene oxides do not show the great stability associated with such groups as the furans, for example, and differ in their chemical characteristics from these and other oxygen heterocycles. They may be regarded as belonging strictly in the aliphatic group of compounds and may be properly considered in this section.

Alkylene oxides may be prepared through the elimination of hydrogen chloride from α-halohydrins by means of alkalies:

$$R_1\underset{Cl}{\underset{|}{CH}}-\underset{OH}{\underset{|}{CHR_2}} + NaOH \rightarrow \underbrace{R_1CH-CHR_2}_{O} + NaCl + H_2O$$

Since α-chlorohydrins may be prepared from many unsaturated aliphatic compounds by the addition of hypochlorous acid, such unsaturated compounds may be thus converted to oxides. Tetrahydrobenzene[26], cyclopentylene[27] and α-naphthoquinone[28] may also be converted to epoxy compounds by this route. Good yields of the oxide are obtained when the caustic solution is added drop by drop to the heated solution of the chlorohydrin.

Homologs of ethylene oxide have been prepared in 47-65% yield by dropping solutions of the chlorohydrins into 1½ equivalent of boiling milk of lime.[83]

Butylenechlorohydrin, $CH_3CH(OH)CH(Cl)CH_3$, is converted to the oxide by warming the halohydrin with the aqueous solution of an alkali metal carbonate or other basic salts. Glycid, $\overbrace{CH_2-CH}^{O}CH_2OH$, is best prepared from glycerol α-chlorohydrin by treatment with cold alcoholic potassium hydroxide. Methylphenylethylene oxide, $C_6H_5\overbrace{C(CH_3)-CH_2}^{O}$ and oxides of the type $ROC_6H_4\overbrace{CH-CH}^{O}CH_3$ may be prepared by heating the chlorohydrin with alcoholic caustic. Glycid acid, $\overbrace{CH_2-CH}^{O}COOH$ may also be prepared by this method.

Styryl oxide, $C_6H_5\overbrace{CH-CH_2}^{O}$, and its homologs are obtained by heating the halohydrins with a suspension of powdered alkali metal hydroxide in ether for one or two days.

Alkylene oxides may be prepared from olefins by direct oxidation. Perbenzoic acid may be used for the purpose.[29] The reaction is carried out, in an indifferent solvent at 0° or in many cases at room temperature:

$$-\overset{|}{C}=\overset{|}{C}- + C_6H_5COO\,OH \rightarrow \underbrace{-\overset{|}{C}-\overset{|}{C}-}_{O} + C_6H_5CO\,OH$$

The general procedure is as follows: The perbenzoic acid is dissolved in a solvent such as ether or chloroform and the available oxygen is determined volumetrically with potassium iodide and standard thiosulfate solution. The compound to be converted to oxide is also dissolved in the solvent, the solution is cooled to 0° and a little more than the calculated quantity of the peracid solution, also cooled to 0°, is added. The mixture is allowed to stand at 0° or, if reaction proceeds slowly at this temperature, it is held at room temperature. The course of the reaction is followed by determining the unreacted peracid. After the completion of the reaction, the benzoic acid formed is eliminated by washing with aqueous caustic, the solution of the oxide is dried with anhydrous calcium chloride, and the oxide is isolated by removing the solvent by distillation.

The solution of perbenzoic acid may be kept unchanged for several days at 0°.

Peracetic acid[85] may be used in the reaction. Satisfactory results are obtained in chloroform or ethereal solution. A hydroxy acetate is formed in many cases if the reaction with peracetic acid is carried out in glacial acetic acid solution.[86] Epoxidation may be brought about successfully in most cases by carrying out the reaction with a glacial acetic acid solution of the peracid at 20-25°. The reaction is generally complete within 2-4 hours with long-chain compounds with a non-terminal double bond, but long-chain compounds with a terminal bond react very slowly, and require treatment for 24 hours.[87] It is important to avoid the presence of strong acids in the reaction mixture. If the reaction with peracetic acid is carried out in acetic acid solution in the presence of 1% sulfuric acid, hydroxy acetates are formed even under mild reaction conditions. The tendency toward the formation of the hydroxyacetate is so marked in some instances that a considerable amount of the hydroxy ester is formed due to the reaction of the acetic acid formed during epoxidation with peracetic acid.[88] *Monoperphthalic acid*[89] has been used successfully for the epoxidation of compounds of the carotene and sterol series.[90] *Camphoric peracid*[91], and *furoic peracid*[92] have also been used in the reaction. Furoic peracid is highly unstable and decomposes above 35°; it is highly reactive, however, and gives epoxides with ethylenic bodies at low temperatures.

Epoxidation with peracids involves the danger of violent or explosive reaction with the more reactive olefins. Such reactions should, therefore, be conducted behind a safety shield. When an epoxidation reaction is carried out for the first time with unknown ethylenic bodies, or those containing more than two positive groups, it is well to carry out a test epoxidation with a small amount of the olefin to determine whether there is any possibility of a violent reaction.

Peracid epoxidation mixtures should not be distilled until one is assured that the peracid is completely utilized, or in the contrary event, that the unreacted peracid is destroyed. Addition of an excess of ferrous sulfate, sodium bisulfite or other reducing agent will destroy the unreacted peracid.

Epoxidation with peracid may be carried out successfully with olefin hydrocarbons and unsaturated alcohols. The velocity of reaction depends to a large extent on the character of the groupings attached to the ethylenic group.[93] Alkyl groups and, to a greater extent, alkoxy groups cause an increase in the velocity. Vinyl ethyl ether, for example, is so readily epoxidized that special care is required to avoid losses due to excessively vigorous action. Negative groups or atoms, including Cl, NO_2, C_6H_5, COOH, CN, cause a decrease in the speed of reaction, or prevent reaction altogether. α-β-Unsaturated acids and ketones, for example, cannot be converted to the oxides with perbenzoic acid, and α,β-unsaturated aldehydes react very slowly. Diarylethylenes, $Ar_2C=CH_2$, are converted to ketones, Ar_2CO, but diphenylpropylene, $(C_6H_5)_2C=CHCH_3$, readily yields an oxide. Compounds with conjugated double bonds give poor yields of the oxide.

The rate of epoxidation with a peracid can be determined by estimating the amount of unconsumed peracid at suitable intervals.[94] The hydrogen peroxide content of peracid solutions may be determined by diluting a 0.2 to 2.0 cc portion of the solution with 50 cc of 4*N* aqueous sulfuric acid at 0° and titrating rapidly with 0.1*N* potassium permanganate. One cubic centimeter of 0.*N* $KMnO_4$ is equivalent to 0.0017 gm of H_2O_2. The peracid content may be determined on this same portion of the solution by adding 2 cc of saturated potassium iodide and rapidly titrating the iodine generated with 0.1*N* sodium thiosulfate solution, using starch as indicator. One cubic centimeter of 0.1*N* thiosulfate is equivalent to 0.0038 gm peracetic acid. Perbenzoic acid and monoperphthalic acid may also be determined by this method.

The velocity constants of various ethylenic compounds in the epoxidation reaction with peracetic acid are given below in decreasing order of magnitude.

	$K \times 10^3$		$K \times 10^3$
1-methylcyclopentane	2200	1,4-dihydronaphthalene	37
2-methyl-2-butene	ca. 1000	cyclobutene	21
oleic acid	384	1-pheny-1-butene	10
1,2-dihydronaphthalene	230-240	eugenol	2.2
cinnamyl alcohol	203	allylbenzene	2.0
isosafrole	148	safrole	1.3
isoeugenol	127	ethylene	0.19
1-phenyl-1-butene	80	cinnamic acid	0.13
1-phenyl-1-propene	46	sorbic acid	0.04

In unsaturated compounds, such as isoprene, geraniol, citral, etc., in which more than one unsaturated linkage is present, and one of the ethylenic groups bears a methyl group, the latter ethylenic group is first attacked by peracids.

In the peracid oxidation of furan and its derivatives, such as furfural, 2-methylfuran, and furfuryl alcohol, resins are formed as the principal product.[95] The initial product is probably an oxide which rapidly resinifies to a great extent, but also undergoes cleavage and hydrolysis to some extent. Aminopyrine and antipyrine do not yield oxides,[96] but thiopyrine yields a diepoxy derivative.[97]

A remarkable transformation takes place in the peracid oxidation of a compound with a carbonyl group adjacent to the double bond: the bond between the carbonyl carbon and the ethylenic group is broken and an oxygen atom enters between these groups, forming a carboxylic ester. Thus, benzalacetone is converted to β-phenylvinyl acetate:

$$C_6H_5CH=CHCOCH_3 \xrightarrow{O} C_6H_5CH=CHOCOCH_3$$

Similar products are obtained from α-methyl-α-benzalacetone, and benzal methyl ketone.[98]

The reaction of acetylene derivatives with perbenzoic acid proceeds in a complex manner and does not result in the formation of oxides.

Ketenes readily combine with oxygen giving oxides in varying yield.[30] Phenylketenes yield appreciable quantities of oxide, diethylketene gives a small amount of oxide, while dimethylketene does not give any oxide. The oxide is the principal product of the oxidation of diphenylketene; the compound exists in two modifications, one of which is readily soluble in ether and melts at 130°, while the other is difficultly soluble in ether and melts at 220°.

Ketene oxides are amorphous, polymeric bodies in which the ketene molecules are probably joined by oxygen bonds.

Alkaline hydrogen peroxide readily converts α,β-unsaturated ketones to the corresponding α,β-oxides:

$$RCH = CHCOCH_3 + H_2O_2 \rightarrow RCH\overset{O}{-}CHCOCH_3 + H_2O$$

The reaction, which is quite general and proceeds well at room temperature in alcoholic or acetone solution, is exothermic and it is necessary to cool the reaction mixture in order to avoid a deep-seated disruptive oxidation of the ketone. Conversion to oxide is generally complete within a few minutes.

All α,β-keto oxides are reconverted to the original unsaturated ketone when heated with potassium iodide and glacial acetic acid, iodine being liberated in the process.

Unsaturated hydrocarbons, including those with conjugated double bonds, do not react with alkaline hydrogen peroxide.

Certain hydroxy amines, such as aminomethyldiphenylcarbinol, when treated with nitrous acid yield oxides:[31]

$$(C_6H_5)_2C(OH)CH_2NH_2 + HNO_2 \rightarrow (C_6H_5)_2\underset{O}{C-CH_2} + 2H_2O + N_2$$

Oxides may result also through the elimination of a tertiary amine from certain hydroxy quarternary ammonium bases. Thus, diphenylhydroxyethyltrimethylammonium hydroxide yields *sym*-diphenylethylene oxide, a compound which has been obtained in two isomeric forms each resulting from the decomposition of one of the two isomeric modifications of the quaternary compound:[32]

$$C_6H_5CH(OH)CH(C_6H_5)N(CH_3)_3OH \rightarrow C_6H_5CH\overset{O}{-}CHC_6H_5 + N(CH_3)_3 + H_2O$$

Another type of reaction leading to the formation of an oxide is exemplified by the cleavage of phenyldimethylmethylmorpholonammonium hydroxide by treatment with caustic:[33]

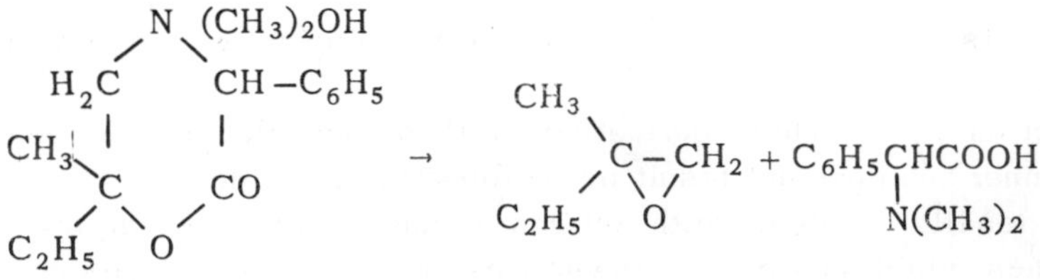

Formation of Oxides Through Condensation Reactions

Erlenmeyer's or Darzens Reaction

Ethylene oxides result through the condensation of ketones and benzaldehyde with certain compounds containing a halomethyl group. Thus ethyl chloroacetate, reacting with benzaldehyde in anhydrous ethereal solution and in the presence of sodium ethoxide or sodium amide, gives phenyl glycidic ester:[34]

$$C_6H_5CHO + ClCH_2COOC_2H_5 + NaOC_2H_5 \rightarrow$$

$$C_6H_5CH\underset{\diagdown O \diagup}{-}CHCOOC_2H_5 + NaCl + C_2H_5OH$$

The work of Claisen[35] and Darzens[36] demonstrated that this reaction is of general applicability for the preparation of oxido carboxylic acids, although aliphatic aldehydes react poorly, and certain hydroaromatic ketones, such as carbone, pulegone, thujone, menthone and isophorone do not react appreciably. Oxido acids were obtained by its use, for example, from acetophenone, ethyl phenyl ketone, acetone, ethyl methyl ketone, methyl propyl ketone and diethyl ketone. The reaction proceeds well with α-chloropropionic acid and halo-bulyrates, but the more complex halo esters fail to undergo the reaction.

The reaction may be carried out in the absence of a solvent, using solid sodium ethoxide as a condensing agent. The procedure is then as follows:

A mixture of 1.6 molecular equivalent of the chloro ester and 1 of the carbonyl compound is cooled well and 1 molecular equivalent of dry, finely powdered sodium ethoxide is added gradually, care being taken to maintain the temperature below 5°. After all the ethoxide has been introduced, the mixture is allowed to stand at room temperature for twelve hours, after which it is heated at 100° for one hour. It is then made slightly acid with acetic acid, washed with water, and the ester is finally separated and fractionally distilled under vacuum.[99] The yield, based on the ketone used in the reaction, is generally quite high. Sodium amide may be used instead of the ethoxide as the condensing agent.

The reaction is preferably carried out in an inert atmosphere. Strong cooling of the reaction mixture to temperatures as low as −80°, during the first stage of the reaction, has been recommended, but the reaction does not proceed at all in certain cases at such low temperatures. The reaction may be complete in the course of a few hours in the case of the more reactive ketones and halo esters.

Glycidic esters have been obtained through the reaction of aldehydes and ketones with dichloroacetic esters in the presence of magnesium amalgam, and subsequent treatment with sodium ethoxide.[113]

$$RCOR' + Cl_2CHCOOC_2H_5 \xrightarrow{Mg} RR'C(OMgCl)-CHClCOOC_2H_5$$

$$\xrightarrow{H_2O} RR'C(OH)CHClCOOC_2H_5 \xrightarrow{C_2H_5ONa} RR'\underset{\diagdown O \diagup}{C-}CHCOOC_2H_5$$

The hydroxy halo ester resulting from the hydrolysis of the original product of the reaction may be dehydrated to an α-chloro unsaturated ester:

$$RR'C(OH)CHClCOOC_2H_5 \xrightarrow{P_2O_5} RR'C{=}C(Cl)COOC_2H_5$$

ω-Bromoacetophenone reacts similarly with benzaldehyde in the presence of sodium ethoxide, forming benzoylphenylethylene oxide (Widmann's reaction):[37]

(1) $C_6H_5CHO + BrCH_2COC_6H_5 + NaOC_2H_5$

$\rightarrow C_6H_5CH-CHCOC_6H_5 + NaBr + C_2H_5OH$
$\qquad\qquad \diagdown O \diagup$

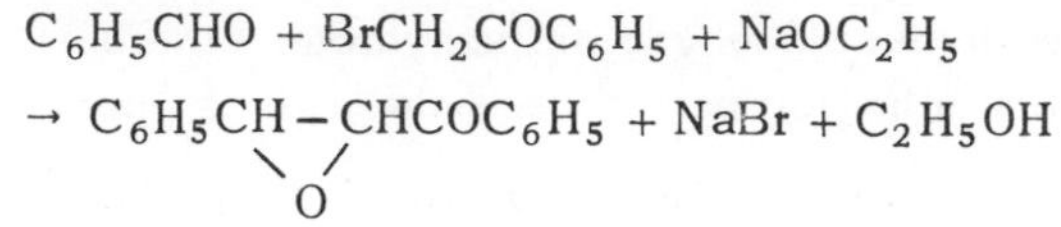

This type of condensation takes place also simultaneously between t he molecules of bromoacetophenone, and the benzoylbromomethyl phenyl ethylene oxide formed at first undergoes rearrangement, the final product being 2-bromo- 3,4-oxido- 3,5-diphenyltetrahydrofuran:

(2) $2\ C_6H_5COCH_2Br \quad\rightarrow\quad C_6H_5\ COCH$
$\qquad\qquad\qquad\qquad\qquad\qquad\qquad\qquad |\!\!>\!\!O$
$\qquad\qquad\qquad\qquad\qquad\qquad\qquad BrCH_2\ C\ C_6H_5$

$\qquad\qquad\qquad C_6H_5CH\text{------}CH$
$\rightarrow\qquad\quad O\diagup\qquad\qquad |\!\!>\!\!O$
$\qquad\qquad\qquad\quad CH(Br)\text{-}CC_6H_5$

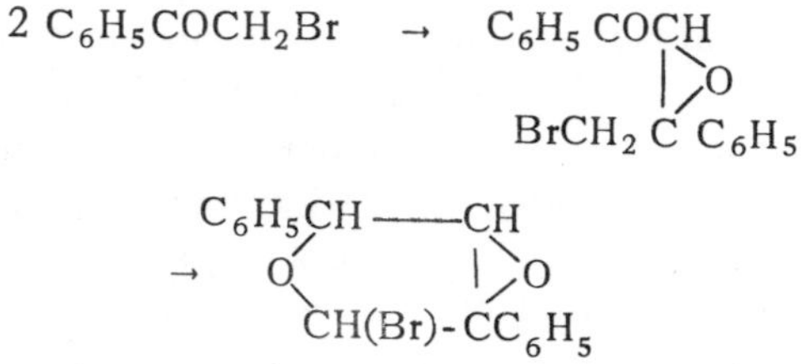

The proportion of the two compounds formed depends upon the relative rate at which the two reactions proceed.

The rate of reaction of type (1) varies greatly depending upon the character of the carbonyl compound reacting with the bromoacetophenone. The presence of negative radicals, such as halogens or nitro groups, in the phenyl group in the carbonyl compound increases the tendency toward glycid condensation (reaction 1), whereas the presence of positive radicals such as CH_3, CH_3O, has the opposite effect. Glycid condensation does not take place at an appreciable rate with acetaldehyde, isobutyraldehyde, oenanthol, citral, anisaldehyde, piperonal, cinnamaldehyde and p-tolualdehyde. Reaction (2) proceeds readily with both bromo and chloroacetophenone, while this type of condensation does not take place, or takes place extremely slowly with chloroacetylanisole, $CH_3OC_6H_4COCH_2Cl$. Bromopinacoline, $(CH_3)_3CCOCH_2Br$, which does not form a self-condensation product, condenses readily with a variety of aldehydes. Aromatic o-hydroxyaldehydes do not form glycids by reaction with ω-bromoacetophenone but yield benzoyl coumarins.[38]

Ketones, in general, cannot be condensed with ω-bromoacetophenone, but oxydo ketones form an exception. Thus, m-nitrophenylbenzoylethylene oxide reacts readily with bromoacetophenone in the presence of sodium ethoxide forming a dioxido compound:

$NO_2C_6H_4CH-CHCOC_6H_5 + Br\ CH_2COC_6H_5 + NaOC_6H_5 \rightarrow$
$\qquad\qquad \diagdown O \diagup$

$\qquad\qquad\qquad\qquad\qquad\quad C_6H_5$
$\qquad\qquad\qquad\qquad\qquad\quad |$
$NO_2C_6H_4CH-CHC \ - \ CHCOC_6H_5 + NaBr + C_2H_5OH$
$\qquad\quad \diagdown O \diagup \quad \diagdown O \diagup$

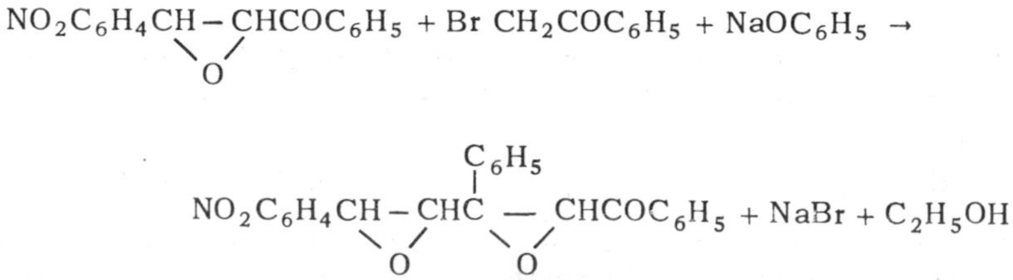

Epicyanohydrin[39], CH_2-CHCH_2CN, and epithiocyanohydrin,[40] CH_2-CHCH_2SCN, may be prepared from epichlorohydrin by reaction with potassium cyanide and potassium thiocyanate respectively. Phenoxypropylene oxide results from the reaction of sodium phenoxide and epichlorohydrin:[41]

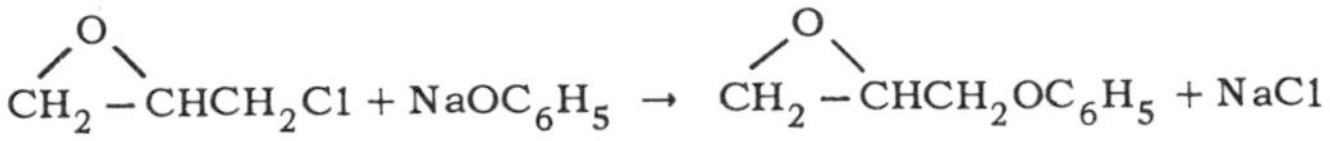

$$CH_2-CHCH_2Cl + NaOC_6H_5 \rightarrow CH_2-CHCH_2OC_6H_5 + NaCl$$

Glycid nitrate[42] $CH_2-CHCH_2ONO_2$, is obtained when epiiodohydrin is made to react with silver nitrate, while diglycid ether[42], $CH_2-CHCH_2OCH_2CH-CH_2$, results when the iodohydrin is treated with moist silver oxide.

A cyclic epoxyketone is formed when 1,4-dibromo-1,4-dibenzoylbutane is treated with sodium cyanide, diethylamine, sodium acetate, or the sodium derivative of malonic ester.

$$\begin{matrix} CH_2CHBrCOC_6H_5 \\ | \\ CH_2CHBrCOC_6H_5 \end{matrix} \rightarrow \begin{matrix} CH_2-CH-CC_6H_5 \\ | \quad\quad | \\ CH_2 \text{——} CBrCOC_6H_5 \end{matrix}$$

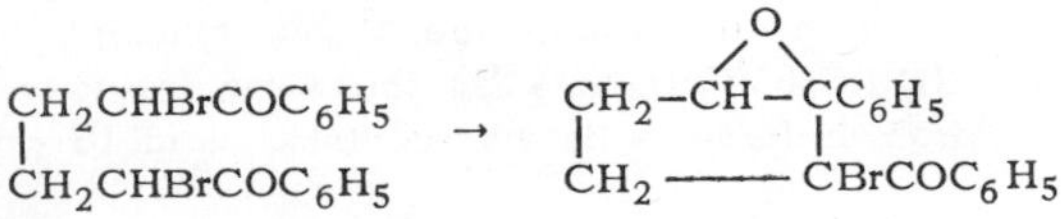

Benzyl and benzal chlorides and other similarly constituted chlorinated compounds have been condensed, under the action of methanolic potassium hydroxide, with aldehydes and ketones to epoxy and haloepoxy compounds:[100]

$$RCH_2Cl + RR'CO \rightarrow RCH-CR'R'' + HCl$$

$$RCHCl_2 + RR'CO \rightarrow RCCl-CR'R'' + HCl$$

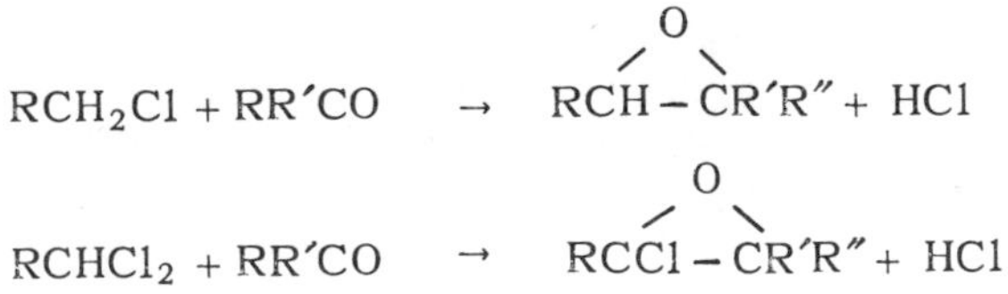

The yields are generally quite high.

Diazomethane, reacting with chloral, forms, a,a,a-trichloro-propylene-β,γ-oxide

Reactions of Alkylene Oxides

Reaction of Alkylene Oxides with Halogen Acids

Alkylene oxides give addition products with compounds containing a reactive hydrogen. The reaction proceeds especially readily with halogen acids, which give halohydrins:

$$CH_2-CH_2 + HCl \rightarrow ClCH_2CH_2OH$$

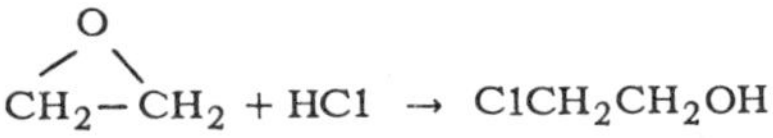

The reaction velicity decreases with increase in the molecular weight of the oxide. Oxides containing an aromatic substituent apparently react more slowly than purely aliphatic oxides. When aqueous hydrochloric acid is used, appreciable isomerization to an aldehyde or ketone may occur with some oxides. The tendency of alkylene oxides to combine with hydrogen chloride is so marked that these compounds cause the formation of the hydroxides of magnesium, aluminum, iron and copper from aqueous solutions of the chlorides of these metals:

$$2\overset{\;O}{CH_2-CH_2} + CuCl_2 + H_2O \rightarrow 2ClCH_2CH_2OH + Cu(OH)_2$$

With unsymmetrical alkylene oxides, the addition of halogen acids proceeds, in general, according to a rule established by Michael,[43] which states that with monoalkylethylene oxides the halogen attaches itself to the carbon atom containing the greater number of hydrogen atoms, while with unsymmetrical dialkylethylene oxides a mixture, of the two isomeric halohydrins results. Isobutylene oxide forms an exception to this rule, giving exclusively 2-chloro-2-methyl-1-propanol by reaction with hydrogen chloride.[44]

The addition of hydrogen chloride to esters of glycidic acids probably takes place in accordance with Markownikow's rule (see). Thus, β,β-dimethyl glycid ethyl ester gives α-hydroxy-β-chloroisovaleric ethyl ester, and trimethyl glycid ethyl ester gives

$$(CH_3)_2CClC(OH)\,(CH_3)COOC_2H_5.$$

Anisoylphenyl ethylene oxide gives the compound $CH_3OC_6H_4COCHClCH(OH)C_6H_5$ when treated with alcoholic hydrogen chloride,[45] but benzoyl *m*-nitrophenylethylene oxide gives $C_6H_5COCH(OH)CHClC_6H_4NO_2$ by the same treatment.[46] *Trans*-2-chloro-3,4-oxido-3,5-diphenyltetrahydrofuran adds hydrochloric acid to give the chlorohydrin $\overline{C_6H_5CHCH(OH)C(Cl)(C_6H_5)CH(Cl)O}$, the reaction proceeding fairly slowly at room temperature unless it is carried out in solution in glacial acetic acid.

The reaction of hydrobromic acid with ethylene oxides is similar to that of hydrochloric acid and usually proceeds with greater ease. Hydriodic acid also reacts similarly with alkyl and aryl substituted ethylene oxides. If, however, a carbonyl group is present in the immediate neighborhood of the oxido group, then hydriodic acid seems to cause the removal, exclusively, of the oxygen of the oxido group, with the formation of an unsaturated compound. This reaction takes place, for example, with compounds of the type $\underset{\;O}{RCOCH-CHR'}$, in which R and R′ are aromatic groups:

$$\underset{\;O}{RCOCH-CH}R' + 2HI \rightarrow RCOCH{=}CHR' + H_2O + I_2$$

It also takes place with dimethylglycid ethyl ester.

Reaction with Sodium Bisulfite

Many 1,2-oxides react with sodium bisulfite when heated at 100° in a sealed tube with the latter, forming a β-hydroxysulfonate:

$$\overline{O.CH_2CH_2} + NaHSO_3 \rightarrow HOCH_2CH_2SO_3Na$$

Hydrocyanic acid reacts additively with ethylene oxide to form ethylene cyanohydrin,[47] $HOCH_2CH_2CN$, although the reaction proceeds slowly unless it is carried out at a temperature in excess of 60° under pressure. The reaction proceeds similarly with epichlorohydrin.[48] Styryl oxide, $\underset{\;O}{C_6H_5CH-CH_2}$, gives phenylacetaldehyde cyanohydrin,[49] $C_6H_5CH_2CH(OH)CN$. Reaction is accelerated by the presence of a small amount of basic substance.

Reaction of Ammonia and Amines with Alkylene Oxides

Ethylene oxide reacts vigorously with aqueous ammonia forming mono-, di- and triethanolamines simultaneously.[50] The reaction proceeds with explosive violence if concentrated ammonia is used. Tetramethylethylene oxide gives with ammonia tetramethylethylene hydroxy ethylamine, $(CH_3)_2C(OH).C(NH_2)(CH_3)_2$, and a small quantity of the secondary base. The reaction of trimethylethylene oxide takes place with rapidity only at 100°, and results in the formation of aminoethyldimethylcarbinol, $(CH_3)_2C(OH)CH(NH_2)CH_3$. Isobutylene oxide, $(CH_3)_2C-CH_2$ (with O bridging), similarly gives aminotrimethylcarbinol, $(CH_3)_2C(OH).CH_2.NH_2$, and small quantities of the secondary and tertiary bases. Glycid gives 1-aminopropanediol, $H_2NCH_2.CH(OH).CH_2(OH)$, as the principal product of the reaction with ammonia.

Oxides of the type $RCOCH-CHR'$ (with O bridging), in which R and R′ are aromatic groups, do not react with ammonia. Addition products are formed, however, with compounds of the type $(CH_3)_2CCOCH-CHR'$ (with O bridging). Phenylmethylglycid ester, $(C_6H_5)(CH_3)C-CHCOOC_2H_5$ (with O bridging), is also unreactive, but phenylglycid esters react readily with ammonia at room temperature to form aminophenyllactic esters, $C_6H_5CH(NH_2)CH(OH)COOR$.

Primary and secondary amines also react with alkylene oxides to form alkyl or arylamino alcohols, the reaction again proceeding in the presence of water.[51]

Imides of dicarboxylic acids react with certain oxides. Thus, ethylene oxide, heated with phthalimide at 170° in a sealed tube, gives β-hydroxyethylphthalimide:

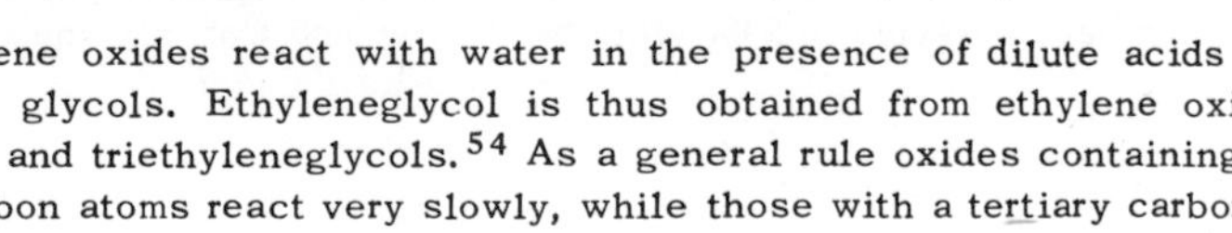

Hydrazine[52] and phenylhydrazine[53] react readily with ethylene oxide, hydrazine giving *asym*-bis-ethylolhydrazine, $(HOCH_2CH_2)_2NNH_2$.

Reaction of Alkylene Oxides with Water and other Hydroxy Compounds

Many alkylene oxides react with water in the presence of dilute acids to form the corresponding glycols. Ethyleneglycol is thus obtained from ethylene oxide, together with some di- and triethyleneglycols.[54] As a general rule oxides containing primary and secondary carbon atoms react very slowly, while those with a tertiary carbon atom, such as isobutylene oxide, $(CH_3)_2C-CH_2$ (with O bridging), and tetramethyl ethylene oxide, $(CH_3)_2C-C(CH_3)_2$ (with O bridging), are hydrolyzed quite readily.[55]

Alcohols and phenols also react with alkylene oxides forming half-ethers of the corresponding glycol, ethylene oxide thus yielding glycol monoethyl ether with ethyl alcohol, and glycol phenyl ether with phenol.[56]

The reaction with carboxylic acids, which is catalyzed with iron chloride or conc. sulfuric acid, proceeds in a similar manner, and results in the formation of half-esters of the corresponding glycol.

Other Reactions

Sodio malonic and acetoacetic esters react readily with certain alkylene oxides. With epichlorohydrin and ethyl acetoacetate, the final product is acetyl chloro-γ-valerolactone,

$$
\begin{array}{ccc}
& \quad \quad COCH_3 & CH_2CHCOCH_3 \\
& \quad \quad / & | \\
ClCH_2CH-CH_2 + H_2C & \rightarrow & \quad \quad COOC_2H_5 \\
\quad \quad \backslash \, / & \quad \quad \backslash & \\
\quad \quad O & \quad \quad COOC_2H_5 & ClCH_2CHOH
\end{array}
$$

$$
\begin{array}{c}
\quad \quad CH_2-CHCOCH_3 \\
\quad \quad | \quad \quad \backslash \\
\rightarrow \quad \quad | \quad \quad \quad CO \\
\quad \quad | \quad \quad / \\
ClCH_2CH-O
\end{array}
$$

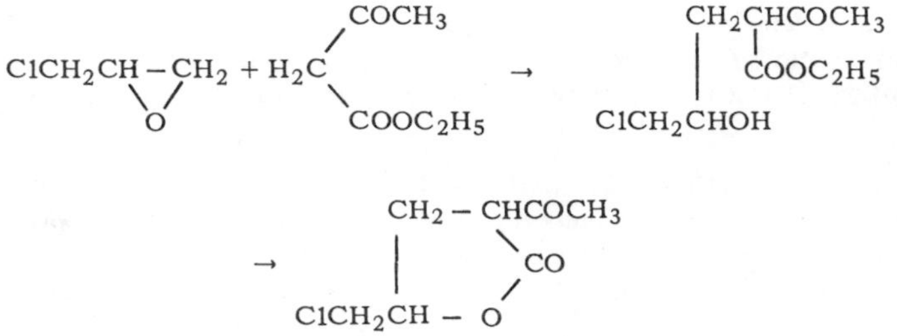

Sodio malonic ester similarly gives with ethylene oxide γ-butyrolactone-α-carboxylic ester,

$$
\begin{array}{c}
CH_2-CHCOOC_2H_5 \\
| \quad \quad \backslash \\
| \quad \quad \quad CO \\
| \quad \quad / \\
CH_2-O
\end{array}
$$

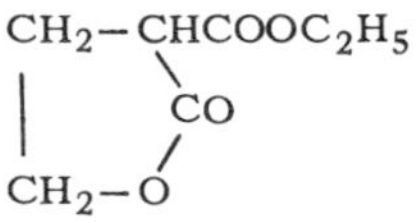

while with β,β'-dimethylglycidic acid ester, it gives 4-methyl-2,3-dicarbethoxypentanolide[57]

$$
\begin{array}{c}
(CH_3)_2C - CHCOOC_2H_5 \\
| \quad \quad | \\
O \quad \quad CHCOOC_2H_5 \\
\backslash \quad / \\
CO
\end{array}
$$

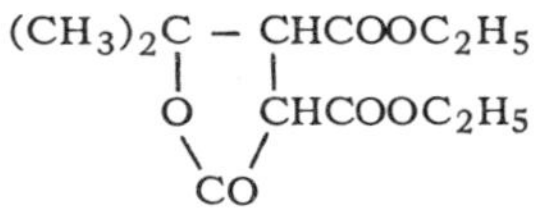

α-Bromo-β-hydroxyethylbenzene has been obtained by the treatment of styrene oxide with the magnesium bromide-ether complex, and hydrolyzing the resulting product:[101]

$$
\begin{array}{ccccc}
O & & & & \\
/ \backslash & \xrightarrow{MgBr_2} & & \xrightarrow{H_2O} & \\
C_6H_5CHCH_2 & \rightarrow & C_6H_5CHBrCH_2OMgBr & \rightarrow & C_6H_5CHBrCH_2OH
\end{array}
$$

Alkylene oxides may be reduced to alcohols with lithium aluminum hydride. α-Phenylethyl alcohol has been obtained in 94% yield by this method from styrene oxide.[102]

Isomerization of Alkylene Oxides

Alkylene oxides have a tendency to isomerize to carbonyl compounds. Isomerization takes place in certain cases by simply heating the compound. Anethole oxide is, thus, converted to anisoylacetone, $CH_3OC_6H_4CH_2COCH_3$, by heating to 200°. Isosafrole oxide can be similarly converted to piperonylacetone, bromoisosafrole oxide to bromopiperonylacetone and dibromoisosafrole oxide to dibromopiperonylacetone. The presence of a contact agent is required, however, in most cases. Thus, ethylene oxide, passed over aluminum oxide heated to 200-300°, changes to acetaldehyde. Propionaldehyde and small quantities of acetone result under the same conditions from propylene oxide, while isobutylene oxide, $(CH_3)_2C{-}CH_2$ (with O bridging the two carbons), gives isobutyraldehyde and trimethylethylene oxide gives methyl isopropyl ketone. Zinc and lead chlorides and finely subdivided metals are also effective catalysts to bring about isomerization. Styryl oxide has thus been isomerized to phenylacetaldehyde by use of metal powders as a catalyst.[58] Dilute acids also promote the isomerization of alkylene oxides. Methylstyryl oxide has been converted, for example, to hydratropoaldehyde, $C_6H_5CH(CH_3)CHO$, by the action of sulfuric acid, sulfurous acid or sodium bisulfide.[59]

The rearrangement of ethylene oxides of the type of $C_6H_5C{-}CHR$ (with O bridging the two carbons) takes place so as to yield the ketones, $(C_6H_5)_2CHCOR$, when R is one of the groups CH_3, C_2H_5, $CH_3CH_2CH_2$, $(CH_3)_2CH$, $CH_3CH_2CH_2CH_2$, $CH_3CH_2CH(CH_3)$, $C_6H_5CH_2$, C_6H_5. The migration takes place in the reverse direction, giving the ketone $C_6H_5COCH(C_6H_5)R$, when R is the anisyl radical, $CH_3OC_6H_4$.[103]

Glycidic esters undergo rearrangement to keto esters when heated:

$$(C_6H_5)_2\overset{O}{\widehat{C-C}}HCOOC_2H_5 \rightarrow (C_6H_5)_2CHCOCOOC_2H_5$$

The ethyl ester of β-phenylglycidic acid is converted to the ethyl ester of phenylmalonic aldehyde acid when its vapors are passed over infusorial earth heated at 310°:

$$C_6H_5\overset{O}{\widehat{CH-C}}HCOOC_2H_5 \rightarrow C_6H_4\begin{cases}CHO\\COOC_2H_5\end{cases}$$

Hydrolysis of glycidic esters and subsequent decarboxylation results in the formation of aldehydes or ketones:

$$RR'\overset{O}{\widehat{C-C}}R''COOC_2H_5 \rightarrow RR'\overset{O}{\widehat{C-C}}R''COOH \rightarrow RR'CHCOR''$$

These esters may be converted to the sodium salt of the acids by adding an equivalent of sodium ethoxide in alcoholic solution. The addition of an equivalent of water, followed by dry ether, causes the precipitation of the sodium salt. The free acid is decarboxylated and converted to the carbonyl compound by the application of heat. The reaction offers a method for the conversion of ketones RCOR′ to aldehydes of the type RCHR′CHO, or ketones of the type RR′CHCOR″.

Aromatic ketoxy compounds of the type of $C_6H_5COCH{-}CHC_6H_5$ (with O bridging the two CH groups) may be converted to α-diketo derivatives by treatment with alcoholic sodium hydroxide or with zinc chloride.[60] These oxido compounds isomerize to 1,3-diketo derivatives when subjected to the action of ultraviolet radiation.[61] Isomerization of α,β-ketooxido compounds proceeds best by allowing a solution of the compound in a mixture of acetic acid and hydrochloric acid to stand at room temperature. The change seems to be preceded by the formation of a halohydrin, which gives rise to a diketone with the liberation of hydrochloric acid. Sulfuric acid may be substituted for hydrochloric acid. Isomerization is at times accompanied by a molecular rearrangement. Phenylacetylacetaldehyde results, for example, through the isomerization of acetylphenylethylene oxide:

$$C_6H_5\overset{O}{\widehat{CH-C}}HCOCH_3 \rightarrow OCHCH(C_6H_5)COCH_3$$

formyldesoxybenzoin, $OCHCH(C_6H_5)COC_6H_5$, results similarly from benzoylphenyl-ethylene oxide.

Alkylene oxides may be converted to alkylene sulfides by the action of thiourea or alkaline thiocyanates: [104]

$$\underset{RCH - CH}{\overset{O}{\diagup \diagdown}} \quad \overset{KCNS}{\longrightarrow} \quad \underset{RCH - CH}{\overset{S}{\diagup \diagdown}}$$

Reaction proceeds at room temperature in aqueous solution and yields are in the range 50 to 73%.

THIOETHERS AND RELATED COMPOUNDS

Methods of Formation

Thioethers are formed when alkyl halides or salts of monoalkyl sulfates are heated with alkali sulfides:

$$2C_2H_5Cl + K_2S \quad \longrightarrow \quad C_2H_5SC_2H_5 + 2KCl$$

$$2KSO_3OC_2H_5 + K_2S \quad \longrightarrow \quad C_2H_5SC_2H_5 + 2K_2SO_4$$

Thioethers are also obtained through the interaction of alkali mercaptides and alkyl iodides. Other methods of preparation include the replacement of the oxygen in ethers with sulfur by means of phosphorus pentasulfide, heating lead mercaptides, and passing vapors of mercaptans over cadmium sulfide heated at 320-330°.

Sulfides result through the reaction of mercaptans with certain olefinic compounds. Addition takes place in accordance with Markownikow's rule in the presence of sulfur or sulfuric acid, but in the reverse direction in the presence of peroxides.[105]

$$RCH = CH_2 + R'SH \quad \overset{H_2SO_4}{\underset{Peroxides}{\rightleftarrows}} \quad \begin{array}{l} RCH(SR')CH_3 \\ \\ RCH_2CH_2SR' \end{array}$$

The yields are generally in the range 60 to 90%. Somewhat lower yields are obtained with vinyl chloride and allyl alcohol.[106] Sulfides are obtained in excellent yield from conjugated olefinic aldehydes, ketones, esters and nitriles.[107]

Aromatic sulfides result from the reaction of sodium thiophenolates and aromatic iodides; as well as through the saponification of aromatic thiocyanates with alkali carbonate. They are formed also when elementary sulfur is made to react with aromatic compounds in the presence of aluminum chloride.

Thioethers give addition compounds of the type R_2SX_2 by reaction with halogens. These are unstable bodies which tend to lose halogen. Many of the halogenated thioethers are decomposed by water to sulfoxides. Hydrolysis takes place more readily with dilute alkalies.

Sulfides with a methylene group attached to sulfur yield additive compounds rather readily. A bromine addition compound may be obtained from diphenyl sulfide in solution in carbon tetrachloride at $-10°$, but the product changes to 4-bromodiphenyl sulfide when allowed to warm to room temperature.

Sulfoxides and sulfones are formed when thioethers are oxidized. Sulfoxides are the first product of oxidation, and are obtained when thioethers are treated with nitric acid. They are also obtained through the controlled oxidation of thioethers with hydrogen peroxide in solution in acetic acid or acetone. Nascent hydrogen reconverts sulfoxides to sulfides. Unsymmetrical sulfones, $RSO.R'$, exist in optically active forms.[62]

Sulfones, R_2SO_2, result when sulfoxides are treated with fuming nitric acid or potassium permanganate. They may also be prepared from alkyl sulfinic acid salts by reaction with alkyl iodides:

$$C_2H_5SO_2K + C_2H_5I \rightarrow (C_2H_5)_2SO_2 + KI$$

Sulfones are highly stable compounds, and are not acted upon by the strongest acids and alkalies. They cannot be oxidized further, and withstand the action of reducing agents. Sodium, reacting with sulfones in boiling toluene, converts them to sulfinates, $RSOONa$.

Sulfonium Compounds

Aliphatic thioethers combine readily with alkyl halides to form sulfonium compounds. Reaction is effected by heating a mixture of the components, or by allowing it to stand at room temperature, whereby the sulfonium compound separates in a crystalline form:

$$\begin{array}{c} R' \\ \diagdown \\ \diagup \\ R'' \end{array} S + RI \rightarrow \begin{array}{c} R' \quad R \\ \diagdown \diagup \\ S \\ \diagup \diagdown \\ R'' \quad I \end{array}$$

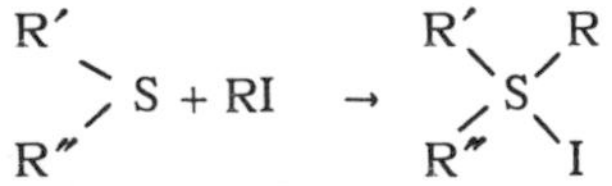

Interchange of sulfur may take place resulting in the formation of the sulfide of the alkyl radical originally attached to the halogen. As a consequence other sulfonium compounds may also form in the course of the reaction, as illustrated in the following example:[63]

$$2CH_3I + (C_6H_5CH_2)_2S \rightarrow 2C_6H_5CH_2I + (CH_3)_2S$$
$$(CH_3)_2S + CH_3I \rightarrow (CH_3)_3SI$$
$$(CH_3)_2S + C_6H_5CH_2I \rightarrow (CH_3)_2S(CH_2C_6H_5)I$$

The velocity of addition of a halide is determined by the degree of mobility of the halogen atoms. Among the primary aliphatic iodides methyl iodide is the most reactive. Ethyl iodide is more reactive than isoamyl iodide. Chloro- and bromoacetone are capable of forming sulfonium compounds, while bromodiphenacyl, $C_6H_5COCH(Br)COOC_2H_5$, and bromocamphor fail to give such compounds. Sulfides of the structure $RS(CH_2)nN(CH_3)I$ in which $n = 2$ do not add methyl iodide; those in which $n = 3$ give unstable addition products, while those in which $n = 4$ yield stable sulfonium salts.[64]

Sulfonium iodides result upon heating certain thioethers with hydrogen iodide, an alkyl iodide and a mercaptan forming as intermediate products:

$$(C_2H_5)_2S + HI \rightarrow C_2H_5I + C_2H_5SH$$

$$(C_2H_5)_2S + C_2H_5I \rightarrow (C_2H_5)_3SI$$

A similar reaction takes place with iodine, an alkyl iodide and a disulfide forming the intermediate products. Acid chlorides react in a similar manner.

Trimethylsulfonium iodide may be obtained through the interaction of methyl iodide with metal sulfides:

$$SnS + 3CH_3I \rightarrow (CH_3)_3SI + SnI_2,$$

or by heating methyl iodide with sulfur at 180° in a sealed tube, whereby a diiodo complex of the sulfonium compound $(CH_3)_3SI{\cdot}I_2$ results.

The bromides and chlorides of sulfonium compounds cannot be prepared directly, as a rule, but are obtained through the interaction of silver chloride or bromide with sulfonium iodides.

Aromatic disulfides and methyl phenyl sulfide do not combine with methyl iodide. Diaryl monoalkyl sulfonium compounds result, however, when certain aromatic disulfides, such as diphenyl and dinaphthyl disulfides, are heated with an equivalent quantity of dimethyl sulfate for several hours at 90 to 100°.[65] The chloroplatinate complexes serve for the isolation of these compounds.[66] Alkyl aromatic sulfonium compounds are also obtained when aromatic lead mercaptides are heated on the water-bath with an excess of dimethyl sulfate:

$$(ArS)_2Pb + 3(CH_3)_2SO_4 \rightarrow 2ArS(CH_3)_2SO_4CH_3 + Pb(OSO_2OCH_3)_2$$

Thiodiphenylamine,

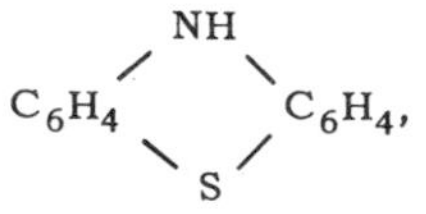

gives a methyl sulfonium salt with dimethyl sulfate. The hydroxide may be prepared from this by treatment with alkalies. The hydroxide may be converted to an anhydride,

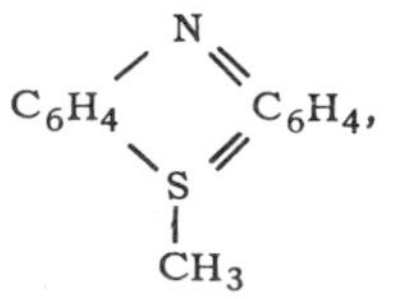

which combines with carbon dioxide in the presence of water to a carbonate,

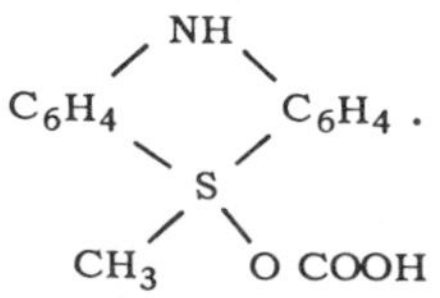

Naphthalene analogs of thiodiphenylamine behave in a similar manner.[67]

Thio aromatic sulfonium compounds result through the interaction of aromatic sulfoxides with phenols or phenol ethers in the presence of sulfuric acid or other condensing agents:[68]

$$Ar_2SO + C_6H_5OH + H_2SO_4 \rightarrow Ar_2S\begin{cases} C_6H_4OH \\ SO_4H \end{cases} + H_2O$$

These compounds may also be prepared from sulfinic acids.

Sulfonium halides are water soluble compounds which resemble quaternary ammonium compounds in many respects. Their solutions react neutral, and the free bases cannot, in general, be liberated by treatment with alkalies. Conversion to the free base is brought about by treating the aqueous solution of the sulfonium halide with moist silver oxide.

Sulfonium bases are frequently more strongly basic than the hydroxides of alkali metals. They are crystalline compounds, readily soluble in water, and are very hygroscopic. They cause the precipitation of metal hydroxides from the solution of heavy metal salts, displace ammonia and other weak bases from their salts, and readily absorb carbon dioxide.

Thetines, $\overline{OCOCH_2S}(R)_2$, which are the sulfur analogs of betains, are slightly basic compounds.

Alkyl Disulfides

Disulfides, RSSR, result from the partial oxidation of mercaptans; they are formed, for example, through the action of iodine or sulfuryl chloride on mercaptans:

$$2C_2H_5SH + I_2 \rightarrow C_2H_5SSC_2H_5 + 2HI$$

$$2C_2H_5SH + SO_2Cl_2 \rightarrow C_2H_5SSC_2H_5 + SO_2 + 2HCl$$

Disulfides may also be prepared by heating salts of monoalkyl sulfates with potassium disulfide:[69]

$$2C_2H_5OSO_3K + K_2S_2 \rightarrow C_2H_5SSC_2H_5 + 2K_2SO_4$$

Mixed disulfides result when the required amount of bromine is added to a mixture in equimolecular quantities of two different mercaptans.[70]

The formation of disulfides from thiophenols proceeds very readily. Partial oxidation takes place, for example, when an alcoholic ammoniacal solution of thiophenol is evaporated to dryness. Mild oxidizing agents, such as alkali ferricyanides, dilute nitric acid or ferric chloride convert aromatic thiophenols to the corresponding disulfides.

Saturated disulfides are hydrolyzed on heating with aqueous alkalies to a mercaptan and a sulfenic acid, RSOH, which however loses oxygen to become converted to a mercaptan.[71] Disulfides in which carbon atoms with double bonds are present adjacent to the sulfur, give by this treatment a mercaptan, an alcohol and sulfur:[72]

$$R_1R_2C = C(R_3)S\text{-}SC(R_3) = C(R_1)R_2 \xrightarrow{H_2O} R_1R_2C = C(R_2)SH + R_1R_2C = C(R_3)OH + S$$

Trisulfides are obtained through the interaction of mercaptans and sulfur dichloride:

$$2C_6H_5SH + SCl_2 \rightarrow C_6H_5SSSC_6H_5 + 2HCl$$

Tetrasulfides are obtained similarly through the interaction of mercaptans with sulfur mochloride, S_2Cl_2.

Disulfides are reduced by nascent hydrogen to mercaptans; heated with zinc dust they yield zinc mercaptides. Potassium mercaptides results when they are heated with potassium sulfide.[73] Metallic sodium converts them to sodium mercaptides, the reaction taking place especially readily with the higher aliphatic disulfides.[74] Dilute nitric acid converts disulfides to sulfonic esters, $RSSO_2R$. Disulfides may be converted to monosulfides by the action of alkali cyanides:

$$RSSR + NaCN \rightarrow RSR + NaSCN$$

Dialkyl Selenides[75]

Dialkyl selenides are obtained by heating alkali metal selenides with salts of monoalkyl sulfates:

$$Na_2Se + 2ROSO_2ONa \rightarrow SeR_2 + 2Na_2SO_4$$

Dialkyl selenides are readily oxidized, and react with halogens to form dihalides. With alkyl halides they give quaternary selenonium compounds, which are salts of the strongly alkaline selenonium hydroxides. Selenonium compounds with three different alkyl groups exist in two optically active forms.

Dialkyl Tellurides[76]

Dimethyl and diethyl tellurides may be prepared in an impure form by heating the alkali metal salts of methyl and ethyl sulfates with alkali tellurides, or by conducting vapors of the corresponding alcohols over heated aluminum telluride, Al_2Te_3.

Dialkyl tellurides may be obtained in the pure form by reducing the dihalides R_2TeX_2, for example, with sulfurous acid; or by the interaction of alkylmagnesium halides with tellurium dihalides.

Dialkyl tellurides give quaternary telluronium compounds with alkyl halides. Quaternary telluronium hydroxides, R_3TeOH, are obtained from these by treatment with moist silver oxide. The hydroxides are soluble in water and are strongly basic in character. Dialky tellurides also readily combine with halogens, forming the *trans*-form of the dihalides, R_2TeX_2. Treated with moist silver oxide, these give the *trans*-dihydroxides $R_2Te(OH)_2$, which when evaporated to dryness change to an anhydride of the *cis*-modification. With concentrated nitric acid dialkyl tellurides give the dinitrates $R_2Te(NO_3)_2$.

Diaryl tellurides are best prepared through the interaction of tellurium iodide or bromide and arylmagnesium bromides:

$$TeBr_2 + 2RMgBr \rightarrow TeR_2 + 2MgBr_2$$

The yields may be as high as 75% of theoretical. The reactions of diaryl tellurides are similar to those of dialkyl tellurides.

References

1. Senderens, *Compt. rend.*, **151**, 3925 (1910). Cf. Schlatter, *J. Ind. Eng. Chem.*, **12**, 1101 (1920).
2. Norris and Rigby, *J. Am. Chem. Soc.*, **54**, 2095 (1932).
3. Norton and Prescott, *Am. Chem. J.*, **6**, 245 (1884).
4. Kraft, *Ber.*, **26**, 2829 (1893).
5. Fischer, *Ber.*, **26**, 2400, 2412 (1893).
6. Schroeber, *Ann.*, **418**, 161 (1919); Haworth, *J. Chem. Soc.*, **107**, 8 (1915).
7. Kremann, *Monatsh.*, **27**, 1265 (1906); Graebe, *Ann.*, **340**, 208 (1905); Witt and Schneider, *Ber.*, **34**, 3173 (1911).
8. Mailhe and de Godon, *Bull. soc. chim.*, (4) **25**, 565 (1919); (4) **27**, 121 (1920).
9. Helferich, Speidel and Toeldte, *Ber.*, **56**, 766 (1923); Helferich, Moog and Jünger, *ibid.*, **58**, 872 (1925).
10. Robinson and Robinson, *J. Chem. Soc.*, **111**, 967 (1917); **123**, 532 (1923); McLeod and Robinson, G.M., *ibid.*, **119**, 1470 (1921).
11. Tschitschibabih and Jelgasin, *Ber.*, **47**, 1843 (1914); Spath, *ibid.*, **47**, 766 (1914); *Monatsh.*, **35**, 319 (1914).
12. Williamson, *J. Chem. Soc.*, **4**, 229 (1852); *J. prakt. Chem.*, (1) **61**, 60 (1854); Wurtz, *Ann.*, **93**, 117 (1855); Lieben and Rossi, *ibid.*, **158**, 165 (1871); **165**, 117 (1873); Cf. Lazinsky and Swadowsky, *J. Russ. Phys.-Chem. Soc.*, **35**, 100; Henry, *Bull. Acad. roy. Belg.*, **1904**, 42.
13. Purdie and Pitkeathly, *J. Chem. Soc.*, **75**, 157 (1899); Purdie and Irvine, *ibid.*, **75**, 485 (1899); **83**, 1021 (1903); McKenzie, *ibid.* **75**, 754 (1899).
14. Haworth, *Constitution of Sugars*, 1929.
15. Plauson and Vielle, *British Patent* 156,121 (1920).
16. *British Patent* 369,297 (1930); *U.S. Patent* 1,959,927 (1934); Reppe and Wolff, *U.S. Patents* 2,066,076 (1937) and 2,021,869 (1936).
17. Wislicenus, *Ann.*, **92**, 106 (1876); Claisen, *Ber.*, **31**, 1021 (1898).
18. Crompton and Vanderstichele, *J. Chem. Soc.*, **117**, 691 (1920).
19. Nehr and Foster, *J. Am. Chem. Soc.*, **31**, 410, 412 (1909); Foster, *ibid.*, **31**, 596 (1909).
20. Claisen, *Ber.*, **29**, 1005 (1896).
21. Moureu, *Compt. rend.*, **138**, 286 (1904); Knorr, *Ber.*, **39**, 1410 (1906).
22. Guest, McDowell and McNamee, *U.S. Patent* 2,421,378 (1947).
23. Hartmann and Gattermann, *Ber.*, **25**, 3531 (1892); Pfeiffer and Haack, *Ann.*, **460**, 156 (1928).
24. Klemenc, *Ber.*, **49**, 1371 (1916).
25. Descudé, *Compt. rend.*, **132**, 1129 (1901); Wedekind, E., and Houssermann, *Ber.*, **34**, 2081 (1901); Knoevenagel, *Ann.*, **402**, 133 (1914); Underwood, Baril and Toone, *J. Am. Chem. Soc.*, **52**, 4087 (1930).
26. Brunel, *Compt. rend.*, **137**, 62 (1903).
27. Meider, *Ber.*, **32**, 2052 (1899).
28. Zincke, *ibid.*, **32**, 3599 (1899).
29. Prileschajew, *ibid.*, **42**, 4811 (1909); **43**, 959 (1910); *Chem. Zentr.* **1911**, **I**, 1279; **II**, 268; *Chem. Zentr.* **1912**, **II**, 2090; *J. Russ. Phys.-Chem. Soc.*, **42**, 1387 (1910); **43**, 609 (1911); **44**, 613 (1912); Nemetkin, *Ber.*, **56**, 1803, 1805, 1808 (1923); **57**, 585 (1924); Boeseken and Elsen, *Rec. trav. chim.*, **48**, 363 (1929); Swern *et al.*, *J. Am. Chem. Soc.*, **68**, 1504 (1946); Byers and Hickinbottom, *J. Chem. Soc.*, **1948**, 284; Swern, *Chem. Revs.*, **48**, 1 (1949).
30. Staudinger, *Die Ketene*, (1912).
31. Paal and Weidenkoff, *Ber.*, **39**, 2062 (1906).
32. Rabe and Hallensleben, *ibid.*, **43**, 884 (1910).
33. Fourneau, *Bull. soc. chim.*, (4) **3**, 407 (1908).
34. Erlenmeyer, Jr., *Ann.*, **271**, 137 (1892).
35. Claisen, *Ber.*, **38**, 693 (1905).
36. Darzens, *Compt. rend.*, **139**, 1214 (1904); **141**, 766 (1905); **144**, 1123 (1907); **145**, 1342 (1907); **151**, 883 (1910).
37. Widmann, *Ann.*, **400**, 86, 104 (1913); *Ber.*, **49**, 477, 2778 (1916); Bodforss, *Ber.*, **49**, 2795 (1916); **51**, 192 (1918); **52**, 142 (1919); Förlander, *Ber.*, **49**, 2782 (1916); **50**, 1457 (1917); Freudenberg and Stoll, *Ann.*, **440**, 41 (1924); Murakami and Ivie, *Proc. Imp. Acad. (Tokyo)*, **10**, 568 (1934).
38. Rap, *Gazz. chim. ital.*, **25**, (2), 285 (1895).
39. Pazschke, *J. prakt. Chem.*, (2) **1**, 82 (1870); Hartenstein, *ibid.*, (2) **7**, 295 (1873).
40. Engle, *J. Am. Chem. Soc.*, **20**, 668 (1898).
41. Lindeman, *Ber.*, **24**, 2145 (1891); Cohn and Plohm, *ibid.*, **40**, 2597 (1907); Fischer and Krämer, *ibid.*, **41**, 2728 (1908); Body and Marle, *J. Chem. Soc.*, **93**, 838 (1908).
42. Nef, *Ann.*, **335**, 238 (1904).
43. Michael, *J. prakt. Chem.*, (2) **64**, 109 (1901).
44. Henry, *Ber.*, **39**, 3677 (1906).
45. Förlander, *ibid.*, **49**, 2783 (1917).

46. Bodforss, *ibid.*, **49**, 2808 (1917).
47. Erlenmeyer, *Ann.*, **191**, 273 (1878).
48. Horman, *Ber.*, **12**, 23 (1879).
49. Fourneau and Tiffeneau, *Compt. rend.*, **146**, 697 (1908).
50. Wurtz, *Ann.*, **114**, 51 (1860); **121**, 226 (1862); Knorr, *Ber.*, **32**, 729 (1899); Krassuski and Duda, *J. prakt. Chem.*, (2) **77**, 84 (1908).
51. Knorr and Schmidt, *Ber.*, **31**, 1072 (1898); Knorr, *ibid.*, **32**, 729 (1899); Knorr and Matthes, *ibid.*, **34**, 3482 (1901); Matthes, *Ann.*, **315**, 104 (1901); **316**, 311 (1901); Emerson, *J. Am. Chem. Soc.*, **67**, 516 (1945); *Chem. Revs.*, **45**, 273 (1949).
52. Knorr and Brownsdon, *Ber.*, **35**, 4474 (1902).
53. Roithner, *Monatsh.*, **15**, 665 (1894).
54. Lourenco, *Ann. chim.*, (3) **67**, 275 (1863); Wilson and Lucas, *J. Am. Chem. Soc.*, **58**, 2400 (1936); **63**, 25 (1941); Moureu and Dode, *Bull. soc. chim.*, (S) **4**, 289 (1937); Winstein, *J. Am. Chem. Soc.*, **64**, 2794 (1942).
55. Eltekow, *Ber.*, **16**, R.395 (1883); Melikow, *ibid.*, **17**, R.420 (1884).
56. Roithner, *Monatsh.*, **15**, 665 (1894).
57. Haller and Blanc, *Compt. rend.*, **142**, 1471 (1906).
58. Fourneau and Tiffeneau, *ibid.*, **140**, 1595 (1905).
59. Tiffeneau, *ibid.*, **140**, 1458 (1905).
60. Förlander, *Ber.*, **50**, 406 (1917); Darmon, *Compt. rend.*, **197**, 1649 (1933); Favorsky *et al.*, *ibid.*, **199**, 1229 (1934).
61. Bodforss, *Ber.*, **51**, 214 (1918).
62. Harrison, Kenyon and Phillips, *J. Chem. Soc.*, **1926**, 658, 3316, 2079.
63. Schöller, *Ber.*, **7**, 1274 (1874).
64. Schneider, Müller and Beck, *Ann.*, **386**, 334 (1912); Schneider, *ibid.*, **375**, 216 (1910).
65. Kehrmann and Duttenhöffer, *Ber.*, **39**, 3559 (1906); **38**, 4197 (1905); Kehrmann and Sava, *ibid.*, **45**, 2895 (1912).
66. Kehrmann and Duttenhöffer, *Ber.*, **38**, 4197 (1905).
67. Kehrmann and Dardel, *ibid.*, **55**, 2346 (1922).
68. Smiles and Le Rossignol, *Proc. Roy. Soc. (London)*, **22**, 24, 87, 158 (1906); *J. Chem. Soc.*, **89**, 696 (1906). *Cf.* Kehrmann, Livermore and Frumkine, *Ber.*, **51**, 474 (1918).
69. Blanksma, *Rec. trav. chim.*, **20**, 121 (1901).
70. Otto and Rössing, *Ber.*, **19**, 3132 (1886).
71. Fromm, *Ann.*, **348**, 146 (1906); **426**, 313 (1922).
72. Price and Twiss, *J. Chem. Soc.*, **97-98**, 1175 (1910); Fromm and Foerster, *Ann.*, **394**, 338 (1912).
73. Otto and Rössing, *Ber.*, **19**, 3129 (1886).
74. Moses and Reid, *J. Am. Chem. Soc.*, **48**, 776 (1926).
75. Krausse and Grosse, *Die Chemie der Metall-Organishen Verbindungen*, (1937), p. 667.
76. Krausse and Grosse, l.c. p. 671; Wohler, *Ann.*, **35**, 111 (1840); Vernon, *J. Chem. Soc.*, **117**, 86, 889 (1920); **119**, 687 (1921); Vernon and Knaggs, *ibid.*, **119**, 105 (1921); Drew, *ibid.*, **117**, 889 (1920); **1929**, 560; Burstall and Sugden, *ibid.*, **1930**, 229.
77. Schorigin and Makaroff - Samljanski, *Ber.*, **65**, 1293 (1932).
78. Schröter and Sondag, *ibid.*, **41**, 1921 (1908).
79. Diels and Blumberg, *ibid.*, **44**, 2848 (1911).
80. Favre, *Compt. rend.*, **119**, 284 (1894); Marvel and Porter, *Organic Syntheses*, Coll. Vol., I, 377 (1941); Henze *et al.*, *J. Am. Chem. Soc.*, **64**, 1222 (1942). *Cf.* Lucien and Mason, *ibid.*, **71**, 258 (1949).
81. Wedekind, *Ber.*, **36**, 1383 (1903).
82. Carlson and Cretcher, *J. Am. Chem. Soc.*, **69**, 1952 (1947).
83. Moureu and Dode, *Bull. Soc. Chim.*, (5) **4**, 281 (1937).
84. Braun, *Organic Syntheses*, Coll. Vol. I, 431 (1941); Kolthoff *et al.*, *J. Polymer Sci.*, **2**, 199 (1947); Swern *et al.*, *J. Am. Chem. Soc.*, **66**, 1925 (1944).
85. Findley *et al.*, *J. Am. Chem. Soc.*, **67**, 412 (1945); Greenspan, *ibid.*, **68**, 907 (1946).
86. Arbuzow and Michailow, *J. Prakt. Chem.*, (2), **127**, 1 (1930); Böeseken *et al.*, *Proc. Acad. Sci. Amsterdam*, **32**, 377 (1929); Smit, *Rec. trav. chim.*, **49**, 675 (1930).
87. Findley *et al.*, *l.c.*, Swern *et al.*, *J. Am. Chem. Soc.*, **68**, 1504 (1946).
88. Arbuzow and Michailow, *J. Prakt. Chem.*, (2) **127**, 192 (1930); Findley *et al.*, *l.c.*
89. Böhme, *Organic Syntheses*, Vol. 2 (1940) p. 70.
90. Karrer and Jucker, *Helv. Chim. Acta*, **28**, 427, 471, 474, 1146 (1945).
91. Milas and McAleny, *J. Am. Chem. Soc.*, **55**, 349 (1933).
92. Milas and Cliff, *ibid.*, **55**, 352 (1933); Milas and McAleny, *ibid.*, **56**, 1221 (1934).
93. Meerwein, *J. Prakt. Chem.*, (2) **113**, 18 (1926); Böeseken, *Rec. trav. chim.*, **45**, 838 (1926); Braun, *J. Am. Chem. Soc.*, **51**, 229 (1929); Smit, *Rec. trav. chim.*, **49**, 686 (1930); Bodendorf, *Arch. Pharm.* **268**, 491 (1930)' Stuurman, *Proc. Acad. Sci. Amsterdam*, **38**, 450 (1935); *C.A.*, **29**, 4657 (1935); Böeseken *et al.*, *Proc. Acad. Sci. Amsterdam.*, **39**, 2 (1936); *C.A.*, **30**, 3304 (1936); *Rec. trav. chim.*, **56**, 1034 (1937); **44**, 90 (1925); **61**, 69 (1942); Heinänen,

Ann. Acad. Sci. Fennicae, **A59**, No. 13, 3 (1943); *C.A.*, **41**, 2307 (1947); Swern, *J. Am. Chem. Soc.*, **69**, 1692 (1947); *Chem. Revs.*, **45**, 1 (1949); *Organic Reactions*, VII, 1953, p. 378.
94. Kolthoff and Menzel, *Die Massanalyse*, Vol. II, 2nd Ed., p. 413, Springer, Berlin 1931; Marks and Morrell, *Analyst*, **54**, 503 (1932); Wheeler, *Oil and Soap*, **9**, 89 (1932).
95. Böeseken *et al.*, *Rec. trav. chim.*, **50**, 1023 (1931).
96. Komada, *J. Chem. Soc. Japan*, **58**, 1295 (1937).
97. Komada, *ibid.*, **59**, 477 (1938).
98. Böeseken *et al.*, *Rec. trav. chim.*, **50**, 827 (1931); **52**, 874 (1933); **55**, 786 (1936).
99. Pointet, *Compl. rend.*, **148**, 417 (1909); Troell, *Ber.*, **61**, 2498 (1928); Kohler *et al.*, *J. Am. Chem. Soc.*, **53**, 211 (1931).
100. Kleucker, *Ber.*, **55**, 1634 (1922); Bergmann and Harvey, *ibid.*, **62**, 902 (1929).
101. Tiffenau and Tchouber, *Compt. rend.*, **207**, 918 (1938).
102. Nystrom and Brown, *J. Am. Chem. Soc.*, **70**, 3739 (1948).
103. Legrave, *Ann. chim.*, (10) **8**, 363 (1928).
104. Culvenor *et al.*, *J. Chem. Soc.*, **1946**, 1050; Snyder *et al.*, *J. Am. Chem. Soc.*, **69**, 2674 (1947).
105. Jones and Reid, *J. Am. Chem. Soc.*, **60**, 2452 (1938); Ipatieff *et al.*, *ibid.*, **60**, 2731 (1938); **61**, 71 (1939); Fuson and Ziegler, *J. Org. Chem.*, **11**, 510 (1946).
106. Fuson *et al.*, *J. Org. Chem.*, **11**, 475 (1946); **14**, 707 (1949); Szabo and Stiller, *J. Am. Chem. Soc.*, **70**, 3667 (1948).
107. Hurd and Gershhein, *J. Am. Chem. Soc.*, **69**, 241, 2328 (1947); Szabo and Stiller, *ibid.*, **70**, 3667 (1948); Pierson *et al.*, *ibid.*, **70**, 1450 (1948); Ross, *ibid.*, **71**, 3458 (1949); Hall and Howe, *J. Chem. Soc.*, **1949**, 2723.
108. Flores - Gallardo and Pollard, *J. Org. Chem.*, **12**, 831 (1947). *Cf.* Koelsch, *J. Am. Chem. Soc.*, **65**, 2460 (1943).
109. Fischer and Baer, *J. Biol. Chem.*, **140**, 397 (1941).
110. Baer *et al.*, *ibid.*, **170**, 337 (1947).

CHAPTER 3

ALIPHATIC CARBONYL COMPOUNDS FORMATION

ALDEHYDES

Formation of Aldehydes by Oxidation or Dehydrogenation of Alcohols[1]

Aldehydes may be prepared from primary alcohols by treatment with various oxidizing agents, in particular with a mixture of sodium bichromate and dilute sulfuric acid. The chromium trioxide-pyridine complex, $CrO_3.2\ C_5H_5N$, converts primary and secondary alcohols to the corresponding carbonyl compounds without affecting double bonds or thio linkages.[152] Oxidation has been brought about by use of *tert*-butyl chromate which is obtained through the reaction of chromic acid and *tert*-butyl alcohol at 0°.[153]

When higher alcohols are oxidized with alkali bichromate and moderately concentrated sulfuric acid, appreciable quantities of esters are formed as a result of the oxidation of the alcohol to the acid stage. Free acids and acetals are also formed, together with the aldehyde. Conditions may be adjusted so as to obtain the esters as the principal product of the reaction.[1]

Unsaturated alcohols give aldehydes in low yield. Cyclic primary alcohols may be successfully converted to the corresponding aldehydes by this method. 1-Methylnaphthyl-4-carbinol gives the aldehyde, but 2-methylnaphthyl-2-carbinol resists oxidation.

The conversion of alcohols to aldehydes may also be accomplished by use of manganese dioxide and sulfuric acid. Narcotine and meconine have been converted by these reagents to opianic acid. The highly sensitive propargyl aldehyde has been prepared by this method in 50% yield.[154] Lead dioxide and sulfuric acid are also suitable for the purpose and nitro ethanol, $NO_2CH_2CH_2OH$, has been converted by their use into nitroacetaldehyde in good yield.[2]

Highly sensitive unsaturated aldehydes, including polyene aldehydes, have been prepared by the action of a suspension of a very active form of manganese dioxide in an indifferent solvent.[155]

This active form of manganese dioxide is obtained by adding a solution of 111 gm manganese sulfate tetrahydrate in 150 cc of water and 117 cc of 40% caustic to a hot solution of 96 gm potassium permanganate in 600 cc water in the course of one hour. The precipitate is washed and dried at 100 to 120°.[156]

N-Chlorosuccinimide converts benzyl alcohol, totyl and naphthyl carbinols to the corresponding aldehydes.[51]

Aromatic alcohols are transformed to aldehydes in almost quantitative yield when they are treated in chloroform solution with liquid nitrogen tetroxide, although reaction proceeds slowly and is complete only after several days.[3]

Some basic primary alcohols may be converted to the corresponding aldehydes by treatment with formaldehyde in acid solution. Pyrrolidylethanol is thus converted to N-methylpyrrolidyl aldehyde, the amino group being methylated in the process:

$$\underset{NH}{\bigcirc} CH_2CH_2OH + H_2CO \rightarrow \underset{\underset{CH_3}{\overset{|}{N}}}{\bigcirc} CH_2CHO + H_2O$$

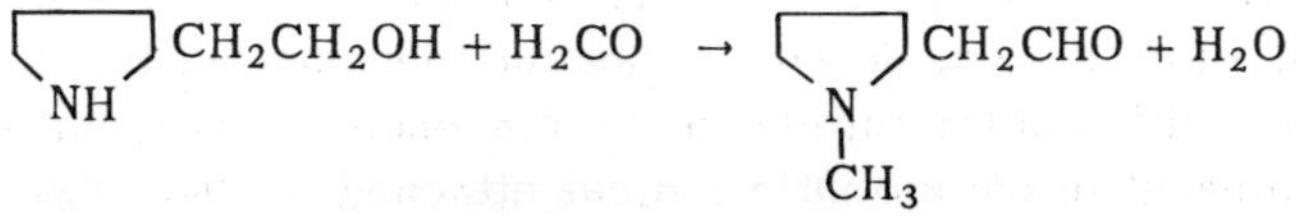

Piperidyl and methylpiperidylethanols also undergo this reaction, which bears a resemblance to the methylation of ammonia, involving the reduction of a molecule of formaldehyde and the simultaneous oxidation of a second molecule to formic acid. The essential requirement is that the compound shall contain a primary or a secondary amino group. Ketones are formed when the compound subjected to the reaction contains a secondary alcohol group.[4]

Aromatic hydroxyaldehydes result through the interaction of phenolic compounds and formaldehyde in the presence of nitro compounds, the latter oxidizing the intermediate phenolic alcohol to the aldehyde.[5]

a,β-Unsaturated aldehydes may be prepared from carbinols $RCH(OH)CH=CH_2$. The halo compound formed on replacing the hydroxyl group by bromine undergoes rearrangement to $RCH=CHCH_2Br$. Hydrolysis of this to the corresponding alcohol followed by oxidation gives the unsaturated aldehyde $RCH=CHCHO$.[52]

Alcohols have been converted to aldehydes through catalytic oxidation using as a catalyst pumice impregnated with ammonium zincate and dried and heated to drive off the ammonia.[53] One liter of finished catalyst should contain about 40 gm of zinc oxide. Isobutyl-, *n*-decyl- and phenylacetaldehyde have been obtained by this method in 60-90% yield.

Oxidation of alkyl halides to the corresponding aldehydes may be accomplished by heating with hexamethylenetetramine; the formaldehyde and ammonia resulting from the dissociation of this compound are the active agents in the reaction:

$$RCH_2Cl + H_2CO + NH_3 \rightarrow RCHO + CH_3NH_2 \cdot HCl$$

The method has been applied to a number of halides, including amyl iodide, allyl iodide and xylyl bromide. The yields are often quite good.

Aromatic methyl chlorides, $ArCH_2Cl$, are readily converted to aldehydes by heating with an aqueous solution of lead- or copper nitrate. The halide is presumably first saponified, the resulting alcohol being then oxidized to the corresponding aldehyde. Benzyl chloride yields benzaldehyde in good yield by this method, and *p*-xylylene chloride, $ClCH_2C_6H_4CH_2Cl$, gives terephthalaldehyde.[6] Benzyl chloride and similar aromatic halides may also be converted to aldehydes by oxidation with sodium bichromate and alkali.

Primary amines may be converted to aldehydes by oxidation with oxygen in the presence of copper powder. The reaction is carried out in hot aqueous solution. Glycine may thus be converted to glyoxylic acid:

$$NaOCOCH_2NH_2 + O_2 + Cu \rightarrow NaOCOCHO + NH_3 + CuO$$

A mixture of aqueous hydrogen peroxide and ferrous sulfate may also be used as the oxidizing agent.[7]

The grouping $-CH_2NH-$ present in certain types of compounds, such as in $C_6H_5CH_2NHC_6H_5$, is susceptible to oxidation to $-CH{=}N-$ with alkaline dichromate and sulfuric acid, or with potassium permanganage. Oxidation may be accomplished with sodium sulfide in the presence of elemental sulfur, if a nitro group is present in the aromatic radical attached to CH_2. The nitro group is reduced to an amino group in the process:

$$2NO_2C_6H_4CH_2NHC_6H_4SO_3H + Na_2S$$
$$\rightarrow 2H_2NC_6H_4CH = NC_6H_4.SO_3H + Na_2SO_4$$

Benzylamino compounds bearing a substituent attached to the carbon in the side chain, such as $C_6H_5CH(CN)NHC_6H_5$, are also subject to this type of oxidation. Hydrazines containing the grouping $-CH_2NH-$ attached to an aromatic ring can be oxidized to hydrazones.[8] With some hydrazines, oxidation proceeds even on simple exposure to atmospheric oxygen. This is true, for example, of benzylhydrazine. Others require treatment with ammoniacal copper hydroxide[9] or with mercuric oxide.[10]

A characteristic transformation involving an oxidation and reduction is observed among the 2-hydroxy derivatives of 1,2-dihydropyridine and quinoline series. These compounds result from the quaternary alkyl ammonium compounds by molecular rearrangement:

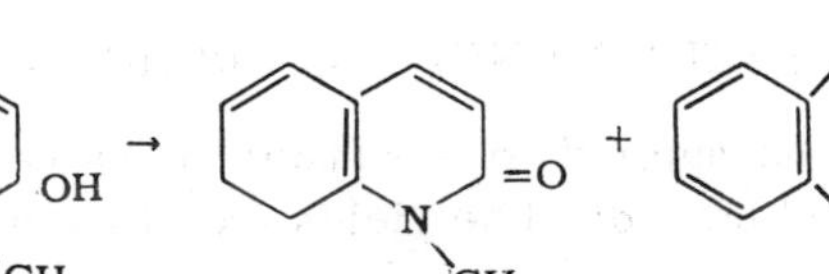

when subjected to distillation they yield a keto and a tetrahydro derivative.[11]

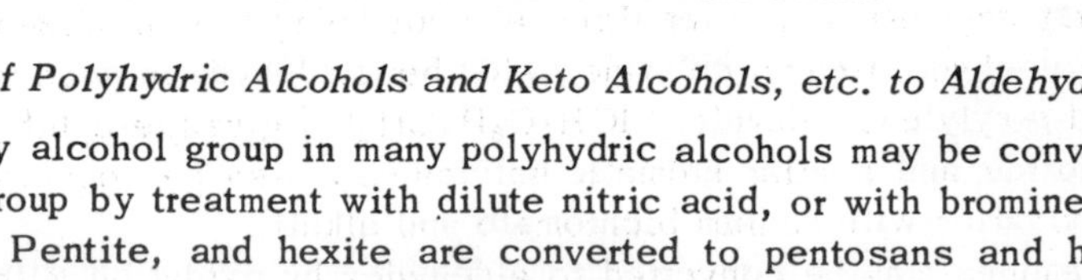

A similar transformation is also observed in the acridine series.

Oxidation of Polyhydric Alcohols and Keto Alcohols, etc. to Aldehydes

A primary alcohol group in many polyhydric alcohols may be converted to the aldehyde group by treatment with dilute nitric acid, or with bromine and sodium hydroxide. Pentite, and hexite are converted to pentosans and hexosans by these reagents. Certain hexose acids, among them galaheptosancarboxylic acid, require treatment with 55% nitric acid.[12]

A method originated by Fenton, which consists in the treatment of the hydroxy compound with dilute aqueous hydrogen peroxide containing ferrous sulfate in solution, converts polyhydric alcohols containing primary hydroxy groups to the corresponding aldehyde alcohols. Dulcite, mannite, glycerine and glycol, all yield the corresponding monoaldehyde by this treatment.[13]

No general method is available for the oxidation of primary alcohols with a keto group in the molecule to the corresponding keto aldehyde. The group $COCH_2OH$ in ketoses is readily converted to the osazone by α-methyl phenylhydrazine.[14] Certain amino ketones are converted to the oxime of the corresponding keto aldehydes on treatment with an excess of hydroxylamine. A transformation of this type is also observed with some chlorinated ketones.

Catalytic Dehydrogenation of Alcohols

Aldehydes may also be obtained through the catalytic dehydrogenation of primary alcohols. The reaction is carried out at 250 to 300°. The catalyst consists of finely subdivided copper supported on copper gauze, and is prepared by reducing with hydrogen at 300° a coating of copper hydroxide on the gauze. Reduction requires 8 to 20 hours.[15] The reaction is one of equilibrium between the alcohol and aldehyde and conversion per pass is, therefore, only partial.

The alcohol is vaporized and passed up through the catalyst tube held vertically. The aldehyde is separated fractionally from the vapors issuing from the catalyst chamber, and the alcohol is returned to the vaporizer. Satisfactory conversions may be obtained with a catalyst tube 1 meter long, 25-30 mm in diameter, packed with the catalyst and heated throughout its length with resistance wire.[16]

The catalyst is prepared in the following manner: The calculated quantity of aqueous sodium hydroxide is added to a solution of copper nitrate; the precipitate of copper hydroxide is washed with warm water until the washings are neutral, and is filtered. The filter cake is spread out in a thin layer on pieces of 10 x 5 cm copper gauze of suitable mesh size. These pieces are then rolled into cylinders and charged into an 80 cm copper tube capable of holding about 30 of the rolls. The tube is heated to 300° and a stream of dry hydrogen is passed through it for eight hours. The tube is then allowed to cool while passage of a current of hydrogen is continued at a slow rate.

A catalyst consisting of finely divided copper coated with silver has been used to advantage. When this catalyst was employed, a certain amount of air was admitted with the alcohol vapors, and the dehydration was carried out at a somewhat higher temperature, namely between 300 and 350°, and under a pressure of 100 mm.[54]

A copper chromite catalyst gives good yields of aldehyde at 300-345° at atmospheric pressure, and retains its activity over long periods.[55] Glycol has been successfully dehydrated to glyoxal,[157] but complications arise due to side reactions with higher glycols.[158]

A three-step synthesis of *dl-glyceraldehyde* from glycerol consists in reacting glycerol with acetone for protecting two of the hydroxyl groups, oxidizing the resulting acetone-glycerol over a silver catalyst, and finally hydrolyzing the product. The overall yield is about 55%.[56]

Methacrolein, $CH_3=C(CH_3)CHO$, has been prepared in 95% yield by the air oxidation of methallyl alcohol.[57]

Butadiene has been obtained in 65% yield by dehydrating ethyl alcohol in the presence of 10% acetaldehyde using magnesium oxide, kaolin, diatomaceous earth, or tantalum oxide supported on diatomaceous earth as catalyst.[159]

The lower primary alcohols may be successfully dehydrogenated at atmospheric pressure, but higher alcohols, those yielding aldehydes boiling above 200°, should be dehydrogenated under reduced pressure. Geraniol and phenylethyl alcohol have been successfully dehydrogenated at atmospheric pressure. Unsaturated alcohols are converted to a large extent to the corresponding saturated aldehydes.

Dihydroxyacetone has been oxidized with excess cupric acetate to hydroxypyruvic aldehyde in 87% yield.[58]

Secondary monohydric alcohols yield the corresponding ketones when dehydrogenated by this method. The method has been successfully applied to the preparation of ketones from secondary aliphatic alcohols as well as from cyclohexanol and some of its homologs, certain keto alcohols and esters of β-hydroxyisohexanecarboxylic acid.

Finely subdivided silver, copper-silver and copper-zinc alloys and zinc oxide are also effective catalysts for the reaction.[17]

A modification of the method, which is suitable for the dehydrogenation of higher alcohols, consists in conducting a current of air through a suspension of finely subdivided copper in a heated solution of the alcohol in cumene containing quinoline and *m*-dinitrobenzene.[18]

Oxidation of Methyl Groups

Oxidation of a methyl group in an aliphatic compound to an aldehyde group may be successfully achieved only if the methyl group is sufficiently activated. Oxidation may be brought about in a satisfactory manner with selenium dioxide.[160] Freshly prepared and sublimed selenium dioxide should alone be used. Dioxane is the preferred solvent, but other solvents have been employed successfully.

Acetaldehyde is converted to glyoxol in 45% yield by treatment with 20% nitric acid at 40° in the presence of sodium nitrite.[161]

Reactive methyl groups may be condensed to oximes with nitric esters in the presence of alkali alcoholates.[162]

Diazonium compounds reacting with methyl ketones in the presence of 20% sodium hydroxide yield α-keto aldehydes.[163]

Rosemund Aldehyde Synthesis[19]

The reduction of carboxylic acids to aldehydes is, in general, impracticable although aromatic *o*-hydroxy acids form a notable exception and give the corresponding aldehydes in good yield on reduction.

Acid chlorides on the other hand, may be catalytically reduced to the corresponding aldehydes. If a highly active catalyst is employed, reduction does not generally stop at the aldehyde stage, but proceeds further and the alcohol corresponding to the acid chloride results. Reduction of the aldehyde is prevented by moderating the activity of the catalyst by the addition of a sulfur compound. This treatment, while preventing the reduction of the aldehyde, does not impair the ability of the catalyst to reduce the highly reactive acid chloride.

Finely divided palladium supported on barium sulfate is used as a catalyst. The sulfur-bearing compound used for moderating the activity of the catalyst is prepared by heating quinoline for several hours with 1/6 its weight of sulfur. The amount of regulator required is about 10 mg per gram of catalyst. In the production of mesityl aldehyde and other similar "hindered" compounds, the addition of the sulfur compound is not necessary, since there is then no danger of reducing the aldehyde.

The usual procedure is to add the catalyst to a solution of the acid chloride in xylene, cumene or tetralin, and to pass a current of hydrogen through the boiling solution under good agitation. An inverted condenser is used to return the solvent to the reaction vessel. Hydrogenation is continued until the theoretical quantity of hydrogen chloride has been evolved. After the completion of the reduction the mixture is acidified and the aldehyde is recovered by distillation with steam. Yields are low if the reaction is carried out without a solvent. The reaction time is 6 to 12 hours.

The solvent should be completely dry; its treatment with sodium or with Raney nickel at about 150° is to be highly recommended. Best yields are obtained when the reaction is carried out at the lowest possible temperature. A 5% palladium catalyst is generally used; its amount should be 5 to 10% of the acid chloride.

Keto groups, nitro groups and aliphatically bound halogens are not attacked.

The method is applicable to the preparation of both aliphatic and aromatic aldehydes. Hydroxyl groups, if present in the acid, must be protected by acetylation or carbomethoxylation. Phthalimide aldehydes have been prepared by this method from phthalimido acid chloride by reduction with palladium-barium sulfate catalyst in the presence of sulfurated quinoline.[59] Phosphorus and sulfur compounds, if formed in the course of the reduction, progressively decrease the activity of the catalyst, and it is desirable to remove them.[20] Nickel and platinum oxide have also been employed as catalysts for the reduction of acid chlorides to aldehydes.[60]

Acid chlorides the reduction of which would lead to ring closure cannot be reduced to aldehydes. Among such chlorides are succinyl chloride and adipic chloride. Basic acid chlorides, such as pyridinecarboxylic chloride, cannot be reduced to aldehydes in general, although di- and trichloropyridinecarboxylic chloride can be reduced to the corresponding aldehyde.

In a useful variation of Rosenmund reaction, reduction is effected in the presence of methyl silicate which converts the aldehyde to methyl acetal as rapidly as it is formed. This procedure makes possible the preparation of certain aldehydes, among them oleic, isovaleric and succinic aldehydes, which are formed in poor yield or are not formed at all by the usual Rosenmund procedure.[164]

Aldehydes from Olefinic Compounds

Acetals and ketals are capable of adding at the double bond of vinyl ethers in the presence of the boron trifluoride-ether complex to form the acetal of a 3-methoxy aldehyde:

$$CH_3CH(OCH_3)_2 + CH_2 = CHOCH_3 \xrightarrow{BF_3\text{-ether}} CH_3CH(OCH_3)CH_2CH(OCH_3)_2$$

The yields are generally very good. The method has been used for the preparation of vitamin A aldehyde from ionone.[117]

Aldehydes also condense with vinyl ethers in the presence of the boron trifluoride-ether complex forming cyclic acetals. Hydrolysis of the latter gives an unsaturated aldehyde with two more carbon atoms than the original aldehyde:

$$2C_3H_7CHO + CH_2 = CHOCH_3 \rightarrow$$

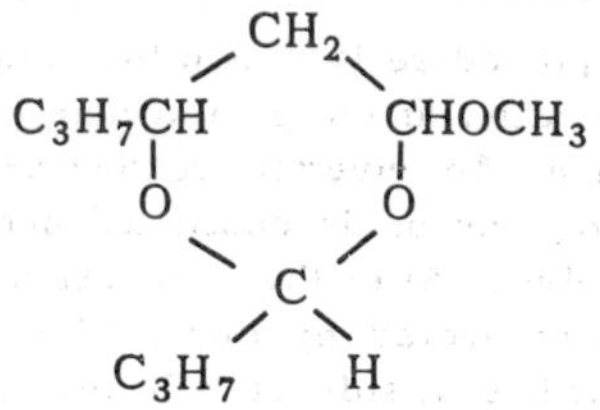

$$\xrightarrow{H_2O} C_3H_7CH = CHCHO + C_3H_7CHO + CH_3OH$$

Ethylenic compounds of the type RCOCH = CHCl react with alcoholic caustic at $-10°$ forming acetals:[118]

$$RCOCH = CHCl \xrightarrow[NaOH]{2R'OH} RCOCH_2CH(OR')_2$$

The ethylenic chlorides RCOCH = CHCl are formed through the condensation of acetylene with acyl halides RCOCl in the presence of aluminum chloride.

Ethylenic ethers ROCOCH = CHOR also react with alcohols, ROH, to form acetals $ROCOCH_2CH(OR)_2$. These ethylenic ethers are formed by the condensation of dialkyl carbonates with acetylene.[119]

Ethylenic ethers of the type $RR'C(OH)CH = CHOC_2H_5$ are readily hydrolyzed under the action of acids to half-acetals $RR'C(OH)CH_2CH(OH)OC_2H_5$. Ethylenic esters of the type in question are obtained by reducing the acetylenic ethers $RR'C(OH)C \equiv COC_2H_5$, which are in turn obtainable through the reaction of ketones RR'CO with ethoxyacetylenemagnesium halides.[120] This constitutes the *Jacobs-Arens-van Dorp method* for the preparation of aldehydes.

Certain unsaturated halo aldehydes with a highly reactive halogen are converted to dialdehydes on heating with caustic. α-Methyl-β-bromoacrolein, for example, gives methylmalonaldehyde by this treatment,[121] and α,β-dibromoacrolein gives bromomalondialdehyde.[122]

Aldehydes may be prepared from compounds with an ethylenic group at the end of a molecule by converting the compound first to a glycol then heating this with an acid:

$$RR'C = CH_2 \rightarrow RR'C(OH)CH_2OH \rightarrow RR'CHCHO$$

Conversion to glycol may be accomplished by oxidation with potassium permanganate, hydrogen peroxide, lead tetraacetate or with the silver benzoate-iodine complex.

Compounds in which the grouping $C = C(R)CH_2OH$ is present are isomerized readily to aldehydes under the influence of acids, the group undergoing transformation to $CHCH(R)CHO$.[123]

Compounds of the type $RCR'(OH)CH = CH_2$ are isomerized with acids to $RCR' = CHCH_2OH$; the latter may be oxidized to the corresponding aldehydes.

Compounds of the type $RR'C(OH)CH{=}CHX$ in which X is a halogen, hydroxyl, alkoxyl, or amino group undergo rearrangement to an aldehyde $RR'C = CHCHO$ under the influence of dilute acids. The method, which is applicable also to cyclic compounds, has been employed in the synthesis of vitamin A.[165]

Vinyl ethers may be rearranged to higher aldehydes; thus, when vapors of allyl vinyl ether are heated at 250°, they are converted to penten-(4)-1-al, and propionaldehyde results when vinyl methyl ether is heated at 280° in contact with aluminum borophosphate.[166]

Trifluoropropene ethers are converted to 3,3,3-trifluoropropanal by hydrogenolysis with Raney nickel:[167]

$$F_3CCH = CHOR + H_2 \rightarrow F_3CCH_2CHO + RH$$

1,2-Dichloroethylene, treated with 65% oleum, is converted to chloroacetaldehydesulfonic acid, $HSO_3CHClCHO$, in good yield.

Aldehydes by Cleavage of Unsaturated Heterocycles

Oxygen heterocycles in which unsaturated bonds are adjacent to the oxygen, and those in which OH, OR, NHR or halogens are attached to a carbon atom adjacent to the oxygen may be hydrolyzed to aldehydes.[73] δ-Hydroxyvaleraldehyde is obtained, for example, from 2-hydroxytetrahydropyran:[124]

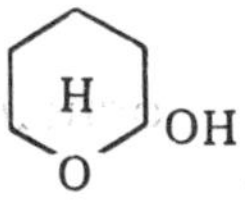

$$\rightarrow HOCH_2CH_2CH_2CH_2CHO$$

2-Hydroxytetrahydropyran may be prepared from tetrahydrofurfuralcohol by molecular rearrangement.

This method is of preparative importance, since many dihydropyran derivatives may be obtained by diene condensation from acrolein and various unsaturated compounds.

Thus, 2-alkoxy derivatives of 2,3-dihydroxypyran-(1,4) may be prepared through the condensation of vinyl ethers with acrolein:[125]

$$CH_2{=}CHCHO + CH_2 = CHOR \rightarrow$$

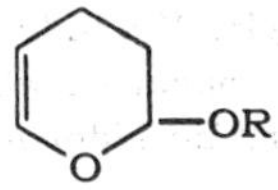

2-Alkoxy-4,5-dihydro-(1,2)-pyrans are hydrolyzed to 5-hydroxypentene-(2)al,

$$HOCH_2CH_2CH = CHCHO.$$[126]

Styrene, condensed with acrolein, gives 2-phenyl-2,3-dihydropyran which, on hydrolysis in dioxane solution with hot 10% sulfuric acid, gives 5-phenyl-5-hydroxypentanal-(1):[127]

$$CH_2 = CHCHO + CH_2 = CHC_6H_5 \quad \rightarrow \quad \underset{O}{\bigcirc}\!\!-C_6H_5$$

$$\overset{H_2O}{\rightarrow} \quad C_6H_5CH(OH)CH_2CH_2CH_2CHO$$

The dimer of acrolein, 2-formyl-2,3-dihydropyran, is converted by dilute mineral acids to α-hydroxyadipaldehyde:[128]

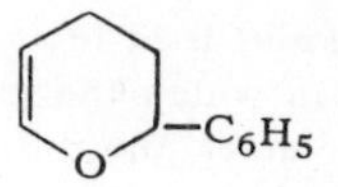

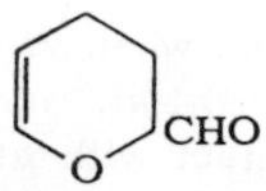

$$\underset{O}{\bigcirc}\!\!CHO \quad \overset{H_2O}{\rightarrow} \quad OCHCH_2CH_2CH_2CH(OH)CHO$$

p-Thioxene, treated with aqueous-alcoholic hydrochloric acid, is converted to hydroxyethylmercaptoacetaldehyde:[129]

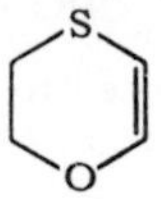

$$\underset{O}{\overset{S}{\bigcirc}} \quad \overset{H_2O}{\rightarrow} \quad HOCH_2CH_2SCH_2CHO$$

Furans are not cleaved, as a rule, by boiling alcoholic hydrochloric acid. 2-Methylfuran (sylvan) behaves exceptionally and is readily converted to levulenic aldehyde acetal by boiling with alcoholic hydrochloric acid.

2,5-Dialkoxy-2,5-dihydrofurans yield maleic and fumaric dialdehydes on mild hydrolysis; these are converted on reduction to succindialdehyde:[74]

$$\underset{RO\ \overset{|}{C}H \quad \overset{|}{C}HOR}{\overset{CH=CH}{\diagdown \diagup}} \quad \rightarrow \quad OCHCH = CH\ CHO \quad \overset{H_2}{\rightarrow} \quad OCHCH_2CH_2CHO$$

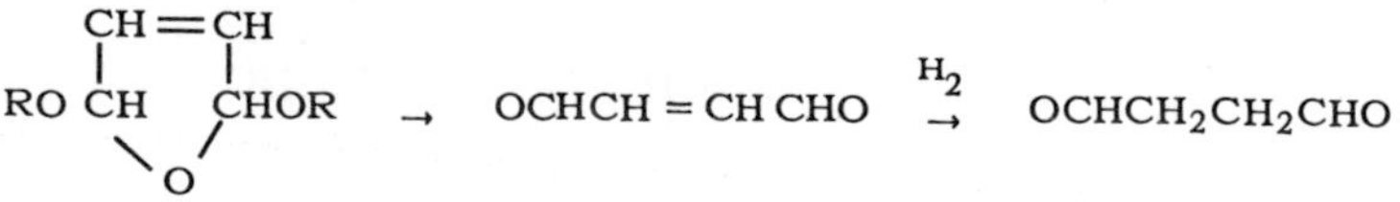

Substituted succinic dialdehydes have been prepared by this method from derivatives of dimethoxydihydrofuran. 2,5-Dialkoxy-2,5-dihydrofurans are obtained by treating furans in alcoholic solution with bromine.[130] The 2,5-dimethoxy derivatives have been prepared in good yield by anodic oxidation of furan in methanolic solution in the presence of ammonium bromide. Electrolysis is effected at $-22°$ under 5 volts potential and a current of 3 amperes.[131] These dialkyldihydrofurans are capable of adding another molecule of alcohol at $0°$ in the presence of hydrobromic acid to form 2,3,5-trialkoxytetrahydrofurans which, when heated at $70°$ for 20 minutes with $0.1N$ aqueous hydrochloric acid, give o-alkylmalic aldehydes.[130] They are capable also of adding hypobromous acid to form bromohydrins which, upon reduction in potassium hydroxide solution and hydrolysis, give malic aldehyde:

$$\underset{C_2H_5O\overset{|}{C}H \quad \overset{|}{C}HOC_2H_5}{\overset{CH=CH}{\diagdown \diagup O}} + HOBr \quad \rightarrow \quad \underset{C_2H_5O\overset{|}{C}H \quad \overset{|}{C}HOC_2H_5}{\overset{BrCH-CHOH}{\diagdown \diagup O}} \quad \overset{H_2}{\rightarrow}$$

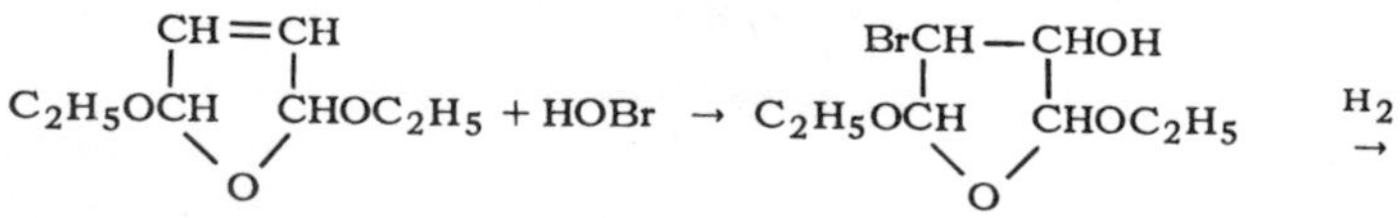

$$
\begin{array}{c}
\underset{|}{CH_2}\!-\!\underset{|}{CHOH} \\
C_2H_5OCH \quad CHOC_2H_5 \\
\diagdown \;O\; \diagup
\end{array}
\qquad
\begin{array}{c}
H_2O\!-\!HCl \\
\rightarrow
\end{array}
\qquad
OCHCH_2CH(OH)CHO
$$

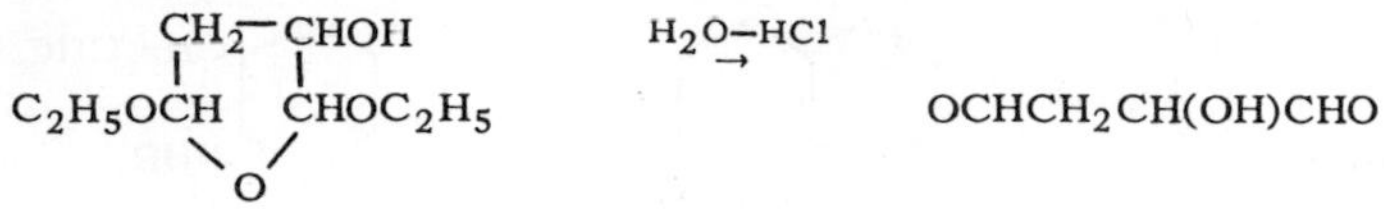

Caution should be exercised in working with 2,5-dialkoxy-3-hydroxy-4-halotetrahydro-furans, as these compounds may decompose violently when distilled.

Furan gives the cyclic acetal of maleic dialdehyde when treated with an alcoholic solution of bromine.[168]

$$
\begin{array}{c}
CH\!-\!CH \\
\|\quad\| \\
CH\quad CH \\
\diagdown O \diagup
\end{array}
\quad
\begin{array}{c}
Br_2 \\
\rightarrow
\end{array}
\quad
\begin{array}{c}
CH\!=\!CH \\
|\quad\; | \\
BrCH\quad CHBr \\
\diagdown O \diagup
\end{array}
\quad
\begin{array}{c}
2\ ROH \\
\rightarrow
\end{array}
\quad
\begin{array}{c}
CH\!=\!CH \\
|\quad\; | \\
ROCH\quad CHOR \\
\diagdown O \diagup
\end{array}
$$

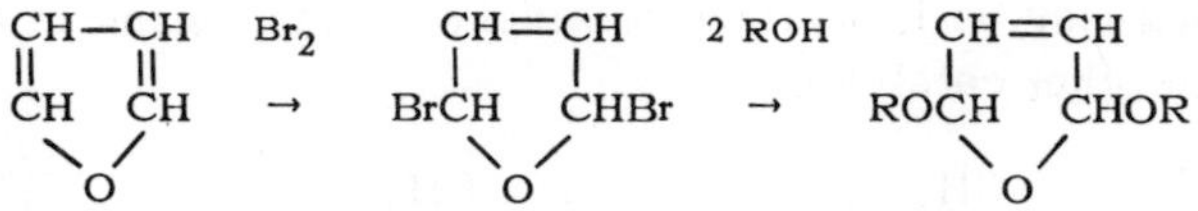

Hydrogenation of the acetal results in the formation of succinaldehyde, and treatment with hypochlorous acid followed by reduction results in the formation of maleic dialdehyde.[169]

Mucochloric acid, $\overline{ClC = CClCH(OH)O.CO}$, is formed through the action of chlorine on furfural, and *mucobromic acid* results similarly by brominating furfural.[170]

Furan is converted to a *cis-trans* mixture of 2,5-diacetoxy-2,5-dihydrofuran in 70% yield when subjected to the action of lead tetraacetate in solution in a mixture of acetic acid and acetic anhydride. Hydrolysis of the product yields maleic dialdehyde,[171] while pyrolysis at 480-500° under 10 atm followed by hydrolysis yields succinic acid half-aldehyde.[172]

Partially reduced nitrogen heterocycles may also be converted to aldehydes by ring fission. Thus, dihydropyridine, which is obtained from pyridine by reduction with sodium and methanol, may be hydrolyzed to glutaraldehyde in 40% yield.[132]

Adducts of chlorosulfonic ethyl ester or of sulfur dioxide with pyridine may be hydrolyzed with alkalies to the sodio derivative of 4-hydroxybutadiene-1-aldehyde. The free aldehyde may be isolated by extracting the acidified solution of the sodium salt with ether and recovering the dissolved aldehyde by evaporating off the ether.[133] An aldehyde is formed from isoquinoline by this method which, however, dimerized to 2-(o-formylphenyl)-5-naphthaldehyde:[134]

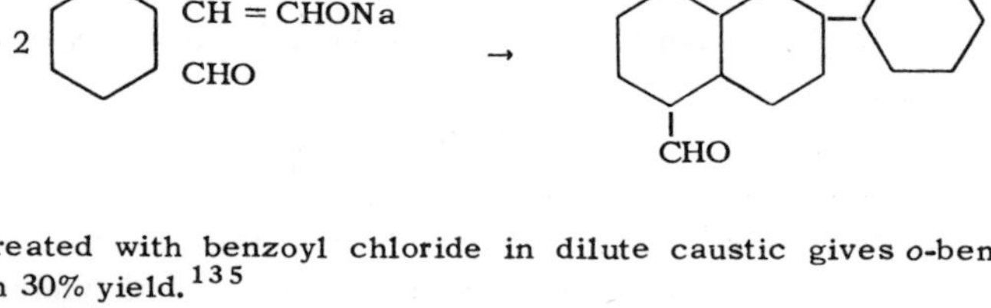

Quinoline treated with benzoyl chloride in dilute caustic gives o-benzoylaminocin-namaldehyde in 30% yield.[135]

The simple quaternary ammonium bases derived from quinoline and isoquinoline undergo rearrangement to the unstable pseudoammonium bases and these, as cyclic aldehyde ammonias, undergo the reactions of aldehyde ammonias:[136]

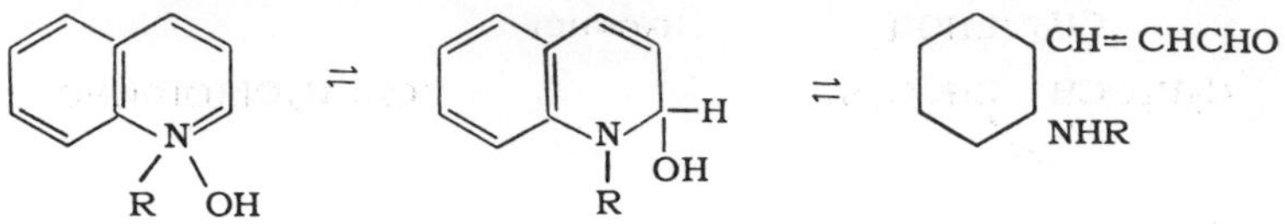

Tetrahydroisoquinoline derivatives of the type of hydrastinine behave similarly.[137]

Aldehydes through the Isomerization of Oxides

Certain oxides may be isomerized to aldehydes by heating in the presence of zinc chloride or other catalyst:

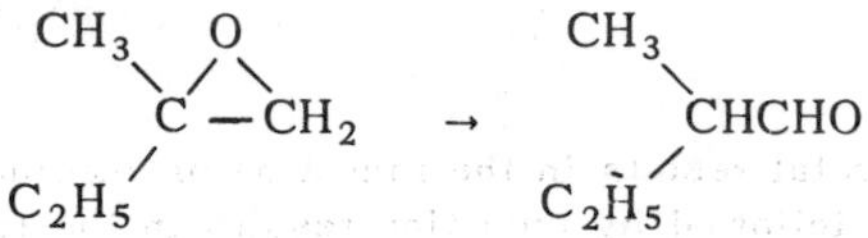

Ethylene oxide may be isomerized to acetaldehyde by heating with sulfuric acid. Glycols and ethers derived from them may be directly converted to aldehydes by heating with anhydrous formaldehyde or oxalaldehyde.[29] Transformation of a,a-diphenylethylene oxide to diphenylacetaldehyde takes place on short heating with concentrated hydrogen sulfite solution.[173] Propylene oxide has been converted to propionaldehyde in good yield catalytically at 280° using potassium alum containing 2% vanadium oxide as catalyst.[174]

Epoxides are converted to aldehyde acetals or enol acetates when they are heated with acetic anhydride.[175]

Glycidic acids may be converted to aldehydes by decarboxylation in the presence of acids:

$$RCH \overset{O}{\overset{\diagup\diagdown}{-}} CHCOOH \quad \rightarrow \quad RCH_2CHO + CO_2$$

This method is of special value since glycidic esters may be prepared from carbonyl compounds by condensation with chloroacetic ester in the presence of sodium alcoholate or sodium amide:[138]

$$RR'CO + ClCH_2COOR \quad \rightarrow \quad RR'C \overset{O}{\overset{\diagup\diagdown}{-}} CHCOOR'' + HCl$$

The method thus makes possible the preparation of aldehydes with one more carbon atom from aldehydes or ketones.[139]

The glycidic ester synthesis is applicable in general to all aliphatic and aromatic aldehydes and ketones; it is applicable even to a,β-unsaturated ketones and Mannich bases. Ketones generally give better yields than aldehydes. Yields vary considerably, but it would appear that failure to work under the optimum conditions for the reaction often account for low yields.[140]

Conversion of glycid esters to aldehydes is effected in two steps: First the ester group is saponified with caustic, then the glycidic acid is decarboxylated by heating with dilute hydrochloric acid.[141] Decarboxylation may also be accomplished by heating the acid under vacuum, preferably in the presence of copper or copper chromite.[142]

Certain glycols containing a primary alcohol group may be dehydrated to aldehydes. Glycols of the type $RR'C(OH)CH_2OH$ have been converted to aldehydes $RR'CHCHO$ simply by heating with dilute acids.[29] Glycols of the type $RCH(OH)CH_2OH$ are transformed into aldehydes somewhat less readily and give ketones and unsaturated alcohols in addition to the aldehydes.[176] The transformation may be brought about catalytically.[177]

Monoglycol ethers, $RR'C(OH)CH_2OR'$, which are readily formed from epoxides by the Grignard reaction, give substituted acetaldehydes $RR'CHCHO$ in 50 to 60% yield by boiling with anhydrous oxalic or formic acid for 3 to 4 hours, a procedure which has been employed for the preparation of intermediates in the synthesis of vitamin A.[178]

Glycols of the type $R'R''C(OH)CH(R)OH$ in which both R′ and R″ are aromatic residues, may be converted to aldehydes $RR'R''CCHO$ by thermal-catalytic treatment.[179]

Chlorohydrins and 1,2-dihalo compounds are converted to aldehydes when heated at 150 to 220° with lead oxide.[180]

Aldehydes through Oxidative Cleavage of Glycols

The bond between adjacent primary or secondary carbon atoms each bearing a hydroxyl group may be ruptured by oxidation with lead tetraacetate:[143]

$$RCH(OH)CH(OH)R' \xrightarrow{Pb(OCOCH_3)_4} \begin{matrix} RCHO \\ | \\ RCHO \end{matrix}\!\!>\!Pb(OCOCH_3)_2$$

$$\rightarrow RCHO + R'CHO + Pb(OCOCH_3)_2$$

This is a valuable method often used for the preparation of aldehydes and ketones.

Oxidation is usually effected with the calculated amount of lead tetraacetate dissolved in benzene or acetic acid. The temperature should not be allowed to rise above 60° in the course of the reaction. The fact that the lead acetate formed in the reaction is insoluble in benzene or chloroform may be taken advantage of in isolating the aldehyde formed. The reaction has been carried out successfully in aqueous media despite the fact that water causes the hydrolysis of lead tetraacetate.[144]

Amino alcohols in which the amino and hydroxyl groups are attached to adjacent carbon atoms, may also be oxidatively cleaved under the action of lead tetraacetate:

$$RCH(OH)CH(NH_2)R' \rightarrow RCHO + R'CH{=}NH$$

The imino compound formed is further oxidized to a nitrile $R'CN$.

Lead tetraacetate is best prepared in the laboratory as follows: 600 gm red lead (lead tetroxide, Pb_3O_4) are added gradually through a sieve to 1.5 lit acetic acid heated at 55 to 60°. Fresh quantities of the oxide are added only after the red color of the oxide previously added has disappeared. After the addition of all the oxide, the mass is cooled and the crystals are filtered and washed with a little acetic acid. The solid is dissolved in 200 cc glacial acetic acid heated at 50°. The tetraacetate separates in the crystalline form on cooling. It is used in the form of the acetic acid-moist paste. The lead tetraacetate content of the paste is determined iodometrically.

Sodium bismuthate has been used instead of lead tetraacetate for the oxidative cleavage of glycols.[145]

Cleavage of glycols to carbonyl compounds may be accomplished by use of periodic acid.[146] This reagent offers an advantage over lead tetraacetate in that it can be used in aqueous media. It may also be used in solution in dioxane, acetic acid and *tert*-butyl alcohol.[147] 9,10-Dihydroxystearic acid has been converted to azelaaldehyde,[148] and 3,4,5,6-diacetonemannite has been converted to diacetone arabinose[149] by use of this reagent.

In *Grundman's method* an acid chloride is converted to a diazoketone by reaction with diazomethane, then successively to an acetoxy ketone and to a glycol by reaction with glacial acetic acid and subsequent reduction of the keto group with simultaneous hydrolysis. The aldehyde is obtained by oxidative cleavage of the glycol with lead tetraacetate or periodic acid:

$$RCOCl \rightarrow RCOCHN_2 \rightarrow RCOCH_2OCOCH_3$$
$$\rightarrow RCH(OH)CH_2OH \rightarrow RCHO$$

In spite of the complexity of the procedure, the yield of aldehyde is generally satisfactory. The method is applicable to aliphatic as well as aromatic acyl chlorides. Sensitive aldehydes, including many olefinic aldehydes and arylacetaldehydes, may be prepared by its use, although α,β-unsaturated aldehydes cannot be prepared by this route because α,β-unsaturated acyl halides react additively with a second molecule of diazomethane giving pyrazoline derivatives.

The procedure followed in preparing the acetoxy ketone is as follows: The diazo ketone is added in portions not exceeding five grams into glacial acetic acid initially warmed to 60 to 70° and maintained at this temperature during the reaction by external cooling. Five to seven hundred cubic centimeters of acetic acid are used per mole of diazoketone. After all the diazoketone has been added and nitrogen evolution has subsided, 0.1 molal equivalent of potassium acetate is added, the temperature is raised slowly to boiling and boiling is continued for an hour.

The preparation of 3-benzyloxy-4-methoxyphenylacetaldehyde may be cited as an example of the procedure followed in oxidizing the glycol.[181] To a solution of 1.5 gm of the corresponding glycol in 75 cc dry benzene are added 2.2 gm of lead tetraacetate in small portions. After cooling the reaction mixture, 75 cc of anhydrous ether are added, the solution is filtered and washed successively with aqueous sodium bicarbonate and water, dried with anhydrous sodium sulfate, and the ether is finally evaporated off to recover the aldehyde.

In *Hershberg's method*[182] a Grignard compound RMgX is made to react with allyl chloride to give $RCH_2CH=CH_2$, which is converted to a glycol $RCH_2CH(OH)CH_2OH$ with benzoyl peroxide, and the glycol is oxidized to RCH_2CHO. This method is suitable for the preparation of unstable aldehydes.

Other Methods of Preparation of Aldehydes

Aldehydes may be obtained in the form of their phenylhydrazones through the reduction of iminoethers, RC(:NH)OR′, with sodium amalgam in the presence of phenyl hydrazine. The aldehyde may be freed from the hydrazone by hydrolysis. If the reduction is carried out in the absence of phenylhydrazine, the yield of aldehyde is low. Other substituted hydrazines or semicarbazones may be used instead of phenylhydrazine.[21]

A method well adapted for the production of hydroaromatic aldehydes consists in reducing amidines of hydroaromatic compounds with sodium and alcohol.[61]

Aldehydes have been prepared through the reduction of the carbazole amide and diphenylene amide of acids with lithium aluminum hydride.[62] The reduction of N-methylanilides of acids with lithium aluminum hydride has also resulted in the formation of aldehydes.[63] The method appears to be of general applicability.

Ortho esters of carboxylic acids have been reduced to the corresponding acetals by boiling with lithium alumium hydride for three hours in a benzene-ether mixture.[183]

Perfluorinated nitriles and cyclopropane nitrile are converted by lithium aluminum hydride to the corresponding aldehydes in moderate yield.[184]

Aldehydes may be prepared from *acids* by distilling under reduced pressure a mixture of the calcium salt of the acid with calcium formate.[64] A more effective method consists in passing a mixture in molecular proportions of the vapors of the acid and formic acid over titanium dioxide heated at 250-300°. Aldehydes may be obtained by this method from acetic acid and its homologs in yields of at least 50% of theoretical. Thoria may also be used as a catalyst, though it gives lower yields of aldehyde.[22] Good yields have been obtained by use of manganous oxide. The method has assumed commercial importance. It is applicable to the preparation of arylaliphatic aldehydes.

Esters of α-hydroxy and α-amino acids may be reduced to aldehydes. Reduction may be carried out catalytically in the presence of platinum hydroxide.[185]

Aldehydes with one carbon atom less may be prepared from acids by a number of methods.

Braun's method involves bromination of the acid followed by conversion to the acid chloride, replacement of the chlorine with the azido group by reaction with sodium azide, finally rearrangement to an isocyano compound and hydrolysis:

$$RCH_2COOH \rightarrow RCHBrCOOH \rightarrow RCHBrCOCl$$

$$\xrightarrow{NaN_3} RCHBrCON_3 \rightarrow RCHBrN=CO$$

$$\xrightarrow{H_2O} RCHBrNH_2 \rightarrow RCHO$$

Blaise and Guerin's method[23] consists essentially in converting the acid to the hydroxy derivative by bromination followed by treatment with alcoholic potassium hydroxide, and distilling the resulting hydroxy acid. Undecaldehyde may be obtained from lauric acid by this method in 62% yield. Conversion of the hydroxy acid to aldehyde proceeds quite rapidly in this case in the temperature range 190 to 200°.

A satisfactory method for the conversion of the hydroxy acid to aldehyde consists in subjecting to steam distillation a mixture of the hydroxy acid with dilute sulfuric acid and lead peroxide.[65] Conversion to aldehyde may be effected also by treating the acid with sodium methylate and distilling the resulting methoxy acid.[66] Yields of 90% are obtained with hydroxy acids containing a chain of five or more carbon atoms. α,α-Diethoxy-ω,ω'-dicarboxylic acids give aldehydes in very low yield. Sodium trichlorolactate, $Cl_3CCH(OH)COONa$, behaves abnormally and gives Cl_2CHCHO.

α-Hydroxy acids may be converted to aldehydes by the action of the calculated amount of lead tetraacetate in benzene or acetic acid solution at about 40 to 60°.[186]

α-Keto acids which do not tend to enolize may, generally, be converted to aldehydes by decarboxylation, although the reaction does not proceed simply because of the great reactivity of aliphatic keto acids. Better results are obtained with the anils of α-keto acids.[187]

Transformation of the hydroxy acid to the aldehyde may be carried out via the

```
           O.CO
          /    \
lactide, RCH      CHR,
          \    /
           CO.O
```

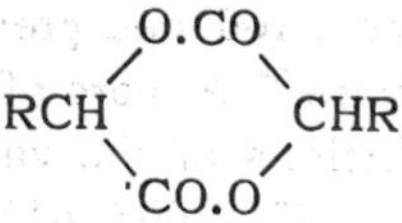

which may be obtained by treatment of the acid with sulfuric acid. The lactide is readily converted to the aldehyde when it is distilled.

Amino acids $RCH(NH_2)COOH$ may also be converted to aldehydes with one carbon atom less, by treating the acid with sodium hypochlorite and heating the sodium salt of the resulting chloroamino acid with water.[24]

These methods are of importance in that they offer the means for passing from an aldehyde or acid to the next lower homolog in the series.

Ozonation of olefins and subsequent treatment with water constitutes another degradative method leading to the formation of aldehydes.[25] Nonyl and azelaic aldehydes may be obtained by this treatment from oleic acid:

$$CH_3(CH_2)_7CH = CH(CH_2)_7COOH \rightarrow CH_3(CH_2)_7CHO + OCH(CH_2)_7COOH$$

Best yields of aldehydes are obtained when ozonization is carried out rapidly at the lowest possible temperature, sometimes as low at −78°, and the ozonide is reduced immediately after its formation.

The reaction of hydrazoic acid with unsaturated compounds results in the rupture of carbon to carbon double bonds with the entrance of a nitrogen atom between the carbon atoms, and the formation of a Schiff base, often in excellent yield:[188]

$$RR'C = CHR'' + HN_3 \rightarrow RR'C = N{-}CH_2R' + N_2$$

Oximes result when nitro olefins are reduced:

$$(CH_3)_2C = CHNO_2 \xrightarrow{H_2} (CH_3)_2CHCH = NOH$$

The oxime is converted to the aldehyde by hydrolysis with acid. Since olefins of this type may be prepared from carbonyl compounds and nitromethane, this offers the possibility of passing from a carbonyl compound to an aldehyde with an additional carbon atom.[26] The method is also applicable to certain saturated aliphatic and cycloaliphatic nitro compounds. The carbonyl compound may be obtained in good yield through the reduction of the nitro compound in the cold with stannous chloride and concentrated hydrochloric acid. The aldehyde is obtained upon steam distilling the resulting product.[27] Hydrogen sulfide may also serve well as the reducing agent in this reaction. The procedure is to add the sodium salt of the nitro compound to dilute sulfuric acid, and at the same time to pass a current of hydrogen sulfide through the solution.

The sodium derivative of nitroparaffins of the type RCH_2NO_2, added to a cold dilute solution of sulfuric or hydrochloric acid, are converted to aldehydes:[67]

$$2RCH = NOONa + 2HCl \rightarrow 2RCHO + N_2O + 2NaCl + H_2O$$

Ketones with a reactive methylene group may be converted to keto aldehydes by condensation with formic ester in the presence of metallic sodium:[68]

$$CH_3COCH_2CH_3 + HCOOC_2H_5 \rightarrow CH_3CO\underset{\overset{|}{CHO}}{C}HCH_3 + HOC_2H_5$$

Reaction proceeds in the cold. Yields range 50 to 80% of the theoretical. The keto aldehyde is often obtained as the sodium salts of the enolic hydroxymethylene form. The point of attachment of the formyl group in unsymmetrical ketones cannot be predicted.[69]

Hydrogen and carbon monoxide may be added simultaneously at ethylenic double bonds to form aldehydes:[125]

$$\begin{matrix} \diagdown \\ \diagup \end{matrix}C = C\begin{matrix} \diagup \\ \diagdown \end{matrix} + CO \rightarrow \begin{matrix} \diagdown \\ \diagup \end{matrix}C\underset{CO}{----}C\begin{matrix} \diagup \\ \diagdown \end{matrix} \xrightarrow{H_2} \begin{matrix} \diagdown \\ \diagup \end{matrix}C\underset{CHO}{----}CH\begin{matrix} \diagup \\ \diagdown \end{matrix}$$

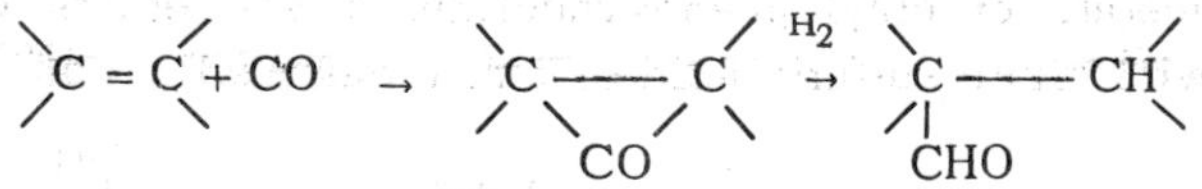

The reaction is carried out at 120-160° under 100-200 atm pressure in the presence of the cobalt catalyst employed in the Fischer-Tropsch coal hydrogenation process. Straight-chain olefins yield 40 to 60% of straight-chain aldehydes. The formyl group never adds to a tertiary carbon. Addition of the formyl group to a carbon atom is hindered by an adjacent tertiary carbon, and is completely prevented by a quaternary carbon, but an isolated tertiary carbon atom does not exert any effect. The ethylenic body generally undergoes isomerization during the reaction. This method is considered in greater detail under chapter 17.

Aminoaldehydes may best be obtained from chlorinated aldehydes by first transforming these to chloroacetals, then replacing the chlorine with an amino group by treatment with ammonia, and finally hydrolyzing the amino acetal with a dilute acid.

The greater resistance of acetals to alkaline reagents is utilized also in preparing acetylenic aldehydes from brominated aldehydes, conversion of the brominated acetal to an acetylenic acetal being accomplished by the conventional method involving dehydrohalogenation with caustic, bromination and a second dehydrohalogenation. The acetylenic acetal is converted to the corresponding aldehyde by heating with a dilute mineral acid.[28]

The sensitive glyceraldehyde acetal is converted to the corresponding aldehyde in 80% yield by the action of dilute sulfuric acid under mild conditions:[70]

Dihydroxy aldehydes may be prepared from olefin acetals by oxidation with potassium permanganate, followed by hydrolysis with a dilute mineral acid.

Another method which renders possible the synthesis of aldehydes with increasing number of carbon atoms is based on the selective hydrogenation of olefinic aldehydes resulting from aldol type condensation and dehydration.

Aldehydes result from the reaction of alkylmagnesium halides with formic esters or with dialkyl formamides:[30]

$$HCOOC_2H_5 + RMgX \rightarrow RCHO + XMgOC_2H_5$$

$$HCON(C_2H_5)_2 + RMgX \rightarrow RCHO + XMgN(C_2H_5)_2$$

The second reaction forms the basis of Bouveault's synthesis.[31]

Acetals result when alkyl magnesium halides are made to react with orthoformic esters:[32]

$$HC(OC_2H_5)_3 + RMgX \rightarrow RCH(OC_2H_5)_2 + XMgOC_2H_5$$

The maximum yields of aldehyde obtained through this reaction, which is the basis of *Bodroux-Tschitschibabin synthesis*, do not exceed 25% of theoretical. The method is applicable to acetylenic Grignard compounds.

Glycol monoalkyl ethers result from the reaction of Grignard reagents with ethyl ethoxyacetate or ethyl phenoxyacetate. These ethers yield aldehydes when treated with dilute sulfuric acid or anhydrous oxalic acid:[71]

$$C_2H_5OCH_2COOC_2H_5 \xrightarrow{RMgX} C_2H_5OCH_2CR_2(OH)$$

$$\xrightarrow{H_2SO_4} [C_2H_5OCH=CR_2] \rightarrow [R_2C=CHOH] \rightarrow R_2CHCHO$$

Yields in the first step range 40 to 80%, and in the second step 50 to 80%. Unsymmetrical dialkyl derivatives of acetaldehyde may be prepared by starting with an α-keto ether:[72]

$$RCOCH_2OC_2H_5 \xrightarrow{RMgX} RR'C(OH)CH_2OC_2H_5 \rightarrow RR'CHCHO$$

Phenyliminoformic ethers reacting with Grignard reagents give aldehyde imines:

$$C_6H_5N=CHOC_2H_5 + RMgX \rightarrow C_6H_5N=CHR + C_2H_5OMgX.$$

Kolbe electrolytic synthesis has been successfully applied by Wohl and Schweitzer to the synthesis of diacetals from acetal acids. The diacetals are readily converted to dialdehydes by hydrolysis. Succinaldehyde has been prepared by this method from the potassium salt of β-diethoxy propionic acid, $(C_2H_5O)_2CHCH_2COOK$. Adipic aldehyde has been obtained similarly from potassium γ-diethoxybutyrate.[33]

Lithium in organolithium compounds may be replaced with the formyl group by reaction with methylphenylformamide and hydrolysis of the resulting addition compound:[150]

$$RLi + OCHN(CH_3)(C_6H_5) \rightarrow RCH(OLi)N(CH_3)(C_6H_5) \xrightarrow{H_2O}$$

$$RCHO + C_6H_5NHCH_3 + LiOH$$

Aldehydes may be prepared from amides with a hydroxyl group in the α-position by the Hofmann transformation followed by hydrolysis:[151]

$$RCH(OH)CONHBr \xrightarrow{CH_3ONa} RCH(OH)NHCOOCH_3 \xrightarrow{H_2O} RCHO$$

Aldehydes may also be obtained from amides with a halogen in α-position, or with an ethylenic bond in α,β-position by the same method:

$$RCH = CHCONHBr \xrightarrow{NaOH} RCH = CHN = CO \xrightarrow{CH_3OH}$$

$$RCH = CHNHCOOCH_3 \xrightarrow{H_2O} RCH_2CHO + H_2NCOOCH_3$$

Substituted malonic esters may be converted to aldehydes via the diazides by the Curtius rearrangement and hydrolysis:

$$RCH_2CH(CON_3)_2 \rightarrow RCHCH(NCO)_2 \xrightarrow{H_2O} RCH_2CHO$$

Hydrogenolysis of thiol esters yields aldehydes or alcohols:[203]

$$RCOSR' \xrightarrow{H + Ni} RCHO \text{ or } RCH_2OH$$

The use of freshly prepared Raney nickel apparently leads to the formation of alcohols. The use of a catalyst which has been partially deactivated by refluxing with acetone gives aldehydes in good yield.[204] The ratio of catalyst to thiol ester should be 10:1. Thiol esters may be reduced to aldehydes with lithium aluminum hydride.[189] Thiol esters are readily prepared by the reaction of acyl chlorides with thiols in the presence of pyridine.

Nitriles and tertiary amides, treated with ¼ molal proportion of lithium hydride, yield an aldimine or an amino alcohol derivative, which on hydrolysis are converted to aldehydes:[190]

$$RCN + LiAlH_4 \rightarrow RCH = NLiAlH_3 \xrightarrow{H_2O} RCHO$$

$$RCONR'_2 + LiAlH_4 \rightarrow RCH(OLiAlH_3)NR'_2 \xrightarrow{H_2O} RCHO$$

N-Methylanilides are especially suitable for the reaction.

In a few instances the nature of the solvent, the concentration of the reactants and temperature are factors of importance, but in most cases no special precautions need to be observed. The difficultly accessible aldehydes

$$C_6H_5(CH = CH)_nCHO, \quad n = 2,4,6,$$

and the unstable aldehydes *p*-methylaminobutyraldehyde, δ-methylaminovaleraldehyde and β-(α-piperidyl) propionaldehyde have been prepared by this method.[191]

KETONES

Formation by Oxidation of Secondary Alcohols

Ketones may be regarded as the products of oxidation of secondary alcohols and may be obtained through the oxidation of such alcohols in the same manner as aldehydes are obtained from primary alcohols. The method is of limited preparative interest, since few secondary alcohols are available or are capable of direct synthesis.

Among the polyhydric alcohols, simple glycols such as ethylmethylglycol, $C_2H_5CH(OH)CH(OH)CH_3$, are oxidized to diketones by bromine water. Methylphenylglycol is converted to the corresponding diketone by heating at 100° with nitric acid of sp. g. 1.30. A keto alcohol results when oxidation is carried out at 0°.[34]

Mannite is converted to fructose with nitric acid or with 3-5% hydrogen peroxide in concentrated ferrous sulfate solution. Aldoses are oxidized to osones by the latter reagent, although with galactose oxidation proceeds beyond the osone stage. The best method for the conversion of carbohydrates and the corresponding polyhydric alcohols to ketoses consists in treatment with lead dioxide and dilute hydrochloric acid of sp. g. 1.095 with good cooling.

Aromatic keto alcohols, the so-called acyloins, are readily oxidized to diketones by treatment at 100° with nitric acid of sp. g. 1.41.[35] Benzoin is converted to benzil on treatment by this reagent for 1 to 2 hours. Anisoin behaves exceptionally and is converted to anisic acid, $CH_3OC_6H_4COOH$. The diketone is obtained when onisoin in solution in 70% aqueous alcohol is treated with Fehling's solution, i.e., a mixture of a concentrated solution of copper sulfate, Rochelle salt and alkali.[36] Benzofuroin is converted to benzofuril by this treatment, a result notable in that it cannot be achieved by many of the other available methods of oxidation.

Secondary alcohols may be converted to ketones by the action of N-halo-amides and imides. Androsteronediol has been converted to androsteronedione by this method.[75] The solvent plays an important role in this reaction. Bromo-amides and -imides have been found to react most readily in *tert*-butyl alcohol.[76]

Diphenylphenylethylcarbinol has been converted to ω-phenylpropiophenone by treatment at 40° for 24 hours with 30% hydrogen peroxide solution in glacial acetic acid containing a little 70% perchloric acid:[211]

$$(C_6H_5)_2C(OH)CH_2CH_2C_6H_5 \quad \rightarrow \quad (C_6H_5)_2C(OOH)CH_2CH_2C_6H_5$$

$$\rightarrow \quad C_6H_5COCH_2CH_2C_6H_5 + C_6H_5OH$$

The method has been employed for the purpose of determining the relative ease of removal of aromatic groups.

Conversion of 1,3-diphenyl-2-acetoxy-1,3-dione to the corresponding 1,2,3-tri-one has been brought about by bromination followed by heating under reduced pressure:[212]

$$C_6H_5COCH(OCOCH_3)COC_6H_5 \quad \rightarrow \quad C_6H_5COCBr(OCOCH_3)COC_6H_5$$

$$\rightarrow \quad C_6H_5COCOCOC_6H_5 + CH_3COBr$$

Keto and aldehyde alcohols, when heated with phenylhydrazine, are converted to the hydrozones of dicarbonyl compounds by a dehydrogenation process involving the reduction of a molecule of hydrazine to aniline and ammonia:

$$\overset{|}{HOCH} - \overset{|}{CO} + 3C_6H_5NHNH_2 \quad \rightarrow \quad C_6H_5NHN = \overset{|}{C} - \overset{|}{C} = NNHC_6H_5$$

$$+ \ C_6H_5NH_2 + NH_3 + 2H_2O$$

The diketones or ketoaldehydes are obtained from the resulting phenylhydra-zones by hydrolysis with a strong mineral acid. The method is of special interest in the chemistry of sugars. The isolation of the carbonyl compounds presents some difficulties. It is usually accomplished by converting them to their lead derivatives.[37]

Oxanthrone, $C_6H_4 \overset{\displaystyle CH(OH)}{\underset{\displaystyle CO}{\diagup \diagdown}} C_6H_4$, is converted to anthraquinone oxime,

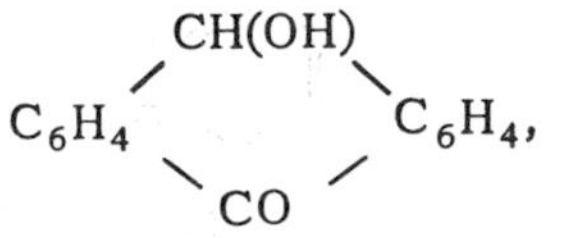

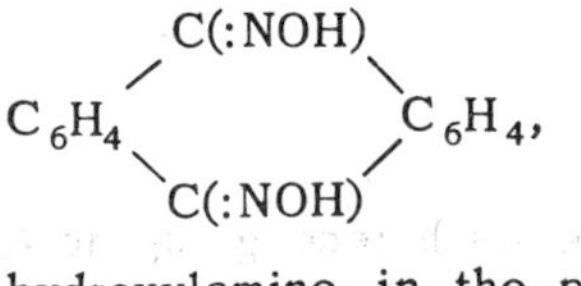

$C_6H_4 \overset{\displaystyle C(:NOH)}{\underset{\displaystyle C(:NOH)}{\diagup \diagdown}} C_6H_4$, on heating an alcoholic solution of the compound with

hydroxylamine in the presence of a little hydrochloric acid. Triphenylvinyl alcohol is oxidized similarly by this treatment.

Keto acids may be prepared from some hydroxy acids by oxidation with cold 4% potassium permanganate. Lactic, mandelic and *o*-nitromandelic acids may be converted to the corresponding keto acids by this reagent. The method fails with *p*-nitromandelic acid.[38]

Nitric acid may be employed successfully with monobasic hexon acids, rhamnose and gluconic acids. Mandelic acid may also be oxidized to benzoylformic acid by nitric acid, though a certain amount of benzoic acid also forms. Nitrotartaric acid, which results through the action of nitric acid on tartaric acid, decomposes spontaneously to dioxytartaric acid, HOCOCO → COCOOH.[39]

Many hydroxy acids are converted to keto acids by *Fenton's method, i.e.*, by the action of hydrogen peroxide in the presence of ferrous sulfate. The peroxide is added to the mixture of the acid and the aqueous solution of ferrous sulfate, in quantity equivalent to the –CH(OH)– group that is to be oxidized. Satisfactory results are obtained by this method with glycolic, lactic, citric and sugar acids. Tartaric acid is converted by this treatment to dihydroxymaleic acid HOCOC(OH) = C(OH)COOH. This may be converted to dioxytartaric acid by shaking with mercuric oxide in the presence of a little water. Heated with water, dioxytartaric acid gives tartronic acid, $CH(OH)(COOH)_2$, in almost quantitative yield.

Secondary alcohols of the pyridine series are readily converted to ketones. The usual procedure is to heat the compound with a mixture of chromic and acetic acids.

The secondary alcohol group in quinine bases are preferably oxidized with a mixture of chromic caid and 33% sulfuric acid at 30 to 50°.

Tropine, subjected to the action of potassium permanganate in acid solution, is converted to tropinone. If oxidation with permanganate is carried out in alkaline solution, the methyl group attached to the nitrogen is removed with the formation of tropigenine. Demethylation of this type takes place with other compounds containing a tertiary nitrogen. N-Methylpyrroleisopropropylcarbinole is, for example, converted to pyrrole propyl ketone, COC_3H_7, when oxidized with potassium permanganate in alkaline solution.

N-Alkyl-2-hydroxypyridine and its derivatives, which result from the quaternary alkylpyridinium hydroxides by molecular rearrangement, are oxidized to keto bases with potassium ferricyanide or, better, electrolytically at iron electrodes in the presence of potassium ferricyanide:

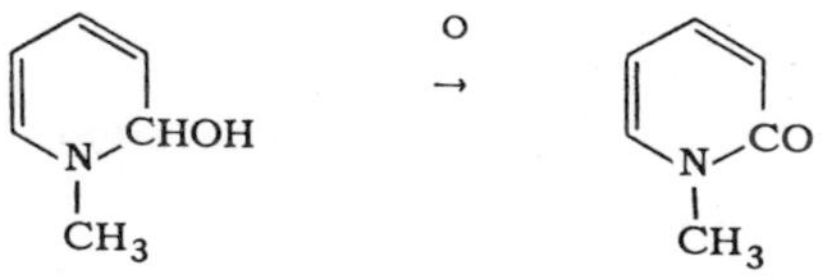

Oxidation with Selenium Dioxide[77]

Selenium dioxide causes the oxidation of an active methylene group to a carbonyl group. Even slightly activated methylene groups, such as those present in simple aliphatic aldehydes and ketones, are susceptible to oxidation.[78]

The oxidation is usually carried out in acetic acid solution, generally at refluxing temperature. In some instances reaction takes place at ordinary temperature; in other cases temperatures in excess of 100° may be required. Dioxane, acetic anhydride, ethanol, water, benzene, etc., may be used as the reaction medium. Oxidation is occasionally carried out in the absence of a solvent.

After the completion of the reaction the excess of selenium dioxide is destroyed with lead acetate, sulfur dioxide, or other reducing agents. Isolation of the products often involves simply the filtration of the solid metallic selenium, and removal of the solvent by distillation. Purification is effected by crystallization or fractional distillation.

Selenium dioxide may be prepared by strongly heating selenium and passing over it a mixture of dry oxygen and nitrogen peroxide, NO_2. The dioxide sublimes and is condensed and collected.

Strongly activated methyl groups, such as those situated between two carbonyl groups, an ester and a carbonyl group, two aromatic groups, etc., are readily converted to carbonyl groups by oxidation with selenium dioxide.[79] Reactive methylene groups present in certain aromatic compounds, such as diphenylmethane, fluorene, etc., are also readily converted to carbonyl groups.[80] The reaction has been used for the conversion of reactive methylene groups in steroids and terpenes to carbonyl groups. 2-Methylcyclohexanone behaves in an anomalous manner and undergoes oxidation as well as partial dehydrogenation when treated with selenium dioxide:[81]

$$\begin{matrix} \text{CO-CH}_2 \\ \diagup \quad \diagdown \\ \text{CH}_3\text{CH} \qquad \text{CH}_2 \\ \diagdown \quad \diagup \\ \text{CH}_2\text{-CH}_2 \end{matrix} \quad \xrightarrow{\text{SeO}_2} \quad \begin{matrix} \text{CO-CO} \\ \diagup \quad \diagdown \\ \text{CH}_3\text{C} \qquad \text{CH}_2 \\ \diagdown \quad \diagup \\ \text{CH-CH}_2 \end{matrix}$$

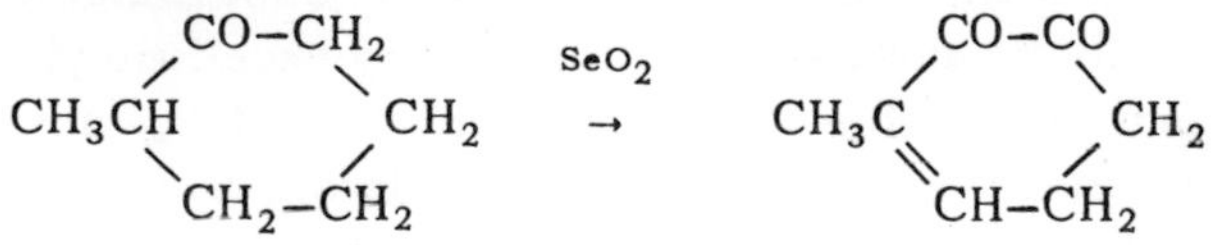

The Oppenauer Dehydrogenation of Secondary Alcohols[33]

This reaction is, in reality, the reverse of the Meerwein-Ponndorf reduction of ketones. It consists in the oxidation of a secondary alcohol with a ketone in the presence of aluminum isopropoxide or -butoxide. The reaction expressing the process may be written as follows:

$$(RR'CHO)_3Al + 3CH_3COCH_3 \;\rightleftharpoons\; [RR'CHOC(CH_3)_2O]_3Al$$

$$\rightarrow \quad RCOR' + [(CH_3)_2CHO]_3Al$$

The general procedure is as follows: Ten parts of the alcohol to be oxidized are added to 100 to 200 molecular equivalents of acetone mixed with a fivefold amount of benzene. Five to thirty parts of aluminum tertiary butoxide are added, and the whole is heated under reflux for nine hours. The reaction mixture is protected from atmospheric moisture during heating. The product is then decomposed with dilute sulfuric acid, and the benzene layer is separated, washed and the benzene is evaporated off to recover the ketone. Purification is effected by fractional distillation, crystallization or other appropriate methods, depending on the character of the ketone.

Cyclohexanone may be used as the oxidizing ketone; this compound has a higher oxidation potential than acetone, and a higher boiling point, and permits a shorter reaction time, generally between 15 minutes and two hours. Acetophenone, which can also be used as the oxidizing ketone, has the advantage that it does not undergo condensation in the presence of the strongly basic catalyst. Quinone would appear to be the most satisfactory hydrogen acceptor for the conversion of triterpenoid alcohols to the corresponding ketones.[82] When cyclohexanone is used as the hydrogen acceptor, 10 to 20 molecular proportions should be employed, and when quinone is employed for the purposee 3 to 10 molecular proportions are sufficient.

In the case of the more resistant carbinol groups, potassium *tert*-butoxide may be employed as the catalyst, in conjunction with benzophenone as the hydrogen acceptor, providing the resulting carbonyl compound will not undergo condensation under the influence of the strongly basic butoxide.

Since the method involves oxidation under very mild conditions, it is applicable to a variety of sensitive compounds. The carbinol group in unsaturated alcohols may be converted to a carbonyl group by this method without affecting the unsaturated bonds. Many alcoholic bodies containing labile substituents such as allyl, vinyl, ethynyl, and other unsaturated side chains have been converted successfully to the corresponding carbonyl compounds.[83]

The assumption that alcoholic groups not activated by a vicinal unsaturated group are resistant to oxidation by this method has proven to be unfounded.[84]

The method is suitable for the oxidation of the carbinol group in acid-sensitive acetals, mercaptals or ketals containing alcoholic groups.[85] The method has found wide application in the field of sterols. Unsaturated steroid alcohols may be oxidized to the corresponding ketones in excellent yield. The method has proven of particular value for the transformation of β,γ-unsaturated steroid alcohols to the related ketones. Halogenated sterols have also been oxidized successfully.[86] The preferential oxidation of the several carbinol groups in polyhydroxysterols may be accomplished by the Oppenauer method. The order of oxidation would appear to be the reverse of that brought about by the chromic anhydride method. A hydroxyl group in position 3 is always attacked first, while one at position 11 is resistant. A carbinol group activated by a double bond is attacked preferentially. An example of a 3,5,19-hydroxy steroid remaining unaffected by the treatment is on record.[87] The oxidation does not always proceed without major breakdown, and a case of the loss of the side-chain during the oxidation of a sterol is known.

Occasionally the carbonyl compound formed in the Oppenauer oxidation condenses with the keto compound employed as a hydrogen acceptor in the reaction. This fact has been successfully utilized in the preparation of compounds of the type of ionone,[88] and of a variety of intermediates useful in polyene synthesis.[89] In such reactions it may be necessary to use larger amounts of aluminum alkoxide, since the water formed in the reaction will destroy an equivalent amount of alkoxide.

Quinine remains unaffected when subjected to the usual conditions of the Oppenauer oxidation,[90] but this compound has been successfully oxidized to the corresponding ketone by use of potassium *tert*-butoxide in conjunction with benzophenone.[91]

Formation of Ketones from Acids

Ketones are formed when alkaline earth metal salts of carboxylic acids are dry distilled:

$$(RCOO)_2Ca \rightarrow RCOR + CaCO_3$$

Mixed ketones are formed on distilling a mixture of the calcium salts of two acids. The method is inconvenient and the yields are usually poor.[40]

Ketones may be obtained in good yield by passing the vapors of an acid over thoria catalyst at an elevated temperature. Yields of ketone ranging from 70 to 90% may be obtained by this method from aliphatic acids.[41] The vapors of the acid are passed through a tube filled with thorium oxide and heated at 400°. The method is applicable to fatty aromatic acids such as phenylacetic acid but fails when applied to purely aromatic acids. As a general rule, acids which are readily decarboxylated do not yield ketones. If the carboxyl group is attached to a secondary carbon, there is a tendency to dehydration; thus, tetraphenylallene, $(C_6H_5)_2C = C = C(C_6H_5)_2$, is obtained when barium diphenylacetate is distilled.

The catalytic preparation of ketones has been extended with marked success to the preparation of cyclic ketones from dicarboxylic acids.

Ketones from Acid Chlorides and Organometallic Compounds

A versatile method of formation of ketones, which is of wide applicability is based on the reaction of acid chlorides with certain organometallic compounds. Freund,[42] who originated this method, used zinc alkyls. The reaction proceeds in two steps:

$$RCOCl + Zn(CH_3)_2 \rightarrow RCCl(CH_3)OZnCH_3$$

$$RCCl(CH_3)OZnCH_3 + RCOCl \rightarrow 2RCOCH_3 + ZnCl_2$$

The reaction is usually carried out at the temperature of melting ice or of an ice-salt bath.

Ketones may be obtained in the first stage of the reaction by decomposing the addition product with water,

$$2RCCl(CH_3)OZnCH_3 + 2H_2O \rightarrow 2RCOCH_3 + ZnCl_2 + Zn(OH)_2 + 2CH_4$$

only half of the zinc alkyl being then utilized for the production of ketone. At times it is of advantage to stop the reaction at the first stage. In that case, the zinc alkyl in a flask is cooled in an ice-salt mixture and two moles of the chloride are added, dropwise in the beginning, then rapidly. After the addition of the zinc alkyl, finely ground ice is introduced to decompose the addition product. In preparing high molecular ketones, it is necessary to heat the mixture of zinc alkyl and acid chloride on a water-bath for half an hour, before the addition of water.

The reaction is applicable also to acid anhydrides, molecular equivalents of the reagents being then required:

$$(C_3H_7CO)_2O + Zn(C_2H_5)_2 \rightarrow C_3H_7COOC(C_3H_7)(C_2H_5)OZnC_2H_5$$

$$2C_3H_7COOC(C_3H_7)(C_2H_5)OZnC_2H_5 + 2H_2O \rightarrow$$

$$2C_3H_7COC_2H_5 + (C_3H_7CO)_2Zn + Zn(OH)_2 + 2C_2H_6$$

Conversion of acid chlorides to ketones has also been carried out by reaction with organozinc halides:

$$RCOCl + R'ZnI \rightarrow RCOR' + ZnClI$$

The alkyl zinc compounds with primary acyclic groups are used in 25% excess; in 33% excess, if the acid chloride cannot be distilled. Organo zinc halides with secondary radicals are used in 100% excess, and aromatic alkyl zinc halides are used in 50% excess. The reaction product is decomposed with ice-water and a few drops of sulfuric acid, the unreacted organozinc halide is decomposed with ammonia or saturated ammonium sulfate solution, and the product is finally washed with dilute sulfuric acid or potassium bicarbonate solution to which some sodium hyposulfite has been added. The yield of ketone varies between 75 to 90% of the theoretical. Aromatic acid chlorides give lower yields of ketones, toluic acid yielding 40-50%, cresotonic acid methyl ester chloride 60-70%, and anisic chloride 25%.

a,β-Unsaturated ketones may be prepared by this method from the corresponding chloride.[92] They may be prepared also from the appropriate hydroxy acid after the hydroxy group has been protected by esterification; the keto esters are subsequently hydrolyzed and boiled with 20% sulfuric acid for a short time. γ-Chloro acid chlorides give γ-halo ketones in good yield if the reaction is carried out at -20 to $-15°$.[93] Diketones may be obtained from pimalic acid dichloride and from dichlorides of other higher dicarboxylic acids. Oxalyl chloride fails to yield the expected product. Half ester chlorides of the lower dicarboxylic acids undergo complex reactions.

a-Chloroacyl chlorides reacting with organozinc halides give esters of chlorinated tertiary alcohols with the chloro acid.[94] The a-chloro ketones can be prepared from such acid chlorides by reaction with a-hydroxyisobutyric acid, conversion of the product to the corresponding acyl chloride and treatment of this with the organozinc halide. The cyclic acetal formed is finally decomposed with acid to obtain the chloro ketone.[94] The reactions representing the successive changes are as follows:

$$RCHClCOCl + (CH_3)_2C(OH)COOH \rightarrow RCHClCOOC(CH_3)_2COOH$$

$$\xrightarrow{SOCl_2} RCHClCOOC(CH_3)_2COCl \xrightarrow{R'ZnI} \begin{array}{c} (CH_3)_2C - CO \\ | \qquad | \\ O \qquad O \\ \diagdown \diagup \\ RCH(Cl).C.R' \end{array}$$

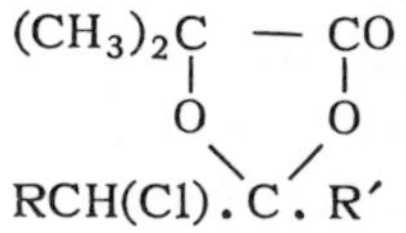

$$\rightarrow RCHClCOR' + (CH_3)_2C(OH)COOH$$

The method may be employed successfully for the preparation of α-di- and trichloro ketones.[95] 1,4-Diketones may be prepared by this method from succinyl dichloride.[96] An α-keto ester has been obtained by the same method from the half ester chloride of oxalic acid,[97] and half ester chlorides of other lower aliphatic dicarboxylic acids.

Ketones have been prepared from acyl halides by reaction with alkyl aluminum chlorides,[98]

$$RCOCl + R'AlCl_2 \rightarrow RCOR' + AlCl_3$$

The reaction is usually carried out in benzene solution at a little above room temperature. Several methyl and ethyl ketones have been prepared by this method, generally in good yield.

Alkyl aluminum halides may be obtained by the reaction of alkyl halides with metallic aluminum. The product of the reaction is an alkyl aluminum sesquihalide, $R_2AlX.RAlX_2$, which may be converted to the dihalide by treatment with the appropriate aluminum trihalide. Induction periods, sometimes of several days, have been reported for the reaction of aluminum with alkyl halides. A highly active form of aluminum turnings has been prepared by protecting the aluminum surface with a blanket of nitrogen during the turning operation. Turnings thus prepared were found to react rapidly at 25° with methyl chloride vapors under a pressure of 3 atm. Of the higher alkyl halides only ethyl and *n*-butyl halides seem to react.

Keto derivatives may be obtained through the reaction of acid chlorides with compounds with a reactive methylene group in the presence of sodium methoxide. Keto derivatives of malonic acid and mono substituted malonic esters may be converted to ketones devoid of an acid function by decarboxylation.[99]

Ketones from Organocadmium Compounds

Ketones result through the reaction of organocadmium compounds with acid chlorides:

$$2RCOCl + R'_2Cd \rightarrow 2RCOR' + CdCl_2$$

The method, which has been developed by Gilman and Nelson,[43] is one of the best and most widely applicable procedures for the preparation of simple and polyfunctional ketones, the yields being generally good. The reaction has been usually carried out in ethereal solution, but improved yields have been obtained when it was conducted in benzene.[100]

Both aliphatic and aromatic acid chlorides react smoothly, the former the more readily. Satisfactory yields of ketone may be obtained even with aliphatic acid chlorides of high molecular weight, such as stearyl chloride. Keto esters have been prepared by the method in good yield from ester chlorides of dibasic acids. While cinnamoyl chloride gives a ketone in good yield by reaction with diphenylcadmium, many cadmiumalkyls give only viscous oils by reaction with cinnamoyl chloride as well as with crotonyl and phenylpropiolyl chlorides. α-Chloroketones are readily obtained by this method. Chloromethyl butyl ketone may, thus, be prepared through the reaction of chloroacetyl chloride and dibutylcadmium.

With the exception of groups containing reactive hydrogen, very few groups interfere with the preparation of ketones from cadmium reagents.

Carbonyl groups usually do not react, or react very slowly, with organocadmium compounds, unless such groups are activated by an adjacent group. The reaction between oxalyl chloride and diethylcadmium, for example, results in the formation of diethylpropionylcarbinol:

$$2ClCOCOCl + 3(C_2H_5)_2Cd \xrightarrow{H_2O} C_2H_5COC(OH)(C_2H_5)_2 + CdCl_2 + Cd(OH)_2$$

Similarly, ester groups that are activated by an adjacent group may react with organocadmium compounds. Ethyl diethylglycolate, $(C_2H_5)_2C(OH)COOC_2H_5$, results, for example, through the reaction of diethylcadmium and diethyl oxalate.

The reaction of the cadmium reagent with the enol form of the ketone formed is always a potential side reaction. With most ketones this reaction is of minor consequence, but with α-chloroketones the loss due to this cause becomes serious and the yield of ketone is correspondingly lower. Enolization and the consequent loss due to reaction with the cadmium reagent appears to be more serious in ether than in benzene. In this connection it is of interest to note that 1-chloro-2-hexanone reacts rapidly with dibutylcadmium with evolution of heat, giving principally higher boiling compounds.

Alkyl cadmium reagents give addition compounds with alkylidenemalonic esters:

$$C_2H_5CH{=}C(COOC_2H_5)_2 + C_{10}H_7CH_2CdCl \rightarrow \begin{array}{l} C_2H_5 \diagdown \\ \qquad\qquad CHC(COOC_2H_5)_2 \\ C_{10}H_7CH_2 \diagup \quad | \\ \qquad\qquad\;\; CdCl \end{array}$$

This reaction, which is similar to that with organomagnesium compounds, gives better yields than is possible to obtain with the corresponding Grignard reagents.

Organocadmium compounds reacting with arylsulfonyl chlorides give sulfones. They fail to react with *tert*-butyl chloride and phenyl isocyanate.

When the reaction of organocadmium compounds with acid chlorides is carried out in ethereal solution, appreciable quantities of ester are formed through the action of the chloride on the ether, a reaction which is apparently catalyzed with the small quantities of organomagnesium compound present in solution:

$$RCOCl + (C_2H_5)_2O \rightarrow RCOOC_2H_5 + C_2H_5Cl$$

Ester formation may be avoided to a large extent by distilling off the ether in which the organocadmium compound was prepared, and carrying the reaction out in benzene.

Organocadmium compounds are prepared readily through the reaction of organomagnesium compounds with cadmium chloride or bromide:[44]

$$2RMgBr + CdCl_2 \rightarrow R_2Cd + MgBr_2 + MgCl_2$$

Organomagnesium bromides react most readily. Good yields of alkylcadmiums are obtained from primary alkyl magnesium halides and from aromatic Grignard compounds. Secondary and tertiary alkylcadmiums are stable only at low temperatures, and while they may be reacted at these temperatures with acyl chlorides, the yields of the resulting ketones are quite low.

Most alkyl cadmium compounds can be stored only for a short time, and when kept for a longer period gradually assume a steel-blue color, especially when exposed to light, finally depositing a black precipitate of finely subdivided cadmium. They are readily oxidized in contact with air giving off fumes, and will ignite spontaneously when dropped on a filter paper exposed to air.

Ketones by Reaction of Acid Chlorides with Sodiomalonic Esters and Similar Compounds

Acyl chlorides react readily with the sodium derivative of malonic esters and substituted malonic esters. On hydrolysis and decarboxylation of the resulting acyl esters, ketones are obtained:

$$RCOCl + NaCR'(COOR'')_2 \rightarrow NaCl + RCOCR'(COOH)_2 \rightarrow RCOCH_2R'$$

The acylation must be carried out in the absence of water.[101]

Amino ketones have been prepared by this route from the phthalamides of acid chlorides.[102] ξ-Aminohexyl methyl ketone has been prepared, for example, from 6-aminoheptanecarboxylic acid phthalimide by the following steps:

$$C_6H_4 \underset{CO}{\overset{CO}{\diagdown\diagup}} N(CH_2)_6COOH \rightarrow C_6H_4 \underset{CO}{\overset{CO}{\diagdown\diagup}} N(CH_2)_6COCl \quad \xrightarrow{NaCH(COOR)_2}$$

$$C_6H_4 \underset{CO}{\overset{CO}{\diagdown\diagup}} N(CH_2)_6COCH(COOR)_2 \rightarrow C_6H_4 \underset{CO}{\overset{CO}{\diagdown\diagup}} N(CH_2)_6COCH(COOH)_2$$

$$\rightarrow 2CO_2 + C_6H_4 \underset{CO}{\overset{CO}{\diagdown\diagup}} N(CH_2)_6COCH_3 \xrightarrow{H_2O} C_6H_4(COOH)_2 + H_2N(CH_2)_6COCH_3$$

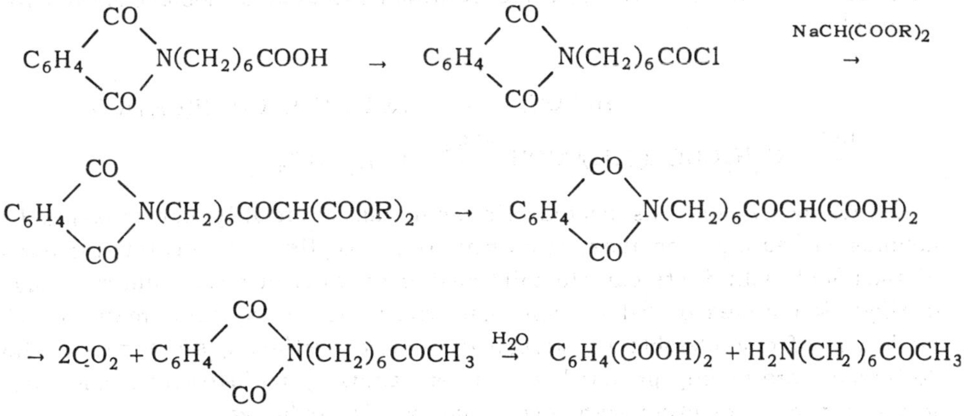

Application of the method to γ-phthalimidobutyryl chloride yields 2-methylpyrroline, $CH_3\overline{C = CHCH_2CH_2NH}$; δ-phthalimidovaleryl chloride also behaves in an exceptional manner and gives 2-methyltetrahydropyridine,

$$CH_3\overline{C = CHCH_2CH_2CH_2NH}.\text{[103]}$$

Conversion of acylated esters to ketones has been accomplished by hydrogenolysis in the presence of palladium catalyst. Esters of the type RCOCH₂R' have been obtained by this method from acylated benzyl esters of substituted malonic acid, $RCOCHR'(COOCH_2C_6H_5)_2$.[104] The method has been utilized for the preparation of long chain ketones, diketones, keto alcohols, acyloins, keto acids, keto esters and keto nitriles.[104]

Acylated acetoacetic esters, which are obtained by the reaction of acyl halides with the sodio derivative of acetoacetic esters, give keto acids by alkali cleavage at 40° in the presence of sodium alkoxides, and diketones by acid cleavage:[105]

$$C_{15}H_{31}COCl + NaOC(CH_3) = CHCOOR \rightarrow NaCl + C_{15}H_{31}COCH(COCH_3)COOR$$

$$\rightarrow C_{15}H_{31}COCH_2COOR \text{ or } C_{15}H_{31}COCH_2COCH_3$$

The claim is made that both straight chain and branched chain ketones may be prepared in good yield through the reaction of Grignard reagents with acid chlorides at low temperatures in the presence of ferric chloride.[192]

Other Methods of Preparation of Ketones

Ketones may also be obtained from acid chlorides of the type RCH_2COCl through the action of anhydrous ferric chloride, which results in the formation of a β-keto acid chloride. The reaction often proceeds in the cold. The keto acid chloride is readily hydrolyzed to the acid and the acid is decarboxylated to a ketone:[45]

$$2C_2H_5COCl \xrightarrow{FeCl_3} HCl + C_2H_5COCH(CH_3)COCl$$

$$\xrightarrow{H_2O} C_2H_5COCH(CH_3)COOH \xrightarrow{-CO_2} C_2H_5COC_2H_5$$

β-Keto acids such as acetoacetic acid can be readily decarboxylated to ketones on heating. Decarboxylation may be accomplished by heating the esters of such acids with dilute caustic solution, baryta water or dilute mineral acids.[46] α-Alkyl derivatives of β-keto acid also yield ketones by this treatment. The method is of considerable importance in organic synthesis, since such α-alkyl derivatives are readily prepared from β-keto acids by replacement of the hydrogen atoms in the reactive methylene group by alkyl radicals.

β-Diketones have been prepared from aliphatic anhydrides and ketones using boron trifluoride as the condensing agent.[193]

Ketones result when a mixture of the potassium salts of a keto acid and an aliphatic acid in aqueous solution is subjected to electrolysis.[47] Methyl propyl ketone is obtained, for example, through the electrolysis of a mixture of the potassium salts of pyruvic and butyric acids:

$$CH_3COCOO^- + C_3H_7COO^- \rightarrow CH_3COC_3H_7 + 2CO_2$$

β-Diketones have been prepared through the condensation of carbonyl compounds with higher esters in the presence of hydrides of alkali or alkaline earth metals.[105]

$$CH_3COCH_3 + C_{11}H_{23}COOC_2H_5 \rightarrow C_{11}H_{23}COCH_2COCH_3 + C_2H_5OH$$

One of the important methods for the preparation of ketones is based on the reaction of organomagnesium compounds with nitriles. This and other methods of synthesis of ketones depending on the use of organomagnesium compounds are discussed in detail in the section dealing with the *Grignard reaction,* Chap. 12.

Methyl ketones may be prepared from aldehydes through the action of diazomethane:[48]

$$C_6H_{13}CHO + CH_2N_2 \rightarrow C_6H_{13}COCH_3 + N_2$$

Chloral gives an oxide $Cl_3CCH - CH_2$ (with O bridging the two carbons), by reaction with diazomethane.[22]

Ketones result when sodio compounds of secondary mononitroparaffins are decomposed with acid:

$$2(CH_3)_2C = NOONa + 2HCl \rightarrow 2(CH_3)_2CO + 2NaCl + N_2O + H_2O$$

The process, known as the *Nef reaction,* is utilized for the preparation of keto acids of the type $RCOCH_2CH_2COOH$ from the condensation products of acrylic esters with nitroparaffins RCH_2NO_2.[207] Nitrocyclohexanes and other cyclic nitro compounds have been converted to cyclic ketones by this reaction.[208] The Nef reaction proceeds normally with the Diels-Alder adduct of nitroethylenes and cyclohexadiene, but not with those of nitroolefins with cyclopentadiene.

Alkylene oxides of certain type are isomerized to ketones when heated with acids. A related reaction is the transformation of secondary and tertiary glycols to ketones under the influence of sulfuric acid in the warm:

$$(C_2H_5)_2C(OH)CH(OH)CH_3 \rightarrow (C_2H_5)_2CHCOCH_3 + H_2O$$

Diketones have been obtained through the condensation of acids with monosubstituted acetylenes in the presence of trifluoroacetic anhydride followed by methanolysis of the product formed.[194]

$$RC \equiv CH + RCOOH + (F_3CCO)_2O \rightarrow F_3CCOOH + F_3CCOOC(R') = CHCOR$$

$$\xrightarrow{CH_3OH} R'COCH_2COR + F_3CCOOCH_3$$

A similar reaction with olefins $R'CH = CHR''$ leads to the formation of α,β-unsaturated ketones $R'CH = CR''COR$.

β-Diketones may be obtained by the acylation of ketones with carboxylic acid anhydrides, which may be brought about under the action of boron trifluoride:

$$CH_3COCH_3 + (CH_3CO)_2O \rightarrow CH_3COCH_2COCH_3 + CH_3COOH$$

The general procedure involves the saturation of the mixture of the ketone and anhydride with boron trifluoride at 0°. A coordination complex is formed from which the β-diketone is liberated by boiling with two molecular equivalents of sodium acetate in aqueous solution. Rapid saturation of the mixture with boron trifluoride generally gives a better yield of the diketone. Ethylene dichloride may be used as a diluent of the reaction mixture where necessary.[209] Acylated acids resulting from the self-condensation of the anhydride and aldol type product resulting from the self-condensation of the ketone are byproducts of the reaction. Acylation may take place at both the methyl and methylene group with ketones CH_3COCH_2R. Some n-alkyl ketones are acylated at the methylene group in the presence of a catalytic amount of p-toluenesulfonic acid. Attempts to acylate acetophenone with benzoic, phthalic and succinic anhydride have failed. The Kostanecky procedure for the preparation of chromones, flavones or isoflavones from aromatic o-hydroxy ketones makes use of acylation with acid anhydrides in the presence of the alkali metal salt of the corresponding acid.[210]

Catalytic reduction of the grouping $CClNO_2$ results in its conversion to a CO group. Certain a-hydroxy ketones have been obtained by this method.[106]

a-*Halo ketones* have been obtained by brominating alkenyl esters:[107]

$$RCOOCR' = CH_2 \overset{Br}{\rightarrow} RCOOCR'BrCH_2Br \rightarrow RCOBr + R'COCH_2Br$$

Breakdown of the dibromide first formed into an acyl bromide and the bromo ketone takes place spontaneously in the cold. The alkenyl esters may be prepared through the addition of acids to acetylenic compounds in the presence of a catalyst.

Isonitroso ketones can be reduced to amino ketones important in the synthesis of pyrrole derivatives.[205]

THIOALDEHYDES AND THIOKETONES

Thioaldehydes in the trimeric form are obtained by the reaction of aldehydes with hydrogen sulfide in the presence of hydrogen chloride:[108]

$$CH_2O + H_2S \rightarrow HSCH_2OH$$

$$CH_2O + 2HSCH_2OH \rightarrow HOCH_2SCH_2SCH_2OH + H_2O$$

$$HOCH_2SCH_2SCH_2OH + H_2S \rightarrow CH_2\begin{matrix} S-CH_2 \\ \diagup \quad \diagdown \\ \quad \quad S \\ \diagdown \quad \diagup \\ S-CH_2 \end{matrix} + 2H_2O$$

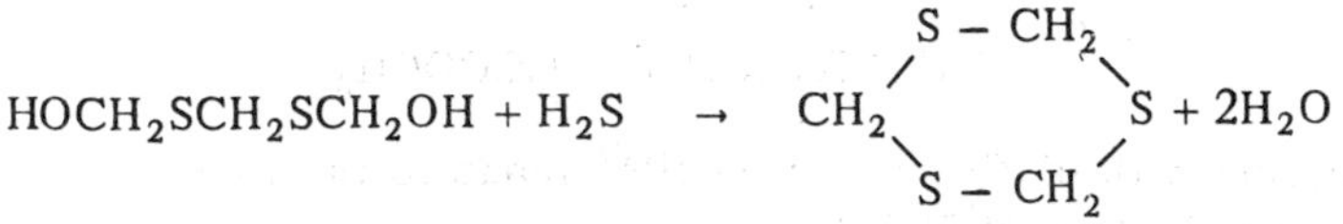

Higher trimeric thioaldehydes may be considered as the homologs of trithiomethylene. These compounds exist in two isomeric modifications, a fact which has not received a fully satisfactory explanation; they are designated as the a and β forms.

Trithioformaldehyde is also formed through the interaction of the formaldehyde with sodium thiosulfate in the presence of hydrochloric acid. Trithioacetaldehyde may also be prepared by this method from acetaldehyde. Tri- and tetrathionic acid may replace thiosulfuric acid in this reaction.

Thialdine, $CH_3CHS.CH(CH_3).NH.CH(CH_3)S$, results through the interaction of hydrogen sulfide with aldehyde ammonia in aqueous solution.

Aromatic aldehydes reacting with hydrogen sulfide in the presence of hydrochloric acid give two isomeric thioaldehydes. Reaction with hydrogen sulfide alone, or with ammonium sulfide, leads to the formation of high molecular polymeric compounds or a mixture of a number of compounds.

As with aliphatic thials, aromatic thials also exist in the trimeric form, in two modifications designated as the α- and β-form. Substituted aromatic aldehydes give the two isomeric trithials if the substituent is positive, but when it is negative only the β-isomer is formed. Phenolic aldehydes give only the β- or *cis-trans* trithials, but benzyl and methyl ethers of such aldehydes give both isomers. Trithials are more readily formed when positive substituents are present. Aldehydes with negative substituents tend to give high polymers.

Thioaldehydes are oxidized by hydrogen peroxide or potassium permanganate, in stages, to trisulfones. The intermediate compounds formed are sulfidisulfoxides, trisulfoxides and sulfidosulfones.

Thioaldehydes undergo a reaction resembling the Wurtz synthesis to form ethylenic compounds:

$$2RCHS \xrightarrow{Na} RCH=CHR.$$

Thioacetals, or mercaptals, result through the interaction of aldehydes and mercaptans in the presence of hydrogen chloride:

$$CH_2O + HSC_5H_{11} \rightarrow HOCH_2SC_5H_{11}$$

$$HOCH_2SC_5H_{11} + HSC_5H_{11} \rightarrow CH_2(SC_5H_{11})_2 + H_2O.$$

These compounds are also obtained through the reaction of alkylene iodides and alkali mercaptides.

Thioacetone results in the trimeric form through the interaction of acetone with hydrogen sulfide in the presence of hydrochloric acid.[109]

Diketones, such as acetylacetone, react with hydrogen sulfide in the presence of hydrogen chloride to form stable sulfurated dimers.[110]

β-Thioketo esters are formed in good yield when β-keto esters are treated in cold alcoholic solution with hydrogen sulfide in the presence of hydrogen chloride:[111]

Duplothioacetone, $CH_3C{-}S{-}C(CH_3)_2S$, is formed by the action of phosphorus pentasulfide on acetone.[49]

Thioketo acids have been prepared through the condensation of aldehydes with rhodanine in acetic acid solution in the presence of sodium acetate, and hydrolysis of the resulting product with caustic:[112]

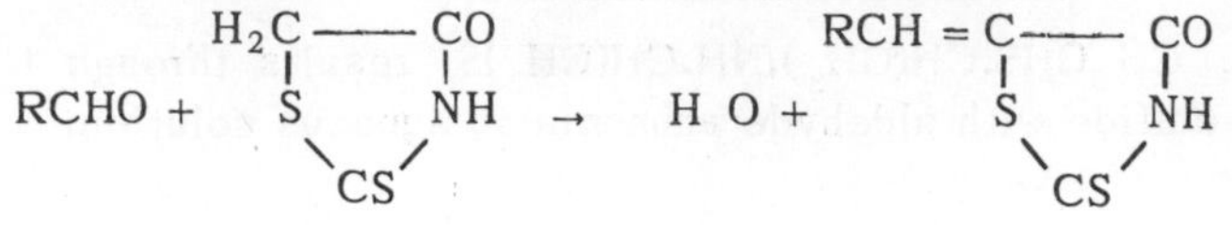

$$\text{RCHO} + \begin{array}{c} \text{H}_2\text{C} \underline{\hspace{1cm}} \text{CO} \\ | \quad\quad | \\ \text{S} \quad\quad \text{NH} \\ \diagdown_{\text{CS}}\diagup \end{array} \rightarrow \text{H O} + \begin{array}{c} \text{RCH} = \text{C} \underline{\hspace{1cm}} \text{CO} \\ | \quad\quad | \\ \text{S} \quad\quad \text{NH} \\ \diagdown_{\text{CS}}\diagup \end{array}$$

$$\rightarrow \quad \text{RCH} = \text{C(SH)COOH} \quad \rightleftarrows \quad \text{RCH}_2\text{CSCOOH}$$

The method is of restricted applicability. Intractable oils have been obtained with acetaldehyde, crotonaldehyde and isovaleraldehyde,[114] and negative results have been obtained with p-aminobenzaldehyde and o-nitrobenzaldehyde.

β-Mercaptocrotonic ester, $\text{CH}_3\text{C(SH)} = \text{CHCOOC}_2\text{H}_5$, is formed, together with the corresponding sulfide, when β-chlorocrotonic ester is treated with potassium sulfide.[113]

Homocyclic ketones also yield thioketones when treated with hydrogen sulfide in the presence of hydrogen chloride, and the majority of known homocyclic thioketones have been obtained by this method.[115] Thiocamphor has been obtained, together with thioborneol, by the pyrolytic decomposition of bornyl disulfide, which is obtained by the action of ammonium sulfide on camphor.[116] Thiomenthone has been prepared by heating menthone with phosphorus trisulfide.[195]

Acetophenone reacts with hydrogen sulfide to form three distinct compounds, monomeric thioacetophenone, trimeric thioacetophenone and anhydrotrithioacetophenone. The last named compound probably has the formula

$$\overline{\text{C}_6\text{H}_5\text{C(CH}_3\text{) SC(C}_6\text{H}_5\text{)} = \text{CH(CH}_3\text{)(C}_6\text{H}_5\text{) S}}$$

Thiobenzophenone is formed on passing first hydrogen sulfide and hydrogen chloride, then hydrogen sulfide alone into a solution of benzophenone in alcohol cooled in ice.[196] Many unsymmetrical arylthiones have also been prepared by this method.[197] The presence of nitro groups in the aromatic ring prevents the formation of thiones. The oxygen in benzophenone may be replaced by reaction with phosphorus pentasulfide, though the resulting thiobenzophenone cannot be obtained in the pure form. Thiobenzophenone results in the desired degree of purity and good yield through the interaction of benzophenone dichloride, $(\text{C}_6\text{H}_5)_2\text{CCl}_2$, and potassium sulfide.[198] A number of aromatic thiones have been prepared by treating diaryl keto dichlorides with thioacetic acid.[199]

N-Alkylated 4,4'-diaminodiarylthiones have been obtained by treating the corresponding diaminodiarylmethanes with polysulfides.[200] Leukauramine is oxidized to Mischler's thioketone in 60% yield on heating with sulfur:[201]

$$[(\text{CH}_3)_2\text{NC}_6\text{H}_4]_2\text{CHNH}_2 + \text{S} \quad \rightarrow \quad [(\text{CH}_3)_2\text{NC}_6\text{H}_4]_2\text{CS} + \text{NH}_3$$

Mischler's thioketone is formed also on warming the corresponding imine or anil with carbon disulfide.[202]

Aromatic thioketones are also formed through the interaction of anils and hydrogen sulfide:

$$(\text{R})_2\text{C} = \text{NR}' + \text{H}_2\text{S} \quad \rightarrow \quad (\text{R})_2\text{CS} + \text{H}_2\text{NR}'.$$

This reaction proceeds most readily with anils containing positive substituents. Phenylauramine, for example, reacts very readily with hydrogen sulfide to form tetramethyldiaminothiobenzophenone:[50]

$$[(\text{CH}_3)_2\text{NC}_6\text{H}_4]_2\text{C} = \text{NC}_6\text{H}_5 + \text{H}_2\text{S} \quad \rightarrow \quad [(\text{CH}_3)_2\text{NC}_6\text{H}_4]_2\text{C} = \text{S} + \text{C}_6\text{H}_5\text{NH}_2$$

While tetraaryl ethylenes may be converted to ketones by oxidation, the parallel reaction with sulfur takes place only in exceptional cases. Dixantylene gives xanthion when melted with sulfur:[206]

$$O \overset{C_6H_4}{\underset{C_6H_4}{\diagup\diagdown}} C = C \overset{C_6H_4}{\underset{C_6H_4}{\diagup\diagdown}} O + 2S \quad \rightarrow \quad 2O \overset{C_6H_4}{\underset{C_6H_4}{\diagup\diagdown}} CS$$

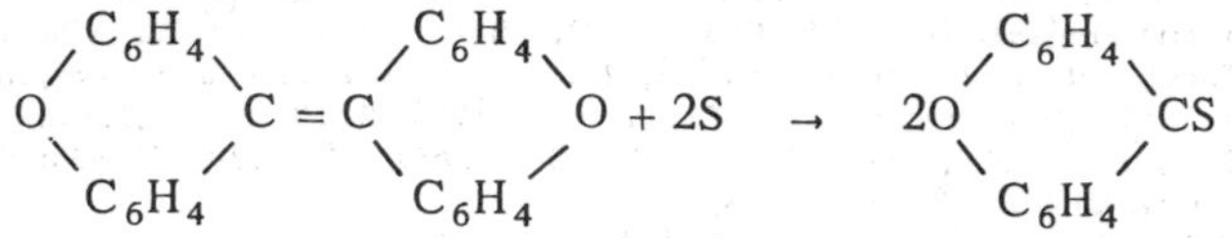

Mercaptals are formed through the reaction of ketones with mercaptans in the presence of hydrogen chloride:

$$(CH_3)_2CO + 2C_2H_5SH \quad \rightarrow \quad (CH_3)_2C(SC_2H_5)_2 + H_2O$$

Mercaptals are oxidized to sulfones by the action of potassium permanganate:

$$(CH_3)_2C(SC_2H_5)_2 \quad \overset{2O_2}{\rightarrow} \quad (CH_3)_2C(SO_2C_2H_5)_2$$

References

1. Liebig, *Ann.*, **14**, 133 (1835); Franchimont and Zincke, *ibid.*, **163**, 197 (1872); Zincke, *ibid.*, **152**, 8 (1869); Pierre and Puchot, *ibid.*, **163**, 271 (1872); Bouveault, *Bull. soc. chim.*, (3) **31**, 1311 (1904); Reilly and Hickinbottom, *Proc. Roy. Dub. Soc.*, **16**, 246 (1921).
2. Wieland and Sekellarios, *Ber.*, **53**, 210 (1920).
3. Cohen and Calvert, *J. Chem. Soc.*, **71**, 1050 (1897); Cohen and Harrison, *ibid.*, **71**, 1057 (1897).
4. Hess, Merck and Uibrig, *Ber.*, **48**, 1886 (1915).
5. Haakk, *British Patent* 157,850.
6. Grimaux and Lauth, *Bull. soc. chim.*, (2) **7**, 106 (1867); Grimaux, *Jahresb.*, **1876**, 490.
7. Suto, *Biochem. Z.* **71**, 169 (1915).
8. Wohl and Österlin, *Ber.*, **33**, 2740 (1900).
9. Elbers, *Ann.*, **227**, 354 (1885).
10. Franzen and Kraft, *J. prakt. Chem.*, (2) **84**, 127 (1911).
11. Decker, *Ber.*, **36**, 2568 (1903); Pictet and Patry, *ibid.*, **35**, 2534 (1902).
12. Kiliani, *ibid.*, **55**, 85 (1922); **56**, 2016 (1923).
13. Fenton and Jackson, *Chem. News.*, **78**, 187 (1898); *J. Chem. Soc.*, **75**, 1 (1899).
14. Neuberg, *Ber.*, **35**, 962 (1902).
15. Sabatier and Senderens, *Compt. rend.*, **136**, 738, 921, 983 (1903); Bouveault, *Bull. soc. chim.*, (3) **11**, 300 (1894); (4) **3**, 119 (1908); Armstrong and Hilditch, *Proc. Roy. Soc. (London)*, A, **97**, 259 (1920); Weizmann and Garrard, *J. Chem. Soc.*, **117**, 324 (1920). Cf. Sabatier, *Catalysis in Organic Chemistry*, pp. 650 et seq. (1923); Conant et al., *J. Am. Chem. Soc.*, **51**, 1246 (1929).
16. Bouveault, *Bull. soc. chim.*, (4) **3**, 118 (1908); Ruzicka and Stoll, *Helv. Chim. Acta*, **7**, 89 (1924).
17. Moureu and Mignonac, *Compt. rend.*, **170**, 258 (1920); Ottensooser, *Bull. soc. chim.*, (4) **41**, 324 (1927); Simington and Adkins, *J. Am. Chem. Soc.*, **50**, 1449 (1928); Lazier, *U.S. patent* 2,178,761 (1935); Halasz, *Compt. rend.*, **209**, 100 (1940); *Concerning Adkin's Catalyst* see Reeve and Adkins, *J. Am. Chem. Soc.*, **62**, 2875 (1940); *U.S. patent* 1,977,750 (1931); Young and Young, *Organic Syntheses*, II, 142; Dunbar and Arnold, *J. Org. Chem.*, **10**, 501 (1945).
18. Rosenmund and Zetzsche, *Ber.*, **54**, 1092, 2033 (1921); Zetsche and Zala, *Helv. Chim. Acta*, **9**, 288 (1926); Rosenmund, *Angew. Chem.* **38**, 145 (1925). Cf. Adkins et al., *J. Am. Chem. Soc.*, **62**, 2874 (1940); Benoit, *U.S. patent* 2,492,614 (1947).
19. Rosenmund, *Ber.*, **51**, 585 (1918); Rosenmund and Zetzsche, *ibid.*, **51**, 594 (1918); **54**, 425, 638, 2038, 2888 (1921); **56**, 1481 (1923); Rosenmund and Pfankuch, *ibid.*, **55**, 2360 (1922); Rosenmund and Zetzsche, *ibid.*, **55**, 609 (1922); Rojahn and Fahr, *Ann.*, **434**, 252 (1923); Zetzsche and Arndt, *Helv. Chim. Acta*, **8**, 591 (1925); **9**, 173, 177 (1926); Rojahn and Schulten, *Arch. Pharm.*, **264**, 348 (1926); Flütsch and Menzi, *Helv. Chim. Acta*, **9**, 177 (1926); Zetsche et al., *ibid.*, **9**, 182, 288 (1926); *Schimmels Ber.*, **1926**, 220. Graf and Meyer, *Ber.*, **61**, 2202 (1928); Graf, *J. prakt. Chem.*, (2) **134**, 177 (1932); *British Patent* 401,502 (1933); *German Patent* 617,763; 621,567 (1935); Hershberg and Cason, *Organic Syntheses*, **2**, 84 (1941); Ferguson, *Chem. Revs.*, **28**, 243 (1946); Dworzak and Zellner,

Monatsh., **80**, 406 (1949); Johnson *et al.*, *J. Chem. Soc.*, **1950**, 2219; Detweiler and Amstutz, *J. Am. Chem. Soc.*, **72**, 2882 (1950); Loftfield, *ibid.*, **73**, 1365 (1951); Balenović *et al.*, *J. Org. Chem.*, **17**, 1459 (1952); **18**, 297 (1953); Brown and Musgrave, *J. Chem. Soc.*, **1952**, 5049; Burger and Hornbaker, *J. Org. Chem.*, **18**, 192 (1953); Wolfram and Usdin, *J. Am. Chem. Soc.*, **75**, 4318 (1953); Mosettig and Mozingo, *Organic Reactions* IV, 362 (1948); Weygand and Meusel, *Ber.*, **76**, 503 (1943); Harris *et al.*, *J. Am. Chem. Soc.*, **67**, 2096 (1945); Jacobs *et al.*, *J. Org. Chem.*, **11**, 236 (1946); Miescher and Heer, *Helv. Chim. Acta*, **20**, 1553 (1947); Johnson *et al.*, *J. Chem. Soc.*, **1950**, 2219; Detweiler and Amstutz, *J. Am. Chem. Soc.*, **72**, 2882 (1950); Todd and Teich, *ibid.*, **75**, 1897 (1953); Burger and Hornbaker, *J. Org. Chem.*, **18**, 192 (1953).

20. Fröschl and Danoff, *J. prakt. Chem.*, (2) **144**, 217 (1936).
21. Henle, *Ber.*, **35**, 3039 (1902); **38**, 1362 (1905); Sonn and Müller, *ibid.*, **52**, 1927 (1919).
22. Sabatier and Mailhe, *Compt. rend.*, **154**, 561 (1912). Sabatier and Mailhe, *Compt. rend.*, **158**, 986 (1914). *Cf.* Moureu *et al.*, *Bull. soc. chim.*, (5) **15**, 96 (1948); Schuler and Lange, *German patent* 825,085 (1949).
23. Blaise, *Compt. rend.* **138**, 697 (1904); *Bull. soc. chim.*, (3) **31**, 483 (1904); Le Sueur, *J. Chem. Soc.*, **85**, 827 (1904); **87**, 1888 (1905).
24. Langheld, *Ber.*, **42**, 2360 (1909); Dakin *et al.*, *Biochem. J.*, **10**, 319 (1916); **11**, 79 (1917); *Proc. Roy. Soc.*, **89**, B, 232 (1917); Traube, *Ber.*, **26**, 384 (1923); Wieland and Bergel, *Ann.*, **439**, 196 (1924); Langenbeck, *Ber.*, **61**, 942 (1928); Fox and Bullock, *J. Am. Chem. Soc.*, **73**, 2754 (1951); Schönberg *et al.*, *J. Chem. Soc.*, **1951**, 2504.
25. Harries, *Ann.*, **343**, 311 (1905); Pummerer and Richtzenhain, *Ann.*, **529**, 33 (1937); Mauthner, *J. prakt. Chem.*, (2) **148**, 95 (1937); Briner *et al.*, *Helv. Chim. Acta*, **21**, 1297 (1938); Späth and Gruber, *Ber.*, **74**, 1498 (1941); Henne and Perilstein, *J. Am. Chem. Soc.*, **65**, 2184 (1943); Hurd and Saunders, *ibid.*, **74**, 5327 (1952); *Concerning reduction of ozonides see* Hurd and Filachione, *ibid.*, **61**, 1156 (1939); Cook and Whitmore, *J. Am. Chem. Soc.*, **63**, 3540 (1941).
26. Bouveault and Wahl, *Compt. rend.*, **134**, 1226 (1902); *Bull. soc. chim.*, (3) **29**, 643 (1903). *Cf.* Gilsdorf and Nord, *J. Am. Chem. Soc.*, **72**, 4327 (1950). v. Braun *et al.*, *Ber.*, **44**, 2526 (1911); **45**, 394 (1912); **46**, 103 (1913); Fischer and Neber, *Ann.*, **496**, 13 (1932); Richter and Koch, *Ark. Pharm.* **273**, 265 (1935); Johnson and Degering, *J. Org. Chem.*, **8**, 11 (1943); Gilsdorf and Nord, *J. Am., Chem. Soc.*, **72**, 4327 (1950). Stein and Bayer, *German patent* 753,470 (1941); Welz, *German patent* 825,544 (1949).
27. Markovnikoff, *Ann.*, **302**, 18, 22 (1898); Konovaloff, *J. Russ. Phys.-Chem. Soc.*, **30**, 960 (1899); **31**, 55 (1899). *Cf.* Wallach, *Ann.*, **336**, 3 (1904); **332**, 323 (1904); v. Braun *et al.*, *Ber.*, **44**, 2526 (1911); **45**, 394 (1912); **46**, 103 (1913).
28. Claisen, *Ber.*, **31**, 1021 (1898).
29. Stoermer, *ibid.*, **39**, 2288 (1906); *Ann. chim. phys.*, (8) **9**, 484 (1906). *Cf.* Klages and Kessler, *Ber.*, **39**, 1753 (1906); Tiffeneau, *et al.*, *Compt. rend.*, **205**, 54 (1936); Mousseron and Granger, *ibid.*, **217**, 483 (1943); Sexton and Britton, *U.S. patent* 2,628,255 (1951); Favorsky and Fikhomolov, *Compt. rend.*, **203**, 726 (1936); Hearne *et al.*, *Ind. Eng. Chem.*, **33**, 805 (1941); Hershtein, *Z. obšč. chim.*, **12**, 132 (1942).
30. Gattermann, *Ann.*, **347**, 348 (1906).
31. Bouveault, *Compt. rend.*, **137**, 987 (1903); *Bull. soc. chim.*, (3) **31**, 1306 (1904); Houben and Doescher, *Ber.*, **40**, 4576 (1907).
32. Bodroux, *Compt. rend.*, **138**, 92 (1904); Tschitschibabin, *J. Russ. Phys.-Chem. Soc.*, **35**, 1284 (1903); *Ber.*, **37**, 186, 850 (1904). *Organic Syntheses*, Coll. vol., II, 323 (1943).
33. Wohl and Schweitzer, *Ber.*, **39**, 890 (1906).
34. Zincke and Zahn, *ibid.*, **43**, 849 (1910).
35. Zinin, *Ann.*, **34**, 188 (1840); Fischer, *ibid.*, **211**, 215 (1882); Scheibler and Emden, *ibid.*, **434**, 265 (1923).
36. Boesler, *Ber.*, **14**, 327 (188); Mason and Dryfoos, *J. Chem. Soc.*, **63**, 1301 (1893).
37. Fischer, *Ber.*, **22**, 88 (1889).
38. Heller, *ibid.*, **44**, 2419 (1911); **46**, 283 (1913).
39. Thiele and Dralle, *Ann.*, **302**, 291 (1898); Osten, *ibid.*, **343**, 153 (1905).
40. Kraft, *Ber.*, **12**, 1664, 1668 (1879); **15**, 1687, 1711 (1882); Young, *Trans. Chem. Soc.*, **59**, 621 (1891); Ludlam, *ibid.*, **81**, 1185 (1902); Morgan and Holmes, *J. Soc. Chem. Ind.*, **44**, 108T, 491T (1925).
41. Squibb, *ibid.*, **14**, 506 (1895); **15**, 612 (1896); *J. Am. Chem. Soc.*, **17**, 187 (1895); Senderens, *Compt. rend.*, **148**, 927 (1909); **149**, 213, 995 (1909); Pickard and Kenyon, *J. Chem. Soc.*, **99**, 56 (1911); **101**, 628 (1912); **103**, 1936 (1913).
42. Freund, *Ann.*, **118**, 1 (1861); Butlerow, *Bull. soc. chim.*, (2) **5**, 18 (1866); Wagner and Saitzew, *Ann.* **175**, 361 (1875); Pawlow, *ibid.*, **188**, 110, 114, 126 (1877); Bertrand, *Bull. Soc. chim.* (3) **15**, 764 (1896). Jones, *J. Am. Chem. Soc.*, **69**, 2353 (1947); Breusch and Baykut, *Ber.*, **36**, 684 (1953).
43. Gilman and Nelson, *Rec. trav. chim.*, **55**, 518 (1936). *Cf.* Cason, *Chem. Revs.*, **40**, 15 (1947);

J. Am. Chem. Soc., **64**, 1106 (1942); **68**, 2078 (1946); Cole and Julian, *ibid.*, **67**, 1369 (1945); Suter and Weston, *ibid.*, **61**, 232 (1939). Pinson and Friess, *J. Am. Chem. Soc.*, **72**, 5333 (1950); Shirley, *Organic Reactions* VIII, 31 (1954).
44. Krause, *Ber.*, **50**, 1813 (1917); de Mahler, *J. Russ. Phys.-Chem. Soc.*, **48**, 1964 (1916).
45. Hamonet, *Bull. soc. chim.*, (2) **50**, 355 (1888); (3) **2**, 334 (1889).
46. Wislicenus, *Ann.*, **190**, 257 (1878); **219**, 308 (1883); Rohn, *ibid.*, **190**, 307 (1878); Jourdan, *ibid.*, **200**, 115 (1880); Böcking, *ibid.*, **204**, 17 (1880); Guthzeit, *ibid.*, **204**, 4, 10 (1880); Bouveault and Locquin, *Bull. soc. chim.*, (3) **31**, 1153 (1904); *Cf.* Clement, *Compt. rend.*, **236**, 718 (1953); **237**, 1421 (1953); Pudles and Lederer, *Biochim. Biophys. Acta*, **11**, 163 (1953).
47. Hofer, *Ber.*, **33**, 651 (1900).
48. Schlotterbeck, *Ber.*, **40**, 481 (1907); **42**, 2559 (1909); Meyer, *Monatsh.*, **26**, 1300 (1905); *Ber.*, **40**, 847 (1907); Lewis *et al.*, *J. Am. Chem. Soc.*, **47**, 1728 (1925); Arndt and Eistert, *Ber.*, **68**, 196 (1935); Wolfrom *et al.*, *J. Am. Chem. Soc.*, **63**, 201 (1941).
49. Autenrieth, *Ber.*, **20**, 374 (1887); Framm and Baumann, *ibid.*, **22**, 1040 (1889).
50. Fehrmann, *Ber.*, **20**, 2857 (1887); Gräbe, *ibid.*, **20**, 3266 (1887); Reddelien and Danilof, *ibid.*, **54**, 3141 (1931).
51. Hebbelynck and Martin, *Bull. soc. chim. Belg.*, **60**, 54 (1951).
52. Delaby, *Bull. soc. chim.*, (5) **3**, 2375 (1936).
53. Ottensooser, *ibid.*, (4) **41**, 324 (1927); *Riechstoff Ind.*, **2**, 192 (1927).
54. Moureu and Mignonac, *Compt. rend.*, **170**, 258 (1920); Aleksandrova, *J. Applied Chem. (U.S.S.R.)*, **10**, 105 (1937); Herne *et al.*, *Ind. Eng. Chem.*, **33**, 805 (1941); Wolf, *Fette u. Seifen*, **49**, 117 (1942); Davies and Hodson, *J. Chem. Soc.*, **1943**, 282; Lunt and Sondheimer, *ibid.*, **1950**, 3361.
55. Adkins *et al.*, *J. Am. Chem. Soc.*, **55**, 2992 (1933); Dunbar, *J. Org. Chem.*, **3**, 242 (1938); Dunbar and Arnold, *Ind. Eng. Chem. Anal. Ed.*, **16**, 441 (1944); *J. Org. Chem.*, **10**, 501 (1945).
56. Gresham and Grigsby, *J. Org. Chem.*, **14**, 1103 (1949).
57. Church and Lynn, *Ind. Eng. Chem.*, **42**, 768 (1950).
58. Evans *et al.*, *J. Am. Chem. Soc.*, **60**, 1628 (1938).
59. Radde, *Ber.*, **55**, 3174 (1922); Balenović *et al.*, *J. Org. Chem.*, **17**, 1459 (1952); **18**, 297 (1953).
60. Grignard and Mingasson, *Compt. rend.*, **185**, 1173 (1927). *Cf. Riechstoff Ind.*, **3**, 63 (1928).
61. Merling, *Ber.*, **41**, 2064 (1908); *Ber. Schimmel & Co. Akt. Ges.*, Oct. 1908, p. 189 ff.
62. Wittig and Hornberger, *Ann.*, **577**, 11 (1952).
63. Wittig and Hornberger, *Ann.*, **577**, 11 (1952); Weygand and Eberhardt, *Angew. Chem.*, **64**, 458 (1952); Weygand *et al.*, *Angew. Chem.*, **65**, 525 (1953); *Ber.*, **84**, 625 (1951). *Cf.* Galinovsky *et al.*, *Monatsh.*, **83**, 114 (1952); *Experientia*, **6**, 377 (1950); Smith and Rogier, *J. Am. Chem. Soc.*, **73**, 4047 (1951); Birkhoffer, *Ber*,, **85**, 288 (1952).
64. *Cf.* Krafft, *Ber.*, **13**, 1413 (1880); **16**, 1716 (1883); Zaar, *J. prakt. Chem.*, (2) **132**, 163 (1931); Behrend and Ludewig, *Ann.*, **379**, 352 (1911); Saha *et al.*, *Ber.*, **73**, 762 (1940).
65. Lewinsohn, *Perfumery Essent. Oil Record*, **15**, 79 (1924).
66. Darzens and Levy, *Compt. rend.*, **196**, 348 (1933); Meyer, *Compt. rend.*, **204**, 508, 1948 (1937).
67. Nef, *Ann.*, **280**, 263 (1894).
68. Tracey and Elderfield, *J. Org. Chem.*, **6**, 63 (1941); Petrow, *J. Chem. Soc.*, **1942**, 694; Plattner, *Helv. Chim. Acta*, **28**, 773 (1945); Levine *et al.*, *J. Am. Chem. Soc.*, **67**, 1510 (1945); Long, *ibid.*, **69**, 992 (1947); Mariella, *ibid.*, **69**, 2670 (1947).
69. Tracey and Elderfield, *J. Org. Chem.*, **6**, 63 (1941); Petrow, *J. Chem. Soc.*, **1942**, 694; Plattner, *Helv. Chim. Acta*, **28**, 773 (1945); Mariella, *J. Am. Chem. Soc.*, **69**, 2670 (1947).
70. Allen and Edens, *Org. Syntheses*, **25**, 92 (1945).
71. Behal and Sommelet, *Bull. soc. chim.*, (3) **31**, 300 (1904); (4) **1**, 401 (1907); Stoermer, *Ber.*, **39**, 2288 (1906).
72. Fieser *et al.*, *J. Am. Chem. Soc.*, **61**, 2136 (1939); Barnes and Budde, *ibid.*, **68**, 2339 (1946).
73. Langley and Emerson, *ibid.*, **72**, 3079 (1950).
74. Sheehan and Bloom, *ibid.*, **74**, 3825 (1952).
75. Reich and Reichstein, *Helv. Chim. Acta*, **26**, 583, 1943); Lardon, *ibid.*, **30**, 597 (1947); Sarett, *J. Am. Chem. Soc.*, **71**, 1165 (1949). *Cf.* Fieser and Rajagopalan, *ibid.*, **71**, 3935, 3938 (1949).
76. Fieser and Rajagopalan, *J. Am. Chem. Soc.*, **72**, 5530 (1950).
77. Babjohn, *Organic Reactions* V, p. 331.
78. Reiley *et al.*, *J. Chem. Soc.*, **1932**, 1875, Mel'nikov and Rokitskaya, *J. Gen. Chem., U.S.S.R.*, **9**, 1158 (1939); *British patent* 354,798.
79. Müller, *Ber.*, **66**, 1668 (1933); Astin *et al.*, *J. Chem. Soc.*, **1933**, 391; Piutti, *Gazz. chim. ital.*, **66**, 276 (1936).
80. DuPont *et al.*, *Bull. soc. chim.*, (4) **53**, 599 (1933); Fischer, *J. Am. Chem. Soc.*, **56**, 2056 (1934); Postowsky and Lugwkin, *Ber.*, **68**, 852 (1935); Badger, *J. Chem. Soc.*, **1941**, 535. *Cf.* Yokoyama, *J. Chem. Soc. Japan*, **59**, 262, 271 (1938).

81. Godchot and Cauquil, *Compt. rend.*, **202**, 326 (1936).
82. Ruzicka and Rey, *Helv. Chim. Acta*, **24**, 529 (1941); Biedebach, *Arch. Pharm.* **281**, 59 (1943); Heilbron *et al.*, *J. Chem. Soc.*, **1949**, 448.
83. Butenandt and Peters, *Ber.*, **71**, 2688 (1938); Ruzicka *et al.*, *Helv. Chim. Acta*, **21**, 373, 597 (1938); **22**, 1297 (1939); Inhoffen *et al.*, *Ber.*, **71**, 1024 (1938); Miescher *et al.*, *Helv. Chim. Acta*, **29**, 632 (1946); **30**, 1025 (1947); **32**, 1764 (1949).
84. Inhoffen *et al.*, *Ber.*, **73**, 457 (1940); Buser, *Helv. Chim. Acta*, **30**, 1390 (1947); Barton and Cox, *J. Chem. Soc.*, **1948**, 783.
85. Reichstein *et al.*, *Helv. Chim. Acta*, **24**, 360 (1941); **21**, 177 (1938).
86. Reichstein *et al.*, *ibid.*, **22**, 1124 (1939); **23**, 136 (1940).
87. Ehrenstein *et al.*, *J. Org. Chem.*, **15**, 264 (1950).
88. Naves *et al.*, *Helv. Chim. Acta*, **30**, 1607 (1947); Ruzicka *et al*, *ibid.*, **30**, 1813 (1947); **32**, 2113 (1949); Winter *et al.*, *ibid.*, **30**, 2215 (1947); Rouvé and Stoll, *ibid.*, **30**, 2220 (1947).
89. Milas *et al.*, *J. Am. Chem. Soc.*, **69**, 2248 (1947); **70**, 1292 (1948); Karrer *et al.*, *Helv. Chim. Acta*, **32**, 232, 436 (1949); Zobrist and Schinz, *ibid.*, **32**, 1195 (1949).
90. McKee and Henze, *J. Am. Chem. Soc.*, **66**, 2021 (1944).
91. Woodward *et al.*, *ibid.*, **67**, 1425 (1945); Jackman and Mills, *Nature*, **164**, 789 (1949); Lutz and Gillespie, *J. Am. Chem. Soc.*, **72**, 345 (1950); Doering and Young, *ibid.*, **72**, 631 (1950); Reichstein, *U.S. Patent* 2,404,768 (1946).
92. Blaise and Mair, *Compt. rend.*, **145**, 18 (1907); *Ann. chim.*, (8) **15**, 556 (1908).
93. Wohlgemuth, *Compt. rend.*, **159**, 80 (1914).
94. Blaise, *ibid.*, **155**, 46 (1912).
95. Blaise, *ibid.*, **155**, 1252 (1912).
96. Blaise, *ibid.*, **158**, 504 (1914).
97. Blaise, *ibid.*, **157**, 1440 (1913).
98. Adkin and Scanley, *J. Am. Chem. Soc.*, **73**, 2854 (1951).
99. Bowman and Fordham, *J. Chem. Soc.*, **1952**, 3945; Fonken and Johnson, *J. Am. Chem. Soc.*, **74**, 831 (1952).
100. Cason, *J. Am. Chem. Soc.*, **68**, 2078 (1946). *Cf.* Stoffer *et al.*, *ibid.*, **69**, 1684 (1947); Cason, *Chem. Revs.*, **40**, 15 (1947).
101. Schneider and Fröhlich, *German patent* 1,586,613 (1937). *Cf.* Auwers and Jacobson, *Ann.*, **426**, 222 (1922).
102. Aschan, *Ber.*, **23**, 3692 (1890); Gabriel, *ibid.*, **42**, 4050 (1909); Gabriel and Colman, *ibid.*, **42**, 1246 (1909).
103. Gabriel and Colman, *Ber.*, **42**, 1247, 1248 (1909).
104. Bawman, *Nature*, **162**, 111 (1948).
105. *Cf.* Hurd and Kelso, *J. Am. Chem. Soc.*, **62**, 2184 (1940).
106. Schmidt and Ascherl, *Ber.*, **58** B, 356 (1925).
107. Slanina, *J. Am. Chem. Soc.*, **58**, 891 (1936).
108. Baumann and Fromm, *Ber.*, **22**, 2600 (1889); Bost and Constable, *Organic Syntheses*, **16**, 81 (1936).
109. Baumann and Fromm, *Ber.*, **22**, 1035 (1889); Leteur, *Compt. rend.*, **136**, 1459 (1903).
110. Fromm and Ziersch, *Ber.*, **39**, 3599 (1906).
111. Mitra, *J. Indian Chem. Soc.*, **10**, 71 (1933).
112. Andreasch, *Monatsh.*, **39**, 426 (1918). *Cf.* Granacher and Mahal, *Helv. Chim. Acta*, **6**, 467 (1923).
113. Scheibler *et al.*, *J. prakt. Chem.*, (2) **124**, 1 (1930). *Cf.* Mitra, *J. Indian Chem. Soc.*, **9**, 633 (1932).
114. Granacher *et al.*, *Helv. Chim. Acta*, **6**, 458 (1923).
115. Fromm, *Ber.*, **60**, 2090 (1927); Ray, *Nature*, **134**, 1010 (1934); Sen, *J. Indian Chem. Soc.*, **12**, 647, 751 (1935); **13**, 268 (1936); **14**, 214 (1937).
116. Wuyts, *Ber.*, **36**, 863 (1903). *Cf.* Müller and Schiller, *J. prakt. Chem.*, (2) **116**, 175 (1927).
117. Copenhaver, *U.S. patent* 2,589,305; 2,586,306 (1949). *Cf.* Starke, *U.S. patent* 2,615,922 (1949); Bougault *et al.*, *Bull. soc. chim.*, (5) **5**, 1699 (1938); **6**, 34 (1939); **7**, 781 (1940); *Compt. rend.*, **208**, 657 (1939); Folkers *et al.*, *J. Biol. Chem.*, **146**, 475 (1942); *J. Am. Chem. Soc.*, **65**, 1013 (1943); Organon, *British patent* 646,586; Levin *et al.*, *U.S. patents* 2,533,124; 2,551,444; 2,623,054 (1947).
118. Nelles and Bayer, *German patent* 642,147; 650,359 (1935); *Frdl.* **23**, 87; **24**, 72; Kroeger *et al.*, *J. Org. Chem.* **1**, 163 (1937); Price and Pappalardo, *J. Am. Chem. Soc.*, **72**, 2613 (1950); Levin *et al.*, *J. Am. Chem. Soc.*, **70**, 1907, 2955 (1948); **71**, 3317 (1949).
119. Croxall *et al.*, *J. Am. Chem. Soc.*, **71**, 1257 (1949); *U.S. patent* 2,535,012 (1948).
120. Jacobs, *et al.*, *J. Am. Chem. Soc.*, **62**, 1849 (1940); **64**, 223 (1942); Van Dorp *et al.*, *Nature*, **160**, 189 (1947); **67**, 973 (1948); **68**, 604 (1949); *Rec. trav. chim.*, **68**, 609 (1949); *French patent* 969,968 (1947); *German patent* 824,943; Arens and Modderman, *Proc. Acad. Sci. Amsterdam, Series B*, **54**, 236 (1951).
121. Pino, *Gazz. chim. ital.*, **80**, 768 (1950); Pino and Ercoli, *ibid.*, **81**, 757 (1951).

122. Grard, *Ann. chim.*, (10) **13**, 363 (1930).
123. Kondakov, *J. Russ. Phys.-Chem. Soc.*, **20**, 154 (1888); Groll *et al.*, *Ind. Eng. Chem.*, **33**, 805 (1941); *U.S. patents* 2,010,076 (1932); 2,046,556 (1934); 2,097,154.
124. Paul, *Bull. soc. chim.*, (4) **53**, 1489 (1933); (5) **1**, 971 (1934); Sawyer and Andrus, *Organic Syntheses*, **23**, 25 (1943); Kline and Turkevich, *J. Am. Chem. Soc.*, **68**, 1646 (1946); Schniepp and Geller, *ibid.*, **68** 1646 (1946); Woods and Sanders, *ibid.*, **68**, 2111 (1946).
125. Smith *et al.*, *J. Am. Chem. Soc.*, **73**, 5267, 5272 (1951); *U.S. patent* 2,514,168; 2,546,018; 2,546,019 (1947); Langley and Emerson, *J. Am. Chem. Soc.*, **72**, 3079 (1950); Hull and Howe, *J. Chem. Soc.*, **1951**, 2480; Parham and Holmquist, *J. Am. Chem. Soc.*, **73**, 913 (1951); Emerson and Langley, *U.S. patent* 2,624,764 (1949).
126. Paul, *Bull. soc. chim.*, (5) **1**, 1397 (1934); Woods and Sanders, *J. Am. Chem. Soc.*, **68**, 2482 (1946); Normant, *Compt. rend.*, **228**, 102 (1949); Quennehen and Normant, *ibid.*, **228**, 1301 (1949); Riobé, *Bull. soc. chim.*, (5) **19**, 305 (1952).
127. Smith *et al.*, *J. Am. Chem. Soc.*, **73**, 5274, 5280 (1951).
128. Schulz and Wagner, *Angew. Chem.*, **62**, 117 (1950); Schulz, *German patent* 863,795 (1943).
129. Parham *et al.*, *J. Am. Chem. Soc.*, **74**, 1824 (1952).
130. Stoll *et al.*, *Helv. Chim. Acta*, **36**, 1500 (1953).
131. Clauson-Kaus *et al.*, *Acta Chem. Scand.*, **6**, 531, 545, 551, 556, 569 (1952); Elming, *ibid.*, **6**, 572 (1952).
132. Shaw, *J. Chem. Soc.*, **1925**, 215; **1937**, 300; Cope *et al.*, *J. Am. Chem. Soc.*, **73**, 3416 (1951).
133. Baumgarten, *Ber.*, **57**, 1622 (1924); **59**, 1166 (1926); *German patent* 438,009 (1924); *Frdl.*, **15**, 1081; Klages, *Ber.*, **86**, 1330 (1953).
134. Baumgarten and Olshausen, *Ber.*, **64**, 925 (1931).
135. Reissert, *Ber.*, **38**, 1603, 3415 (1905).
136. *Cf.* Kaufmann and Strübin, *ibid.*, **44**, 680 (1911).
137. Richter-Anschutz, *Chemie der Kohlenstoffverbindungen*, 12th ed. III, p. 367 (1931).
138. Dullagham and Nord., *J. Org. Chem.*, **17**, 1183 (1952); Johnson *et al.*, *J. Am. Chem. Soc.*, **75**, 4995 (1953).
139. Darzens *et al.*, *Compt. rend.*, **139**, 1214 (1904); **141**, 786 (1905); **142**, 714 (1906); **144**, 1123 (1907); **145**, 1342 (1907); **150**, 1243 (1910); **151**, 758 (1910); **152**, 443, 1105 (1911); **154**, 1812 (1912); **196**, 348, 489 (1933); **204**, 272 (1937); *German patents* 174,239; 174,279 (1904); Newman, *Organic Reactions* **5**, 413 (1949); Houben-Weyl, *Die Methoden der Organische Chemie VII*, p. 326 (1954); VIII, 513 (1952). *Cf.* Yarnall and Wallis, *J. Org. Chem.*, **4**, 270 (1939); Howton, *ibid.*, **12**, 379 (1947); Ecary, *Ann. chim.*, (12) **3**, 445 (1948); Goerman and Pearce, *J. Am. Chem. Soc.*, **73**, 2304 (1951); Nerdel *et al.*, *Ber.*, **84**, 972 (1951); **85**, 173 (1952); Johnson *et al.*, *J. Am. Chem. Soc.*, **75**, 4995 (1953).
140. *Cf.* Schmitt, *Ann.*, **547**, 261 (1941); Isler *et al.*, *Helv. Chim. Acta*, **30**, 1911 (1947); **32**, 489 (1949); Lindlar, *U.S. patent* 2,451,740 (1947); 2,451,742 (1948); *Swiss patent* 255,097 (1946); Linnel and Shen, *J. Pharm. Pharmacol.*, **1**, 971 (1949); Karrer and Leumann, *Helv. Chim. Acta*, **34**, 1408 (1951); Inhoffen *et al.*, *Ann.*, **570**, 54 (1950).
141. Dullagham and Nord, *J. Org. Chem.*, **18**, 878 (1953).
142. Sommers and Westen, *J. Am. Chem. Soc.*, **73**, 575 (1951).
143. Criegee, *Ann.*, 481,263 (1930); *Ber.*, **64**, 260 (1931), *Angew Chem.*, **53**, 321 (1940); *Cf.* Scanlan and Swern, *J. Am. Chem. Soc.*, **62**, 2305 (1940); Ohle and Melkonian, *Ber.*, **74**, 291 (1941); Paul and Tchelitcheff, *Bull. soc. chim.*, (5) **15**, 197 (1948); Kransz, *Ann. chim.*, (12) **4**, 811 (1949); Reeves, *Ind. Eng. Chem.*, **21**, 751 (1949); English and Barber, *J. Am. Chem. Soc.*, **71**, 3310 (1949); Jensen *et al.*, *Acta Chem. Scand.*, **4**, 692, 703 (1950); Reid and Yost, *J. Am. Chem. Soc.*, **72**, 5232 (1950); Hurd and Saunders, *ibid.*, **74**, 5326 (1952); Mathes and Souermilch, *Ber.*, **85**, 1008 (1952).
144. Baer *et al.*, *J. Am. Chem. Soc.*, **61**, 2607 (1939); Grosheintz, *ibid.*, **61**, 3379 (1939).
145. Rigly, *Nature*, **164**, 185 (1949); *J. Chem. Soc.*, **1950**, 1907; Stoll *et al.*, *Helv. Chim. Acta*, **36**, 268 (1953).
146. Malaprade, *Bull. soc. chim.*, (4) **43**, 683 (1928); Fleury *et al.*, *Compt. rend.*, **195**, 1395 (1932); **196**, 1416 (1933); Jackson and Hudson, *J. Am. Chem. Soc.*, **59**, 2049 (1937); **60**, 989 (1938); Criegee, *Angew. Chem.*, **53**, 321 (1940); Fleury and Bon-Bernates, *J. pharm. chim.*, (8) **23**, 85 (1936); Reeves, *J. Am. Chem. Soc.*, **61**, 664 (1939); Salmon Powell, *ibid.*, **61**, 3507 (1939); English and Griswold, *ibid.*, **70**, 1390 (1948); Schöpt and Kühne, *Ber.*, **83**, 390 (1950); Brown *et al.*, *J. Chem. Soc.*, **1952**, 3172.
147. Willard and Boyle, *Ind. Eng. Chem. Anal. Ed.*, **13**, 137 (1941).
148. King, *J. Chem. Soc.*, **1936**, 1791; **1938**, 1826.
149. English and Griswald, *J. Am. Chem. Soc.*, **70**, 1390 (1948).
150. Adams and Mathieu, *ibid.*, **70**, 2120 (1948); Gilman *et al.*, *ibid.*, **61**, 951 (1939); **68**, 427 (1946).
151. Arens and Greenwood, *J. Chem. Soc.*, **1953**, 1937.
152. Sarrett *et al.*, *J. Am. Chem. Soc.*, **75**, 422 (1953); Hershberg *et al.*, *ibid.*, **75**, 5751 (1953).
153. Oppenauer *et al.*, *Germ. patent Anm. Sch.* 2261 (1942); *C.A.*, **44**, 387 (1950).

154. Wille and Saffer, *Ann.*, **568**, 40 (1950); Deichsel, *U.S. patent* 849,547 (1943).
155. Bell *et al.*, *Biochem. J.*, **42**, 516 (1948); Attenburrow *et al.*, *J. Chem. Soc.*, **1952**, 1094.
156. Attenburrow *et al.*, *J. Chem. Soc.*, **1952**, 1104.
157. Bohmfalk *et al.*, *Ind. Eng. Chem.*, **43**, 786 (1951); McNamee and Dunn, *U.S. patent* 2,339,347 (1940).
158. *German patents* 833,291; 857,359.
159) *French patent* 665,917 (1928); *German patent* 577,630 (1928); Lebedev, *Russian patent* 35,182 (1927); Jackson *et al.*, *Ind. Eng. Chem.*, **39**, 120 (1947); Kampmeyer and Stahly, *ibid.*, **41**, 550 (1949); Corson *et al.*, *ibid.*, **41**, 1012 (1949).
160. Kačer, *German patent* 557,249; *Frdl.*, **19**, 2124; Reiley *et al.*, *J. Chem. Soc.*, **1932**, 2342; *Nature*, **159**, 571 (1947).
161. Kölln, *Ann.*, **416**, 230 (1918); Mugdan and Sixt, *German patent* 573,721 (1932); *Frdl.*, **19**, 215.
162. Müller and Pechmann, *Ber.*, **22**, 2557 (1889); Pinner, *ibid.*, **35**, 4132 (1902); **38**, 1531 (1905).
163. Bamberger and Wulz, *Ber.*, **24**, 2793 (1891).
164. Escourrou, *Bull. soc. chim.*, (5) **6**, 1172 (1939).
165. Seifert and Schinz, *Helv. Chim. Acta*, **34**, 728 (1951).
166. Hull and Hagemeyer, *U.S. patent* 2,642,460 (1948).
167. Hazeldine, *J. Chem. Soc.*, **1952**, 3490.
168. Jones, *U.S. patent* 2,515,304 (1946); Clauson-Kaas, *Acta Chem. Scand.*, **1**, 379, 415 (1947); **2**, 109 (1948).
169. Stoll *et al.*, *Helv. Chim. Acta*, **35**, 1263 (1952). *Cf.* Fakstrop *et al.*, *J. Am. Chem. Soc.*, **72**, 869 (1950); Hufford *et al.*, *ibid.*, **74**, 3014 (1952).
170. Hill and Palmer, *Am. Chem. J.*, **9**, 147 (1887); Dunlap *ibid.*, **19**, 641 (1897); Simonis, *Ber.*, **32**, 2085 (1899); Heilbron, *J. Chem. Soc.*, **1932**, 264; *J. Am. Chem. Soc.*, **74**, 326 (1952); Kuh, *U.S. patent* 2,588,852 (1950); Kuh and Shepard, *J. Am. Chem. Soc.*, **75**, 4597 (1953).
171. Elming and Clauson-Kaas, *Acta Chem. Scand.*, **6**, 535 (1952).
172. Clauson-Kaas and Elming, *ibid.*, **6**, 560 (1952).
173. Klages and Kessler, *Ber.*, **39**, 1753 (1906).
174. Baur, *Germ. patents* 528,822; 538,651 (1929); 618,972 (1932); *Frdl.*, **18**, 772, 774; **21**, 95.
175. Ramart-Lucas and Labaune, *Ann. chim.*, (10) **16**, 276 (1931).
176. *Cf.* Zinke, *Ann.*, **216**, 286, 301 (1882); Kötz and Richter, *J. prakt. Chem.*, (2) **111**, 382 (1925).
177. Walh *et al.*, *Ber.*, **32**, 1353 (1899); **45**, 2046 (1912); Groll and Berkeley *U.S. patent* 2,042,224 (1934); Emerson, *U.S. patent* 2,444,400 (1943); Gear, *U.S. patent* 2,501,042 (1947); Hoyt and Manninen, *U.S. patent* 2,558,520 (1948); *Organic Syntheses* Coll. Vol. 1, p. 45.
178. Inhoffen and Leibner, *Ann.*, **575**, 105 (1951).
179. Zinke and Brauer, *Ber.*, **9**, 1769 (1876); Daniloff, *ibid.*, **59**, 1041 (1926); **60**, 2390 (1927); Urion, *Compt. rend.*, **190**, 1512 (1930); *Ann. chim.*, (11) **1**, 1 (1934); Urion and Baum, *Compt. rend.*, **204**, 595 (1937); Tiffeneau and Levy, *Bull. soc. chim.*, (4) **49**, 1746 (1931); Tiffeneau, *Helv. Chim. Acta*, **21**, 404 (1938); Roger and Harper, *Rec. trav. chim.*, **56**, 203 (1937).
180. Lieben, *Monatsh.*, **23**, 60 (1902); Askenasy and Heller, *U.D. patent* 1,928,240 (1930); Amos and Hooker, *U.S. patent* 2,208,557 (1938); Ziese, *French patent* 850,752 (1938); Emerson, *U.S. patent* 2,397,412 (1943).
181. Schöpf *et al.*, *Ann.*, **544**, 30 (1940).
182. Hershberg, *Helv. Chim. Acta*, **17**, 351 (1934); Jensen and Dynesen, *Acta Chem. Scand.*, **4**, 692 (1950); *C.A.*, **45**, 798 (1951).
183. Claus and Morgen, *J. Am. Chem. Soc.*, **73**, 5005 (1951); Marvel *et al.*, *ibid.*, **64**, 1824 (1942); Roedig and Degener, *Ber.*, **86**, 1473 (1953).
184. Henne *et al.*, *J. Am. Chem. Soc.*, **72**, 3370 (1950); Smith and Rogier, *ibid.*, **73**, 4047 (1951); Lowy, *ibid.*, **74**, 1355 (1952).
185. Adkins, *Org. Syntheses*, **8**, 98 (1928); Glattfeld *et al.*, *J. Am. Chem. Soc.*, **49**, 2305 (1927); **57**, 2204 (1935); Schmidt and Müller, *Ber.*, **76**, 344 (1943).
186. Oeda, *Bull. Chem. Soc. Japan*, **9**, 13 (1934); Klenk and Clarenz, *Z. physiol. Chem.* **257**, 272 (1939); Lauer *et al.*, *J. Am. Chem. Soc.*, **63**, 1153 (1941); *Cf.* Soffer *et al.*, *ibid.*, **74**, 1556 (1952).
187. Soffer *et al.*, *l.c.*
188. Schmidt, *Angew. Chem.*, **36**, 511 (1923); Wolf, *Org. Reactions* III, 307 (1946); Schmidt and Klavehn, *Germ. patent* 583,565 (1929).
189. Brandt, *Acta Chem. Scand.*, **3**, 1050 (1949).
190. Mosettig, *Org. Reactions*, VIII, 218 (1954); Henne *et al.*, *J. Am. Chem. Soc.*, **72**, 3370 (1950); Claus and Morgenthau, *ibid.*, **73**, 5005 (1951); Smith and Rogier, *ibid.*, **73**, 4047 (1951); Yandik and Larsen, *ibid.*, **73**, 3534 (1951); Weygand *et al.*, *Ber.*, **84**, 625 (1951); *Angew. Chem.*, **65**, 525 (1953); Brown and Musgrave, *J. Chem. Soc.*, **1952**, 5049; Husted and Ahlbrecht, *J. Am. Chem. Soc.*, **74**, 5442 (1952); Birkofer and Birkofer, *Ber.*, **88**, 286 (1952); Arth, *J. Am. Chem. Soc.*, **75**, 2413 (1953); Pierce and Kane, *ibid.*, **76**, 300 (1954).

191. Wittig and Hornberger, *Ann.*, **577**, 11 (1952); Galinovsky *et al.*, *Monatsh.*, **82**, 551 (1951); **83**, 114 (1952).
192. Percival *et al.*, *J. Am. Chem. Soc.*, **75**, 3731 (1953).
193. Manyik *et al.*, *ibid.*, **75**, 5030 (1953).
194. Henne and Tedder, *J. Chem. Soc.*, **1953**, 3628.
195. Speranski, *J. Russ. Phys.-Chem. Soc.*, **38**, 1288 (1906); *C.A.*, **1**, 2118 (1907).
196. Staudinger and Freudenberger, *Ber.*, **61**, B, 1576 (1928).
197. Bost and Cosby, *J. Am. Chem. Soc.*, **57**, 1404 (1935).
198. Freudenberg, *Organic Syntheses*, Coll. Vol. II, p. 573 (1943).
199. Schönberg *et al.*, *Ber.*, **61**, B, 1375 (1928); Kitamura, *J. Pharm. Soc. Japan*, **57**, 893 (1937).
200. *British patent* 20,615 (1914); *C.A.*, **10**, 2389 (1916).
201. Mohlau *et al.*, *Ber.*, **35**, 377 (1902).
202. Fehrmann, *ibid.*, **20**, 2869 (1895).
203. Wolfrom and Karabinos, *J. Am. Chem. Soc.*, **68**, 724, 1455 (1946); Prelog *et al.*, *Helv. Chim. Acta*, **29**, 360 (1946).
204. Spero *et al.*, *J. Am. Chem. Soc.*, **70**, 1907 (1948); McIntosh *et al.*, *ibid.*, **70**, 2955 (1948).
205. Fischer and Orth, *Die Chemie des Pyrrols*, vol. 1, p. 410 (1934).
206. Schönberg, *Ber.*, **58**, 1793 (1925).
207. Schickh and Grieshaber, *Angew. Chem.*, **62**, 547 (1950); Kloetzel, *J. Am. Chem. Soc.*, **70**, 3571 (1948). *Cf.* Buckley *et al.*, *J. Chem. Soc.*, **1947**, 1514.
208. Schickh and Grieshaber, *l.c.*, Wildman *et al.*, *J. Org. Chem.*, **17**, 581 (1952); *J. Am. Chem. Soc.*, **75**, 1912 (1953).
209. Hauser *et al.*, *J. Am. Chem. Soc.*, **66**, 345 (1944); **72**, 3635 (1950); **74**, 3231 (1952); **75**, 4109, 5030 (1953); *Organic Reactions* VIII, p 98 ff (1954).
210. Hauser *et al.*, *Organic Reactions*, VIII, p. 91 (1951); Chakravarti and Madjundar, *J. Indian Chem. Soc.*, **16**, 151 (1939); Ali *et al.*, *Proc. Indian Acad. Sci.*, **13 A**, 184 (1941); *C.A.*, **36**, 91 (1942).
211. Kharasch and Burt, *J. Org. Chem.*, **16**, 150 (1951).
212. Roberts *et al.*, *J. Am. Chem. Soc.*, **73**, 618 (1951); Kohler and Erickson, *ibid.*, **53**, 2301 (1931).

CHAPTER 4

REACTIONS INVOLVING CARBONYL COMPOUNDS: Part 1

The carbonyl group in aldehydes and ketones is capable of various reactions. The reactivity of the group varies, depending on the character of the rest of the molecule.

α-Hydroxy carbonyl compounds in general undergo oxidation readily. Aromatic hydroxy ketones are transformed to 1,2-diketones, but the oxidation of aliphatic α-hydroxy ketones proceeds vigorously and cannot be stopped at the diketone stage. A method of oxidation which is generally applicable depends on the use of Fehling's solution or of copper sulfate and pyridine. Chlorine, nitric acid, chromic acid and alkaline permanganate solution may also be used for the purpose in many cases.[1]

Aliphatic α-hydroxy ketones may be conveniently dehydrogenated to the corresponding diketones by passing the vapors of the hydroxy ketone over reduced copper at 250-270°.[2]

Enolization

The grouping $-CH_2CO-$ in simple ketones shows some tendency to change in part to the enolic form $-CH = C(OH)-$.[3] This tendency is much more pronounced in 1,3-diketones and β-keto esters. The two forms in general exist simultaneously in the liquid diketones or keto esters.

The presence of the enol form may be demonstrated in various ways. Thus, the enol gives a characteristic coloration with ferric chloride, and from the sodium derivative of the enol, solutions of copper salts give a precipitate of the copper salt of the enol form. Bromine reacts with an alcoholic solution of the enol, probably forming a monobromoketone:

$$-\overset{|}{\underset{|}{C}} = \overset{|}{C}OH + Br_2 \rightarrow -\overset{Br}{\underset{|}{\overset{|}{C}}} -\overset{|}{C}(OH)Br \rightarrow -\underset{|}{C}Br.\overset{|}{C}O + HBr$$

This reaction may be employed for the estimation of the quantity of the enol form.[4] The amount of the enol may also be determined from the index of refraction of the liquid, if the indices of refraction of the pure enol and keto forms are known.

The equilibrium between the enol and keto forms is influenced by temperature and the solvent employed. The effect of the solvent is especially marked. Thus, the enol form of ethyl acetoacetate exists in water to the extent of only 0.4%; the amount rises to 48%

in hexane, and to 56% in pyridine. Acetonylacetone exists largely in the enol form in many organic solvents.

Special factors play an important role in enolization which may result in ring closure. For example, while α,δ-diacetylbutene shows the characteristics of a true diketone, its $\beta,\beta,\gamma,\gamma$-tetramethyl derivative passes into the cyclic form,

$$CH_3\overline{C(OH)CH_2CH_2C(CH_3)_2C}HCOCH_3,$$

at the moment of its formation.[156]

The rearrangement

$$-\overset{|}{C}H-CO- \rightleftarrows -\overset{|}{C}=C(OH)-$$

can be forced in the direction of enol formation. The change may be brought about in diketones by use of alkali hydroxide. Monoketones are not enolized by alkalies; enolization may be induced in this case by use of alkali metals, though the free enolates have not been isolated. Acids also bring about enolization, and to a greater extent in nonionizing than in ionizing media. No corresponding treatment is known which forces the formation of the keto form, although the transformation of the enol form to the keto form may be catalytically accelerated.

Ketones of the type of pulegone and menthone, subjected to the action of Grignard reagents, yield the enol magnesium halides. These have been transformed to the acetyl and benzoyl derivatives of the enols by the action of acetyl and benzoyl chlorides respectively. The free enols have been obtained from the acetyl compounds by hydrolysis.[5]

The pure enolic form of ethyl acetoacetate may be prepared by fractional distillation. This is accomplished by first fractionally distilling the ester in a glass apparatus to obtain a condensate rich in the enol form. When the distillate is immediately fractionated in a quartz apparatus the enol may be obtained in the pure form. The enolic form of acetonylacetone may also be prepared by this method.[6]

α-Diketones are also tautomeric in character, and both isomeric forms of phenyl benzyl, phenyl anisyl and benzyl methyl ketones have been isolated. Keto - enol tautomerism is also possible in γ-diketones.

β-Keto aldehydes are apparently incapable of existence, changing immediately to hydroxymethylene ketones, RCOCH = CHOC, compounds of pronounced acid character which dissolve in aqueous solutions of alkali carbonates to form stable alkaline salts. These salts yield neutral acetates and benzoates by treatment with acetic anhydride and benzoyl chloride, respectively. With ethyl iodide, they give ethoxymethyleneketones, which show the character of esters and are saponified by alcoholic alkalies.

Triketones of the type RCOCH(COR′)COR″ have been isolated both in the keto form and the enol form, RC(OH) = C(COR′)COR″. According to Claisen, the tendency toward enolization increases with increase in the number of acyl groups attached to the carbon atom adjacent to the carbonyl group, and in proportion to the acidic character of the acyl group. The acetyl group thus shows a greater potency than the benzoyl group in inducing enolization.

The enols are acidic in character and readily give alkali metal derivatives; many dissolve in aqueous alkali. Enol salts of other metals have also been prepared. Among the best known are the salts of acetylacetone, of which more than sixty have been prepared.[7] Most of these metallic compounds cannot be regarded as normal salts, since they are sparingly soluble in water, soluble in hydrocarbons and may be volatilized without decomposition. They should be regarded, rather, as coordination compounds with the carbonyl group attached to the metal by a coordinate valency,

$$CH_3.C - O$$
$$CH \qquad Me$$
$$CH_3C = O$$

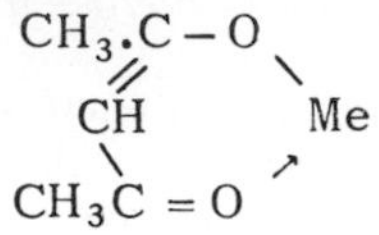

The alkali metal derivatives of enols, reacting with alkyl and acyl halides give, as a rule, not the expected enol ethers or esters, but an alkyl or acyl substituted ketone. a-Methylacetoacetic ester results, for example, through the reaction of methyl iodide with the sodium derivative of ethyl acetoacetate:

$$CH_3C = CHCOOC_2H_5 + CH_3I \quad \rightarrow \quad CH_3COCH(CH_3)COOC_2H_5 + NaI$$
$$\underset{ONa}{|}$$

Acetylmethyl ethyl ketone, $CH_3COCH(COCH_3)CH_3$, results similarly from sodio acetylacetone and methyl iodide.

The ether of the enolic form of acetoacetic ester may be prepared in low yield from the silver derivative of the enol and an alkyl halide. The alkyl ether of the enol form of ethyl oxalacetate has been prepared by this method from the silver derivative of the enol.[6]

A remarkable characteristic of the enolic forms of 1,3-diketones or β-keto esters is their ability to give azo derivatives by reaction with diazo compounds. The reaction is best carried out by adding to the ketone first the solution of the diazo compound, then sodium acetate.[8] Cleavage of certain groups may take place during the reaction. Cleavage takes place, for example, when azo compounds are prepared from 3-methylacetylacetone and from malonic ester.[9]

Polymerization of Aldehydes

Aliphatic aldehydes polymerize under the influence of substances such as sulfuric acid, hydrogen chloride, sulfur dioxide or zinc chloride.

Formaldehyde in the pure form polymerizes spontaneously to *trioxymethylene*,

$$\begin{array}{ccc} & O - CH_2 & \\ CH_2 & & O \\ & O - CH_2 & \end{array}$$

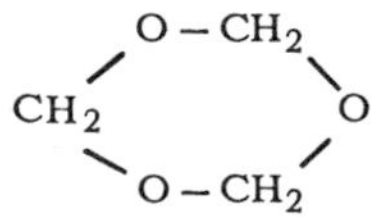

traces of water favoring the change. This polymer is readily decomposed on heating to monomeric formaldehyde. When aqueous solutions of the aldehyde are evaporated, a water-soluble polymer of unknown molecular weight, *paraformaldehyde,* results containing loosely combined water. Various polymers of formaldehyde are formed when sulfuric acid is added to aqueous solutions of the aldehyde. The a- and β-polyoxymethylenes are formed by the action of sulfuric acid on aqueous, methanol-free formaldehyde solutions, while β- and γ-isomers result when sulfuric acid is added to commercial formaldehyde solutions, which contain methanol. A fourth polymer, δ-polyoxymethylene is obtained when an aqueous solution of the γ-isomer is subjected to prolonged heating.[10] An isomeric form of trioxymethylene is obtained when the various polyoxymethylenes are sublimed and the vapors are led into water. The polyoxymethylenes are considered by Staudinger as long chains of oxymethylene, $-O-CH_2-(OCH_2)_n-OCH-$. Variations in the terminal group are assumed to account for differences in the chemical properties.

The terminal grouping in the α-isomer is assumed to be $-CH_2OH$, while that of the γ-isomer $-OCH_3$.[11]

The addition of a drop of sulfuric acid to *acetaldehyde* causes the rapid polymerization of the compound. The reaction proceeds violently if concentrated sulfuric acid is used. The compound is transformed largely to *paraldehyde*, a liquid which shows none of the characteristic reactions of aldehydes. It is unreactive toward Schiff's reagent, hydroxylamine, phenylhydrazine and ammoniacal silver nitrate. Molecular weight determinations show that it is a trimer of acetaldehyde. It may be considered as a homolog of trioxymethylene with the structure[12]

$$CH_3CH \begin{array}{c} O-CH-CH_3 \\ \diagup \qquad \diagdown \\ \qquad \qquad O \\ \diagdown \qquad \diagup \\ O-CH-CH_3 \end{array}$$

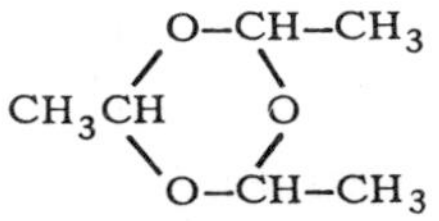

The transformation of acetaldehyde to paraldehyde is a reversible process and an equilibrium condition exists between the monomeric aldehyde and the trimer:

$$3CH_3CHO \rightleftarrows (CH_3CHO)_3$$

The trimer may be transformed completely into the monomer by distilling in the presence of sulfuric acid. Treated with bromine at $0°$, paraldehyde yields dibromoparaldehyde with small amounts of tribromoparaldehyde.[13]

A solid polymer, *metaldehyde*, results, together with some paraldehyde, when the polymerization of acetaldehyde is carried out at $0°$ by the use of dry hydrogen chloride or sulfuric acid.[14] Like paraldehyde, metaldehyde shows none of the characteristic reactions of aldehydes. The structure of this polymer has not yet been established, although it is probable that it contains ether-like linkages.

Higher homologs of acetaldehyde also give two types of polymers, designated as the para and meta series.[15] Aldehydes with eleven or more carbon atoms have a tendency to polymerize spontaneously on keeping; polymerization is accelerated by acids or sodium bisulfite.[16] Hexahydrobenzaldehyde also polymerizes on keeping. The spontaneous polymerization of halogenated aliphatic aldehydes is probably due to the action of small amounts of hydrogen halide resulting from the hydrolysis of the haloaldehyde.[17]

Dialdehydes such as glyoxal and succinaldehyde, polymerize quite readily to glassy bodies. The monomeric dialdehydes may be stored unchanged for only a short period below $-20°$. Dialdehydes of the type of succinic and maleic dialdehyde react as monomers in aqueous solution.

Alpha and beta hydroxy aldehydes polymerize very readily. The polymers are mostly di- and trimeric compounds.[245]

Polymeric aldehydes may be depolymerized more or less readily by heat. An equilibrium exists between monomeric and polymeric forms in solution. The transformation is catalyzed by hydrogen ions. Low temperatures favor the formation of the polymer, while higher temperatures cause the reverse change. The depolymerization of paraformaldehyde by heating should be stopped short of complete disappearance of the polymer in order to avoid a possible explosive decomposition.

Reaction with Alkali Bisulfites[157]

Aldehydes in aqueous solution react with sulfurous acid with evolution of heat to form additive compounds which, however, are decomposed to the original aldehyde upon the evaporation of the solution. Well defined crystalline compounds result, on the other hand, through the interaction of aldehydes and alkali bisulfites in aqueous solution. Raschig showed that the compounds formed are α-hydroxy-sulfonic acids:[18]

$$RCHO + NaHSO_3 \rightarrow RCH\begin{matrix} \diagup OH \\ \diagdown SO_3Na \end{matrix}$$

The correctness of this structure has been confirmed by observations of X-ray spectra.[19] The instability of the free acid is explained by the fact that the hydroxy and sulfonic acid radicals are attached to the same carbon atom.

The *procedure* followed in preparing bisulfite compounds is to shake the carbonyl compound with a concentrated aqueous solution of sodium bisulfite. Alcohol is often employed as a solvent or is added toward the end of the reaction in order to bring about more complete precipitation of the bisulfite compound. The use of emulsifying agents including soaps is of advantage when large quantities of neutral impurities are present.

Bisulfite compounds of sensitive aldehydes containing reactive double bonds are made by reaction with hydrogen sulfite freshly prepared from equivalent quantities of pure sodium sulfite and acetic acid. Another method consists in mixing the carbonyl compound with neutral aqueous sodium bisulfite and leading sulfur dioxide into the mixture, or gradually adding an acid to keep the solution neutral to phenolphthalein.

The aldehyde-bisulfite compounds are only slightly soluble in concentrated aqueous alkali bisulfite, and they may be isolated in the crystalline form by the addition of an excess of bisulfite to their solution.

The tendency toward the formation of bisulfite compounds is so marked with most aldehydes and some ketones, including cyclic ketones such as cyclohexanone, that they partially react with sodium sulfite with liberation of free alkalies,

$$RCHO + Na_2SO_3 + H_2O \rightarrow RCH(OH)SO_3Na + NaOH$$

and the reaction may be employed for the estimation of the more reactive carbonyl compounds, simply by titrating the alkali liberated.[20]

Aldehydes, with few exceptions, readily react with alkali bisulfites. Among the exceptions are phenyldimethylacetaldehyde, diphenylethylacetaldehyde,[21] and aldehydes derived from thymol and carvacrol.[22]

Bisulfite compounds may be obtained from chloral and bromal. *n*-Butyl-*n*-hexylacetaldehyde reacts very slowly, and the bisulfite compound of 2-methyl-5-isopropylcyclohexane is decomposed even by cold water. A polymeric body is obtained from undecanal, while phenyldimethylacetaldehyde and diphenylethylacetaldehyde fail to react with sodium bisulfite. Bisulfite compounds of aldehydic sugars, such as *d*-glucose and arabinose are much less stable than those of simple aldehydes.

Unsaturated aldehydes combine with particular ease with bisulfite to form sulfonic acid.[158]

Ketones of the type CH_3COR in which R is a primary alkyl group react readily with sodium bisulfite, while ketones of this type in which R is a secondary or tertiary alkyl group react less readily. Aliphatic ketones, RCOR′, in which both groups R and R′ contain two or more carbon atoms react with alkali bisulfites with difficulty, while purely aromatic and aromatic aliphatic ketones show no tendency to react at all. Cyclohexanone and similar cyclic ketones readily yield bisulfite compounds.[23]

Bisulfite compounds have been obtained from 3,5-dimethylcyclohexanone and 3-methyl-5-isopropylcyclohexanone, and surprisingly also from 2-isopropyl and 2-methyl-6-isopropylcyclohexanone; 2,3,6-trimethylcyclohexanone fails to react with sodium bisulfite. 3,5,-5-trimethyl-2-cyclohexanone and isopulegone do not react, while camphorphorone yields a stable sulfonic acid. β-Thujone is capable of reacting with sodium bisulfite, but α-decalene gives an unstable addition compound, while carone and camphor do not react.

Nearly all unsaturated ketones add sodium bisulfite at the ethylenic double bond. Pulegone gives the normal addition product with bisulfite; but addition at the double bond takes place with sulfur trioxide in alcoholic solution at 20°. Mesityl oxide combines with sodium bisulfite to form an isopropylacetone sulfonic acid, and phorone gives a disulfonic acid:[160]

$$(CH_3)_2C = CHCOCH_3 + NaHSO_3 \rightarrow (CH_3)_2C(SO_3Na)CH_2COCH_3$$

$$(CH_3)_2C = CHCOCH = C(CH_3)_2 + 2NaHSO_3 \rightarrow [(CH_3)_2CHCH(SO_3Na)]_2CO$$

The separation of the bisulfite compound in the crystalline form does not always take place readily. The bisulfite derivative of pulegone, for example, could only by obtained in the solid form by carrying out the reaction in aqueous alcoholic solution, and allowing the reaction mixture to stand for ten days.[159]

Alkali cyanides react with carbonyl bisulfite compounds to form cyanohydrins:[24]

$$RCH(OH)SO_3Na + NaCH \rightarrow RCH(OH)CN + Na_2SO_3$$

The reaction offers an excellent method for the preparation of cyanohydrins difficult to prepare directly from the carbonyl compound.

Ammonia and amines react with bisulfite compounds forming alkylideneamino sulfites:[25]

$$RCH(OH)SO_3Na + NH_3 \rightarrow RCH(NH_2)SO_3Na + H_2O$$

Carbonyl bisulfite compounds are reduced with zinc dust and acetic acid to sulfoxylates:[26]

$$RCH(OH)SO_3Na + 2H \rightarrow RCH(OH)SO_2Na + H_2O$$

Decomposition of Bisulfite Compounds

The sulfonic group in aldehyde bisulfite compounds may be removed by treatment with acids or alkalies. Decomposition takes place at ordinary temperature in some instances, but heating is necessary in many cases.

Decomposition is usually brought about by boiling with sodium carbonate or bicarbonate solution. Decomposition by this method proceeds very slowly in some cases, as for example, with the pulegone bisulfite compound, and it is then best carried out with potassium hydroxide solution. Barium hydroxide has been used for the decomposition of tiglic aldehyde bisulfite compound.[161] Removal of the sulfonic group from the bisulfite compound of diketohexamethylene has been effected by boiling with dilute sulfuric acid.

The acid cleavage procedure is employed with aldehydes which undergo aldol condensation with caustic. Carbonates or bicarbonates are used with sensitive aldehydes, and the aldehyde is removed by steam distillation as it is formed. The bisulfite group may be removed from bisulfite compounds by reaction with a carbonyl compound with a strong affinity for the bisulfite residue. Formaldehyde, benzaldehyde, *p*-nitro- and 2,4-dinitrobenzaldehyde have been employed for the purpose.

The bisulfite compound of citral, if left in contact with the mother liquors for a considerable time, undergoes a change, and can no longer be reconverted to the aldehyde. This behavior is shown by the bisulfite compound of other carbonyl compounds in which an unsaturated group is present in the neighborhood of the carbonyl group.

α-Hydroxysulfinic Acids

α-Hydroxysulfinic acids or sulfoxylic acids are formed through the reduction of α-hydroxysulfonic acids. They act as dibasic acids and give salts of the type $RCH(OH)SO_2M$ and $RCH(OM)SO_2M$. *Rongalite* is the primary sodium salt of hydroxymethanesulfinic acid.[162] In the free acids the carbon to sulfur bond is stronger than in α-hydroxysulfonic acids. The bond strength is greatest in hydroxymethanesulfinic acid; it is of a lower order in acids derived from the bisulfite compounds of acetaldehyde, benzaldehyde and acetone. The carbon to sulfur bond is weak in anilidomethanesulfinic acid, $C_6H_5NHCH_2SO_2H$. Salts of hydroxysulfinic acids are stable to alkalies even at higher temperatures.

Reaction with Hydrocyanic Acid

Aldehydes and ketones react with hydrocyanic acid in the presence of small quantities of substances of basic character,(*) yielding cyanohydrins:[27]

$$RCOR' + HCN \rightarrow RC(OH)(CN)R'$$

The reaction is reversible, although the cyanohydrin largely predominates at the equilibrium point. In the case of aldehydes the reaction is more rapid and proceeds further in the direction of formation of the cyanohydrin than with ketones. The formation of cyanohydrins proceeds in the absence of catalysts though at a slow rate. Mixed aliphatic-aromatic ketones react slowly with hydrocyanic acid even in the presence of catalysts, while purely aromatic ketones do not react at all. Cyanohydrins may be obtained from aldoses such as glucose, fructose and arabinose.[28]

A satisfactory procedure is to add a few drops of a concentrated sodium hydroxide solution to the hydrocyanic acid and to introduce the carbonyl compound gradually, while the temperature of the mixture is maintained at a point where reaction proceeds rapidly. The reaction rate is usually rapid with aldehydes at room temperature, but in the case of ketones it may be necessary to warm the liquid somewhat above this temperature. Sodium or potassium cyanide, ammonia and amines may also serve as catalysts.

The hydrocyanic acid may be generated as it is utilized in the reaction, by gradually adding concentrated hydrochloric acid to a suspension of an alkali cyanide in a strongly cooled ethereal solution of the carbonyl compound. Reaction usually proceeds quite rapidly. The carbonyl compound remains largely in solution in the ether and may be isolated by separating the ether layer and evaporating off the solvent.

(*) It is of interest to note that certain addition reactions of carbonyl compounds are catalyzed by acids.

Cyanohydrins may also be prepared through the interaction of potassium cyanide with the bisulfite compound of the aldehyde or ketone in aqueous solution at room temperature.[29] Cyanohydrins may be purified by distillation under vacuum providing they are properly neutralized, or are slightly acidified.

Cyanohydrins tend to dissociate into hydrocyanic acid and the carbonyl compound, alkaline substances favoring dissociation. Aldehyde cyanohydrins dissociate to a lesser degree than ketone cyanohydrins. Cyanohydrins of phenyl alkyl ketones are relatively stable, with the higher members showing somewhat greater instability. The dissociation of cyanohydrins is catalyzed by amines in all solvents, while the degree of dissociation is enhanced by amines in water and unaffected in alcohols and in acetone.

Aminonitriles Derived from Aldehydes and Ketones

α-Aminonitriles result through the interaction of cyanides of ammonia or amines with aldehydes or ketones:[30]

$$RR'CO + NH_4CN \rightarrow RR'C(NH_2)CN + H_2O$$

Instead of the amine cyanide, a mixture of solutions of a salt of the amine and of an alkali cyanide may be employed. Amino nitriles may be prepared by this method from sugars as well as from other aliphatic carbonyl compounds. The reaction may be applied successfully to most aliphatic aldehydes. Aminonitriles of the less reactive aldehydes, such as *o*-nitrobenzaldehyde, may best be prepared by adding sodium cyanide with good stirring to a solution of amine acetate and the aldehyde in glacial acetic acid.[31] Aralkyl ketones react with ammonium cyanide at a comparatively high temperature to give unstable aminonitriles that are difficult to isolate and purify.[32] Purely aromatic ketones, such as benzophenone, do not react with ammonium cyanide.

Aminonitriles may also be prepared from condensation products of amines and aldehydes. Methyleneimine, $CH_2 = NCH_3$, reacting with hydrocyanic acid gives methylglycinonitrile,[33] CH_3NHCH_2CN; aldehyde ammonia gives with hydrocyanic acid di α-cyanoethyamine. This same compound results, together with α-aminopropionitrile, from the reaction of hydrocyanic acid with ethyleneimine,[33] $CH_3CH. = NH$. Schiff reagents, $RN = CHR_2$, give with hydrocyanic acid compounds of the type $RNHCH(CN)R_2$. Some among these reagents, such as benzoin anilide, react with difficulty. Pyrotartaric anilide does not react.[34] Hydrazones and oximes of aliphatic aldehydes or ketones also react with hydrocyanic acid in like manner, but those of the aromatic series do not react.[35]

Aminonitriles may also be prepared from bisulfite compounds of aldehydes and ketones by adding a slight excess of the amine to their solution, then introducing the required quantity of sodium cyanide in concentrated solution.[36]

α-Hydroxylaminoisobutyronitrile is oxidized by chlorine at 0° to α-nitrosoisobutyronitrile, $(CH_3)_2C(NO)CN$ (*Piloty's reaction*).[237]

Reaction with Amino Compounds

The ability of carbonyl compounds to give addition compounds is manifested in their reactions with amines. The reaction often proceeds with cleavage of water, however, giving rise to compounds with a grouping C = N—.

The reaction of aliphatic aldehydes with ammonia generally leads to the formation of crystalline addition compounds, the so-called aldehyde ammonias. These are insoluble in ether and may, therefore, be conveniently prepared by passing gaseous ammonia into an ethereal solution of the aldehyde. They are comparatively unstable, decomposing into the aldehyde and an ammonium salt when treated with acids. They are transformed to pyridine bases when subjected to strong heating.

The reaction of ammonia with formaldehyde in aqueous solution normally leads to the formation of hexamethylene tetramine.[37] Aliphatic amines give methylolalkylamines with formaldehyde.[154]

$$(CH_3)_2NH + CH_2O \rightarrow (CH_3)_2NCH_2OH.$$

These compounds may be made to react with a second molecule of amine to form bisaminomethanes. When distilled over solid potassium hydroxide, methylalkylamines lose water to form alkylmethylimines, usually as the cyclic trimers,

$$\overline{RNCH_2N(R)CH_2N(R)CH_2}.$$ [164]

Pyridine derivatives are formed when vapors of an aliphatic aldehyde mixed with ammonia are passed over alumina heated at 300-400° (*Tschitschibabin reaction*).[165] The probable course of the reaction appears to be as follows:

$$RCH_2CHO + NH_3 \rightarrow RCH_2CH = NH + H_2O$$

$$3RCH_2CH = NH \rightarrow RCH_2CH(NH_2)CH(R)CH(NH_2)CH(R)CH = NH$$

→ 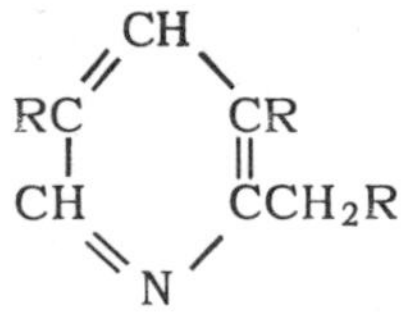 $+ 2NH_3 + H_2$

Crotonaldehyde gives a compound of the probable formula $C_{12}H_{24}N_4$.[166]

The reaction of formaldehyde with aromatic amines proceeds in a complex manner.[167] Aniline forms a methylenediamine which, when heated with aniline hydrochloride, gives a derivative of anhydro-*p*-aminobenzyl alcohol. The latter adds a molecule of the amine with the formation of a benzylaniline derivative, and this finally is converted to a ditan derivative:

$$2C_6H_5NH_2 \xrightarrow{CH_2O} C_6H_5NHCH_2NHC_6H_5 \rightarrow C_6H_5NH_2 + \overline{CH_2C_6H_4NH} \rightarrow$$

$$C_6H_5NHCH_2C_6H_4NH_2 \rightarrow H_2NC_6H_4CH_2C_6H_4NH_2$$

Reaction with *o*-phenylenediamine in weakly acid solution results in the formation of N-methylbenzoimidazole:

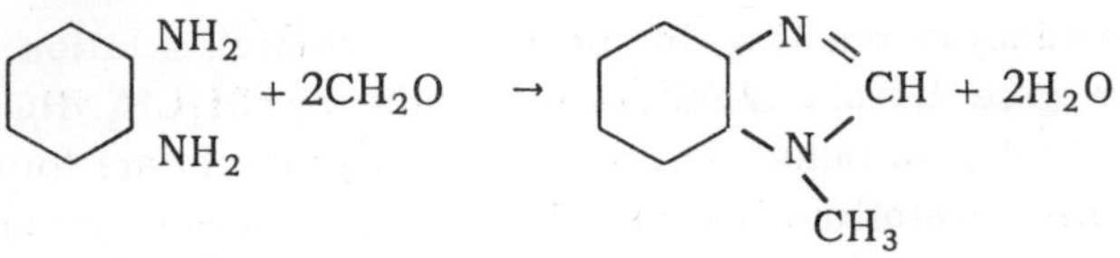

m-Methyl-*o*-phenylenediamine reacts similarly. Products corresponding empirically to the dimers of Schiff bases are formed when the reaction is carried out in neutral solution.[168]

Formaldehyde, reacting with secondary alkyl aromatic amines in neutral or alkaline solution, gives alkyldiphenylaminomethanes:[169]

$$2RNHAr + CH_2O \rightarrow ArN(R)CH_2N(R)Ar + H_2O$$

A benzidine type of rearrangement occurs with the formation of *p*-alkylaminodiphenylmethane when the reaction is carried out at higher temperatures in acid medium:[170]

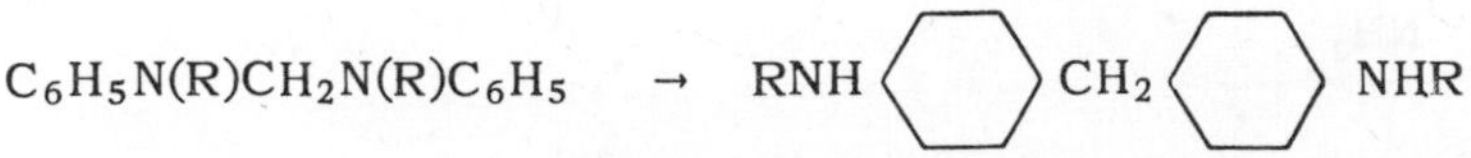

The reaction of acetaldehyde and higher aliphatic aldehydes with secondary amines in the presence of potassium carbonate results in the formation of bisamino compounds:

$$RCH_2CHO + 2HNR'_2 \rightarrow RCH_2CH(NR'_2)_2 + H_2O$$

When such compounds are distilled, they generally yield α,β-unsaturated amines:

$$RCH_2CH(NR'_2)_2 \rightarrow RCH = CHNR'_2 + HNR'_2$$

In the case of phenylacetaldehyde and dibenzylamine, the unsaturated amine $C_6H_5CH = CHN(CH_2C_6H_5)_2$ is formed spontaneously. With α,β-unsaturated aldehydes, $R'CH = CHCHO$, crystalline condensation products of the type $R'CH(NR_2)CH = CHNR_2$ are obtained at low temperatures, sometimes as low as -10 and $-20°$; at higher temperatures resins or complex aldol-like products result.[171] The crystalline bisamino compounds decompose on distillation into aminoallenes $R'CH = C = CHNR_3$. The reaction of ethyl- and allylamines with acetaldehyde gives cyclic compounds of the type

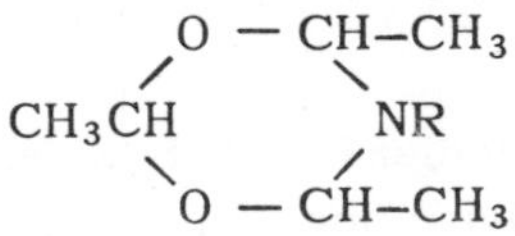

Formaldehyde also gives similar ring compounds with these amines.

The reaction of aliphatic aldehydes RCHO with diamines of the type

$$Ar(CH_2)_nNHCH_2CH_2NH(CH_2)_nAr$$

results in the formation of tetrahydroimidazoles.[172]

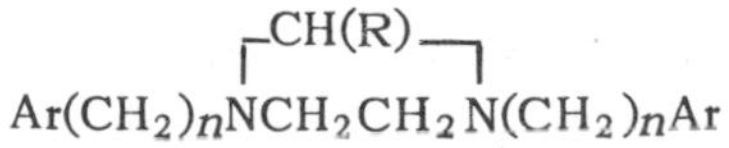

Aniline and acetaldehyde reacting in the cold in neutral solution or in the presence of sodium give 1,1-bis (phenylamino) ethane, $CH_3CH(NHC_6H_5)_2$.[173] Under loosely controlled conditions amorphous or oily products are formed along with some well-defined crystalline bodies.[174] Diphenylaminoethanes are readily obtained from para substituted anilines and acetaldehyde.[175] Propionaldehyde and valeraldehyde yield dimeric products with aniline;[176] butyraldehyde, isobutyraldehyde, isovaleraldehyde and heptaldehyde give anhydro products presumably of the Schiff base type.[177]

Quinolines are formed by a reaction resembling the Skraup synthesis when aliphatic aldehydes are heated with aromatic amines and concentrated hydrochloric acid.[178] 1-Methylquioline is obtained, for example, with acetaldehyde and aniline:

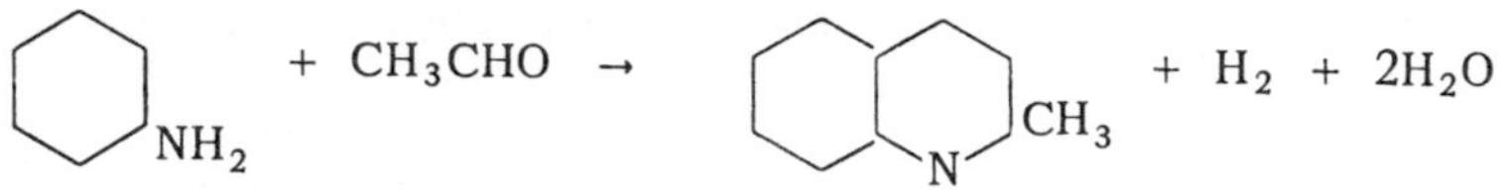

Aliphatic α-chloro aldehydes react with aromatic amines to form α-hydroxy-β-chloroethylarylamines and bis-(arylamino)-chloromethanes. The hydroxy amines readily combine, as a rule, with an additional molecule of amine to form the bisamine derivatives.

Amides give methylol derivatives with formaldehyde. The reaction usually proceeds best in the presence of basic agents such as sodium hydroxide, barium hydroxide, triethylamine, etc., although acid catalysts are employed with aromatic and chlorinated aliphatic amides. Acetamide combines with formaldehyde on heating in the presence of a catalyst. N-Alkylated amides do not give the reaction.[155]

The reaction of ketones with ammonia is unlike that of aldehydes. Acetone gives principally diacetoneamine and triacetoneamine,[38] compounds which also result from the interaction of ammonia with mesityl oxide and phorone:

$$(CH_3)_2C = CHCOCH_3 + NH_3 \rightarrow (CH_3)_2C(NH_2)CH_2COCH_3$$

$$(CH_3)_2C = CHCOCH = C(CH_3)_2 + NH_3 \rightarrow (CH_3)_2C\begin{matrix} / & CH_2COCH_2 & \backslash \\ \backslash & NH & / \end{matrix}C(CH_3)_2$$

The latter also gives diacetonediamine, $(CH_3)_2C(NH_2)CH_2COCH_2C(NH_2)(CH_3)_2$. It appears possible that the formation of these compounds from acetone is preceded by a condensation of the ketone to mesityl oxide and phorone. Other ketones may also give similar products with ammonia. Triacetoneamine, which is a weaker base than diacetoneamine, gives an N-bromide on treatment with bromine, and a nitrosoamine, $C_9H_{16}ON.NO$ with nitrous acid. N-alkyltriacetoneamines result from the reaction of phorone with primary aliphatic amines.[39] Ketimines of aromatic ketones result when vapors of the ketone mixed with ammonia are passed over thorium oxide heated at 300-400°. Aliphatic ketones do not react under these conditions.[40]

Schiff Bases

Aldehydes in general react with primary bases to form condensation products of the type RCH = NR′, known as azomethines or Schiff bases.[41] Reaction may be brought about by heating a mixture of the aldehyde and amine in equimolecular proportions alone or in a diluent such as alcohol or acetic acid.[42] The reaction proceeds most readily with aromatic aldehydes and aromatic amines which yield, as a rule, stable crystalline substances. Condensation may be effected between aliphatic aldehydes and aromatic amines under the proper conditions, but the resulting azomethines are usually unstable and tend to polymerize.

Azomethines derived from formaldehyde are the least stable. Thus *p*-toluazomethine $CH_2 = NC_6H_4CH_3$ readily polymerizes to a dimer and a trimer and is capable of combining with a further molecule of *p*-toluidine to form the compound $CH_2(NHC_6H_4CH_3)_2$.[43] The azomethine $CH_3CH = NC_6H_5$ derived from acetaldehyde and aniline is also unstable, and polymerizes rapidly; it reacts readily with a molecule of aniline forming $CH_3CH(NHC_6H_5)_2$.[44]

The reaction between ketones and amines proceeds much less readily than with aldehydes. The reaction of mixed aromatic aliphatic and purely aromatic ketones with aromatic aliphatic amines and that of purely aromatic ketones with aromatic amines proceeds only in the presence of catalysts, such as zinc chloride.[45] An accumulation of substituents in the immediate vicinity of the carbonyl group appears to retard the reaction due to steric hindrance. In the aromatic series substituents in the ortho position have a retarding effect for the same reason.[46]

Reaction with Hydroxylamine, Hydrazines and Semicarbazide

The end product of the reaction of aldehydes and hydroxylamine are aldoximes, RCH:NOH. Unstable addition products are often formed as intermediates:

$$RCHO + H_2NOH \rightarrow RCH(OH)NHOH \rightarrow RCH{:}NOH + H_2O$$

Ketones react with hydroxylamine less readily than aldehydes, forming ketoximes RR′C = NOH.

The general procedure followed in preparing oximes is to bring together the carbonyl compound and the equivalent quantity of hydroxylamine hydrochloride in aqueous solution, and to add a 25 to 50% excess of sodium carbonate or bicarbonate. The reaction proceeds to completion at room temperature with aldehydes, but in preparing ketoximes heat must be applied to the mixture.[47] Cyclic ketones react more readily than open chain ketones; trimethyl derivatives form an exception however and react less readily than open chain ketones. If the carbonyl compound is insoluble in water, sufficient alcohol is added to bring it into solution. Sodium hydroxide may be employed for liberating the free hydroxylamine from the chloride, but it is then necessary to saturate the solution with carbon dioxide at the end of the reaction to precipitate out the oxime.

The reaction between ketones and hydroxylamine is accelerated by sodium hydroxide in proportion to its concentration. The reaction rate is also increased by hydrochloric acid up to a concentration of half-molal hydrogen chloride, beyond which a rapid decrease in rate is observed with increase in concentration.[48] The rate of reaction may be determined by a titration of free acid formed when the hydrochloride of hydroxylamine is employed as the reagent.[239] The ketoxime of acetone may be prepared by treating acetone with the zinc chloride complex of hydroxylamine.

The rate of oxime formation from acetone and hydroxylamine is greatest at pH 4.7, while the rate of hydrolysis of the oxime reaches its peak at pH 2.3. Optimum conditions for oxime formation are assured by using a solution of hydroxylamine acetate in acetic acid buffered with sodium acetate.

Diketones react very readily with hydroxylamine to form monoximes. Dioximes are obtained only when the diketones are heated with an excess of hydroxylamine.[240]

The extent of oxime formation from a number of ketones on reaction in 1/100 normal solution within an hour at room temperature is given below:

	% Oxime Formed		% Oxime Formed
Acetone	82	ethyl *n*-propyl ketone	36.8
Methyl ethyl ketone	79.2	di *n*-propyl ketone	31.4
Methyl propyl ketone	74.6	methyl ethyl ketone	67.6
Diethyl ketone	37.9		

Branched-chain ketones react less readily than straight-chain ketones.

Oximes of flavones and naphthoflavones have been prepared by reaction of the flavone with a mixture of hydroxylamine hydrochloride and pyridine.[241]

Propargyl oxime condenses to a cyclic compound immediately after it is formed.[246]

$$HC \equiv CCH = NOH \rightarrow \overline{CH = CHCH = NO}$$

Potassium ethoxide converts the cyclic body to $CNCH_2CHO$.

A reaction resembling osazone formation has been observed with 2,4-dihydroxy ω-aminoacetophenone

$$(HO)_2C_6H_3COCH_2NH_2 + 3H_2NOH \rightarrow (HO)_2C_6H_3C(=NOH)CH = NOH + 2NH_3 + 2H_2O$$

Chloral also reacts with two molecular equivalents of hydroxylamine. Complications arise in the reaction of *o*-phthalaldehyde with hydroxylamine.[247]

Oximes are decomposed with acids to the original carbonyl compound and the hydroxylamine salt of the acid. Ketoximes differ from aldoximes in that they yield an O-acyl derivative and an acid amide on reaction with acid chlorides or anhydrides. Oximes are reduced by nascent hydrogen to primary amines. The hydrogen may be generated by the action of sodium on alcohol or through the reaction of acetic acid and sodium amalgam. Amines may be obtained in good yield from certain oximes by electrolytic reduction at lead cathodes.[49]

When chlorine is passed through a solution of acetaldoxime, nitrosochloroethane, $CH_3CH(Cl)NO$, precipitates out in the crystalline form. The ethereal solution of the latter compound is at first blue but becomes colorless on standing due to the transformation of the compound to $CH_3C(:NOH)Cl$. With chlorine this compound gives nitrosodichloroethane, CH_3CCl_2NO, a deep blue colored oil.[242] Nitrosodichloroethane may be obtained directly from acetaldoxime, by chlorination in hydrochloric acid solution.

No stereoisomeric modifications have been isolated from simple aliphatic ketoximes, although cases of stereoisomerism have been observed with some complex aliphatic ketoximes. Isomerism has also been observed among simple aliphatic aldoximes.[243]

The question as to whether an oxime is of the *α* (*syn*) or *β* (*anti*) form may be decided by warming the compound for a short time with acetic anhydride, then adding sodium carbonate; only the *β*- compounds yield a nitrile under these conditions.

In general aromatic compounds give *α*-oximes, while aliphatic compounds tend to form *β*-oximes. Cinnamaldehyde and other intermediate types give a mixture of *α*- and *β*-isomers.[248] An *α*-isomer is converted to the *β*-form by concentrated acids, and the reverse change is caused by dilute acids.

Aldehydes of the aliphatic series react with hydrazine to form aldazines, $RCH = N-N = CHR$. Aromatic aldehydes may be made to react with one amino group in hydrazine forming hydrazones, $RCH = N{\cdot}NH_2$, or with both amino groups to give an aldazine. Aliphatic ketones also give azines, $RR'C = N-N = CRR'$, by reaction with both amino groups in hydrazine, but a hydrazone $(CH_3)_2C = NNH_2$ may also be prepared from acetone and hydrazine.[50]

The reaction between carbonyl compounds and hydrazine is usually carried out by adding the carbonyl compound to an aqueous solution of a salt of hydrazine and the required quantity of sodium carbonate or sodium hydroxide. An excess of sodium acetate may be used instead of sodium carbonate or hydroxide.[51]

Hydrazone formation generally proceeds at pH 5. Precipitation of the hydrazone in dilute solution is rendered more complete by the addition of sodium chloride. Pyridine is sometimes used as a catalyst. Reaction often takes place at room temperature and proceeds to completion in almost all cases on warming on the water bath. It is desirable to acylate free hydroxyl groups and to esterify free carboxyl groups prior to the preparation of the hydrazone.

Phenylhydrazine and other aromatic hydrazines react readily with carbonyl compounds to form hydrazones, $RR'C = N.NHR''$.

Phenylhydrazones are generally prepared by adding the carbonyl compound to a solution of phenylhydrazine in ether or alcohol or in an aqueous solution of acetic acid containing 30 to 50% of the acid. The reaction proceeds to completion at room temperature with most aldehydes and ketones.[179]

Hydrazone formation with a weakly basic hydrazine, such as 2,4-dinitrophenylhydrazine, is best carried out in the presence of a mineral acid.[249]

Diphenylmethanedimethylhydrazine, $H_2NN(CH_3)C_6H_4CH_2C_6H_4N(CH_3)NH_2$, reacts with aldehydes much more readily than with ketones and has been used for the separation of aldoses of certain configuration from a mixture of sugars. The reagent may be employed in very dilute solution.

Acylated hydrazines, such as benzhydrazide, $C_6H_5CONHNH_2$, have been used for the precipitation of carbonyl compounds from very dilute solutions.[250] Benzhydrazide and certain other acylated hydrazines do not react with ketoses and bioses and may serve for the separation of these from aldoses.

Hydrazone formation takes place with particular ease with aldehyde and keto acids. Reaction proceeds even in the cold and in dilute solution, occasionally in the presence of mineral acids. The hydrazones separate as crystalline precipitates.

Hydrazones of oxo compounds which contain a carbonyl group in β or γ-position undergo ring closure readily. Ring compounds are also formed with carbonyl compounds containing an unsaturated bond in the neighborhood of the carbonyl group and those having an amino group in the β-position. Acyl cyanides, RCOCN, react with hydrazines $RNHNH_2$ to form hydrazides, $R'NHNHCOR$.

The original carbonyl compounds may be freed from hydrazones by reaction with pyruvic acid: [180]

$$(CH_3)_2C = N \cdot NHC_6H_5 + CH_3COCOOH \rightarrow (CH_3)_2CO + CH_3C(=NNHC_6H_5)COOH$$

Hydrazones of aliphatic aldehydes and ketones add hydrocyanic acid to form hydrazido nitriles. Hydrazones of aromatic carbonyl compounds do not undergo this reaction. [181]

A characteristic reaction of hydrazones is their conversion into indole derivatives on heating with zinc chloride: [182]

$$C_6H_5NHN = C(CH_3)_2 \rightarrow C_6H_4 \underset{NH}{\overset{CH}{<}} CCH_3 + NH_3$$

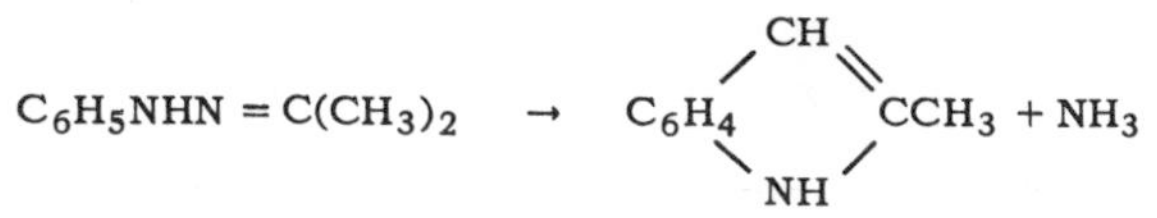

The reaction product of phenylhydrazine and acetoacetic ester is probably benzene hydrazocrotonic ester; when heated at 200° under vacuum, it is quantitatively converted to phenylmethylpyrazolone: [183]

$$C_2H_5OCOCH = C(CH_3)NHNHC_6H_5 \rightarrow C_6H_5N \underset{NHC \cdot CH_3}{\overset{COCH}{<}} + C_2H_5OH$$

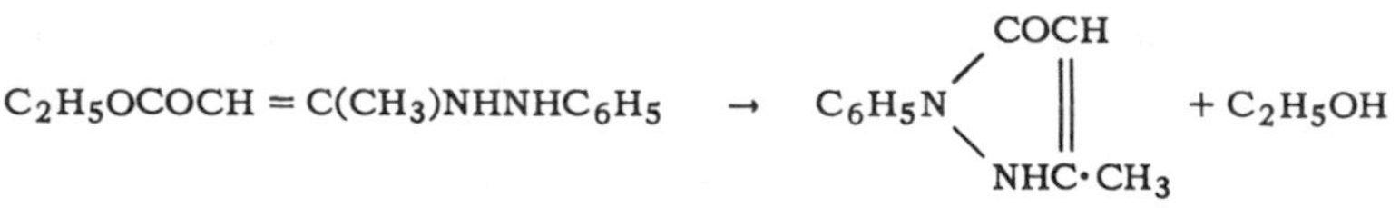

Compounds in which two adjacent hydrazone groups are present are termed osazones. Most osazones are converted to osotetrazones when oxidized with ferric chloride.[184] Dimethyldiphenylozotetrazine is obtained, for example, from the osazone of diacetyl:

$$\begin{array}{c} CH_3C = NNHC_6H_5 \\ | \\ CH_3C = NNHC_6H_5 \end{array} + 2FeCl_3 \rightarrow \begin{array}{c} CH_3C = N-NC_6H_5 \\ | \quad\quad | \\ CH_3C = N-NC_6H_5 \end{array} + 2HCl + 2FeCl_2$$

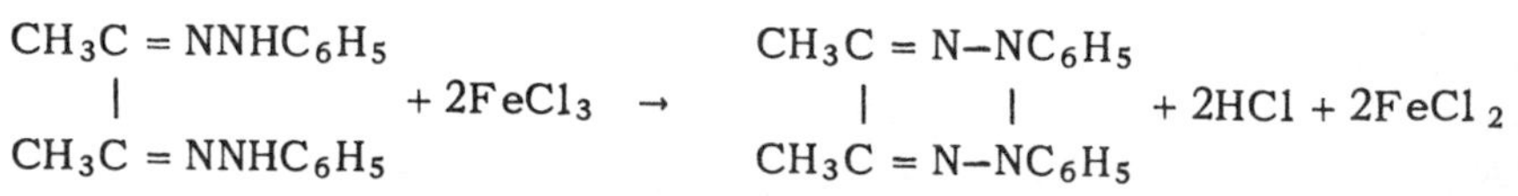

When hydrazine and substituted hydrazines are made to react with a warm solution of an aldose or ketose in an inert solvent, the carbon atom at position 2 in aldoses, and at position 1 in ketoses is oxidized to a carbonyl group and reacts with a further molecule of the hydrazine to form an osazone.

Semicarbazide, $H_2NCONHNH_2$, thiosemicarbazide and other derivatives of hydrazine, including benzoylhydrazine, aminoguanidine and semioxamazide, $H_2NCOCONHNH_2$, react with carbonyl compounds in the same manner as aromatic hydrazines.

The reaction with semicarbazide is carried out by adding a concentrated aqueous solution of the hydrochloride of the base to a solution of the carbonyl compound. Water is used as the solvent if the carbonyl compound is soluble in water, otherwise dilute acetic acid or alcohol are employed. The semicarbazone usually precipitates out immediately, and the reaction is completed by the addition of solid potassium acetate. With some carbonyl compounds precipitation of the semicarbazide may require several days.

Certain aldehydes which fail to form oximes and hydrazones react with semicarbazide. Aldehydes may be liberated from their semicarbazones with great difficulty.

Thiosemicarbazide formation with aldehydes takes place very readily by reaction with acetone thiosemicarbazone in dilute acetic acid solution.[251] Much interest has centered on thiosemicarbazones since the discovery of the high antitubercular activity of some of these compounds.[252]

In the reaction of hydroxylamine, semicarbazide and other amines, with carbonyl compounds containing a reactive unsaturated bond, addition at the double bond may take place. The hydrochloride of the base may react otherwise than the sulfate.

Carbonyl compounds may be regenerated from oximes and hydrazones by hydrolysis. Keto derivatives are the easiest to hydrolyze. The oximes and hydrazones derived from aromatic, α,β-unsaturated and saturated aliphatic aldehydes decompose with increasing difficulty in the order named. Aromatic and $\alpha,\ \beta$-unsaturated hydrazones are usually decomposed with dilute oxalic or phthalic acid.[253] Sulfurous acid has also been used with success.[254] More stable hydrazones are hydrolyzed with dilute hydrochloric or sulfuric acid.[255] Sometimes the use of more concentrated acid is required. In exceptional cases heating with an acetic acid-hydrochloric acid mixture is resorted to.[256] Oximes in general are more readily hydrolyzed than hydrazones, and the latter more readily than semicarbazones. Semicarbazones of unsaturated aldehydes that are sensitive to warm acids are hydrolyzed with cold 6-normal sulfuric acid, and the freed aldehyde is continuously extracted with petroleum ether. This procedure is not applicable to carbohydrates since aldoses are not extractable with petroleum ether.

Carbonyl compounds may be regenerated from hydrazones by displacement with a second carbonyl compound. Benzaldehyde, p-nitro- and 2,4-dinitrobenzaldehyde or formaldehyde have been used as the displacing aldehyde. With carbohydrates and related compounds benzaldehyde should be used to avoid the formation of stable acetals or other difficulties. The procedure is to mix the hydrazone with a molecular equivalent of the aldehyde in alcoholic solution or in aqueous suspension and to heat under reflux.

Oxidative regeneration of carbonyl compounds from their oximes is employed when other methods of regeneration would cause secondary changes, as for example in the case of succinaldehyde dioxime, which is cyclized under the influence of acids. The oxidizing agents usually employed are nitric acid and amyl nitrite in the cold, and in special cases halogens or ferric halides.

Isolation and Purification of Carbonyl Compounds with Girard Reagents

Girard reagents are quaternary aminohydrazides; *reagent T* is trimethylaminoacetylhydrazide, $(CH_3)_3\overset{+}{N}CH_2CONHNH_2.\overset{-}{Cl}$, *reagent P* is the triethylamino analog of reagent T. These reagents yield water soluble hydrazones with water soluble ketones. These hydrazones are not isolated, but the carbonyl compounds are freed in aqueous solution. By adjusting the pH of the solution in stages it is possible to separate various carbonyl compounds fractionally from a mixture.[257]

Wolff–Kishner Reaction[147]

When aldehyde- or ketone hydrazones are heated with aqueous alkali, they remain unaffected or are converted to azines. When, however, they are heated in a sealed tube with absolute alcohol in the presence of sodium alcoholate, decomposition takes place with evolution of nitrogen. The reaction involves the replacement of the hydrazone group with two hydrogen atoms:

$$>C=N.NH_2 \rightarrow >CH_2 + N_2$$

and indirectly brings about the complete reduction of the carbonyl group. It has an advantage over the Clemmensen's method, in that it leaves intact any unsaturated bonds present in the carbonyl compound, although the possibility of a shift in the position of the unsaturated bond is not excluded.

An identical transformation may be brought about by heating semicarbazones in the presence of a limited quantity of water. The semicarbazone is first transformed to a hydrazone by hydrolysis:

$$>C=N.NHCONH_2 + H_2O \rightarrow >C{:}N.NH_2 + CO_2 + NH_3$$

$$>C=N.NH_2 \rightarrow >CH_2 + N_2$$

Disemicarbazones may also be decomposed in this manner. Camphene is best reduced to acenaphthene through the corresponding disemicarbazone.[148] Decomposition is brought about by heating with 96-98% ethanol.

The method is generally applicable to aliphatic, aromatic and cyclic ketones and aldehydes, as well as to keto acids. The yields range between 75 to 90% of the theoretically expected quantity. The method has been especially useful in the sterol series.

In preparing the hydrazone required for the reaction, it is of advantage to use the hydrazine hydrate in slight excess. It is not necessary to purify the hydrazone; it is filtered, dissolved in ether, the solution is dried and the hydrazone is isolated in the anhydrous condition by evaporating the solvent. The sodium alkoxide acts as a catalyst, and comparatively small amounts of this reagent are usually required. Sodium ethylate may be conveniently prepared from 1 part of sodium and 12 parts of absolute alcohol under anhydrous conditions. The decomposition temperature varies between rather wide limits. Heating at 160° for 6 to 8 hours is usually sufficient for most hydrazones, but hydrazones of cyclic ketones, such as camporhydrazone, require heating for a longer period or at higher temperatures, up to 200°. *p*-Nitrobenzalhydrazone and furfuralhydrazone decompose below 80°.

A recent modification of the method[149] makes possible the decomposition of the hydrazone under atmospheric pressure. The hydrazone is heated in solution in triethylene glycol in the presence of a half molecular equivalent of sodium methylate at 190-200° under a reflux condenser until the evolution of nitrogen ceases. The operation is usually complete within ½ to 1½ hours; during this period about 80 to 85% of the theoretically expected quantity of nitrogen is evolved. The hydrazone is conveniently prepared by heating under a reflux condenser, at 125° or higher, a mixture of 1 mole of the ketone, 2 moles of hydrazine hydrate with 180-200 cc of triethylene glycol and 5 cc of glacial acetic acid. The aqueous hydrazine hydrate which distills over is trapped and separated. Heating is continued until the calculated quantity of hydrazine has been collected. The residual solution is rapidly cooled and is employed directly in the final decomposition step by mixing it with a solution of a half mole of sodium methoxide in 200 cc of triethylene glycol.

Kishner accomplished the decomposition of hydrazones by heating with solid potassium hydroxide under atmospheric pressure. Staudinger obtained the hydrocarbon directly from the carbonyl compounds by heating these with hydrazine to an elevated temperature.[150]

The products from aliphatic unsaturated aldehydes and ketones are olefins or cyclopropane derivatives, while alicyclic α, β-unsaturated carbonyl compounds give exocyclic methylene compounds.[185] Citral, for example, gives 1-methylene-2,2,6-trimethylcyclohexane:

$$\begin{array}{ccc} & C(CH_3)_2 & \\ \diagup & & \diagdown \\ CH_2 & & CCHO \\ | & & \| \\ CH_2 & & CCH_3 \\ \diagdown & & \diagup \\ & CH_2 & \end{array} \quad \rightarrow \quad \begin{array}{ccc} & C(CH_3)_2 & \\ \diagup & & \diagdown \\ CH_2 & & C=CH_2 \\ | & & | \\ CH_2 & & CHCH_3 \\ \diagdown & & \diagup \\ & CH_2 & \end{array}$$

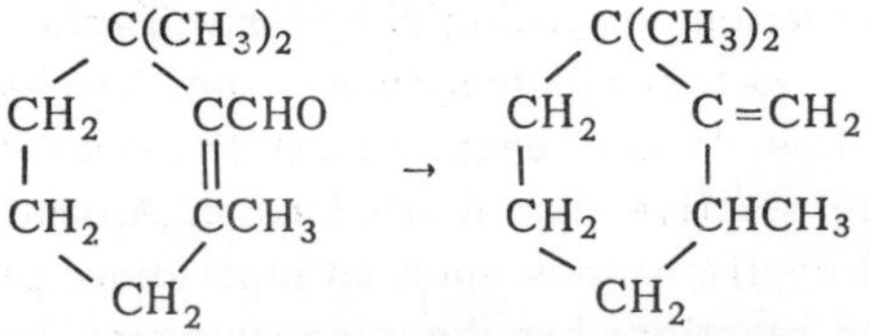

The Wolff-Kishner reaction is applicable to pyrazolones;[151] these compounds decompose with ring cleavage to nitrogen and an acid:

$$\begin{array}{ccc} & NH & \\ \diagup & & \diagdown \\ CO & & N \\ | & & \| \\ CH_2 & - & C-CH_3 \end{array} \quad \xrightarrow{H_2O} \quad CH_3CH_2CH_2COOH + N_2$$

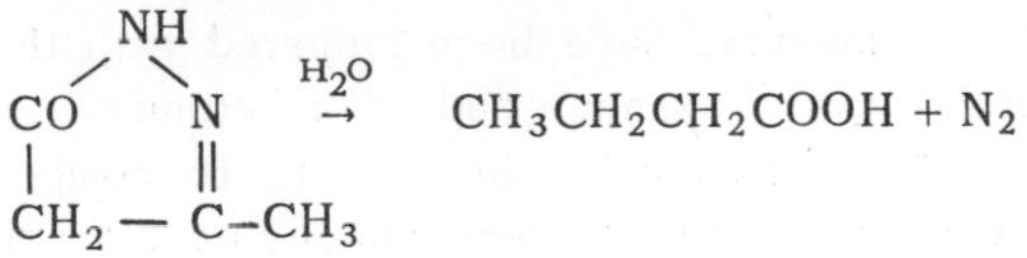

Alkylation may take place simultaneously with some pyrazolones. Thus, 3-methylpyrazolone heated at 220° for 15 hours with sodium methoxide yields both 3,4-dimethylpyrazolone and butyric acid in almost equimolecular proportions. Alkylation takes place exclusively below 230°; above this temperature alkylation is retarded in proportion to increase in temperature. Occasionally union between two rings may take place, 1-phenyl-3-methylpyrazolone giving, for example, bis-1-phenyl-3-methylpyrazolone, which is subsequently alkylated.

2-Hydrazinopyridine and other compounds of this type do not yield the expected dihydro product, but are converted to the pyridine derivative. The reaction fails in the pyrazole series.[152]

Mannich Reaction [52]

The Mannich reaction involves the formation of an aminomethylated product through the simultaneous reaction of an amine and formaldehyde with a compound having a reactive hydrogen, generally a carbonyl compound:

$$RCOCH_3 + CH_2O + R'_2NH.HCl \quad \rightarrow \quad RCOCH_2CH_2NR'_2.HCl + H_2O$$

Active hydrogens are present in ketones in general and Mannich bases have been prepared from a large number of these compounds, including aliphatic, unsaturated, cyclic, aralkyl ketones and ketones of the heterocyclic series. o-Aminoacetophenone and its acetyl and benzoyl derivatives, m-aminoacetophenone, *p*-aminoacetophenone, β-tetralone, barbituric acid and certain pyrazolones from exceptions, and do not give the Mannich reaction. Aldehydes may also undergo the Mannich reaction, the aminomethylene group entering the α-position with respect to the carbonyl group.[53]

Ammonia as well as primary and secondary amines are all capable of giving the reaction. The products resulting from ammonia and primary amines are themselves primary and secondary bases, and are capable of further reaction with formaldehyde and the carbonyl compound. The reaction with ammonia is complicated by the fact that this base reacts with formaldehyde to form methylamine, which reacts to form methylated products. Many aliphatic amines take part in the Mannich reaction, including β-hydroxy, β-chloro and β-phenylethylamines, benzylamine, ω-aminoacetophenone and tetrahydro-β-naphthylamine. Hydrazine and guanidine do not react. Among the secondary aliphatic amines dimethylamine is more reactive than diethylamine. Aromatic and alkyl aromatic amines and saturated cyclic amines such as piperidine, piperazine and morpholine give the Mannich reaction, but dicyclohexylamine and tetrahydroquinoline are unreactive.

Other aldehydes, as for example acetaldehyde, phenylacetaldehyde, benzaldehyde and anisaldehyde may be substituted for formaldehyde in the Mannich reaction, and addition compounds have been prepared with these aldehydes in conjunction with acetone, cyclohexanone and other ketones.

The Mannich reaction is applicable, in general, to compounds with active hydrogen, such as cyanoacetic acid,[54] *p*-nitrophenylacetic acid, benzoylacetic acid, acetoacetic ester, and malonic acid. The ortho and para hydrogen atoms in phenols are also reactive.[55] Di- and trisubstituted products may be obtained from those phenols in which 2, 4 and 6 positions are unoccupied. Phenylacetylenes and some substituted phenylacetylenes also give the Mannich reaction, yielding bases of the type $RC \equiv C.CH_2NR'_2$. α-Picoline and quinaldines also react, α-picoline forming 2-β-diethylaminoethylpyridine with diethylamine and formaldehyde.[56]

General Procedure

The general procedure followed in carrying out the Mannich reaction is to mix the carbonyl compound with 5 to 10% excess of the hydrochloride of the amine and 50 to 100% excess of 20-40% aqueous formaldehyde and to heat the mixture under agitation until the reaction is complete. It is preferable to add the excess formaldehyde in portions at intervals. The reaction is generally complete within a few minutes, but occasionally continued heating for 6 to 8 hours may be necessary. Paraformaldehyde may be used in place of aqueous formaldehyde, and an organic solvent, usually 95% ethyl alcohol may be employed to bring the product into solution. If the carbonyl compound used in the reaction is a liquid, it may serve as the solvent. In condensations involving 2-, 3- and 9- acetylphenanthrene it is of advantage to use isoamyl alcohol as a solvent.

The mixture is acidified, as a rule, after the completion of the reaction, but sometimes it is of advantage to add sufficient hydrochloric acid to the liquid in the beginning to make it acid to Congo red.

The base resulting from the reaction may be isolated as the hydrochloride, but if the free base may be distilled without decomposition, isolation and purification may be more effectively achieved by distillation.

Byproducts formed in the reaction are condensation products between formaldehyde and amines or ketones, and substances resulting from reactions of the primary products.

Ring Formation through the Mannich Reaction

Mannich bases resulting through the interaction of primary bases with two molecules of a ketone and two of aldehyde are usually unstable and readily undergo cyclization.[57] Two isomeric forms of an acetyldimethyltetrahydropyridine result, for example, from the condensation product of methylamine hydrochloride, acetone and formaldehyde:

$$2CH_3COCH_3 + 2CH_2O + H_2NCH_3.HCl \rightarrow CH_3COCH_2CH_2N(CH_3)CH_2CH_2COCH_3.HCl$$

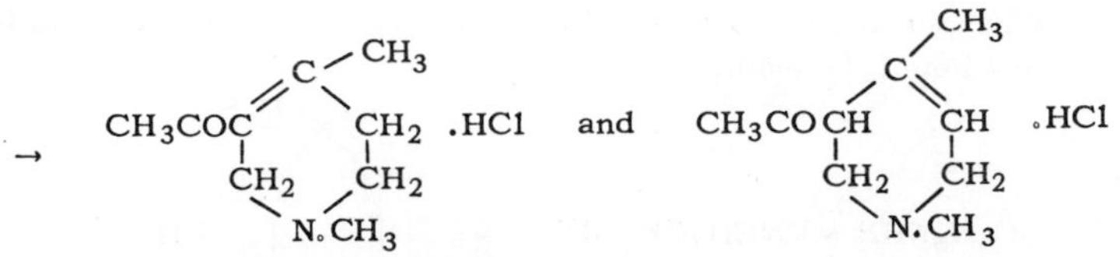

Pyridones are formed directly through the interaction of a primary amine hydrochloride with a ketone having two active hydrogen atoms attached to carbon atoms adjacent to the carbonyl group. An example is the reaction of acetone dicarboxylic esters with an amine and an aldehyde:[58]

$$CO(CH_2COOR)_2 + R'NH_2.HCl + 2CH_3CHO$$

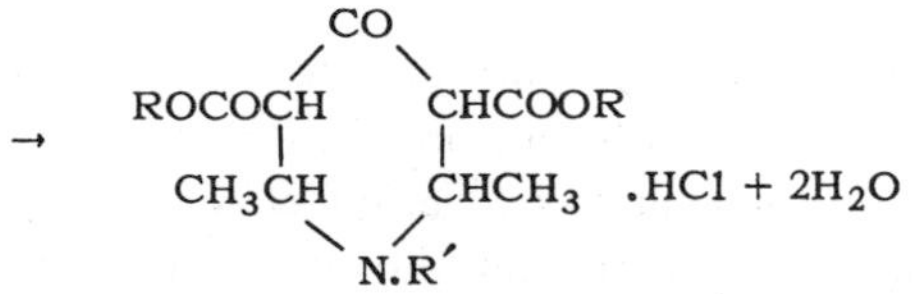

A pyridone also results through the interaction of aniline hydrochloride, benzaldehyde and acetone:

$$CH_3COCH_3 + C_6H_5NH_2.HCl + 2C_5H_5CHO \rightarrow$$

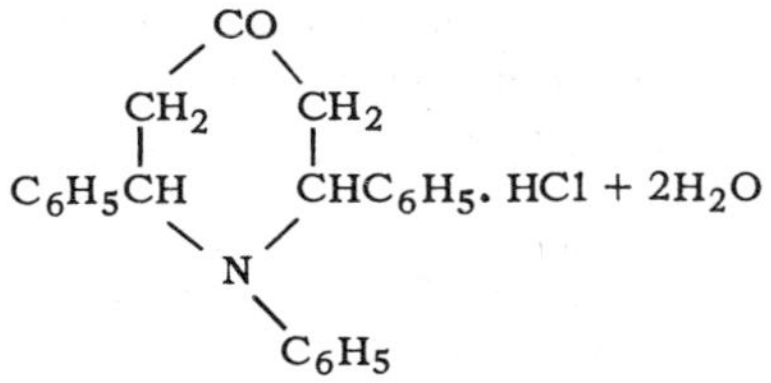

The cyclic compounds are formed from tetrahydropyrones.[59]

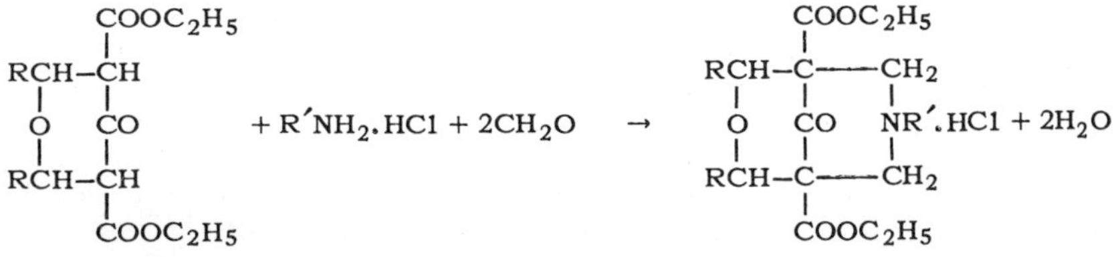

Pyridones resulting from the condensation of acetonedicarboxylic esters with primary amines and aldehydes also yield bicyclic compounds by reaction with two additional molecules of aldehyde and a mole of amine:[60]

$$
\begin{array}{c}
\text{COOR}'' \\
|
\end{array}
\qquad\qquad
\begin{array}{c}
\text{COOR}'' \\
|
\end{array}
$$

$$
\begin{array}{cc}
\text{RCH—CH} \\
| \quad | \\
\text{RN} \quad \text{CO} \\
| \quad | \\
\text{RCH—CH} \\
| \\
\text{COOR}''
\end{array}
+ \text{R}'\text{NH}_2.\text{HCl} + 2\text{CH}_2\text{O}
\;\rightarrow\;
\begin{array}{ccc}
\text{RCH—C——CH}_2 \\
| \quad | \quad | \\
\text{R}'\text{N} \quad \text{CO} \quad \text{NR}'.\text{HCl} + 2\text{H}_2\text{O} \\
| \quad | \quad | \\
\text{RCH—C——CH}_2 \\
| \\
\text{COOR}''
\end{array}
$$

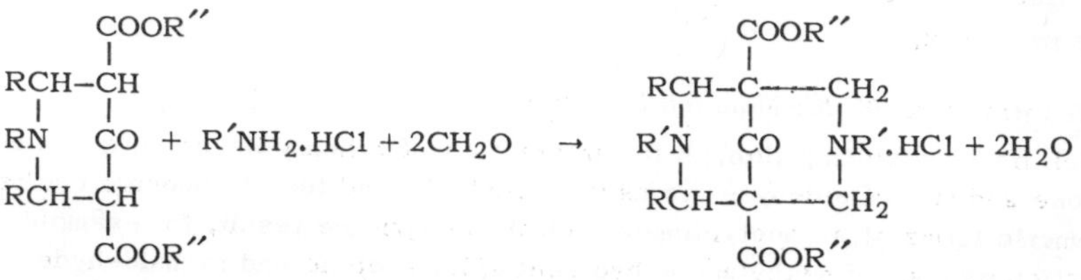

The bicyclic nucleus of these compounds is designated by the term bispidin ring.

Phenylhydrazones of ketonic Mannich bases undergo internal condensation to pyrazolines by elimination of the amino group:[186]

$$
\text{C}_6\text{H}_5\text{NHN} = \text{CRCH}_2\text{CH}_2\text{NR}' \quad\rightarrow\quad
\begin{array}{c}
\text{N}^{-\text{C}_6\text{H}_5} \\
/ \quad \backslash \\
\text{N} \quad \text{CH}_2 \\
\| \quad | \quad + \text{HNR}'_2 \\
\text{RC} - \text{CH}_2
\end{array}
$$

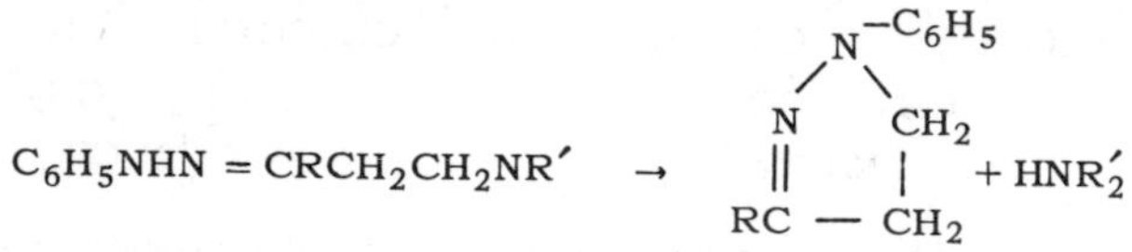

Some Mannich bases can be distilled without decomposition under diminished pressure, but many decompose into an amine and an unsaturated compound when heated or distilled with steam:[61]

$$
\text{C}_6\text{H}_5\text{COCH}_2\text{CH}_2\text{NR}_2.\text{HCl} \quad\rightarrow\quad \text{C}_6\text{H}_5\text{COCH} = \text{CH}_2 + \text{R}_2\text{NH}.\text{HCl}
$$

In some instances decomposition may proceed spontaneously. The condensation product resulting from the interaction of ethyl monoethylmalonate, diethylamine and formaldehyde, decomposes to ethyl acrylate as it is formed. The reaction involves cleavage of an amine and simultaneous decarboxylation:

$$
(\text{HOCO})_2\text{C(R)CH}_2\text{N(CH}_3)_2 \quad\rightarrow\quad \text{HOCOC(R)} = \text{CH}_2 + (\text{CH}_3)_2\text{NH} + \text{CO}_2
$$

This forms the basis of a satisfactory method of preparation of a-alkylacrylic acids from alkylmalonic acids.[62]

Mannich bases may be employed for the introduction of organic groups into the molecule of compounds with a reactive methylene:

$$
\text{RCH}_2\text{NR}' + \text{CH}_2\text{R}''\text{R}''' \rightarrow \text{RCH}_2\text{CHR}''\text{R}''' + \text{HNR}'_2
$$

Compounds with a methylene group of moderate activity, as for example, simple ketones, require the presence of strong bases, preferably sodium amide, capable of converting them to enolates. Among Mannich bases only those capable of undergoing transformation to unsaturated systems by amine elimination are suitable for the reaction. Ionization of the methylenic compound is an essential condition of the reaction. Ionization may be caused by the basic character of the Mannich base itself, as in the case of ethyl nitroacetate.[187] Ionization may be brought about also by the addition of a small amount of a basic substance such as sodium hydroxide, sodium ethoxide or sodium amide. The base chosen should be no stronger than is just sufficient to catalyze the reaction in order to avoid multiple substitutions and other condensation reactions. It is desirable in most cases to carry out the reaction under a nitrogen atmosphere. Gramine reacting with aliphatic nitro compounds gives a skatyl derivative of the nitro body:[188]

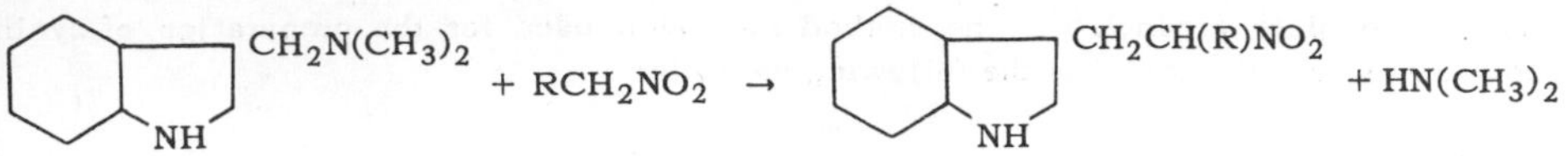
CH2N(CH3)2
NH
+ RCH2NO2 →
CH2CH(R)NO2
NH
+ HN(CH3)2

A diskatyl compound is obtained with nitromethane. Monosubstituted products have been obtained from nitromethane in the presence of sodium ethoxide with Mannich bases of acetone, cyclohexanone, acetophenone, 4-methoxy- and 3,4-dimethoxyacetophenone.[189] 1- And 2-nitropropane have been alkylated by the Mannich base derived from 1-nitropropane.[190] The reaction failed with the Mannich base of 2-nitropropane.

Condensation products have been prepared by this reaction with various Mannich bases and ethyl acetoacetate,[191] cyanoacetic ester,[192] malonic ester derivatives,[193] tricarbethoxymethane,[194] and dibenzoylmethane.[195] Condensations of this type have been carried out also with ketonic Mannich bases and ketones or keto esters.[196] The resulting δ-ketones may be converted to cyclohexanone derivatives by an internal aldol condensation; cyclization often occurs spontaneously during the primary condensation reaction. The reaction has been utilized for the preparation of the terpenes carvone and piperitone,[197] bicylcic terpenes containing angular methyl groups such as the cyperones,[198] polynuclear hydrocarbons with fused ring systems related to steroids and containing angular methyl groups,[199] and compounds related to alkaloids and containing angular ethyl and phenyl groups.[200]

Reaction proceeds with diethylphthalimidomalonate,

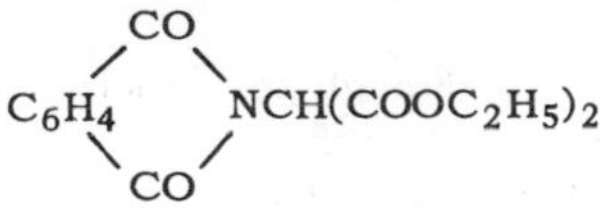
CO
C6H4
NCH(COOC2H5)2
CO

under the optimum experimental conditions.[201]

Indole reacts with diethylpiperidinomethylformamidomalonate to give diethyl skatylformamidomalonate, which is readily hydrolyzed to triptophan in one step.[202]

2-Dimethylaminomethylpyrole reacts with diethyl acetamidomalonate in toluene or xylene in the presence of sodium hydroxide to give a 70 to 80% yield of the compound

[203]

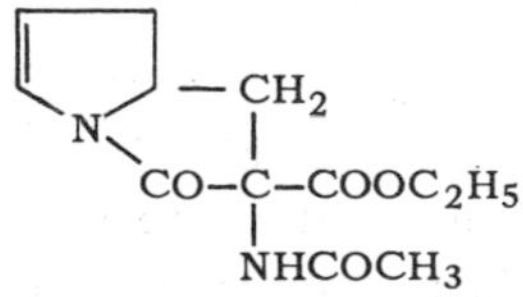
CH2
N
CO–C–COOC2H5
NHCOCH3

The reaction of Mannich bases with compounds having reactive methylene groups often proceeds slowly. Robinson introduced a modification of the reaction which consisted in using the quaternary methiodide of the base formed by the reaction of the base with methyl iodide.[63] The reaction proceeds much more rapidly with the quaternary compound, as a rule, than with the free base, but requires the use of an stoichiometric amount of the base, whereas in the reaction of the free base only a catalytic quantity of the base is required. The reaction mixture is held at room temperature for several hours, and is then heated under reflux for two to twenty hours, until the evolution of amine ceases.[204] It is claimed that yields are improved when the quaternary salt is formed *in situ* by the addition of two equivalents of ethyl iodide or dimethyl sulfate to the Mannich base, and the reaction is carried out with the sodio derivative of the methylenic compound in solution in absolute alcohol.[205] The method has been used for the preparation of cyclic compounds, as illustrated in the following example:

$$
\begin{array}{c}
\text{CH}_2 \\
\text{CH}_2 \quad\quad \text{CO} \\
| \quad\quad\quad | \\
\text{CH}_2 \quad\quad \text{CH}_2 \\
\text{CH}_2
\end{array}
+ \text{CH}_3\text{COCH}_2\text{CH}_2\text{N(C}_2\text{H}_5)_2\text{CH}_3 \cdot \text{I} \quad\rightarrow\quad (\text{C}_2\text{H}_5)_2\text{NCH}_3 \cdot \text{HI}
$$

$$
+
\begin{array}{c}
\text{CH}_2 \\
\text{CH}_2 \quad\quad \text{CO} \\
| \quad\quad\quad | \\
\text{CH}_2 \quad\quad \text{CHCH}_2\text{CH}_2\text{COCH}_3 \\
\text{CH}_2
\end{array}
\rightarrow
\begin{array}{c}
\quad\quad\quad \text{OH} \\
\text{CH}_2 \; | \; \text{CH}_2 \\
\text{CH}_2 \quad \text{C} \quad \text{CO} \\
| \quad\quad\quad | \quad\quad | \\
\text{CH}_2 \quad \text{CH} \quad \text{CH}_2 \\
\text{CH}_2 \quad \text{CH}_2
\end{array}
\rightarrow
\begin{array}{c}
\text{CH}_2 \quad \text{CH} \\
\text{CH}_2 \quad \text{C} \quad \text{CO} \\
| \quad\quad\quad | \quad\quad | \\
\text{CH}_2 \quad \text{CH} \quad \text{CH}_2 \\
\text{CH}_2 \quad \text{CH}_2
\end{array}
$$

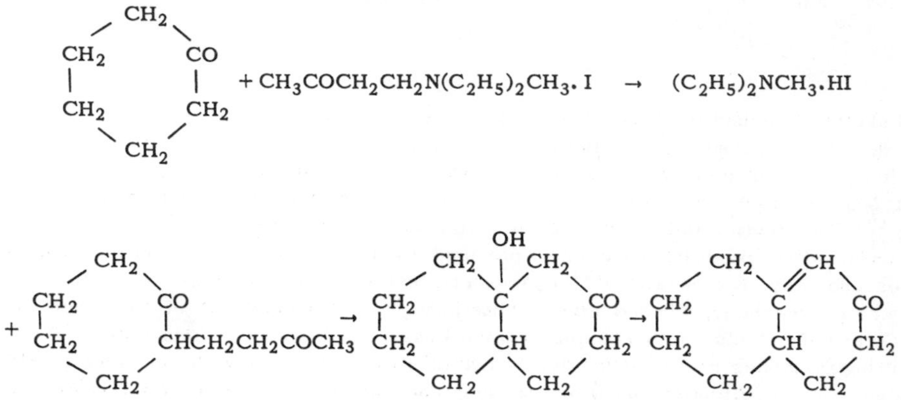

The amino group in many Mannich bases of the type $\text{RCOCRR'CH}_2\text{N(CH}_3)_2$ may be replaced with the *cyano* group by reaction of the hydrochloride of the base with aqueous potassium cyanide.[206]

Mannich bases of phenols and indoles, reacting with hot aqueous alcoholic sodium cyanide, give the sodium salt of aryl- and indoleacetic acids.[207] The nitriles may be obtained by carrying out the reaction with a benzene solution of hydrogen cyanide at 150° in an autoclave.

Nitriles have been obtained also through the reaction of quaternary halides derived from Mannich bases with sodium cyanide.[208]

Certain Mannich bases have been converted to aldehydes by heating them in acetic acid solution with hexamethylenetetramine. The reaction is applicable to Mannich bases derived from indole, 2-phenylindole, 2-carbethoxyindole, phenol, and β-naphthol.[209]

Mannich bases may be readily reduced to amino alcohols, which, in contrast to the corresponding ketones, are quite stable.

Biginelli's Reaction [153]

Biginelli effected a condensation between urea, an aldehyde and a β-keto ester, which probably involved first a union between the carbonyl carbon in the aldehyde, the reactive methylene in the keto ester and an amino group in urea. On this basis, the final product, a pyrimidine derivative, would be the result of a union between the second amino group in urea and the carbonyl group of the keto ester:

$$
\text{C}_6\text{H}_5\text{CHO} + \text{H}_2\text{C(COOC}_2\text{H}_5)\text{COCH}_3 + \text{H}_2\text{NCONH}_2 \quad\rightarrow
$$

$$
\text{H}_2\text{O} + \text{C}_6\text{H}_5\underset{\underset{\text{NHCONH}_2}{|}}{\text{CH}}\text{CH(COOC}_2\text{H}_5)\text{COCH}_3
$$

$$
\rightarrow \quad \text{C}_6\text{H}_5\underset{\underset{\text{NH}-\text{CONH}}{|}}{\text{CH}}\text{C(COOC}_2\text{H}_5)\text{:CCH} \quad + \text{H}_2\text{O}
$$

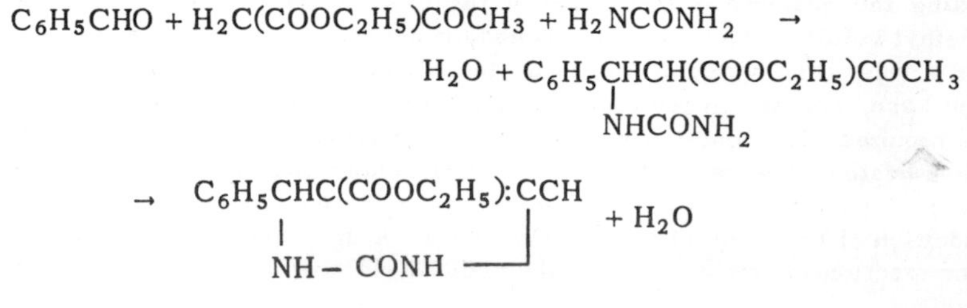

The reaction may be carried out in alcoholic or in acetic acid solution, in the presence of hydrogen chloride, which acts as a catalyst. Excellent results are obtained with benzaldehyde, β-hydroxybenzaldehyde, anisaldehyde and styrylaldehyde and moderate yields are obtained with many other aldehydes. Yields are low in a few exceptional cases.

The reaction of certain carbonyl compounds with ammonium formate leads to the formation of an amine through the intermediate appearance of a hydroxy amine and its subsequent partial reduction (see *Leuckart Reaction,* Chap. 9).

Schmidt Reaction[64]

Hydrazoic acid reacts with carbonyl compounds in the presence of sulfuric acid to form amides:

$$CH_3COCH_3 + HN_3 \rightarrow CH_3CONHCH_3 + N_2$$

Since an aldehyde gives an unsubstituted amide $RCONH_2$, this may be dehydrated to a nitrile, in the presence of sulfuric acid. The reaction of acetaldehyde with hydrazoic acid in the presence of concentrated sulfuric acid thus leads to the formation of acetonitrile, while benzaldehyde yields both benzonitrile and formanilide.

The mechanism of the reaction is not definitely established, but it appears probably that an unstable addition compound,

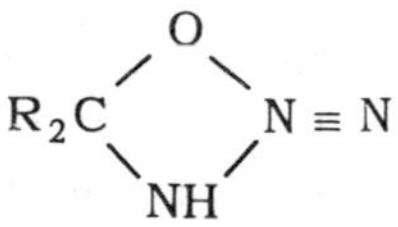

is first formed which undergoes immediate rearrangement to the amide, with cleavage of nitrogen.

General Procedure

In carrying out the reaction, a solution of hydrazoic acid in chloroform is added with good stirring to a mixture of the ketone with sulfuric acid. Stirring is continued until the evolution of nitrogen ceases. As a rule the hydrazoic acid is used in 20% excess. Alternatively the sulfuric acid may be added drop by drop and with good agitation to the mixture of the ketone and the solution of hydrazoic acid, or *vice versa.*

Tetrazoles, RC:NN = N.NR′ (ring closed between C and the last N), are formed as byproducts of the reaction of hydrazoic acid with carbonyl compounds. Tetrazoles may be obtained as the principal product of the reaction when hydrazoic acid is used in at least twofold excess. When the reaction between ketones and hydrazoic acid is carried out in the presence of alcohol and hydrochloric acid imino ethers are obtained:

$$RCOR + HN_3 + R'OH + HCl \rightarrow RC(=NR)OR'.\ HCl + H_2O + N_2$$

Unsymmetrical ketones give two different amides. Substituted acylacetic esters

$$RCOC(R')(R'')COOC_2H_5$$

yield amides of the type $RCONHC(R')(R'')COOC_2H_5$, which may be hydrolyzed to substituted α-amino acids, $H_2NC(R')(R'')COOH$. Some otherwise difficultly accessible amino acids may be prepared by this route.

The Schmidt reaction is applicable to cyclic ketones and results in the formation of a cyclic amide such as $\overline{CH_2(CH_2)_4NHCO}$, for example, from cyclohexanone. These amides are readily hydrolyzed to amino acids.

Benzoylbenzoic acid gives anhydro-N-benzoylanthranilic acid

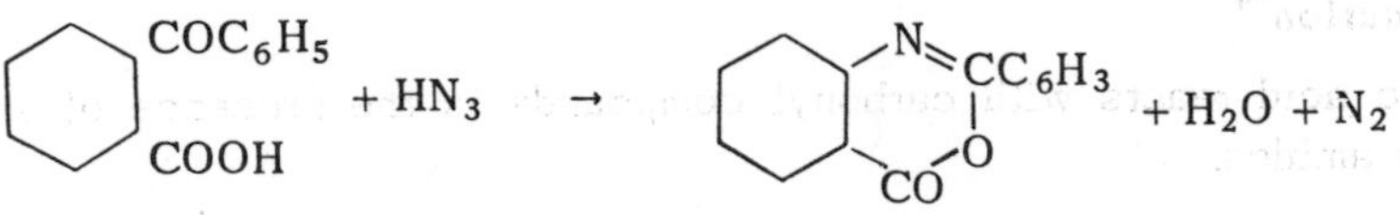

Benzophenone reacts abnormally giving a phenyliminodihydrotetrazole. Benzil yields as the final product of the reaction benzoylphenylurea,

$$C_6H_5NHCONHCOC_6H_5,$$

with some oxanilide.

Cannizzaro Reaction

A process of mutual oxidation and reduction between two molecules of an aldehyde or between molecules of two different aldehydes, resulting in the formation of an alcohol and an acid, is known as the Cannizzaro reaction after its discoverer.[65] The transformation, which is referred to as a disproportionation or dismutation, is brought about under the influence of an alkali, such as sodium hydroxide:

$$2RCHO + NaOH \rightarrow RCH_2OH + RCOONa$$

The aldehyde is added to 50% aqueous or alcoholic caustic, and the mixture is agitated in the cold. Alkali metal alcoholates in alcoholic solution are also used in place of alkaline hydroxides.[66] When the process involves two different aldehydes it is termed a "crossed" Cannizzaro reaction.

A probable mechanism of the reaction is expressed by the following scheme.[211]

$$RCHO + NaOH \rightleftharpoons RCH\begin{matrix}ONa \\ OH\end{matrix} \xrightarrow{RCHO} \overset{OH}{\underset{|}{}}\!\!RCHO-\overset{ONa}{\underset{|}{C}}HR$$

$$\rightarrow RCH_2OCOR + NaOH \rightarrow RCH_2O\overset{OH}{\underset{|}{C}}\begin{matrix}-R \\ ONa\end{matrix}$$

$$\rightarrow RCH_2OH + RCOONa$$

In the aliphatic series the Cannizzaro reaction proceeds best, as a general rule, between aldehydes with no α-hydrogen, i.e., with tertiary aldehydes.[67] Dismutation of the Cannizzaro type takes place only to a small extent with acetaldehyde and with other aldehydes of the normal aliphatic series.[68] Electronegative groups, such as halogens and nitro groups, in the molecule, favor the reaction, while electropositive groups such as methyl, alkoxy and amino radicals have the opposite effect. Acetylenic aldehydes are broken down into an acetylenic hydrocarbon and a formate when treated with an alkali. This type of cleavage also takes place with triphenylacetaldehyde and trihaloacetaldehydes, which yield triphenylmethane and a haloform respectively when treated with an alkali.

It is noteworty that the Cannizzaro reaction does not take place with benzaldehyde, *p*-tolualdehyde, or anisaldehyde if peroxides are carefully removed from these aldehydes.[266] The conversion of benzaldehyde to benzoic acid is greatly enhanced by use of solubilizing agents.[267]

Disproportionation of the Cannizzaro type has been observed with certain aldehydes having an α-hydrogen atom, but under conditions differing from those of the normal Cannizzaro reaction. For example, isobutyraldehyde is converted quantitatively into isobutyl alcohol when it is heated with barium hydroxide in a sealed tube at 150°.[69] Simple alkoxides of magnesium and aluminum induce the disproportionation of normal aliphatic aldehydes such as acetaldehyde. Conversion of the latter to ethyl acetate is quantitative.[70] Very pure starting materials are required for successful results, and the method presents some difficulties. These reagents convert isobutyraldehyde and chloral into isobutyl isobutylacetate and trichlorethyl trichloroacetate respectively. Mildly basic ethoxides, such as $Mg(OC_2H_5)_2$, $Mg[Al(OC_2H_5)_4]_2$ and $Na_2Mg(OC_2H_5)_4$ convert aldehydes containing a CH_2 group in α-position to trimeric glycol esters. Such catalysts give the simple esters with aldehydes containing no methylene group in α-position to the carbonyl group, but the strongly basic sodium ethoxide may convert these aldehydes to glycol esters.[212]

The Cannizzaro reaction may take place between an aldol of the type RCH(R′)CH(OH)CRR′CHO and the aldehyde RCHR′CHO, yielding an alcohol $RCHR'CH(OH)CRR'CH_2OH$.[71]

A crossed Cannizzaro reaction between formaldehyde and the condensation products of formaldehyde and aldehydes of the type RCHR′CHO gives dimethylhydroxy compounds:

$$RCR'(CH_2OH)CHO + CH_2O + NaOH \rightarrow RCR'(CH_2OH)_2 + HCOONa$$

The condensation products of aliphatic aldehydes of the normal series with formaldehyde also undergo this reaction, forming trimethylolalkanes, $RC(CH_2OH)_3$,[72] while acetaldehyde gives pentaerythritol $C(CH_2OH)_4$. Attempts to prepare a dimethylol compound from phenylacetaldehyde have not met with success.

Hydroxy groups apparently favor a dismutation of Cannizzaro type. Hydroxypivalic aldehyde, $HOCH_2(CH_2)_2CHO$ for example, readily undergoes the Cannizzaro reaction yielding hydroxypivalic acid.

α-Keto aldehydes of the type of phenylglyoxal undergo an internal dismutation to form α-hydroxy acids: [73]

$$RCOCHO + NaOH \rightarrow RCH(OH)COONa$$

Glyoxal yields sodium glyoxylate, OCHCOONa, when treated with strong sodium hydroxide. [74]

Lactones have been obtained in good yield through an internal Cannizzaro reaction from certain readily accessible derivatives of glutaraldehyde, such as ethyltrimethylglutaraldehyde: [75]

$$OCHC(CH_3)_2CH(C_2H_5)CH(CH_3)CHO \rightarrow \overline{COC(CH_3)_2CH(C_2H_5)CH(CH_3)CH_2O}$$

Reformatsky's Reaction

α-Haloesters react with zinc under anhydrous conditions to form organozinc compounds characterized by the grouping XZnC.COOR, X representing a halogen atom. These react with carbonyl compounds to form addition products, which on decomposition with acids give β-hydroxyesters: [76]

$$-\overset{|}{C}=O + XZn-\underset{|}{\overset{|}{C}}COOR \rightarrow -\underset{|}{\overset{XZnO}{\overset{|}{C}}}-\underset{|}{\overset{|}{C}}COOR \rightarrow -\underset{|}{\overset{HO}{\overset{|}{C}}}-\underset{|}{\overset{|}{C}}COOR$$

The organozinc compound is not prepared separately, but is formed in the course of the reaction from metallic zinc and the halo ester.

General Procedure

The zinc is added to a portion of the solution of the carbonyl compound and halo ester in benzene or other solvent in a flask provided with a reflux condenser. A vigorous reaction soon begins. The remainder of the solution is added gradually, at a rate to maintain a smooth reaction. It is important to assure the complete absence of water from the reagents and the apparatus, and to protect the latter from atmospheric moisture. Zinc dust, granular or mossy zinc may serve equally well on condition that the surface of the metal be clean. A few crystals of iodine, a little amalgamated zinc or a trace of methylmagnesium iodide may be added to initiate the reaction, if necessary. Occasionally the reaction is retarded due to the adherence of the reaction product to the surface of zinc. This may be overcome usually by adequate agitation, or through the proper choice of a solvent. In carrying out the reaction with ketones it is desirable to use a mixture in equal quantities of benzene and toluene.

A good method for cleaning the zinc is to heat it to 100° for about 15 minutes with sulfuric acid containing a few drops of nitric acid. The metal is then washed successively with water and acetone and dried. The zinc may be activated by immersing it in a warm solution of copper sulfate, thus depositing a layer of copper on its surface.

It has been claimed that a great improvement in yields is brought about if the reaction is carried out in dilute ethereal solution, first adding the aldehyde and the zinc and then gradually introducing the bromo ester. [213]

The reaction is generally applicable, with few exceptions, to saturated or unsaturated aliphatic and aromatic aldehydes and ketones as well as to cyclic ketones; it follows an abnormal course with halo aliphatic ketones, and does not succeed with phenolic ketones. The reaction proceeds more readily with aldehydes than with ketones. Among halo esters, iodides are the most reactive, chlorides the least reactive. Chloroacetic esters hardly react at all; on the other hand secondary or tertiary α-chloro esters are more reactive. Bromo esters are commonly used in carrying out the reaction because of their high reactivity and ready availability.

Side reactions are normally of little consequence in Reformatsky's reaction, and may be further repressed by using an excess of halo ester and introducing it in small successive portions. Coupling of two molecules of the halo ester by elimination of two atoms of bromine as zinc bromide is a possible side reaction. Some carbonyl compounds give rise to aldols, and the water resulting from this reaction decomposes an equivalent of the intermediate organozinc compound. Certain carbonyl compounds are partially enolized under the influence of the organozinc compound, and the enolic form escapes reaction.

Methyl bromozincmalonate and ethyl α-bromozincisobutyrate react abnormally with benzalacetophenone to give 1,4-addition products.[77] Acetone is apparently converted under the action of methyl bromozincmalonate to mesityl oxide; the organozinc compound reacts with this forming a 1,4-addition product.[78]

β- and γ-bromo and iodo esters take part in the Reformatsky reaction only to a very slight extent; on the other hand, certain reactive halogen compounds, as for example benzyl halides, undergo the reaction. Vinylogs of α-halo esters, such as $ICH_2CH = CHCOOC_2H_5$, readily take part in the reaction.

β-Hydroxy esters, the final product of Reformatsky's reaction, show a tendency to lose a molecule of water to yield unsaturated compounds, loss of water sometimes being occasioned by heating alone. Dehydration may be readily brought about by use of various dehydrating agents, including acetic anhydride, acetyl chloride, zinc chloride, or sulfuric acid of moderate concentration.[79] Dehydration may be conveniently carried out by refluxing a mixture of the hydroxy ester, dehydrating agent and benzene and continuously separating from the condensate the water carried away by the vapors of benzene.

It can be seen that Reformatsky's reaction offers the possibility not only of passing from a carbonyl compound to a β-hydroxy ester with at least two more carbon atoms, but also of preparing unsaturated esters from such hydroxy compounds. The latter may be readily hydrogenated to the corresponding saturated ester. Esters of both types may be transformed to an aldehyde with the same number of carbon atoms and the synthesis repeated. It is thus possible, by starting with a carbonyl compound, to increase the chain length by steps of two carbon atoms through the successive application of Reformatsky's reaction. Phytol[80] and natural polyenes[90] [81] have been prepared synthetically by this procedure.

Reformatsky's reaction is applicable to esters and results in the formation of ketonic bodies. Ethyl γ-ethoxyacetoacetate has been obtained in 10 to 33% yield by this reaction from ethyl ethoxyacetate and ethyl bromoacetate by use of amalgamated zinc:[268]

$$C_2H_5OCH_2COOC_2H_5 + BrCH_2COOC_2H_5 + Zn(Hg)$$
$$\rightarrow C_2H_5OCH_2C(OC_2H_5)(OZnBr)CH_2COOC_2H_5$$
$$\xrightarrow{H_2O} C_2H_5OCH_2COCH_2COOC_2H_5$$

Ethyl 3,4-diketoadipate, $C_2H_5OCOCH_2COCOCH_2COOC_2H_5$, has been obtained similarly from ethyl oxalate, ethyl chloroacetate and zinc.[269] Ethyl α-bromoisobutyrate and oxalic ester give ethyl α,α-dimethylmaleate, $C_2H_5OCOCH(OH)C(CH_3)_2COOC_2H_5$.[270] Ethyl trimesate, the aldehyde ester formed, polymerizes to an aromatic tricarboxylic ester.[271] Ethyl α-bromopropionate and ethyl formate give ethyl 2,4-dimethyl-3-hydroxyglutarate.[272]

The application of Reformatsky's reaction to nitriles leads to the formation of ketones in a manner comparable with the Grignard reaction:[258]

$$RCN + BrCR'_2COOR'' + Zn \rightarrow BrZnN = C(R)C(R')_2COOR'' \rightarrow RCOC(R')_2COOR''$$

Aldol Condensation
(Wurtz Reaction)

The condensation reaction between two molecules of a carbonyl compound, involving the transfer of the α-hydrogen from one molecule to the oxygen of the carbonyl group in the other with simultaneous linkage of the molecules through the carbon valencies is known as aldol condensation:[82]

$$2CH_3CHO \rightarrow CH_3CH(OH)CH_2CHO$$

The reaction is usually brought about under the influence of alkalies or other basic substances. The reaction is one of equilibrium. The aldol is associated with a molecule of aldehyde with which it forms a compound with a 1,3-dioxane structure. The presence of at least one hydrogen atom in the α-position in the molecule of the carbonyl compound is an essential requirement of the reaction. Thus, homologs of acetaldehyde containing the groupings $-CH_2CHO$ and $-\overset{|}{C}H.CHO$ undergo the reaction readily. Aldehydes with the grouping $-\overset{|}{\underset{|}{C}}-CHO$, such as $(CH_3)_3CCHO$ and aromatic aldehydes ArCHO, which have no hydrogen in the α-position, are incapable of yielding aldols through self-condensation, but condense with the aldehydes of the aforementioned types to form mixed aldols. Formaldehyde fails to yield an aldol by self-condensation, but can condense with aldehydes having at least one hydrogen in the α-position. Diprimary glycols result through the interaction of aldehydes of the type ArCH(Alk). CHO with formaldehyde in the presence of basic catalysts:[83]

$$C_6H_5CH(CH_3)CHO + 4CH_2O + K_2CO_3$$
$$\rightarrow C_6H_5C(CH_3)(CH_2OH)_2 + 2HCOOK + CO_2 + CO + H_2O$$

Crossed aldol condensation between formaldehyde and acetaldehyde results in the formation of pentaerythritol, $C(CH_2OH)_4$, in 74% yield.

The mobility of a α-hydrogen in the Cannizzaro reaction is greater the fewer the number of hydrogen atoms attached to the α-carbon atom. Thus, acetaldehyde and propionaldehyde react to form α-methyl- β-hydroxy butyraldehyde:

$$CH_3CHO + CH_3CH_2CHO \quad \rightarrow \quad CH_3CH(OH)CH(CH_3)CHO$$

Aldehyde disulfonic acids, bis-diphenylenesuccinaldehyde and *ms*-fluorenealdehydes are decomposed by alkalies with cleavage of the carbonyl group, and therefore fail to give aldols.[84] The condensation product of acetophenone with phthalaldehyde is a lactone of the expected aldol,

$$C_6H_4 \underset{CO}{\overset{CHCH_2COCH_3}{\diagup \diagdown}} O$$

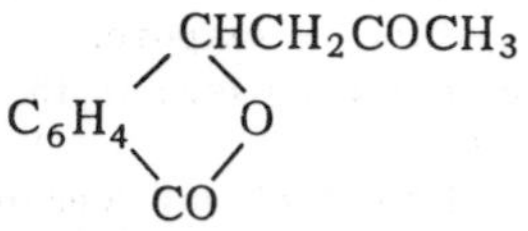

The carbonyl group in acetone and other ketones is less reactive than that in aldehydes. Reactive hydrogen atoms are present in acetone, and aldol condensation proceeds to a limited extent in the presence of alkalies, equilibrium being reached when only a comparatively small amount of the aldol, diacetone alcohol, has formed.

The normal aldol condensation of aldehydes and ketones under the action of alkaline catalysts, which takes place readily with methyl ketones and especially with acetone, proceeds with difficulty in the case of ketones in which both alkyl groups attached to the carbonyl group contain more than one carbon atom. All aldehydes do not react with equal ease, reactivity decreasing with molecular weight.

In the reaction of aldehydes with higher aliphatic ketones condensation takes place with a methyl group adjacent to the carbonyl group. Isobutyraldehyde reacting with diethyl ketone in 10% alcoholic potassium hydroxide solution gives 2,4-dimethyl-3-heptanol-5-one; butyraldehyde and methyl ethyl ketone reacting in the presence of alcoholic or solid potassium hydroxide give 5-methyl-4-heptane-6-one, $CH_3CH_2CH_2CH = C(CH_3)COCH_3$, with the intermediate formation of the aldol.

Aliphatic ketones of the type RCH_2COCH_2R' may be condensed with aldehydes under the action of hydrogen chloride, to β-chloro ketones:

$$RCHO + CH_3CH_2COR' + HCl \quad \rightarrow \quad RCHClCH(CH_3)COR' + H_2O$$

These compounds readily lose hydrogen chloride when heated, forming unsaturated ketones.

Condensations of the aldol type take place also, in general, between aldehydes and compounds containing reactive methylene groups, such as malonic esters, cyanoacetic esters, etc.:[85]

$$RCHO + H_2C(COOC_2H_5)_2 \quad \rightarrow \quad RCH(OH)CH(COOC_2H_5)_2$$

In many cases such reactions proceed further; a molecule of water is eliminated from the product and an unsaturated compound results. This is the basis of the Claisen and Knoevenagel condensations.

General Procedure

The reaction is carried out at a comparatively low temperature, usually between 8 and 15°. A satisfactory procedure is to shake a fairly concentrated aqueous solution of the condensing agent with an ethereal solution of the aldehyde.[86] The aldol formed is retained in solution in the ether and is thus protected from the action of the condensing agent, and furthermore, the aldehyde comes in contact with the catalyst gradually in small quantities at a time.[*]

Alkali metal hydroxides or carbonates are generally employed as condensing agents, potassium compounds being more effective than sodium compounds. Many other substances may be used as condensing agents. Lime-water, calcium ethoxide, strontium oxide and sulfite have been employed for the purpose.

Aldol condensation takes place in many cases in the absence of a catalyst, under the action of heat or ultraviolet rays.

It has already been pointed out that an aldol may combine with a molecule of aldehyde to form a compound with a 1,3-dioxane structure.[214] Acetaldol, for example, is obtained principally in the form of the compound:

$$
\begin{array}{c}
\quad\quad\quad O \text{---} CH\text{--}CH_3 \\
\quad\quad / \quad\quad\quad\quad \backslash \\
CH_2CH \quad\quad\quad\quad CH_2 \\
\quad\quad \backslash \quad\quad\quad\quad / \\
\quad\quad\quad O \text{---} CH\text{--}CH_3
\end{array}
$$

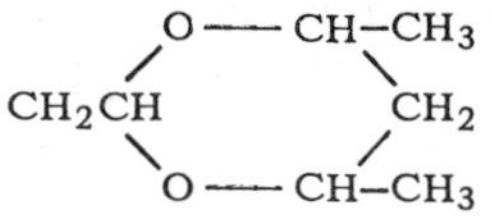

The aldol may be obtained from this slow distillation under 10-15 mm pressure in the presence of acid or alkaline catalysts. The compound distills under reduced pressure without decomposition. It breaks down into its components in aqueous solution.

Diacetone has been condensed with acetaldehyde to β-hydroxyisovaleralaldehyde in the presence of glycine as a catalyst.[215]

An aldol type condensation takes place in the reaction of acetone with chloroform in the presence of a suspension of potassium hydroxide in acetal or glycol dialkyl ethers.[216] The reaction results in the formation of trichloro-*ter*-butyl alcohol in high yield:

$$CH_3COCH_3 + HCCl_3 \quad \rightarrow \quad (CH_3)_2C(OH)CCl_3$$

The reaction is applicable to other ketones and even to aldehydes which do not readily resinify in contact with potassium hydroxide.

Condensation to Esters

The condensation of certain aldehydes takes a different course when carried out in the presence of aluminum alkoxides. A transfer of hydrogen takes place between the carbon atoms of the carbonyl groups and an ester results. Ethyl acetate is obtained, for example, when acetaldehyde is condensed under the influence of aluminum methoxide:

$$2CH_3CHO \quad \xrightarrow{\text{Al(OCH}_3)_3} \quad CH_3COOCH_2CH_3.$$

Methyl formate and propyl propionate result similarly from trioxymethylene and propionaldehyde respectively. Chloral yields trichloroethyl trichloroacetate.

(*) It should be noted that many aldehydes are converted to dark resinous products under the action of alkalies.

Acyloin Condensation

The acyloin condensation which takes place readily with many aromatic aldehydes is applicable to few aldehydes that are not purely aromatic. An acyloin has been obtained from phenyl glyoxal.[244]

Formation of α, β-Unsaturated Carbonyl Compounds

Aldols resulting from the condensation of a carbonyl compound with a secondary α-carbon show a tendency to lose the elements of water to yield α,β-unsaturated aldehydes or ketones. Simple heating is sufficient, in some cases, to cause dehydration. Unsaturated compounds of this type may form if aldol condensation is carried out under drastic conditions, and a second aldol condensation also takes place with the aldol first formed. Dehydration of the aldol in the course of its formation may be brought about by the use of zinc chloride as a condensing agent.[87]

Dehydration of the aldol may be accomplished by treatment with a dehydrating agent. Hydracetyl acetone, $CH_3CH(OH).CH_2COCH_3$, may be converted to ethylidene acetone by heating with anhydrous oxalic acid, and 2,4-dimethyl-3-heptene-5-one results from 2,4-dimethyl-3-heptanol-5-one by the same treatment.

In some instances the formation of the unsaturated compound proceeds readily, as with isovaleraldehyde which, reacting with acetone in very dilute aqueous sodium hydroxide solution, gives methylheptenone, $(CH_3)_2CHCH_2CH{:}CHCOCH_3$. Citral, condensing with acetone in the presence of barium hydroxide, or preferably sodium ethoxide, gives pseudoionone, $(CH_3)_2C = CHCH_2CH_2C(CH_3) = CHCH = CHCOCH_3$, a compound from which the isomeric α- and β-ionones are prepared.

Benzaldehyde reacting at 11° with crotonaldehyde in solution in alcoholic caustic gives 5-phenylpentadienal, $C_6H_5CH = CHCH = CHCHO$, in 10% yield.

An important synthesis of *polyethylenic aldehydes* has been accomplished by Kuhn through the condensation of cinnamaldehyde and crotonaldehyde in solution in 70% alcohol in the presence of piperidine acetate, which resulted in the formation of 7-phenylheptatrienal in 50% yield.

$$C_6H_5CH = CHCHO + CH_3CH{:}CHCHO \rightarrow$$
$$C_6H_5CH = CHCH = CH.CH = CHCHO + H_2O$$

Simultaneously 11-phenylundecapentaenal, $C_6H_5(CH = CH)_5.CHO$, was formed in 20% yield. This latter, condensed in benzene solution with a molecule of crotonaldehyde, in the presence of piperidine acetate, gives phenylpentadecaheptaenal $C_6H_5(CH = CH)_7.CHO$ in 80% yield.

Aromatic aldehydes reacting with acetone generally yield the unsaturated compound. Dibenzylideneacetone, $(C_6H_5CH = CH)_2CO$, is thus obtained through the condensation of benzaldehyde with acetone in the presence of sodium hydroxide solution or of aqueous alcoholic potassium cyanide. Benzalacetone (chalcone) similarly results through the interaction of benzaldehyde and acetophenone in the presence of sodium methoxide:

$$C_6H_5CHO + CH_3COC_6H_5 \rightarrow C_6H_5CH = CHCOC_6H_5 + H_2O$$

Salicylaldehyde gives both a monosalicylidene and a disalicylidene compound with acetone when the condensation is carried out in the presence of sodium hydroxide solution, while ceracidine results, when the reaction is carried out in the presence of sulfuric acid, through the condensation of two molecules of salicylideneacetone:

$$2OHC_6H_4CH = CHCOCH_3 \rightarrow$$

$$HOC_6H_4CH = CH\overline{C = CH.C(=C}H)CH = CHC_6H_4OH + 2H_2O$$

Compounds of this type may also be obtained with salicylaldehyde and ketones of the type CH_3COR. *o*-Nitrobenzaldehyde, reacting with acetone in the presence of a solution of sodium hydroxide or other alkaline agent, such as sodium sulfide and trisodium phosphate, gives the β-hydroxyketone,

$$NO_2C_6H_4CH(OH)CH_2COCH_3,$$

which is very readily transformed to *o*-nitrobenzylideneacetone.

Pyrrole-2-aldehyde gives with acetone 2-(β-acetylvinyl)-pyrrole,

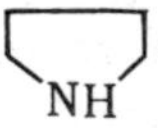 $.CH = CHCOCH_3,$

at water-bath temperature, in the presence of dilute aqueous potassium hydroxide.[146]

Benzaldehyde and its homologs may be condensed with halo ketones in the presence of hydrogen halides with the intermediate formation of an α,β-unsaturated ketone, which reacts with the hydrogen halide to yield a saturated dihalo ketone:

$$C_6H_5CHO + H_2CBrCOC_6H_5 \rightarrow H_2O + C_6H_5CH = CBrCOC_6H_5$$

$$\xrightarrow{HBr} C_6H_5CHBrCHBrCOC_6H_5$$

The dehydration of aldols resulting from ketones is of some practical importance since the unsaturated ketone may be obtained in good yield in spite of the fact that the aldol-ketone equilibrium does not favor the formation of aldol. Mesityl oxide, $(CH_3)_2C = CHCOCH_3$, results when the self-condensation of acetone is conducted under vigorous conditions, as, for example by use of quick-lime, sodium alkoxides or hydrogen chloride as condensing agents.[88] Condensation may proceed further, with the formation of phorone,

$$(CH_3)_2C = CHCOCH = C(CH_3)_2,$$

isophorone, xylitone and finally mesitylene.[89]

Mesityl oxide is obtained as the principal product when acetone is made to condense in the presence of alkalies, diacetone alcohol being the intermediate product of the reaction.

Ketones other than acetone also undergo condensations of the same type. Thus, diethyl ketone yields homomesityl oxide, $(CH_3CH_2)_2C = C(CH_3)COCH_2CH_3$, when condensed under the influence of sodium ethoxide, and homoisophorone, $(C_2H_5)_2C.CH(CH_3)C(C_2H_5):C(CH_3)COCHCH_3$, results from this by further reaction. Condensations of this type may also be caused to take place between two different ketones.

Dypnone (7-methylbenzalacetophenone) results when acetophenone is made to undergo self-condensation under the influence of zinc chloride or iodine; further condensation leads to the formation of *sym*-1,3,5-triphenylbenzene:

$$2C_6H_5COCH_3 \rightarrow C_6H_5C(CH_3) = CHCOC_6H_5$$

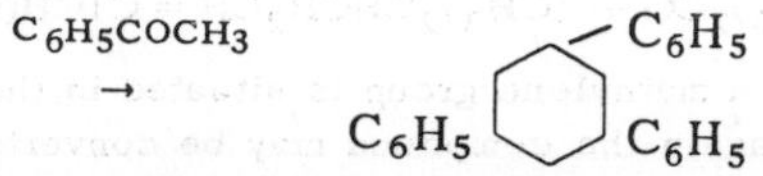

This transformation takes place with improved yields when acetophenone is dissolved in an equal volume of aniline containing a little aniline hydrochloride, and the mixture is heated to 180°. This method may be successfully applied to other aralkyl ketones, but with purely aliphatic ketones the reaction proceeds in a different direction, and quinolines, indoles, etc. are formed.

Diacetyl has been condensed with unsaturated aldehydes of the type $R(CH = CH)_nCHO$ to polyeneones $R(CH = CH)_{n+1}COCO(CH = CH)_nR$.[217]

Cyclopentenone and cyclohexenone have been obtained through the internal condensation of 1,4- and 1,5-diketones.[218] The method has been employed for the preparation of macrocyclic ketones. Muscone has been obtained, for example, through the condensation of hexadeca-2,15-dione under the action of the Grignard compound of N-methylaniline, and hydrogenation of the unsaturated ketone formed:[219]

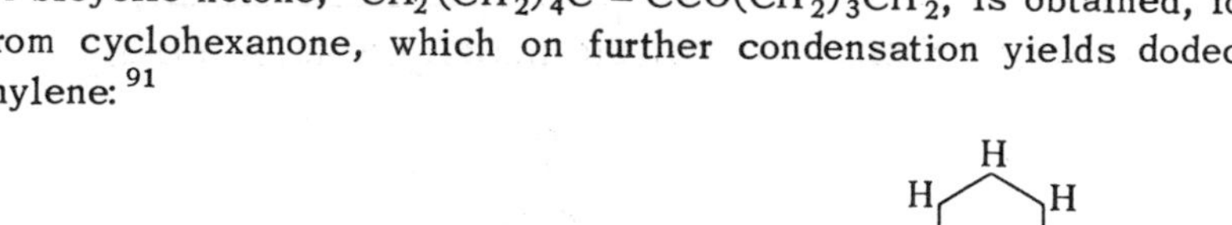

Cyclic ketones are also capable fo forming unsaturated condensation products. A bicyclic ketone, $CH_2(CH_2)_4C = CCO(CH_2)_3CH_2$, is obtained, for example, from cyclohexanone, which on further condensation yields dodecahydrotriphenylene:[91]

$$CH_2(CH_2)_4C = C\,CO(CH_2)_3CH_2 + CO(CH_2)_4CH_2 \rightarrow$$

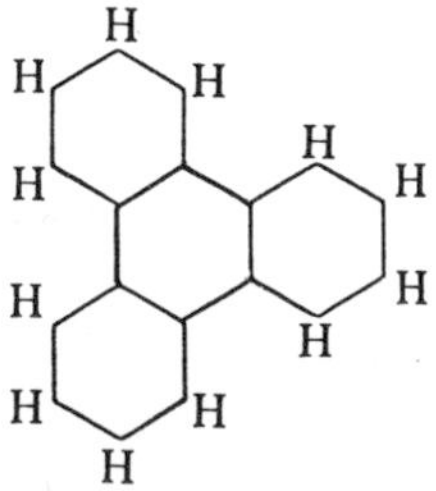

The last named may be dehydrogenated to triphenylene by passing its vapors over heated copper.

Ethylmethylacrolein, reacting with acetone in alkaline medium, yields an unsaturated compound with conjugated double bonds, $CH_3CH_2CH = C(CH_3)CH = CHCOCH_3$. When this is heated with zinc chloride, internal condensation takes place with elimination of water and the formation of pseudocumol,[143]

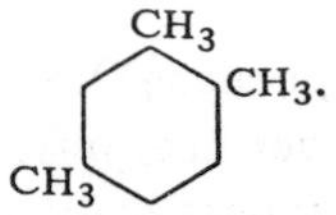

A similar unsaturated compound is obtained through the condensation of isovaleraldehyde with acetone:

$$2(CH_3)_2CHCH_2CHO + (CH_3)_2CO \rightarrow (CH_3)_2CHCH_2CH = C[CH(CH_3)_2]CH = CHCOCH_3$$

As in the previous example, a methylene group is situated in the 6 position with respect to the carbonyl group, and again the compound may be converted by internal condensation to a cyclic hydrocarbon, diisopropyltoluene,

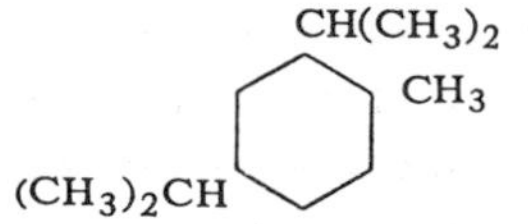

α,β-Diketones yield substituted quinones when condensed under the action of alkalies. The first product of condensation of diacetyl is an unsaturated triketone, which, by internal condensation, gives *p*-xyloquinone:

$$2CH_3COCOCH_3 \rightarrow CH_3COC(CH_3) = CHCO.COCH_3$$

$\rightarrow$ 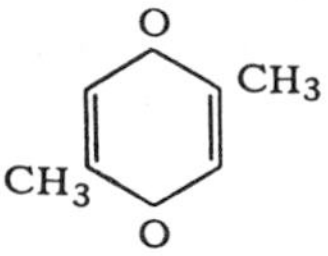

Duroquinone similarly results through the condensation of acetyl propionyl.[144]

A complex bicyclic compound is formed by the condensation of diacetyl with benzaldehyde. The first stage in this reaction would appear to be the formation of a cyclic dihydroxy diketone through the self-condensation of diacetyl; condensation with benzaldehyde then gives the bicyclic product:[145]

$$2CH_3COCOCH_3 \rightarrow CH_3C(OH)COCH_2C(OH)(CH_3)COCH_2$$

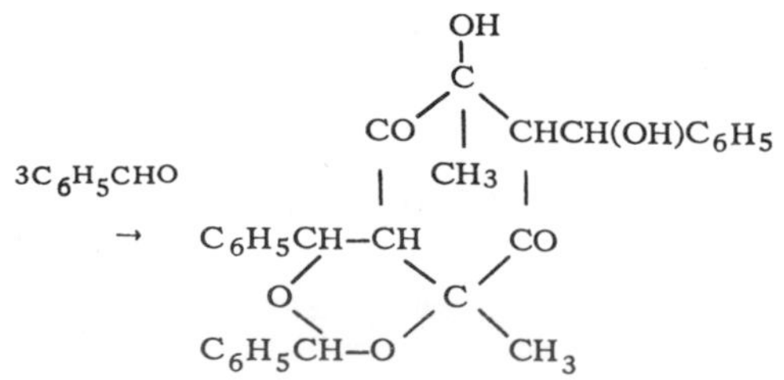

The sodio derivative of nitromalonaldehyde condenses with acetone to the sodio derivative of an unsaturated nitroketone, which is converted by hydrochloric acid to *p*-nitrophenol:[220]

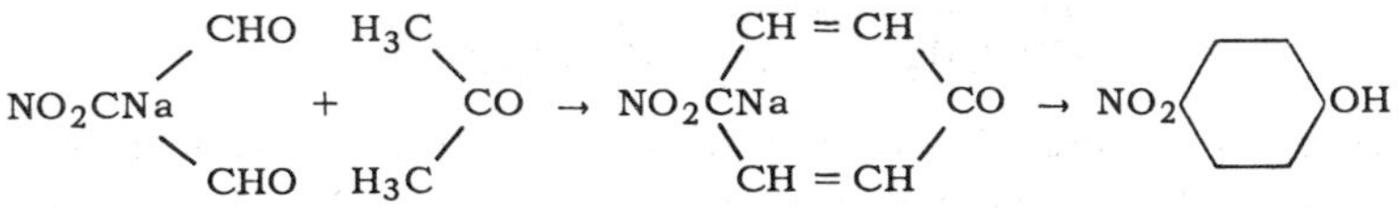

The method has been applied to the preparation of phenols of the type

$$\overline{CH_2(CH_2)_nCH_2C(=CH)C(OH)} = \underline{C \cdot CH = CNO_2}$$

from the macrocyclic ketones $\overline{CH_2(CH_2)_nCH_2CO}$.[221]

Aminoanthraquinone reacts with acetone in the presence of alkalies to form a cyclic base:

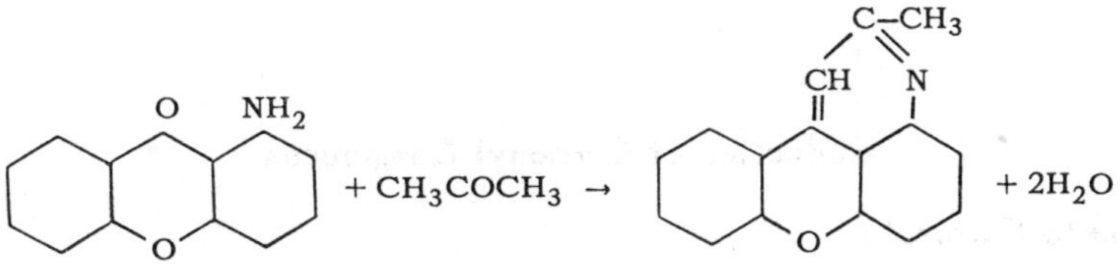

Polymerization of Aldols

Aldols show a tendency to form polymeric bodies. Freshly distilled pure acetaldol gradually changes on standing to a dimeric body known as paraldol:[222]

$$2CH_3CH(OH)CH_2CO \rightarrow CH_3CH(OH)CH_2CH(OH)OCH(CH_3)CH_2CHO$$

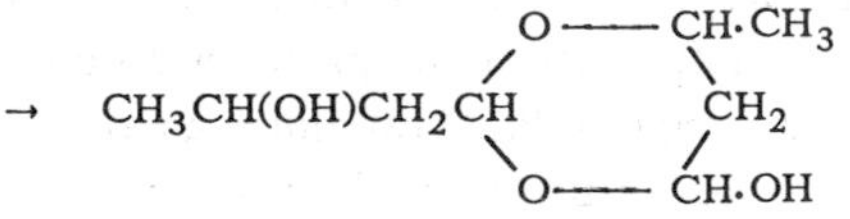

Dimerization of acetaldol in the free state is complete within a few hours at ordinary temperature. Acetic acid greatly accelerates the transformation, and the process comes to an end within a few minutes, although dimerization is not complete, and an equilibrium is reached when 80% of the aldol is converted to paradol.[223] In dilute aqueous solution the monomer preponderates at equilibrium. Paraldol is depolymerized to aldol when it is heated under reduced pressure.

Further condensation of paraldol to a tetrameric acetaldol, termed *tetraldam,* takes place in the presence of hydrocyanic acid.[224] A tetrameric aldehyde, *dialdan,* is obtained on heating acetaldehyde with concentrated hydrochloric acid; on boiling this compound with water, acetaldehyde is liberated and a dimeric dialdan is formed.[225]

Reduction of Unsaturated Aldehydes [259]

An unsaturated bond in a carbonyl compound may often be reduced in preference to the carbonyl group. An olefinic bond in α, β-position is more readily reduced than one in a more distant position. In hydroxymethylene ethers with a carbonyl group in conjugation with the olefinic bond, such as in 2-alkoxymethylenecyclohexanones,

$$\overline{CH_2CH_2CH_2CH_2COC} = CHOR,$$

the carbonyl group is preferencially reduced by lithium aluminum hydride.[260] Unsaturated carbonyl compounds in which the olefinic bond is difficult to reduce are converted to acetals prior to hydrogenation. This procedure makes possible the hydrogenation of furfural catalytically to the tetrahydro stage, and of pyridine α-aldehyde to the corresponding piperidine aldehyde with sodium and alcohol.[261] Catalytic reduction of aromatic acetals results in the cleavage of alkoxyl groups.

Acetylenic acetals are readily converted to ethylenic acetals by catalytic reduction.[262]

Reduction of Carbonyl Compounds

Conversion to Carbinols

Carbonyl compounds may be reduced with a variety of reagents. Zinc dust and an acid or an alkali, sodium or aluminum amalgam used in conjunction with alcohol or an acid, phosphorus and hydriodic acid bring about this reduction. Carbonyl compounds may also be reduced by catalytic methods. Many of these methods cause the partial reduction of the carbonyl compounds to carbinols. The various types of carbonyl compounds behave differently toward different reducing agents, and occasionally groups sensitive to reduction, if present in the molecule of the ketone or aldehyde, may be affected.

Sodium or sodium amalgam used in conjunction with an alcohol is well adapted for the reduction of aliphatic, alkyl aromatic and purely aromatic ketones to the corresponding hydroxy compounds. Aluminum amalgam and an alcohol, zinc dust and an acid or alkali are also suitable for the reduction of this class of compounds.

Aliphatic and *alicyclic ketones* are reduced to carbinols with sodium or sodium amalgam and strong caustic. The higher aliphatic ketones are best reduced with sodium in moist benzene solution.[92] Flavanone is converted to flavanol with aluminum amalgam, a pinacone forming as a byproduct.[93] Camphonic acids and compounds of similar structure cannot be reduced with sodium and alcohol, and require electrolytic reduction at an overvoltage induced by potassium amalgam at the electrode. This method is also applicable to camphorcarboxylic acid and epicamphorcarboxylic acid.

Aliphatic aldehydes and ketones may be smoothly reduced to the corresponding alcohols with hydrogen in the presence of reduced nickel heated to 100-165°. Alkyl aromatic and purely aromatic ketones are reduced by this method at 200°

to the corresponding hydrocarbons.[141] Aldehydes and ketones may be reduced catalytically in the liquid phase by use of a platinum oxide catalyst activated with iron salts. The carbonyl group is reduced to a carbinol group by this method.[142]

Alkyl aromatic ketones are best converted to carbinols with sodium and boiling alcohol.[94] In individual cases the use of sodium amalgam is of advantage, as for example, in the reduction of acylated ketones. Homoveratroyl-ω-aminoacetoveratrone can be converted to homoveratroylhydroxyaminoveratylamine only by this treatment.

Purely aromatic and *heterocyclic ketones* are effectively reduced to carbinols, with few exceptions, with zinc dust and alkali. Fluorenone is best reduced with zinc dust and ammonia, and xanthone with zinc dust and alcoholic sodium hydroxide. Sodium amalgam used with alcohol is also an effective reducing agent for this class of compounds. Michler's ketone, $[(CH_3)_2NC_6H_4]_2CO$, may be reduced with sodium and ethyl or amyl alcohol, sodium amylate, or with sodium amalgam which gives the hydrol in quantitative yield. Ketones of the quinone group, such as dihydrocinchonine and cinchotoxine, are reduced to the corresponding secondary alcohols with zinc dust and alcoholic sodium ethylate or with aluminum powder in boiling alcoholic solution. Aminolyl amino ketones are also effectively reduced with similar treatment,[95] or with zinc dust and formic acid. Alloxan is converted to dialuric acid, $\overline{\text{CONHCOCH(OH)CONH}}$, with stannous chloride in strongly acid solution.

Keto acids are readily converted to α-hydroxy acids with sodium amalgam or preferably with aluminum amalgam. Thus valerolactone results from levulinic acid, and malic acid from oxalacetic acid.[96] Reduction with sodium amalgam also proceeds satisfactorily in alkaline solution, acetoacetic acid giving β-hydroxybutyric acid in 96% yield by this treatment, although the method is not uniformly successful. Thus, α-dimethylacetoacetic ester gives the corresponding acid in only 30% yield, and α-diethylacetoacetic ester resists reduction by this method.[97] Tropinonecarboxylic acid is preferably reduced with sodium amalgam in a solution maintained slightly acidic during the operation.[98] The best procedure for the reduction of *m*-benzoylbenzoic acid appears to be treatment with sodium amalgam in the presence of a large quantity of water. *o*-Benzoylbenzoic acid may be reduced under the prolonged action of zinc dust and glacial acetic or hydrochloric acid. Certain aromatic aldehydes have been reduced with zinc dust and acetic acid, the resulting alcohol combining with the acid to form the acetate. Hydroxyaldehydes give considerable quantities of complex condensation products. *o*-Nitrobenzaldehyde, treated with zinc dust and 33% acetic acid, yields α-aminobenzaldehyde and some anthranil.

Reduction of Amino Ketones

Ketones in which an amino group is attached to the α-carbon atom generally lose this group when reduced with sodium amalgam. Piperidine is detached, for example, from piperidineacetone, and ammonia from ω-aminoacetophenone when these compounds are reduced with sodium amalgam in alkaline solution. Cleavage of the amino group apparently takes place the more readily, the greater the molecular weight of the radicals in the amino group. Reduction may be carried out successfully, in some cases, without cleavage of the amino group. Thus, phenylaminoacetone, $C_6H_5CH(NH_2)COCH_3$, may be converted to phenylaminopropanol by reduction with 4% sodium amalgam in a weakly acidic solution at 0°. The isomeric phenyl aminoethyl ketone, $C_6H_5COCH(NH_2)CH_3$, can also be successfully reduced in a similar manner.

The reduction of α-amino ketones may be accomplished without cleavage of the amino group with aluminum amalgam in neutral solution, or catalytically. Electrolytic reduction also accomplishes the purpose well, and has been applied successfully to the reduction of adrenalone, $CH_3NHCH_2COC_6H_3(OH)_2$, to adrenaline, and of aminopropionylveratrol to aminoveratrylcarbinol, as well as of the analogous pyrocatechine derivatives of ω-aminoacetophenone, ω-aminoalkylquinoline ketone, etc., to the corresponding hydroxy compounds. Excellent results have been obtained through the combined use of catalytic and electrolytic reduction.[99]

The reduction of ketones, in which an amino group is attached to the β-carbon atom, by use of sodium or aluminum amalgam, generally proceeds without cleavage of the amino group, although fissure has been observed in some cases. Zinc dust and hydrochloric acid can also be used for the purpose.[100] Treatment with sodium and alcohol causes the removal of the amino group.

Heterocyclic β-amino ketones may be satisfactorily reduced to the corresponding hydroxy compounds with zinc dust and concentrated hydriodic acid, and with sodium amalgam. Electrolytic reduction also gives satisfactory results.[101] The combined use of zinc powder and sodium ethylate gives excellent results with ketones of the pyridine series. γ-Ketones of the quinoline series may be reduced satisfactorily with zinc dust and acetic acid, those of the pyrrole series with sodium and alcohol, or catalytically.[102]

Reduction of Diketones

One or both carbonyl groups in diketones may be reduced to hydroxymethylene groups, depending upon the conditions under which the operation is carried out. Diacetyl and the homologous diketones may be reduced to keto alcohols by means of granular zinc and hot, dilute sulfuric acid,[103] but pinacones result when the reduction is carried out by the use of zinc and acetic acid. Benzil in alcoholic solution is reduced to benzoin by treatment with zinc and hydrochloric acid, iron turnings and acetic acid or with sodium hydrosulfite.[104] Treated with sodium amalgam, furil is converted to furoin which then undergoes further reduction.[105] Both carbonyl groups in diketones may, sometimes, be reduced by the use of sodium amalgam and ammonium chloride. The methyl acetal of the diketo aldehyde $CH_3CH_2COCH_2COCHO$ is, thus, transformed to the corresponding dihydroxymethylal hy this treatment, and p-diketohexamethylene,

$\overline{OCCH_2CH_2COCH_2CH_2}$, is changed to 1,4-dihydroxycyclohexane, or chinite. Diketoapocamphoric ester is similarly reduced to the dihydroxy derivative. Keto alcohols may be further reduced to the corresponding glycols with 3-4% sodium amalgam, by taking care to neutralize the alkali as it is formed during the reaction.[106]

Pinacone Formation

In the reduction of acetone and other ketones with sodium amalgam and moist ether, a part of the ketone undergoes condensation, two molecules becoming joined with carbon bonds to form a 1,2-dihydric alcohol or a pinacone:

$$2(CH_3)_2CO + H_2 \rightarrow (CH_3)_2C(OH)C(OH)(CH_3)_2$$

This type of condensation is common to all carbonyl compounds, although it is often a secondary reaction, and the principal product is the monohydric alcohol corresponding to the carbonyl compound. In the aliphatic series the tendency toward the formation of pinacones is greater in ketones than in aldehydes. Pinacones may be obtained readily, in general, from aromatic carbonyl compounds. Aliphatic aldehydes do not show a tendency to give pinacones, although under special conditions small quantities of this type of condensation products may be obtained.[139]

Pinacones result in low yield (about 10% of theoretical) when aliphatic ketones are treated with sodium or strong caustic solution. The yield of pinacone is materially improved when sodium and moist ether or petroleum ether are used as the reducing agents. The yields are further improved when the reduction is carried out with magnesium or sodium amalgams. Amino ketones may be converted to pinacones successfully with the last mentioned reducing agents.[107] Aliphatic ketones are converted to pinacones with excellent yields through electolytic reduction at lead cathodes containing 4% copper, or better still, at graphite cathodes.

Some diketones are capable of forming cyclic compounds through an internal pinacone condensation. For example, diacetylpentane, treated in ethereal solution with a large excess of sodium and concentrated sodium hydroxide solution under cooling, gives dihydroxydimethylheptamethylene:

$$CH_2(CH_2CH_2COCH_3)_2 \rightarrow CH_3\overline{C(OH)(CH_2)_5C}(OH)CH_3,$$

the corresponding open-chain disecondary alcohol being formed simultaneously. Cyclic pinacones are also obtained from 1,5- and 1,6- diketones when these are treated with sodium amalgam in a carbon dioxide atmosphere, or with zinc dust and glacial acetic acid. Diphenyldihydroxypentane results, for example, from the reduction of 1,3-dibenzoylpropane:

$$CH_2(CH_2COC_6H_5)_2 \rightarrow C_6H_5\overline{C(OH)(CH_2)_3C}(OH)C_6H_5$$

Cyclic dihydric alcohol are also formed through the reduction of the ketone in moist ethereal solution with sodium, or in alcoholic solution with aluminum amalgam. Triphenyldihydroxypentamethylene has been obtained by a similar method from benzaldiacetophenone, $C_6H_5COCH_2CH(C_6H_5)CH_2COC_6H_5$. 1,8-Diacylnaphthalenes are converted to acenaphthene glycols when boiled with zinc dust and alcoholic potassium hydroxide, o-Diacetophenone,

$$CH_3COC_6H_4C_6H_4COCH_3,$$

has been converted by the same method to dihydroxydimethyldihydrophenanthrene.

Pinacones are formed in very good yield when alkyl aromatic ketones in alcoholic solution are reduced with sodium amalgam.[108] Better yields are obtained in this case also when aluminum amalgam is used as the reducing agent.[109] Pinacones result from alkyl aromatic ketones when they are reduced with zinc dust and alcoholic potassium hydroxide. Isopropylphenyl pinacone has been prepared by this method from isopropylphenyl ketone.[110] Treatment of aralkyl ketones with zinc dust and acetic acid at 100° also leads to the formation of pinacones. This method gives excellent results with purely aromatic ketones, but it fails with the aliphatic ketones.[111] Alkyl aromatic ketones, such as acetophenone, are reduced slowly by this method, while purely aromatic ketones are reduced vigorously. The general procedure is to dissolve the ketone in acetic acid and to add twice the calculated quantity of zinc gradually while the mixture is heated on a water-bath. Heating is continued until the zinc dust has been completely converted to zinc acetate.

Benzaldehyde, reduced with magnesium amalgam or sodium and alcohol, yields a mixture of hydrobenzoin and isohydrobenzoin. Piperonal behaves in a like manner.[140]

The electrolytic reduction of ketones in solution in alcoholic sodium hydroxide leads to the formation of pinacones. Acetophenone pinacone has been prepared by this method from acetophenone and benzoin pinacone,

$$C_6H_5CH(OH)CH(OH)(C_6H_5).C(OH)(C_6H_5)CH(OH)C_6H_5,$$

from benzil.

Isocyclic ketones also give pinacones, the best method of preparation consisting of the treatment of the compound in moist ethereal solution with sodium.[112]

When a concentrated alcoholic solution of benzophenone is heated with zinc dust and hydrochloric acid for a long period α- and β-benzopinacolines result:

$$2C_6H_5COC_6H_5 \quad \begin{matrix} \rightarrow \\ \rightarrow \end{matrix} \quad \begin{matrix} (C_6H_5)_2C \overset{O}{\overset{\diagup\diagdown}{\longrightarrow}} C(C_6H_5)_2 \\ (C_6H_5)_3CCOC_6H_5 \end{matrix}$$

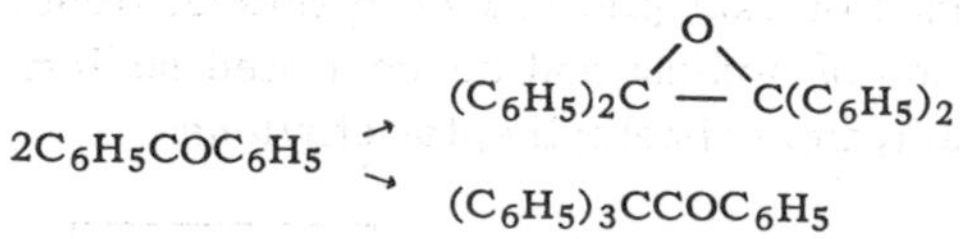

Pinacones undergo a characteristic transformation under the influence of mineral acids which involves the migration of a hydrocarbon group and cleavage of the elements of water, resulting in the formation of a saturated monoketone, a so-called *pinacoline:*

$$(R)_2C(OH)C(OH)(R)_2 \quad \rightarrow \quad (R)_3CCOR + H_2O$$

In the process of reduction of carbonyl compounds, elimination of oxygen from two molecules may take place with the formation of an unsaturated linkage between carbon atoms, uniting the two molecules. A small quantity of tetraphenylethylene results when benzophenone is reduced with zinc dust, and fluorenone gives an appreciable quantity of diphenyleneethylene[113] when treated in ethereal solution with zinc dust and acetyl chloride:

$$\text{CO} + 2H_2 \rightarrow \text{C}=\text{C} + 2H_2O$$

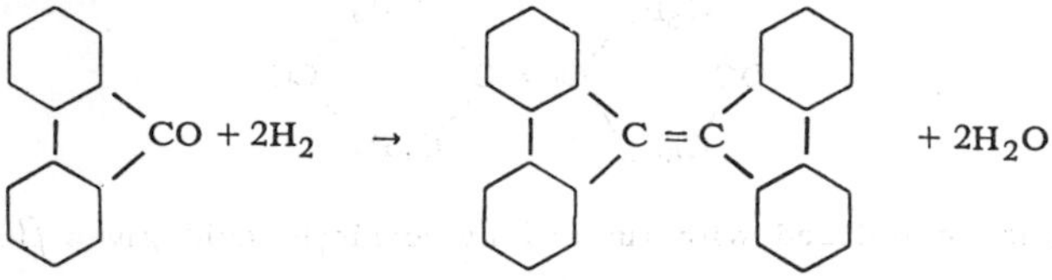

This type of condensation may take place exclusively with certain carbonyl compounds. Michler's ketone for example, reduced with tin and hydrochloric acid, gives an ethylenic compound in nearly quantitative yield:

$$2[(CH_3)_2NC_6H_4]_2CO + 2H \rightarrow [(CH_3)_2NC_6H_4]_2C = C[C_6H_4N(CH_3)_2]_2 + 2H_2O$$

An ethylenic compound, dixanthylene, also forms exclusively from xanthone when this is reduced with zinc dust and acetic acid:

$$2O \begin{matrix} C_6H_4 \\ \\ C_6H_4 \end{matrix} CO + 2H_2 \rightarrow O \begin{matrix} C_6H_4 \\ \\ C_6H_4 \end{matrix} C = C \begin{matrix} C_6H_4 \\ \\ C_6H_4 \end{matrix} O + 2H_2O$$

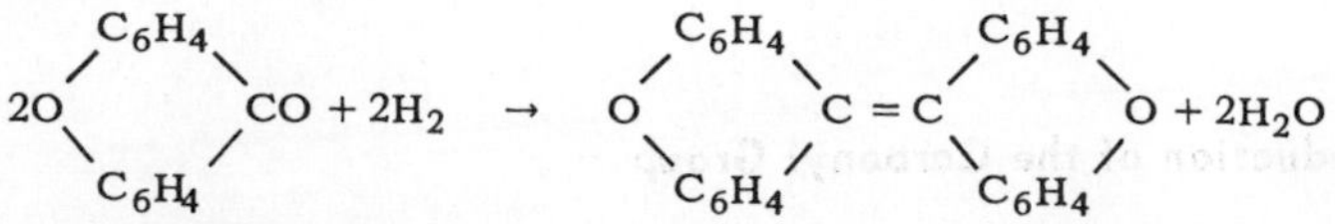

Reduction is carried out by adding zinc to the acetic acid solution of the compound, then introducing a few drops of hydrochloric acid from time to time while the mixture is kept agitated. The yield is almost quantitative. This type of condensation readily takes place also with the homologs of xanthone.[114]

N-Methylacridine subjected to the same treatment yields dimethyl-bis-acridine, while 3,6-diamino-N-methylacridine gives bis-trypaflavin:[115]

$$2CH_3N \begin{matrix} C_6H_3(NH_2) \\ \\ C_6H_3(NH_2) \end{matrix} \begin{matrix} CH_3 \\ \\ CO \\ \\ Cl \end{matrix} \rightarrow N \begin{matrix} C_6H_3(NH_2) \\ \\ C_6H_3(NH_2) \end{matrix} C - C \begin{matrix} C_6H_5(NH_2) \\ \\ C_6H_5(NH_2) \end{matrix} N \begin{matrix} CH_3 \\ \\ Cl \end{matrix}$$

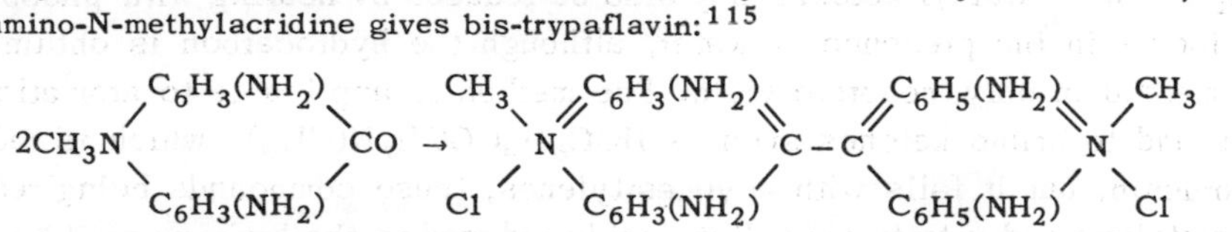

Coupling with carbon bonds and the simultaneous reduction of the second carbonyl group takes place when anthraquinone is heated with zinc dust and ammonia, or with tin and hydrochloric acid in glacial acetic acid solution, the final product being dianthryl:

$$2CO \begin{matrix} C_6H_4 \\ \\ C_6H_4 \end{matrix} CO \rightarrow CH_2 \begin{matrix} C_6H_4 \\ \\ C_6H_4 \end{matrix} C(OH).COH \begin{matrix} C_6H_4 \\ \\ C_6H_4 \end{matrix} CH_2$$

$$\rightarrow CH \begin{matrix} C_6H_4 \\ \\ C_6H_4 \end{matrix} C - C \begin{matrix} C_6H_4 \\ \\ C_6H_4 \end{matrix} CH$$

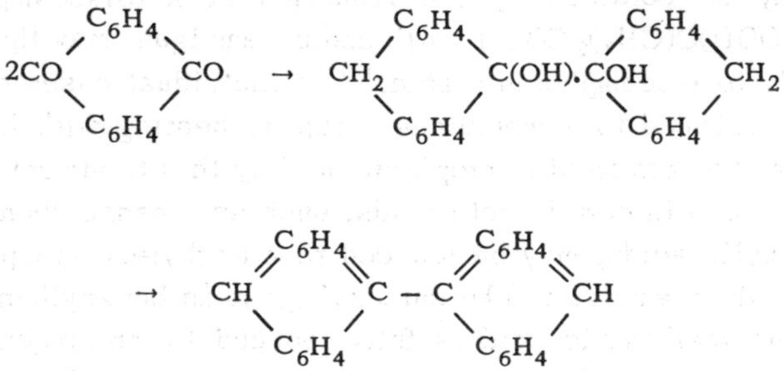

Dianthranol is obtained when anthraquinone is reduced with an excess of zinc dust and 10% sodium hydroxide in a sealed tube at 160°.[116]

$$2CO \begin{matrix} C_6H_4 \\ \\ C_6H_4 \end{matrix} CO \rightarrow HOC \begin{matrix} C_6H_4 \\ \\ C_6H_4 \end{matrix} C - C \begin{matrix} C_6H_4 \\ \\ C_6H_4 \end{matrix} C.OH$$

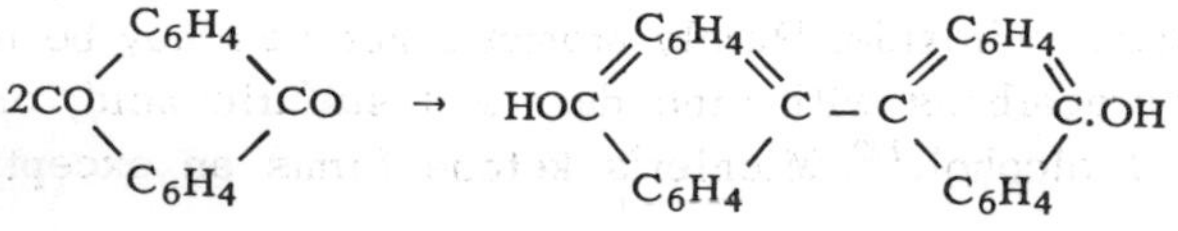

Reduction with copper or aluminum powder and sulfuric acid at 100-120° results in the formation of dianthrone,

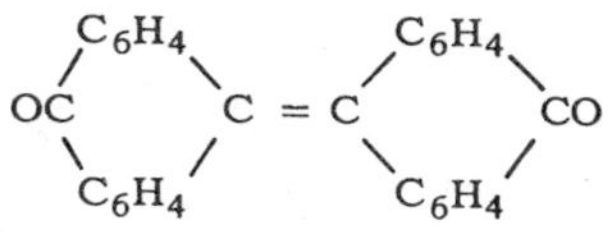

β-Naphthoquinone reduced with tin and hydrochloric acid gives β-naphthyldihydroquinone:[117]

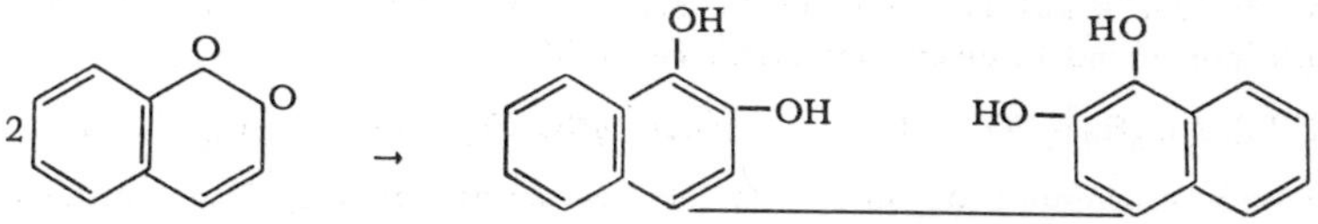

Complete Reduction of the Carbonyl Group

The reduction of carbonyl compounds by the usual methods proceeds partially as a rule, leading to the formation of hydroxy compounds. Aralkyl ketones thus reduced with sodium and alcohol to hydroxy compounds may be further reduced to the corresponding hydrocarbons by heating to 120° with hydriodic acid and phosphorus.[118] Aralkyl ketones may also be reduced by heating with phosphorus and iodine in the presence of water, although the hydrocarbon is obtained by this method in only moderate yield. The method is applicable to aromatic keto acids and to amino ketones such as $HOC_6H_4COCH_2N(CH_3)_2$ which is reduced to hordenin, but it fails with acylmesitylenes, these compounds being reduced to mesitylene and a fatty acid. Keto acids reduced to the hydroxy acid by treatment with sodium amalgam may be reduced to the corresponding acid by heating with concentrated hydriodic acid. The lactone of α-hydroxyisocamphoronic acid which may be obtained by the reduction of ketoisocamphoronic acid, $HOCOCH(CH_2COOH)C(CH_3)_2COOH$, with sodium amalgam, may thus be converted quantitatively to isocamphoronic acid.[119] In individual cases the keto group may be directly reduced to a methylene group by heating with hydriodic acid. Pyruvic acid may be converted to propionic acid by this treatment.[120]

The carbonyl group in certain keto acids, such as *o*-benzoylbenzoic acid and fluorenonecarboxylic acids, may be reduced to a methylene group by prolonged treatment with sodium amalgam. The carbonyl group in benzoylbenzoic acid and *o,p*-benzophenonedicarboxylic acid is fully reduced by prolonged heating with zinc dust and ammonia in the presence of a little copper hydroxide-ammonia complex.[121] Complete reduction of the carbonyl group in phenylbenzoyl-*o*-benzoic and α-naphthoylbenzoic acids may be brought about by heating with zinc dust and aqueous sodium hydroxide. Purely aromatic ketones may be reduced to the corresponding hydrocarbons with zinc dust and sulfuric acid, or with sodium and ethyl or amyl alcohol.[122] Michler's ketone forms an exception, requiring treatment with zinc and acetic acid. Xanthone gives xanthene, and 9,9-diethylanthron yields 9,9-diethyl-9,10-dihydroanthracene when reduced with zinc dust and acetic acid. Camphorquinone is reduced to camphor by heating to 100° in alcoholic solution with ammonium sulfhydrate.

The carbonyl group in aromatic and alkyl aromatic ketones may be fully reduced by catalytic hydrogenation over nickel at 190-195°. The aromatic ring is not reduced by this treatment, but unsaturated cyclic ketones are converted to saturated hydrocarbons.[123] Aliphatic ketones can be converted to the corresponding hydrocarbons by electrolytic reduction at a cadmium electrode.[124]

The most important method for the complete reduction of the carbonyl group is that originated by Clemmensen.

Clemmensen Reduction

The method consists in treating the compound with amalgamated zinc in boiling hydrochloric acid solution, and leads to the formation of the fully hydrogenated compound:[125]

$$RCOR' + 4H \rightarrow RCH_2R' + H_2O$$

The readiness with which reduction proceeds depends both upon the character of the carbonyl compound and the conditions under which the reduction is carried out.

General Procedure

The usual procedure is to heat the carbonyl compound under reflux with an excess of amalgamated zinc and aqueous 20 to 40% hydrochloric acid. The hydrochloric acid is replenished as it is consumed, through the intermittent addition of concentrated hydrochloric acid. The reduction of the more reactive compounds may be complete within about four hours. When dealing with more resistant carbonyl compounds, it may be necessary to prolong the time of reduction to ten hours or longer.

When reducing compounds that are insoluble in aqueous hydrochloric acid, it is of advantage to employ a water-miscible solvent for the carbonyl compound. A mixture of hydrochloric acid and acetic acid is suitable in many cases, particularly for the reduction of natural keto compounds. Satisfactory results are obtained sometimes by gradually introducing a solution of the carbonyl compound in alcohol into the mixture of boiling hydrochloric acid and amalgamated zinc. The use of a water-insoluble solvent, such as toluene, is desirable in special cases, where the prevention of the contamination of the zinc surface by insoluble polymolecular products and minimizing side reaction are important.

Certain sensitive compounds may best be reduced at room temperature. The mixture of the carbonyl compound and the reducing medium is agitated at room temperature for one or two days and is then heated under reflux for about twenty hours. Occasionally reduction is accomplished by the use of zinc dust and alcohol alone.

Mossy zinc is the most generally used form of the metal but zinc turnings, granular zinc or zinc powder may be employed with equal success. The metal is amalgamated by treating it for one hour with 2 parts of 5% aqueous mercuric chloride solution and is then rinsed before use.

Aliphatic and saturated cyclic ketones are generally reduced smoothly, the reduction proceeding slowly with compounds of larger molecules. Aliphatic hydroxy ketones undergo reduction without removal of the hydroxy group.[126] Alkyl aromatic ketones react normally as a rule, the presence of carboxyl and hydroxy groups in the aromatic nucleus favoring the reaction.[127] Ortho and meta-acetophenone carboxylic acids are not reduced to ethyl benzoic acids. m-Amino-acetophenone and isophthalophenone also are not fully reduced. Diphenyl-truxones are reduced to the corresponding diphenyltruxandioles. Benzophenone is transformed to benzhydrol. The reduction of β-diketones proceeds normally, and it is possible to reduce selectively one of the carbonyl groups. Benzil is transformed to diphenylethane in good yield.[128] Aliphatic hydroxy ketones also undergo the Clemmensen reduction normally. Thineyl alkyl ketones give alkyl-thiophenes.[129] Ring enlargement to substituted methylpiperidines takes place when 2-acyl-1-methylpyrrolidines are subjected to reduction:[226]

$$\begin{array}{c} CH_2-CH_2 \\ | \qquad | \\ CH_2 \quad CHCOR \\ \diagdown \diagup \\ NCH_3 \end{array} \rightarrow \begin{array}{c} H \\ \diagup \diagdown \\ \quad \quad -R \\ N-CH_3 \end{array}$$

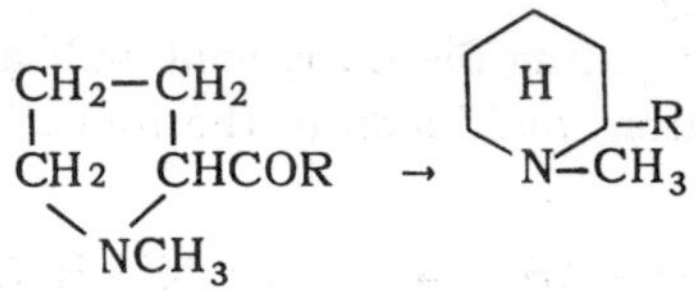

but 2-propionyl-1-methylpyrrolidine is converted to 5-ethyl-3,4-trimethylene ox-azolidine:[236]

$$\begin{array}{c} CH_2-CH \\ | \qquad | \\ CH_2 \quad CHCOC_2H_5 \\ \diagdown \diagup \\ NCH_3 \end{array} \rightarrow \begin{array}{c} CH_2-CH_2 \\ | \qquad | \\ CH \quad CH \\ \diagup \diagdown \diagdown \\ N \qquad CHC_2H_5 \\ \diagdown \diagup \\ O \end{array}$$

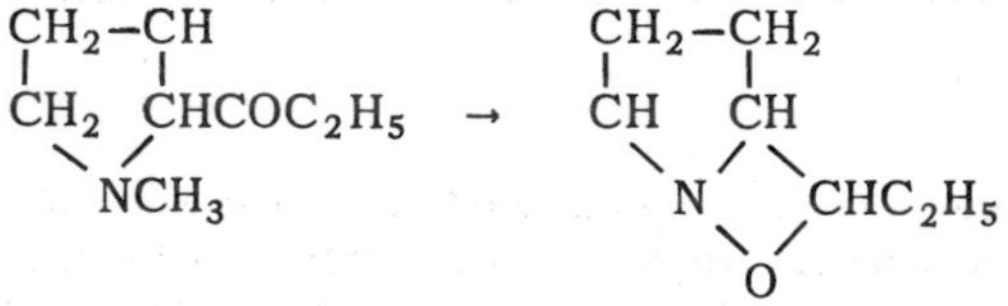

Cyclic ketones of the type of hydrindone and α-ketotetrahydronaphthalene are reduced to hydrocarbons.[130] Most indandiones are reduced normally.[131] With the exception of α-keto acids[132] which give α-hydroxy acids, the carbonyl group in keto acids is fully reduced,[133] although partial resinification may take place, especially with γ-keto acids. Acetoacetic ester and levulinic ester give the corresponding fatty acids in poor yield.[134] Anthraquinone and some of its derivatives are reduced to dihydroanthracenes. The reaction has been applied to few aldehydes. Poor yields of toluene are obtained in the reduction of benzaldehyde, but phenolic aldehydes generally give the corresponding methyl phenols in excellent yield.

Side reactions take place in the reduction of many aliphatic aromatic ketones leading principally to condensation to pinacolines or to unsaturated compounds, and the formation of resinous products, due to polymerization.[134]

Certain sensitive groups may be reduced under the conditions of the Clemmensen reaction. Active hydroxyl groups, such as those present in β-hydroxy acids, are removed. Benzoin is transformed to diphenylethane. α,β-Unsaturated bonds, i.e., olefinic bonds conjugated with the carbonyl bonds are reduced in general,[135] but isolated double bonds apparently are not affected. The unsaturated linkages in chromanones and coumarins are not affected,[136] but pyrroles and isoquinolines are reduced to pyrrolines and tetrahydroisoquinolines.[137] The halogen in α-halo ketones in the aromatic nucleus of certain aromatic aliphatic ketones are removed.[138] The reduction of the aromatic ring in some aromatic aliphatic ketones has also been noted.

Peroxides of Carbonyl Compounds

Dialdehyde peroxides are formed through the reaction of concentrated hydrogen peroxide, or of Caro's acid, $HOOSO_2OH$, with aldehydes:[227]

$$2RCHO + H_2O_2 \rightarrow \underset{\substack{OH \quad HO}}{RCH \overset{O-O}{\diagup \quad \diagdown} CHR}$$

$$2RCHO + 2H_2O_2 \rightarrow \underset{\substack{O-O}}{RCH \overset{O-O}{\diagup \quad \diagdown} CHR} + 2H_2O$$

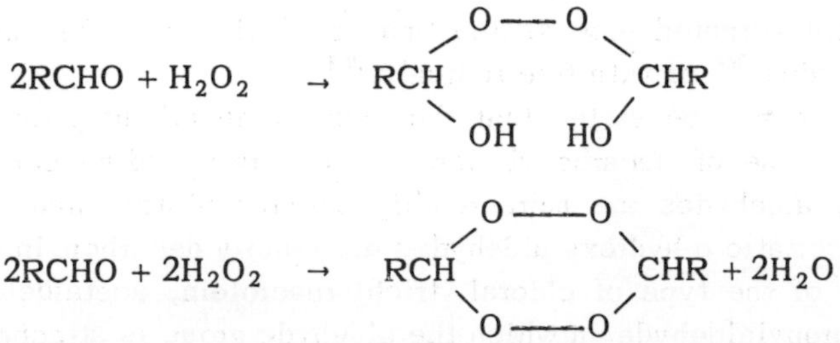

The methyl and ethyl compounds are obtained in good yield when the reactants are brought together in ethereal solution.[228]

Acetone triperoxide is obtained by the action of hydrogen peroxide on acetone:[229]

$$3(CH_3)_2CO + 3H_2O_2 \rightarrow (CH_3)_2CO \cdot OC(CH_3)_2O \cdot OC(CH_3)_2O \cdot O + 3H_2O$$

The diperoxide is formed through the reaction of acetone with Caro's acid.[230]

Monoaldehyde peroxides result through the direct action of concentrated ozone on aldehydes. They result also by the degradation of ozonides.[231]

Peroxides of aldehydes cannot be isolated directly, but aldehyde acyl peroxides are precipitated on adding acid anhydrides to the mixture containing the aldehyde peroxide.[232]

Trimethylene peroxide azine has been obtained through the reaction of formaldehyde with hydrogen peroxide and hydrazine.[233] The compound has been assigned the formula

$CH_2 = N \cdot NCH_2O \cdot O \cdot CH_2$. A triperoxide obtained from hexamethylenetetramine[234] is believed to be a peroxide derivative of trimethylamine

$$\underset{\substack{O-CH_2}}{\overset{O-CH_2}{\mid \quad \diagdown}} NCH_2O \cdot OCH_2N \underset{\substack{CH_2O}}{\overset{CH_2O}{\diagup \quad \mid}}$$

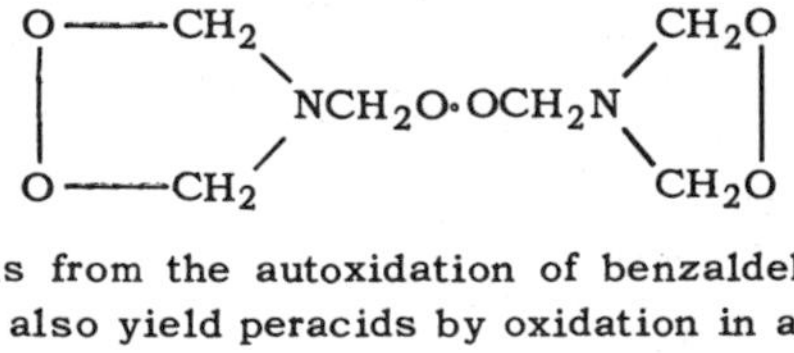

Perbenzoic acid results from the autoxidation of benzaldehyde in acetone solution. Other aromatic aldehydes also yield peracids by oxidation in acetone solution. Complete decomposition takes place when autoxidation occurs in certain other solvents, due to reaction with unchanged aldehyde.[235]

Anhydrous acetaldehyde takes up oxygen to form principally peracetic acid. Only a small amount of peracid is formed when oxidation takes place in aqueous solution.

Decarbonylation of Aldehydes

The thermal decarbonylation of certain aldehydes is possible. Partial decarbonylation of benzaldehyde, furfural, vanillin, piperonal and cinnamaldehyde may be brought about by passing the vapors of these compounds over Raney nickel at 370 to 390°.[263] The reaction involves the removal of a molecule of carbon monoxide with attachment of the hydrogen atom of the aldehyde group to the organic residue:

$$RCHO \rightarrow RH + CO$$

It is a radical actuated process that may be facilitated, for example, by the addition of iodine,[264] or with free radicals.[265]

In general it may be stated that the ease of decarbonylation of aldehydes parallels the ease of decarboxylation of the corresponding carboxylic acids. α-Substituted aldehydes are more readily decarbonylated than straight chain aldehydes. Aromatic o-hydroxy aldehydes are readily decarbonylated.

Aldehydes of the type of chloral, trichloroacrolein, acetaldehydedisulfonic acid, phenylpropylaldehyde, in which the aldehyde group is attached to a strongly negative group, liberate formic acid when treated with alkalies in the cold or at slightly elevated temperature.

References

1. Laurent, *Ann.*, **17**, 91 (1836); Zinin, *ibid.*, **34**, 188 (1840); Widman, *Ber.*, **14**, 610 (1881); Irvine and Moodie, *J. Chem. Soc.*, **91**, 544 (1907).
2. Bouveault and Loquin, *Bull. soc. chim.*, (3) **35**, 650 (1906).
3. Lapworth, *J. Chem. Soc.*, **93**, 2189 (1908); Dawson *et al.*, *ibid.*, **95**, 1860 (1909); **97**, 2048 (1910); **101**, 1503 (1912). *Cf.* Mannich, *Ber.*, **39**, 1594 (1906); Semmler, *ibid.*, **42**, 584, 1161 (1909); Hâncu, *ibid.*, **42**, 1052 (1909); Meyer, *Ber.*, **45**, 2852 (1912).
4. Meyer, *Ann.*, **380**, 212 (1911); *Ber.*, **45**, 2843 (1912); Dieckmann, *ibid.*, **55**, 2470 (1922); Taylor and Ewbank, *J. Chem. Soc.*, **1926**, 2818; Martius, *Ann.*, **499**, 228 (1932).
5. Grignard and Savard, *Compt. rend.*, **179**, 1573 (1924); **182**, 422 (1926); Grignard and Blanchon, *C.A.*, **24**, 1342 (1930); Gordon, *ibid.*, **22**, 584 (1928).
6. Meyer and Schoeller, *Ber.*, **53**, 1410 (1920); Meyer and Hopff, *ibid.*, **54**, 579 (1921).
7. Combes, *Compt. rend.*, **105**, 868 (1887); Tanatar and Kurovski, *J. Russ. Phys.-Chem. Soc.*, **40**, 580 (1906); *Ber.*, **63**, 1078 (1910); Morgan *et al.*, *J. Chem. Soc.*, **105**, 189 (1914); **125**, 372, 1264 (1924); **125**, 1252 (1924). Cf. Schlenk *et al.*, *Ber.*, **46**, 2840 (1913); **47**, 486 (1914); Kamm and Kamm, *J. Am. Pharm. Assoc.* **11**, 599 (1922); Blicke, *J. Am. Chem. Soc.*, **46**, 2560 (1924); Acree, *ibid.*, **47**, 229 (1925).
8. Bulow, *Ber.*, **32**, 197 (1899); Morgan and Reilly, *J. Chem. Soc.*, **103**, 810 (1913). *Cf.* Meyer, *Ber.*, **10**, 2075 (1877); Züblin, *ibid.*, **11**, 1417 (1878); v. Richter and Münzer, *ibid.*, **17**, 1926 (1884); Beyer and Claisen, *ibid.*, **21**, 1697 (1888).
9. Morgan and Reilly, *J. Chem. Soc.*, **103**, 810 (1913); v. Pechmann, *Ber.*, **25**, 3175 (1892); Busch and Wolbring, *J. prakt. Chem.*, (2) **71**, 370 (1905).
10. Auerbach and Barschall, *Chem. Zentr.* **1907 II**, 1734. *Cf.* Cambier and Brochet, *Compt. rend.*, **119**, 607 (1894).
11. Staudinger *et al.*, *Ber.*, **53**, 1073 (1920); *Ann.*, **474**, 155 (1929). *Cf.* Zeyewetz and Gibello, *Compt. rend.*, **138**, 1226 (1904).
12. Brühl, *Ber.*, **24**, 650 (1891); Troeger, *ibid.*, **25**, 3316 (1892).
13. Stepanow, *et al.*, *Ber.*, **58**, 1718 (1925).
14. Kekulé and Zincke, *Ann.*, **162**, 146 (1872). *Cf.* Hantzsch and Oechslin, *Ber.*, **40**, 4341 (1907).
15. Francke *et al.*, *Monatsh.*, **33**, 349 (1912); **34**, 804 (1913); **43**, 659 (1923); Orndorff, *Am. Chem. J.*, **12**, 353 (1890); Blaise and Guerin, *Bull. soc. chim.*, (3) **29**, 1203 (1903); Le Sueur, *J. Chem. Soc.*, **87**, 1893 (1904); Neustädter, *Monatsh.*, 898 (1900); Richard, *Ann. chim.*, (8) **21**, 394 (1911).

16. Blaise and Guérin, *Bull. soc. chim.*, (3) **29**, 1202 (1903); le Sueur, *J. Chem. Soc.*, **85**, 833 (1904); **87**, 1892 (1905).
17. Hibbert and Hill, *J. Am. Chem. Soc.*, **45**, 743 (1923); Grabowski, *Ber.*, **8**, 1436 (1875). *Cf.* Kolbe, *Ann.*, **54**, 183 (1845) footnote; Jacobsen, *Ber.*, **8**, 88 (1875); Grimaux and Adam, *Bull. soc. chim.*, (2) **36**, 23, 136 (1881).
18. Raschig, *Ber.*, **59**, 589, 2025 (1926); Raschig and Prahl, *Ann.*, **448**, 265 (1926). *Cf.* Binz, *Ber.*, **59**, 1695 (1926); Schroeter, *ibid.*, **59**, 2341 (1926).
19. Bazlen, *Ber.*, **60**, 1470 (1927).
20. Sadtler, *Am. J. Pharm.*, **76**, 84 (1904).
21. Tiffeneau and Dorlencourt, *Compt. rend.*, **143**, 1242 (1906).
22. Kobek, *Ber.*, **16**, 2097 (1883); Nordmann, *ibid.*, **17**, 2364 (1884).
23. Petrenko-Kritschenko, *Ann.*, **341**, 163 (1905); Steart, *J. Chem. Soc.*, **87**, 186 (1905).
24. Knoevenagel and Lange, *Ber.*, **37**, 4060 (1904); Knoevenagel, *ibid.*, **38**, 213 (1905).
25. Knoevenagel, *Ber.*, **37**, 4075 (1904); Reinking *et al.*, *ibid.*, **38**, 1077 (1905).
26. Reinking *et al.*, *Ber.*, **38**, 1073 (1905).
27. Ultée, *Ber.*, **39**, 1856 (1906); *Rec. trav. chim.*, **28**, 1, 248, 257 (1909); Corette, *Compt. rend.*, **134**, 477 (1902); Richard, *Ann. chim.*, (8) **21**, 378 (1910); Böeseken, *Rec. trav. chim.*, **37**, 165 (1918); Le Sueur, *J. Chem. Soc.*, **85**, 834 (1904); Jones, W.J., *ibid.*, **105**, 1560 (1914); Lapworth and Manske, *ibid.*, **1928**, 2533; **1930**, 1976.
28. Kilian, *Ber.*, **18**, 3066 (1885); **19**, 221, 770, 3029 (1886); Fischer, *Ann.*, **270**, 64 (1892); Philippe, *Ann. chim. phys.*, (8) **26**, 289 (1912); *Compt. rend.*, **152**, 1774 (1911).
29. Bucherer and Grolée, *Ber.*, **39**, 1224 (1906). *Cf.* Albert, *ibid.*, **49**, 1382 (1916).
30. Zelinski and Stadnikoff, *Ber.*, **39**, 1725 (1906); **41**, 2063 (1908); *J. Russ. Phys.-Chem. Soc.*, **40**, 790 (1908); Bucherer and Steiner, *J. prakt. Chem.*, (2) **140**, 291 (1934); Jacobsen, *J. Am. Chem. Soc.*, **67**, 1996 (1946).
31. Walther and Hübner, *J. prakt. Chem.*, (2) **93**, 121 (1916).
32. Lavelof, *J. Russ. Phys.-Chem. Soc.*, **36**, 27 (1904).
33. Delépine, *Bull. soc. chim.*, (3) **29**, 1178 (1903).
34. Miller and Plöchl, *Ber.*, **25**, 2020 (1892).
35. Miller and Plöchl, *ibid.*, **25**, 2070 (1892). *Cf.* Porter and Hallerman, *J. Am. Chem. Soc.*, **66**, 1652 (1944).
36. Knoevenagel and Mercklin, *Ber.*, **37**, 4094 (1904).
37. Henry, *Bull. Acad. roy. Belg.*, **1902**, 721 (1903); Cambier and Brochet, *Bull. soc. chim.*, (3) **13**, 392 (1895); Duden and Scharff, *Ber.*, **28**, 938 (1895).
38. Heintz, *Ann.*, **174**, 133, 154, 166 (1874); **178**, 305, (1875); **183**, 276 (1876); **189**, 214 (1877); **198**, 42 (1879); **203**, 336 (1880); Traube, *Ber.*, **42**, 3298 (1909).
39. Guareschi, *Ber.*, **28**, R160 (1895).
40. Mignonac, *Compt. rend.*, **169**, 237 (1917).
41. Laurent and Gerhardt, *Ann.*, **76**, 304 (1850); Schiff, *ibid.*, Spl. **3**, 343 (1864).
42. Lowy and Downey, *J. Am. Chem. Soc.*, **43**, 346 (1921); Lowy and King, *ibid.*, **43**, 626 (1921).
43. Ingold and Piggott, *J. Chem. Soc.*, **123**, 2745 (1923); Miller and Wagner, *J. Am. Chem. Soc.*, **54**, 3698 (1932).
44. v. Miller, Plöchl and Eckstein, *Ber.*, **25**, 2030 (1892); Eibner, *ibid.*, **30**, 1446 (1897); *Ann.*, **328**, 121 (1903).
45. Reddelien, *Ann.*, **388**, 165 (1912).
46. Stewart, *Stereochemistry*, 1907, pp. 416-426.
47. Auwers, *Ber.*, **22**, 605 (1889); Barrett and Lapworth, *J. Chem. Soc.*, **93**, 85 (1908).
48. Barrett and Lapworth, *J. Chem. Soc.*, **93**, 85 (1908); *Cf.* Acree and Johnson, *Am. Chem. J.*, **38**, 308 (1907); Acree, *ibid.*, **39**, 300 (1908).
49. Tafel and Pfeffermann, *Ber.*, **35**, 1510 (1902).
50. Curtius and Thun, *J. prakt. Chem.*, (2) **44**, 164 (1891); Curtius and Pflug, *ibid.*, (2) **44**, 543 (1891).
51. Robinson and Robinson, *J. Chem. Soc.*, **113**, 644 (1918). Cerf. *Bull. soc. chim.*, (5) **4**, 1451, 1460 (1937); Desai, *J. Indian Chem. Soc.*, **10**, 663 (1938); Feldman and Wagner, *J. Org. Chem.*, **7**, 31 (1942); Senkus, *J. Am. Chem. Soc.*, **68**, 10 (1946); Johnson, *ibid.*, **68**, 12, 14 (1946); Bruson and Butler, *ibid.*, **68**, 2348 (1946); Horning and Horning, *J. Org. Chem.*, **11**, 95 (1946); Hartough and Meisel, *J. Am. Chem. Soc.*, **70**, 4018 (1948).
52. Mannich *et al.*, *Arch. Pharm.*, **250**, 647 (1912); *ibid.*, **265**, 684 (1924); *Ber.*, **39**, 608 (1930); *ibid.*, **55**, 3510 (1922); *Arch. Pharm.*, **276**, 206 (1938); Petrenko-Kritschenko and Zoneff, *Ber.*, **39**, 1358 (1906); **42**, 3683 (1909); Kermack and Muir, *J. Chem. Soc.*, **1931**, 3089; Levy and Nisbet, *ibid.*, **1938**, 1053; Burger and Mosettig, *J. Am. Chem. Soc.*, **58**, 1570 (1936); Blicke and Burchhalter, *ibid.*, **64**, 451 (1942); Blicke, *Chemical Reactions*, Vol. I, p. 303 (1942).
53. Mannich, *et al.*, *Ber.*, **65**, 378 (1932); **55**, 3486 (1922).
54. Mannich and Kather, *ibid.*, **53**, 1368 (1920).
55. Decombe, *Compt. rend.*, **196**, 866 (1933); **197**, 258 (1933); Bruson and MacMullen, *J. Am. Chem. Soc.*, **63**, 270 (1941); Caldwell and Thompson, *ibid.*, **61**, 765 (1939).

56. Tseon Héon-Féo, *Compt. rend.*, **192**, 1242 (1931); Mannich, *Arch. Pharm.*, **255**, 261 (1917).
57. Mannich and Ball, *Arch. Pharm.*, **264**, 65 (1926); Mannich and Ritsert, *ibid.*, **264**, 164 (1926).
58. Mannich and Schumann, *Ber.*, **69**, 2299 (1936).
59. Mannich and Mück, *ibid.*, **63**, 604 (1930).
60. Mannich and Viet, *ibid.*, **68**, 506 (1935); Mannich and Moss, *ibid.*, **63**, 608 (1930).
61. Mannich *et al.*, *Arch. Pharm.*, **265**, 598 (1927); *Ber.*, **55**, 356 (1922); **57**, 1116 (1924).
62. Mannich and Bauroth, *Ber.*, **55**, 3504 (1922).
63. Robinson *et al.*, *J. Chem. Soc.*, **1937**, 53; **1941**, 586; Wilds and Shunk, *J. Org. Chem.*, **7**, 469 (1942).
64. Schmidt, *Z. angew. Chem.*, **36**, 511 (1923); *Ber.*, **57**, 704 (1924); **58**, 2413 (1925); Briggs and Lyttleton, *J. Chem. Soc.*, **1943**, 421; Adamson and Kenner, *ibid.*, **1934**, 838; **1939**, 181; v. Braun, *Ann.*, **490**, 100 (1931); Briggs and De Ath, *J. Chem. Soc.*, **1937**, 456; Ruzicka *et al.*, *Helv. Chim. Acta*, **16**, 1323 (1933); Wolff, *Organic Reactions*, vol. III, p. 307; Newman and Gildenhorn, *J. Am. Chem. Soc.*, **70**, 317 (1948).
65. Cannizzaro, *Ann.*, **88**, 129 (1853); Tischtschenko, *et al.*, *J. prakt. Chem.*, **86**, 322 (1912); Hammarsten, *Ann.*, **420**, 262 (1920); Lock, *Monatsh.*, **55**, 307 (1930); **64**, 178, 341 (1934); **67**, 320 (1936); Weissberger and Haase, *J. Chem. Soc.*, **1934**, 535; Hazlet and Callison, *J. Am. Chem. Soc.*, **66**, 1248 (1944); Geissmann, *Organic Reactions*, vol. II, p. 94.
66. Claisen, *Ber.*, **20**, 646 (1887); Tischtschenko, *ibid.*, **20**, 246 (1887); Child and Adkins, *J. Am. Chem. Soc.*, **45**, 3013 (1923); **47**, 798 (1925); Marshall, *J. Chem. Soc.*, **127**, 2184 (1925).
67. Franke, *Monatsh.*, **17**, 666 (1896); **21**, 1122 (1900); Wessely, *ibid.*, **22**, 66 (1901); Neustädter, *Ann.*, **351**, 295 (1907).
68. Perkin, Jr., *Ber.*, **15**, 2803 (1882); **16**, 210 (1883); Hammersten, *Ann.*, **420**, 262 (1920).
69. Lederer, *Monatsh.*, **22**, 536 (1901).
70. Tischtschenko, *J. Russ. Phys.-Chem. Soc.*, **38**, 355 (1906); Childs and Adkins, *J. Am. Chem. Soc.*, **45**, 3013 (1923); **47**, 798 (1925).
71. Herrmann, *Monatsh.*, **25**, 188 (1904); Neustädter, *ibid.*, **27**, 879 (1906).
72. Tollens *et al.*, *Ann.*, **265**, 316 (1891); **276**, 82 (1893); *ibid.*, **289**, 46 (1896); *Ber.*, **36**, 1342 (1903); Hasaens, *Ann.*, **276**, 76 (1893).
73. Pechmann, *Ber.*, **20**, 2904 (1887); **22**, 2558 (1889); Meyerhoff, *Naturwiss.*, **24**, 689 (1936); **26**, 443 (1937).
74. Debus, *Ann.*, **100**, 116 (1856).
75. Meerwein, *Ber.*, **53**, 1829 (1920).
76. Reformatsky, *Ber.*, **20**, 1210 (1887); **28**, 2838, 2842 (1895); *J. Russ. Phys.-Chem. Soc.*, **22**, 44 (1890); *J. prakt. Chem.*, (2) **54**, 469 (1896); Reformatsky and Pleskonossow, *Ber.*, **28**, 2838 (1895); Dain, *J. Russ. Phys.-Chem. Soc.*, **28**, 593 (1896); Jaworsky and Reformatsky, *Ber.*, **35**, 3633 (1902); Zelinsky and Gutt, *ibid.*, **35**, 2140 (1902); Rupe and Lutz, *ibid.*, **36**, 15 (1903); Bouveault and Blanc, *Bull. soc. chim.*, (3) **31**, 1208 (1904); Haller and Brochet, *Compt. rend.*, **150**, 500 (1910); Willstätter and Hatt, *Ann.*, **418**, 153 (1918); Nieuwland and Daly, *J. Am. Chem. Soc.*, **53**, 1842 (1931); Shriner, *Organic Reactions*, vol. I, p. 1 (1942); Harvey *et al.*, *J. Chem. Soc.*, **1930**, 426; Abbott *et al.*, *ibid.*, **1928**, 2518; Bardhan, *ibid.*, **1928**, 2603, 2615; Colonge and Joly, *Ann. chim.*, (11) **18**, 310 (1943); Colonge, *Bull. soc. chim.*, (5) **9**, 732 (1942); Fieser *et al.*, *J. Am. Chem. Soc.*, **70**, 3209 (1948); Tsatsas, *Ann. chim.*, (12) **1**, 352 (1946); Kuhn and Grundmann, *Ber.*, **70** B, 1899 (1940). *Cf.* Kuhn and Stabb, *Angew. Chem.*, **65**, 371 (1953); Dreiding and Pratt, *J. Am. Chem. Soc.*, **75**, 3717 (1953).
77. Kohler *et al.*, *Am. Chem. J.*, **46**, 221 (1911); *J. Am. Chem. Soc.*, **41**, 683 (1919).
78. Iyer, *J. Indian Chem. Soc.*, **17**, 215 (1940).
79. Stoermer and Frederici, *Ber.*, **41**, 324 (1908); Wallach, *Ann.*, **365**, 255 (1909); Rupe, *ibid.*, **369**, 321 (1909); Cook, *J. Chem. Soc.*, **1931**, 2524; Bachmann, *J. Org. Chem.*, **3**, 434 (1938); Bergmann and Boograchov, *J. Am. Chem. Soc.*, **62**, 3017 (1940).
80. Fischer, *Ann.*, **475**, 183 (1929).
81. Kuhn and Hoffer, *Ber.*, **65**, 651 (1932).
82. Wurtz, *Compt. rend.*, **74**, 1361 (1872); **76**, 1165 (1873); **83**, 255 (1876); **92**, 1438 (1881); **97**, 1169 (1883); *J. prakt. Chem.*, (2) **5**, 457 (1872); Kolbe, *ibid.*, (2) **5**, 465 (1872); Lieben, *Monatsh.*, **4**, 11 (1883); **22**, 289 (1901); Franke and Kohn, *ibid.*, **19**, 354, 519 (1898); Claisen, *Ann.*, **306**, 322 (1899); Franke, *Monatsh.*, **21**, 1122 (1900); Nef. *Ann.*, **318**, 160 (1901); Rosinger, *Ber.*, **22**, 545 (1901); *Ann.*, **322**, 131 (1902); Euler, *Ber.*, **38**, 2551 (1905); Neustädter, *Monatsh.*, **27**, 879 (1906); *Ann.*, **351**, 294 (1907); Tischtschenko, *J. Russ. Phys.-Chem. Soc.*, **38**, 398 (1906); McLeod, *Am. Chem. J.*, **37**, 20 (1907); Taipale, *J. Russ. Phys.-Chem. Soc.*, **41**, 815 (1909); Zelinski and Wolkowski, *ibid.*, **45**, 1451 (1913); Mammarten, *Ann.*, **420**, 262 (1920); **421**, 293 (1920); Fischer and Wiedemann, *Ber.*, **64**, 2825 (1931); *Ann.*, **513**, 251 (1934); Braun and Manz, *Ber.*, **67**, 1696 (1934).
83. Fourneau, *Bull. soc. chim.*, (4) **47**, 858 (1930).

84. Schroeter, *Ber.*, **31**, 2189 (1898); *Ann.*, **303**, 114 (1898); Wislicenus and Russ, *Ber.*, **43**, 2719 (1910).
85. Wurtz, *Ber.*, **14**, 2069 (1881); Newbury, *ibid.*, **24**, R89 (1891); Orndorff and Newbury, *ibid.*, **25**, R732 (1892).
86. Grignard and Abelmann, *Bull. soc. chim.*, (4) **7**, 638 (1910); Kyriakides, *J. Am. Chem. Soc.*, **36**, 531 (1914).
87. Lieben, *Monatsh.*, **22**, 289 (1901); Neustadter, *ibid.*, **22**, 903 (1906); Raper, *J. Chem. Soc.*, **91**, 1831 (1907); Schmidt, *Ber.*, **14**, 1459 (1881); Claisen, *ibid.*, **14**, 2468 (1881); **25**, 3164 (1892).
88. Kane, *J. prakt. Chem.*, (1) **15**, 129 (1838); Fittig, *Ann.*, **110**, 32 (1859); Baeyer, *ibid.*, **140**, 301 (1886); Claisen, *ibid.*, **180**, 1 (1876).
89. Kerp, *Ann.*, **290**, 137 (1896); Kerp and Müller, *ibid.*, **299**, 93 (1897); Knoevenagel, *ibid.*, **297**, 185 (1897); Crossley and Gilling, *J. Chem. Soc.*, **95**, 18 (1909).
90. Bodroux and Taboury, *Bull. soc. chim.*, (4) **3**, 829 (1908); Becker and Thorpe, *J. Chem. Soc.*, **121**, 1303 (1922); Ekeley and Howe, *J. Am. Chem. Soc.*, **45**, 1917 (1923); Abbot *et al.*, *J. Chem. Soc.*, **1928**, 2514.
91. Wallach, *Ber.*, **40**, 70 (1907); Mannich, *ibid.*, **40**, 153 (1907).
92. Munch, *Ann.*, **180**, 333 (1875).
93. Freudenberg and Orthner, *Ber.*, **55**, 1749 (1922).
94. Klages and Allendorff, *ibid.*, **31**, 1003 (1898); **35**, 2245 (1902).
95. Rabe and Kindler, *ibid.*, **51**, 466, 1363 (1918); Rabe, *ibid.*, **55**, 531 (1922).
96. Wolff, *Ann.*, **208**, 104 (1881); Wislicenus, *Ber.*, **24**, 3416 (1891); **25**, 2448 (1892).
97. Salkowski, *J. prakt. Chem.*, (2) **106**, 253 (1923).
98. Willstätter *et al.*, *Ann.*, **326**, 43, 61, 79 (1903); **434**, 111 (1923).
99. Ishiwara, *Ber.*, **57**, 1125 (1924).
100. Mannich and Lammering, *ibid.*, **55**, 3510 (1922).
101. Harries, *ibid.*, **29**, 2731 (1896).
102. Kaufmann *et al.*, *Ber.*, **46**, 62 (1913); Hess, *ibid.*, **46**, 3120, 3124, 4110 (1913); **52**, 988 (1919).
103. v. Pechmann and Dahl, *ibid.*, **23**, 2421 (1890); Diels and Stephan, *ibid.*, **40**, 4336 (1907).
104. Grandmougin, *J. prakt. Chem.*, (2) **76**, 137 (1907).
105. Fischer, *Ann.*, **211**, 221 (1882).
106. Perkin and Freer, *J. Chem. Soc.*, **51**, 836 (1887); Possanner and Ehrenthal, *Monatsh.*, **24**, 353 (1903).
107. Mannich and Heilner, *Ber.*, **55**, 358 (1922).
108. Buchka, *ibid.*, **10**, 1714 (1877).
109. Tutin *et al.*, *J. Chem. Soc.*, **95**, 2113 (1909).
110. Claus, *J. prakt. Chem.*, (2) **46**, 481 (1892).
111. Elbs and Schmitz, *ibid.*, (2) **51**, 591 (1895).
112. Kerp, *Ann.*, **290**, 143 (1896).
113. Städel, *ibid.*, **194**, 307 (1878); Klinger and Lonnes, *Ber.*, **29**, 2154 (1896); Gurgenjanz and Kostanecki, *ibid.*, **28**, 2310 (1895).
114. Gurgenjanz and Kostanecki, *Ber.*, **28**, 2310 (1895).
115. Ehrlich and Bendu, *ibid.*, **46**, 1941, 1946 (1912).
116. Meyer, *ibid.*, **42**, 143 (1919); *Monatsh.*, **30**, 165 (1909).
117. Liebermann and Jacobson, *Ann.*, **211**, 58 (1882); Korn, *Ber.*, **17**, 3024 (1884).
118. Klages and Stamm, *Ber.*, **37**, 1715 (1904).
119. Baeyer, *ibid.*, **29**, 2792 (1896); Wagner and Slawinski, *ibid.*, **32**, 2080 (1899); Tiemann, *ibid.*, **29**, 2612, 3018 (1896).
120. Wislicenus, *Ann.*, **126**, 229 (1863).
121. Lampricht, *ibid.*, **309**, 115 (1899).
122. Zincke and Thörner, *Ber.*, **10**, 1473 (1877); Gräbe, *ibid.*, **7**, 1624 (1874); Klages and Allendorff, *ibid.*, **31**, 998 (1898).
123. Darzens, *Compt. rend.*, **139**, 868 (1904); Darzens and Rost, *ibid.*, **146**, 933 (1908); Sabatier and Murat, *ibid.*, **158**, 760 (1914); Skita, *Ber.*, **41**, 2938 (1908); Zelinski, *ibid.*, **44**, 2781 (1911); Ipatiev, *ibid.*, **45**, 3205 (1912).
124. Tafel, *Ber.*, **42**, 3146 (1909).
125. Clemmensen, *ibid.*, **46**, 1838 (1913); **47**, 51, 681 (1914); Johnson and Hodge, *J. Am. Chem. Soc.*, **35**, 1014 (1913); Najima and Nakamura, *Ber.*, **46**, 4092 (1913); Martin, *Organic Reactions* vol. 1, p. 155; *J. Am. Chem. Soc.*, **58**, 1438 (1936).
126. Marker and Lawson, *J. Am. Chem. Soc.*, **61**, 852 (1939); Lutz and Small, *J. Org. Chem.*, **4**, 220 (1939).
127. Cox, *J. Am. Chem. Soc.*, **52**, 352 (1930); Klarmann, *ibid.*, **48**, 791 (1926); Klarmann and Figdor, *ibid.*, **48**, 803 (1926).
128. Ballard and Dehn, *J. Am. Chem. Soc.*, **54**, 3969 (1932).
129. Steinkopf and Schubart, *Ann.*, **424**, 20 (1921).

130. Clemmensen, *Ber.*, **47**, 681 (1914); Auwers and Saurwein, *ibid.*, **55**, 2373 (1922); Krollpfeiffer and Schäfer, *ibid.*, **56**, 620 (1923); Harvey *et al.*, *J. Chem. Soc.*, **1930**, 2537 Heilbron and Wilson, *ibid.*, **1930**, 2537; Haworth *et al.*, *ibid.*, **1932**, 1784, 2248.
131. v. Braun *et al.*, *Ber.*, **53**, 1155 (1920); Fleischer *et al.*, *ibid.*, **53**, 1255 (1920); **56**, 228 (1923); *Ann.*, **422**, 231, 272 (1921).
132. Steinkopf and Wolfram, *Ann.*, **430**, 113 (1923); Wislicenus and Weitemeyer, *ibid.*, **436**, 1 (1924).
133. Borsche, *Ber.*, **52**, 2077 (1919); Windaus, *Ann.*, **447**, 233 (1926); Ruzicka *et al.*, *Helv. Chim. Acta*, **11**, 496 (1928); Guha, *Ber.*, **72**, 1359 (1939); Plant and Tomlinson, *J. Chem. Soc.*, **1935**, 1092.
134. Steinkopf and Wolfram, *Ann.*, **430**, 113 (1923).
135. Dippy and Lewis, *Rec. trav. chim.*, **56**, 1000 (1937); Burton and Shoppee, *J. Chem. Soc.*, **1939**, 567.
136. Bridge *et al.*, *J. Chem. Soc.*, **1937**, 1530; George and Robertson, *ibid.*, **1937**, 135; Anderson and Marrian, *J. Biol. Chem.*, **127**, 647 (1939).
137. Awe, *Ber.*, **67**, 836 (1934); Awe and Unger, *Ibid.*, **70**, 472 (1937).
138. Johnson and Hodge, *J. Am. Chem. Soc.*, **35**, 1014 (1913); Fincke and Ristic, *J. prakt. Chem.*, **146**, 151 (1936).
139. Meunier, *Compt. rend.*, **134**, 473 (1902); Ciusa and Milani, *Atti accad. Lincei*, (5) **22**, 681 (1913).
140. Fittig and Remsen, *Ann.*, **159**, 130 (1871); Fittig and Ammann, *ibid.*, **168**, 70 (1873).
141. Sabatier and Senderens, *Compt. rend.*, **137**, 301, 1025 (1903); Mailhe, *Bull. soc. chim.*, (4) **15**, 327 (1914).
142. Voorhees and Adams, *J. Am. Chem. Soc.*, **44**, 1397 (1922); Carothers and Adams, *ibid.*, **45**, 1071 (1923); **46**, 1675 (1924); **47**, 1047 (1925).
143. Barbier and Bouveault, *Compt. rend.*, **120**, 1420 (1895).
144. Pechmann, *Ber.*, **21**, 1418 (1888).
145. Diels, *Ann.*, **434**, 1 (1923).
146. Lubrzynska, *J. Chem. Soc.*, **109**, 1119 (1916).
147. Wolff, *Ann.*, **394**, 86 (1912); Wolff and Tielepape, *ibid.*, **420**, 275 (1920); Thielepape, *Ber.*, **55**, 136 (1922); Knorr and Hess, *ibid.*, **44**, 2760 (1911); Kishner, *J. Russ. Phys.-Chem. Soc.*, **43**, 582, 1398 (1911); **44**, 165 (1912); **45**, 1779 (1913); Campbell and Eby, *J. Am. Chem. Soc.*, **63**, 2683 (1941); Moffett and Hunter, *ibid.*, **73**, 1973 (1951).
148. Schönberg, *Ber.*, **54**, 2838 (1921).
149. Whitmore *et al.*, *J. Am. Chem. Soc.*, **67**, 2061 (1945); Soffer *et al.*, *ibid.*, **67**, 1435 (1945); Huang and Minlon, *ibid.*, **68**, 2487 (1946); **70**, 2802 (1948); **71**, 3301 (1949); Drake and Melamed, *ibid.*, **70**, 364 (1948); Campbell *et al.*, *J. Chem. Soc.*, **1949**, 1742; Nunn and Rapson, *ibid.*, **1949**, 1051; Rytina *et al.*, *J. Am. Chem. Soc.*, **71**, 751 (1949); Fand and Lutonski, *ibid.*, **71**, 3301 (1949).
150. Staudinger and Kupfer, *Ber.*, **44**, 2197 (1911).
151. Wolff and Thielepape, *Ann.*, **420**, 275 (1920).
152. Thielepape and Spreckelsen, *Ber.*, **55**, 2929 (1922).
153. Biginelli, *Gazz. chim. ital.*, **23**, 360 (1893); *Atti accad. Lincei*, (5) **3**, 195 (1894); *Ber.*, **24**, 1317 (1891); Hinkel and Hey, *Rec. trav. chim.*, **48**, 1280 (1929); Falkers, Harwood and Johnson, *J. Am. Chem. Soc.*, **54**, 3751 (1932).
154. Henry, *Ber.*, **26**, Ref. 934 (1893); **28**, Ref. 851, 924 (1895); Kolotow, *ibid.*, **26**, Ref. 611 (1893).
155. Einhorn *et al.*, *Ann.*, **343**, 207 (1905); **361**, 113 (1908).
156. Vogel, *J. Chem. Soc.*, **1927**, 594.
157. Bertagnini, *Ann.*, **85**, 179, 268 (1853); Mendeleer, *ibid.*, **110**, 243 (1859); Cannizzaro, *ibid.*, **119**, 254 (1861); Chancel, *ibid.*, **151**, 302 (1869); Bunte, *ibid.*, **170**, 308 (1873); Etard, *Ann. chim.*, (5) **22**, 248 (1881); Lipp., *Ann.*, **205**, 3 (1880); V. Richter and Schuchner. *Ber.*, **17**, 1933 (1884); Julsin, *ibid.*, **17**, 2505 (1884); Kahn, *ibid.*, **18**, 3365 (1885); Colmann and Perkin, *J. Chem. Soc.*, **51**, 238 (1887); Freer and Perkin, *ibid.*, **53**, 214 (1888); v. Miller and Rohde, *Ber.*, **23**, 1075 (1890); **24**, 1359 (1891); Kraft, *ibid.*, **23**, 2361 (1890); Kraut, *Ann.*, **258**, 105 (1890); Stoermer, *Ber.*, **39**, 2300 (1906); Demjanow and Fortunatow, *ibid.*, **40**, 4398 (1907); Darzens, *Compt. rend.*, **144**, 1124 (1907).
158. Ludwig, *Monatsh.*, **9**, 661 (1889).
159. Baeyer, *Ber.*, **28**, 652 (1895).
160. Pinner, *ibid.*, **16**, 1727 (1883).
161. Herzig, *Monatsh.*, **3**, 119 (1883).
162. Bazlen, *Ber.*, **60**, 1470 (1927).
163. Sprung, *Chem. Revs.*, **26**, 297 (1940).
164. Henry, *Bull. acad. roy. belg.*, (3) **26**, 206 (1893); **28**, 359 (1894); **29**, 26 (1895); Cambier and Brochet, *Bull. soc. chim.*, (3) **13**, 404 (1895); Franchimont and van Epps, *Rec. trav. chim.*, **15**, 169 (1896); Einhorn and Prettner, *Ann.*, **334**, 217 (1904).
165. Tschitschibabin *et al.*, *J. Russ. Phys.-Chem.*, **37**, 1229 (1905); *J. prakt. Chem.*, (2) **107**, 109, 122, 129, 132, 138, 145, 154 (1924); Strain, *J. Am. Chem. Soc.*, **54**, 1221 (1932); Haskelberg, *Chemistry and Industry*, **54**, 261 (1935).

166. Délépine, *Compt. rend.*, **144**, 853 (1907).
167. *Cf.* Auerbach and Barschall, *Chem. Zentr.*, **1907 II**, 1735.
168. Bischoff, *Ber.*, **31**, 3248 (1898); Scholtz and Jaross, *ibid.*, **35**, 413 (1902).
169. v. Braun, *Ber.*, **41**, 2145 (1908).
170. Gnehm and Blumer, *Ann.*, **304**, 115 (1899); v. Braun, *Ber.*, **41**, 2145 (1908); Wagner, *J. Am. Chem. Soc.*, **55**, 724 (1933); **56**, 1944 (1934); Craig, *ibid.*, **55**, 3723 (1933). *Cf.* Young and Wagner, *ibid.*, **59**, 854 (1934).
171. Mannich *et al.*, *Ber.*, **69**, 2112 (1936).
172. Lob, *Rec. trav. chim.*, **55**, 859 (1936); Rameau, *ibid.*, **57**, 194 (1938).
173. Eibner, *Ber.*, **30**, 1444 (1897); Miller and Wagner, *J. Am. Chem. Soc.*, **54**, 3698 (1932).
174. Schiff, *Ann. Suppl.* **3**, 343 (1864); Tollen, *Ber.*, **17**, 653 (1884); von Miller, *ibid.*, **25**, 2072 (1892); von Miller and Plochl, *ibid.*, **27**, 1296 (1894); **29**, 1462 (1896); Eibner and Koch, *Z. angew. Chem.*, **39**, 1514 (1926).
175. Eiber, *Ann.*, **302**, 334 (1898).
176. v. Miller and Plochl, *Ber.*, **25**, 2033, 2044 (1892).
177. *Cf.* Lipmann and Strecker, *ibid.*, **12**, 831 (1879); von Miller *et al.*, *ibid.*, **25**, 2028, 2033, 2039, 2050 (1892); Friedjung and Mosler, *Monatsh.*, **22**, 460 (1901).
178. Doebner and v. Miller, *Ber.*, **16**, 2464 (1863); **17**, 1698, 1712 (1884); v. Miller and Kinkelin, *ibid.*, **20**, 1916 (1887).
179. Fischer, *Ber.*, **16**, 661 Anm. (1883); **17**, 572 (1884); **22**, 90 (1889); Fischer and Jordan, *ibid.*, **16**, 2241 (1883); Overton, *ibid.*, **26**, 20 (1893).
180. Fischer and Ach, *Ann.*, **253**, 57 (1889).
181. Miller and Plochl, *Ber.*, **25**, 2023, 2036, 2057 (1892).
182. Fischer and Hess, *ibid.*, **17**, 559 (1884); Fischer, *ibid.*, **19**, 1563 (1886); *Ann.*, **236**, 116 (1886); Brunner, *Monatsh.*. **16**, 183, 849 (1895).
183. Knorr, *Ann.*, **238**, 147 (1886); Wef., *ibid.*, **266**, 70 (1891).
184. v. Pechmann, *Ber.*, **21**, 2751 (1888).
185. Lurdelli and Jeger, *Helv. Chim. Acta*, **32**, 1817 (1949).
186. Mannich and Bauroth, *Ber.*, **57**, 1108 (1924); Nisbet *et al.*, *J. Chem. Soc.*, **1933**, 839; **1938**, 1053, 1237, 1568, 1572; **1945**, 126; Harradence and Lions, *J. Proc. Roy. Soc., N.S. Wales*, **73**, 14 (1939); *C.A.*, **33**, 8196 (1939); Blicke, *Organic Reactions*, I, p. 303 (1942).
187. Lyttle and Weisblat, *J. Am. Chem. Soc.*, **69**, 2118 (1947); *U.S. patent* 2,557,041; *C.A.*, **46**, 1593 (1952). *Cf.* Snyder and Eliel, *J. Am. Chem. Soc.*, **71**, 663 (1949).
188. Snyder and Katz, *J. Am. Chem. Soc.*, **69**, 3140 (1947). *Cf.* Lyttle and Weisblat, *ibid.*, **69**, 2118 (1947); **71**, 3079 (1949); *U.S. patents* 2,557,041; 2,528,928; *C.A.*, **46**, 1593 (1952); **45**, 3870g (1951).
189. Reichert and Posemann, *Arch. Pharm.*, **275**, 67 (1937).
190. Snyder and Hamlin, *J. Am. Chem. Soc.*, **72**, 5082 (1950); Gill *et al.*, *ibid.*, **74**, 4923 (1952).
191. Mannich *et al.*, *Ber.*, **70**, 355 (1937).
192. Snyder *et al.*, *J. Am. Chem. Soc.*, **66**, 200 (1944).
193. Snyder and Smith, *ibid.*, **66**, 350 (1944); *U.S. patent* 2,447,545; *C.A.*, **43**, 2643 (1949); Suter *et al.*, *J. Am. Chem. Soc.*, **66**, 500 (1944); Snyder and Eliel, *ibid.*, **70**, 3855 (1948).
194. Snyder and Eliel, *J. Am. Chem. Soc.*, **71**, 663 (1949).
195. Lieberman and Wagner, *J. Org. Chem.*, **14**, 1001 (1949).
196. *Cf.*, Barltrop and Saxton, *J. Chem. Soc.*, **1952**, 1038; Gunstone and Heggie, *ibid.*, **1952**, 1437.
197. Lions *et al.*, *Austalian J. Sci.* **10**, 147 (1948); *C.A.*, **42**, 7257 (1948); *J. Am. Chem. Soc.*, **72**, 3464, 3468 (1950).
198. Simonsen *et al.*, *J. Chem. Soc.*, **1937**, 1576; McQuillin, *ibid.*, **1951**, 716.
199. Robinson *et al.*, *J. Chem. Soc.*, **1943**, 491; **1949**, 1855, 1866.
200. Ghosh and Robinson, *ibid.*, **1944**, 506.
201. Hellmann, *Z. physiol. Chem.*, **284**, 163 (1949); Vejdelek, *Chem. Listy*, **44**, 73 (1950); *C.A.*, **45**, 8004 (1951).
202. Butenandt *et al.*, *Z. physiol. Chem.*, **284**, 175 (1949); Meyers, *Doctoral thesis, Univ. of Illinois, Urbana, Ill.*, (1951).
203. Herz *et al.*, *J. Am. Chem. Soc.*, **70**, 504 (1948).
204. Wilds and Shunk, *ibid.*, **65**, 469 (1943); Prelog *et al.*, *Helv. Chim. Acta*, **29**, 1425 (1946); **33**, 356 (1950); **31**, 92 (1948); **32**, 1284 (1949).
205. Suter, *et al.*, *J. Am. Chem. Soc.*, **67**, 36, 502 (1945); *U.S. patent* 2,451,310; 2,468,912; *C.A.*, **43**, 1442, 5806 (1949). *Cf.* Rydon, *J. Chem. Soc.*, **1948**, 705; Rydon and Siddapa, *ibid.*, **1951**, 2462; Kornfeld, *J. Org. Chem.*, **16**, 806 (1951); Hamlin and Fischer, *J. Am. Chem. Soc.*, **73**, 5007 (1951); Jackman and Archer, *ibid.*, **68**, 2105 (1946); Herz *et al.*, *ibid.*, **70**, 504 (1948); Albertson, *ibid.*, **70**, 669 (1948).
206. Khott, *J. Chem. Soc.*, **1947**, 1190, Sneyder and Brewster, *J. Am. Chem. Soc.*, **71**, 1061 (1949).
207. Salzer and Andersag, *U.S. patent* 2,315,661; *C.A.*, **37**, 5418 (1943); *U.S. PB706, Dept. of Commerce, Washington, D.C.*
208. Eliot and Peckham, *J. Am. Chem. Soc.*, **72**, 1209 (1950).
209. Snyder *et al.*, *ibid.*, **74**, 5110 (1952).

210. Smith, *ibid.*, **70**, 320 (1948).
211. Haber and Willstätter, *Ber.*, **64**, 2844 (1931); Weiss, *Trans. Faraday Soc.*, **37**, 782 (1941); *Chemistry and Industry, (London)*, **1949**, No. 17 p. 274; Alexander, *J. Am. Chem. Soc.*, **69**, 289 (1947).
212. Kulpinski and Nord, *J. Org. Chem.*, **8**, 256 (1943); Villani and Nord, *J. Am. Chem. Soc.*, **69**, 2605 (1947).
213. Stoll, *Helv. Chim. Acta*, **34**, 679 (1951).
214. Hanschke, *Ber.*, **76**, 180 (1943); Späth *et al.*, *ibid.*, **76**, 57, 1196 (1943). *Cf.* Saunders *et al.*, *J. Am. Chem. Soc.*, **65**, 1714 (1943); **66**, 206 (1944).
215. Kuzin and Nevraeva, *Biokhimiya*, **6**, 261 (1941); *C.A.*, **35**, 7427 (1941). *Cf.* Fischer and Marshall, *Ber.*, **64**, 2825 (1931).
216. Bergmann and Sulzbacher, *British patent* 587,275 (1947).
217. Karrer *et al.*, *Helv. Chim. Acta*, **28**, 1181, 1185 (1945); **29**, 1836 (1946); Sörensen *et al.*, *Acta Chem. Scand.* **1**, 458 (1947). *Cf.* Karrer and Eugster, *Helv. Chim. Acta*, **32**, 1013, 1934 (1949).
218. Prelog *et al.*, *Helv. Chim. Acta*, **31**, 92 (1948).
219. Stoll and Rouvé, *ibid.*, **30**, 2019 (1947); **20**, 525 (1937).
220. Jones and Kenner, *J. Chem. Soc.*, **1931**, 1849.
221. Prelog *et al.*, *Helv. Chim. Acta*, **30**, 1465 (1947); **31**, 870, 877, 1325 (1948).
222. Späth and Schmidt, *Ber.*, **74**, 859 (1941).
223. Owen, *J. Chem. Soc.*, **1943**, 445.
224. Späth *et al.*, *Ber.*, **76**, 722 (1943).
225. Späth *et al.*, *ibid.*, **76**, 520 (1943).
226. Clemo *et al.*, *J. Chem. Soc.*, **1949**, 2095.
227. Nef, *Ann.*, **298**, 284 (1897); Baeyer and Villiger, *Ber.*, **31**, 1581, 2479 (1900); Wieland and Wingler, *Ann.*, **431**, 301 (1923).
228. Wieland and Wingler, *Ann.*, **431**, 301 (1923).
229. Baeyer and Villiger, *Ber.*, **33**, 858 (1900); Wolffenstein, *ibid.*, **28**, 2265 (1895).
230. Baeyer and Villiger, *Ber.*, **33**, 124 (1900). *Cf.* Baeyer and Villiger, *ibid.*, **33**, 2479 (1900).
231. Harries, *Ber.*, **42**, 446 (1909).
232. Nef, *Ann.*, **298**, 284 (1877).
233. Girswald and Siegens, *Ber.*, **54**, 492 (1921).
234. Legler, *Ber.*, **18**, 3343 (1885); Baeyer and Villiger, *ibid.*, **33**, 2479 (1900); v. Girsewald, *ibid.*, **45**, 2571 (1912); v. Girsewald and Siegens, *ibid.*, **54**, 410 (1921).
235. Wieland, *Ber.*, **54**, 2356 (1921); Jorrisen and van der Beek, *Rec. trav. chim.*, **45**, 245 (1926); **46**, 42 (1927); *Chem. Zentr.*, **1926 I**, 2616; **1927 I**, 2625.
236. Clemo and Vipond, *Chemistry and Industry (London)*, **1949**, 856. *Cf.* Leonard and Ruyle, *J. Am. Chem. Soc.*, **71**, 3094 (1949).
237. Piloty and Schwerin, *Ber.*, **34**, 1864, 1870, 2354 (1901). *Cf.* Miller and Plochl, *ibid.*, **25**, 2070 (1892).
238. Pinner, *Ber.*, **15**, 594 (1882); Wislecenus *et al.*, *Ann.*, **275**, 315, 362 (1893); Wallach, *ibid.*, **277**, 135 (1893); Markownikoff, *J. prakt. Chem.*, (2) **49**, 414 (1894); Zelinsky and Reformatsky, *Ber.*, **28**, 2944 (1895); Knoevenagel, *Ann.*, **297**, 163 (1897); Petrenko-Kritschenko, *ibid.*, **341**, 164 (1905); Brunel, *Compt. rend.*, **140**, 793 (1905); *Bull. soc. chim.*, (3) **33**, 569 (1905); Kishner, *J. Russ. Phys.-Chem. Soc.*, **39**, 923 (1907); *Cehm. Zentr.*, **1908 I**, 123.
239. Vavon *et al.*, *Bull. soc. chim.*, (4) **43**, 231 (1928); *Compt. rend.*, **207**, 926 (1938).
240. Sidgwick, *Organic Chemistry of Nitrogen*, p. 169 (1937).
241. Gulati and Ray, *Current Sci. (India)*, **5**, 75 (1936).
242. Piloty and Steinbock, *Ber.*, **35**, 3101 (1902). *Cf.* Wieland, *ibid.*, **40**, 1677 (1907).
243. *Cf.* Dunstan and Dymond, *J. Chem. Soc.*, **65**, 206 (1894).
244. Soderbaum, *Ber.*, **25**, 3468 (1892).
245. *Cf.* Levene and Walti, *J. Biol. Chem.*, **94**, 353 (1931); Späth and Raschik, *Monatsh.*, **76**, 65 (1946).
246. Claisen, *Ber.*, **36**, 367 (1903); v. Auwers and Seyfried, *Ann.*, **484**, 178 (1930).
247. Kampfschmidt and Wibaut, *Rec. trav. chim.*, **71**, 601 (1952).
248. Freudenberg, *Stereochemie*, p. 974 (1933); Lamart-Lucas and Hoch, *Bull. soc. chim.*, (5) **5**, 987 (1938).
249. Birkit and Michalek, *Ind. Eng. Chem.*, **42**, 1864 (1952).
250. Curtius *et al.*, *J. prakt. Chem.*, (2) **50**, 275 (1894); **51**, 165, 353 (1895); *Ber.*, **28**, 522 (1895).
251. Goth and Selzer, *Germ. patent* 819,241 (1949); 823,446 (1949).
252. Bernstein *et al.*, *J. Am. Chem. Soc.*, **73**, 906 (1951); Drain, *Chem. Products.*, **15**, 286 (1952); Campaigne *et al.*, *J. Am. Chen. Soc.*, **75**, 988 (1953).
253. Tiemann, *Ber.*, **33**, 3721 (1900); Wallach, *Ann.*, **347**, 333 (1906); Semmler and Feldstein, *Ber.*, **47**, 2688 (1914); Kiliani, *ibid.*, **56**, 2017 (1923).
254. Gluud, *Ber.*, **48**, 422 (1915).

255. v. Auwers, *Ann.*, **439**, 172 (1924).
256. Liebermann and Lindenbaum, *Ber.*, **40**, 3579 (1907).
257. Houben-Weyl, *Die Methoden* VII, 1 p. 480 (1954).
258. Cason *et al.*, *J. Org. Chem.*, **18**, 1594 (1953).
259. Bewley and Keeble, *U.S. patent* 2,501,708 (1946); Geyer and Mortimer, *U.S. patent* 2,514,156 (1946); Prelog and Frick, *Helv. Chim. Acta*, **31**, 420 (1948); Heilbron, *J. Chem. Soc.*, **1949**, 737; Lunt and Sondheimer, *ibid.*, **1950**, 2957; Colombi *et al.*, *Helv. Chim. Acta*, **34**, 269 (1951); Cornubert and Real, *Bull. soc. chim.*, (5) **19**, 407 (1952); Huford *et al.*, *J. Am. Chem. Soc.*, **74**, 3017 (1952).
260. Seifert and Schinz, *Helv. Chim. Acta*, **34**, 728 (1951); Agarwal *et al.*, *J. Indian Chem. Soc.*, **28**, 95 (1951).
261. Harries and Lénart, *Ann.*, **410**, 105 (1915).
262. Wohl *et al.*, *Ber.*, **48**, 339 (1912); *Ann.*, **481**, 11, (1930); Schöpf and Arnold *Ann.*, **558**, 117 (1947); Raphael and Sondheimer, *J. Chem. Soc.*, **1951**, 2693; Sondheimer, *J. Am. Chem. Soc.*, **74**, 4040 (1952); Herbertz, *Ber.*, **85**, 478, 482 (1952).
263. Padoa and Pont, *Atti acad. nazl. Lincei class sci. fis. mat. e nat.*, (5) **15**, II, 610 (1916); Mailhe, *Bull. soc. chim.*, (4) **39**, 922 (1926); Whitman, *U.S. patent* 2,374,149 (1943); Wilsom, *J. Chem. Soc.*, **1945**, 61; Cass. *Ind. Eng. Chem.*, **40**, 216 (1948).
264. Thompson and Frewing, *Trans. Faraday Soc.*, **31**, 1660 (1935); Ebert, *J. phys. Chem.*, **39**, 421 (1935); Paul, *Bull. soc. chim.*, (5) **8**, 504 (1941); Schwab, *Handbuch der Katalyse*, VII, **2**, 217 (1943); Balcet and Calvert, *J. Am. Chem. Soc.*, **73**, 661 (1951).
265. Waters *et al.*, *Nature*, **170**, 211, 212 (1952); *Discuss. Faraday Soc.*, **14**, 221 (1953). *Cf.* Winstein and Seubold, *J. Am. Chem. Soc.*, **69**, 2916 (1947); Curtin and Hurwitz, *ibid.*, **74**, 5380 (1952).
266. Alexander, *J. Am. Chem. Soc.*, **69**, 289 (1941); Lachmann, *ibid.*, **45**, 2356 (1923).
267. McKee, *Ind. Eng. Chem.*, **38**, 382 (1946).
268. Sommelet, *Bull. soc. chim.*, (4) **29**, 553 (1921); *Compt. rend.*, **154**, 706 (1912); Johnson, *J. Am. Chem. Soc.*, **35**, 582 (1913); Johnson and Chernoff, *ibid.*, **35**, 585 (1913); **36**, 1742 (1914).
269. Fittig and Daimler, *Ber.*, **20**, 202 (1887).
270. Rassow and Bauer, *ibid.*, **41**, 963 (1908).
271. Reformatsky, *J. Russ. Phys.-Chem. Soc.*, **30**, 280 (1898); *J. prakt. Chem.*, (2) **54**, 477 (1896).
272. Reformatsky, *Ber.*, **28**, 3262 (1895); Blaise, *Compt. rend.*, **126**, 1808 (1898).

CHAPTER 5

REACTIONS INVOLVING CARBONYL COMPOUNDS: Part 2

ACETALS

Formation of Acetals, R(R′)C(OR″)$_2$

Acetals result through the reaction of a hydroxy compound with a carbonyl group:

$$RCHO + 2HOR' \rightarrow RCH(OR')_2 + H_2O$$

The reaction proceeds only with the simpler alcohols and with aliphatic and certain aromatic aldehydes, in the presence of hydrogen chloride or other substances acting as catalysts.[1] The reaction velocity is extremely small in the absence of catalysts. Acetals of ketones and those of phenols are obtained by indirect methods to be discussed below.

The ease of acetal formation decreases in the order formaldehyde, other aliphatic aldehydes, α,β-unsaturated aldehydes, aromatic aldehydes, ketones. Very energetic reaction conditions are necessary in the preparation of ketals. In general acetals are obtained with greater ease from primary alcohols, less readily from secondary and tertiary alcohols.

The formation of acetals from alcohols and aldehydes is a reversible process, and both aldehyde and acetal are present in a definite proportion at equilibrium. The rate of reaction and the proportion of acetal at equilibrium depend, to a large extent, upon the character of the alcohol and the aldehyde.[2] With acetaldehyde, starting with approximately a fivefold excess of alcohol, and carrying out the reaction at 25°, conversions in excess of 90% have been observed with methyl, ethyl, *n*-propyl and isobutyl alcohols. With the same aldehyde and under the same conditions, the extent of acetal formation was somewhat more than 60% with *sec*-butyl alcohol and a little below this figure with isopropyl alcohol, while with *tert*-butyl alcohol it was somewhat more than 30%. With benzaldehyde, conversion under the same conditions was in the neighborhood of 36% with ethanol and only 16% with isopropyl alcohol.

There is no dependence between the reaction velocity and the degree of conversion at equilibrium. Thus, the rate of reaction is lowest with methanol and highest with tertiary alcohols, the secondary alcohols also reacting quite rapidly. Aromatic aldehydes react with great rapidity.

General Procedure

The aldehyde is added to 4-8 parts of 1% alcoholic hydrogen chloride and the mixture is allowed to stand at room temperature for a day or two; or alternatively the mixture is heated on the water bath for a few hours. After the reaction is complete, the acid is neutralized with sodium carbonate or preferably by the addition of alcoholic sodium ethylate. Water is then added and the acetal is isolated by solvent extraction or by fractional distillation. Water should not be added before complete neutralization, since dilute acids cause the decomposition of the acetal.

The unconverted aldehyde may be removed by conversion to oxime and extraction with aqueous caustic, or, preferably, by treatment with a saturated solution of potassium phenylhydrazine sulfonate followed by extraction with water. The first procedure is inapplicable to acetals derived from phenolic products. Other methods of purification are, treatment with an aqueous solution of sodium bisulfite free of excess sulfur dioxide,[3] or shaking with alkaline hydrogen peroxide heated to 65°.[4]

Acetals of formaldehyde may be prepared by the above method with aqueous formaldehyde, providing sufficient anhydrous calcium chloride is added to eliminate practically all of the water from the sphere of reaction.

The addition of calcium chloride improves the yield of acetal in the preparation of acetals from lower alcohols. This is not necessary with the higher alcohols, since the water formed separates as a second layer.

As a rule, acetals of unsaturated aldehydes cannot be prepared by this method, since generally, addition of the alcohol at the double bond takes place. Cinnamic aldehyde forms an exception and yields aldols in the normal manner. α,β-Unsaturated aldehydes give cyclic acetals with α- and β-glycols, without addition at the double bond.

Hydroxy aldehydes and ketones give the anhydro compounds of the half-acetals, the so-called cycloacetals or lactolides:[5]

$$CH_3CH(OH)CH_2CH_2CHO + CH_3OH \xrightarrow{HCl} CH_3\overline{CHCH_2CH_2CH(OCH_3)O} + H_2O$$

Acetal formation proceeds well with polyhydric alcohols. Propylidene glycol acetal results in about 75% yield by heating a mixutre of propionaldehyde and glycol at 100° for several days. The reaction can be greatly accelerated, if the boiling point of the aldehyde employed lies above that of water, by heating the mixture to a point where the water resulting from the reaction is driven off as rapidly as it is formed. Catalysts accelerate the reaction.[6] Hydrogen chloride, phosphoric acid or sublimed ferric chloride, calcium chloride or zinc chloride may be employed for the purpose.[177]

Cyclic acetals or ketals result, in general, through the interaction of aldehydes and ketones with dihydric alcohols in the presence of the usual catalysts, hydrochloric and sulfuric acids, *p*-toluene sulfonic acid, tin tetrachloride, boron trifluoride, etc. Acetal formation takes place occasionally in the absence of a condensing agent.

The procedure followed varies according to the catalyst employed.

When *hydrogen chloride* is used as a catalyst, the alcohol is mixed with slightly more than the equivalent amount of the carbonyl compound, hydrochloric acid of sp.g 1.19 is added and the mixture is heated under reflux. Alternatively, the mixture is saturated with gaseous hydrogen chloride at 0°, allowed to stand for several hours, and the hydrogen chloride is then swept out with a current of carbon dioxide.[171]

The best procedure, when sulfuric acid is used as a catalyst, is to heat a mixture of equivalent quantities of the dihydric alcohol and carbonyl compound and a few drops of 40% sulfuric acid over the water bath for 10 hours. The yields of cyclic acetals obtained from aliphatic compounds by this method are low.

Excellent yields of cyclic acetals are generally obtained by use of *p-toluenesulfonic acid* as a catalyst. The procedure followed when this reagent is used is to add a small quantity of the acid to a solution of equivalent quantities of the alcohol and carbonyl compound in benzene. The water formed is continuously removed by distillation of the benzene through a reflux condenser into a water trap, from the top of which the benzene is returned to the reaction vessel. This method is applicable to the preparation of acetals and ketals of polyhydric alcohols, tartaric esters, and pyrocatechine. Cyclic ketals may be obtained by this method from acetoacetic ester, cyclohexanone, menthone and camphor.

Phosphorus pentoxide may be employed as a dehydrating agent in the preparation of acetals of pyrocatechine: One mole of the phenol is dissolved in two to three moles of the carbonyl compound at 10° and the required quantity of phosphorus pentoxide is added, together with some quartz sand. The liquid is agitated until it becomes viscous. The amount of phosphorus pentoxide required per gram of pyrocatechine is about 1.3 grams. The acetaldehyde compound is prepared by adding phosphorus pentoxide to the mixture of pyrocatechine and paraldehyde cooled to −5°. Yields of ketals range 65-80% of theory, while yields of acetals range 45-50% of theory.

Six-membered cyclic acetals form more readily than five-membered rings. Alkyl substituents in the alcohol component increase the tendency toward ring formation, whereas such substituents in the aldehyde component adversely influence the stability of the cyclic acetal. Yields of isobutyral acetals obtained from a number of dihydric alcohols were as follows:

Alcohol	Yield of isobutylacetal % of theory
Dimethyltrimethylene glycol, $(CH_3)_2C(CH_2OH)_2$	67
2-Methylpentane-1,3-diol, $C_2H_5CH(OH)CH(CH_3)CH_2OH$	69
Butane-1,3-diol, $CH_3CH(OH)CH_2CH_2OH$	63
2,4-Dimethylpentane-2,4-diol, $(CH_3)_2C(OH)CH_2C(CH_3)_2OH$	25
Pinacone, $(CH_3)_2C(OH)C(OH)(CH_3)_2$	58

Many-membered cyclic acetals are often obtained in the polymeric form, but they may be depolymerized by distillation at about 170° under vacuum.[172]

Glycolic acetals may be obtained through the interaction of alkylene oxides $RCHCH_2O$ with carbonyl compounds in the presence of tin tetrachloride. The yields range from 25 to 35% of the theoretical.[173] Undesirable side reactions are repressed by adding the reactants dissolved in dry carbon tetrachloride to a dilute solution of the catalyst in the same solvent at 20-30°. The reaction is practically instantaneous in most cases.

Formaldehyde, reacting with propylene in the presence of boron trifluoride at 0-20°, gives 4-methyl-1,3-dioxane,[174] $CH_3CHCH_2CH_2OCH_2O$

Acetals of acetaldehyde are formed in 80 to 90% yield by the reaction of primary aliphatic alcohols with vinyl acetate in the presence of an acidic mercury-boron catalyst:[178]

$$CH_2 = CHOCOCH_3 + 2ROH \rightarrow CH_3CH(OR)_2 + CH_3COOH$$

Ketals of acetone are obtained in a similar manner from isopropyl acetate.

β-Keto dimethyl acetals are obtained in 80 to 90% yield by the reaction of an absolute methanolic solution of sodium hydroxide at −10° with β-chlorovinyl ketones:[179]

$$RCOCH = CHCl + 2CH_3OH + NaOH \rightarrow RCOCH_2CH(OCH_3)_2 + NaCl + H_2O$$

β-Chlorovinyl ketones are formed in 60 to 80% yield through the reaction of acyl halides with acetylene in the presence of aluminum chloride:

$$RCOCl + HC \equiv CH \rightarrow RCOCH = CHCl$$

Ketals are formed by the addition of alcohols to acetylenic compounds in the presence of boron trifluoride and mercuric oxide.[180]

$$RC \equiv CH + 2R'OH \rightarrow RC(OR')_2CH_3$$

The reaction of alcohols with vinylacetylene results in the formation of β-alkoxyketals.[181]

$$CH_2 = CHC \equiv CH + 3ROH \rightarrow ROCH_2CH_2C(OR)_2CH_3$$

Glycols give cyclic acetals.[86] Allylacetylene, $CH_2 = CHCH_2C \equiv CR$, on the other hand, adds only two molecules of methanol to yield 5, 5-dimethoxy-1-alkenes,

$$CH_2 = CHCH_2C(OCH_3)_2R \quad ^{182}$$

Vapors of 2,3-butanedial passed over aluminum oxide heated at 350-400° give 2,4,5-trimethyl-2-ethyl-1,3-dioxocyclopentane:[88]

$$2CH_3CH(OH)CH(OH)CH_3 \rightarrow CH_3\overline{C(C_2H_5)OCH(CH_3)CH(CH_3)O} + 2H_2O$$

d-Glucose reacts with acetone to form diacetone glucose,

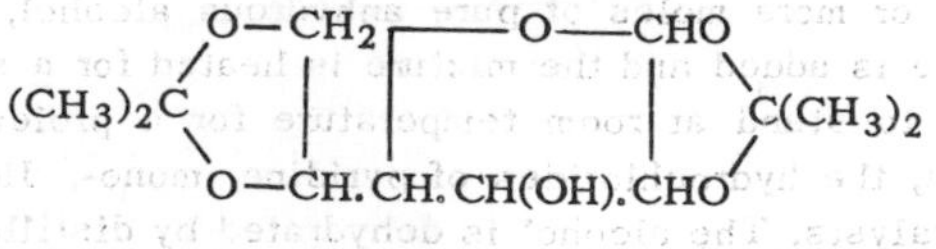

Hydrochloric acid, sulfuric acid and copper sulfate catalyze the reaction. Acetaldehyde is also an accelerator of the reaction. Monoacetone glucose is formed as a byproduct.

Benzal acetals of polyhydric alcohols may be obtained through the interaction of benzaldehyde and the alcohol in solution in a mixture of acetic acid and concentrated sulfuric acid, whereby the insoluble acetal separates out of solution. Mannite combines with three molecules of aldehyde; sorbite, erythrite and dulcite with two, while arabite and glucoheptite react with only one. Benzaldehyde reacting with glucose gives glucopyranose,

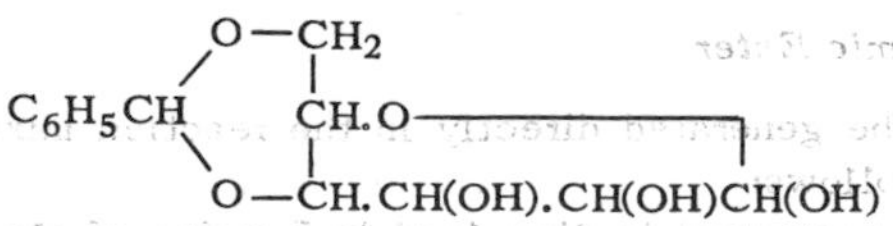

Glycol heated with *o*-nitrobenzaldehyde in a sealed tube at 150° for 30 hours gives *o*-nitrobenzylidene glycol, $NO_2C_6H_4\overline{CHOCH_2CH_2O}$

Fatty aromatic aldehydes in which the carbonyl group is separated from the

nucleus by one or more carbon atoms behave like aliphatic aldehydes. Acetals are obtained, for example, from phenylacetaldehyde, cinnamaldehyde and hydrocinnamaldehyde by direct reaction with an alcohol in the presence of hydrogen chloride.

While the method is applicable to benzaldehyde, with good results, low yields of acetals are obtained in general, although aromatic aldehydes which contain negative substituents are readily converted to acetals in good yield. Acetals are obtained, for example, by this method, in yields ranging from 70 to over 80% of theoretical, from *o*-nitro-, 2,4-dichloro- and 2-nitro-3,6-dichlorobenzaldehydes. It is a remarkable fact that steric hindrance due to *ortho* substitution is not observed in this reaction.

The reaction of phenols with aldehydes in the presence of acids generally leads to the formation of compounds of the type $RCH(C_6H_4OH)_2$. *Para*-substituted phenols form an exception, and yield acetals in the normal manner.

Preparation of Acetals by Use of Orthoformic Esters

A method of wide applicability for the preparation of acetals consists in the reaction of orthoformic esters or other ortho esters with carbonyl compounds:[7]

$$RR'CO + HC(OC_2H_5)_3 \rightarrow RR'C(OC_2H_5)_2 + HCOOC_2H_5$$

Ketals, i.e., acetals of ketones, which cannot be obtained by the direct action of alcohols with ketones, and acetals which are obtained only in poor yield by the direct method, may be prepared in good yield by this method.

Procedure

One molecule of the carbonyl compound is dissolved in a mixture of 1.1 moles of orthoformic ester and 3 or more moles of pure anhydrous alcohol, a small quantity of anhydrous ferric chloride is added and the mixture is heated for a short period or, alternatively, it is allowed to stand at room temperature for a prolonged period. Mineral acids, salts of ammonia, the hydrochlorides of pyridine, mono-, di- and triethyl amines may also be used as catalysts. The alcohol is dehydrated by distillation over sodium.

The amount of catalyst added has a marked influence on the yield of acetal. There is an optimum concentration of catalyst, and quantities lower than this optimum or in excess of it give less satisfactory yields. The use of a milder catalyst is generally desirable. There is also an optimum reaction period which should not be exceeded since otherwise side reactions which continue to take place are apt to decrease the yield of acetal seriously. The optimum time must be determined experimentally for each particular case.

Use of Nascent Orthoformic Ester

The ortho ester may be generated directly in the reaction mixture. The procedure to be followed is then as follows:

One mole of carbonyl compound is dissolved in 5 moles of alcohol and 1.25 moles of formiminoether hydrochloride of the alcohol are added gradually with stirring while the mixture is cooled. After the introduction of all of the iminoether, the liquid is kept in an ice chest for a time, and is then allowed to remain at room temperature for 4 to 8 days. In order to isolate the acetal a large quantity of ether is first added, the mixture is stirred and the precipitated ammonium chloride is filtered off, the filtrate is made slightly basic by the addition of a few drops of aqua ammonia and is shaken with ice water. The ether layer is then drawn off, dried over anhydrous potassium carbonate and the acetal is isolated by fractional distillation. The distillation is carried out under vacuum, if the acetal is of high molecular weight.

Lower boiling acetals, which are difficultly separated from the residual alcohol by distillation, may be purified by adding anhydrous calcium chloride to the crude acetal fraction and allowing the liquid to remain in contact with this compound for a long period. The calcium chloride absorbs the major portion of the remaining alcohol, and the comparatively pure acetal may be poured off.

It should be noted that forminoether hydrochlorides are unstable and should be made as they are needed. The mercuric chloride complex of forminoether hydrochlorides may be employed instead of the iminoether salts. This complex is obtained in good yield through the reaction of mercuric cyanide with alcohols in the presence of mercuric chloride and hydrochloric acid:[8]

$$Hg(CN)_2 + 2ROH + HgCl_2 + 4HCl \rightarrow 2HC(OR){:}NH.HCl.HgCl_2$$

The complex reacts readily with alcohols even at room temperature to give the orthoformic ester of the alcohol.

The velocity of acetal formation decreases with increase in the molecular weight of ketones. Ketones with a normal chain react more rapidly than those with branched chains. Yields of ketals obtained by this method from various ketones were as follows: acetone 90%, methyl ethyl ketone 88%, dimethyl ketone 87%, methyl hexyl ketone 85%, acetophenone 67%, propiophenone 64%, benzophenone 31%, methyl *tert*-butyl ketone 12%.[183]

Use of Orthosilicic Esters

Acetals may be prepared through the interaction of carbonyl compounds with orthosilicic esters. The reaction is carried out in alcoholic solution in the presence of mineral acids or compounds with an acid reaction.[9] This method presents the advantage that orthosilicic esters may be prepared readily from silicon tetrachloride but is not generally applicable.

The *procedure* is as follows: One mole of the carbonyl compound and 2 to 3 moles of the alcohol are mixed with 1.1 mole of orthosilicic ester and 10 cc of a saturated solution of hydrogen chloride in alcohol are added. The mixture is allowed to stand at room temperature for a few days, or heated under reflux for a short time.

The isolation of the ester is usually accomplished by fractionating the liquid and pouring the acetal fraction into 30% potassium hydroxide solution, using half a liter of this solution to every mole of ester, a treatment which decompose the excess orthosilicic ester. Esters of methyl and ethyl alcohol are decomposed by shaking the liquid at room temperature for 10 minutes, while orthosilicates of the higher alcohols require heating under reflux for a short period. Following this treatment, the alcoholic solution of the acetal is obtained free of silicic esters and may be separated, dried with potassium carbonate and fractionally distilled; or the organic components may be taken up in ether, the extract dried, and fractionated.[9]

Other ortho esters may also serve for the preparation of acetals by reaction with carbonyl compounds. Acetals may also be prepared through the interaction of dimethyl sulfite with carbonyl compounds.[10] Higher alkyl sulfites also react similarly to form higher acetals, but such acetals may be prepared more conveniently by heating the carbonyl compound with a mixture of dimethyl sulfite and the desired alcohol.

Acetals result by the reaction of aldehyde dichlorides with alkali metal alcoholates or phenolates:

$$RCHCl_2 + 2NaOR' \rightarrow RCH(OR')_2 + 2NaCl$$

This method is employed in cases where the acetal sought is not accessible by other methods.[11] The method is employed, in particular, for the preparation of acetals of phenols. The chloroether RCH(Cl)OR′ may be employed in place of the dichlorides. Acetals of chloral may be obtained by this route.[12]

Acetals of benzaldehyde are obtained readily by the cautious treatment of the solution of banzalaniline in the alcohol with a mineral acid. Gaseous hydrochloric acid or concentrated sulfuric acid may be used for the purpose.

Acetals of Ketenes

The simplest ketene acetal has been obtained from diethylsodio acetylorthoacetate, the intermediate in the synthesis of acetoacetic ester, by treatment with water:[13]

$$CH_3COCH_2C(ONa)(OC_2H_5)_2 \xrightarrow{H_2O} CH_2 = C(OC_2H_5)_2 + CH_3COONa$$

The compound is largely freed of alcohol and the unconverted ethyl acetate before being treated with water. Acyl ortho esters of the same type also result from the treatment of other carboxylic esters capable of enolization, by treatment with sodium ethoxide, and can be similarly converted to ketene acetals. Methyl ketene diethyl acetal, $CH_3CH = C(OC_2H_5)_2$, and ethoxy ketene diethyl acetal, $C_2H_5OCH = C(OC_2H_5)_2$, have been prepared by this method, but efforts, to prepare phenyl ketene acetal have failed. This latter has been obtained by the repeated distillation of ethyl orthophenylacetate, $C_6H_5CH_2C(OC_2H_5)_3$, under vacuum.[14]

Two general methods have been employed for the preparation of ketene acetals.[185] One depends on the dehydrohalogenation of α-halo acetals, which is brought about by treatment with potassium *tert*-butoxide in solution in *tert*-butane:

$$BrCH_2CH(OC_2H_5)_2 + KOC(CH_3)_3 \rightarrow CH_2 = C(OC_2H_5)_2 + KBr + HOC(CH_3)_3$$

Primary and secondary alkoxides cannot be used in the reaction, since they tend to react additively with the ketene acetal. The method is not applicable to alkyl halo acetals $AlkCHXCH(OC_2H_5)_2$ owing to the preferential formation of α,β-unsaturated acetals by elimination of the elements of a hydrogen halide.

Removal of the bromine atom and an alkoxy group from α-bromo ortho esters forms the basis of the second method:[186]

$$RCHBrC(OC_2H_5)_3 + 2Na \rightarrow RCH = C(OC_2H_5)_2 + NaBr + NaOC_2H_5$$

This method is not suitable for the preparation of phenylketene acetal from the ortho ester of phenylbromoacetic acid.

Pyrolysis of aliphatic ortho esters yield ketene acetals only when a negative substituent is present in α-position.

Ethyl diethoxyorthoacetate has been converted to diethoxyketene diethyl acetal in 39% yield by the action of sodium ethoxide:[187]

$$(C_2H_5O)_2CHC(OC_2H_5)_3 + NaOC_2H_5 \rightarrow C_2H_5OH + (C_2H_5O)_2CNaC(OC_2H_5)_3$$
$$\rightarrow (C_2H_5O)_2C = C(OC_2H_5)_2 + C_2H_5ONa$$

Ketene diphenyl acetal results when an alkaline phenoxide is made to react with trichloroethane:

$$CH_3CCl_3 + 3C_6H_5ONa \rightarrow CH_2 = C(OC_6H_5)_2 + C_6H_5OH + 3NaCl$$

The interesting compound $C(OC_2H_5)_2$, which may be considered as the acetal derived from carbon monixide, results when chloroethoxymethylene, C_2H_5OCCl, is treated with an alkaline ethoxide. Chloroethoxymethylene is obtained from the reaction product of ethyl formate and sodium ethoxide by treatment with phosphorus trichloride.

Ketene acetal and its homologs, like the corresponding ketenes, are highly reactive. Ketene acetals polymerize under the influence of even traces of acids.[188] A cyclic trimer, 1,1,3,3,5,5-hexaethoxycyclohexane is obtained from this acetal by the action of hydrogen fluoride. Methylketene diacetal is converted to ethyl propionate when treated with hydrogen fluoride:[189]

$$CH_3CH = C(OC_2H_5)_2 + HF \rightarrow CH_3CH_2CF(OC_2H_5)_2$$
$$\rightarrow CH_3CH_2COOC_2H_5 + C_2H_5F$$

Diene type addition reactions take place between certain ketene acetals and maleic anhydride, in which two molecules of the ketene acetal react simultaneously as if they formed a diene. 3,4-Ethoxyphthalic anhydride is obtained from ketene diethylacetal and maleic anhydride:[190]

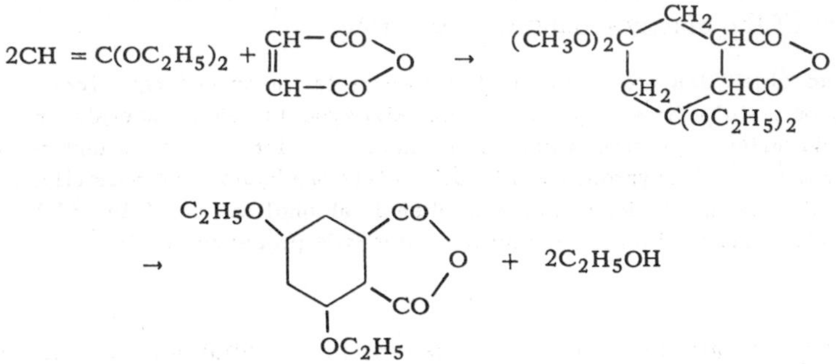

Dimethylmaleic anhydride fails to give an adduct.

Benzoquinone reacts additively with ketene diethyl acetal; the addition product yields homogenistic acid when hydrolyzed:[191]

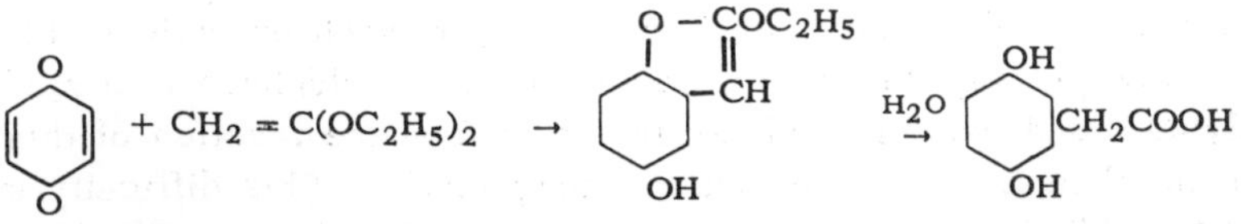

Other quinones give similar addition products, although generally in poor yield.

Hydrolysis of Acetals

Acetals are notable for their stability toward alkalies but they are readily decomposed under the action of dilute minearl acids. The ease of hydrolysis depends upon the character of both the carbonyl and alcohol constituents. The rate of hydrolysis increases with increase in the molecular weight of the carbonyl or the alkyl constituent. Acetals of secondary alcohols are decomposed more rapidly than those of primary alcohols. As an illustration of the great differences in the rates of decomposition, it may be noted that the ethyl acetal of acetone decomposes several thousand times more rapidly than acetaldehyde ethyl acetal, while this latter is hydrolyzed hundreds of times more rapidly than formaldehyde ethyl acetal. The decomposition of the ethyl ketal of acetone and other ketals of aliphatic alcohols proceeds rapidly in the cold under the action of dilute acids; this is true also of the acetals of β-hydroxypropionaldehyde and acrolein.[15] The rate of hydrolysis increases in direct proportion to the hydrogen ion concentration. Acetals of the heterocyclic series are rapidly hydrolyzed.

Hydrolysis of acetals generally requires, however, boiling under reflux with about 5% sulfuric acid for several hours.[16] Acetals which are insoluble in water may be successfully hydrolyzed by heating with a mixture of 25% aqueous sulfuric acid and a volume of acetic acid equal to that of the acetal. The use of concentrated hydrochloric acid may be of advantage occasionally, as in the case of aminoacetal.

Organic acids or anhydrides are used if the carbonyl compounds resulting from hydrolysis are susceptible to change under the action of strong mineral acids. Decomposition with anhydrides is accompanies with the formation of an ester of the acid. Acid halides may also be employed for the purpose, providing the use of an excess is avoided. An excess of acid chloride causes the replacement of the alkoxy groups with chlorine.

Few amino aldehydes are stable in the free state; many undergo aldol condensation when freed, or yield polymeric Schiff bases. Alkoxyacetaldehyde acetals are difficult to hydrolyze and under the vigorous conditions necessary for hydrolysis undergo condensation reactions.[222] β-Alkoxypropionaldehyde acetals are hydrolyzed normally, but β-phenoxypropionaldehyde acetal decomposes to phenol, alcohol and acrolein.[223] Hydrolysis of glycolaldehyde acetal and α-bromophenylacetaldehyde proceeds poorly.[224]

Methylenedioxy groups, $CH_2\begin{matrix}/O-\\ \backslash O-\end{matrix}$, present in formaldehyde acetals of *o*-dihydroxy aromatic compounds, such as in piperonal and its derivates, do not show the ready tendency to hydrolysis characteristic of other types of acetals. They resemble rather phenolic ethers, and are only hydrolyzed on prolonged heating with moderately concentrated sulfuric acid. Since formaldehyde is a product of the hydrolysis, condensation products resulting from the reaction of this aldehyde with the phenols generated cause a complication. This difficulty may be eliminated by adding to the reaction mixture other phenolic compounds capable of reacting more readily with the formaldehyde formed. Phlorglucinol or resorcinol may be used for this purpose.

The procedure is to add the methylenedioxy compound and an equivalent quantity of phlorglucinol or resorcinol to sulfuric acid of sp.g. 1.39, in an amount equal to ten times the weight of the compound to be hydrolyzed, and to heat on a boiling water bath for a period of 10 to 15 hours.

The hydrolysis may be accomplished more rapidly with concentrated sulfuric acid at room temperature, providing the compound is not basic and resists sulfonation. The same proportion of acid is used by weight as above, and the reaction is complete within 2 to 5 hours. Treatment with concentrated hydrochloric acid in a shaking autoclave at 100-130° also accomplishes the purpose. In either case, the reaction is carried out in the presence of phlorglucinol or resorcinol, in order to prevent attack of the phenol generated by formaldehyde.

Pyrolysis of acetals of unsaturated aldehydes results in the formation of conjugated unsaturated systems. 1-Ethoxybutadiene, $CH_2=CHCH=CHOC_2H_5$, is obtained in 80% yield, for example, when crotonaldehyde diethyl acetal is passed at 350° and under 14 atm pressure over primary sodium phosphate supported on pumice.[225] Butin-2-al-acetal, $CH_3C\equiv CCH(OC_2H_5)_2$, treated with potassium hydroxide, is converted to 1-alkoxy-buten-(1)-in-(3), $CH\equiv CCH=CHOC_2H_5$, which changes to butin-(3)- al-(1), $CH\equiv CCH_2CHO$, on treatment with hydrochloric acid.[226]

Acetals are resistant to the action of many reducing and oxidizing agents. Among oxidizing agents only ozone seems to attack acetals, a fact which may be related to the autoxidation tendency of acetals.

Hydrazines and hydroxylamine fail to react with acetals in alkaline solution, but reaction proceeds readily in acid medium.

MERCAPTALS

Formation of Mercaptals

Mercaptans are also capable of forming compounds of the type of acetals by reaction with carbonyl compounds in the presence of hydrogen chloride:[17]

$$>CO + 2HSC_2H_5 \rightarrow >C(SC_2H_5)_2 + H_2O$$

The reaction apparently takes place in two steps. The resulting compounds are termed mercaptals, or mercaptols when derived from ketones. The reaction proceeds less readily with ketones. Cyclic mercaptans have been prepared from difunctional mercaptans of the type $HS(CH_2)_nSH$.

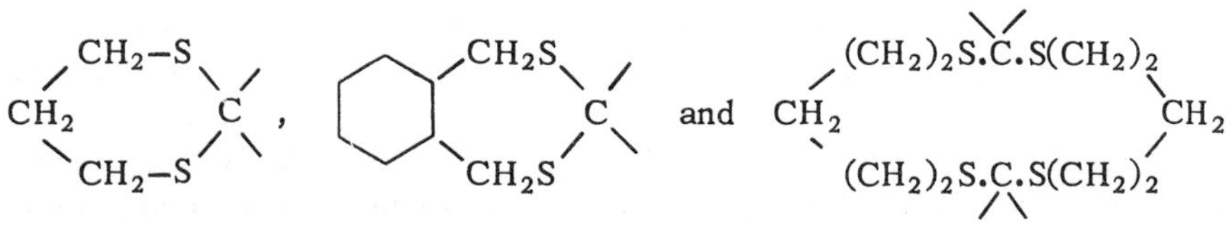

are examples.[18]

In contrast to acetals, mercaptals and mercaptols are quite stable toward acids. The hydrogen atom in the group $-CH(SR)_2$ in mercaptals is reactive and may be replaced with alkali metals by reaction with caustic, and for this reason mercaptals are more soluble in aqueous alkalies than in water.

Mercaptals may be converted to the corresponding aldehydes by treatment in acetone solution with mercuric chloride.[227] The mercuric chloride is generally employed in admixture with cadmium carbonate or mercuric oxide.[228] The mercaptal group may be reduced to a methyl group by treatment with a large excess of Raney nickel.

HYDRATES AND PEROXIDES

Hydrate Formation

Certain aldehydes react with water to form relatively stable hydrates. The reaction is, of course, strictly comparable with acetal formation from aldehydes and alcohols:

$$RCHO + H_2O \rightarrow RCH(OH)_2$$

Hydrate formation is observed with aldehydes showing the greatest tendency to form acetals. These include formaldehyde, fluoral, glyoxal, glyoxylic acid, phenylglyoxal, chloral, sodium acetaldehydedisulfonate, phenoxyacetaldehyde, tetrahydrofurfurylhydroxyacetaldehyde, chloroacetaldehyde, heterocyclic aldehydes containing the grouping $N = C(-C)CHO$, such as quinoline- and 3-hydroxyquinoline-2-aldehyde. Fluoral hydrate appears to possess the greatest stability. *Ortho*-derivatives of aldehydes, RCH(OH)OCH(OH)R, are formed through the addition of a molecular equivalent of aldehyde hydrate to one of the aldehyde.

Half acetals of aldehydes, RCH(OH)OR′, are more stable than the corresponding aldehyde hydrates. Aliphatic aldehydes are generally present in alcoholic solution in part as half acetals; the proportion of the latter may be as high as 50% of the total aldehyde.

Peroxides from Carbonyl Compounds[230]

1-Hydroxyalkyl hydroperoxides are formed through the reaction of hydrogen peroxide with carbonyl compounds in non-aqueous media:[231]

$$RR'CO + H_2O_2 \rightarrow RR'C(OH)OOH$$

Bis-(1-hydroxyalkyl)-Peroxides, RR′C(OH)O.OC(OH)RR′, are formed when the reaction is carried out in an aqueous medium, or when an excess of carbonyl compound is used.[232] The compound derived from formaldehyde is unstable and explosive; higher members of the series are stable at ordinary temperature. Bishydroperoxides prepared from normal carbonyl compounds with more than seven carbon atoms are solids.

Alkyl-1-hydroxyalkyl peroxides are obtained by the interaction of a hydroperoxide with an excess of aldehyde or ketone in the presence of an acid catalyst in ethereal solution:[233]

$$RR'CO + R''OOH \rightarrow RR'C(OH)OOR''$$

Alkyl-1-hydroxyalkyl peroxides are in general liquids sufficiently stable to be distilled without decomposition.

Peroxyacetals are formed when an aldehyde or ketone is allowed to react with an excess of a hydroperoxide in the presence of an acid: [234]

$$RR'CO + 2R''OOH \rightarrow RR'C(OOR'')_2 + H_2O$$

The reaction occurs more readily with ketones than with aldehydes.

OTHER ADDITIVE COMPOUNDS

Formation of Esters of the Type RCH(OCOR')$_2$

Anhydrides of certain acids react with aldehydes in the presence of a small quantity of sulfuric acid or other catalyst to form addition compounds which are esters of the unstable hydrated form of the aldehyde, $RCH(OH)_2$: [19]

$$RCHO + (R'CO)_2O \rightarrow RCH(OCOR')_2$$

Ketones do not seem to undergo this reaction.

Reaction with Acid Chlorides

Acid chlorides react with many carbonyl compounds to form α-chloroalkyl esters as the initial product of the reaction:

$$\text{>CO} + \text{ClCOR} \rightarrow \text{C}\underset{\text{Cl}}{\overset{\text{OCOR}}{<}}$$

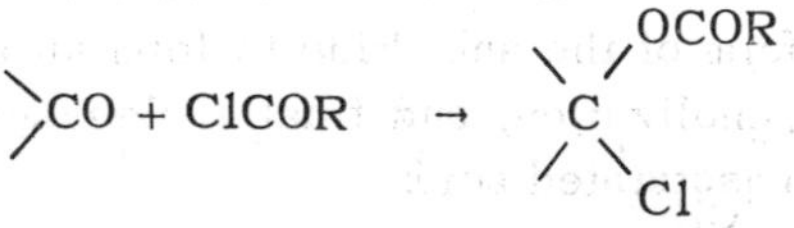

These chloroesters are unstable and lose hydrogen chloride, and are thereby transformed to the ester of an unsaturated alcohol: [20]

$$\begin{array}{c} R' \\ \diagdown \\ R''CH_2 \end{array} C \begin{array}{c} OCOR \\ \diagup \\ \diagdown \\ Cl \end{array} \rightarrow \begin{array}{c} R' \\ \diagdown \\ R''CH \end{array} COCOR$$

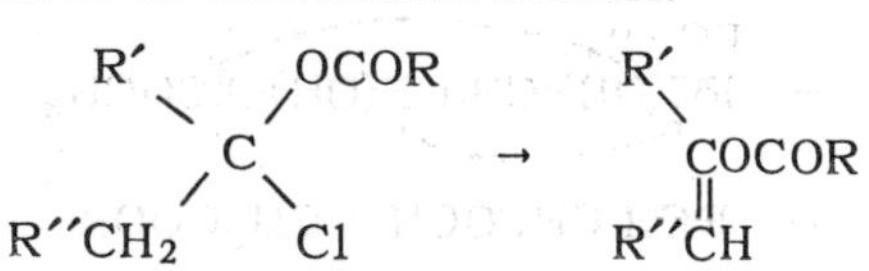

Reaction with Alkyl Halides

Alkyl halides are capable of reacting with carbonyl compounds to form α-chloroethers. The reaction may be carried out, for example, by saturating a mixture of the aldehyde and alcohol with hydrogen chloride: [21]

$$CH_3CHO + C_2H_5Cl \rightarrow CH_3CH\underset{C_2H_5}{\overset{Cl}{<}}$$

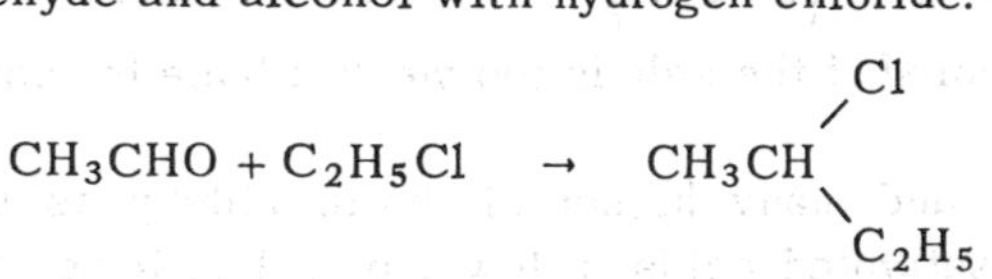

Hydrogen chloride also gives addition products with carbonyl compounds, but ether formation takes place simultaneously and the final product is an α-dichloroether:

$$2CH_3CHO + 2HCl \rightarrow 2CH_3CH\begin{matrix} Cl \\ OH \end{matrix} \rightarrow (CH_3CHCl)_2O + H_2O$$

REACTION WITH METHYLENE GROUPS; PERKIN, CLAISEN AND KNOEVENAGEL CONDENSATIONS

The carbonyl group in aldehydes and ketones is capable of reaction with methyl or methylene groups in certain compounds. *Aldol condensation,* discussed in Chapter 4, is a reaction of this type.

Perkin Reaction[22]

A reaction of aldehydes with the α-methylene group in carboxylic acids, involving the elimination of a molecule of water and the formation of an α,β-unsaturated acid is known as the Perkin reaction. It is generally brought about by heating a mixture of the aldehyde with the anhydride and the alkaline salt of the acid:

$$RCHO + H_2C(R')COONa \rightarrow RCH = C(R')COONa + H_2O$$

This reaction was discovered by Bertagnini,[23] and was first carefully studied by Perkin. It ranks among the most important in organic synthesis.

The present view of the mechanism of the reaction[24] is that the aldehyde reacts with the enolic form of the anhydride to form an aldol type of compound, which itself undergoes enolization, and finally cleavage takes place resulting in the formation of the unsaturated acid:

$$RCHO + CH_2 = C(OH)OCOCH_3 \rightarrow \underset{(I)}{RCOCH_2CH(OH)OCOCH_3}$$

$$\rightarrow RC(OH){:}CH.CH(OH)O|COCH_3$$

$$\rightarrow RCH{:}CHCOCH + CH_3COOH$$

The salt acts merely as a base, and promotes the enolization of the anhydride and of the addition product. Cleavage of the first addition product (I) may occur in such a manner as to give an aldehyde:

$$RCOCH_2CH(OH)|OCOCH_3 \rightarrow RCOCH_2CHO + CH_3COOH$$

This reaction is favored if the salt is too weak a base to induce the enolization of (I).

Isobutyraldehyde and many higher aliphatic aldehydes ungergo the Perkin reaction, giving unsaturated acids in low yield. The lower aliphatic aldehydes do not react well, giving extremely low yields of the unsaturated acid, or undergo reaction in an entirely different direction. The reaction generally proceeds well with aromatic aldehydes.

Procedure

The application of the reaction to the preparation of cinnamic acid from benzaldehyde and acetic anhydride may serve to illustrate the procedure: A mixture of two parts by weight of benzaldehyde with three parts of acetic anhydride and one part freshly fused sodium acetate is heated for about eight hours at 175-180°. The melt is then poured into water and the unconverted benzaldehyde is removed by distillation with steam. The residual liquid is decolorized with carbon, cooled and acidified to precipitate the cinnamic acid which is filtered, washed and dried.

The use of an indifferent solvent, such as toluene or nitrobenzene, causes a marked drop in the yield and may even inhibit the reaction completely.

Acetic acid exerts a retarding effect in many cases and its removal by distillation usually increases the yield considerably.

Potassium salts are more effective catalysts than sodium salts. Alkali carbonates, especially potassium carbonate, are also effective catalysts. Pyridine often promotes the reaction. The salt may be replaced by a tertiary base. The catalytic effect of the base is greater in proportion to its strength. Increase in the quantity of the base produces an increase in the yield, up to a certain point, beyond which an increase in the amount of the amine causes a decrease in yield. The optimum quantity of the base, i.e., the amount producing the best yield, is smaller the stronger the base.

Extensive decarboxylation in the course of the reaction has been observed in exceptional cases, as for example with isovaleric acid,[25] although it may take place in many other cases to a slight extent and become marked at excessively high temperatures.

Benzaldehyde, reacting with acetic anhydride under the normal conditions of the Perkin reaction, gives cinnamic acid in moderate yield; about 45-50% in the time usually allowed to the reaction. The presence of a strong negative substituent in the *o*- or *p*-position has a marked favorable action on the yield of the cinnamic acid.[26] Nitro groups exert a greater effect than chlorine. 2,6-Dichlorobenzaldehyde gives a better yield than 2-chlorobenzaldehyde, but 2,4-dinitrobenzaldehyde gives a somewhat lower yield than 2-nitrobenzaldehyde. A hydroxy group in the *p*-position exerts a moderately favorable effect, though 3,5-dihydroxybanzaldehyde does not react. Methoxy groups in the *o*-position have no effect, but exert an unfavorable influence if present in the *p*-position.

Methyl groups cause a marked decrease in the reaction rate and the yield. The effect of substitution in various positions decreases in the order *ortho* > *meta* > *para*. 2,4,6-Trimethylbenzaldehyde gives the corresponding cinnamic acid only in 7-8% yield. The methyl groups in the 2 and 6 positions inhibit the reaction completely. A dimethylamino group in the *p*-position also inhibits the reaction. The inhibitive effect of methyl groups may be counteracted by nitro groups. Ethyl and phenyl groups generally exert a more marked retarding influence than methyl groups.

Hydroxyl groups in the *meta* and *para* position are acylated in the course of the reaction; *o*-hydroxybenzaldehyde yields a coumarin. Aminocinnamic acids cannot be prepared directly from aminobenzaldehydes and must be obtained indirectly from the nitrated acids by reduction.

The Perkin synthesis has been carried out with generally good results with the following aldehydes: 4-cyanobenzaldehyde, 4-carbethoxybenzaldehyde, cinnamaldehyde, 1-naphthaldehyde, 4-bromo-1-naphthaldehyde, furfural and 2-thiophenealdehyde. 2-Naphthaldehyde and 2-hydroxy-2-naphthaldehyde give lower yields of the unsaturated acids.

Bifunctional aldehydes are generally converted to diacrylic acids.[27] Such acids are obtained, for example, from phthaladehyde, isophthalaldehyde, and terephthalaldehyde. The last named may be converted to a monoacrylic acid under mild conditions. 2-Formylcinnamic aldehyde gives a mixture of mono and diacrylic acids.

Perkin's reaction is applicable to phthalic anhydride, one of the carboxyl groups in this compound acting as an aldehyde function.[28]

Simple aliphatic and aromatic ketones do not undergo the reaction. On the other hand α-keto acids react to form unsaturated acids with loss of the carboxyl group originally present in the keto acids:[29]

$$RCOCOOH + (CH_3CO)_2O \rightarrow RCH = CHCOOH + CO_2 + CH_3COOH$$

In the Perkin synthesis union takes place between the carbonyl carbon of the aldehyde with the α-methylene group in the acid. The reaction is practically limited, for this reason, to acids of the type RCH_2COOH, *i.e., mono-substituted* acetic acids. Acids in which R is a straight chain alkyl residue react readily. Higher homologs of acetic acid react at lower temperatures and give somewhat better yields of the unsaturated acids than acetic acid. While isocaproic acid reacts normally, isovaleric acid gives only a small yield of the unsaturated acid, decarboxylation taking place with the formation of an unsaturated hydrocarbon as the principal product.

Crotonic acid, reacting in the form of its anhydride with benzaldehyde, in the presence of a tertiary base, gives the vinyl cinnamic acid,

$$C_6H_5CH = C(CH = CH_2)COOH,$$

in 40% yield; β,β-dimethylacrylic anhydride gives α-isopropenylcinnamic acid in 38% yield.

Phenylacetic acid, in common with other acetic acid derivatives with an activating substituent, is highly reactive; on the other hand, β-phenylpropionic acid and γ-phenylburytic acid are much less reactive. The latter, reacting with benzaldehyde in the presence of acetic anhydride and the usual catalyst, gives α-phenylcinnamic acid in only 14% yield.[30] The vinylog of phenylacetic acid, $C_6H_5CH = CHCH_2COOH$, reacts in a satisfactory manner.

Succinic acid is capable of reacting with aromatic as well as with aliphatic aldehydes, but the primary product is a γ-substituted paraconic acid:

$$RCHO + HOCOCH_2CH_2COOH \rightarrow \overline{RCHCH(COOH)CH_2COO} + H_2O$$

On heating, these compounds lose water and carbon dioxide and are thereby converted to unsaturated acids:

$$\overline{RCHCH(COOH)CH_2COO} \rightarrow RCH = CHCH_2COOH + CO_2$$

A small quantity of an α,γ-butyrolactone is also formed simultaneously. The paraconic acid and the unsaturated acid are often obtained together at the temperatures at which the reaction is carried out, the proportion of the unsaturated acid rising with increasing temperature. The usual procedure is to heat the mixture of the sodium salt of the acid and the aldehyde with acetic anhydride.[31] Phenylsuccinic acid gives with benzaldehyde β,γ-diphenylvinylacetic acid,[32] $C_6H_5CH = C(C_6H_5)CH_2COOH$. Cinnamaldehyde reacts with succinic acid to form the diethenyl acid in low yield, with a large proportion of 2,5-diphenylphenol. On heating two molecular proportions of cinnamaldehyde with one of succinic acid in the presence of acetic anhydride and litharge, 1,8-diphenyloctatetrene is obtained. Glutaric acid, $HOCO(CH_2)_3COOH$, reacts poorly with benzaldehyde, but phenylglutaric acid reacts in a fairly satisfactory manner to form γ,δ-diphenyl-γ,δ-pentenoic acid:

$$C_6H_5CHO + HOCOCH(C_6H_5)CH_2CH_2COOH$$
$$\rightarrow \quad C_6H_5CH = C(C_6H_5)CH_2CH_2COOH + CO_2 + H_2O$$

α-Aryloxyacetic acids generally react well in the Perkin synthesis. Thiodiglycolic acid, $S(CH_2COOH)_2$, reacts with two molecular proportions of benzaldehyde forming α-thio-bis-cinnamic acid,[33] $S[C(:CHC_6H_5)COOH]_2$. α-Halo acids do not react, or react only to a very slight extent.

Many derivatives of aminoacetic acids undergo the Perkin reaction with aromatic aldehydes. Hippuric acid gives an azlactone in good yield (Erlenmeyer's azlactone synthesis):[34]

$$C_6H_5CHO + H_2C(NHCOC_6H_5)COOH \rightarrow C_6H_5CH = \overline{CN:C(C_6H_5)O.CO} + 2H_2O$$

Acetylaminoacetic acid behaves similarly. Acylated N-phenyl acetic acids fail to undergo this reaction.

Azlactones may be hydrolyzed in steps to α-acylaminocinnamic acids and to arylpyruvic acids:[35]

$$RCH = \overline{CN = C(R').OCO} \xrightarrow{H_2O} RCH = C(NHCOR')COOH$$
$$\rightarrow RCH_2C(=NCOR')COOH \rightarrow RCH_2COCOOH$$

Azlactones derived from acetylaminoacetic acid are preferable for this purpose since they are more readily hydrolyzed. On oxidation with hydrogen peroxide, the arylpyruvic acids are converted to arylacetic acids.

Creatine condenses with benzaldehyde on heating in the presence of acetic anhydride and sodium acetate to N-acetylbenzalcreatine,

$$C_6H_5CH = \overline{CN(CH_3)C(=NCOCH_3)NHCO}$$

This condensation can be carried out also with other aromatic aldehydes. The resulting products may be converted to β-substituted N-methylalanines,[36] $RCH_2CH(NHCH_3)COOH$.

Hydantoin and acetylthiohydantoin also undergo the Perkin condensation with aromatic aldehydes, giving $RCH{=}\overline{CNHCONHCO}$ and $RCH = \overline{CN(COCH_3)CSNHCO}$ respectively. The acetylthiohydantoin condensation product may be obtained in excellent yield when the aldehyde and acetylthiohydantoin are made to react in pyridine solution in the presence of a small amount of piperidine or diethylamine. This type of condensation takes place also with rhodanine, $H_2\overline{CSCSNHCO}$. The condensation products may be converted by hydrolysis with caustic to arylthiopyruvic acids:

$$RCH = \overline{CSCSNHCO} \rightarrow RCH = C(SH)COOH \rightarrow RCH_2CSCOOH$$

They may also be transformed to other compounds, such as arylalanines, arylacetonitriles, etc.[37]

When the Perkin reaction is applied to isobutyric acid, a compound in which the α-carbon bears but one atom of hydrogen, the acyl derivative of a β-hydroxy acid is obtained,[38] partly in the form of the mixed anhydride with isobutyric acid. On stronger heating this loses a molecule of isobutyric acid and is simultaneously decarboxylated, giving an unsaturated hydrocarbon:

$$\underset{\displaystyle OCOCH(CH_3)_2}{RCHC(CH_3)_2COOH} \rightarrow RCH = C(CH_3)_2 + (CH_3)_2CHCOOH + CO_2$$

This transformation takes place at about 100° with the furfural derivative.[39]

Claisen Condensation

Aldehydes undergo condensation with esters of the type RCH_2COOR' in the presence of metallic sodium or sodium ethylate to form unsaturated esters[40] $R''CH = C(R)COOR'$. The mechanism of the reaction parallels that of acetoacetic ester condensation. An addition compound of the ester and sodium ethylate is first formed which is transformed into an unsaturated sodio ether; an addition compound between this ether and the aldehyde forms next, and through a molecular rearrangement and cleavage of sodium hydroxide, changes to the unsaturated ester:

$$CH_3COOC_2H_5 \xrightarrow{NaOC_2H_5} CH_3C(ONa)(OC_2H_5)_2$$

$$\rightarrow CH_2 = C(ONa)OC_2H_5 \xrightarrow{RCHO} \underline{RCH.CH_2C(O})(ONa)OC_2H_5$$

$$\rightarrow RCH = CHC(OH)(ONa)OC_2H_5 \rightarrow RCH = CHCOOC_2H_5 + NaOH$$

Amides of alkali metals are excellent catalysts for the reaction, but they tend to form some amide byproducts.[196]

In the Claisen reaction as in that of Perkin, union with the carbonyl carbon takes place at the α-carbon in the acid.

Claisen's reaction often proceeds quite smoothly, giving the unsaturated ester in excellent yield, and has the further advantage over Perkin's method that the final product can be readily obtained in a pure form, since it is not accompanied by impurities that are difficult to eliminate. The condensation between benzaldehyde and ethyl acetate proceeds quite well, for example, at a temperature in the neighborhood of 0°, giving ethyl cinnamate in 68 to 74% yield.

The usual procedure is to dissolve the aldehyde in the ester, and to add a little alcohol and metallic sodium cut in small pieces. The mixture is cooled and agitated during the reaction. The methyl esters react particularly well.

The Claisen reaction proceeds readily with succinic esters.[41] Ketones as well as aldehydes may be condensed with these esters. One or both methylene groups may be made to react. The compounds obtained by the condensation of two aldehyde molecules, $HOCOC(=CHR)C(=CHR)COOH$, are known as fulginic acids; their anhydrides, termed fulgides, show the interesting phenomenon of thermochromy and phototropy, i.e., undergo change of color on heating and upon being subjected to the action of light rays.[42] In a number of instances the condensation of ketones with esters assumes a normal course at low temperatures, while at higher temperatures alcoholysis takes place with decomposition of the α,γ-diketone.

The condensation of aldehydes and ketones with α-chloro esters in the presence of alkaline substances results in the formation of glycid carboxylic acids,

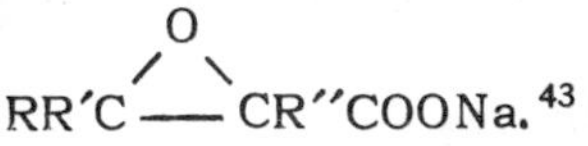

$$RR'C \overset{O}{\overset{/\backslash}{-\!\!-\!\!-}} CR''COONa.$$ [43] Sodium amide is the best catalyst for this reaction.

Ketones in which the carbonyl group is situated between two tertiary carbon atoms are cleaved into a hydrocarbon and an amide when boiled with sodamide in benzene or toluene solution:

$$(CH_3)_3CCOC(CH_3)_3 \overset{NaNH_2}{\longrightarrow} (CH_3)_3CCONH_2 + HC(CH_3)_3$$

$$(CH_3)_3CCOC_6H_5 \overset{NaNH_2}{\longrightarrow} (CH_3)_3CCONH_2 + C_6H_6$$

The Claisen condensation of phenylpropiolic ester with acetophenone results in the formation of products which cyclize spontaneously to γ-pyrone derivatives:[197]

$$C_6H_5C \equiv CCOOC_2H_5 + C_6H_5COCH_3 \longrightarrow [C_6H_5C \equiv CCOCH_2COC_6H_5]$$

$$\longrightarrow C_6H_5 - \underset{O}{\overset{CO}{\bigcirc\!\!\!\bigcirc}} - C_6H_5$$

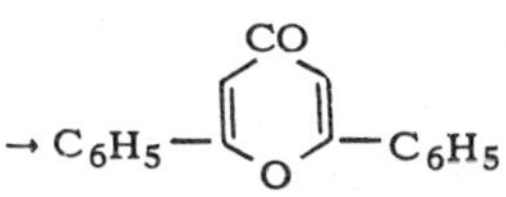

6-Phenyl-2,3-indeno-γ-pyrone has been obtained through the condensation of phenylpropiolic ester with α-hydrindone:[198]

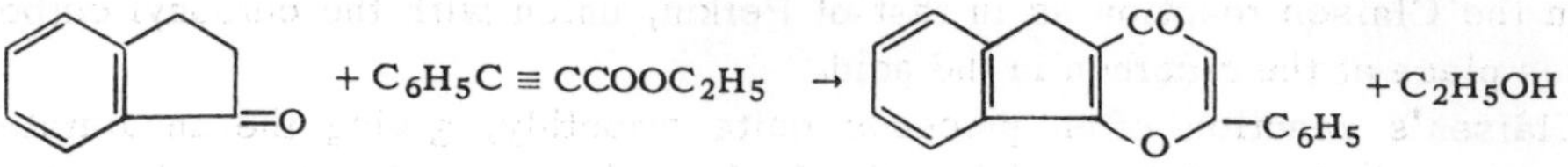

The condensation of phenylpropiolic ester with desoxybenzoin gives 4,5,6-triphenyl-α-pyrone:

$$C_6H_5CH_2COC_6H_5 + C_6H_5C \equiv CCOOC_2H_5$$

$$\rightarrow O\langle\begin{matrix} CO-CH \\ C_6H_5-C=C-C_6H_5 \end{matrix}\rangle CC_6H_5 + C_2H_5OH$$

A reaction between an aromatic aldehyde and acetaldehyde leading to the formation of an unsaturated aldehyde, $RCH = CHCHO$, is known as the *Claisen-Schmidt Condensation*. It takes place under the action of aqueous alkalies. It may be regarded as an aldol condensation, and probably involves the formation of an aldol as the first stage in the reaction, followed by dehydration, giving the unsaturated aldehyde:

$$C_6H_5CHO + H_3CCHO \rightleftharpoons C_6H_5CH(OH)CH_2CHO$$

$$\rightarrow C_6H_5CH = CHCHO + H_2O$$

Condensation takes place simultaneously, to some extent, between two molecules of acetaldehyde, giving the corresponding aldol, β-hydroxybutyraldehyde.

An important extension of this reaction is the condensation of benzaldehyde with crotonaldehyde, resulting in the formation of a series of polyene aldehydes.

Condensations with Reactive Methylene Groups – Knoevenagel Type Condensations

The reaction of a carbonyl group with a methylene group proceeds with particular ease when there are attached to the latter certain types of radicals which exert an activating influence varying in degree in accordance with their character. Among such radicals are the carboxyl and related groups as, for example, the ester residue $-COOR$, amide groups $-CONH_2$ or $-CONHR$, the cyano group; also carbonyl groups, aromatic radicals, the thionyl group, arylsulfonyl groups, $ArSO_2$-, nitro groups, nitroso groups and carbon atoms with ethylenic or acetyl-bonds. The activating influence comes to evidence best when two of these groups are attached to a methylene. The methylene group in dibenzoylmethane does not react in the normal manner, as the compound presumably exists in the enol form $C_6H_5C(OH) = CHCOC_6H_5$.

The activating influence is manifested in a remarkable manner in methyl groups attached to certain nitrated aromatic radicals, the pyridine or quinoline nucleus and finally the pyrylium group. Thus, the methyl group in 2,4-dinitrotoluene, 2-cyano-4-nitrotoluene, α-and γ-picolines,

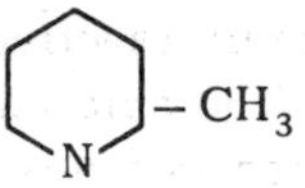

and

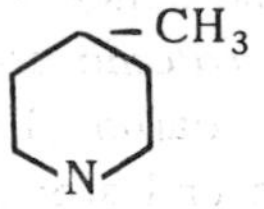

in quinaldine,

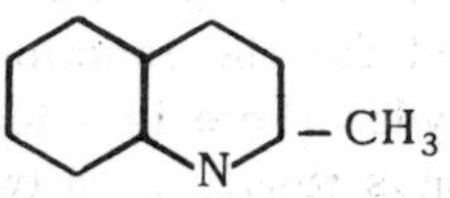

in 2- and 4-methyl diphenyl pyrylium salts,

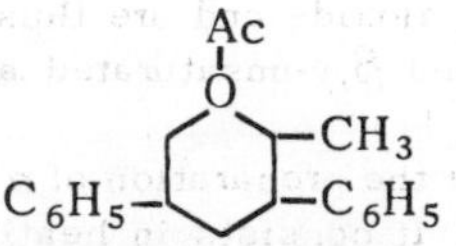

and

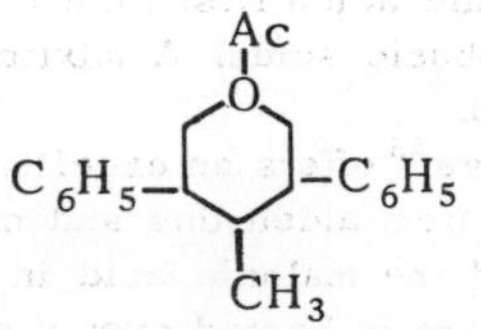

are reactive, and under the proper conditions are capable of condensing with carbonyl groups.

The reaction between a carbonyl compound and a compound containing an active methylene group usually involves molecular proportions of each reactant, resulting in the formation of an unsaturated product:

$$C_6H_5CHO + H_2C(COOC_2H_5)_2 \rightarrow C_6H_5CH=C(COOC_2H_5)_2 + H_2O$$

With some carbonyl compounds combination takes place with two molecules of the methylene compound. For example, aliphatic aldehydes combine with two molecules of malonic ester:

$$CH_3CHO + 2H_2C(COOC_2H_5)_2 \rightarrow CH_3CH[CH(COOC_2H_5)_2]_2 + H_2O$$

Products derived through the condensation of aldehydes with malonic acid may undergo decarboxylation. Decarboxylation may be brought about in most instances by drastic treatment during the initial reaction. Condensation products with cyanoacetic acid may also be decarboxylated.

Except in a few isolated cases, the reaction between carbonyl compounds and compounds with an active methylene proceeds only in the presence of catalysts. Alkali metal alcoholates, which are the condensing agents employed in the Claisen reaction, may serve as catalysts, but as a general rule, the reaction is best catalyzed with secondary bases, especially piperidine. Ammonia and primary amines may also serve the purpose. Small quantities of acid added to the base have a beneficial effect. In many cases a mixture in equivalent quantities of piperidine and acetic acid to which a little alcohol has been added is a particularly good catalyst.[81] It would appear that the amine gives an addition product with the carbonyl compound, such as RCH(OH)NHR′, which then reacts with the methylene group to form the final unsaturated body.[44]

Dehydrating agents, like acetic acid, zinc chloride, etc., have also been used effectively to bring about the condensation.

The methylene group in *malonic acid* is highly reactive because of the presence in the molecule of two carboxyl groups. The acid reacts readily with aldehydes of both the aliphatic and aromatic series in the presence of amines. Reaction is generally brought about by the application of heat, although many aromatic aldehydes react at moderate temperature. A small amount of piperidine appears to be the best catalyst for the reaction of aliphatic aldehydes with malonic acid. With these aldehydes there is a tendency to form alkylidenebis-malonic acids and these compounds result when two molecular proportions of the acid are used.

The reaction may be carried out in acetic acid solution using an amine as a catalyst. The alkylidene malonic acids first formed lose carbon dioxide and are thus transformed to unsaturated monobasic acids. A mixture of α,β- and β,γ-unsaturated acids are obtained by this method.

Doebner's procedure[45] offers an excellent method for the preparation of α,β-unsaturated monobasic acids from aldehydes and malonic acid. It consists in heating a mixture of the aldehyde and the malonic acid in pyridine solution in the presence of a little piperidine. The mixture is heated over a steam bath until the evolution of carbon dioxide ceases. Complete decarboxylation of alkylidene malonic acids to the monocarboxylic acid generally requires heating for a few hours. Crotonic acid is, thus, obtained in 60% yield from acetaldehyde.[46] The α,β-isomer is also obtained almost exclusively with most other aliphatic aldehydes. *n*-Heptaldehyde gives 5 to 10% of the β,γ-isomer, which, however can be removed readily as the lactone by shaking with 85% sulfuric acid at 80°, and extracting the acid from the crude mixture of acid and lactone by shaking with aqueous sodium carbonate. When the reaction is carried out in the presence of tertiary bases other than pyridine, the β,γ-acids are formed.[47] When dimethylaniline or triethanolamine are used as catalyst the β,γ-isomer is formed almost exclusively.

Acrolein and crotonaldehyde can be condensed with malonic acid by Doebner's procedure to give butadiene carboxylic acid and sorbic acid, respectively, in good yield.

Cinnamic acid and its derivatives may be prepared by the same method from aromatic aldehydes and malonic acid. The reaction proceeds readily ,and it is only necessary to heat the mixture over a water bath for a short time and then to boil under a reflux condenser for a few minutes.[48]

Aromatic aldehydes react with malonic acid in the presence of amines, giving exclusively arylidene malonic acids:

$$C_6H_5CHO + H_2C(COOH)_2 \rightarrow C_6H_5CH = C(COOH)_2 + H_2O$$

These compounds are readily decarboxylated on heating to the corresponding unsaturated monocarboxylic acids.

Coumarin derivatives have been obtained through the condensation of malonic acid or its esters with aromatic o-hydroxy aldehydes.[199] Coumar-3-carboxylic acid has been obtained, for example, from salicylaldehyde and malonic acid:

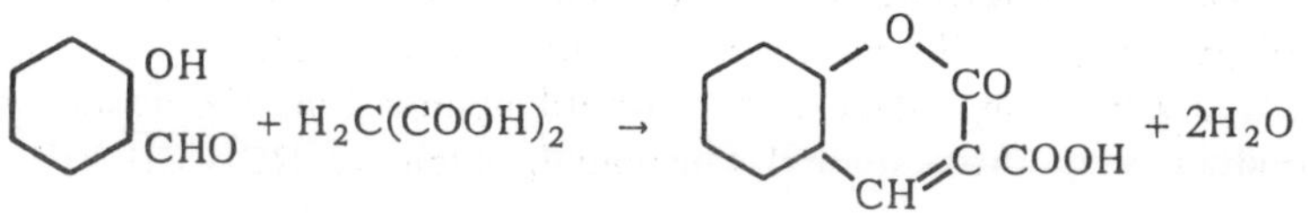

β-Amino- or β-methylamino-β-arylpropionic acids are obtained in 50 to 60% yield, if the reaction is carried out in the presence of a large quantity of ammonia or methylamine, although a certain amount of the unsaturated acid forms simultaneously.[49]

Cinnamaldehyde reacts with malonic acid in the presence of ammonia, aniline or pyridine. Cinnamalonic acid is obtained if the reaction is carried out at moderate temperature, while at higher temperatures partial decarboxylation takes place and cinnamalacetic acid is obtained.[50]

Acetone may be condensed with malonic acid in the presence of ammonia or pyridine to β,β′-dimethylacrylic acid.[51] Diethyl ketone gives the corresponding acrylic acid in fair yield, whereas cyclohexanone reacts poorly.

The reactions of *esters of malonic acid* with carbonyl compounds parallel those with malonic acid. The ready decarboxylation common to condensation products of the acid is not observed with those of the esters. It has been noted that when the condensation of malonic esters with aliphatic aldehydes is carried out by use of an acid condensing agent, alkylidene malonic esters, $RCH = C(COOC_2H_5)_2$, are obtained; on the other hand, if condensation is brought about by use of basic catalysts, alkylidene-bis-malonic esters, $RCH[CH(COOC_2H_5)_2]_2$, are obtained. Aromatic aldehydes always yield the arylidene malonic esters, $ArCH = C(COOC_2H_5)_2$.

The reaction of carbonyl compounds with *cyanoacetic ester* normally proceeds in much the same manner as with malonic acid or malonic ester. Arylidene cyanoacetates, $ArCH = C(CN)COOC_2H_5$, are obtained as a rule with aromatic aldehydes. The free acids, which may be obtained directly through the condensation of aromatic aldehydes with cyanoacetic acid, may be decarboxylated by heating to the corresponding cinnamonitriles.[52] With benzylidene cyanoacetic acid decarboxylation proceeds at 180°.

Bis-cyanoacetates are obtained through the condensation of ethyl cyanoacetate with oxomalonic ethyl ester, $(C_2H_5OCO)_2CO$, salicylaldehyde and phenylacetaldehyde.

Aralkyl ketones, reacting with cyanoacetic ester and ammonia, give cyclodicyanoglutaramides. β-Benzyl-β-methyl-α-dicyanoglutaramide is obtained, for example, with benzyl methyl ketone.[200]

Ethyl acetoacetate condensing with cyanoacetic ethyl ester gives α-cyano-β-methylgluconic ethyl esther, $C_2H_5OCOCH(CN)C(CH_3) = CHCOOC_2H_5$. Only one carbonyl group in benzil reacts with ethyl cyanoacetate to form $C_6H_5COC(C_6H_5) = C(CN)COOC_2H_5$. This is true also of camphoquinone. Benzoin gives the cyanolactone $C_6H_5\overline{C = C(CN)COOC}HC_6H_5$. Benzophenone gives with ethyl cyanoacetate a deeply colored compound which on hydrolysis is converted to hydroquinone-α,β′-diacetic acid,

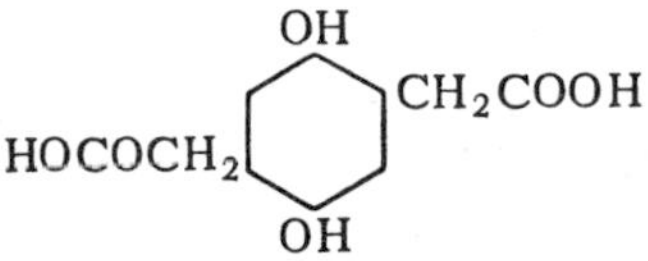

Acetone reacts with one and two molecular proportions of cyanoacetic ester giving $(CH_3)_2C = C(CN)COOC_2H_5$ and $(CH_3)_2C[CH(CN)COOC_2H_5]_2$.

Cyanoacetamide and *malononitrile* react with carbonyl compounds in the same manner as the related compounds such as cyanoacetic ester, considered above. Some reactions are specific to cyanoacetamide, and are due to the presence of the amide group in the molecule.

Ketones, R_1R_2CO, react with cyanoacetamide to form, initially, the substituted cyanoacrylamides $R_1R_2C = C(CN)CONH_2$, which add a molecule of cyanoacetamide, forming

$$\begin{array}{l} R_1R_2CCH(CN)CONH_2 \\ \quad\;\; | \\ \quad CNCHCONH_2 \end{array}$$

and its *trans* isomer. These undergo condensation to six-membered rings, the *trans* isomer giving

$$R_1R_2CCH(CN)CONHCOCHCN,$$

and the *cis* isomer $R_1R_2CCH(CN)CONHC(:NH)CHCONH_2$. The compound resulting from the *trans* isomer predominates, since the isomer forms 95% of the total bis-cyanoacetamides obtained.

A different type of condensation takes place with the initial product resulting from the reaction of ethyl acetylpyruvate, $CH_3COCH_2COCOOC_2H_5$, and cyanoacetamide, also leading to the formation of a ring compound

$$C_2H_5OCOC = C(CN)CONHC(CH_3) = CH.$$

This type of condensation is also observed with benzoylacetone, which gives 3-cyano-6-phenyl-4-methyl-2-pyridone, $CH_3C = C(CN)CONHC(C_6H_4) = CH$. The reaction with benzoyl formanilide, $C_6H_5COCONHC_6H_5$, illustrates another type of condensation, as this compound yields with cyanoacetamide the formamido pyrrolidone $C_6H_5C(OH)CON(C_6H_5)C(:NH)CHCONH_2$. Benzalacetophenone apparently gives $C_6H_5CHCH(CN)CONHC(OH)(C_6H_5)CH_2$, and this is dehydrated to $C_6H_5CHCH(CN)CON{:}C(C_6H_5)CH_2$. Hydroxymethylene ketones, $RCOCH = CHOH$, give pyridones.

The reactions of *malononitrile* with carbonyl compounds generally parallel those of malonic ester or cyanoacetic ester. With acetaldehyde two types of condensation products have been reported, the normal ethylene-bis-malononitrile, $CH_3CH[CH(CN)_2]_2$ and a ring product, 1-3-dimethylcyclobutane-2,2,4,4-tetranitrile, $(CN)_2CCH(CH_3)C(CN)_2CHCH_3$.

Aromatic aldehydes react normally with malononitrile. *o*-Nitrobenzaldehyde reacts in the absence of a condensing agent.[53] Resorcinaldehyde and *p*-dimethylaminobenzaldehyde condense with malononitrile in alcoholic solution in the presence of a little sodium hydroxide solution.[54] Acetone and other ketones give the normal alkylidene malononitriles, $R_1R_2C = C(CN)_2$. Benzophenone gives diphenyldicyanoethylene; benzoyl formanilide also reacts in this manner giving $(CN)_2C = C(C_6H_5)CONHC_6H_5$. Acetylacetone gives 3-cyano-ψ-lutidostyryl and 3-cyano-4-methyl-6-phenyl-2-pyridone. Isatin, reacting with malononitrile in alcoholic solution in the presence of sodium hydroxide, gives isatomalononitrile,

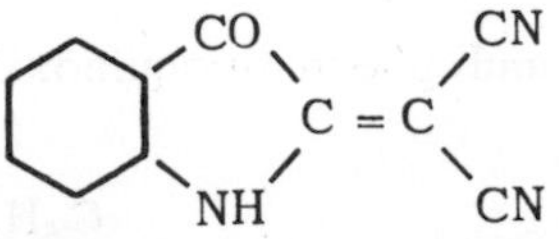

The methylene group in *acetoacetic ester* is reactive due to the influence of the adjacent carbonyl and carboxyl groups, and, as a consequence, reactions characteristic of active methylene groups take place with acetoacetic ester and carbonyl compounds. Simple products due to the intermolecular condensation of carbonyl and methyl groups in acetoacetic ester have not been reported. When acetoacetic ester is heated with 1/3 molecular equivalent of sodium ethoxide, the complex bicyclic compound

$$\begin{array}{l} \quad\;\; CH_3C.CH_2.C \text{———} O \text{—} CO \\ \qquad\quad\;\, \| \qquad\quad \| \qquad\qquad\;\; | \\ C_2H_5OCO\,C.CO.\;C.C(CH_3) = CCOCH_3 \end{array}$$

is obtained.[55]

Acetaldehyde may react with one molecular proportion of acetoacetic ester to form ethylidene acetoacetic ester, or with two molecular proportions to give ethylidene-bis-acetoacetic ester. Under suitable conditions the last named compound can undergo internal aldol condensation forming dimethylcyclohexanolone dicarboxylic diethyl ester:

$$CH_3CH\begin{cases} CH(COOC_2H_5)COCH_3 \\ CH(COOC_2H_5)COCH_3 \end{cases} \rightarrow CH_3CH\begin{cases} CH(COOC_2H_5)\,CO \diagdown \\ \qquad\qquad\qquad\qquad\;\; CH_2 \\ CH(COOC_2H_5)\,C(CH_3)OH \diagup \end{cases}$$

Similar condensation products are also obtained with other aliphatic aldehydes.[56] Benzaldehyde[57] and other aromatic aldehydes, such as *m*- and *p*-nitrobenzaldehydes, *p*-tolualdehyde, cuminol, methoxybenzaldehyde and piperonal, also give these three types of condensation products. Similar products have been prepared with furfural. Benzylidene acetoacetic ester forms through the interaction of equimolecular quantities of benzaldehyde and ethyl acetoacetate at $-5°$ in the presence of piperidine.[58] Arylidene acetoacetic esters cannot be hydrolyzed to the corresponding acids, treatment with alkalies regenerating the original aldehyde and acetoacetic ester which undergoes hydrolysis and ultimately decomposes.

The condensation of chloral with acetoacetic ester may be brought about by heating the mixture of the two compounds with acetic anhydride for a prolonged period. The resulting product is trichloroethylidene acetoacetic ester. [59]

Isopropylidene acetoacetic ester results when a mixture of one part of acetone and two parts of acetoacetic ester saturated with hydrogen chloride at $-5°$ is heated with quinoline. [60] Benzalacetone, $C_6H_5CH = CHCOCH_3$, reacting with a molecular proportion of acetoacetic ester in the presence of a little diethylamine, gives acetone and methylphenylcyclohexanolonedicarboxylic diethyl ester. [61]

Acenaphthoquinoxylene and phenanthroquinoxiline acetoacetic ethyl ester,

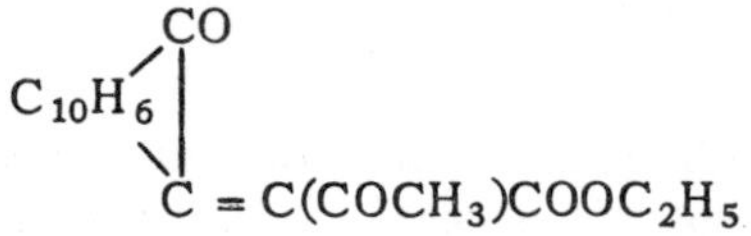

$$C_{10}H_6 \begin{array}{c} CO \\ | \\ C = C(COCH_3)COOC_2H_5 \end{array} \quad \text{and} \quad \begin{array}{c} C_6H_4-CO \\ | \quad\quad | \\ C_5H_4-C = C(COCH_3)COOC_2H_5, \end{array}$$

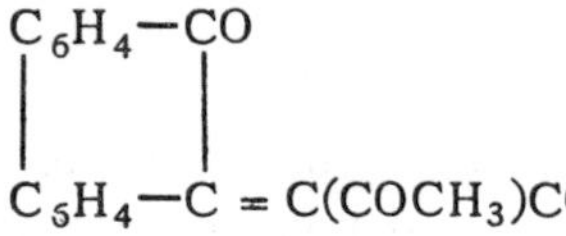

have been obtained through the condensation of acetoacetic ester with acenaphthoquinone and phenanthraquinone. Acenaphthoquinone may also be condensed with two molecular proportions of acetoacetic ester, in the presence of ammonia, to form the compound

$$C_{10}H_6 \begin{array}{c} C = C(COCH_3)COOC_2H_5 \\ | \\ C = C(COCH_3)COOC_2H_5 \end{array}$$

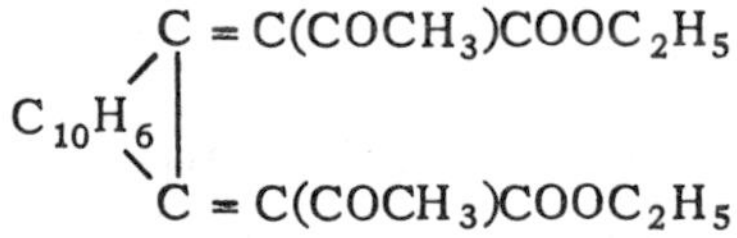

Salicylaldehyde gives with an equimolecular quantity of acetoacetic ethyl ester acetocoumarin, [62]

$$C_6H_4 \begin{array}{c} O - CO \\ | \\ CH = CCOCH_3 \end{array}$$

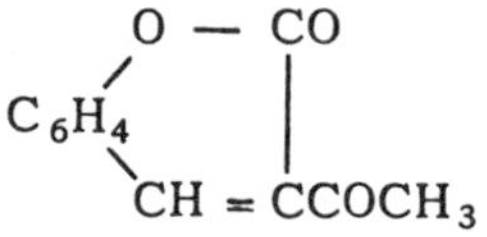

β-Hydroxynaphthaldehyde reacts in a similar manner.

The condensation product of aldehydes, RCHO, with oxalacetic acid, namely alkylidene-bis-oxalacetic esters, undergo ketone cleavage on boiling with hydrochloric acid to yield a,a-diketo pimelic acid derivatives,

$$HOCOCOCH_2CH(R)CH_2COCOOH.$$

These compounds yield on dehydration pyrandicarboxylic acid derivatives,

$$\begin{array}{c} HOCOC — O — CCOOH \\ \| \quad\quad\quad \| \\ CH.CH(R).CH \end{array}$$

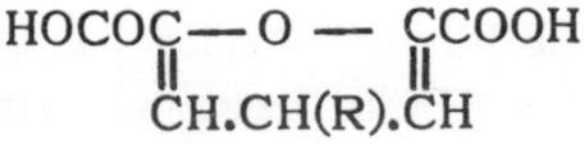

Both methylene groups in succinic acid and its esters are capable of reacting, under the proper conditions, with carbonyl compounds (*Stobbe condensation*). The free acids of the type $RCH = C(COOH)CH_2COOH$ are generally unstable and change to paraconic acids, $\overline{RCHCH(COOH)CH_2COO}$, by internal condensation. An exceptional case is that of desoxybenzoin which gives the acid $C_6H_5CH_2C(C_6H_5)=C(COOH)CH_2COOH$; this changes to γ-benzylidene-γ-phenylpyrotartaric acid, $C_6H_5CH = C(C_6H_5)CH(COOH)CH_2COOH$, through internal rearrangement.[63] The acids resulting from the condensation of two molecules of a carbonyl compound are knownas fulgenic acids, HOCOC(:CRR')C(:CRR')COOH. These may be decarboxylated to the corresponding dienes.

The condensation of succinic esters with carbonyl compounds proceeds well under the action of sodium ethoxide; better results are obtained, however, with potassium *tert*-butoxide.[221] It is possible to prepare mixed condensation products through the stepwise reaction of the ester, first with one molecule of one carbonyl compound, followed by reaction with a molecule of a second carbonyl compound. Thus, α-veratroyl-δ,δ-dimethylfulginic acid ester,

$$(CH_3O)_2C_6H_3CH = C(COOC_2H_5)C[=C(CH_3)_2]COOC_2H_5,$$

may be prepared through the successive condensation of succinic ester with acetone and veratraldehyde.

Under the more or less drastic conditions under which the condensation has to be carried out, *succinonitrile* yields products of partial hydrolysis. Thus benzaldehyde, heated with an alcoholic solution of succinonitrile in the presence of sodium ethoxide, gives α-benzylidene-β-cyanopropionamide,

$$CNCH_2C(:NC_6H_5)CONH_2,$$

while anisaldehyde, reacting with succinonitrile under the same conditions, gives anisylidene succinamide.[64] Condensation with formaldehyde in acetic acid solution in the presence of sulfuric acid gives methylenedisuccinimide,

$$(\overline{COCH_2CH_2CON})_2CH_2.$$

Aromatic aldehydes do not react with equal ease with *benzyl cyanide*.[65] Many react well in the presence of sodium ethoxide; salicylaldehyde and vanilline fail to give condensation products. Benzaldehyde can combine with one or two molecular proportions of benzyl cyanide, forming α-pheynlcinnamonitrile, and α,β,γ-triphenylglutaronitrile, $C_6H_5CH[CH(CN)C_6H_5]_2$. *o*-Hydroxybenzaldehyde yields α-phenyl-β-(*o*-hydroxyphenyl)acrylonitrile, $HOC_6H_4CH = C(CN)C_6H_5$; this is convetted to α-phenylcoumarin,

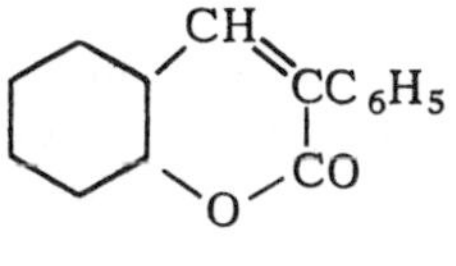

when the cyano group is hydrolyzed. The condensation product with *o*-nitrobenzaldehyde, which is also an unsaturated nitrile, gives on reduction of the nitro group, Py-1-amino-Py-2-phenylquinoline:

$$\text{(structure) } CH = CC_6H_5,\ CN,\ NO \quad \xrightarrow{H_2} \quad \text{(structure) } CH, CC_6H_5, CNH_2, N$$

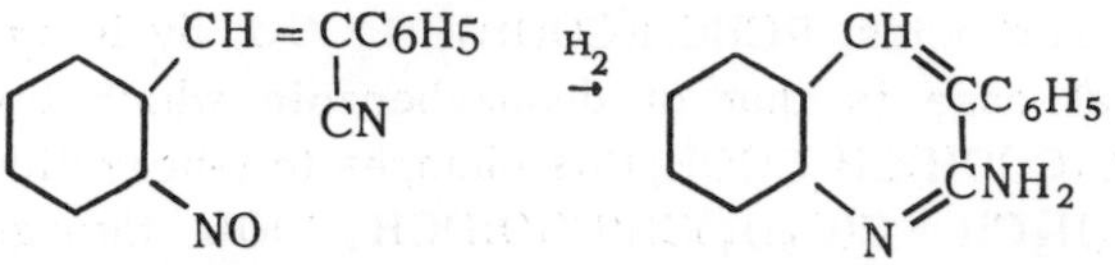

Benzophenone reacts only to a limited extent with benzyl cyanide in the presence of sodium ethoxide, giving a small yield of triphenylacrylonitrile. Triphenylacrylonitrile, $(C_6H_5)_2C = C(C_6H_5)CN$, may be obtained in 30% yield through the interaction of benzyl cyanide with benzophenone dichloride,[66] $(C_6H_5)_2CCl_2$. Camphorquinine reacting with benzyl cyanide gives

$$C_8H_4 \begin{matrix} C = C(CN)C_6H_5 \\ | \\ CO \end{matrix}$$

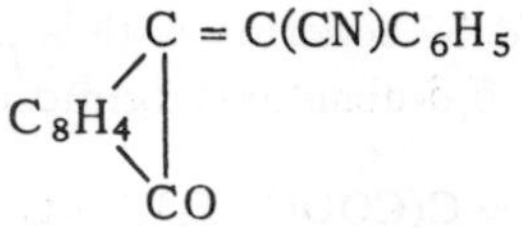

Pyruvic acid reacts with benzyl cyanide in the presence of potassium hydroxide at 2°, giving the potassium salt of a-hydroxy-β-cyano-β-phenylisobutyric acid, $C_6H_5CH(CN)C(OH)(CH_3)COOH$, in 55% yield. On hydrolysis with concentrated hydrochloric acid, this is partially converted to phenylmaleic anhydride, $C_6H_5\overline{C = CHCOOCO}$. Benzylpyrivic acid reacts similarly, while phenylpyruvic acid gives the unsaturated benzylcinnamic acid,

$$C_6H_5C(CN = C(COOH)CH_2C_6H_5$$

which is decomposed by concentrated alkalies to the original components, benzyl cyanide and phenylpyruvic acid.

Substituted benzyl cyanides react with carbonyl compounds as a rule in the same manner as benzyl cyanide.

Phenylacetic acid and *arylacetic acids* in general undergo condensation with carbonyl compounds yielding products similar to those obtained with benzyl cyanide. Reaction proceeds most readily with aromatic aldehydes. The resulting arylidene arylacetic acids may be decarboxylated by heating in pyridine in the presence of some piperidine. Thus, when the reaction of benzaldehyde with *p*-nitrophenylacetic acid is carried out at 150-160°, condensation and decarboxylation take place simultaneously and *p*-nitrostilbene results.[67] The two compounds react in the absence of a catalyst at 205° (in sealed tube) giving *p*-nitrophenylcinnamic acid.[68]

Formylacetic ethyl ester, which contains both a carbonyl and an active methylene group, is capable of self-condensation, three molecules combining to form trimesic acid ethyl ester:

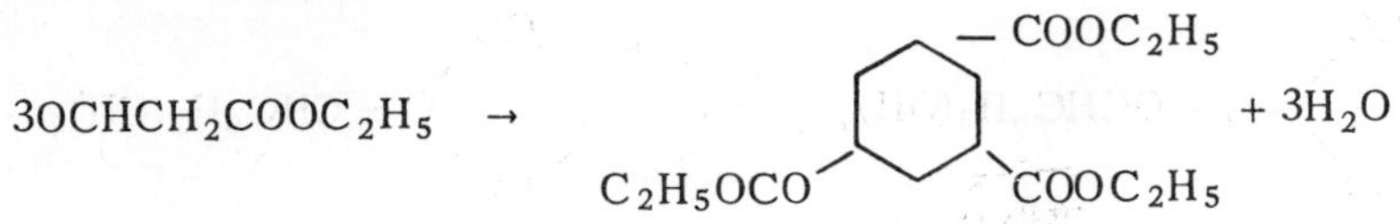

Benzoylacetic ester condenses with benzaldehyde under the action of hydrogen chloride giving benzalbenzoylacetic ester, $C_6H_5CH = C(COC_6H_5)COOC_2H_5$; under the same conditions benzoylpyruvic ester gives ketophenylparacophenone:[69]

$$C_6H_5COCH_2COCOOC_2H_5 + OCHC_6H_5 \quad \rightarrow \quad C_6H_5COCHCH(OH)C_6H_5$$
$$\underset{\textstyle COCOOC_6H_5}{|}$$

$$\rightarrow \quad C_6H_5COCH\!\!-\!\!-\!\!-\!\!-CHC_6H_5 + H_2O$$
$$\underset{\textstyle CO}{|} \quad \underset{\textstyle O}{|}$$
$$\searrow\!\!\nearrow$$
$$CO$$

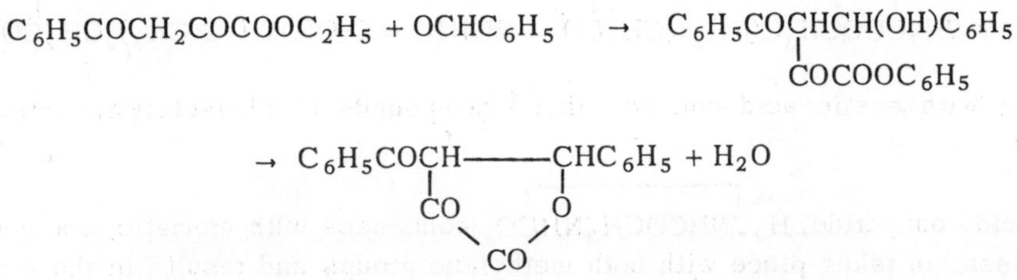

Desoxybenzoin reacts with one molecular proportion of benzaldehyde to form benzylidene desoxybenzoin,[70] $C_6H_5CH = C(C_6H_5)COC_6H_5$; or with two molecular proportions, to yield benzamaron,[71] $C_6H_5CH[CH(C_6H_5)COC_6H_5]_2$. This compound reacts with hydroxylamine to form pentaphenylpyridine:

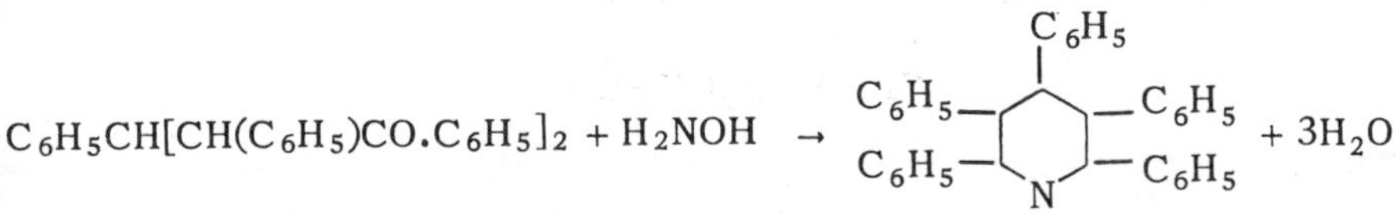

Aryl sulfonylacetonitriles, $ArSO_2CH_2CN$, react with aromatic aldehydes, RCHO, forming unsaturated α-sulfonylnitriles, $RCH = C(CN)SO_2Ar$.

Acetylacetone, condensing with benzaldehyde in the presence of hydrogen chloride, gives $C_6H_5CHClCH(OCH_3)_2$, which can be converted to benzylidene acetylacetone, $C_6H_5CH = C(COCH_3)_2$by distillation under vacuum.[201]

Barbituric acid, a compound which may be considered an acylated malonamide and possesses a reactive methylene group, is capable of condensing with certain aldehydes in the manner of malonic acid. With furfural it forms furfuralbarbituric acid:[72]

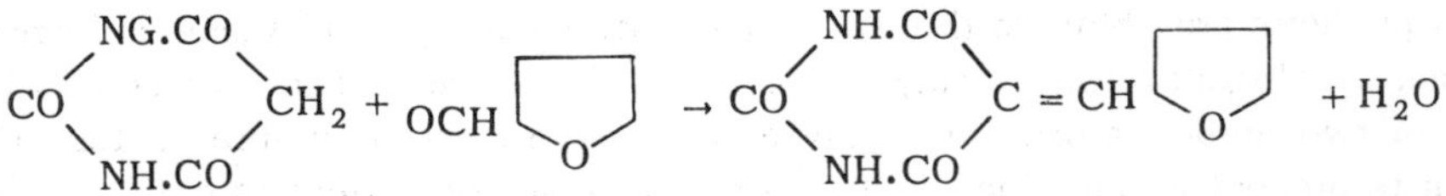

1,3-Hydrindanedione, which possesses a methylene group situated between two carbonyl groups, reacts with aldehydes. For example, it yields a condensation product with protocatechualdehyde:[73]

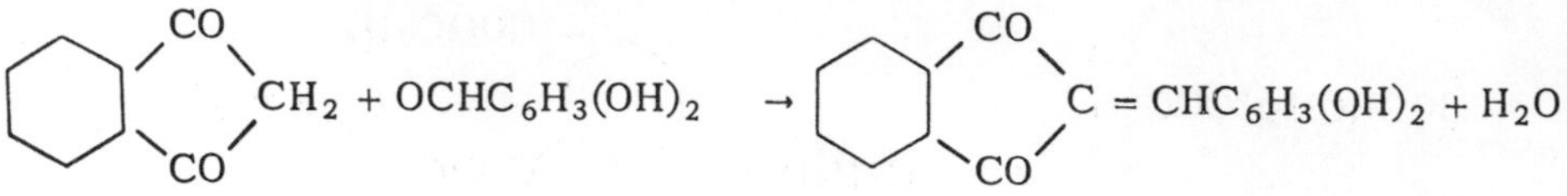

Another example of a diketone of this type is dimedon or dimethylcyclohexanedione, which reacts with simple aldehydes to form water-insoluble condensation products: [74]

$$RCHO + 2H_2CCOCH_2C(CH_3)_2CH_2CO \rightarrow RCH[C = C(OH)CH_2C(CH_3)_2CH_2CO]_2$$

Boiling with acetic acid converts these compounds to characteristic internal ethers.

Glycide anhydride, $H_2CNHCOCH_2NHCO$, condenses with aromatic aldehydes. Condensation takes place with both methylene groups and results in the formation of diarylidene derivatives, $RCH = CNHCOC(:CHR)NHCO$. Other dipeptide anhydrides having the glycide group also form condensation products with aromatic aldehydes. [75]

Examples of activation due to a pair of carbon atoms with ethylenic linkages attached to a methylene group are offered by cyclopentadiene,

$$CH:CHCH_2CH=CH,$$

indene,

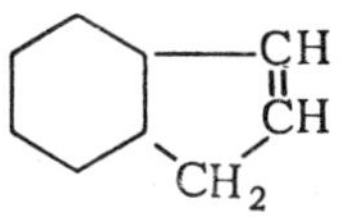

and fluorene,

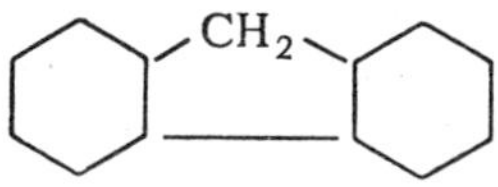

Cyclopentadiene gives with acetone dimethylfulvene,

$$CH = CHCH = CHC = C(CH_3)_2;$$

similar products are obtained through condensation with acetophenone and benzophenone. Analogous product may be obtained from indene and fluorene. [76] The effect of two carbon atoms with ethylenic bonds is inappreciable, unless ring tension is present as an added factor, although a marked effect is obtained by a combination of a carbonyl and ethylenic or acetylenic groups.

Activation by nitro groups may be illustrated with the example of nitroparaffins, RCH_2NO_2, which react with aromatic aldehydes to form arylnitroolefins: [77]

$$C_6H_5CHO + H_2C(R)NO_2 \rightarrow C_6H_5CH = C(R)NO_2 + H_2O$$

The reaction takes place in the presence of potassium hydroxide, nitroethane reacting especially readily.

The potassium salt of the *aci* form of the nitro alcohol, RCH(OH)C(R′)NOOK, is first formed. In individual cases this changes spontaneously to the nitroethylene derivative by cleavage of water, but dehydration has to be brought about by heating or other means in many instances.

The lower aliphatic nitroethylenes are quite unstable and polymerize readily; nitrobutylenes and higher homologs are fairly stable compounds.

Aliphatic aldehydes combine with nitromethane and nitroparaffins, in general, in the presence of potassium carbonate, to form nitro alcohols,

$$RCH(OH)CH(R')NO_2$$

The reaction may be considered to consist in the replacement of a hydrogen atom attached to the carbon atom adjacent to the nitro group with a carbonyl group, RCH(OH)-, a process which can be repeated until all hydrogens originally attached to this carbon atom are thus replaced.[78]

In 2,4-dinitrotoluene and similar nitrated aromatic compounds with a methyl group attached at the 2 or 4 position in the nucleus with respect to the nitro group, the activating influence of the nitro groups appears in the methyl group, which reacts with ease with aromatic aldehydes in the presence of piperidine or other secondary amine:[79]

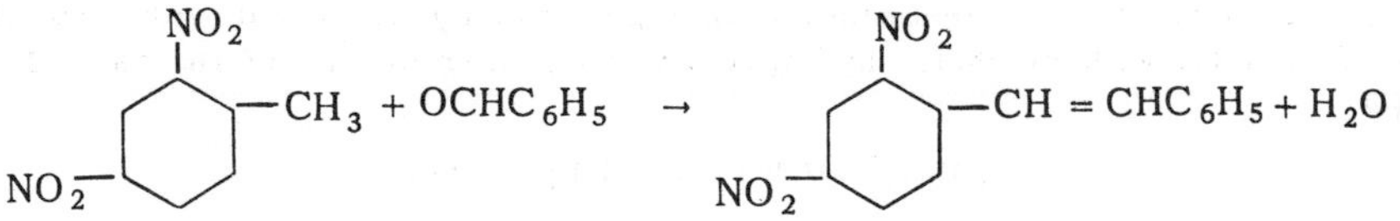

The methyl group in 2-cyano-4-nitrotoluene is reactive, and this compound may be condensed with benzaldehyde in the presence of pyridine at 120-140°, to 2-cyano-4-nitrostilbene. This type of condensation takes place readily also with α- and γ-methyl pyridines and with quinaldine:[80]

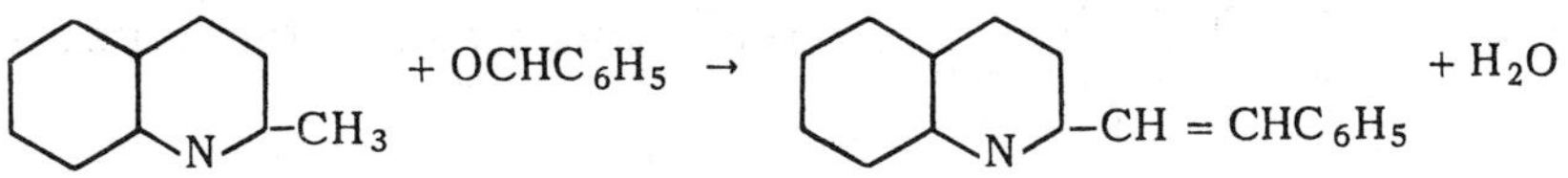

Bases of the type of α- and γ-methylpyridine may be converted to alcohols of the type

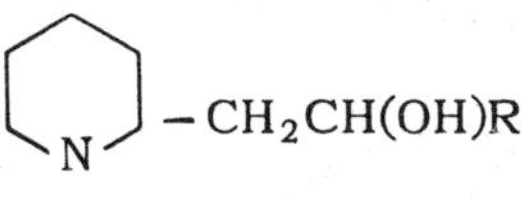

by heating at 130-150° in a sealed tube with a little water and the aldehyde.

Acetone reacts with benzaldehyde in the presence of dilute caustic to form benzylideneacetone.[202] Acetone, heated with pyrivic acid in a mixture of acetic and sulfuric acids, gives an anhydride of the so-called acetone dipyruvic acid $CO[CH{:}C(CH_3)COOH]_2$. The anhydride, which probably has the structure $OCOC(CH_3)CHCCHC(CH_3)COO$, is converted to the alkaline salt of the acid on treatment with aqueous alkalies.

Chloralacetophenone, $C_6H_5COCH = CHCCl_3$, is obtained through the condensation of acetophenone with chloral.[203]

Replacement of Reactive Hydrogens with Organic Radicals

A characteristic of reactive methylene groups is the ready replacement of the hydrogens with an alkali metal. In the resulting compound the metal can, in turn, be replaced with an organic radical by reaction with an organic halide:

$$>CHNa + XR \rightarrow >CHR + NaX$$

This subject is taken up in the present chapter since carbonyl groups are among the more important activating combinations, and since the subject formed a logical sequel of the matter treated in the proceeding section.

The groups bringing about the activation of methylene have been listed in the preceding section. Activating residues have a common characteristic; they are strongly electronegative. In this connection, a method for the determination of the relative electronegativity of a given organic residue, originated by Kharasch, may be mentioned. The method involves the treatment of an organomercury compound with two different radicals, RHgR′, with alcoholic hydrogen chloride, whereby one of the radicals is removed:

$$RHgR' + HCl \rightarrow RHgCl + R'H$$

The residue which preferentially captures the proton, namely R′, is the more electronegative.

The ranking of some of the organic radicals in *decreasing order of negativity*, determined by this method, is as follows:

$$C_6H_5 > (CH_3)_3Si\text{-}CH_2 > CH_3 > n\text{-}C_6H_{13} > (CH_3)_3CCH_2$$

CN > 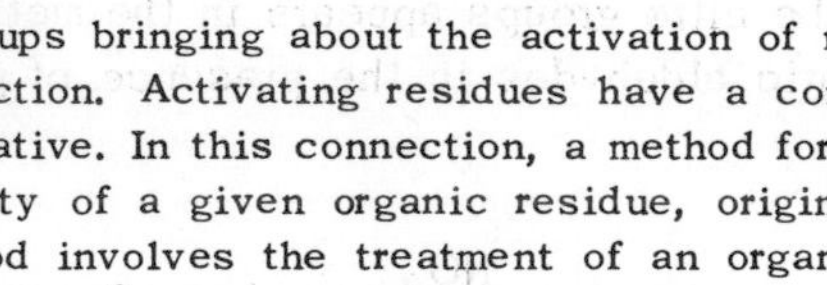 > C_6H_5 > CH_3 > CH_3CH_2

$$> CH_3CH_2CH_2 > CH_3(CH_2)_3 > (CH_3)_2CHCH_2CH_2 > C_6H_5CH_2 >$$

> 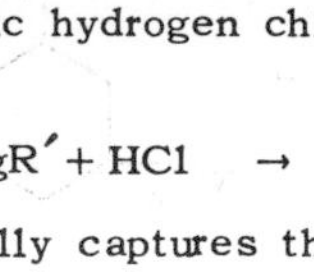 > $CH_3(CH_2)_{15}$

This sequence is referred to as the *Kharasch Series.*[82]

Halogens in the nucleus generally cause an intensification of the negative character of the aromatic group, substitution in the para position exerting the least influence, fluorine in this position being wholly without action.

Vorlaender has observed that the hydrogen atom is active in a combination of the type HC.C:C, but not in HC:C or HC.C.C:C. This rule is of general applicability and holds true when the carbon atoms 1 and 3 are replaced by other multivalent negative elements. The activating capacity is limited, however, and in compounds such as H_3CCOOH, for example, it is largely oriented in the direction of the hydroxyl group, with the hydrogen atoms in the methyl group practically unaffected.

One or both hydrogen atoms in the methylene group in *malonic acid* and its *esters* may be replaced with alkali metals. Alkyl malonic acids or esters are obtained through the interaction of alkyl halides with these alkali metal derivatives. Alkyl sulfates, nitrates and toluenesulfonates may be employed in the reaction in special cases instead of the halides, but nitrites, acetates and benzoates are unreactive.[83]

The sodium derivative of malonic ester may be prepared by treating the compound with the required quantity of 10% alcoholic sodium ethoxide solution. The sodio compound need not be isolated and can be used directly in alcoholic solution for the preparation of alkylated esters.[84]

Solid alkali hydroxides and even dry silver oxide may be effectively utilized in some cases in place of sodium ethoxide. The reaction is carried out in ethereal solution, or in the absence of a sulvent.

Magnesium compounds such as $C_2H_5OMgCH(COOC_2H_5)_2$, which are readily obtained by the action of activated magnesium on an anhydrous alcoholic solution of the ester, may be used in the reaction with excellent results.

Iodides are the most reactive among alkyl halides, but the reaction generally proceeds at a satisfactory rate with the bromides. Compounds with an active chlorine react quite readily. The reaction invariably results in the formation of a C-substituted malonic ester.

Methyl iodide reacting with sodio malonic diethyl ester gives the monomethylated ester, together with other products; ethyl iodide yields principally the monosubstituted product with some disubstituted ester. Monoethylmalonic diethyl ester results when a mixture of ethyl iodide and diethyl malonate is heated with solid potassium hydroxide.[85] The monosubstituted products have been obtained from normal and isopropyl iodides. Allyl iodide gives the mono- or the disubstituted product, depending on the proportions used. Monosubstituted products have been obtained also through the reaction of sodio malonic ester with benzyl chloride, ω-bromacetophenone, ethyl chloroformate, ethyl α-bromopropionate, β-bromolevulinate, and picryl chloride. Both mono- and disubstituted products have been obtained with chloracetic ester. The pentamethyl ester of dicarboxytricarballylic acid, $CH_3OCOCH(CHCOOCH_3)_2$, results through the interaction of sodio methyl malonate and methyl dichloracetate.[86] Ethyl trichloracetate reacting with sodio ethyl malonate gives tetraethyl propylenetetracarboxylate.[87]

Only one chlorine is replaceable by the malonic ester residue in dichloroindene, and in 2,3-dichloro-1,4- and 3,4-dichloro-1,2-naphthoquinone. Chloranil gives with sodio ethyl malonate 3,6-dichloroquinone-2,5-bis-malonic ester.[88] 2,3,4,5-Tetrachloropyridine gives γ-(2,3,5-trichloropyridyl)-malonic ester.[89] Carbon tetrachloride yields tetraethyl propylenetetracarboxylate and the tetraethyl ester of *sym*-ethanetetracarboxylic acid.[90] The compound

$$HOC[CH(COOCH_3)_2]_3$$

has been prepared by the reaction of carbon tetrachloride with methyl malonate in the presence of sodium methoxide.[91] The reaction of chloroform with sodio ethyl malonate leads to the formation of

$$CH[CH(COOC_2H_5)_2]_3,\ C_2H_5OCOCHCH=C(COOC_2H_5)_2$$

and other products.

An interesting application of the reaction is the preparation of carboxylic acids with an aldehyde function. For this purpose a bromoacetal is condensed with sodio malonic ester, the ester is converted to the acid with caustic and the acid heated in a sealed tube with water, this treatment regenerating the aldehyde and at the same time causing the partial decarboxylation of the acid to a monocarboxylic acid:

$$(C_2H_5O)_2CHCH_2Br + NaCH(COOC_2H_5)_2 \rightarrow NaBr + (C_2H_5O)_2CHCH_2CH(COOC_2H_5)_2$$

$$\rightarrow (C_2H_5O)_2CHCH_2CH(COOH)_2 \xrightarrow{H_2O} OCHCH_2CH_2COOH + CO_2 + 2C_2H_5OH$$

With bromoacetal the condensation with sodiomalonic ester is carried out at 130-140° and the final hydrolysis at 180-190°.

Amino acids are prepared in a similar manner from bromoalkylphthalimides such as

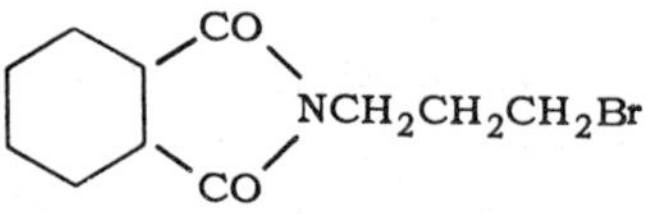

by condensation with sodiomalonic ester, and heating the resulting product with aqueous sodium hydroxide.

Methylenemalonic ester, $CH_2=C(COOC_2H_5)_2$, results in the reversible *para* polymeric form when methylene iodide reacts with malonic ester in the presence of two molecular equivalents of sodium ethoxide. The compound may be depolymerized to the monomer by distillation, but the monomer changes on standing to the *meta* form of the polymer which cannot be depolymerized, decomposing above 240° when heated.[168]

Dibromo paraffins in which the bromine is in the 1,2 and 1,3 positions give with sodiomalonic ester, according to the conditions, cyclic derivatives, unsaturated homologs of malonic ester or symmetrical ethane- or propanetetracarboxylic esters and, in some instances, unsaturated brominated hydrocarbons.[92] Ethylene dibromide, for example, gives cyclopropane-1, 1-dicarboxylic ester, $\overline{CH_2.CH_2C}(COOC_2H_5)_2$ and butane-$\alpha,\alpha,\delta,\delta$-tetracarboxylic ester,[93] $(C_2H_5OCO)_2CHCH_2CH_2CH(COOC_2H_5)_2$. The formation of the cyclic compound from the monosodio derivative may be explained by the following series of reactions:

$$BrCH_2CH_2Br + NaHC(COOC_2H_5)_2 \rightarrow BrCH_2CH_2CH(COOC_2H_5)_2$$

$$\xrightarrow{NaCH(COOC_2H_5)_2} BrCH_2CH_2C(Na)(COOC_2H_5)_2 \rightarrow \overline{CH_2CH_2C}(COOC_2H_5)_2$$

Similar products are obtained with trimethylene dibromide $Br(CH_2)_3Br$. Propylene dibromide yields the cyclic product with some *sym*-ethanetetracarboxylic ethyl ester and, under certain conditions, also α- and β-bromopropylene.[94] 1,3-Dibrom-2-methylpropane gives the cyclic product, but 2,4-dibrom-2-methylbutane gives δ-methyl-γ-pentylene-α,α-dicarboxylic ethyl ester,

$$(CH_3)_2C = CHCH_2CH(COOC_2H_5)_2,$$

and 2,3-dibrom-2-methylbutane yields trimethylethylene. In both last mentioned cases *sym*-ethanetetracarboxylic ethyl ester also forms.

sym-Tetrabromtetramethylmethane yields a bicyclic compound with disodiomalonic ester, which may be converted by saponification followed by partial decarboxylation to spiroheptanedicarboxylic acid:

$$(BrCH_2)_2C(CH_2Br)_2 + 2Na_2C(COOC_2H_5)$$

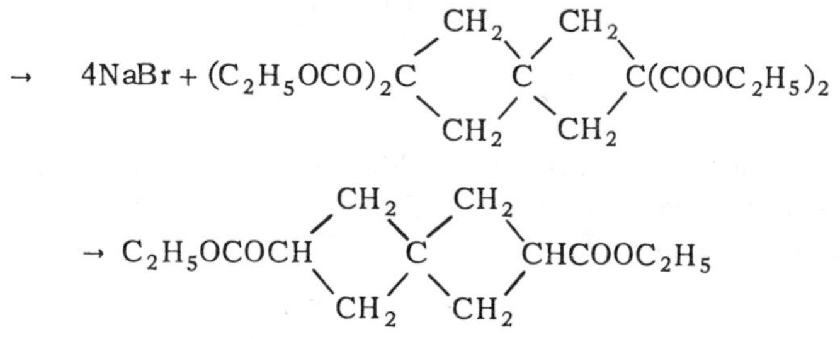

Dibromosuccinic ethyl ester gives with disodiomalonic ester a cyclic compound

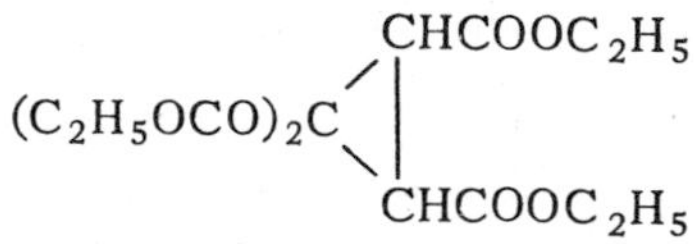

A cyclic compound,

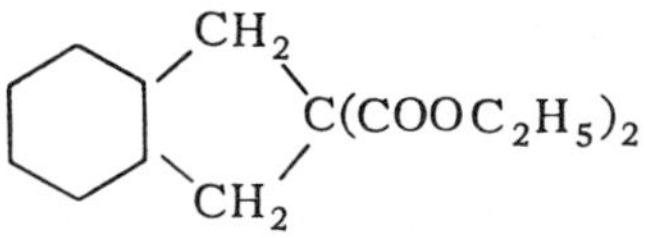

is also obtained from *o*-xylene dibromide and disodiomalonic ester.

Chlorides of acids of both aliphatic and aromatic series react with sodiomalonic esters to give acylated malonic esters. Acetyl chloride gives the mono- and diacetyl derivatives, $CH_3COCH(COOC_2H_5)_2$ and $(CH_3CO)_2C(COOC_2H_5)_2$.

Phenylacetyl chloride reacts similarly. Chloracetyl chloride gives tetron-α-car boxylic ethyl ester, $C_2H_5OCO\overline{CHCOCH_2OCO}$ and a compound of the empirica formula $C_9H_{12}O_5$. Succinyl chloride gives succinylmalonic diethyl ester $\overline{COCH_2CH_2COC}(COOC_2H_5)_2$. Phthalyl chloride gives the compounds.[95]

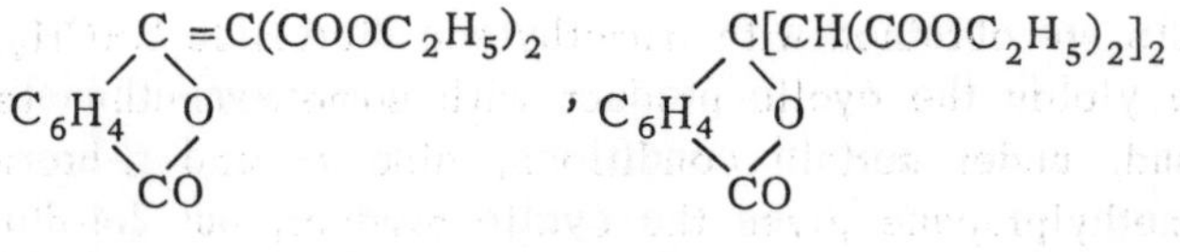

and probably

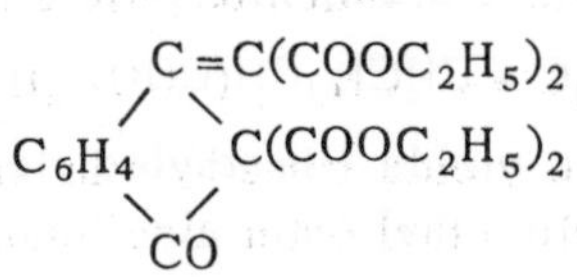

Acetylsalicyclic acid chloride reacting in ethereal solution with sodiomaloni ethyl ester gives carbethoxybenzotetronic acid,[96]

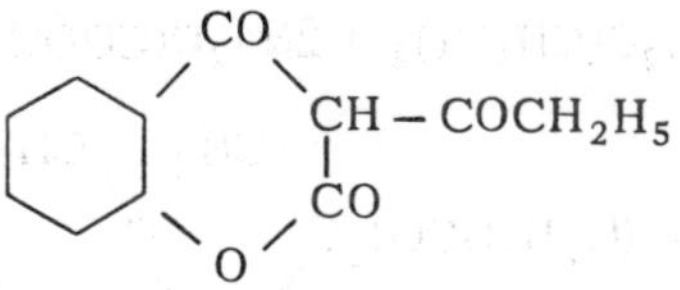

Other aromatic acetyl *o*-hydroxy acyl chlorides react in a like manner.

Cyclic bodies have been obtained through the intramolecular condensation o ω-haloacylacetic esters:[204]

$$XCH_2(CH_2)_nCOCH_2COOC_2H_5 \rightarrow \overline{CH_2(CH_5)_nCOC}HCOOC_2H_5$$

Compounds with 14 to 17 membered rings have been prepared by this method.

The hydrogen atoms in the methylene group in *cyanacetic acid* and *its ester* are replaceable with alkali metals, and, as in the case of sodiomalonic esters the alkali metal may be exchanged with organic groups by reaction with organo halogen compounds. Substitution by alkyl groups takes place readily by reactio with alkyl iodides or bromides, the monosubstituted compounds resulting as rule from monosodium-cyanacetic ester. An exception is the reaction with α-bro mopropionic ester which gives a disubstituted product.

One or both chlorine atoms in dibromindone and dichloronaphthoquinone ma be replaced with the cyanacetic ester group. The highly reactive chlorine i 2,4-dinitrochlorobenzene, picryl chloride and other similar compounds may b readily exchanged by the cyanacetic ester residue. The reaction of disodio cyanacetic ester with chloroform leads to the formation of sodiodicyanoglutari ester,[97] $C_2H_5OCOC(CN)(Na)CH:C(CN)COOC_2H_5$. Carbon tetrachloride gives the same compound.[98]

The reaction of sodiocyanacetic ester with acid chlorides proceeds readily. Unlike sodiomalonic ester, sodiocyanacetic ester does not yield the tetronic acid derivatives on condensation with chloracetyl chloride or acetylsalicylyl chloride, but gives chloracetyl- and acetylsalicylylcyanoacetic-esters. The normal acyl derivatives are also obtained with ethyl chloroformate and ethoxalyl chloride. A cyclic compound, methyloxycyanocoumarin,

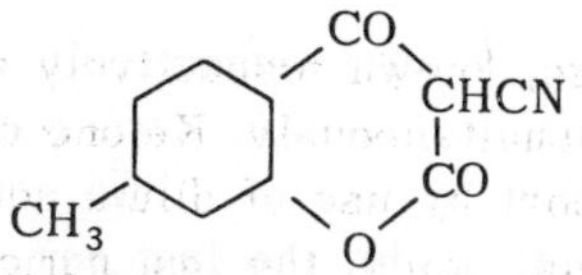

is afforded, however, by *o*-acetoxy-*m*-toluic acid chloride.[99]

Cyclic derivatives as well as open chain products may result through the reaction of 1,2- or 1,3- or other dihalo compounds with the halogens attached to different carbon atoms. Cyclopropylcyanocarboxylic ester $\overline{CH_2CH_2C}(CN)COOC_2H_5$ and ethyl *a*,*δ*-dicyanovalerate, $CN(CH_2)_3CH(CN)COOC_2H_5$ have been prepared, for example, from ethylene dibromide and ethyl sodiocyanacetate.[100]

The hydrogen atoms of the methylene group in *acetoacetic ester*, as in malonic and cyanoacetic esters, may be replaced with alkali metals and these in turn may be exchanged for organic groups by reaction with organic halogen compounds.

The general procedure in preparing the alkylated acetoacetic esters is as follows: An atomic equivalent of metallic sodium is dissolved in sufficient 95% alcohol to produce a 10% sodium ethoxide solution; a molecular equivalent of acetoacetic ester is added and the desired halide is introduced in slight excess with cooling. The mixture is heated under reflux, if necessary. The reaction is complete when the mixture no longer reacts alkaline to litmus. The alcohol is then removed from the product by distillation, water is added to the residue and the ester is taken up in ether. The ethereal solution is finally washed, dried with anhydrous sodium sulfate, and the compound is isolated by fractionation under reduced pressure.

A second alkyl group can be introduced in the same manner after the reaction with the first mole of alkyl halide is complete. The crude neutral alcoholic solution is used for the purpose without further treatment and the required quantity of 10% sodium ethylate solution and the additional quantity of the halide are added.[101]

The alkylation of keto-enols is usually carried out by mixing the alcoholic alkaline solution of the keto-enol with the halide at a suitable temperature without the necessity of isolating the enolate.

Alkylation of aliphatic *β*-diketones proceeds readily, but the sodio compound of certain aromatic *β*-diketones fails to react with alkyl halides. This is the case, for example, with bis-(*p*-methoxybenzoyl)-methane,[178] though not with dibenzoylmethane. In such cases alkylation proceeds well with the potassium derivative of the diketone.[179]

While it is possible to introduce two alkyl groups simultaneously into the molecule of malonic esters, this is not possible with acetoacetic ester and *β*-diketones. Dialkylated products may be prepared from the mono substituted products by reaction with sodium, followed by refluxing with the alkyl halide.

Alkylacetoacetic esters may be decomposed by hydrolysis in two distinct ways:

$$CH_3COCH(R)COOC_2H_5 \xrightarrow{H_2O} CH_3COCH_2R + CO_2 + C_2H_5OH \qquad (I)$$

$$CH_3COCH(R)COOC_2H_5 \xrightarrow{H_2O} CH_3COOH + RCH_2COOC_2H_5 \qquad (II)$$

These two types of cleavage, known respectively as the *ketone cleavage* and *acid cleavage,* take place simultaneously. Ketone cleavage predominates when decomposition is brought about by use of dilute aqueous potassium hydroxide, baryta water, or dilute mineral acids, the last named giving the most satisfactory results. Acid cleavage predominates when the ester is heated with concentrated alcoholic potassium hydroxide or sodium alcoholate. Ethyl diethylacetoacetate resists the action of cold 5% aqueous potassium hydroxide, while the monoethyl derivative is readily decomposed. The ketonic fission of β-keto esters $CH_3COCRR'COOC_2H_5$ is favored by a low concentration of alkali, but the yield of ketonic products varies widely with the nature of R and R′. In difficult cases, for example when R is *n*-butyl and R′ isobutyl, ketonic fission has been brought about by pyrolysis.[205]

The normal substitution products are obtained with alkyl halides and many other organic halogen compounds. Chlorodimethyl ether reacts in an exceptional manner giving ethyl β-(methoxymethoxy)-crotonate,

$$CH_3OCH_2OC(CH_3) = CHCOOC_2H_5.$$

Dibromindone gives bromindoylacetoacetic ester. In chloranil one or two chlorine atoms, those in position 1 and 5, are replaceable with the acetoacetic ester residue. Chloroform reacting with sodioacetoacetic ester yields a product which on saponification with caustic followed by treatment with acid is converted to *m*-hydroxyuvitic acid,[102]

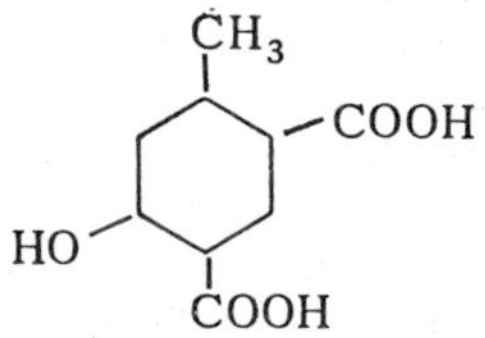

Dihalo compounds in which the halogen atoms are attached to different carbon atoms react with sodioacetoacetic acid to form cyclic as well as open chain derivatives,

$$C_2H_5OCO\overline{C(COCH_3)(CH_2)_{n-1}CH_2} \quad \text{and}$$

$$C_2H_5OCOCH(COCH_3)(CH_2)_nCH(COCH_3)COOC_2H_5$$

Removal of hydrogen halides with the formation of unsaturated products may also take place. Ethylene dibromide gives principally 1-acetylcyclopropane-1-carboxylic ester with some 2-methyl-4,5-dihydrofurane-3-carboxylic ethyl ester and ethyl α,α'-diacetyladipate.[103] When an excess of the dibromide is used, a certain amount of bromoethylacetoacetic ester results. One molecular equivalent of trimethylene dibromide gives with two molecular equivalents of sodioacetoacetic ester the ethyl ester of methyldihydropyrancarboxylic acid,[104]

$$C_2H_5OCOC = C(CH_3)OCH_2CH_2CH_2$$

1,5-dibromopentane gives 1-acetylcyclohexane-1-carboxylic ethyl ester and ethyl α,α'-diacetylpimelate.[105] Orthoxylylene bromide gives the cyclic compound

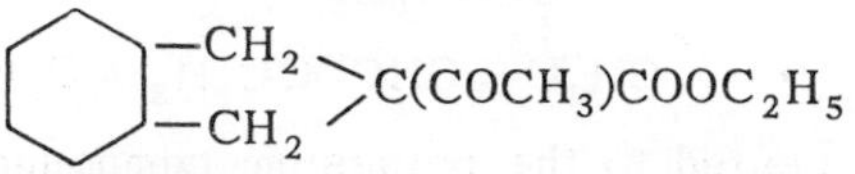

but the meta and para isomers yield the bisacetoacetoacetic ester derivatives.

The acylation of ethyl acetoacetate through its sodio compound should be carried out in the absence of any alcohol. The sodio compound is prepared for this purpose by the reaction of metallic sodium with acetoacetic ester in solution in anhydrous ether, ligroin or benzene. Some acylated compounds, such as the benzoyl derivative, show a tendency to combine with the sodium of the sodioacetoacetic ester during the reaction, and on further reaction with the acyl chloride yield the diacylated ester. The mono compound is generally obtained in good yield when two moles of the sodioacetoacetic ester are used. The monosubstitution products obtained by this method are C-acyl derivatives. Like the alkylated derivatives, they may undergo the ketone or acid cleavage:[106]

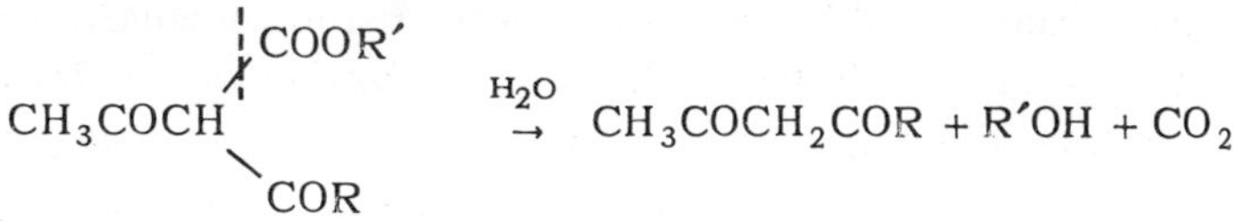

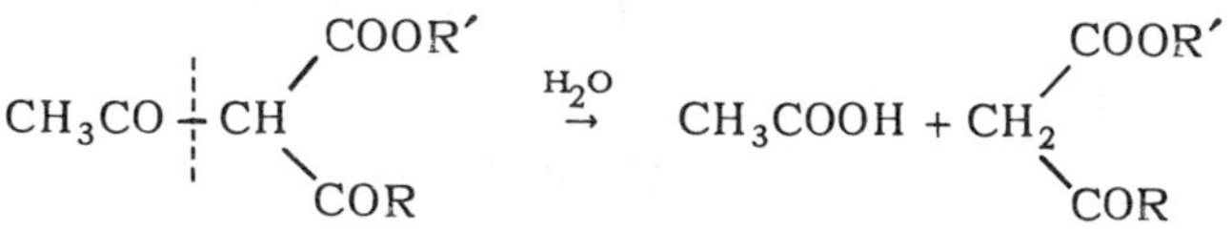

A third type of cleavage which is a combination of the preceding two also takes place

Ketone cleavage takes place on boiling the acylated product with water. Acid

cleavage takes place on treating the compound with 8 to 10% aqua ammonia. Benzoylacetoacetic ester shaken with aqueous ammonia of this strength, first dissolves, then an automatic rise in temperature takes place, followed by the separation of an oil, which is practically pure benzoyl acetic ester. The method serves for the preparation of various acylated acetic esters.

The third type of cleavage takes place when the C-acylated ester is heated in a sealed tube at 130-140° with concentrated hydrochloric acid. Heating with an excess of dilute potassium hydroxide also causes this type of hydrolysis.

When acid chlorides react with acetoacetic ester in the presence of tertiary bases, such as pyridine, O-acyl derivatives are obtained:[170]

$$CH_3COCH_2COOC_2H_5 + ClCOC_6H_5 + C_6H_5N \rightarrow$$

$$\begin{array}{l} \;\;\;\;\;OCOC_6H_5 \\ \;\;\;\;\;| \\ CH_3C = CHCOOC_2H_5 + C_6H_5N.HCl \end{array}$$

O-Acyl esters are converted to the potassium compound of C-acyl derivatives $CH_3C(OK) = C(COC_6H_5)COOC_2H_5$ by treatment with potassium carbonate.

In contrast to alkylated derivatives of acetoacetic ester and other enolizable keto compounds, acylated derivatives are more acidic than the parent enolic substance. As a consequence, acylation of these compounds proceeds until both hydrogen atoms attached to the methylene group are replaced with acyl groups.[180] The yield of monoacylated compound may be increased by forming the enolic compound in successive fractions, causing each fraction to react with the required quantity of acyl chloride, until all the carbonyl compound is consumed. During acylation the tendency to enolization may undergo variation, increasing in some cases and decreasing in others, an enhanced degree of enolization rendering acylation more difficult.

Acetyl chloride in ethereal solution reacting with *sodioacetoacetic ester* gives acetylacetoacetic ester; benzoyl chloride gives, according to the proportions used, mono or dibenzoylacetoacetic ester. Monoacyl derivatives are obtained from *o*-nitro, 3,5-dinitro,3,4,5-trimethoxybenzoyl chlorides and with cinnamyl chloride. Phenylpropiolic acid[107] gives the compound

$$\begin{array}{l} C_6H_5CH = C - O - CH \\ \qquad\qquad\;\; | \qquad\quad \| \\ \qquad\qquad CO \;—\; CCOOC_2H_5 \end{array}$$

while phthalyl chloride yields

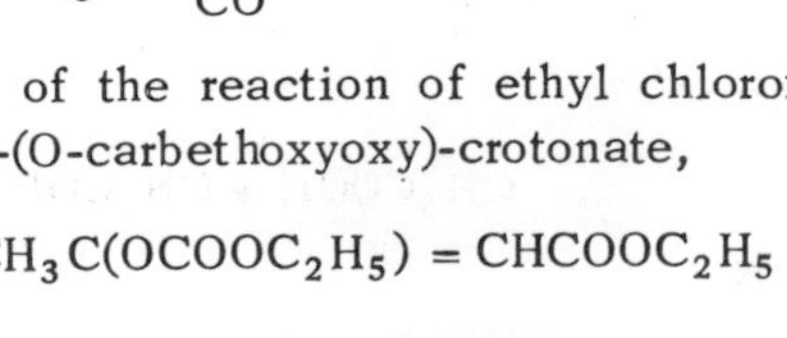

The principal product of the reaction of ethyl chloroformate and sodioacetoacetic ester is ethyl β-(O-carbethoxyoxy)-crotonate,

$$CH_3C(OCOOC_2H_5) = CHCOOC_2H_5$$

with a little diethyl acetylmalonate. An O-derivative is also obtained from monochloromethyl ether. Phosgene in benzene solution, reacting with ethyl sodioacetoacetate, gives ethyl α-chloroacetoacetate, but thiocarbonylacetoacetic ester,

$$CH_3COC(=CS)COOC_2H_5$$

is obtained with thiophosgene. Acetylcyanacetic ester, $CH_3COCH(CN)COOC_2H_5$, is obtained through the reaction of cyanogen chloride with ethyl sodioacetoacetate. The sodio compound of the cyano ester gives O-substituted derivatives of the enolic form, $CH_3C(OR) = C(CN)COOC_2H_5$, on reaction with organic halides. Diazomethane reacts with acetoacetic ester to form methoxy crotonic ethyl ester. The condensation of acetylsalicylyl chloride with sodioacetoacetic ester leads to the formation of acetyloxycoumarin,[108]

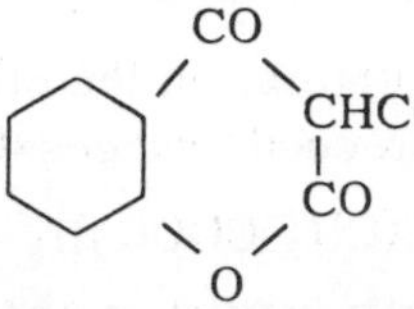

Homologs and derivatives of acetylsalicylyl chloride and *o*-acetoxynaphthoyl chloride react similarly.

The behavior of *benzyl cyanide* is much the same as that of compounds with an active methylene group previously discussed. The sodio derivative may be prepared through the interaction of benzyl cyanide and sodium amide in ethereal solution. The metal may be replaced in the sodio derivative with organic groups by reaction with organic halides. Alkylation[109] generally proceeds in a normal manner. It is preferable to carry out the reaction by use of alkyl iodides. As a rule, both hydrogens of the methylene group can be replaced with alkyl groups. Thus, a second organic radical may be introduced in the molecule of methylphenyl- and diphenylacetonitrile; benzylphenylacetonitrile forms an exception, and it is not possible to introduce a second group in this compound. Benzophenone dichloride, $(C_6H_5)_2CCl_2$, may be condensed with the nitrile to form phenylcyanostilbene,[110] $(C_5H_5)_2C = C(CN)C_6H_5$. Cyclic derivatives may be prepared with dihalo compounds in which the halogen atoms are attached to different carbon atoms; phenylcyclopropyl cyanide, $\overline{CH_2.CH_2C}(C_6H_5)CN$, has been prepared, for example, with chlorobromethylene,[111] $ClCH_2CH_2Br$.

The reaction between sodiobenzyl cyanide and acid chlorides proceeds readily. Acetyl chloride reacts violently and, it would appear, in a rather complex manner. The sodio derivative of the enolic form of monoacetylbenzyl cyanide evidently is among the compounds initially formed, the interaction of this with another molecule of acetyl chloride giving an acetylated unsaturated hydroxy nitrile:

$$CH_3COCl + 2NaCH(CN)C_6H_5 \rightarrow CH_3C(ONa) = C(CN)C_6H_5 + C_6H_5CH_2CN + NaCl$$

$$CH_3C(ONa) = C(CN)C_6H_5 + CH_3COCl \rightarrow CH_3C(OCOCH_3) = C(CN)C_6H_5 + NaCl$$

Benzoyl chloride yields the benzoylated product, $C_6H_5COCH(CN)C_6H_5$. Sodiobenzyl cyanide does not react with phthalic anhydride.

Attempts to alkylate esters of diketo acids through their sodio derivative have not led to the expected products, but have generally resulted in the cleavage of one acyl group and its replacement with an alkyl group:

$$\begin{array}{l} CH_3C(ONa) \\ \qquad \backslash\backslash \\ \qquad\quad CCH_2COOC_2H_5 + CH_3I + C_2H_5OH \rightarrow CH_3COCH(CH_3)CH_2COOC_2H_5 \\ \qquad / \\ CH_3CO \end{array}$$

$$+ CH_3COOC_2H_5 + NaI$$

The acylation of alkylacetoacetic esters, on the other hand, which reverses the order of addition of substituents, proceeds successfully:

$$CH_3C(ONa){:}C(CH_3)COOC_2H_5 + C_3H_7COCl \rightarrow$$

$$CH_3COC(CH_3)(COC_3H_7)COOC_2H_5 + NaCl$$

Aliphatic nitriles may be alkylated by the simultaneous action of alkyl halides and sodium amide. The reactive halides are mixed with the sodamide and the mixture is added gradually to the solution of the nitrile in benzol heated to about 60°. The less reactive halides are mixed with the nitrile, the mixture is heated and a suspension of the sodamide in an inert solvent is added gradually.[112] γ-Chlorobutyronitrile may be condensed by this method to cyclopropyl cyanide.[113]

Use of Magnesium for the Replacement of Active Hydrogen

One hydrogen atom of a reactive methylene group may be replaced with the ethyoxymagnesium group by reaction with metallic magnesium in the presence of anhydrous ethyl alcohol and an activator such as iodine. Ethyl ethoxymagnesium-malonate, $C_2H_5OMgCH(COOC_2H_5)_2$, is obtained by this method, for example, from ethyl malonate. Alkyl iodides or organic halides with a mobile halogen, reacting with these ethoxymagensium compounds, replace the metallic group with the organic radical. Alkyl iodides yield with ethoxymagnesiummalonic ester dialkyl malonic esters.

Reaction of Active Methylene Groups with Nitroso Compounds

Reactive methylene groups may be condensed with nitroso compounds, in the presence of alkalies, to form azomethines:

$$>CH_2 + ONC_6H_4N(CH_3)_2 \rightarrow >C = NC_6H_4N(CH_3)_2 + H_2O$$

Azomethines are decomposed by dilute acids to a keto compound and an amine:

$$>C = NC_6H_4N(CH_3)_2 + H_2O \rightarrow >CO + H_2NC_6H_4N(CH_3)_2$$

This reaction offers a means for the preparation of certain triketones, such as triketopentane, $CH_3COCOCOCH_3$ and 2,3,4-triketohexane, $CH_3COCOCOC_2H_5$. In this connection, mention may be made of the fact that purely aromatic triketones have been prepared through the action of nitrous gases on dibenzoylmethane or its derivatives.

Ketones of the general type RCH_2COR' react with nitrous esters in the presence of hydrochloric acid to form isonitroso derivatives:[114]

$$RCH_2COR' + ONOC_5H_{11} \rightarrow RC(:NOH)COR' + C_5H_{11}OH$$

Reactions with Nitric Oxide and Nitrous Acid

Sodio ethyl acetoacetate is converted to disodio ethyl isonitraminoacetoacetic ester, $CH_3COC(Na)(N_2O_2Na).COOC_2H_5$, under the simultaneous action of nitric oxide and sodium ethoxide.

Nitrous acid reacting with ethyl acetoacetate gives ethyl isonitrosoacetoacetate, $CH_3COC(:NOH)COOC_2H_5$.[169] This compound readily decomposes to isonitrosoacetone, carbon dioxide and alcohol. With monoalkylacetoacetic esters, $CH_3COCH(R)COOR'$, nitrous acid yields α-isonitroso fatty acid esters, $RC(:NOH)COOR'$, whereas with the free acids isonitrosoketones

$$CH_3COC(:NOH)R'$$

are obtained with liberation of carbon dioxide and water.

REACTION WITH AROMATIC COMPOUNDS; MISCELLANEOUS OTHER REACTIONS.

Condensation of Carbonyl and Aromatic Compounds

Aliphatic aldehydes react with aromatic compounds in the presence of sulfuric acid or other condensing agent, two aromatic residues uniting with the carbonyl carbon, with elimination of a molecule of water:

$$RCHO + 2C_6H_6 \rightarrow RCH(C_6H_5)_2 + H_2O$$

The reaction takes place more readily with phenols and their derivatives and with certain aromatic amines than with the straight hydrocarbons. The readiness with which the reaction takes place depends also on the character of the aldehyde. Chloral, for example, reacts more readily than acetaldehyde. The reaction takes place also with naphthalene and its derivatives.

The *procedure* is to add concentrated sulfuric acid to a well-stirred solution of two moles of the aromatic compound and one of the aldehyde in acetic acid, at such a rate that the temperature does not exceed 40°. It is often necessary to apply external cooling toward the end. The reaction is generally complete, or nearly so, if the addition of more sulfuric acid does not cause a further increase in temperature. The mixture is usually allowed to stand for several hours before the isolation of the product, which is accomplished by pouring the liquid in water, filtering the solid and crystallizing from alcohol, ether or benzene. The yields often range between 60 to 90% of the theoretical. Concentrated sulfuric acid alone may also be used as a condensing agent; its effectiveness may be increased by the addition of sulfur trioxide. Tin tetrachloride, aluminun chloride, hydrogen chloride and potassium acid sulfate also act as condensing agents

In many cases, as for example, in the reaction of acetaldehyde with phenol, tin tetra chloride is a more effective condensing agent.[115] The condensation product of pheno with acetaldehyde is formed in the cold when tin tetrachloride is added dropwise to th liquefied mixture of phenol and paraldehyde with good stirring. When aluminum chlorid is used as a condensing agent the reaction may be carried out in carbon disulfide; o the condensing agent may be added directly to the mixture of the aldehyde with th aromatic compound.

The reaction takes place readily with formaldehyde, acetaldehyde, mono-, di and trichloracetaldehydes, bromal, crotonaldehyde and the acetals of these alde hydes.

In the reaction with phenols, ethers are apparently formed at first, and sub sequently undergo molecular rearrangement to the isomeric aryl-substitute hydrocarbon:

$$RCHO + 2C_6H_5OH \rightarrow H_2O + RCH(OC_6H_5)_2 \rightarrow RCH(C_6H_4OH)_2$$

Union with the carbonyl carbon atom takes place to a large extent at the *par* position in the aromatic nucleus with respect to the hydroxyl group. If thi pi sition is occupied, then union takes place at the *ortho* position.

The reaction takes place also with phenol ethers, although less readily tha with the free phenols.[116] Condensation products have been prepared from aniso methyl ethers of *p*- and *o*-cresols, with benzaldehyde. Many polyhydric phenol and β-naphthol give, on condensation with aldehydes, internal anhydrides o the type.[116]

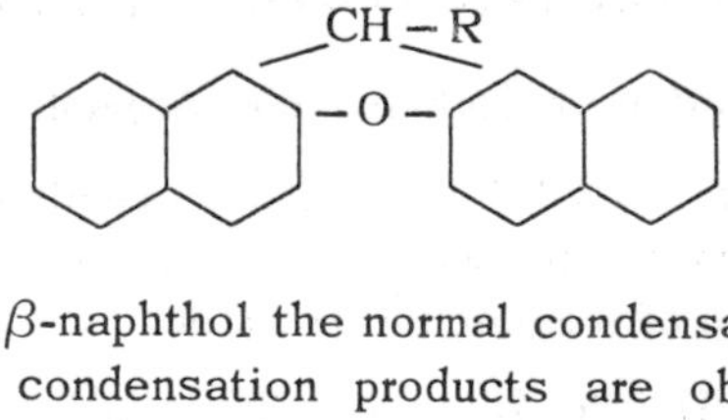

formaldehyde gives with β-naphthol the normal condensation product and not th anhydride. The normal condensation products are obtained with α-naphtho these are soluble in dilute alkalies, in contrast to the anhydrides obtained fro β-naphthol.

The activity of the carbonyl group in aromatic aldehydes is influenced b substituents in the aromatic nucleus. Thus, while benzaldehyde fails to reac with aromatic hydrocarbons in the presence of sulfuric acid, condensation take place readily with *meta*- and *para*-nitrobenzaldehydes. Benzaldehyde may b condensed with aromatic hydrocarbons under more vigorous conditions, namely by heating in a sealed tube at 250-270° in the presence of zinc chloride.

Union of a single aromatic radical with a carbonyl compound without cleavage o water may be brought about under certain circumstances. Condensation takes place i this manner when the reaction is carried out in dilute solution and mild condensin agents are used:

$$RCHO + C_6H_5OH \rightarrow RCH(OH)C_6H_4OH$$

The reaction proceeds in this way also when the components are heated with excess mineral acid.[118] Condensation of this type may be brought about with aromatic hydroxy acids and aromatic aldehydes under the influence of sulfuric acid of 60 to 66° Be., and with salts of aromatic amines and aromatic aldehydes in the presence of alcohols. Certain aliphatic aldehydes also give diphenylcarbinol derivatives with aromatic amines.[119] *p*-Dimethylaminophenyltrichloroethyl alcohol, $Cl_3C\ CH(OH)C_6H_4N(CH_3)_2$, results for example, through the interaction of chloral and dimethylaniline.

Amorphous condensation products result from the reaction of phenols with many aromatic aldehydes, among them anisaldehyde, *p*-nitrobenzaldehyde, nitrovanillin, bromohydroxybenzaldehyde, bromopiperonal and bromocinnamaldehyde. The nature of the product obtained depends upon the solvent employed, the temperature, and the reaction time.[120] Amorphous products are also obtained, as a rule, when aromatic aldehydes are condensed with polyhydric phenols. In a few exceptional cases crystalline, well-defined products are obtained, as for example, with guaiacol and phenol, or *o*-aminobenzaldehyde and phlorglucine, in the latter case dihydroxyacridine,

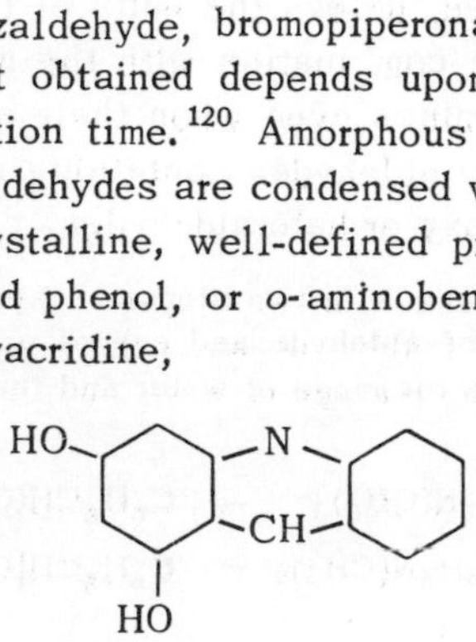

being the product of the reaction.[121]

Condensation products of the normal type have been obtained with salicylaldehyde and certain phenolic compounds, such as thymol[122] and resorcinol.

A number of aromatic aldehydes containing carboxyl groups have been successfully condensed with phenol. Leuco-piaurin,

$$(CH_3O)_2C_6H_2(COOH)CH(C_6H_4OH)_2,$$

has been obtained, for example, from phenol and opianic acid,[123] and hydroxyphenylphthalide,

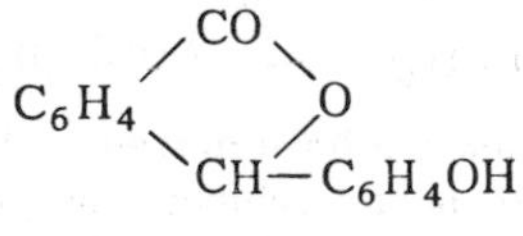

from phenol and *o*-phthalaldehyde.[124] Aldehydes may also be condensed with aromatic hydroxyaldehydes under carefully controlled conditions in the presence of zinc chloride:[125]

$$RCHO + 2C_6H_4(OH)CHO \rightarrow RCH[C_6H_3(OH)CHO]_2 + H_2O$$

Aromatic aldehydes with negative substituents react more readily, than benzaldehyde.[126]

Aldehydes react with many aromatic amines in much the same manner as with phenols. The reaction proceeds in the presence of the same condensing agents that act as effective catalysts in the reaction with phenols, namely, zinc chloride, hydrogen chloride, sulfuric acid, alkali bisulfite, anhydrous oxalic acid, phosphorus oxychloride,[127] etc. The leuco-base of Malachite Green results, for example, when phosphorus oxychloride is added gradually to a boiling alcoholic solution containing one molecular equivalent of benzaldehyde and two of dimethylaniline. The carbonyl carbon attaches itself preferentially at the *para* position in the aromatic group, as in the case of phenols, and if this position is occupied, union takes place at the ortho position. N-Substituted products are obtained with primary amines, unless the salts of these amines are used, preferably the sulfate, although combination with the nitrogen atom takes place to some extent with certain amines even when their salts are used. The reaction proceeds best with aromatic aldehydes containing negative substituents in the nucleus such as nitro, hydroxy or halo aldehydes.

Condensation apparently proceeds in two stages: a hydrol is formed first through the combination of one molecule of aldehyde and one of amine, and reacts further with a second molecule of amine, with cleavage of water and the formation of a triphenylmethane derivative:

$$C_6H_5CHO + C_6H_5N(CH_3)_2 \rightarrow C_6H_5CH(OH)C_6H_4N(CH_3)_2$$

$$C_6H_5CH(OH)C_6H_4N(CH_3)_2 + C_6H_5N(CH_3)_2 \rightarrow C_6H_5CH[C_6H_4N(CH_3)_2]_2 + H_2O$$

The second stage proceeds the more slowly the greater the acidity of the reaction mixture; it fails to proceed in 70% sulfuric acid.[128] The second reaction is favored, when sulfuric acid is used in conjunction with a dehydrating agent, or when dilute sulfuric or hydrochloric acid is used as the condensing agent.

Hydrols are formed readily only from aldehydes with strong negative substituents, such as *p*-nitrobenzaldehyde. Chloral gives a hydrol with dimethylaniline if the temperature is not allowed to rise above 40° during the reaction,[129] while at water-bath temperature it gives decamethylpentaminopentaphenylethane,

$$[(CH_3)_2NC_6H_4]_3C.CH[C_6H_4N(CH_3)_2]_2.$$

The hydrol is decomposed with hot caustic solution to a dialkylaminoaldehyde and chloroform:

$$Cl_3CCH(OH)C_6H_4N(CH_3)_2 \rightarrow OCHC_6H_4N(CH_3)_2 + Cl_3CH$$

Hydrols derived from aromatic amines have played an important role in dye chemistry, and an extensive literature exists in the subject. Such hydrols may be condensed with primary, secondary and tertiary bases to triphenylmethane derivatives.

m-Aminophenols in alcoholic solution reacting with aromatic aldehydes in the presence of zinc chloride yield leuco-bases of the triphenylmethane series. The reaction proceeds well also in concentrated sulfuric acid or in acetic acid in the presence of sulfuric acid. Substituted amino aldehydes may also be condensed with aromatic amines. Hexamethyl-*p*-leucaniline results, for example, from dimethylaminobenzaldehyde and dimethylaniline. The reaction often proceeds more readily and with formation of smaller amounts of by-products when sulfuric acid rather than hydrochloric acid is used as a condensing agent. It is possible to bring about the union of two different aromatic groups with the carbonyl carbon. Thus, tetramethyldiaminodiphenylxylylmethane is obtained in quantitative yield when one molecular equivalent of *p*-dimethylaminobenzaldehyde is heated for 24 hours with a solution of one molecular equivalent of dimethylaniline in 70% sulfuric acid and an excess of *meta*-zylene:[128]

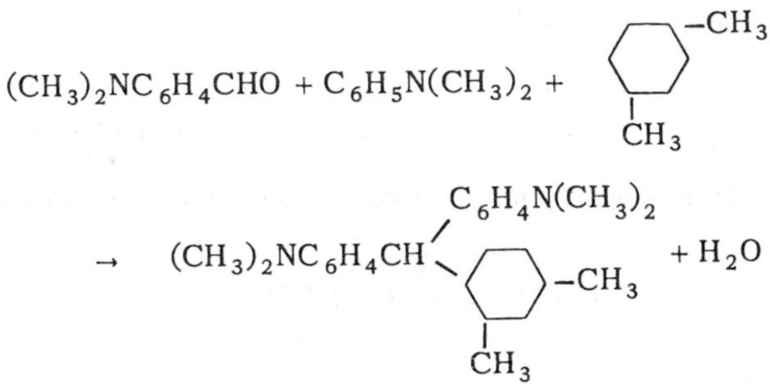
$(CH_3)_2NC_6H_4CHO + C_6H_5N(CH_3)_2 +$
$-CH_3$
CH_3
$\rightarrow (CH_3)_2NC_6H_4CH$
$C_6H_4N(CH_3)_2$
$-CH_3$
$+ H_2O$
CH_3

Aromatic aldehydo carboxylic acids may be condensed with aromatic amines to mordant dyes of the triphenylmethane series. Tetramethyldiaminotriphenylmethanehydroxycarboxylic acid, $[(CH_3)_2NC_6H_4]_2CHC_6H_3(OH)COOH$, may be obtained, for example, from *o*-aldehydosalicylic acid and diethylaniline. The condensation is effected in the presence of sulfuric acid by heating the reaction mixture at 90° for a day.

In contrast to dimethyl- or diethylaniline, *o*-toluidine fails to condense with aldehydes under the usual conditions, but condensation proceeds readily with monoalkyl *o*-toluidines. For example, methyl-*o*-toluidine reacts readily with dichlorobenzaldehyde in alcoholic solution in the presence of sulfuric acid to form dimethylamino-*o*-ditolyldichlorophenylmethane,

$$Cl_2C_6H_3CH[C_6H_3(CH_3)NHCH_3]_2$$

Phenylisoindole undergoes condensation with aldehydes in the same manner as dimethylaniline.[130] α-Methylindole condenses with aliphatic and aromatic aldehydes as follows:[131]

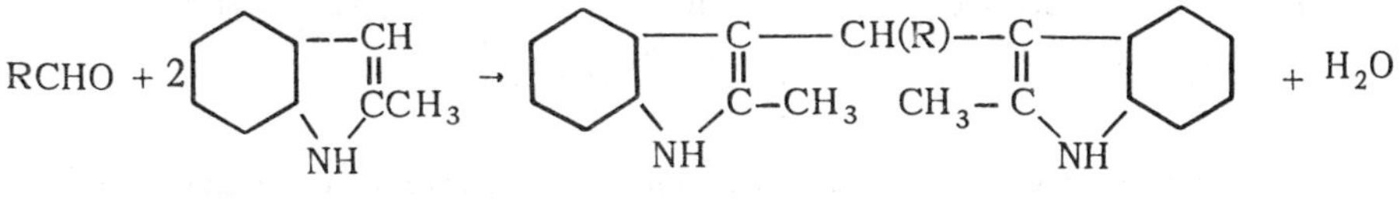
RCHO + 2
CH
CCH3
NH
C—CH(R)—C
C–CH3
CH3–C
NH
NH
+ H2O

Aliphatic ketones react with aromatic compounds in the presence of hydrogen chloride or ferric chloride to form alkyldiphenylmethane derivatives:[132]

$$R_1R_2CO + 2C_6H_5OH \rightarrow R_1R_2C(C_6H_4OH)_2 + H_2O$$

The reaction proceeds best in the temperature range 50-60°. Hydrogen chloride exerts an accelerating influence on the reaction in proportion to its concentration, although the use of an excessive amount of this acid should be avoided. Ketones of low molecular weight are much more reactive than those of high molecular weight. Polyhydric phenols may combine with more than one molecular proportions of the ketone; thus resorcinol combines with two and pyrogallol with three molecular equivalents of acetone, although hydroquinone and pyrocatechin combine only with a single molecular proportion of the ketone. [133]

Chloracetone reacts with one molecular proportion of phenol to give p-hydroxyphenylacetone, which then reacts with two additional moles of phenol to form 1,2,2,tri-(hydroxyphenyl)-propane: [134]

$$CH_3COCH_2Cl + C_6H_5OH \rightarrow CH_3COCH_2C_6H_4OH + HCl$$

$$CH_3COCH_2C_6H_4OH + 2C_6H_5OH \rightarrow CH_3C(C_6H_4OH)_2CH_2C_6H_4OH + H_2O$$

Cyclohexanone condenses with phenol to dihydroxyphenylcyclohexane,

$$\overline{CH_2(CH_2)_4}C(C_6H_4OH)_2.$$

Diphenylene ketone,

$$\begin{array}{c} CO \\ \diagup \quad \diagdown \\ C_6H_4 \text{——} C_6H_4, \end{array}$$

reacts similarly at 115-120° in the presence of tin chloride, while anthraquinone yields phenol anthraquinone, [135]

$$\begin{array}{c} C(C_6H_4OH)_2 \\ \diagup \\ C_6H_4 \text{-} CO \text{-} C_6H_4 \end{array}$$

Substituted benzophenones react with tertiary bases in the presence of dehydrating agents to give triphenylmethane derivatives; hexamethylrosaniline results, for example, in the form of its chloride, through the interaction of tetramethyldiaminobenzophenone and dimethylaniline hydrochloride.

Alloxan reacts with benzene in the presence of oleum of 20% SO_3 content to form 5,5'-diphenylbarbituric acid in 50% yield: [206]

$$\begin{array}{c} NH-CO \\ OC \diagup \quad \diagdown CO + C_6H_6 \\ \diagdown \quad \diagup \\ NH-CO \end{array} \rightarrow \begin{array}{c} NH-CO \\ OC \diagup \quad \diagdown C(C_6H_5)_2 + H_2O \\ \diagdown \quad \diagup \\ NH-CO \end{array}$$

Heterocyclic oxygen ring compounds result when α,β-unsaturated ketones, such as benzalacetone, react with phenol:

$$\begin{array}{c} \bigcirc \\ OH \end{array} + RCOCH = CHR' \rightarrow \begin{array}{c} R \\ \diagup \\ C \\ \bigcirc \diagdown CH \\ \diagdown \quad | \\ CHR' \\ O \end{array} + H_2O$$

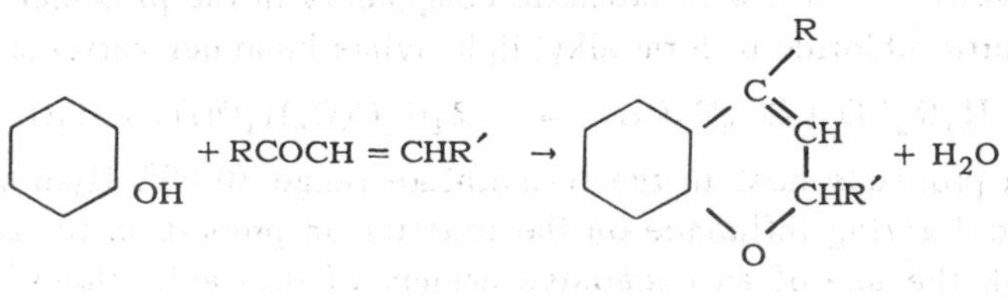

Chloro ketones of the type, $RCOCH_2CHCl.R'$, also yield such ring compounds on reactions with phenols.

1,3-Diketones combine with certain aromatic amines forming nitrogen ring compounds.

Examples are the formation of 2-methyl-4-phenyl-7-hydroxyquinoline from *m*-aminophenol and benzoylacetone, and of 2,4,6-trimethylquinoline from *p*-toluidine and acetyl acetone.

Lederer-Manasse Reaction

The condensation of formaldehyde with aromatic compounds leading to the formation of methylol derivatives is known as the Lederer-Manasse reaction. Formaldehyde may react with one or with two molecules of an aromatic compound to form a methylol or a diarylmethane derivative:

$$(CH_3)_2C_6H_3OH + CH_2O \rightarrow (CH_3)_2C_6H_2(OH)CH_2OH$$

$$2(CH_3)_2C_6H_3OH + CH_2O \rightarrow [(CH_3)_2C_6H_2(OH)]_2CH_2$$

The *procedure* is to add a molar equivalent of aqueous formalin to a solution of one molar equivalent of phenol in a slight excess of dilute sodium hydroxide solution and to allow the mixture to stand until the odor of formaldehyde disappears. An acid is added in moderate excess at the end of the reaction and the product is isolated by extraction with ether. Paraformaldehyde or methylal may be substituted for the formalin. The dimethylol derivative may also be formed as a byproduct in some cases in small amounts.

The formation of diarylmethane is favored by vigorous condensing agents. Thus, while *meta*-xylol, reacting with formaldehyde in the presence of slaked lime, gives the hydroxymethylene derivative, the product obtained when the reaction is carried out in the presence of even very dilute sodium hydroxide is the diphenylmethane derivative. The type of product obtained is determined, in a large measure, by the character of the phenolic compound, the diarylmethane derivative being obtained, for example, from β-naphthol and *vic-m*-xylol.[136]

Condensation takes place under the influence of alkaline or neutral condensing agents, the methylol group entering the *ortho* and *para* positions with respect to the hydroxyl group. Suitable condensing agents are alkali hydroxides and carbonates, the oxides of calcium, barium, zinc and lead. Strong alkalies favor the formation of the *para* compound.[137] The reaction takes place more readily with alkylated phenols such as metaxylol, than with phenol itself. 2-Methyl-4-bromophenol and many other halogenated and nitrated phenols fail to react.[138] The reaction generally proceeds well with tertiary aromatic bases.[139] Pyrrole[140] and pyridine and their derivatives are also capable of undergoing this reaction.

If the aromatic component contains an active methylene, the methylol group preferentially attaches itself to this.

Polyhydric phenols, such as resorcinol, pyrogallol, and hydroxyquinone condense readily with formaldehyde, but the products obtained are often amorphous, some tending to form inner anhydrides.[141] Amorphous, resin-like condensation products are obtained also from phenol itself, and the reaction forms the basis of the commercial preparation of the so-called phenolic resins.[142]

The reaction with *p*-nitrophenol takes a different course; it would appear that S-nitrosaligenin is first formed, and reacts with an additional molecule of formaldehyde to give an internal methylene ether:[140]

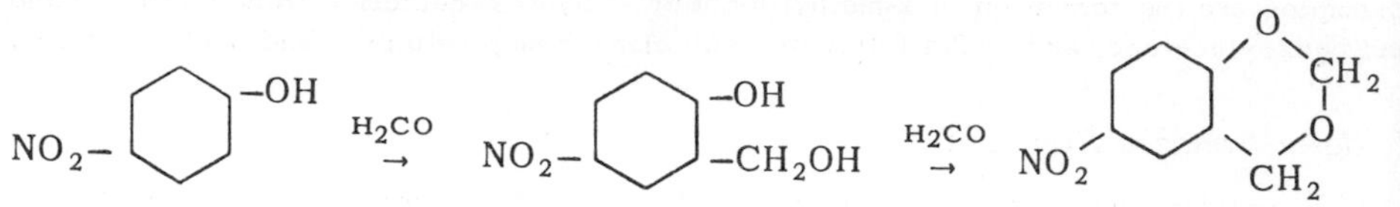

Some homologs of *p*-nitrophenol, such as 2- and 3-methyl *p*-nitrophenols, react similarly.

Chloromethylation

A chloromethylated product usually results when the condensation of formaldehyde with aromatic compounds is carried out in the presence of hydrogen chloride:

$$C_6H_6 + CH_2O + HCl \rightarrow C_6H_5CH_2Cl + H_2O$$

The reaction which is applicable to most aromatic hydrocarbons and their derivatives, takes place, in general, in the presence of a catalyst. Sulfuric acid, the chlorides of zinc, aluminum and tin are effective catalysts.

The introduction of alkyl groups in the benzene nucleus enhances the reactivity of the hydrocarbon, the highly alkylated homologs reacting rapidly in the absence of a catalyst. The chloromethyl group preferentially enters the *para* position with respect to an alkyl group, but a small amount of *o*-chloromethylated isomer also forms. Dichloromethylated products are obtained in many cases; these may be formed as the principal product from *meta*-xylene and mesitylene under the proper conditions.

Halogens, nitro, carboxyl and chloromethyl groups in the aromatic nucleus retard the reaction. *m*-Dinitrobenzene, 1,3,5-trinitrobenzene and *o*- and *p*-halonitrobenzenes fail to react. Aromatic compounds with three or more halogen atoms in the nucleus also fail to react. The presence of alkyl groups in the nucleus counteracts the influence of these substituents however. Monobromomesitylene, for example, may be chloromethylated quite readily. Hydroxyl groups in the nucleus greatly increase the rate of reaction, condensation proceeding vigorously, but the products obtained are often polymeric bodies. The activating influence of hydroxyl groups may be sufficiently attenuated by a deactivating group to make a smooth reaction possible; thus, nitrophenols may be chloromethylated without difficulty.[143] Phenol ethers react smoothly and well, as a rule; phenolic bodies and phenol ethers containing an aldehyde group also react in a satisfactory manner. Salicylic acid gives the 5-chloromethyl derivative in good yield.[217] Highly alkylated aromatic ketones may be chloromethylated successfully. Aromatic amines react vigorously with formaldehyde in the presence of hydrogen chloride, but complex condensation products are invariably the result of the reaction, and it has not been possible to isolate simple chloromethylated products derived from these bodies.[144]

Procedure

A variety of procedures have been utilized for the chloromethylation of aromatic compounds. The following is generally applicable to liquid bodies of moderate reactivity:

A mixture of paraformaldehyde and an equal weight of powdered zinc chloride with an excess of the aromatic compound is heated with stirring to 60° and a current of gaseous hydrogen chloride is led through the mixture until absorption ceases. The oily layer is washed with water and dilute aqueous sodium carbonate solution, dried over calcium chloride and the chloromethylated compound is isolated by fractional distillation.

In chloromethylating solid bodies, 40% aqueous formaldehyde may be employed, although it then becomes necessary to increase the amount of the catalyst. Trioxymethylene or acetals of formaldehyde may also be substituted for paraformaldehyde.

Sulfuric acid or aluminum chloride may be used as condensing agents, though these catalysts tend to favor the formation of diphenylmethane derivatives. Stannic chloride is employed with success occasionally with compounds which normally resist chloromethylation.[145]

Highly alkylated benzene derivatives usually can be chloromethylated without the use of a catalyst.[146] Anisidine and cresol methyl ethers may best be chloromethylated in the temperature range 0 to 15°, and without a catalyst, higher temperatures and the presence of catalysts favoring the formation of diphenylmethane- and dichloromethyl derivatives. Many other compounds require mild conditions for successful chloromethylation. Among such compounds are phenol ethers, nitrophenyl ethers, and highly alkylated aromatic ketones.

m-Xylene gives 2,4-dimethylbenzyl chloride with great ease; chlorobenzene gives *p*-chlorobenzyl chloride though requiring somewhat vigorous treatment. *o*-Chlorotoluene gives *m*-chloro-*p*-methyl benzyl chloride; nitrobenzene reacts to a slight extent forming *m*-nitrobenzyl chloride. *p*-Chlorobenzene and *p*-chlorotoluene fail to react. Naphthalene, chloronaphthalene and tetralin have been successfully chloromethylated.[218]

Chloromethylation may be accomplished by use of chloromethyl ether, CH_3OCH_2Cl, the reaction often proceeding in the absence of a catalyst; stannic chloride may be employed as a catalyst with the less reactive compounds. Carbon disulfide or other indifferent solvents may be employed as diluents. The chloromethyl ether is preferably used in excess.

Chloromethyl ether may be prepared by simply passing dry hydrogen chloride through a cooled mixture of 3 parts of paraformaldehyde and 2 parts of methanol, until all the solid paraformaldehyde disappears. The upper layer, which contains the chloroether, is dried with calcium chloride and is fractionally distilled. The product may be further purified by washing with concentrated hydrochloric acid. It is possible to obtain a product of 95% purity by this procedure.

Thiophene and benzothiophene undergo chloromethylation to furnish the respective 2- and 3-chloromethyl derivative.[219]

Glycols have been chloromethylated by passing hydrogen chloride into a mixture of glycol and trioxymethylene.[220] A few aliphatic ketones have been successfully chloromethylated with formaldehyde and hydrochloric acid:[117]

$$RCOCH_3 + CH_2O + HCl \rightarrow RCOCH_2CH_2Cl + H_2O$$

The bromomethyl group may be introduced into many aromatic compounds by the method employed for chloromethylation, although bromomethylation proceeds much less readily and the yields obtained are very much lower.[147] Iodomethylation appears to be of very rare occurrence.[148]

By using aldehydes other than formaldehyde, other chloroalkyl groups have been introduced into aromatic compounds in a few instances.[149] Chloroethylated products show a marked tendency to lose hydrogen chloride to be converted to vinyl derivatives.

Hydroxymethylation

Cyclohexanone has been hydroxymethylated by reaction with formaldehyde in the presence of calcium oxide at 40°, giving 2,2,6,6-tetramethylcyclohexanol in 73 to 85% yield.[164]

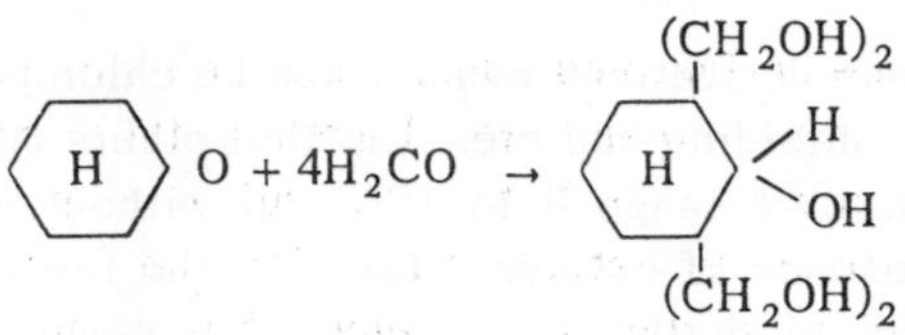

Willgerodt Reaction[150]

A remarkable transformation takes place when an alkyl aromatic ketone is heated in a sealed tube at an elevated temperature with an aqueous solution of yellow ammonium polysulfide, and the amide of an acid with the same number of carbon atoms results:

$$RCOCH_3 \xrightarrow{(NH_4)_2S_x, H_2O} RCH_2CONH_2$$

The mechanism of the reaction has not been elucidated. Willgerodt assumed that the oxygen migrated in some unknown manner to the end of the chain. Kindler considered it possible, on the contrary, that the aromatic radical as a unit wandered to the end of the chain, following the formation of a hydramine and other successive changes resulting in the appearance of an unsaturated sulfurated amine, such as $RC(NH_2 = S) = CHCH_3$, rearranging to $H_2NCSCH_2CH_2R$. Other hypotheses advanced in explanation of the reaction involve the assumption that an unsaturated hydrocarbon is formed as an intermediate, and this, on further reaction, gives rise to an amino compound or an isomercaptan, the latter then undergoing a series of changes ending in the formation of the thioamide.[151] The amide is presumably formed by hydrolysis of the thioamide. It has been demonstrated that the carbon skeleton is retained during the reaction, and that the transformation does not involve a migration of carbon atoms.

Procedure

A mixture of the ketone with the polysulfide reagent, in the proportion of five cubic centimeters of the reagent to every gram of the ketone, is heated in a sealed tube at 160-180° for a prolonged period, generally 12 hours or longer. The tube is then thoroughly cooled, the contents are removed and the amide is isolated.

The polysulfide reagent is best prepared by passing a current of hydrogen sulfide through a suspension of ten parts by weight of powdered sulfur in one part concentrated ammonia until all the sulfur dissolves. High concentrations of free hydrogen sulfide are not desirable since the compound causes the reduction of the carbonyl group.

It is of advantage to add *dioxane* to the reaction mixture, in the proportion of four volumes to every five volumes of the reagent. The reaction then proceeds at a lower temperature, side reactions are minimized and a higher yield of the product is obtained. The amide usually precipitates out of the dioxane- water solution upon cooling, and on simple filtration is obtained in a fair degree of purity. *Pyridine* will also serve as a solvent, although many amides remain in solution in the pyridine-water mixture after cooling. If the amide does not precipitate out of solution or does so partially, it is best recovered by distilling off the solvent, and extracting the residue with hot water, alcohol or other suitable solvent. Alternatively, the amide may be hydrolyzed with a mixture of acetic and concentrated hydrochloric acids; the organic acid formed isolated as its sodium salt by extraction with water and then freed by the addition of excess mineral acid.

Good yields of amide are obtained with some ketones, such as acetophenone, with a mixture of sulfur and concentrated aqueous ammonia in the presence of a solvent, such as pyridine or dioxane. Better yields are obtained by this method with aliphatic and certain other types of ketones when a small amount of hydrogen sulfide is introduced into the ammonia-sulfur mixture.

The reaction proceeds best with aryl methyl ketones, but alkyl aromatic ketones with higher aliphatic groups also undergo the transformation, the amide group appearing at the end of the aliphatic chain:

$$RCO(CH_2)_nCH_3 \rightarrow R(CH_2)_{n+1}CONH_2$$

The yield becomes smaller with increasing length of the alkyl chain, groups with 5 and 6 atoms giving the amide in very small yield.

Alkyl and alkoxy groups and halogens, if unreactive, do not interfere with the reaction and are not themselves affected; amino, nitro and formyl groups, on the other hand, undergo oxidative or other changes during the reaction. Ketones with branched chains give low yields of the amide, or do not react at all.

The reaction has been applied to some purely aliphatic ketones. Amides have been obtained, for example, from pinacolone and heptanone. Various heptanones such as methyl pentyl- and ethyl butyl ketone and heptaldehyde all give heptoic amide $CH_3(CH_2)_5CONH_2$; the best yield is obtained from the aldehyde and the next best from methyl pentyl ketone. The yield of amide from aliphatic ketones is improved when the proportion of sulfide is increased to correspond to 10 to 20 atoms sulfur per mole of ketone.

A number of byproducts are formed in the Willgerodt reaction. The amide is accompanied by small amounts of the ammonium salt of the corresponding acid. Reduction of the carbonyl group may take place, resulting in the formation of a hydrocarbon. Acetophenone and other methyl aryl ketones give appreciable quantities of diarylthiophenes. Anthracene is the principal product when ethyl 9-anthryl ketone is subjected to the reaction.

The Kindler Modification

The Willgerodt transformation may be brought about by a modified procedure originated by Kindler which utilizes a mixture of an amine and sulfur in the absence of water.[152] The reaction results in the formation of a thioamide:

$$RCOCH_3 + R_2NH + S \rightarrow RCH_2CSNR_2 + H_2O$$

Secondary aliphatic amines or morpholine are well suited for the reaction, though primary aliphatic amines or even anhydrous ammonia may also be employed with success. The amine and sulfur are generally used in 50% excess over the amount required by theory. The method offers the distinct advantage that, by the proper choice of the amine, the reaction may be carried out at atmospheric pressure.

The yields of thioamide are often quite satisfactory. Thus, a 73% yield of the thiomorpholide has been obtained from *o*-benzyloxyacetophenone, and about 90% yield from 2-acetylnaphthalene. With ketones, $ArCO(CH_2)_nCH_3$, yields of thioamide decrease with increase in the aliphatic chain length. The reaction fails to occur with arylaliphatic ketones, if the alkyl group contains a quaternary carbon. The thioamides may be converted to the corresponding acid in high yields; thus β-naphthylacetic acid has been obtained in 89.5% yield from the corresponding thiomorpholide.[153]

Aromatic olefin or acetylene hydrocarbons are transformed to amides under the conditions of the Willgerodt procedure, or to thioamides under those of Kindler's modification.[207] Phenylacetamide is obtained, for example, from phenylacetylene, and β-phenylpropionamide from either methylphenylacetylene or methylstyrene. The reaction of aldehydes and imines with ammonium polysulfide is also closely related to the Willgerodt reaction.[208]

Passerini's Reaction

Aldehydes and ketones react with aromatic isonitriles in the presence of organic acids to form the esters of α-hydroxy N-Arylamides:[154]

$$RN = C + R'CHO + CH_3COOH \rightarrow RNH.COCH(OCOCH_3)R'$$

The reaction proceeds well with many ketones, including cyclic ketones, but is not applicable to ketones in which an ethylenic linkage is present in 2,3-position with respect to the carbonyl group.

Halogenation of Carbonyl Compounds

The replacement of hydrogen atoms attached to a carbon atom with halogens proceeds with comparative ease if a carbonyl group is attached to the carbon atom. A methylene group is halogenated in preference to a methyl group.

In the halogenation of carbonyl compounds, enolization apparently precedes halogenation, the first process taking place slowly, the second vary rapidly.[155]

Aldehydes are readily halogenated, but extensive oxidative changes generally accompany normal halogenation. Substitution may take place at the carbonyl as well as the α-carbon atom.

Monohaloaldehydes are obtained in good yield when halogenation is carried out in an inert solvent such as methylene chloride, chloroform, and carbon tetrachloride at the lowest possible temperature. Cooling to –25° may be necessary in some cases. Monohalo compounds are formed also when the reaction is carried out in concentrated hydrochloric acid.[124]

Di- and tribromoaldehydes have been obtained by bromonation of paraldehyde in solution in a little more than twice its weight of acetic acid.

Acetaldehyde chlorinated in aqueous solution yields dichloracetaldehyde and chloral hydrate. Acetyl chloride is the product of the reaction if chlorination is carried out in the absence of water. Monochloroacetaldehyde may be obtained very readily from vinyl chloride $CH_2 = CHCl$ by the action of hypochlorous acid.[229]

Halogenated acetals are obtained through the chlorination of alcohols.

Aromatic aldehydes yield acid chlorides on chlorination, through the replacement of the carbonyl hydrogen with a chlorine atom. Bromination of benzaldehyde in carbon tetrachloride solution leads to the formation of bromobenzyl benzoate:

$$C_6H_5CHO + Br_2 \rightarrow C_6H_5COBr + HBr$$

$$C_6H_5COBr + C_6H_5CHO \rightarrow C_6H_5COOCH(Br)C_6H_5$$

n-Valeraldehyde has been directly brominated in chloroform solution at $-15°$, and α-bromo-*n*-valeraldehyde has been obtained in 70% yield.[210] Cyclohexanealdehyde has been converted similarly to the 1-bromo derivative by bromination in chloroform solution at 0°.[211] The reaction mixture containing the bromoaldehyde is often treated with absolute alcohol and the compound is obtained as the bromodiethyl acetal.[212]

Isovaleraldehyde in chloroform solution, treated successively with bromine and ethanol, gives α-bromoethylisovaleracetal:[156]

$$(CH_3)_2CHCH_2CHO + Br_2 + 2C_2H_5OH \rightarrow (CH_3)_2CHCH(Br)CH(OC_2H_5)_2 + HBr + H_2O$$

Removal of hydrogen bromide from this compound, followed by hydrolysis, results in the formation of β-methylcrotonaldehyde which is an important intermediate in the synthesis of natural polyene chains.

Bromination of acetals affords α-bromoacetals in satisfactory yield. The reaction is carried out in cold chloroform solution in the presence of calcium carbonate which removes the liberated hydrogen bromide.[213]

Bromination of enol acetates of aldehydes with subsequent reaction of the brominated product with methanol results in the formation of α-bromo acetals:[214]

$$RCH = CHOCOCH_3 + Br_2 \rightarrow RCHBrCHBrOCOCH_3 \xrightarrow{CH_3OH} RCHBrCH(OCH_3)_2$$

The enol acetates may be obtained in yields ranging 40-60% from aldehydes by treatment with a mixture of acetic anhydride and potassium acetate. Brominated keto acetals have also been prepared by this method from ketones capable of undergoing enolization.[215]

Ketones are readily halogenated, yielding a mixture of various haloketones. The hydrogen halides formed in the reaction, if allowed to accumulate, cause condensation reactions to take place. If more than one halogen atom enters the molecule, they tend to combine with the same carbon atom, although if halogenation is carried out first with chlorine and then with bromine, the latter combines with a carbon atom bearing no chlorine. Thus, chlorodibromacetone, $ClCH_2COCHBr_2$ results from the bromination of monochloracetone, and bromodichloroacetone, $Cl_2CH.COCH_2Br$ and dibromodichloroketone, $Cl_2CHCOCHBr_2$, result from *unsym*-dichloroacetone.

Acetophenone and its analogs are halogenated readily. The bromides are obtained simply by mixing equivalent quantities of the ketone and bromine in a suitable solvent. Most phenacyl bromides are crystalline bodies.

Monochloracetone[157] is obtained when chlorine is led through cold acetone in the presence of fragments of marble. Ten parts of marble and 40 parts of acetone are placed in a flask cooled with water and a current of chlorine is passed through the liquid, while 18 to 20 parts of water are added dropwise. The liquid separates in two layers; it is allowed to stand for 24 hours, and the upper layer is drawn off. The monochloroacetone is recovered from this by fractional distillation. Condensation products are formed when the reaction is carried out in the absence of calcium carbonate, and purification of the chloroacetone becomes difficult.

Dichloracetones[158], and pentachloracetone[159] are also obtained by the direct chlorination of acetone. Unsymmetrical dichloracetone results through the reaction of phosgene and acetone.

Sym-dichloracetone results also when α-dichlorohydrin is oxidized with potassium chromate and sulfuric acid.[160] Chloranilic acid or triaminophenol subjected to the action of potassium chlorate and hydrochloric acid give *sym*-tetrachloracetone;[161] this compound results also through the chlorination of phloroglucinol.[162] *Unsym*-tetrachloracetone results when isopropyl alcohol is chlorinated.[163]

Nitrosyl chloride, NOCl, reacts with methyl ketones, $RCOCH_3$, in carbon tetrachloride solution forming chloroisonitrosoketones, $RCOCCl = NOH$.

In neutral aqueous solution bromine reacts with acetone very slowly, but reaction proceeds vigorously in alkaline solution. The reaction is also accelerated by acids, in proportion to the hydrogen ion concentration, although the anion also seems to have an effect.[164] Mono-, di-, and tribromoacetone may be prepared by varying the conditions.[216] Acetone may be converted in aqueous solution by dilute bromine vapors to monobromacetone;[165] cyclohexanone may be similarly converted to 2-brom-1-cyclohexanone. Monobromacetone results in quantitative yield through the action of diazobenzo perbromide on acetone in the cold:

$$CH_3COCH_3 + C_6H_5N_2Br.Br_2 \rightarrow CH_3COCH_2Br + C_6H_5N_2Br + HBr$$

The perbromide dissolves in the ketone, an immediate reaction follows and crystals separate out. A quantitative yield of the monobromo product may also be obtained from acetophenone by this method.

Acetone dicarboxylic acid in dilute aqueous solution, subjected to the action of bromine gives pentabromoacetone.

Perbromoacetone, $Br_3CCOCBr_3$, is obtained by treating triaminophenol or bromanilic acid with bromine water.[165] Tribromacetone, Br_3CCOCH_3, results on bromination of isopropyl alcohol.

Dichloroacetophenone, dissolved in acetic acid containing fused sodium acetate in solution and treated with chlorine at 95°, is converted to trichloroacetophenone.[209]

Picoline, brominated in chloroform solution at −15° in the presence of tin chloride, gives monobromopinacoline.[176]

Iodoacetone results through the interaction of monochloracetone and potassium iodide in aqueous alcoholic solution.[92] Iodine trichloride reacting with acetone yields *sym*-diiodoacetone in good yield.

β-Chloropropionacetal, $(C_2H_5O)_2CHCH_2CH_2Cl$, and other similar compounds are converted to the corresponding iodo compounds by treatment with hydrogen iodide in the presence of a trace of potassium iodide (*Wohl's method*).

Aldehydes and ketones react with iodine in acid solution to form α-iodo derivatives, the reaction apparently proceeding between the enolic form and iodine:[178]

$$CH_3CHO \rightleftharpoons CH_2 = CHOH \xrightarrow{I_2} ICH_2CHIOH \rightarrow ICH_2CHO + HI$$

Fresh solutions of iodine in aqueous alkalies react with compounds containing the groupings CH_3CO- or $CH_3CH(OH)-$, etc., to form iodoform, triiodosubstituted products being formed as intermediates:[179]

$$CH_3COCH_3 + 3KOI \rightarrow 3KOH + CH_3COCI_3 \rightarrow CH_3COOK + HCI_3$$

Replacement of the Oxygen of Carbonyl Groups by Chlorine

Phosphorus pentachloride acting upon carbonyl compounds causes the replacement of the oxygen of the carbonyl group with two chlorine atoms:[192]

$$CH_3CHO + PCl_5 \rightarrow CH_3CHCl_2 + POCl_3$$
$$(CH_3)_2CO + PCl_5 \rightarrow (CH_3)_2CCl_2 + POCl_3$$

The reaction generally does not stop at this stage, however, especially with ketones, and an unsaturated monochloro compound forms with the separation of hydrogen chloride:

$$(CH_3)_2CCl_2 \rightarrow CH_3C(Cl) = CH_2 + HCl$$

Maximum yields of chlorides are obtained by adding the ketone dropwise to a slight excess of phosphorus pentachloride in a glass vessel cooled to 0°. The chlorides are obtained in 91% yield by using freshly powdered phosphorus pentachloride, maintaining the temperature at 0° to 5° and agitating the reaction mixture effectively. Diisopropyl ketone and pentamethylacetone react at higher temperatures and yield α-chloro ketones as a result of a chlorination reaction. Phosphorus pentabromide causes mainly α-bromination.[193]

Some ketones yield unsaturated chloro compounds when subjected to the action of phosphorus pentachloride.[195] Dibenzyl ketone, for example, gives 1,3-diphenyl-2-chloropropylene:

$$C_6H_5CH_2COCH_2C_6H_5 + PCl_5 \rightarrow C_6H_5CH_2CCl = CHC_6H_5 + POCl_3 + HCl$$

Acetaldehyde has been converted to ethylidene bromide by the action of bromine and phosphorus:

$$CH_3CHO + 5Br + P \rightarrow CH_3CHBr_2 + POBr_3$$

Phosphorus tribromide may be used instead of a mixture of bromine and phosphorus.

Oxyalyl chloride reacts with many carbonyl compounds replacing the oxygen with two chlorine atoms:

$$R_1R_2CO + ClCO.COCl \rightarrow R_1R_2CCl_2 + CO + CO_2$$

This method is applicable to the preparation of unstable keto chlorides which are otherwise difficult to obtain, such as dibenzal and dianisal chlorides. It is not suitable for the preparation of benzal and benzophenone dichlorides and other similar compounds.

Phosgene reacts with benzaldehyde in a sealed tube at 120-130° to form benzal chloride, a reaction which takes place also with ketones.

Preparation of Ring Compounds from Diketones

The presence of two carbonyl groups in diketones makes possible the formation of ring structures through condensations resulting in the union of the two carbonyl carbons with an atom or with one or two distinct reactive centers in the molecule. Self-condensation resulting in ring formation may also take place, involving one or more molecules of the carbonyl compounds. The following are representative of such condensations.

α-Diketones combine with *o*-phenylenediamine to form quinoxalines:

$$RCOCOR' + H_2NC_6H_4NH_2 \rightarrow RC = NC_6H_4N = CR' + 2H_2O$$

Glyoxilines are obtained through the reaction of *α*-diketones with ammonia and an aldehyde:

$$RCOCOR' + CH_3CHO + 2NH_3 \rightarrow HNC(R) = C(R')N = CCH_3 + 3H_2O$$

α-Diketones containing methyl or methylene groups adjacent to the carbonyl groups may undergo self-condensation to quinones:

$$2CH_3COCOCH_3 \rightarrow COC(CH_3) = CHCOC(CH_3) = CH + 2H_2O$$

1,3-Diketones yield cyclic products with hydroxylamine and with hydrazines; isoxazoles are obtained with the former and pyrazoles with the latter:

$$RCOCH_2COR' + H_2NOH \rightarrow H_2O + RC(:NOH)CH_2COR'$$

$$\rightarrow N = C(R)CH = C(R')O$$

$$RCOCH_2COR' + H_2NNHC_6H_5 \rightarrow N = C(R)CH = C(R')NC_6H_5 + 2H_2O$$

Semicarbazide also yields a pyrazole derivative.

1,4-Diketones are capable of internal condensation leading to the formation of furan derivatives:

$$CH_3COCH_2CH_2COCH_3 \rightarrow CH_3C = CHCH = C(CH_3)O + H_2O$$

These ketones are converted to cyclopentanone derivatives in weakly alkaline solution:[194]

$$RCH_2COCH_2CH_2COCH_3 \rightarrow CH_3C = C(R)COCH_2CH_2 + H_2O$$

By reaction with ammonia, such ketones give pyrrole derivatives:

$$CH_3COCH_2CH_2COCH_3 + NH_3 \rightarrow NH.C(CH_3):CHCH = CCH_3 + 2H_2O$$

Thiophene derivatives are obtained by reaction with phosphorus pentasulfide:

$$CH_3COCH_2CH_2COCH_3 + H_2S \rightarrow \overline{SC(CH_3) = CHCH = CCH_3} + 2H_2O$$

References

1. Fischer and Giebe, *Ber.*, **30**, 3053 (1897); **31**, 545 (1898); Delépine, *Bull.soc.chim.*, (3) **25**, 574 (1901); Haworth and Lapworth, *J. Chem. Soc.*, **121**, 79 (1922); Adkins, et al., *J. Am. Chem. Soc.*, **44**, 2749 (1922); **47**, 1358, 1368 (1925); **50**, 178 (1928). Ghysels and Bédowe, *Bull.soc.chim. Belg.* **34**, 41 (1925). Cf. Gilman and Blatt, "*Organic Syntheses*", Coll. vol. 1, 2nd ed. (1941) p. 1.
2. Delépine, *Bull. soc. chim.*, (3) **25**, 364 (1900); *Ann. chim.*,(7) **23**, 378 (1901); Adkins and Adams, *J. Am. Chem. Soc.*, **47**, 1368 (1925).
3. Haworth and Lapworth, *J. Chem. Soc.* **121**, 82 (1922).
4. Adams and Adkins, *J. Am. Chem. Soc.* **47**, 1366 (1925).
5. Helferich and co-workers, *Ber.* **52**, 1126, 1804 (1919); **55**, 703 (1922); **56**, 759 (1923); **57**, 1912 (1924); **58**, 1246 (1925); Bergmann and Ludwig, *Ann.* **436**, 173 (1924); Bergmann and Kann, *ibid.*, **438**, 280 (1924); Bergmann and Gierth, *ibid.*, **448**, 48 (1926); Fischer and Milbrand, *Ber.* **57**, 707 (1924).
6. Delépine, *Bull. soc. chim*, (3) **23**, 915 (1900); Trillat and Cambier, *Compt. rend.*, **118**, 1277 (1894); Verley, *Bull. soc. chim.*, (3) **21**, 275 (1899).
7. Claisen, *Ber.* **29**, 1005 (1896); **31**, 1010 (1898); **40**, 3903 (1907). Guest *et al.*, *U. S. patent* 2,421,559 (1944).
8. Hill and Black, *J. Am. Chem. Soc.*, **31**, 207 (1901).
9. Helfrich and Hansen, *Ber.* **57**, 795 (1924); Skrabal and Bilger, *Z. physik. Chem.*, **130**, 30 (1927).
10. Voss, *Ann.* **485**, 283 (1931) *Cf.* Voss and Blanke, *ibid.*, **485**, 258 (1931).
11. Fosse, *Compt. rend.*, **130**, 725 (1900); Mackenzie, *J. Chem. Soc.* **69**, 985 (1896); **79**, 1204 (1901); Mackenzie and Joseph, *ibid.*, **85**, 790 (1904).
12. Favre, *Bull. soc. chim.*, (3) **11**, 879 (1894); Wurtz and Frapolli, *Jahresb.* **1872**, 438; Pergami, *Gazz. chim. ital.*, **26II**, 466 (1887).
13. Scheiber, Marhenkel and Nikolič, *Ann.*, **458**, 21 (1927).
14. Staudinger and Rathsam, *Helv. Chim. Acta*, **5**, 645 (1922).
15. Wohl, *Ber.*, **31**, 1798 (1898); **41**, 3608 (1908).
16. Cf. Fischer, *ibid.*, **26**, 93 (1893); Jacobsen and Neumeister, *ibid.*, **15**, 602 (1882).
17. Baumann, *Ber.* **18**, 883 (1885). Posner, *ibid.*, **32**, 2801 (1899); **33**, 2983 (1900); **34**, 2643 (1901); **35**, 493, 799, 2343 (1902); **36**, 296 (1903); **37**, 502 (1904); **38**, 646 (1905); **40**, 4788 (1907).
18. Autenrieth, et al., *Ber.* **35**, 1388 (1902); **36**, 183 (1903); **41**, 4249 (1908); **42**, 4346 (1909); Koetz, *ibid.*, **33**, 729 (1900).
19. Geuther, *Ann.* **106**, 249 (1858); Guthrie and Kolbe, *ibid.*, **109**, 299 (1859); Skraup, *Montsh.*, **19**, 458 (1898); Wegscheider and Späth, *ibid.*, **30**, 840 (1909); Whol and Maag, *Ber.*, **43**, 3292 (1910); Hurd and Green, *J. Am. chem. soc.*, **63**, 2201 (1941).
20. Simpson, *Ann.*, **109**, 156 (1859); Rubencamp, *ibid.*, **225**, 274 (1884); Franchimant, *Rec. trav. chim.*, **1**, 243 (1882); Descudé, *Ann. chim.*, (7) **29**, 488, 501 (1903); Lees, *J. Chem. Soc.* **83**, 145 (1903); Ulich and Adams, *J. Am. Chem. Soc.*, **43**, 660 (1921); Späth and Schmid, *Ber.*, **73**, 248 (1940).
21. Wurtz and Frapolli, *Ann.*, **108**, 226 (1858); Schiff, *Zeitschrift für Chemie*, **1870**, 74; Bachmann, *Ann.*, **218**, 38 (1883); Guther and Rübencamp, *ibid.*, **225**, 269 Ann. (1884); Claus and Trainer, *Ber.*, **19**, 3004 (1886).
22. Perkin, *J. Chem. Soc.* **21**, 53, 181 (1868)1 **31**, 388 (1877); **32**, 669 (1878), **35**, 138 (1879); **49**, 317 (1886); Fittig, *Ann.* **195**, 169 (1879); **216**, 97 (1883); **227**, 48 (1885); *Ber.*, **14**, 1824 (1881); **16**, 1436 (1883); **27**, 2658 (1897); Fittig and Jayne, *Ann.* **216**, 115 (1883); Fittig and Ott, *ibid.*, **227**, 119 (1885); Baeyer and Jackson, *Ber.*, **13**, 115 (1880); Conrad and Bischoff, *Ann.*, **204**, 183 (1880); Michael, *J. prakt. Chem.*, (2) **60**, 364 (1899); *Am. Chem. J.*, **50**, 411 (1913); Michael and Hartman, *Ber.*, **34**, 918 (1901). Watson *Ann. Repts. Chem. Soc.* (London), **36**, 210 (1939); Johnson, "*Chemical Reactions*" (J. Wiley & Sons, (1942)I, p. 210.
23. Bertagnini, *Ann.* **100**, 126 (1856).
24. Perkin, *J. Chem. Soc.* **49**, 317 (1886); Nef, *Ann.* **298**, 309 (1897); Michael, *Ber.*, **34**, 918 (1901); Conrad and Bischoff, *Ann.*, **204**, 183 (1880); Kalnin, *Helv. Chim. Acta*, **11**, 983

(1928); Müller, *Ann.*, **491**, 252 (1931); **515**, 97 (1935); Breslow and Hawser, *J. Am. Chem. Soc.*, **61**, 786, 793 (1939); Arndt and Eistert, *Ber.*, **69**, 2381 (1936).

25. Schaarschmidt, Georgeacopol and Herzenberg, *Ber.*, **51**, 1059 (1918).
26. Böck, Lock and Schmidt, *Monatsh.* **64**, 401 (1934); Lock and Boyer, *Ber.*, **72**, 1064 (1939).
27. Löw, *Ann.*, **231**, 375 (1885); Ephraim, *Ber.* **34**, 2784 (1901); Thiele and Falk, *Ann.* **347**, 117 (1906); Ruggli and Staub, *Helv. Chim. Acta*, **17**, 1523 (1934).
28. Gabriel and Michael, *Ber.* **10**, 1554 (1877); **11**, 1683 (1878); Gabriel, *ibid.*, **17**, 2521 (1884); Gabriel and Neumann, *ibid.*, **26**, 952 (1893); Bromberg, *ibid.*, **29**, 1439 (1896).
29. Homolka, *Ber.*, **18**, 987 (1885); Claus and Wollmer, *ibid.*, **18**, 1861 (1885).
30. Rupe, *Ann.*, **395**, 106, 411 (1913).
31. Fittig and Jayne, *ibid.*, **216**, 99 (1882); Perkin and Sen, *J. Chem. Soc.* **31**, 394 (1877).
32. Fichter and Latzko, *J. prakt. Chem.*, (2) **74**, 330 (1906).
33. Loeven, *Ber.* **18**, 3242 (1885); Hinsberg, *J. prakt. Chem.*, (2) **84**, 192 (1911).
34. Erlenmeyer, *Ann.* **271**, 164 (1892); **337**, 265 (1904).
35. Buck and Ide, *"Organic Syntheses"*, **15**, 33 (1935).
36. Nicolet and Campbell, *J. Am. Chem. Soc.*, **50**, 1155 (1928); Deulofeu and Mendivelzua, *Ber.*, **68**, 783 (1935).
37. Gränacher, *Helv. chim. Acta*, **5**, 610 (1922); Julian and Sturgis, *J. Am. Chem. Soc.*, **57**, 1126 (1935); Plucker and Amstutz, *ibid.*, **62**, 1512 (1940).
38. Hauser and Breslow, *J. Am. Chem. Soc.*, **61**, 793 (1939).
39. Baeyer and Tonnies, *Ber.*, **10**, 1364 (1877).
40. Claisen, *ibid.*, **23**, 978 (1890); Young, *ibid.*, **25**, 2103 (1892); Posner, *J. prakt. Chem.*, (2) **82**, 435 (1910); Scheibler and Friese, *Ann.*, **445**, 141 (1925).
41. Stobbe, *Ann.*, **282**, 283 (1894); **308**, 90 (1899); *Ber.* **44**, 1297 (1911).
42. Stobbe, *Ann.* **349**, 333, 361 (1906); **351**, 1 (1908); **380**, 1 (1911); *Ber.* **38**, 3674 (1905).
43. Claisen, *Ber.* **38**, 701, 707 (1905); Neustädter, *Monatsh.* **27**, 887 (1906); Darzens, *Compt. rend.*, **139**, 1214 (1904).
44. Mannich and Ganz, *Ber.*, **55**, 3486 (1922); Dilthey, *ibid.*, **62**, 1609 (1929); Radionow and Postovskaja, *J. Am. Chem. Soc.*, **51**, 841 (1929); Blanchard, Klein and Donald, *ibid.*, **53**, 2809 (1931); Fischer and Marshall, *Ber.*, **64**, 2825 (1931); Drobnick, *Diss.*, Prague, (1933); Smith and Welch, *J. Chem. Soc.*, **1934**, 1136; Kuhn, Badstübner and Grundmann, *Ber.*, **69**, 98 (1936); Bernhauer and Irrgang, *Ann.* **525**, 45 (1936).
45. Doebner, *Ber.* **33**, 2140 (1900); **35**, 1137 (1902); Rosenmund and Boehm, *Ann.*, **437**, 125 (1924); Haworth, Perkin and Pink, *J. Chem. Soc.*, **127**, 1709 (1925); *J. prakt. Chem.*, (2) **110**, 125 (1925).
46. v. Auwers, Meissner, Seydel and Wisseback, *Ann.*, **432**, 46 (1923).
47. Boxer and Linstead, *J. Chem. Soc.* **1931**, 740. Cf. v. Auwers, *Ann.* **432**, 58 (1923).
48. Vorsatz, *J. prakt. Chem.* (2) **45**, 265 (1936); Kurien et al., *J. Indian Chem. Soc.*, **11**, 823 (1934).
49. Rodionov et al., *Ber.* **59**, 2952 (1926); *Arch Pharm.* **266**, 116 (1928) *J. Am. Chem. Soc.* **51**, 847 (1929).
50. Riedel, *Ann.* **361**, 89 (1908).
51. Massot, *Ber.*, **27**, 1225, 1574 (1844); Dutt, *J. Indian Chem. Soc.*, **1**, 297 (1925).
52. Fiquet, *Bull. soc. chim.*, (3) **7**, 11 (1892), *Ann. chim.*, (6) **29**, 433 (1893).
53. Haller and Wunderlich, *Ber.*, **47**, 1617 (1914).
54. Walter, *ibid.*, **35**, 1320 (1902).
55. Collie and Chrystall, *J. Chem. Soc.*, **91**, 1802 (1907).
56. Knoevenagel and Klages, *Ann.* **281**, 104 (1894); Knoevenagel, *ibid.*, **288**, 323 (1895); Rabe and Elze, *ibid.*, **323**, 87, 100 (1902); Wallach, *ibid.*, **323**, 145 (1902); Rabe and Rahm, *ibid.*, **332**, 3 (1904).
57. Rabe, *Ann.*, **312**, 167 (1900); Rabe and Elze, *ibid.*, **323**, 103 (1902).
58. Knoevenagel, *Ber.*, **29**, 172 (1896); **31**, 738 (1898).
59. Claisen and Matthews, *Ann.*, **218**, 175 (1883).
60. Merling and Wolde, *ibid.*, **366**, 131 (1909); Pauly, *Ber.*, **30**, 482 (1897).
61. Knoevenagel, *Ber.* **35**, 399 (1902).
62. Knoevenagel, *ibid.*, **31**, 732 (1898).
63. Stobbe, *Ann.*, **308**, 67 (1899); Russwurm, *ibid.*, **308**, 156 (1899).
64. Bechert, *J. prakt. Chem.*, (2) **50**, 1 (1894). Cf. Baker and Lapworth, *J. Chem. Soc.* **127**, 560 (1925).
65. Frost, *Ann.* **250**, 157 (1889); Meyer, *Ber.*, **21**, 355 (1888); Garrick, *J. prakt. Chem.*, (2) **45**, 500 (1892); Walther, *ibid.* (2) **53**, 454 (1896); Heuck, *Ber.* **28**, 2253 (1895); Brand and Löhr, *J. prakt. Chem.*, (2) **109**, 365 (1925).
66. Heyl and Meyer, *Ber.*, **28**, 2785 (1895).
67. Pfeiffer and Sergiewskaja, *Ber.*, **44**, 1107 (1911).
68. Walther and Wetzlich, *J. prakt. Chem.*, (2) **61**, 181 (1900).
69. Knoevenagel and Schmidt, *Ann.*, **281**, 47 (1894).
70. Knoevenagel and Weissgerber, *Ber.*, **26**, 436, 441 (1893); Klages and Knoevenagel, *ibid.* **26**, 447 (2893); Cf. Klingemann, *Ann.* **275**, 59 (1893).

71. Zinin, *Jahresb.* **1870**, 586; Knoevenagel, *Ber.*, **21**, 1356 (note) (1888); Japp and Klingemann, *ibid.* **21**, 2934 (1888); Knoevenagel and Weissgerber, *ibid.*, **26**, 436, 441 (1893); Klingemann, *ibid.*, **26**, 818 (1893); *Ann.* **275**, 50 (1893).
72. Jager and Unger, *Ber.*, **35**, 4440 (1902); Conrad and Reinbach, *ibid.*, **34**, 1339 (1901).
73. Noelting, *Chem. Zentr.* **1903 II**, 34.
74. Vorländer, *Ber.* **30**, 1801 (1897); *Ann.* **294**, 253 (1896).
75. Sasaki, *Ber.*, **54**, 168 (1921).
76. Thiele, *ibid.*, **33**, 666 (1900); Thiele and Büchner, *Ann.*, **347**, 249 (1906); Thiele and Henle, *ibid.*, **347**, 296 (1906); Sieglitz, *Ber.*, **52**, 1514 (1919); **53**, 1232 (1920); Wislicenus and Hentrich, *Ann.*, **436**, 11 (1924).
77. Knoevenagel and Walter, *Ber.* **37**, 4502 (1905). Cf. Thiele and Haeckel, *Ann.*, **325**, 7 (1902); Priebs, *ibid.*, **225**, 321 (1884).
78. Henry, *Compt. rend.*, **120**, 1265 (1895); **121**, 210 (1895); *Bull. soc. chim.*, (3) **13**, 999 (1895); *Rec. trav. chim.*, **16**, 189, 193 (1897). Schmidt and Wilkendorf, *Ber.*, **52**, 389 (1919); **55**, 316 (1922).
79. Thiele and Escale, *Ber.*, **34**, 2842 (1901); Borsche, *Ann.*, **386**, 351 (1911). Cf. Ruggli, Zimmermann and Thouvay, *Helv. Chim. Acta*, **14**, 1250 (1931).
80. Ladenburg, *Ber.*, **19**, 439, 2578 (1886); **22**, 2583 (1889). Matzdorff, *ibid.*, **23**, 2709 (1890); Königs and Happe, *ibid.*, **35**, 1343 (1902); **36**, 2904 (1903); Lipp *et al. ibid.*, **37**, 737 (1904); **38**, 2276, 247 (1905); **39**, 1045 (1906). Shaw, *J. Chem. Soc.*, **125**, 2363 (1924).
81. Komnenos, *Ann.* **218**, 145 (1883); Fittig and McKenzie, *Ber.* **26**, 2080 (1893); *Ann*, **283**, 82 (1894); Braunn, *Monatsh.*, **17**, 213 (1896). Cf. Massot, *Ber.*, **27**, 1225, 1574 (1894).
82. Kharasch and Marker, *J. Am. Chem. Soc.*, **48**, 3140 (1926).
83. Nef, *Ann.* **309**, 177 (1899).
84. Conrad, *ibid.*, **204**, 127 (1880); Schey, *Rec. trav. chim.*, **16**, 357 (1897); Michael, *J. prakt. Chem.* (2) **72**, 537 (1905).
85. Michael, *J. prakt. Chem.*, (2) **72**, 553 (1905).
86. Anschütz and Deschauer, *Ann.*, **347**, 6 (1906).
87. Ruhemann, *Ber.* **29**, 1017 (1896).
88. Stieglitz, *Am. Chem. J.*, **13**, 38 (1891).
89. Sell and Dootson, *J. Chem. Soc.*, **83**, 398 (1903).
90. Dimroth, *Ber.*, **35**, 2883 (1902); Dimroth and Feuchter, *ibid.*, **36**, 2239 note 5 (1903); Zelinsky and Doroschewsky, *ibid.*, **27**, 3375 (1894); Bischoff, *ibid.*, **28**, 2829 (1895).
91. Zelinsky and Porchunow, *Ber.* **28**, 2946 (1895).
92. Ipatjew, *J. prakt. Chem.* (2) **59**, 542 (1899); Perkin, *Ber.*, **17**, 54 (1884); **19**, 2039 (1886); *J. Chem. Soc.* **47**, 807 (1885); **65**, 578 (1894); Fittig and Röder, *Ann.*, **227**, 13 (1885).
93. Perkin, *Ber.*, **18**, 3246 (1885); *J. Chem. Soc.*, **51**, 241 (1887); Perkin and Prentice, *ibid.*, **59**, 824 (1891).
94. Marburg, *Ann.*, **294**, 112 (1897).
95. Wislicenus, *ibid.*, **242**, 23 (1887).
96. Anschütz, *ibid.*, **368**, 43, (1909).
97. Errera, *Gazz. chim. ital.*, **27 II**, 393 (1897); *Ber.*, **31**, 1241 (1898).
98. Dimroth, *Ber.*, **35**, 2881 (1902).
99. Anschütz and Wagner, *Ann.*, **367**, 232 (1909).
100. Carpenter and Perkin, *J. Chem Soc.*, **75**, 921 (1899); Barthe, *Bull. soc. chim.*, (3) **35**, 40 (1906). Cf. Barthe, *Compt. rend.*, **118**, 1268 (1894).
101. Wislicenus, *Ann.*, **186**, 216 (1877); Conrad and Limpach, *ibid.*, **192**, 153 (1878).
102. Oppenheim and Precht, *Ber.* **9**, 321 (1876).
103. Perkin, *Ber.* **16**, 2134 (1883); *J. Chem. Soc.* **47**, 829 (1885); Perkin and Obremsky, *Ber.* **19**, 2045 (1886); Freer and Perkin, *J. Chem. Soc.* **51**, 822 (1885); Perkin, *ibid.*, **57**, 215 (1890).
104. Perkin, *J. Chem. Soc.* **51**, 702, 709 (1887); Perkin and Kipping, *J. Chem. Soc.* **55**, 331 (1889).
105. v. Braun, *Ber.* **40**, 3944 (1907).
106. Claisen and Haase, *Ber.* **33**, 1244 (1900); Fischer and Bülow, *ibid.*, **18**, 2132 (1885).
107. Ruhemann and Merriman, *J. Chem. Soc.* **87**, 1383 (1905).
108. Anschütz, *Ann.* **367**, 193 (1909).
109. Zelinsky and Feldmann, *Ber.*, **22**, 3289 (1899); Bodroux and Taboury, *Bull. soc. chim.*, (4) **7**, 666, 670, 732 (1910); Haller and Bower, *Compt. rend.*, **155**, 1582 (1912); Lévy and Jullien, *Bull. soc. chim.*, (4) **45**, 941 (1929); Knowles and Cloke, *J. Am. Chem. Soc.*, **54**, 2036 (1932); Corré and Liebermann, *Compt. rend.*, **196**, 17 (1933); Jullien, *Bull. soc. chim.*, (5) **3**, 1347 (1936); (5) **6**, 1252 (1939).
110. Heyl and Meyer, *Ber.* **28**, 1799 (1895).
111. Knowles and Cloke, *J. Am. Chem. Soc.* **54**, 2036 (1932); Carré and Liebermann, *Compt. rend.*, **196**, 117 (1933).
112. Ziegler and Ohlinger, *Ann.* **495**, 84 (1932); Kisanor and Poliakova, *Bull. soc. chim.*, (5) **3**, 1601 (1936); Bergstrom and Agostino, *J. Am. Chem. Soc.*, **67**, 2152 (1945).
113. Cloke, Anderson, Lachmann and Smith, *J. Am. Chem. Soc.*, **53**, 2791 (1931).
114. Claisen, *Ber.*, **20**, 252 (1887); Claisen and Manasse, *ibid.*, **22**, 526 (1889); Sandmeyer, *ibid.*,

20, 639 (1887); Behrend and Tryller, *Ann.*, **283**, 244 (1894). Cf. Claisen, *Ber.* **27**, 655 (1887); Claisen and Manasse, *ibid.*, **20**, 2194 (1887); *Ann.*, **273**, 71 (1892).
115. Fabinyi, *Ber.*, **11**, 283 (1878).
116. Claisen, *Ann.*, **237**, 264 (1887).
117. Colonge, *Bull. soc. chim.*, (5e) **3**, 2116 (1936).
118. Albrecht, *Ber.*, **21**, 3292 (1878); Danckwortt, *ibid.*, **42**, 4163 (1909).
119. Böessneck, *ibid.*, **18**, 1516 (1886); Knöfler and Böessneck, *ibid.*, **20**, 3193 (1887).
120. Baeyer and Villiger, *Ber.*, **35**, 1197 (1902); Sen and Sinha, *J. Am. Chem. Soc.*, **45**, 2984 (1923); Danckwortt, *Ber.*, **42**, 4164 (1909); Claisen, *Ann.*, **237**, 262 (1887); Liebermann and Lindenbaum, *Ber.*, **37**, 1172 (1904); Kahl, *ibid.*, **31**, 143 (1898).
121. Eliasberg and Friedländer, *Ber.*, **25**, 1760 (1892).
122. Llorens, *Chem. Zentr.* **1921**, **III**, 785.
123. Liebermann and Seidler, *Ber.*, **20**, 873 (1887).
124. Bistrzycki and Öhlert, *ibid.*, **27**, 2632 (1894).
125. Rogow, *ibid.*, **34**, 3882 (1901).
126. Rogow, *ibid.*, **35**, 1961 (1902).
127. Mazzara, *Gazz. chim. ital.*, **15**, 44 (1885); *Ber.*, **18**, R.334 (1885); Tschacher, *Ber.*, **19**, 2463 (1886); **21**, 188 (1888); Stolz, *ibid.*, **20**, R.615 (1887); Wallach and Wünsten, *ibid.*, **16**, 149 (1883), Anschütz, *ibid.*, **17**, 1078 (1884); Kaeswurn, *ibid.*, **19** 744 (1886); Necki, *Monatsh.*, **9**, 1148 (1888).
128. Conzetti, *Chem. Zeit.*, **34**, 1099 (1910).
129. Böessneck, *Ber.*, **18**, 1516 (1885); **19**, 365 (1886); Knoefler and Böessneck, *ibid.*, **20**, 3193 (1887); Rousset, *Bull. soc. chim.*, (3), **11**, 318 (1894); Weil, *Ber.*, **27**, 3316 (1894); Sachs and Appenzeller, *ibid.*, **41**, 97 (1908).
130. Scholtz and Wolfrum, *Ber.*, **43**, 2305 (1910).
131. Fischer, *Ann.*, **242**, 373 (1887); Wenzing, *ibid.*, **239**, 241 (1887).
132. Meyer, *Chem. Zeit.*, **45**, 632 (1921).
133. Schmidlin and Lang, *Ber.*, **43**, 2808 (1910).
134. Lippmann, *ibid.*, **45**, 2489 (1912).
135. Graebe and Aubin, *Ann.*, **247**, 285 (1888).
136. Manasse, *Ber.* **27**, 2412 (1894); v. Auwers, *ibid.*, **40**, 2526 (1907).
137. Auwers, *Ber.* **40**, 2525 (1907); Auwers and Ercklentz, *Ann.*, **302**, 115 (1895); Manasse, *Ber.* **27**, 2409 (1894); Lederer, *J. prakt. Chem.*, (2) **50**, 223 (1894).
138. Auwers, *Ber.*, **40**, 2524 (1907).
139. v. Braun, Kruber and Aust, *ibid.*, **45**, 2977 (1912); **46**, 3056, 3460 (1913).
140. Borsche and Berkhout, *Ann.*, **330**, 82 (1904).
141. Caro, *Ber.*, **25**, 947 (1892); Kahl, *ibid.*, **31**, 143 (1898); Liebermann and Lindenbaum, *ibid.*, **37**, 1176 (1904); Möhlau and Koch, *ibid.*, **27**, 2887 (1894).
142. Baeyer, *Ber.*, **6**, 223 (1873); **7**, 1190 (1874); ter Meer, *ibid.*, **7**, 1200 (1874); Hsaeus, *ibid.*, **25**, 3213 (1892); Kleeberg, *Ann.*, **263**, 284 (1891); Abel, *Ber.*, **25**, 3477 (1892). van Marle and Tollens, *ibid.*, **36**, 1348 (1903); Lederer, *J. prakt. Chem.*, (2) **50**, 223 (1894). Concerning Bakelite type resins see Lebach, *Z. angew. Chem.*, **22**, 1598 (1909); Baekeland, *Chem. Zeit.* **33**, 317, 326, 347, 358, 857 (1909).
143. Stoermer and Behn, *Ber.*, **34**, 2455 (1901); Buehler, Kirchner and Diebel, *Organic Syntheses*, **20**, 59 (1940). Cf. Sommelet, *Bull. soc. chim.*, (4) **53**, 853, (1933); *Compt. rend.*, **197**, 256 (1933); Sommelet and Morszak, *Compt. rend.*, **198**, 2256 (1934).
144. Wagner, *J. Am. Chem. Soc.*, **55**, 724 (1933).
145. Sommelet, *Compt. rend.*, **157**, 1443 (1913).
146. v. Braun and Nelles, *Ber.*, **67**, 1094 (1934); Nauta and Dienska, *Rec. trav. chim.*, **55**, 1000 (1936).
147. Stephen, Short and Gladding, *J. Chem. Soc.*, **117**, 510 (1920); Vavon, Bolle and Colin, *Bull. soc. chim.*, (5) **6**, 1025 (1939); Darzens and Lévy, *Compt. rend.*, **202**, 73 (1936); Darzens, *ibid.*, **208**, 818 (1939).
148. Sandin and Fieser, *J. Am. Chem. Soc.*, **62**, 3098 (1940).
149. Quelet, *Bull. soc. chim.*, (5) **1**, 904 (1934); (5) **7**, 196, 205 (1940); *Compt. rend.*, **199**, 150 (1934); Quelet and Allard, *Bull. soc. chim.*, (5) **7**, 215 (1940); Ducasse, *ibid.*, (3) **3**, 2202 (1936).
150. Willgerodt, *Ber.*, **20**, 2467 (1887); **21**, 534 (1888); Willgerodt and Merck, *J. prakt. Chem.*, (2) **80**, 92 (1909); Willgerodt, *ibid.*, **80**, 183 (1909); Willgerodt and Hambrecht, *ibid.*, (2) **81**, 74 (1910); Willgerodt and Scholtz, *ibid.*, (2) **81**, 382 (1910); Willgerodt and Albert, *ibid.*, (2) **84**, 387 (1911); Weitzenböck and Lieb, *Monatsh.*, **33**, 556, 563 (1912); Mosetting and deKamp, *J. Am. Chem. Soc.*, **55**, 3444 (1933); Smith and MacMullen, *ibid.*, **58**, 633 (1936); Fieser and Kilmer, *ibid.*, **62**, 1354 (1940); Bachmann and Cormack, *ibid.*, **63**, 2494 (1941); Schwenk and Bloch *ibid.*, **64**, 3051 (1942); Cavalieri *et al.*, *ibid.*, **67**, 1783 (1945); Cormack *et al.*, *ibid.*, **68**, 2025, 2029, 2033, 2755 (1946); *J. Org. Chem.*, **12**, 76 (1947); Pattison and Cormack, *J. Am. Chem. Soc.*, **68**, 2033 (1946). King and McMillan, *ibid.*, **68**, 525, 632, 1369, 2335 (1946); **69**, 1207 (1947); **70**, 4143 (1948); McMillan, *ibid.*, **70**, 868 (1948);

Shantz and Rittenberg; *ibid.*, **68**, 2109 (1946); Dauben *et al.*, *ibid.*, **68**, 2117 (1946); Gilman and Avakian, *ibid.*, **68**, 2104 (1946); Ott *et al.*, *ibid.*, **68**, 2633 (1946); Campaigne and Rutan, *ibid.*, **69**, 1211 (1947); Molan and Dean, *ibid.*, **69**, 1797 (1947); Turner, *ibid.*, **70**, 396 (1948); Horton and Van den Berghe, *ibid.*, **70**, 2425 (1948); Corse *et al.*, *ibid.*, **70**, 2837, 2843 (1948); Kindler and Li, *Ber.*, **74**, 321 (1941); Schwenk and Papa, *J. Org. Chem.*, **11**, 798 (1946); Stank, *Coll. Czech. Chem. Comm.*, **12**, 691 (1946).

151. De Tar and Cormak, *J. Am. Chem. Soc.*, **68**, 2025, 2029 (1945); King and McMillan, *ibid.*, **68**, 525, 632 (1946).
152. Kindler, *Ann.*, **431**, 193, 222 (1923); *Arch. Pharm.*, **265**, 389 (1927); Kindler and Li, *Ber.*, **74B**, 321 (1941); Schwenk and Bloch, *J. Am. Chem. Soc.*, **64**, 3051 (1942).
153. Newman, *J. Org. Chem.*, **9**, 521 (1944); Schwenk and Bloch, *J. Am. Chem. Soc.*, **64**, 3051 (1942).
154. Passerini, *Gazz. chim. ital.*, **51**, 181 (1921); **53**, 410 (1923); **54**, 529 (1924); Baker and Schlesinger, *J. Am. Chem. Soc.*, **67**, 1499 (1945).
155. Watson, *Chem. Revs.*, **7**, 174 (1930).
156. Fischer and Löwenberg, *Ber.* **64**, 31 (1931); *Ann.*, **494**, 272 (1932).
157. Fritsch, *Ann.* **279**, 313 (1894); Fritsch, *Ber.*, **26**, 597 (1893); Darzens, *Compt. rend.*, **208**, 818 (1939); Kubiczek and Neugebauer, *Monatsh.*, **81**, 917 (1950).
158. Meyer and Janny, *Ber.*, **15**, 1165 (1882).
159. Fritsch, *Ann.*, **279**, 317 (1894); Quelet, *Bull. soc. chim.*, (5e) **7**, 196, 205 (1940).
160. Posner and Rohde, *Ber.*, **42**, 3233 (1909).
161. Levy and Curchod, *Ann.*, **252**, 330 (1889).
162. Zincke and Kegel, *ibid.*, **22**, 1478 (1889).
163. *Chem. Zentr.*, **1897 I**, 281.
164. Wittcoff, *Organic Syntheses*, **31**, 101 (1951).
165. Scholl and Matthaiopoulos, *Ber.*, **29**, 1555 (1896).
166. Widman and Wahlberg, *ibid.*, **44**, 2066 (1911).
167. Scholl and Matthaiopoulos, *ibid.*, **29**, 1557 (1896).
168. Zelinsky, *ibid.*, **22**, 3294 (1889); Tanatar, *Ann.*, **273**, 48 (1893); Haworth and Perkin, *J. Chem. Soc.*, **73**, 333 (1898); Komppa, *Chem. Zentr.* **1898, II**, 1169.
169. Traube, *Ann.*, **300**, 89 (1898).
170. Claisen, *Ber.*, **33**, 1242 (1900); Auwers, *ibid.*, **37**, 3900 (1904).
171. Delépine, *Bull. soc. chim.*, (3) **25**, 581 (1901); Apel and Tollens, *Ann.*, **289**, 44 (1896); Dworzak and Lasch, *Monatsh.*, **51**, 59 (1929).
172. Spangel and Carothers, *J. Am. Chem. Soc.*, **57**, 929 (1935).
173. Bogert and Roblin, *ibid.*, **55** 3741 (1933); Willfang, *Ber.*, **74**, 145 (1941); **70**, 2167 (1937).
174. Nieuwland, Vogt and Foohey, *ibid.*, **52**, 1018 (1930).
175. Brit. Patent 483, 828 (1938).
176. Backer, *Rec. trav. chim.*, **55**, 1036 (1936).
177. Adams and Adkins, *J. Am. Chem. Soc.*, **47**, 1358, 1368 (1925).
178. Croxall *et al.*, *ibid.*, **70**, 2805 (1948).
179. Price and Pappalardo, *ibid.*, **72**, 2613 (1950).
180. Nieuwland *et al.*, *ibid.*, **52**, 1130 (1934).
181. Hennion *et al.*, *ibid.*, **56**, 1786 (1934).
182. Nieuwland *et al.*, *ibid.*, **58**, 892 (1936).
183. Carswell and Adkins, *J. Am. Chem. Soc.*, **50**, 235 (1928).
184. Voss, *Ann.*, **485**, 283 (1931).
185. McElvain *et al.*, *J. Am. Chem. Soc.*, **58**, 529 (1936); **59**, 2266 (1937); **60**, 2210 (1928); **62**, 964, 1281, 1482 (1940); **64**, 254, 260, 1059, 1966, 2525 (1942); **65**, 2236, 2239 (1943); **66**, 1077 (1944); McElvain and Kundiger, *Organic Syntheses*, **23**, 45 (1943); McElvain, *Chem. Revs.*, **45**, 453 (1949).
186. McElvain *et al.*, *J. Am. Chem. Soc.*, **62**, 1482 (1940); **64**, 1966, 2525 (1942).
187. McElvain and Stevens, *ibid.*, **68**, 1917 (1946); McElvain and Clark, *ibid.*, **69**, 2661 (1947).
188. McElvain *et al.*, *J. Am. Chem. Soc.*, **62**, 964 (1940).
189. McElvain *et al.*, *ibid.*, **58**, 529 (1936); **62**, 1281 (1940); **64**, 254 (1942).
190. McElvain and Cohen, *ibid.*, **64**, 260 (1942).
191. McElvain *et al.*, *ibid.*, **64**, 260 (1942); **66**, 1077 (1944) *Cf*, Hagemeyer, *Ind. Eng., Chem.*, **41**, 765 (1949); Young, *J. Am. Chem. Soc.*, **71**, 1346 (1949).
192. Friedel, *Compt. rend.*, **67**, 1192 (1868); *Ann. chim.*, (4) **16**, 310 (1869); Delacre, *Bull. soc. chim.*, (3) **35**, 343 (1906); *Acad. roy. Belg. Classe Sci. Mem.*, (2) **1**, 1 (1904-1096); Risseghem, *Bull. soc. chim. Belg.*, **31**, 62 (1922); de Graef, *ibid.*, **34**, 427 (1925); Bartlett and Rosen, *J. Am. Chem. Soc.*, **64**, 543 (1942); *Cf.* Favorskii, *J. prakt. Chem.*, (2) **88**, 641 (1913); *J. Russ. Phys. -Chem. Soc.*, **44**, 1339 (1912); Vassliev, *Bull. soc. chim.*, (4) **43**, 563 (1928); Bourguel, *ibid.*, (4) **35**, 1629 (1924); Charpentier, *ibid.*, (5) **1**, 1407 (1934).
193. Faworsky, *J. prakt. Chem.*, (2) **88**, 641 (1913).
194. Hunsdiecker, *Ber.*, **75**, 455 (1942).
195. Wieland, *ibid.*, **37**, 1143 (1904).

196. Hauser *et al., J. Am. Chem. Soc.*, **66**, 1220, 1768 (1944); **67**, 1510 (1945); **68**, 26 (1946); **69**, 2325, 2649 (1947); Zellars and Levine, *J. Org. Chem.*, **13**, 160 (1948). *Cf.* Swamer and Hauser, *J. Am. Chem. Soc.*, **68**, 2647 (1946); La Forge *et al., ibid.*, **69**, 186, 2677, 293: (1947); **70**, 2287 (1948); Jackman *et al., ibid.*, **70**, 2884 (1948); Cristol *et al., ibid.*, **71** 1863 (1949); Hauser *et al., ibid.*, **62**, 2611 (1940); **65**, 2051 (1943); **69**, 2951 (1947); **70** 606 (1948); **71**, 770, 1350 (1949); Zook *et al., ibid.*, **68**, 2404 (1946).
197. Ruhemann, *J. Chem. Soc.*, **93**, 431, 1281 (1908); **97**, 457 (1910); Kalff, *Rec. trav. chim.*, **46** 594 (1927). *Cf.* Ingold, *J. Chem. Soc.*, **127**, 1199 (1925).
198. Ruhemann, *J. Chem. Soc.*, **101**, 1729 (1912).
199. Stuart, *ibid.*, **49**, 366 (1886); Knoevenagel, *Ber.*, **31**, 2168 (1898); Pechmann and Kraft *ibid.*, **34**, 426 (1901); Knoevenagel and Schröter, *ibid.*, **37**, 4487 (1904); Betti and Mundici *Gazz. chim. ital.*, **35 II**, 45 (1905); Chuit and Bolsing, *Bull. soc. chim.*, (3) **35**, 78, 8: (1906); Pandya and Vahidy, *Proc. Indian Acad. Sci.*, **A 6**, 181 (1937).
200. Guareschi, *Gazz. chim. ital.*, **48 II**, 83 (1918).
201. Knoevenagel, *Ann.*, **281**, 79 (1894).
202. Engler and Leist, *Ber.*, **6**, 754, 257 (1873); Schmidt., *ibid.*, **14**, 1460 (1881); Claisen and Claparede, *ibid.*, **14**, 2460 (1881); Claisen, *ibid.*, **14**, 2470 (1881); Baeyer and Becker *ibid.*, **16**, 1969 (1883); Claisen and Ponder, *Ann.*, **223**, 138 (1884); Fischer, *Ber.*, **17** 576 (1884); Knorr, *ibid.*, **20**, 1099 (1887); Zelinsky, *ibid.*, **20**, 922 (1887); Claisen and Manasse, *ibid.*, **22**, 529 (1889); Goldschmidt, *ibid.*, **28**, 818 (1895); Harries and Eschenbach, *ibid.*, **29**, 380 (1896).
203. Koenigs, *Ber.*, **25**, 797 (1892); Wislicenns and Sattler, *ibid*, **26**, 911 (1893).
204. Hunsdiecker, *Ber.*, **75**, 1190 (1942).
205. *Cf.* Hauser *et al., J. Am. Chem. Soc.*, **69**, 1264 (1947); **70**, 3957, 4250 (1948).
206. Barnes and McElvain, *ibid.*, **59**, 2348 (1937).
207. Carmack and De Tar, *J. Am. Chem. Soc.*, **68**, 2029 (1946).
208. Kindler, *Arch. Pharm.*, **265**, 389 (1927); Kindler and Peschke, *ibid.*, **270**, 340 (1932); **272**, 236 (1934).
209. Cohen *et al., J. Am. Chem. Soc.*, **72**, 3952 (1950).
210. Erlenmeyer and Jung, *Helv. Chim. Acta*, **32**, 37 (1949).
211. Heilbron *et al., J. Chem. Soc.*, **1949**, 737.
212. Kuhn and Grundmann, *Ber.*, **70**, 1894 (1937); Fischer *et al., ibid.*, **64**, 30 (1931).
213. Hartung and Adkins, *J. Am. Chem. Soc.*, **49**, 2517 (1927); McElvain *et al., ibid.*, **64**, 196- (1942). Fischer and Löwenberg, *Ber.*, **66**, 667 (1933); Harries and Krützfeld, *ibid.*, **39** 3675 (1906). *Cf.* Haganz *et al., ibid.*, **86**, 148, 1398 (1953).
214. Bedoukian, *ibid.*, **66**, 1325 (1944); *Org. Syntheses*, **29**, 14 (1949).
215. Bedoukian, *J. Am. Chem. Soc.*, **67**, 1430 (1945).
216. Levene, *Organic Syntheses*, Coll. vol. II, p. 88 (1934); Weygand and Schmied-Kowarzik *Ber.*, **82**, 333 (1949).
217. Buehler, *J. Tenn. Acad. Sci.*, **22**, 303 (1947).
218. Badger *et al., J. Chem. Soc.*, **1947**, 1432; Horn and Warren, *ibid.*, **1946**, 144.
219. Griffling and Salisbury, *J. Am. Chem. Soc.*, **70**, 3416 (1948); Avakian *et al., ibid.*, **70**, 3075 (1948); Blicke and Sheets, *ibid.*, **70**, 3768 (1948); Wiberg and McShane, *Organic Syntheses*, **29**, 31 (1949).
220. Lichtenberger and Martin, *Bull. soc. chim.*, (5) **12**, 114 (1945).
221. Johnson *et al., J. Am. Chem. Soc.*, **67**, 1357 (1945). *Cf.* Hewett, *J. Chem. Soc.*, **1942**, 555; Johnson *et al., J. Am. Chem. Soc.*, **69**, 792 (1947); Newman and Hart, *ibid.*, **69**, 298 (1947); Cook and Robinson, *J. Chem. Soc.*, **1938**, 505.
222. Rotbart, *Ann. chim.*, (11), **1**, 439 (1934); *Compt. rend.*, **196**, 1508, 2013 (1933); Halasz and Rovira, *Bull. soc. chim.*, (5) **8**, 185 (1941). *Cf.* Drake, *U.S. patent* 2,629,741 (1950).
223. Schorigin and Korschak, *Ber.*, **68**, 838 (1935).
224. Bedoukian, *J. Am. Chem. Soc.*, **66**, 1326 (1944).
225. Flaig, *Ann.*, **568**, 21 (1950); *Chem. Ber. des Reichsamtes f. Wirtschaftsaushau*, 1942, 1095.
226. Viguier, *Compt. rend.*, **154**, 218 (1912); *Ann. chim.*, (8) **28**, 515 (1913).
227. Fischer, *Ber.*, **27**, 637 (1894).
228. Wolfram, *J. Am. Chem. Soc.*, **51**, 2190 (1920); Overend *et al., J. Chem. Soc.*, **1949**, 2844. *Cf* Pacsu, *Ber.*, **58**, 509 (1925).
229. Ernst and Lange, *Germ. patents* 496,062; 521,723 (1927); *Frdl.*, **16**, 183; **17**, 202; *French patent* 979,133 (1948).
230. Tobolsky and Mesrobian, *Organic Peroxides.* Interscience Publ. (1954).
231. Rieche, *Ber.*, **64**, 2328 (1931); Rieche and Meister, *ibid.*, **68**, 1465 (1935); Milas *et al., J. Am. Chem. Soc.*, **61**, 2430 (1939). *Cf.* Criegee and Dietrich, *Ann.*, **560**, 135 (1948).
232. Hawkins, *Quart. Revs. (London)* **4**, 251 (1950); Criegee, *Fortschr. Chem. Forsch.*, **1**, 508 (1950).
233. Rieche, *Ber.*, **63**, 2642 (1930); *U.S. patents* 2,400,041; 2,455,569 Shell Development Co., *British patent* 444,544.
234. *U.S. patent* 2,455,569; Vaughan *et al., Ind. Eng. Chem.*, **41**, 1673, 1679 (1949); *J. Am. Chem. Soc.*, **71**, 1432 (1949).

CHAPTER 6

ALIPHATIC CARBOXYLIC ACIDS

ACIDS WITH NO OTHER FUNCTIONAL GROUPS

Methods of Formation

Conversion of Alcohols to Acids

Primary alcohols may be converted to carboxylic acids by oxidation with alkaline permanganate[1] or a mixture of chromic and sulfuric acids. Oxidation by the latter leads to the formation of a certain amount of byproducts, but these can be readily separated from the acid formed. The use of alkaline permanganate is preferable when aromatic aldehydes are oxidized to the corresponding acids, since the chromic acid mixture usually carries the oxidation largely to the aldehyde stage.

When more than one primary alcohol group is present in the compound, selective oxidation of one of these groups to a carboxyl group is possible by the use of dilute nitric acid. Glycerine may be oxidized in this manner to glyceric acid,[2] and sugars may be similarly converted to sugar acids.[3]

A method of restricted applicability consists in heating the alcohol with solid caustic in an autoclave at 200 - 250°.[4] Soda-lime may be employed instead of caustic. Palmitic acid may be obtained in quantitative yield, for example, when cetyl alcohol is heated at 210 - 220° with soda-lime.

Oxidation of Aldehydes to Acids

Aldehydes are readily oxidized to the corresponding acids by treatment with *potassium permanganate* or with dilute *nitric acid*. The permanganate may be used in aqueous solution containing sodium carbonate or in acetone solution. Saturated aliphatic aldehydes, benzaldehyde and its halogen, nitro and alkoxy substituted derivatives may be effectively oxidized by this reagent. In applying the method to homologs of benzaldehyde, the amount of permangenate used should be carefully regulated in order to prevent the oxidation of the alkyl groups present.

Nitric acid is used in dilute or concentrated form. Halogenated[5] and polyhydroxy[6] aldehydes have been converted to the corresponding acids by the use of this reagent.

Peracids are effective oxidizing agents for the conversion of many aldehydes, among them oenanthaldehyde and aromatic aldehydes, to the corresponding acids.[7] However, *p*-hydroxy benzaldehyde, treated with this reagent, yields quinol, a reaction which is comparable to the formation of *o*- and *p*-quinones from aromatic *o*- and *p*-hydroxy aldehydes by treatment with hydrogen peroxide *(Dakin's reaction).*

Very sensitive aldehydes may be converted to the corresponding acids by means of an aqueous suspension of silver oxide. A satisfactory procedure is to add slowly and with agitation three molecular equivalents of half normal caustic to a mixture of two molecular equivalents of an aqueous silver nitrate solution and one of aldehyde dissolved in aqueous alcohol. After the completion of the reaction, the acid formed is neutralized and the mixture is allowed to stand overnight. The acid may be isolated by the usual procedure.[8] Ammoniacal silver nitrate containing some alkali may also be used for the purpose. Unsaturated and amino aldehydes have been successfully converted to the corresponding acids by this reagent.[9]

Mercuric oxide[10] is a satisfactory reagent for the conversion of some reducing sugars to the corresponding acids, though bromine water[11] is used more generally for the purpose.

An indirect method of oxidation of aldehydes to acids involves their reaction with nitrohydroxylaminic acid,[12] $Na_2N_2O_3$, or benzenesulfonylhydroxylamine,[13]

$$C_6H_5SO_2NHOH,$$

resulting in the formation of hydroxamic acids RC(OH):NOH. These are converted to the corresponding acids, RCOOH, on hydrolysis with dilute mineral acids. Salicyladehyde and *o*-nitrobenzaldehyde fail to give hydroxamic acids with the above reagents.[14]

The catalytic oxidation of aldehydes, though of some technical importance, is of little preparative value in the laboratory.

Certain aldehydes, including benzaldehyde and its homologs, are gradually oxidized to acids on contact with atmospheric oxygen. A peracid appears to be the initial product of oxidation.

Oxidation of Ketones and Olefin Hydrocarbons to Acids

The oxidation of ketones results in the cleavage of the molecule at the carbonyl group with the formation of carboxylic acids. Oxidation may be accomplished with chromic acid or other vigorous oxidizing agents. It may be presumed that a group adjacent to the carbonyl group is first attacked, a hydroxy ketone is formed and cleavage takes place at this point. In general, a carbon atom with fewer hydrogen atoms is preferentially attacked, ketones of the type RCH_2COCH_3, for example, giving the acids RCOOH and CH_3COOH.[15] If the carbonyl group is attached to a tertiary carbon, it remains joined to this carbon after oxidation and cleavage. With unsymmetrical ketones RCH_2COCH_2R', the formation of four different acids, RCH_2COOH, R'COOH, $R'CH_2COOH$ and RCOOH, is possible, and all four are generally formed in varying quantities.

When aliphatic methyl ketones are treated with sodium hypochlorite, an acid and chloroform result:

$$(CH_3)_3C.COCH_3 \rightarrow (CH_3)_3CCOOH + CHCl_3$$

Sodium hypobromite gives an acid and bromoform.

The formation of acids through the oxidation of cyclic ketones is of considerable preparative importance. Lactones result when such ketones are treated with ammonium persulfate or with sulfomonoperacids.

Oxidizing agents, such as alkaline potassium permanganate, chromic acid or ozone,[16] attack the unsaturated bond in olefin hydrocarbons causing cleavage of the molecule at this point. An acid or an aldehyde results, depending on the degree of oxidation, providing hydrogen atoms are attached to the unsaturated carbon atoms. This method, while of little preparative value, is of considerable importance for the determination of the structure of unsaturated compounds.

Acids from Cyclic Esters and Carbon Monoxide

Tetrahydrofuran reacts with carbon monoxide and water under pressure at elevated temperatures in the presence of metals capable of forming metal carbonyls, with the formation of adipic acid:

$$\overline{CH_2CH_2CH_2CH_2O} + 2CO + H_2O \rightarrow HOCO(CH_2)_4COOH$$

The reaction is strongly exothermic (72 Cal/mole) and proceeds with extreme rapidity at 240-270° under a carbon monoxide pressure of 240 to 270 atm.

Formation of Acid from Nitriles

Carboxylic acids may be prepared from nitriles by hydrolysis with strong mineral acids or alkalies:

$$RCN + 2H_2O + HCl \rightarrow RCOOH + NH_4Cl$$

This method is of considerable preparative importance, since the nitrile group may be introduced into the molecule of organic compounds by a variety of methods, often simply and with excellent yields. One of the important methods, for example, is the replacement of halogens or negative groups by the cyano group by reaction with an alkaline cyanide. The subject is dealt with fully in the chapter on nitriles.

It may be pointed out that organic halides may be prepared from carboxylic acids by reducing these to the corresponding alcohols. The alcoholic hydroxyl may be replaced with a halogen atom by various methods. The iodides may be obtained by treating the alcohol with phosphorus triiodide. The nitrile corresponding to the next higher acid may be prepared from the iodide by reaction with an alkaline cyanide. Thus, the conversion of a given acid to the next higher homolog involves the following series of reactions:[17]

$$RCOOH \rightarrow RCH_2OH \xrightarrow{PI_3} RCH_2I \xrightarrow{NaCN} RCH_2CN$$

$$\xrightarrow{H_2O} RCH_2COOH$$

The method has been successfully applied to the preparation of higher fatty acid up to $C_{26}H_{52}O_2$.

Long chain acetylenic acids have been prepared via the acetylenic chloro compounds resulting from the reaction of ω, ω'-chloroido compounds, $I(CH_2)_nCl$, with monosubstituted acetylenes, $RC{\equiv}CH$, in the presence of sodium amide. The acids obtained by hydrolysis of the nitriles have been reduced to ethylenic acids.[254]

Formation of Acids from Organometallic Compounds

Sodium compounds of mono substituted acetylenes, such as sodium phenylacetylide, react with carbon dioxide to form acetylenic acids:[18]

$$C_6H_5C{\equiv}CNa + CO_2 \rightarrow C_6H_5C{\equiv}CCOONa$$

A more satisfactory method of preparing acetylenic acids consists in the reaction of sodium acetylides with chloroformic ester:

$$C_6H_5C{\equiv}CNa + ClCOOC_2H_5 \rightarrow C_6H_5C{\equiv}CCOOC_2H_5 + NaCl$$

acid is obtained from the ester formed by hydrolysis.

The reaction of organomagnesium compounds with carbon dioxide, giving the halomagnesium salt of a carboxylic acid, is similar in type to the Kolbe – Schmidt synythesis:[19]

$$RMgX + CO_2 \rightarrow RCOOMgX$$

Zinc alkyls, reacting with two molecular equivalents of phosgene, give acid chlorides:

$$Zn(CH_3)_2 + 2ClCOCl \rightarrow 2CH_3COCl + ZnCl_2$$

The chloride may be converted to the acid by hydrolysis.

Salts of organic acids are obtained when alkali alcoholates are heated at an elevated temperature with carbon monoxide:

$$CH_3ONa + CO \rightarrow CH_3COONa$$

This reaction is of little preparative value since yields are poor with the higher alkali alcoholates.

Long chain acids with up to 34 carbon atoms have been made through the reaction of cadmium alkyls with the half ester chlorides of dicarboxylic acids and reduction of the resulting keto acid by the Wolff-Kishner method:[151]

$$CdR_2 + ClCO(CH_2)_nCOOC_2H_5 \rightarrow ClCdR + RCO(CH_2)_nCOOC_2H_5$$

$$\rightarrow RCO(CH_2)_nCOOH \rightarrow RCH_2(CH_2)_nCOOH$$

Coupling reactions using acetylenic magnesium compounds and reactive halides have been employed for the synthesis of long chain carboxylic acids.[25] As an example the preparation of octadecadiyne-9, 12-oic acid may be mentioned,[257] which has been obtained by condensing 1-bromooctyne-2 with the halomagnesium compound derived from 8-chlorooctyne-1, converting the resulting chloro compound to the corresponding iodo compound and proceeding with a malonic ester synthesis:[258]

$$CH_3(CH_2)_4C{\equiv}CCH_2Br + BrMgC{\equiv}C(CH_2)_6Cl \rightarrow$$

$$MgBr_2 + CH_3(CH_2)_4C{\equiv}CCH_2C{\equiv}C(CH_2)_6Cl$$

$$\xrightarrow{KI} CH_3(CH_2)_4C{\equiv}CCH_2C{\equiv}C(CH_2)_6I \xrightarrow{\text{Malonic ester synth.}}$$

$$CH_3(CH_2)_4C{\equiv}CCH_2C{\equiv}C(CH_2)_7COOH$$

Acetylenic acetals have been employed in such coupling reactions, and the acids have been prepared from the resulting acetals by oxidation with potassium periodate.[259]

Miscellaneous other Methods of Formation of Acids

Organic groups may be introduced into the molecule of malonic ester to replace the hydrogen atoms of the reactive methylene group and to form the esters of dicarboxylic acids of the types $R_1CH(COOC_2H_5)$ and $R_1C(R_2)(COOC_2H_5)_2$. This is brought about through the reaction of sodio malonic ester and organic halides, and offers an elegant method for the synthesis of acids of these types. Monocarboxylic acids, R_1CH_2COOH and $R_1CH(R_2).COOH$, may be prepared from these dicarboxylic acids by partial decarboxylation.[152]

Alkylated derivatives of acetoacetic ester, $CH_3COCH(R_1)COOC_2H_5$, and $CH_3COC(R_2)(R_1)COOC_2H_5$, which may be prepared from acetoacetic ester similarly by replacing the active hydrogen of the methylene group with the organic groups R_1, R_2, may be subjected to acid cleavage to obtain acids of the types R_1CH_2COOH and $R_1CH(R_2)COOH$:

$$CH_3COCH(R_1)COOC_2H_5 + 2KOH \quad \rightarrow \quad CH_3COOK + R_1CH_2COOK + C_2H_5OH$$

Trialkyl derivatives of acetophenone may be readily prepared by the alkylation of acetophenone.[20] They are decomposed with sodamide to benzene and the sodium derivative of a trialkylacetic amide:

$$C_6H_5COC(R_1)(R_2)R_3 + NaNH_2 \quad \rightarrow \quad C_6H_6 + R_1C(R_2)(R_3)CONHNa$$

The reaction is carried out in the following manner: One mole of the ketone is dissolved in four to five times its volume of benzene or toluene, one and a half moles of finely pulverized sodamide is added and the mixture is heated under reflux for 4 to 5 hours. Decomposition of the sodium derivative with water yields the amide. The method is not applicable to dialkyl derivatives of acetophenone.

Trialkylacetamides are resistant to alkalies, but they may be converted to the corresponding acids by Bouveault's method: The amide is dissolved in concentrated sulfuric acid, the theoretically required quantity of nitrosyl sulfate is introduced and a little water is added. After the completion of the reaction, the mixture is diluted with water and the acid is isolated by extraction with ether.

Esters of aliphatic acids may be alkylated in α-position by the action of triphenylmethyl sodium and an alkyl halide:[153]

$$RR'CHCOOC_2H_5 + NaC(C_6H_5)_3 + IR'' \rightarrow$$
$$RR'R''CCOOC_2H_5 + NaI + HC(C_6H_5)_3$$

The method gives tertiary acids in excellent yield.

Acids branched in the γ-position may be readily obtained by cyanoethylation of ketones followed by hydrolysis and reduction of the product:[154]

$$RCOCHR'R'' + H_2C=CHCN \quad \rightarrow \quad RCOCR'R''CH_2CH_2CN$$
$$\rightarrow \quad RCH_2CR'R''CH_2CH_2COOH$$

α-Methyl-α-octylcapric acid has been prepared by condensing methyldioctylmethyl chloride with furan-1-carboxylic acid in the presence of aluminum chloride and oxidizing the product with potassium permanganate:[155]

$$(C_8H_{17})_2CClCH_3 + \underset{O}{\boxed{}}COOH \xrightarrow{AlCl_3} (C_8H_{17})_2C(CH_3)\underset{O}{\boxed{}}COOH$$
$$\xrightarrow{KMnO_4} (C_8H_{17})_2C(CH_3)COOH$$

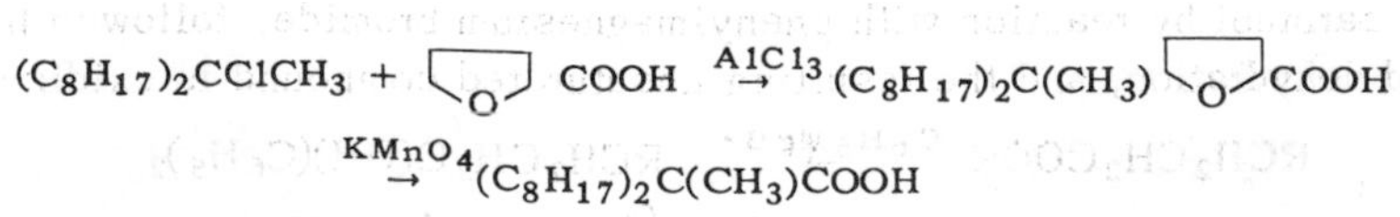

The electrolysis of a mixture of the alkali metal salts of a monobasic acid and of the monoester of a dibasic acid leads to the formation of the ester of a monobasic acid as one of the products in the anode section:

$$CH_3COOK + NaOCOCH_2CH_2COOC_2H_5 \rightarrow$$
$$Na^+ + K^+ + CH_3COO\text{-} + \text{-}OCOCH_2CH_2COOC_2H_5$$
$$\rightarrow CH_3CH_2CH_2COOC_2H_5 + 2CO_2$$

Racemic 3, 13, 19-trimethyltricosanoic acid has been synthesized by this method.[219] The method has been extended to the preparation of other long chain acids.[255]

Carboxylic acids may be prepared by the action of metallic sodium on a mixture of an alkyl halide and chlorocarbonic ester.[21] This reaction, which is a special case, of Wurtz synthesis, is of little preparative importance. Thiophene β-carboxylic acid has been prepared by this method from β-iodothiophene and chlorocarbonic ester in good yield.

The oxidation of a methyl group to a carboxyl group, while it may be carried out successfully in the aromatic series, is usually impracticable with aliphatic compounds, since it generally leads to a more or less complete break down of the molecule. However, satisfactory results are obtained in some exceptional cases. For instance, isovaleric acid may be oxidized with nitric acid to methylmalic acid, $HOCOCH_2C(OH)(CH_3)COOH$;[22] isocaprolactone, $(CH_3)_2\overline{CCH_2CH_2COO}$, to valerolactone carboxylic acid, $HOCO\overline{C(CH_3)CH_2CH_2COO}$;[23] and terebenic acid, to valerolactone γ, β-dicarboxylic acid.

The oxygen or the hydroxy group in carbonyl or hydroxy acids may be replaced with hydrogen atoms by reduction. α-Hydroxy acids may be reduced quite readily by heating with hydrogen iodide. Halogenated acids may be reduced to the corresponding halogen-free acids with sodium amalgam.

Dicarboxylic acids may be prepared by the general methods employed for the preparation of monocarboxylic acids. Thus, dicarboxylic acids may be obtained by the oxidation of diprimary alcohols; from monohalo carboxylic acids by Wurtz's reaction, or through conversion to a cyano compound by reaction with sodium cyanide and subsequent hydrolysis. Aliphatic dihalo compounds can be converted by this last method to dicarboxylic acids. Dicarboxylic acids may be prepared from γ- and δ-lactones by reaction with an alkali cyanide and subsequent hydrolysis of the γ- or δ-cyanocarboxylic acid formed. The conversion of a dicarboxylic acid ester by reduction with sodium and ethanol to the corresponding dihydric alcohol, followed by the conversion of the alcohol formed successively to a dihalide, dicyanide and finally to a dicarboxylic acid with two more carbon atoms than the original acid, succeeds particularly well with acids containing 7 to 17 carbon atoms.[24]

The elimination of the carboxyl group from acids RCH_2CH_2COOH, with the formation of an acid with one carbon atom less is possible by the application of the Barbier-Wieland degradation. The ester of the acid is converted to a diphenyl carbinol by reaction with phenylmagnesium bromide, followed by hydrolysis and dehydration, and the resulting unsaturated compound is oxidized:[253]

$$RCH_2CH_2COOR \xrightarrow{C_6H_5MgBr} RCH_2CH_2C(OH)(C_6H_5)_2$$
$$\rightarrow RCH_2CH{=}C(C_6H_5)_2 \xrightarrow{O_2} RCH_2COOH$$

ACIDS WITH OTHER FUNCTIONAL GROUPS

HYDROXY ACIDS

Methods of Formation

Many of the general methods of preparation of acids are applicable to the synthesis of hydroxy acids. Thus, hydroxy acids result through the selective oxidation of dihydroxy compounds containing a primary alcohol group. Glycolic acid is obtained, for example, through the oxidation of glycol with dilute nitric acid, or with atmospheric oxygen in the presence of platinum sponge:

$$HOCH_2CH_2OH \xrightarrow{O_2} HOCH_2COOH$$

Halogen compounds containing a hydroxy group give rise to hydroxy nitriles on reaction with alkali cyanides, hydrolysis of the nitrile giving a hydroxy acid.

Halo acids may be converted to hydroxy acids by treatment with silver oxide, or by heating with aqueous alkali. γ-Halo acids yield γ-lactones on distillation. Certain unsaturated acids heated with aqueous caustic at 100° yield hydroxy acids.[25] β, γ-and γ, δ-unsaturated acids give lactones on distillation. The oxidation of acids containing a tertiary carbon may lead to the formation of hydroxy acids.[26]

Aldehyde and ketone carboxylic acids may be reduced to the corresponding hydroxy acids. Reduction may be carried out with sodium amalgam, or with zinc and hydrochloric or dilute sulfuric acid. Sodium and alcohol, or electrolytic reduction also accomplish the result effectively. Dicarboxylic acids may be reduced by similar methods to hydroxy acids.

The reaction of organomagnesium halides with keto acid esters leads to the formation among other products, of halomagnesiumoxyesters, from which the hydroxy ester may be obtained by treatment with dilute acids:

$$CH_3COCOOC_2H_5 + R\,MgI \rightarrow CH_3C(R)(OMgI)COOC_2H_5$$
$$\rightarrow CH_3C(R)(OH)COOC_2H_5$$

Amino acids may be converted to hydroxy acids by treatment with nitrous acid.

Several excellent methods are available for the preparation of *α-hydroxy acids*. The reaction of hydrocyanic acid with aldehydes or ketones may serve for the synthesis of α-hydroxy acids, as the resulting cyanohydrins are hydrolyzed quite readily to the corresponding acids on treatment with warm aqueous mineral acids:

$$R_1R_2CO + HCN \rightarrow R_1R_2C(OH)CN \rightarrow R_1R_2C(OH)COOH$$

Reformatsky's reaction offers a general method for the preparation of various types of hydroxy acids from ketones. A reaction originated by Frankland and Duppa, utilizing organozinc compounds also leads to the formation of α-hydroxy acids.

Frankland and Duppa's Method[27]

Zinc alkyls reacting with oxalic esters give alkyl derivatives of zincoxy acetic esters; on hydrolysis these are converted to esters of hydroxy acids:

$$C_2H_5OCOCOOC_2H_5 + Zn(R)_2 \rightarrow C_2H_5OZnOC(R)_2COOC_2H_5$$
$$\rightarrow HOC(R)_2COOC_2H_5$$

The reaction may be carried out also with a mixture of an alkyl halide in the presence of granular zinc. The reaction may then be represented as follows:

$$C_2H_5OCOCOOC_2H_5 + RI + 3Zn \rightarrow C_2H_5ZnO\,C(ZnI)(R)COOC_2H_5 + ZnO$$
$$C_2H_5ZnOC(ZnI)(R)COOC_2H_5 + RI \rightarrow ZnI_2 + C_2H_5ZnOC(R)_2COOC_2H_5$$
$$\xrightarrow{H_2O} HOC(R)_2COOC_2H_5$$

The procedure is as follows: A mixture of the calculated quantities of the alkyl iodide and oxalic ester is heated with granular zinc under reflux at 30 to 60° for two to four days; water and an excess of barium hydroxide are then added to the reaction mixture, and the alcohol formed is distilled with steam. The residual liquid is cooled, filtered, and shaken with silver oxide or lead hydroxide to eliminate the iodine. A current of steam and carbon dioxide is finally passed through the liquid to precipitate the barium as barium carbonate; the liquid is then filtered and evaporated to crystallization.

The zinc used should be freshly ignited, or it may be activated with dilute hydrochloric acid, iodine or by amalgamation with a small amount of mercury. Amalgamation may be accomplished by immersing the granules of zinc for a moment in a dilute solution of mercuric chloride, washing and drying.

Occasionally it may be necessary to initiate the reaction by the addition of a little zinc alkyl in ethereal solution.

The reaction may be suspended at the first stage to obtain a monoalkyl hydroxy acetic acid:[28]

$$C_2H_5OCO.COO\,C_2H_5 + (CH_3)_2CHI + 3Zn \rightarrow$$
$$ZnO + C_2H_5ZnOC(ZnI)[CH(CH_3)_2].COOC_2H_5$$
$$\xrightarrow{H_2O} (CH_3)_2CH.CH(OH).COO\,C_2H_5$$

It is also possible to introduce two different organic groups in stages:

$$C_2H_5OCO.COOC_2H_5 + CH_3I + 3Zn \rightarrow C_2H_5ZnOC(CH_3)(ZnI)COOC_2H_5 + ZnO$$
$$C_2H_5ZnOC(CH_3)(ZnI).COOC_2H_5 + C_2H_5I \rightarrow$$
$$ZnI_2 + C_2H_5ZnOC(CH_3)(C_2H_5).COOC_2H_5$$
$$\xrightarrow{H_2O} HOC(CH_3)(C_2H_5)COOC_2H_5$$

Chemical Behavior of Hydroxy acids

α-Hydroxy acids are capable of forming cyclic esters, the hemilactides. The transformation takes place with loss of water when the acids are heated:

$$2CH_3CH(OH)COOH \rightarrow CH_3\overline{CHOCOCH(CH_3)OCO} + 2H_2O$$

When heated with dilute sulfuric or hydrochloric acid, another type of transformation takes place with the hydroxy acid undergoing cleavage to a carbonyl compound and formic acid:

$$CH_3CH(OH)COOH \rightarrow CH_3CHO + HCOOH$$
$$(CH_3)_2C(OH)COOH \rightarrow (CH_3)_2CO + HCOOH$$

Extensive investigations have shown that these two types of transformations take place independently.[29] Acids of the type RR′C(OH)COOH give, on heating, both a ketone and an unsaturated acid. In the lower members of the series, the proportion of olefinic acid formed increases with increase in the number of carbon atoms in the molecule.[30]

β-Hydroxy acids suffer the loss of the elements of water when heated with dilute sulfuric acid to form unsaturated acids. Thus, β-hydroxybutyric acid gives crotonic acid on distillation with 50% aqueous sulfuric acid:

$$CH_3CH(OH)CH_2COOH \rightarrow CH_3CH{\equiv}CHCOOH + H_2O$$

β-Hydroxyvaleric acid gives a mixture of unsaturated acids when distilled, or on heating in alkaline solution.[31]

β-Hydroxy acids show no tendency to form lactones.

Internal esters, the so-called lactones, are obtained readily from γ- and δ-hydroxy acids on heating:

$$HOCH_2CH_2CH_2COOH \rightarrow \overline{CH_2CH_2CH_2COO} + H_2O$$

The transformation is accelerated by mineral acids.[32] Lactone formation takes place with varying ease depending upon the structure of the acid. The transformation takes place with greater ease with increase in the number of substituents attached to the carbon atom in the lactone ring, and with increase in the magnitude of these substituents.[33]

γ-Lactones are characterized by their great stability and are only partially converted to γ-hydroxy acids on prolonged heating with water. δ-Lactones are gradually hydrolyzed with water at ordinary temperature.[34]

Many γ-lactones combine with halogen acids forming γ-halo acids. Some γ-lactones resist the action of aqueous hydrogen halides; these may be converted to the halo acids by heating with halogen acids in alcoholic solution. Esters of hydroxy acids are obtained from lactones upon heating with an alcoholic solution of sulfuric acid.[36]

γ-Lactones combine with ammonia without separation of water.[37] Sodium and alcohol reduce lactones to glycols.[38]

ε-Hydroxy acids, and hydroxy acids, in which the hydroxy group is still further removed from the carboxyl group, do not show any tendency to form lactones. These acids lose water when heated to form unsaturated acids.

ALDEHYDE AND KETO ACIDS

ALDEHYDE ACIDS

Methods of Formation

No general method is available for the introduction of the aldehyde group into the molecule of aliphatic acids. Special methods are available, however, for the preparation of certain types of aldehyde acids.

Ethyl α-formylpropionate, $CH_3CH(CHO)COOC_2H_5$, is obtained when ethyl formate is condensed with ethyl propionate.[39] The compound exists also in the tautomeric form $CH_3C(:CHOH)COOC_2H_5$. Formylacetic ester results in the form of its sodium derivative, $NaOCH{=}CH.COOC_2H_5$, when metallic sodium acts upon a mixture of ethyl formate and ethyl acetate.[40] The free formyl ester is unstable and condenses rapidly to formylglutamic ester,

$$C_2H_5OCOC(CHO){:}CHCH_2COOC_2H_5.$$

Succinic aldehyde acid may be obtained from bromacetal and sodiomalonic ester by a series of reactions involving the saponification of the resulting acetal malonic ester and the hydrolysis and partial decarboxylation of the acetal acid formed:[41]

$$(C_2H_5O)_2CHCH_2Br + NaCH(COOC_2H_5)_2 \rightarrow$$
$$NaBr + (C_2H_5O)_2CHCH_2CH(COOC_2H_5)_2$$
$$\rightarrow (C_2H_5O)_2CHCH_2CH(COOH)_2 \rightarrow OCHCH_2CH_2COOH$$

The method may be employed for the preparation of γ-formylbutyric acid from β-chloropropacetal and sodiomalonic ester.[42]

Succinaldehyde acid may be prepared also from aconic acid $HOCOC{=}CHOCO\,CH_2$, or from formyl succinic ester, $C_2H_5OCOC({=}COH)CH_2COOC_2H_5$, by heating with water. Ozonization of allylacetic acid, followed by hydrolysis of the ozonide, also results in the formation of the aldehyde acid:

$$CH_2{=}CHCH_2CH_2COOH \xrightarrow{O_3} \overset{O-O-O}{\overline{CH_2-CH}}CH_2CH_2COOH$$
$$\rightarrow OCHCH_2CH_2COOH$$

Another method of preparation consist in the treatment of glutamic acid with hypochlorite and hydrolysis of γ-azidobutyric acid with boiling hydrochloric acid.

Succinaldehyde acid polymerizes on standing to a dimer melting at 147°, which is reconverted to the monomeric aldehyde acid on distillation under vacuum.

Maleic aldehyde acid, $OCHCH = CHCOOH$, is obtained in good yield by the action of an alkaline solution of bromine on furan α-carboxylic acid:

$$\overline{OCH{=}CHCH{=}C}COOH + BrOH + H_2O \rightarrow \overline{OCH(OH)CHBrCH_2C}(OH)COOH$$
$$\rightarrow \overline{OCH\,(OH)CH{=}CH.CO} \rightarrow OCHCH{=}CHCOOH$$

The reaction of bromine and furancarboxylic acid may be conducted so as to yield mono- and dibromomaleic aldehyde acids. The dihalo derivative, termed mucobromic acid,[43] yields esters which are derived from its pseudo isomer, ROCHCBr = CBrCOO.

An anilino derivative, $C_6H_5NH.C = CHBrCH(OR)OCO$, results from the reaction of the ester with aniline.

Aldehyde acids may be prepared from unsaturated acids by treatment with ozone and hydrolytic cleavage of the resulting ozonide:

$$>C = C< + O_3 \rightarrow >\overset{O.O.O.}{C - C}< \xrightarrow{H_2O} >CO + OC< + H_2O_2$$

The aldehyde group occupies the same position as the unsaturated bond with respect to the carboxyl group. Azelaic aldehyde, $OCH(CH_2)_7COOH$, may be obtained, for example, from oleic acid.[44] Aldehyde acids may also be prepared through ozonization from unsaturated cyclic hydrocarbons. For example, adipic aldehyde acid, $OCH(CH_2)_4COOH$, may be obtained from cyclohexene.

The ethyl acetal ester of the semialdehyde of oxalic acid, $(C_2H_5O)_2CHCOOC_2H_5$, treated with sodium ethoxide, gives an enolic derivative which, when treated with water, is converted to *dimethoxymethyl*, $C(OC_2H_5)_2$.[251] The same compound is obtained from the sodio derivative of ethyl formate, $NaOCOC_2H_5$, by chlorination with phosphoryl chloride followed by treatment with sodium ethoxide.

KETO ACIDS

Methods of Formation

Ketonic acids may be obtained by the cautious oxidation of hydroxy acids containing a secondary alcohol group. Lactic acid, for example, can be oxidized to pyruvic acid:[249]

$$CH_3CH(OH)COOH \rightarrow CH_3COCOOH$$

α-Alkylated acetoacetic esters may be transformed to α-keto esters by conversion to α-oximino esters by a method developed by Meyer and Zublin, which consists in the treatment of the acylated ester with nitrous acid

$$CH_3COCH(R)COOC_2H_5 + HNO_2 \rightarrow RC(=NOH)COOC_2H_5 + CH_3COOH$$

The reaction is carried out at 0° in concentrated sulfuric acid, using nitrosyl bisulfate as the source of nitrous acid.[45] Transformation to the keto ester is brought about through the action of nitrosyl bisulfate, $HOSO_2ONO$, in the presence of 85% formic acid at a maximum temperature of 30°:

$$RC(=NOH)COOC_2H_5 + HNO_2 \rightarrow RCOCOOC_2H_5 + N_2O + H_2O$$

Conversion to the keto compound is generally poor, although yields of 90% have been reported in some cases. Phenylpyruvic acid cannot be prepared by this method; this acid has been obtained by boiling α-acetaminocinnamic acid for three hours with normal hydrochloric acid:[156]

$$C_6H_5CH = (NHCOCH_3)COOH + HCl + 2H_2O$$
$$\rightarrow C_6H_5CH_2COCOOH + CH_3COOH + NH_4Cl$$

The reaction of nitrous acid and α-alkylacetoacetic ester in the absence of a solvent leads to the formation of true α-nitroso esters, $RCH(NO)COOC_2H_5$. These are converted to α-keto esters by treatment with a small amount of alkali.

α-Oximino esters may be prepared also from aliphatic α-bromo esters by reaction with alkali nitrites.[46]

Acyl cyanides, RCOCN, which may be obtained through the reaction of acyl chlorides with silver cyanide,[47] give α-keto acids in poor yield when hydrolyzed. A large proportion of the acid RCOOH is formed in this hydrolysis with loss of the cyano group as hydrogen cyanide.[48]

α-Keto acids have been prepared through the hydrolysis of ethyl esters of oxalo acids which are obtained by the reaction of an ester with ethyl oxalate in the presence of sodium ethoxide:[157]

$$RCH_2COOC_2H_5 + C_2H_5OCOCOOC_2H_5 \xrightarrow{NaOC_2H_5} C_2H_5OH + RCH(COCOOC_2H_5)COOC_2H_5$$
$$\rightarrow RCH_2COCOOH$$

Hydrolysis is brought about by boiling with 10% sulfuric acid for six hours. The yield of ketone is quite high in some cases, but yields as low as 9% have been observed.

α-Keto acids may be prepared from the reaction product of Grignard compounds with diethyl oxamates by hydrolysis:[158]

$$C_2H_5OCOCON(C_2H_5)_2 \xrightarrow{RMgX} RCOCON(C_2H_5)_2 \xrightarrow{H_2O} RCOCOOH$$

The reaction with the Grignard reagent is carried out at -15°. The oxamates are obtained by boiling a mixture of diethyl oxalate and the secondary amine under reflux for a long period:

$$C_2H_5OCOCOOC_2H_5 + HN(C_2H_5)_2 \rightarrow C_2H_5OCOCON(C_2H_5)_2 + H_2O$$

Yields are in the neighborhood of 60%.

Certain α-keto acids have been obtained by oxidation of a methyl group or an aldehyde group adjacent to a keto group. The difficulty accessible α, β β-trimethylglutaric acid has been obtained by oxidizing the methyl group in α, β, β-trimethyllevulinic acid:

$$CH_3COC(CH_3)_2CH(CH_3)COOH \rightarrow HOCOCOC(CH_3)_2CH(CH_3)COOH$$

Pyruvic acid has been prepared in 90% yield by oxidizing methylglyoxal by bromine water:[159]

$$CH_3COCHO \rightarrow CH_3COCOOH$$

Some aromatic unsaturated azlactones yield α-keto acids when treated successively with sodium hydroxide and hydrochloric acid:[160]

$$\overline{RCH = CCOOCR' = N} \rightarrow RCH_2COCOOH + R'COOH$$

Azlactones are readily obtained by reaction of aromatic aldehydes and hippuric acid.

Ester condensation, a highly important synthetic method leading to the formation of β-keto esters, is of limited applicability, as the condensation of esters of higher aliphatic acids proceeds in a very unsatisfactory manner. A general method of synthesis of β-keto esters is based on acid cleavage of acylated acetoacetic esters:

$$CH_3COCH(COR)COOR' \xrightarrow{H_2O} CH_3COOH + RCOCH_2COOR'$$

β-Keto acids may be prepared through the reaction of acyl chlorides with sodio malonic esters or the sodio derivative of other esters having a reactive methylene group and hydrolysis of the resulting product. Monocarboxylic keto acids are formed through the partial decarboxylation of acylated malonic acids. Monocarboxylic keto acid esters are obtained by Bawman's method[161] by reductive cleavage of the carbobenzyloxy group from the mixed ethyl benzyl ester of an acylated malonic acid:

$$RCOCH\begin{cases} COOCH_2C_6H_5 \\ COOC_2H_5 \end{cases} \rightarrow RCOCH_2COOC_2H_5$$

Reduction is carried out caralytically in the presence of finely divided palladium.

Chlorides of α-substituted β-keto acids result through the self-condensation of aliphatic acid chlorides under the action of iron chloride:[49]

$$2RCH_2COCl \rightarrow RCH_2COCH(R)COCl + HCl$$

Keto acids may be prepared from nitriles by various methods. Aliphatic nitriles are condensed to dimers under the influence of sodium. These dimers are β-imino nitriles, which on hydrolysis are converted to β-keto acids:[50]

$$2RCH_2CN \rightarrow RCH_2C(:NH)CH(R)CN \xrightarrow{H_2O} RCH_2COCH(R)COOH$$

Nitriles, subjected to a modified Reformatsky reaction with aliphatic α-bromo esters give bromozinc derivatives of β-imino esters which, on hydrolysis, yield the corresponding β-keto esters:[51]

$$RCN + Zn + BrC(CH_3)_2COOC_2H_5 \rightarrow (RC(=NZnBr)C(CH_3)_2COOC_2H_5)$$
$$\rightarrow RCOC(CH_3)_2COOC_2H_5$$

Organomagnesium compounds reacting with α-cyano esters give, among other products, halomagnesium imino esters; these on hydrolysis with dilute acids yield the corresponding β-keto esters:

$$RMgI + CNCH_2COOC_2H_5 \rightarrow RC(:NMgI)CH_2COOC_2H_5$$
$$\rightarrow RCOCH_2COOC_2H_5$$

β-keto esters may be converted to γ-*keto acids via* their sodio derivatives through reaction with α-halo esters, followed by hydrolysis and partial decarboxylation of the resulting dicarboxylic acids:[52]

$$CH_3C(ONa){:}CHCOOC_2H_5 + ClCH(R)COOC_2H_5$$

$$\rightarrow NaCl + CH_3COCH(COOC_2H_5)CH(R)COOC_2H_5$$

$$\xrightarrow{H_2O} CH_3COCH_2CH(R)COOH + CO_2 + 2C_2H_5OH$$

γ-keto esters are obtained through the interaction of α-halo ketones or their derivatives with sodio malonic ester, followed by hydrolysis and partial decarboxylation:[53]

$$RCOCH_2Br + NaCH(COOC_2H_5)_2 \rightarrow NaBr + RCOCH_2CH(COOC_2H_5)_2$$

$$\rightarrow RCOCH_2CH_2COOH + CO_2 + 2C_2H_5OH$$

This reaction is capable of many modifications.

Half-ester acid chlorides of succinic acid and its alkylated derivatives may be converted to γ-keto esters by reaction with zinc alkyls:[54]

$$2C_2H_5OCOCH_2CH_2COCl + ZnR_2 \rightarrow 2C_2H_5OCOCH_2CH_2COR + ZnCl_2$$

β,γ-Unsaturated acids are converted to β-hydroxy γ-lactones on oxidation with potassium permanganate; on distillation, the hydroxy lactone yields an unsaturated lactone which may be hydrolyzed to a γ-keto acid.[55] Unsaturated acids of this type can also be converted to γ-keto acids by bromination followed by partial hydrolysis, dehydrohalogenation and finally hydrolysis:

$$RCH = CHCH_2COOH \xrightarrow{Br_2} RCHBrCHBrCH_2COOH$$

$$\rightarrow RCH(OH)CHBrCH_2COOH \rightarrow \overline{RCHCHBrCH_2COO}$$

$$\rightarrow \overline{RC = CHCH_2COO} \rightarrow RCOCH_2CH_2COOH$$

γ-Keto acids result through the isomerization of β,γ-unsaturated α-hydroxy acids:

$$CH_3CH = CHCH(OH)COOH \rightarrow CH_3COCH_2CH_2COOH$$

δ-Keto acids may be prepared from the sodio derivatives of β-keto esters by reaction with β-iodopropionic ester, hydrolyzing and partially decarboxylating the resulting dicarboxylic ester:

$$RC(ONa){:}CR'COOC_2H_5 + ICH_2CH_2COOC_2H_5$$

$$\rightarrow NaI + RCOCR'(COOC_2H_5)CH_2CH_2COOC_2H_5$$

$$\rightarrow RCOCR'(COOH)CH_2CH_2COOH \rightarrow RCOCHR'CH_2CH_2COOH$$

The reaction of β-haloketones with sodiomalonic ester and subsequent hydrolysis and partial decarboxylation of the resulting acid also yields δ-keto acids:

$$RCOCH_2CH_2Cl + NaCH(COOC_2H_5)_2 \rightarrow NaCl + RCOCH_2CH_2CH(COOC_2H_5)_2$$
$$\rightarrow RCOCH_2CH_2CH(COOH)_2 \rightarrow RCOCH_2CH_2CH_2COOH$$

Substituted dihydroresorcinol carboxylic esters result from the condensation of sodio acetoacetic ester with α, β-unsaturated esters. Ring rupture takes place, accompanied by partial decarboxylation, when these are heated with baryta water, with the formation of a δ-keto acid:

$$RCH = CHCOOC_2H_5 + CH_3C(ONa) = CHCOOC_2H_5$$

$$\rightarrow \overline{RCHCH_2COCH_2COCH}COOC_2H_5 + C_2H_5ONa$$

$$\xrightarrow{2H_2O} CH_3COCH_2CH(R)CH(COOH)COOH \rightarrow CH_3COCH_2CH(R)CH_2COOH$$

The reaction of zinc alkyls with ester chlorides of glutaric acid or its derivatives yields δ-keto acids:

$$2C_2H_5OCOCH_2CH_2CH_2COCl + ZnR_2 \rightarrow 2C_2H_5OCOCH_2CH_2CH_2COR + ZnCl_2$$

This reaction may be utilized for the preparation of keto acids in which the carbonyl group is still further removed from the carboxyl group. The reaction of halo acids with sodio β-keto esters may be used for the same purpose:

$$RC(ONa) = CHCOOC_2H_5 + Cl(CH_2)_nCOOC_2H_5$$
$$\rightarrow NaCl + RCOCH(COOC_2H_5)(CH_2)_nCOOC_2H_5$$
$$\rightarrow RCO(CH_2)_{2n+1}COOH$$

Symmetrical keto esters, $C_2H_5OCO(CH_2)_nCO(CH_2)_nCOOC_2H_5$, have been obtained by converting the acid chlorides, $C_2H_5OCO(CH_2)_nCOCl$, to the corresponding ketene by dehydrochlorination with triethylamine and reducing the diketene formed to the symmetrical keto acid.[162]

The triple bond in long chain acetylene carboxylic acids, if sufficiently distant from the carboxyl group, may be hydrated to give keto acids:

$$RC \equiv C(CH_2)_nCOOH \xrightarrow{H_2O} RCO(CH_2)_{n+1}COOH$$

This reaction is of little preparative value, but offers a method for locating the position of the multiple bond in acetylenic acids. To this end the oxime of the keto acid obtained is subjected to the Beckmann transformation, and the resulting amide is hydrolyzed. The position of the triple bond is indicated by the nature of the acid and amide obtained.

Hydration of the acetylenic acid may be effected by treating it with mercuric acetate in acetic acid solution and subjecting the product to the action of hydrochloric acid.[163] Several long chain keto acids have been prepared by this method.[164]

α-Amino dicarboxylic acids generally react with acetic anhydride to form the N-acylated derivative of an α-amino keto acid:

$$HOCOCH(NH_2)(CH_2)_nCOOH \xrightarrow{Ac_2O + C_6H_5N} CH_3COCH(NHCOCH_3)(CH_2)_nCOOH$$

The reaction bears the name of its discoverers, *Dakin and West.*[165] Picoline- and alkylamino acids do not react in this manner but give the corresponding N-acylated acids. α-Aminohydratropic acid, which lacks an α-hydrogen atom, also yields the N-acylated product.

Diketo Acids

Acylation of sodio β-keto esters yields keto esters in which the carbonyl groups are separated by one carbon atom.[56] Such diketo esters are obtained also through the interaction of bromacetic ester with acid anhydrides in the presence of granular zinc:[57]

$$2(RCO)_2O + 2Zn + 2BrCH_2COOC_2H_5 \rightarrow 2(RCO)_2CHCOOC_2H_5 + ZnBr_2 + Zn(OH)_2$$

and through the reaction of sodio derivative of acetylacetone with halo esters:[58]

$$CH_3C(ONa) = CHCOCH_3 + ClCH_2COOC_2H_5 \rightarrow (CH_3CO)_2CHCH_2COOC_2H_5 + NaCl$$

The condensation of oxalic ester with ketones in the presence of sodium ethoxide gives 1,3-diketo esters:[59]

$$CH_3COCH_3 + C_2H_5OCOCOOC_2H_5 \rightarrow CH_3COCH_2COCOOC_2H_5 + C_2H_5OH$$

Diketo esters in which the carbonyl groups are separated by two carbon atoms are obtained through the reaction of α-halo ketones with the sodio derivative of β-keto esters:[60]

$$RC(ONa) = CR'COOC_2H_5 + ClCH_2COR'' \rightarrow RCOCR'(CH_2COR'')COOC_2H_5 + NaCl$$

Furfuralacetone is hydrolyzed to a diketo acid of this type by boiling with an aqueous alcoholic solution of hydrochloric acid:[61]

$$CH_3COCH = CH\overline{C = CHCH = CHO} + 2H_2O \rightarrow CH_3COCH_2CH_2COCH_2CH_2COOH$$

Chemical Behavior of Keto Acids

Many *α-keto acids* lose carbon monoxide, when heated with concentrated sulfuric acid, giving an acid devoid of the carbonyl function:[62]

$$RCOCOOH \rightarrow RCOOH + CO$$

Some aliphatic α-keto acids are decarboxylated on heating at 150° with 10% aqueous sulfuric acid, yielding an aldehyde:[63]

$$RCOCOOH \rightarrow RCHO + CO_2$$

Keto acids of this type may be oxidized to acids RCOOH, by treatment with the calculated quantity of 30% aqueous hydrogen peroxide.[64] The method is employed for the preparation of phenyl aliphatic acids.[65]

α-Keto acids are converted readily to an aldehyde with one less carbon atom by heating with aniline; the aniline compound of the aldehyde formed liberates the aldehyde when treated with dilute sulfuric acid.[66]

The dimethyl keto dicarboxylic acid, $HOCOCH_2C(CH_3)_2COCOOH$, is stable in the open chain form; the corresponding trimethyl acid exists both in the open chain and the lactone form, $\overline{OCOCH(CH_3)C(CH_3)_2C}(OH)COOH$, while the tetramethyl acid is stable only in the lactone form.[250]

β-Keto acids, in contrast to other acids containing the carbonyl group, are unstable in the free state and readily lose carbon dioxide to give a ketone:

$$RCOCH_2COOH \rightarrow RCOCH_3 + CO_2$$

These acids and their salts cannot, therefore, be stored, except under special conditions. It is of interest to note that β-halo and β-sulfo carboxylic acids show a similar instability. The esters of these acids are stable, however, and are characterized by the great reactivity of the hydrogen atoms attached to the carbon atom between the carbonyl and carboxyl groups. This offers a typical example of a *reactive methylene* group. These hydrogen atoms may be replaced by alkali metals. It has been demonstrated that these metal compounds are derived from the enol form of the ester, with the metal combined with the enol oxygen, $CH_3C(ONa) = CHCOOC_2H_5$. This is in accord with a rule enunciated by Michael which states that in oxygenated organic compounds yielding alkali metal derivatives of the type under discussion, the metal is always joined to an oxygen atom and never directly to a carbon atom.

The alkali metal in these derivatives of β-keto esters may be exchanged for an organic radical by reaction with an organic halide. The resulting bodies are C-substituted esters. The second hydrogen remaining in the substituted ester may also be replaced by an alkali metal, and this in turn may be similarly exchanged with an organic group.

The reactive methylene group may be condensed with carbonyl groups and with other reactive oxygenated groups.

α,β-Dialkyl acetoacetic esters undergo cleavage under the action of a hot solution of ethanolic sodium ethoxide, giving a dialkyl acetic ester:[166]

$$CH_3COCRR'COOC_2H_5 \rightarrow RR'CHCOOC_2H_5$$

Keto-Enol Isomerism

It has been demonstrated that acetoacetic ester exist in keto and enol forms,

$$CH_3COCH_2COOC_2H_5 \rightleftharpoons CH_3C(OH){:}CHCOOC_2H_5$$

Enolization is possible also with β-keto esters in which not more than one α-hydrogen atom is replaced with an organic group. The enol form reacts rapidly with bromine to give a C-brominated keto ester:

$$CH_3C(OH) = CHCOOC_2H_5 + Br_2 \rightarrow CH_3CBr(OH)CHBrCOOC_2H_5$$
$$\rightarrow CH_3COCHBrCOOC_2H_5 + HBr$$

This makes possible the determination of the quantity of the enol form present in a sample of the ester.

The determination is carried out in the following manner: An alcoholic solution of bromine is added gradually to a solution of the ester in alcohol until the color of bromine persists; the excess of bromine is destroyed with a little β-naphthol dissolved in alcohol. A solution of potassium iodide is then added, the mixture is warmed slightly and the liberated iodine is titrated with $N/10$ sodium thiosulfate solution. The reaction leading to the formation of iodine may be expressed as follows:

$$CH_3COCHBr.COOC_2H_5 + 2KI + H_2O \rightarrow CH_3COCH_2COOC_2H_5 + KBr + KOH + I_2$$

It has been shown that acetoacetic ester normally contains 2% of the enol isomer.

Acetoacetic ester has been obtained in the enolic form by treating a suspension of dry sodioacetoacetic ester in ether at -78° with a slight deficiency of dry hydrogen chloride, filtering and eliminating the solvent under vacuum at -78°. The enol isomer of acetoacetic ester may be preserved for 10 to 14 days when protected from atmospheric impurities. Impurities which induce the reversion bring about the conversion of the enol to the keto form within a few seconds. Hydrogen chloride greatly accelerates the reversion of the enol form in non-dissociating solvents, but the effect is much less marked in aqueous or alcoholic solution.

Two stereoisomeric modifications of the enol form are possible, and there are some indications of their existence.[67]

Characteristic Reactions of Acetoacetic Ester

Acetoacetic ester undergoes self-condensation under the action of concentrated sulfuric acid forming isodehydroacetic acid. Dehydroacetic acid is obtained on heating acetoacetic ester under a reflux condenser:

$$2CH\ COCH_3COOC_2H_5 \rightarrow \overline{COOC(CH_3) = CHCOCHCOCH_3} + 2C_2H_5OH$$

The reaction of acetoacetic ester with phenylhydrazine in ethereal solution gives a hydrazone which, on heating or on treatment with acids or alkalies, gives methylphenylpyrozolone,[68] $CH_3\overline{C = NN(C_6H_5)COCH_2}$. Higher β-keto esters reacting with hydrazine, also yield substituted pyrazolones:

$$C_3H_7COCH(C_2H_5)COOC_2H_5 + H_2NNH_2$$

$$\rightarrow C_3H_7\overline{C = NNHCOCHC_2H_5} + C_2H_5OH + H_2O$$

With amidines, $RC(=NH)NH_2$, acetoacetic ester gives 6-hydroxy-4-methylpyrimidines, $\overline{RC = NC(CH_3) = CHC(OH) = N}$; with aldehyde ammonias, pyridine derivatives, while with arylamines quinoline derivatives result.

α-Monoalkyl acetoacetic esters subjected to the action of nitrous acid give a variety of products, such as α-nitroso and isonitroso acids and α-isonitroso ketones, depending upon the conditions. Nitrous fumes reacting with β-keto esters, $RCOCH(Alk).COOC_2H_5$, give α-nitroso esters $NOCH(Alk)COOC_2H_5$. The reaction takes place most readily when R is H or CH_3.[69] α,α-Dialkyl acetoacetic esters are not attacked with nitrous gases.[70] Nitric acid converts α-monoalkyl acetoacetic esters to *gem*-dinitroparaffins, $(NO_2)_2CHR$.

γ-Keto acids are stable in the free state and do not decompose in the cold. They may be distilled under vacuum without decomposition. When heated to boiling at atmospheric pressure under a reflux condenser, they give two isomeric unsaturated γ-lactones of the types $\overline{RCHCH = CHCOO}$ and $\overline{RC = CHCH_2COO}$. This transformation takes place more readily if side chains are present in the acid moiety.[71] γ-Keto acids do not show any tendency to give enolic isomers. The methylene group adjacent to the carbonyl group in these acids is only slightly reactive. These acids yield stable mercaptides, $RC(SR')_2CH_2CH_2COOC_2H_5$ and disulfones, $RC(SO_2R)_2CH_2CH_2COOC_2H_5$, which may be converted to the free acids.[72]

1,3-Diketo acids have a reactive methylene group situated between the carbonyl groups, and yield sodio derivatives. These acids cannot be alkylated, in the usual manner, through the interaction of their sodio derivatives with alkyl halides, since the reaction results in the cleavage of an acyl group and its replacement with an alkyl group.[73]

AMINO ACIDS

Methods of Preparation

Amino acids may be prepared from halo acids by replacement of the halogen by an amino group by reaction with ammonia[167] or ammonium carbonate.[168] In this reaction primary, secondary and tertiary amino acids are formed simultaneously through the interaction of the base with one, two or three molecular proportions of the halo acid. Secondary bases react with one molecular proportion of the halo acid:[74]

$$2(CH_3)_2NH + ClCH_2COOH \rightarrow (CH_3)_2NCH_2COOH.(CH_3)_2NH$$

Leucine, isoleucine and *valine* have been obtained in 30-40% yield by this method from the corresponding halo acids.[169] *dl*-Phenylalanine has been prepared in a somewhat better yield from α-bromo-β-phenylpropionic acid.[170]

Lysine has been prepared from N-benzoyl-6-aminohexoic acid by bromination, followed by replacement of the bromine with an amino group, and hydrolysis:[171]

$$C_6H_5CONH(CH_2)_4CH_2COOH \xrightarrow{Br} C_6H_5CONH(CH_2)_4CHBrCOOH$$

$$\xrightarrow{NH_3} C_6H_5CONH(CH_2)_4CH(NH_2)COOH \rightarrow H_2N(CH_2)_4CH(NH_2)COOH$$

Benzoylaminohexoic acid is obtained from the oxime of cyclohexanone by treatment with sulfuric acid and benzoylation of the resulting cyclic amide.[172]

Histidine has been prepared from α-chloro-β-glyoxaline propionic acid by reaction with ammonia:[173]

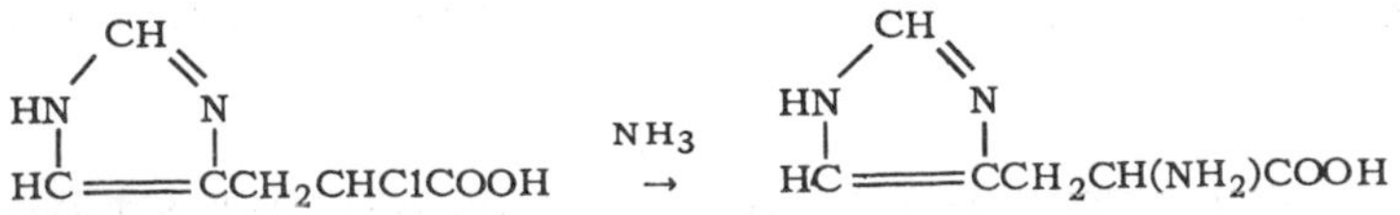

The chloro acid was obtained through the condensation of chloromalonic ester with

4-chloromethylglyoxaline hydrochloride and hydrolysis and decarboxylation of the resulting product:

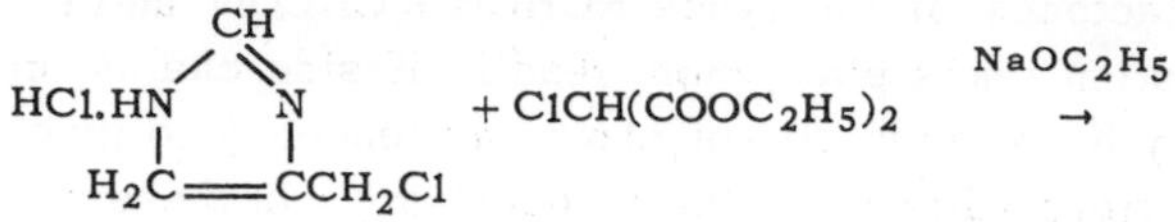

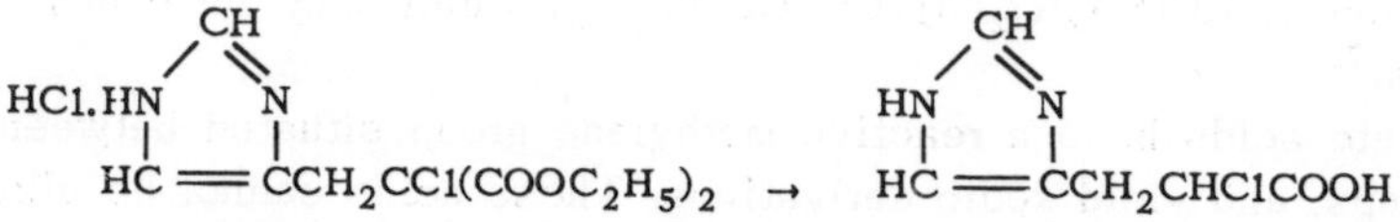

$$\underset{\underset{H_2C=CCH_2Cl}{|}}{\overset{\overset{CH}{\diagup\diagdown}}{HCl.HN\quad N}} + ClCH(COOC_2H_5)_2 \quad \overset{NaOC_2H_5}{\rightarrow}$$

$$\underset{\underset{HC=CCH_2CCl(COOC_2H_5)_2}{|}}{\overset{\overset{CH}{\diagup\diagdown}}{HCl.HN\quad N}} \rightarrow \underset{\underset{HC=CCH_2CHClCOOH}{|}}{\overset{\overset{CH}{\diagup\diagdown}}{HN\quad N}}$$

4-Chloromethylglyoxaline hydrochloride has been prepared from acetonedicarboxylic acid by conversion to diaminoacetone dihydrochloride via the dinitroso compound, and condensation of the diamino compound with potassium thiocyanate to obtain 4-aminomethylthioglyoxaline:

$$HOCOCH_2COCH_2COOH \quad \overset{HNO_2}{\rightarrow} \quad HON=CHCOCH=NOH \quad \overset{HCl+ZnCl_2}{\rightarrow}$$

$$H_2NCH_2COCH_2NH_2 \quad \overset{KCNS}{\rightarrow} \quad \underset{\underset{HC=CCH_2NH_2}{|}}{\overset{\overset{CSH}{\diagup\diagdown}}{HN\quad N}}$$

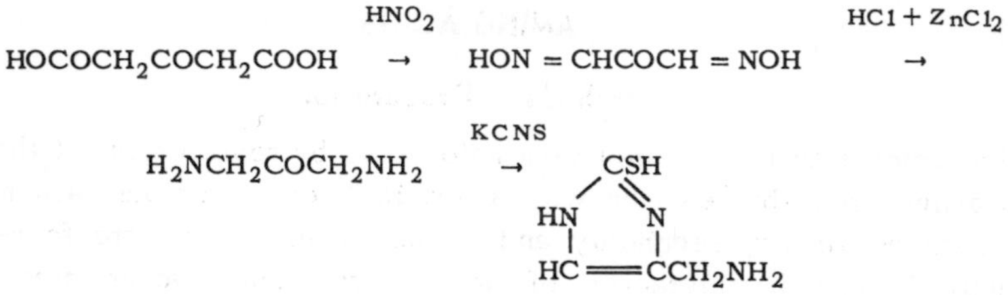

Conversion of this to 2-chloromethylglyoxaline was accomplished by treatment with nitrous acid followed by treatment with phosphorus pentachloride:

$$\underset{\underset{HC=CCH_2NH_2}{|}}{\overset{\overset{CSH}{\diagup\diagdown}}{HN\quad N}} \quad \overset{HNO_2}{\rightarrow} \quad \underset{\underset{HC=CCH_2OH}{|}}{\overset{\overset{CSH}{\diagup\diagdown}}{HN\quad N}} \quad \overset{PCl_5}{\rightarrow} \quad \underset{\underset{HC=CCH_2Cl}{|}}{\overset{\overset{CSH}{\diagup\diagdown}}{HN\quad N}}$$

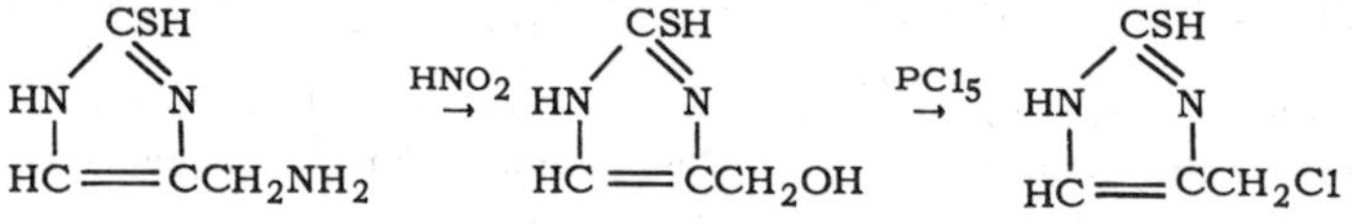

γ-Hydroxyproline has been prepared from α-bromo-δ-chlorovalerolactone by reaction with ammonia, and hydrolysis of the resulting diamino-γ-valerolactone:[174]

$$\underset{\underset{CO-O}{|\quad\quad|}}{BrCHCH_2CHCH_2Cl} \overset{NH_3}{\rightarrow} \underset{\underset{CO-O}{|\quad\quad|}}{H_2NCHCH_2CHCH_2NH_2} \overset{H_2O}{\rightarrow} \underset{\underset{\underset{COOH}{|}}{CHCH_2-CHOH}}{\overset{NH-\!-\!-CH_2}{|\quad\quad\quad|}}$$

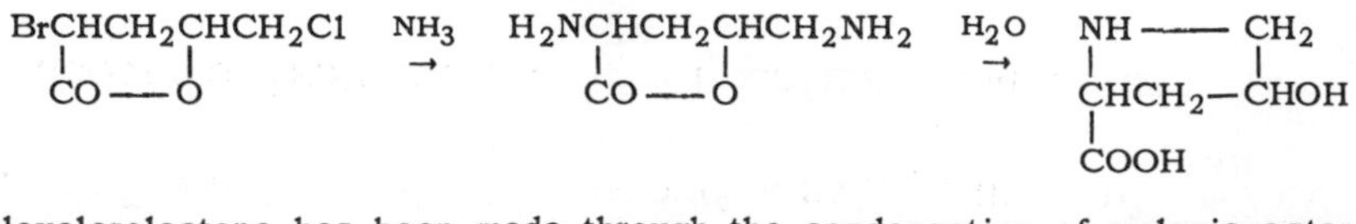

The halovalerolactone has been made through the condensation of malonic ester with epichlorohydrin, and bromination of the resulting δ-chlorolactone, followed by hydrolysis and decarboxylation:

$$\underset{}{ClCH_2CH\overset{\overset{O}{\diagup\diagdown}}{-\!\!-\!\!-}CH_2}+CH_2(COOC_2H_5)_2 \quad \overset{NaOC_2H_5}{\rightarrow} \quad ClCH_2CH(OH)CH_2CH(COOC_2H_5)_2$$

$$\rightarrow \underset{\underset{CO-O}{|\quad\quad|}}{C_2H_5OCOCHCH_2CHCH_2Cl} \quad \overset{Br_2}{\rightarrow} \quad \underset{\underset{CO-O}{|\quad\quad|}}{C_2H_5OCOCBrCH_2CHCH_2Cl}$$

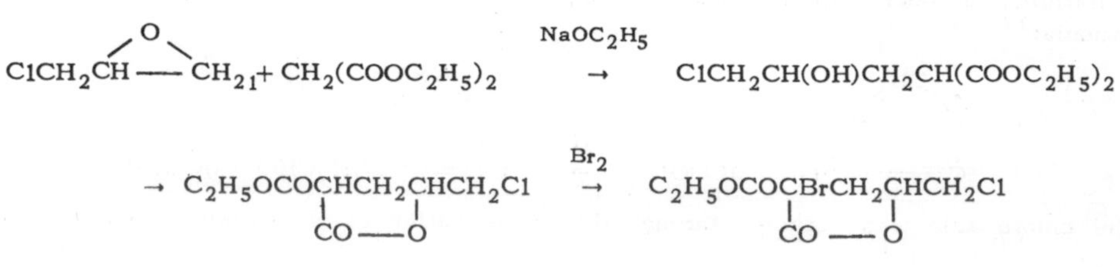

$$\xrightarrow{H_2O} \quad \underset{\underset{CO-\!\!\!-O}{|}}{BrCHCH_2CHCH_2Cl}$$

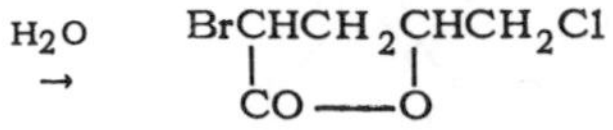

Two of the four possible stereoisomeric γ-hydroxyprolines, the two inactive forms, have been isolated by fractional crystallization of their copper salts.

α-Bromo acids may be obtained in satisfactory yield by the Hell-Volhard reaction from aliphatic acids, i.e., by reaction with a mixture of bromine and red phosphorus. α-Halo-β-alkoxy acids are formed by the reaction of a halogen with the addition product of an α,β-unsaturated acid with mercuric acetate and an alcohol. Methyl α-bromo-β-methoxy-propionate prepared by this method from methyl acrylate has been converted to serine by hydrolysis followed by reaction with ammonia: [175]

$$CH_2 = CHCOOCH_3 + Hg(OCOCH_3)_2 + CH_3OH$$

$$\rightarrow \quad CH_3COOH + CH_3OCH_2CH(HgOCOCH_3)COOCH_3$$

$$\xrightarrow{Br_2 + KBr} CH_3OCH_2CHBrCOOCH_3 \xrightarrow{HBr + H_2O} CH_3OCH_2CHBrCOOH$$

$$\xrightarrow{NH_3} CH_3OCH_2CH(NH_2)COOHNH_4 \rightarrow CH_3OCH_2CH(NH_2)COOH$$

α-Bromo monocarboxylic acids have been prepared from substituted malonic acids by bromination and partial decarboxylation:

$$RCH(COOC_2H_5)_2 + Br_2 \rightarrow RCBr(COOC_2H_5)_2 \rightarrow RCHBrCOOH$$

Many amino acids, including *histidine* and *methionine,* have been synthesized by this route, by replacement of the halogen in the brominated acid with an amino group.

A particularly effective method for the preparation of amino acids is offered by *Gabriel's amine Synthesis* based on the reaction of halo acids with the potassium derivative of phthalimide. Hydrolysis of the product by boiling hydrochloric acid gives the amino acid: [75]

$$C_6H_4 \underset{CO}{\overset{CO}{<}} NK + ClCH_2COONa \rightarrow KCl + C_6H_4 \underset{CO}{\overset{CO}{<}} NCH_2COONa$$

$$\rightarrow \quad C_6H_4(COOH)_2 + H_2NCH_2COOH$$

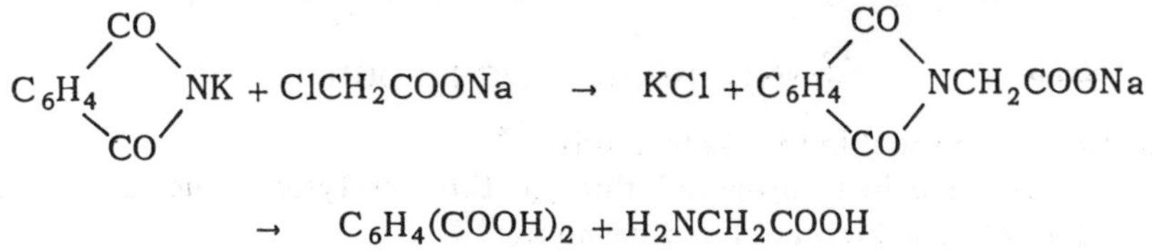

Amino acids may be prepared by Gabriel's method by causing ethylene dibromide or other dibrominated hydrocarbons to react with one molecular equivalent of potassium phthalimide. The bromine in the resulting product is replaced with the malonic ester residue by reaction with sodiomalonic ester, and the imido compound obtained is finally hydrolyzed with boiling hydrochloric acid, partial decarboxylation taking place simultaneously: [76]

$$C_6H_4 \underset{CO}{\overset{CO}{<}} NK + BrCH_2CH_2Br \rightarrow KBr + C_6H_4 \underset{CO}{\overset{CO}{<}} NCH_2CH_2Br$$

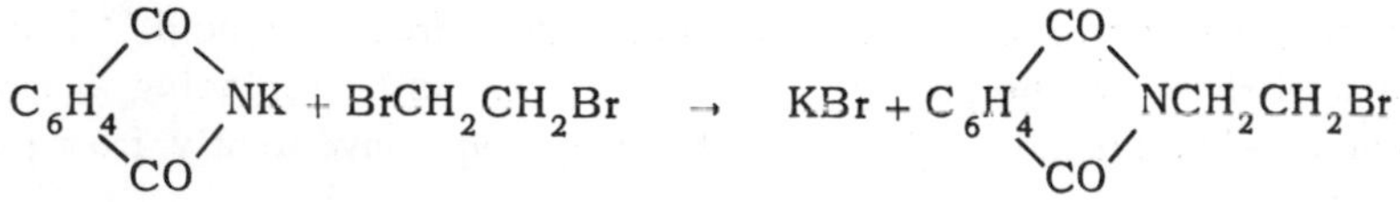

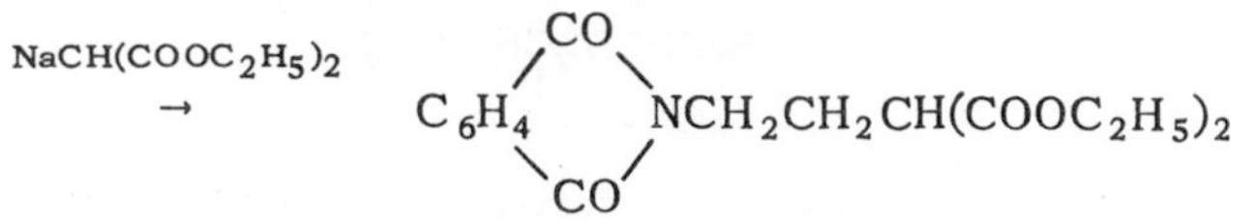

$$NaCH(COOC_2H_5)_2 \rightarrow C_6H_4 \underset{CO}{\overset{CO}{\diagdown}} NCH_2CH_2CH(COOC_2H_5)_2$$

$$\xrightarrow{H_2O} C_6H_4(COOH)_2 + H_2NCH_2CH_2CH_2COOH + CO_2 + 2C_2H_5OH$$

Tyrosine,

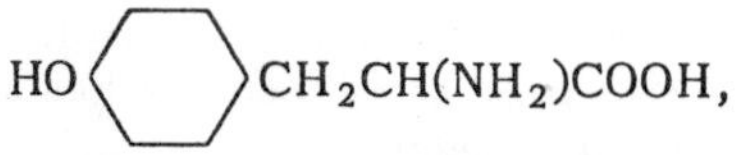

has been synthesized in about 35% yield from potassium phthalimidomalonic ester and anisyl bromide.[176]

Proline has been obtained in 70% yield from sodio phthalimidomalonic ester and α,γ-dibromopropane:[177]

$$\underset{CO}{\overset{CO}{\diagdown}} NCNa(COOC_2H_5)_2 + Br(CH_2)_3Br \rightarrow \underset{CO}{\overset{CO}{\diagdown}} NC\underset{COOC_2H_5}{\overset{COOC_2H_5}{\diagup}} CH_2CH_2CH_2Br$$

$$\rightarrow \underset{CH_2}{\overset{CH_2---CH_2}{|}} \underset{NH}{\diagdown} \underset{CHCOOH}{|}$$

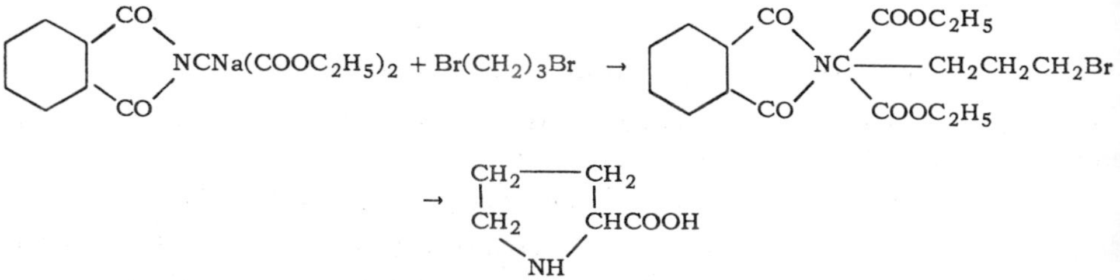

Ring closure was effected by treatment with alcoholic potassium hydroxide.

Keto acids may be converted to amino acids through the reduction of their oximes or hydrazones with sodium amalgam or other reducing agents:

$$CH_3COCH_2CH_2COOH \xrightarrow{H_2NOH} CH_3C(:NOH)CH_2CH_2COOH$$

$$\xrightarrow{H_2} CH_3CH(NH_2)CH_2CH_2COOH$$

The reaction is applicable to α-keto acids.[178]

Amino acids have been prepared through the catalytic reduction of the reaction product of an α-keto acid and ammonia:[179]

$$RCOCOOH \xrightarrow{NH_3,\ H_2} RCH(NH_2)COOH$$

A number of other excellent methods are available for the preparation of α-amino acids. Nitriles of α-amino acids are obtained from aldehyde or ketone cyanohydrins through the replacement of the hydroxy group with an amino group by reaction with ammonia.[77] α-Amino nitriles may be prepared directly through the interaction of the carbonyl compound with ammonium cyanide,[78] or with a mixture of ammonium chloride and an alkali cyanide;[79] they are formed also through the reaction of aldehyde ammonias with hydrocyanic acid.[80] N-substituted amino nitriles may be prepared by these methods by replacing ammonia with an amine. α-Alkylamino nitriles may be prepared conveniently from potassium cyanide and amino sulfites derived from aldehyde sodium bisulfite compounds by reaction with alkyl amines:[81]

$$HOCH_2OSO_2Na + HN(C_2H_5)_2 \rightarrow H_2O + (C_2H_5)_2NCH_2OSO_2Na$$

$$\xrightarrow{KCN} (C_2H_5)_2NCH_2CN$$

These α-amino nitriles may be converted to the corresponding acids by hydrolysis with aqueous mineral acids and alkalies.

Acid hydrolysis may be carried out successfully with 50% sulfuric acid. The nitrile is added gradually to 2.2 molal equivalent of the cold acid with cooling and stirring. After all the nitrile has been introduced, the mixture is heated at 80° for an hour. A suspension of somewhat more than the required amount of lime water is then added to neutralize the acid and precipitate out the sulfate radical; then ammonium carbonate is added to eliminate the excess lime and the solution is filtered. The amino acid is recovered by evaporating the solution to dryness under vacuum. The yields are usually quite high.[180]

Alkali hydrolysis may be accomplished successfully providing the concentration of the nitrile in solution is kept below 2 molal and that of caustic above 5 normal. A little over 0.6 molal equivalent of caustic is used for every mole of amino nitrile. If the reaction is carried out in the cold, the caustic solution is added to the nitrile, while if it is conducted at a higher temperature, the nitrile is added to the caustic solution. The concentration of ammonia in solution must be kept at a high level during the reaction. In carrying the reaction in the cold, the caustic solution is added slowly, and the reaction mixture is allowed to stand 24 hours after all the caustic has been introduced. The excess ammonia is then evaporated off by heating, the solution is acidified with hydrochloric acid, evaporated to dryness and the amino acid hydrochloride is extracted with alcohol.

These methods have been employed for the preparation of alanine,[181] glutamic acid,[182] glycine,[183] isoleucine,[184] leucine,[185] methionine,[186] norleucine,[187] phenylalanine,[188] serine,[189] and valine.[190]

Carboxymethylation of an amine may be brought about through the reaction of the amine with sodium cyanide and formaldehyde:[191]

$$R_2NH + CH_2O + H_2O + NaCN \rightarrow R_2NCH_2COONa + NH_3$$

Best yields are obtained by carrying out the reaction at a moderate temperature, removing the ammonia under reduced pressure, raising the pH during the reaction by the addition of sodium hydroxide, and using an excess of sodium cyanide and formaldehyde.

The catalyzed addition of mercaptans to crotonaldehyde offers a means for the preparation of sulfur-containing amino acids of the methionine type:[192]

$$CH_2 = CHCHO + HSR \rightarrow RSCH_2CH_2CHO \xrightarrow[NH_3]{HCN} RSCH_2CH_2CH(NH_2)CN$$

Conversion of the amino nitrile to the acid may be achieved by Bucherer's hydantoin reaction followed by hydrolysis.[193]

α-Amino acids with two more carbon atoms than the original aldehyde may be prepared from aldehydes by *Erlenmeyer's* or the *azlactone method*. The carbonyl compound is condensed with hippuric acid and the product is reduced with sodium amalgam or hydriodic acid; the amino acid is obtained by the hydrolytic cleavage of the resulting benzoylamino acid: [82]

$$RCHO + H_2C(COOH)NHCOC_6H_5 \rightarrow \begin{bmatrix} RCH = C - CO \\ | \quad\quad | \\ \quad\quad O \\ | \quad\quad | \\ N = CC_6H_5 \end{bmatrix} \rightarrow$$

$$RCH = C(COOH)NHCOC_6H_5$$

$$\underset{\substack{\text{in acetic} \\ \text{acid}}}{\overset{HI + P}{\rightarrow}} RCH_2CH(COOH)NHCOC_6H_5 \overset{H_2O}{\rightarrow} RCH_2CH(NH_2)COOH + C_6H_5COOH$$

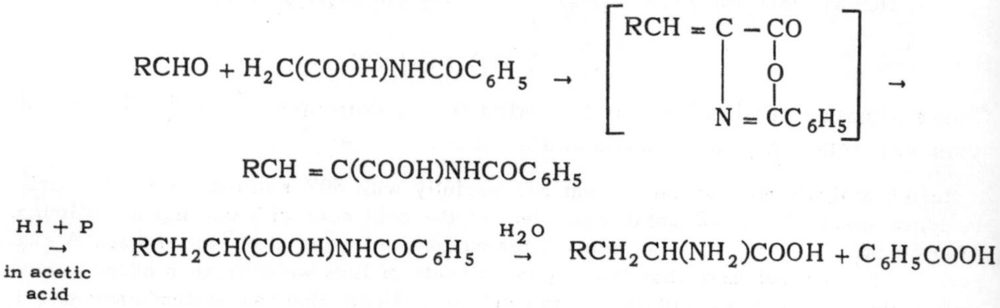

Histidine has been prepared by the azlactone method starting with formylglyoxaline: [194]

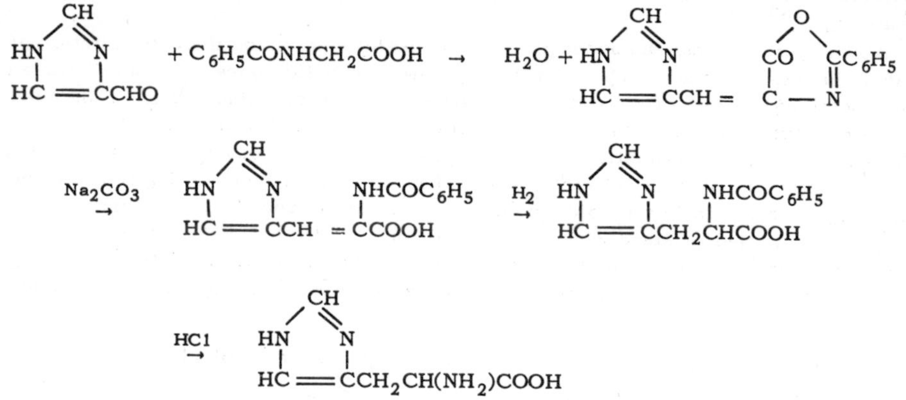

Formylglyoxaline was obtained by oxidizing 4-hydroxymethylglyoxaline with nitric acid. *Triptophane* has also been obtained by this route, starting with 3-formylindole: [195]

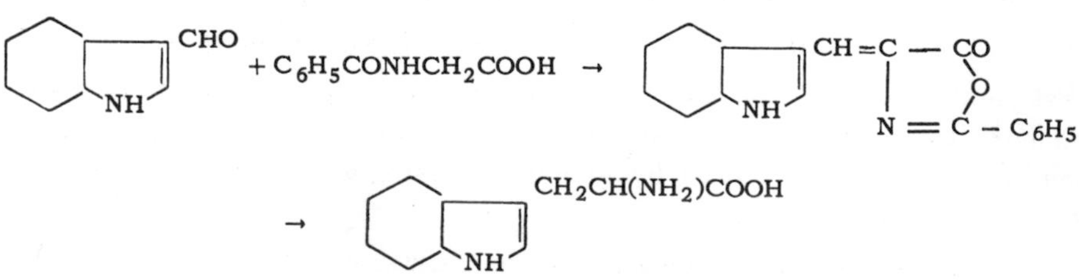

3-Formylindole may be prepared by the Reimer-Tiemann method.

   Thyroxine has been prepared by this method from 3,5-diodo-4-(4′-methoxyphenoxy)-benzaldehyde: [196]

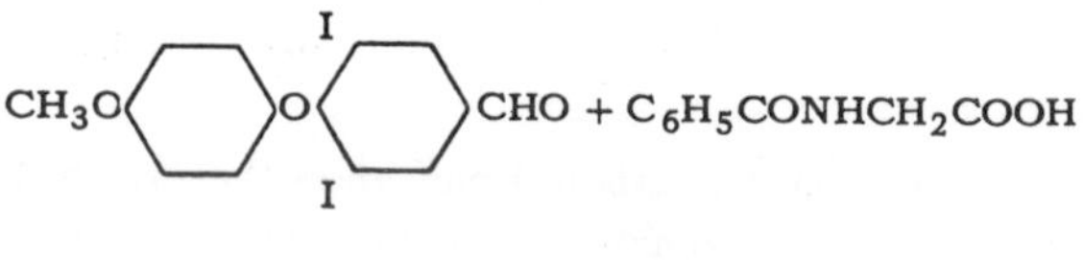

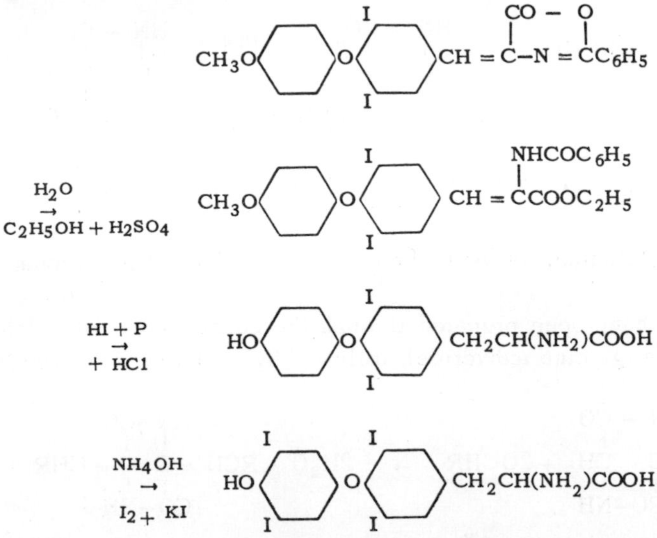

The aldehyde was obtained from 3,5-diiodo-4-(4′-methoxyphenoxy)-nitrobenzene, by reduction of the nitro group to an amino group, replacement of the amino group with a cyano group via the diazo compound, and conversion of the cyano group to the aldehyde group.

Tyrosine has been synthesized from anisaldehyde by the azlactone method:[197]

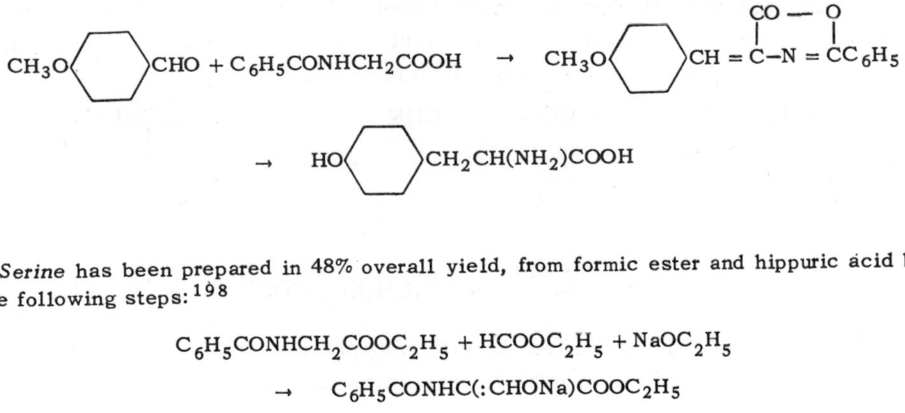

Serine has been prepared in 48% overall yield, from formic ester and hippuric acid by the following steps:[198]

$$C_6H_5CONHCH_2COOC_2H_5 + HCOOC_2H_5 + NaOC_2H_5$$

$$\rightarrow C_6H_5CONHC(:CHONa)COOC_2H_5$$

$$\xrightarrow{HCl} C_6H_5CONHC(:CHOH)COOC_2H_5$$

$$\xrightarrow{H_2} C_6H_5CONHCH(CH_2OH)COOC_2H_5$$

$$\xrightarrow[H_2SO_4]{H_2O} HOCH_2CH(NH_2)COOH$$

In a few cases *hydantoin* may be used with success instead of hippuric acid. The reaction appears to be restricted to benzaldehyde, anisaldehyde and β-indolealdehyde. Condensation is effected in acetic acid solution in the presence of acetic anhydride and sodium acetate:[83]

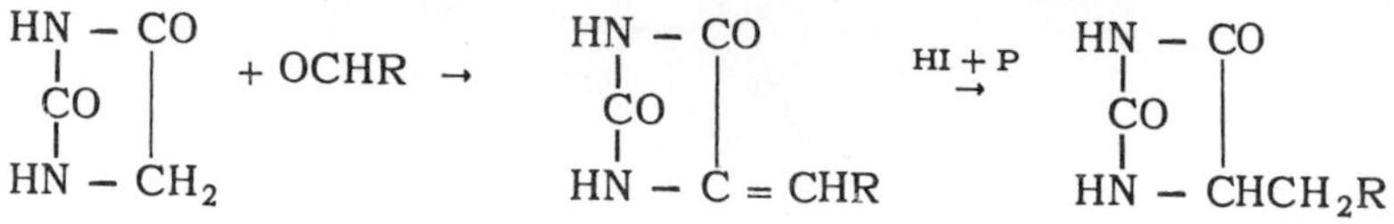

$$\begin{matrix} \text{HN} - \text{CO} \\ | \quad\quad | \\ \text{CO} \quad\quad | \\ | \quad\quad | \\ \text{HN} - \text{CH}_2 \end{matrix} + \text{OCHR} \;\rightarrow\; \begin{matrix} \text{HN} - \text{CO} \\ | \quad\quad | \\ \text{CO} \quad\quad | \\ | \quad\quad | \\ \text{HN} - \text{C} = \text{CHR} \end{matrix} \quad\overset{\text{HI} + \text{P}}{\rightarrow}\quad \begin{matrix} \text{HN} - \text{CO} \\ | \quad\quad | \\ \text{CO} \quad\quad | \\ | \quad\quad | \\ \text{HN} - \text{CHCH}_2\text{R} \end{matrix}$$

$$\overset{\text{H}_2\text{O} + \text{HI}}{\rightarrow} \quad \text{RCH}_2\text{CH(NH}_2\text{)COOH}$$

Alanine, phenylalanine, tyrosine and tryptophan have been prepared by this method.

Amino acids have been prepared through the condensation of aldehydes with diketopiperazine (glycine anhydride), followed by reduction and hydrolysis[199]

$$\begin{matrix} \text{HN} - \text{CO} \\ | \quad\quad | \\ \text{H}_2\text{C} \quad \text{CH}_2 \\ | \quad\quad | \\ \text{CO} - \text{NH} \end{matrix} + 2\text{OCHR} \;\rightarrow\; 2\text{H}_2\text{O} + \text{RCH} = \begin{matrix} \text{HN} - \text{CO} \\ | \quad\quad | \\ \text{C} \quad\quad \text{C} = \text{CHR} \\ | \quad\quad | \\ \text{CO} - \text{NH} \end{matrix}$$

$$\overset{\text{HI} + \text{P}}{\rightarrow} \quad \begin{matrix} \text{HN} - \text{CO} \\ | \quad\quad | \\ \text{RCH}_2\text{CH} \quad \text{CHCH}_2\text{R} \\ | \quad\quad | \\ \text{CO} - \text{NH} \end{matrix} \quad \overset{\text{H}_2\text{O} + \text{HI}}{\rightarrow} \quad 2\text{RCH}_2\text{CH(NH}_2\text{)COOH}$$

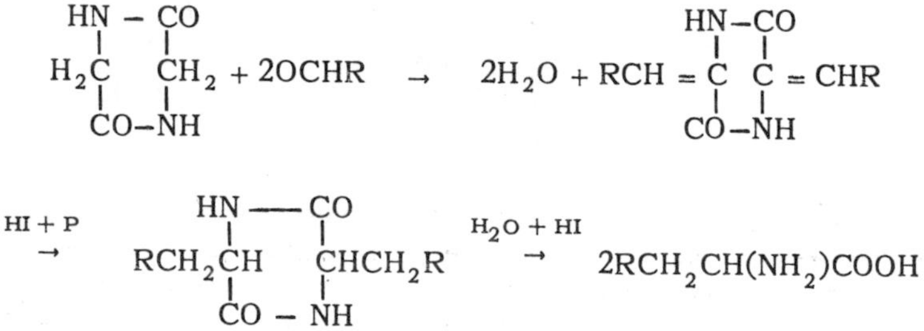

Condensation of aldehydes with thiazolones and reduction of the product with zinc and acetic acid followed by treatment with methanolic hydrogen chloride has also been employed for the preparation of a-amino acids:[200]

$$\begin{matrix} \text{CO} - \text{CH}_2 \\ | \quad\quad | \\ \text{S} \quad\quad \text{NH} \\ \diagdown \;/ \\ \text{CS} \end{matrix} + \text{OCHR} \;\rightarrow\; \begin{matrix} \text{CO} - \text{C} = \text{CHR} \\ | \quad\quad | \\ \text{S} \quad\quad \text{NH} \\ \diagdown \;/ \\ \text{CS} \end{matrix} \quad \overset{\text{Zn}}{\underset{\text{acetic acid}}{\rightarrow}} \quad \begin{matrix} \text{CO} - \text{CHCH}_2\text{R} \\ | \quad\quad | \\ \text{S} \quad\quad \text{NH} \\ \diagdown \;/ \\ \text{CS} \end{matrix}$$

$$\overset{\text{HCl} + \text{CH}_3\text{OH}}{\rightarrow} \quad \text{RCH}_2\text{CH(NH}_2\text{)COOH}$$

The reduction may also be effected with phosphorus and hydriodic acid. The reaction may be carried out at room temperature, and the yields are high.

Thiazolone is obtained through the reaction of carbon disulfide with aminoacetamide:

$$\text{H}_2\text{NCH}_2\text{CONH}_2 + \text{CS}_2 \;\rightarrow\; \begin{matrix} \text{CO} - \text{CH}_2 \\ | \quad\quad | \\ \text{S} \quad\quad \text{NH} \\ \diagdown \;/ \\ \text{CS} \end{matrix} + \text{NH}_3$$

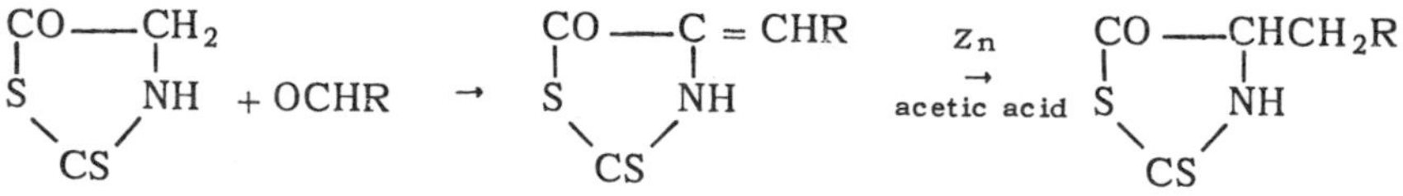

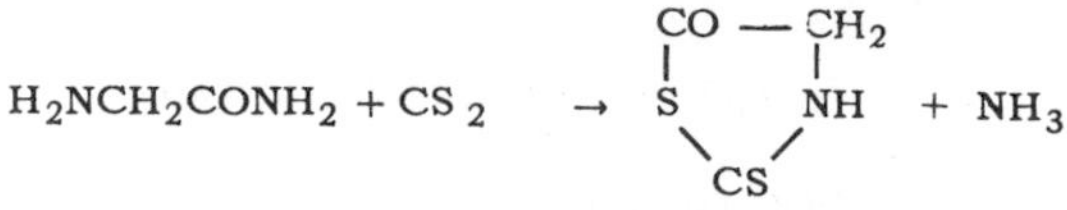

Aminoacetamide, in turn, may be obtained from glycinonitrile by reaction with acetone in the presence of sodium methoxide, and hydrolysis of the resulting cyclic imide:

$$\text{H}_2\text{NCH}_2\text{CN} + (\text{CH}_3)_2\text{CO} \;\overset{\text{NaOCH}_3}{\rightarrow}\; \begin{matrix} \text{H}_2\text{C} - \text{C} = \text{NH} \\ | \quad\quad | \\ \text{HN} \quad\quad \text{O} \\ \diagdown \;/ \\ \text{C(CH}_3)_2 \end{matrix}$$

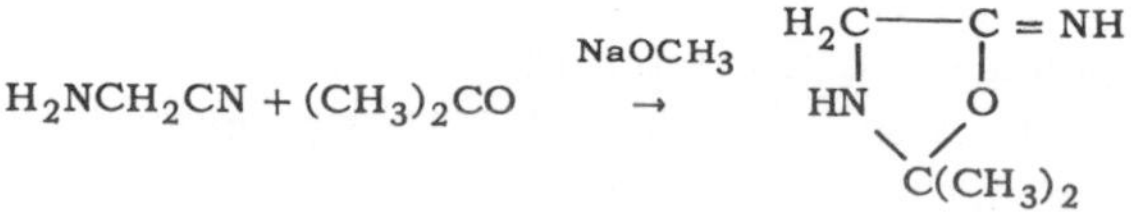

$$\xrightarrow{H_2O} \quad H_2NCH_2CONH_2$$

Glycine, H_2NCH_2COOH, results from the hydrolysis of thiazolone.

Many syntheses of amino acids have been developed depending on the use of malonic acid or its esters. A method for the preparation of α-amino acids of varying chain length utilizes the reaction of alkyl halides with acylaminomalonic esters in the presence of sodium ethoxide:[201]

$$RX + AcNHCH(COOC_2H_5)_2 \xrightarrow{NaOC_2H_5} AcNHC(R)(COOC_2H_5)_2$$

The amino acids, $RCH(NH_2)COOH$, are obtained on hydrolysis and partial decarboxylation of the product. Acylaminomalonic esters are obtained from aminomalonic ester by acylation, while aminomalonic acid is prepared from malonic ester by nitrosation and reduction.[202]

In this synthesis the order in which the amino group and the group R are introduced may be reversed.

Nitroso derivatives of substituted malonic acids may be converted to α-amino acids by partial decarboxylation followed by reduction with tin and hydrochloric acid:[203]

$$RC(NO)(COOH)_2 \rightarrow RCH(NO)COOH \xrightarrow{Sn + HCl} RCH(NH_2)COOH$$

Nitroso or oximino derivatives are obtained in good yield from substituted malonic acids by reaction with nitrosyl chloride. Reduction of the oximino group to an amino group may be accomplished catalytically.

Tryptophan has been obtained in 45% yield through the reaction of 3-iodomethylindole with acetylaminomalonic ester, and subsequent hydrolysis and partial decarboxylation:[204]

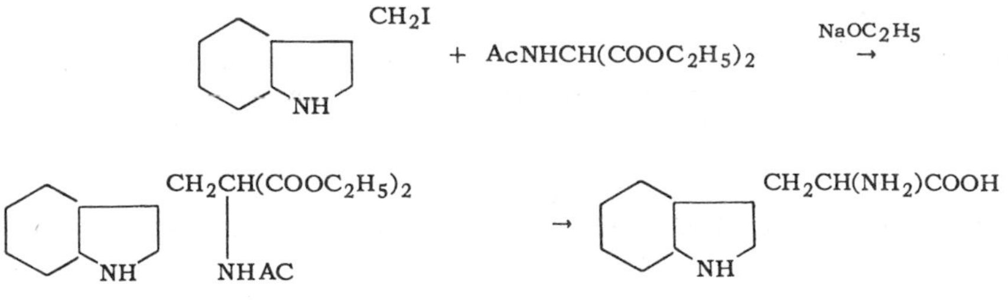

The compound has been obtained in 90% yield from formamiomalonic ester and diethylaminomethylindole.[260]

Cystine has been prepared by condensing formaldehyde with thiobenzoylaminomalonic ester, treating the resulting product with thionyl chloride to form a thiazolone, and hydrolyzing this and oxidizing the product of hydrolysis:[205]

$$C_6H_5CSNHCH(COOC_2H_5)_2 \xrightarrow{H_2CO} RCSNHC(CH_2OH)(COOC_2H_5)_2$$

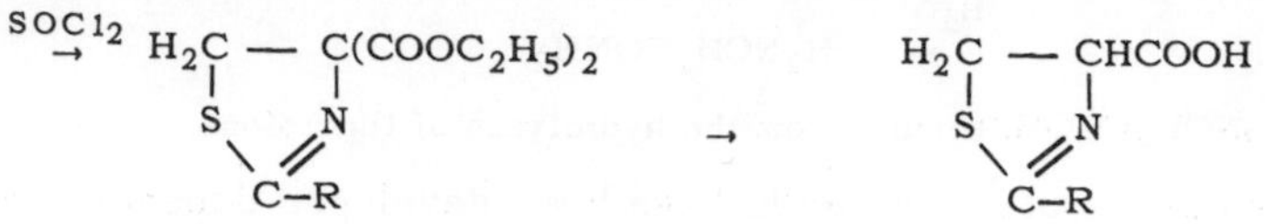

$$\xrightarrow[\text{and oxidation}]{\text{hydrolysis}} HSCH_2CH(NH_2)COOH$$

Lysine has been prepared from the condensation product of acraldehyde and acetylaminomalonic ester by reaction with hydrocyanic acid, acetylation and reduction of the resulting cyanohydrin, followed by acetylation, hydrolysis and decarboxylation of the resulting amino compound:[206]

$$OCHCH=CH_2 + AcNHCH(COOC_2H_5)_2 \xrightarrow{NaOC_2H_5} OCHCH_2CH_2C(NHAc)(COOC_2H_5)_2$$

$$\xrightarrow{HCN} CNCH(OH)CH_2CH_2C(NHAc)(COOC_2H_5)_2 \rightarrow H_2NCH_2CH_2CH_2CH_2C(NHAc)(COOC_2H_5)_2$$

$$\rightarrow H_2NCH_2CH_2CH_2CH_2CH(NH_2)COOH$$

Ornithine has been made from the condensation product of acrylonitrile and acetylaminomalonic ester, by reduction in the presence of Raney nickel followed by hydrolysis and decarboxylation:[207]

$$CNCH=CH_2 + HC(NHAc)(COOC_2H_5)_2 \xrightarrow{NaOC_2H_5} CNCH_2CH_2C(NHAc)(COOC_2H_5)_2$$

$$\xrightarrow{H_2} H_2NCH_2CH_2CH_2C(NHAc)(COOC_2H_5)_2 \rightarrow H_2NCH_2CH_2CH_2CH(NH_2)COOH$$

The compound has also been prepared from the condensation product of acraldehyde and acetylaminomalonic ester by reaction with phenylhydrazine, reduction with Raney nickel to a cyclic amide and hydrolysis:[207]

$$OCHCH=CH_2 + AcNHCH(COOC_2H_5)_2 \xrightarrow{NaOC_2H_5} OCHCH_2CH_2C(NHAc)(COOC_2H_5)_2$$

$$\xrightarrow{C_6H_5NHNH_2} C_6H_5NHN=CHCH_2CH_2C(NHAc)(COOC_2H_5)_2 \xrightarrow{H_2}$$

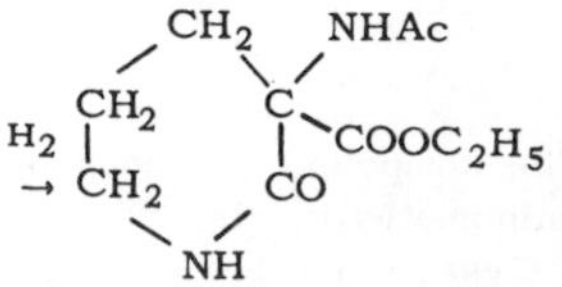
CH_2
NHAc
CH_2
C
$COOC_2H_5$
CH_2
CO
NH

$$\rightarrow H_2NCH_2CH_2CH_2CH(NH_2)COOH$$

Proline has been synthesized starting with γ-aminopropylaminomalonic ester, by condensing this to α,α-pyrrolidinedicarboxylic diamide and hydrolyzing and partially decarboxylating the latter:[208]

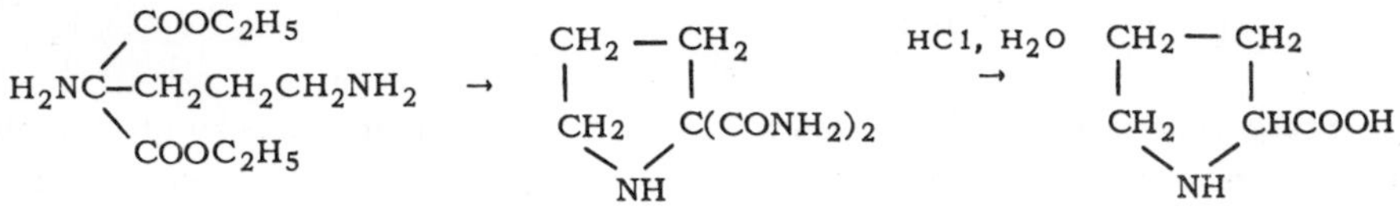

In this synthesis the yield of pyrolidinedicarboxylic diamide was quite low, only 12% of the theoretically expected quantity. The required γ-aminopropylaminomalonic ester was prepared from γ-bromopropylbromomalonic ester. *Proline* has been synthesized in 20% overall yield from malonic ester and acrylonitrile.[261] The method involves the catalytic reduction of the condensation product which results in the formation of a piperone carboxylic acid; chlorination of this with SO_2Cl_2 followed by hydrolysis yields proline hydrochloride.

Isoleucine has also been synthesized by the malonic ester route.[209]

An amino group may be introduced into malonic ester by reaction with an aryldiazo acetate and reduction of the resulting arylhydrazone with zinc dust and alcohol or other suitable reducing agent:[210]

$$ArN = NOAc + H_2C(COOC_2H_5)_2 \rightarrow AcOH + ArNHN = C(COOC_2H_5)_2$$
$$\rightarrow H_2NCH(COOC_2H_5)_2 + ArNH_2$$

The reaction of benzenediazonium chloride with α-methylacetoacetic acid leads to the formation of the monophenylhydrazide of diacetyl:[211]

$$CH_3COCH(CH_3)COOH + ClN_2C_6H_5 \rightarrow CH_3COC(:NNHC_6H_5)CH_3 + CO_2 + HCl$$

This is known as the *Japp and Klingemann reaction.*

Reactions involving the reactive methylene in malonic esters are generally applicable to acetoacetic ester and esters of other acids with a reactive methylene group.

Threonine has been synthesized starting with benzamidoacetoacetic ester.[212] Hydrogenation followed by treatment with thionyl chloride gave an oxazoline:

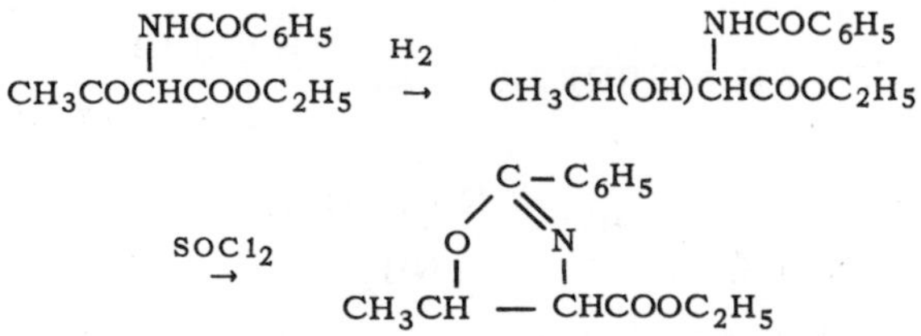

Hydrolysis with caustic followed by treatment with hydrochloric acid gave threonine, $CH_3CH(OH)CH(NH_2)COOH$, in 60% overall yield. The benzamidoacetoacetic ester required for the synthesis was obtained indirectly from benzaminoacetic ester by reaction with acetic anhydride in the presence of β-picoline, and esterification of the lactone formed:

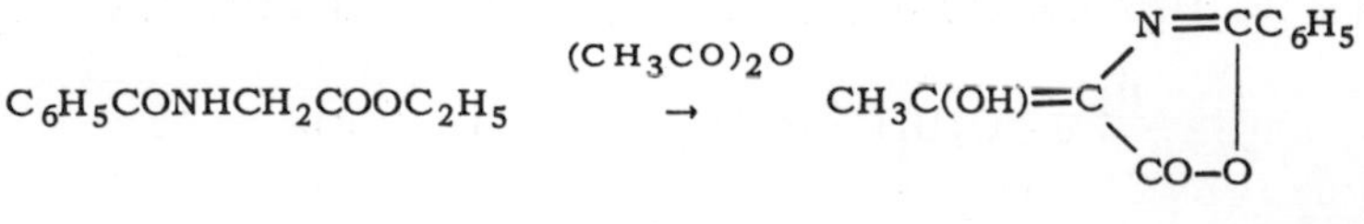

$$C_2H_5OH \to \begin{matrix} NHCOC_6H_5 \\ | \\ CH_3COCHCOOC_2H_5 \end{matrix}$$

An interesting method of preparation of amino acids from α-alkylated aceto-acetic esters depends on the reaction of hydrazoic acid with these esters. It involves a remarkable molecular rearrangement resulting in the formation of an acetylamino acid, hydrolysis of which yields an amino acid:

$$CH_3COCH(R)COOC_2H_5 + HN_3 \to N_2 + CH_3CONHCH(R)COOC_2H_5$$

$$\to H_2NCH(R)COOH$$

Another reaction involving a similar rearrangement and forming the basis for a method of preparation of amino acids, depends on the conversion of the half-azide of substituted malonic acids to a cyclic anhydrobromide. The azide is prepared from the half-ester of the acid by reaction first with hydrazine, then with nitrous acid:[213]

$$RCH(COONa)COOC_2H_5 + H_2NNH_2 \to C_2H_5OH + RCH(COONa)CONHNH_2$$

$$\overset{HNO_2}{\to} RCH(COOH)CON_3 \to \overline{RCHNHCOOCO}$$

The cyclic anhydroamide, subjected to hydrolysis, gives an amino acid:

$$\overline{RCHNHCOOCO} + H_2O \to RCH(NH_2)COOH + CO_2$$

Leucine has been prepared by condensing 2-methylallyl chloride with acetaminocyano-acetic ester and hydrogenating the resulting product.

Substituted cyanoacetic esters, $CNCRR'COOC_2H_5$, may be converted to amino acids $RR'C(NH_2)COOH$ by hydrolysis to the amide $H_2NCOCRR'COOH$, and application of the Hofmann degradation.[214]

α-Amino acids are formed by a process of transamination from α-keto acids by reaction with an α-amino acid:[215]

$$RCOCOOH + H_2NCH(R)COOH \to \begin{matrix} R'CCOOH \\ || \\ NCH(R)COOH \end{matrix} \to$$

$$\begin{matrix} R'CHCOOH \\ | \\ N=C(R)COOH \end{matrix} \overset{H_2O}{\to} \begin{matrix} R'CHCOOH \\ | \\ NH_2 \end{matrix} + CO_2 + RCHO$$

α-Amino acids with three additional carbon atoms may be synthesized from aromatic aldehydes and pyruvic acid by condensing the latter with a Schiff base derived from the aldehyde and reducing the product with hydrogen in the presence of colloidal platinum or palladium. This method is especially useful for the preparation of N-alkylated amino acids:

$$C_6H_5CH=NC_2H_5 + CH_3COCOOH \to H_2O + C_6H_5CH=CHC(:NC_2H_5)COOH$$

$$\overset{H_2}{\to} C_6H_5CH_2CH_2CH(NHC_2H_5)COOH$$

Cystine has been made from α-acetaminoacrylic acid by reaction with thioacetic acid, hydrolysis of the addition product, and finally oxidation of the thio amino acid:[216]

$$2CH_2=C(NHCOCH_3)COOH + CH_3COSH \rightarrow 2CH_3COSCH_2CH(NHCOCH_3)COOH$$

$$\xrightarrow{HCl} 2HSCH_2CH(NH_2)COOH \xrightarrow{O_2} HOCOCH(NH_2)CH_2SSCH_2CH(NH_2)COOH$$

Acetaminoacrylic acid is obtained through the reaction of acetamide with pyruvic acid. Cystine has also been prepared from methyl α-chloroacrylate by reaction with thiourea in the presence of hydrogen chloride, reduction of the aminothiazolinecarboxylic acid formed and oxidation of the resulting 1-amino-2-mercaptopropionic acid:[217]

$$2\ (HCl.HN=)(H_2N)CSH + CH_2=CClCOOCH_3 \rightarrow 2\ (HCl.HN=)(H_2N)CSCH_2CHClCOOCH_3$$

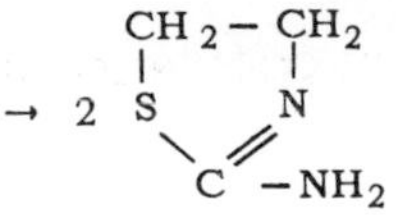

$$\xrightarrow{H_2} 2\ HSCH_2CH(NH_2)COOH$$

$$\xrightarrow{O_2} HOCOCH(NH_2)CH_2SSCH_2CH(NH_2)COOH$$

Cystine has also been prepared from the ethyl ester of benzoylserine by treatment with phosphorous pentasulfide, followed by hydrolysis and oxidation with ferric chloride and ammonia:[218]

$$2\ HOCH_2CH(NHCOC_6H_5)COOC_2H_5 \xrightarrow{P_2S_5} 2\ HSCH_2CH(NHCOC_6H_5)COOC_2H_5 \xrightarrow{HCl}$$

$$2\ HSCH_2CH(NH_2HCl)COOH \xrightarrow{O_2} HOCOCH(NH_2)CH_2SSCH_2CH(NH_2)COOH$$

Another method utilizes the reaction of toluene-ω-thiol with α-chloroacrylonitrile; the addition product is successively aminated, hydrolyzed and debenzoylated:[220]

$$CH_2=CClCN + C_6H_5CH_2SH \rightarrow C_6H_5CH_2SCH_2CHClCN \rightarrow HSCH_2CH(NH_2)COOH$$

Glutamine has been prepared from dimethyl-1-benzylcarbaminoglutarate by reaction with ammonia, hydrolysis and hydrogenolysis:[221]

$$CH_3OCOCH_2CH_2CH(C_6H_5CH_2OCONH)COOCH_3 \xrightarrow{NH_3} H_2NCOCH_2CH_2CH(C_6H_5CH_2OCONH)NONH_2$$

$$\xrightarrow{H_2O} H_2NCOCH_2CH_2CH(C_6H_5CH_2ONH)COOH \xrightarrow{H_2} H_2NCOCH_2CH_2CH(NH_2)COOH$$

The synthesis of *glutathione* in the form of its dimethyl ester has been accomplished through the interaction of glutamic acid monobromide with cystine dimethyl ester:[222]

$$CH_3OCOCH(NH_2)CH_2SSCH_2CH(NH_2)COOH + 2BrCOCH_2CH_2CH(NH_2)COOH$$

$$\rightarrow HOCOCH(NH_2)CH_2CH_2CONHC(COOCH_3)CH_2SSCH_2C(COOCH_3)NHCOCH_2CH_2CH(NH_2)COOH$$

The monobromide was prepared by heating glutamic acid with phosphorus tribromide.

Glutathione has also been obtained through the reaction of hydantoin propionyl bromide with cystine dimethyl ester hydrochloride, cleavage of the hydantoin ring in the resulting product with calcium hydroxide, and finally treatment with nitrous acid:[223]

$$[CH_3OCOCH(NH_2)CH_2S-]_2 + 2BrCOCH_2CH_2\overline{CHCONHCONH}$$

$$\rightarrow \left[\begin{array}{l}-SCH_2CHCOOCH_3 \\ \quad\quad | \\ \quad\quad NHCOCH_2CH_2\overline{CHCONHCONH}\end{array}\right]_2$$

$$\xrightarrow{Ca(OH)_2} \left[\begin{array}{l}-SCH_2CHCOOH \\ \quad\quad | \\ \quad\quad NHCOCH_2CH_2CH(COOH)NHCONH_2\end{array}\right]_2$$

$$\xrightarrow{HNO_2} \left[\begin{array}{l}-SCH_2CHCOOH \\ \quad\quad | \\ \quad\quad NHCOCH_2CH_2CH(NH_2)COOH\end{array}\right]_2$$

Hydantoinpropionic acid was made from glutamic acid by Dakin's method, i.e., by reaction with potassium cyanate, and was converted to the bromide by treatment with phosphorus tribromide.

Glutathion may be isolated by forming its mercuric sulfate compound and liberating the acid from this by treatment with hydrogen sulfide.

β-Hydroxyglutamic acid has been obtained in 60% overall yield from acetonedicarboxylic ester by reaction with ethyl nitrite in solution in ethereal hydrogen chloride and catalytic reduction of the resulting oxime, in the presence of palladium catalyst deposited on carbon, in alcoholic hydrochloric acid:[224]

$$C_2H_5OCOCH_2COCH_2COOC_2H_5 \xrightarrow{C_2H_5NO_2} C_2H_5OCOCH_2COC(:NOH)COOC_2H_5$$

$$\xrightarrow{H_2} HOCOCH_2CH(OH)CH(NH_2)COOH$$

Isoleucine has been prepared similarly by reduction of the oxime of ethylmethylpyruvic acid obtained by the action of nitrosyl sulfate on the condensation product of acetoacetic ester and *sec*-butyl iodide:[225]

$$CH_3CH_2CHICH_3 + CH_3COCH_2COOC_2H_5 \xrightarrow{NaOC_2H_5} \begin{array}{c}CH_3COCHCOOC_2H_5 \\ | \\ CH_3CHCH_2CH_3\end{array}$$

$$\xrightarrow[\text{sulfate}]{\text{nitrosyl}} CH_3CH_2CH(CH_3)C(:NOH)COOH \xrightarrow{H_2}$$

$$CH_3CH_2CH(CH_3)CH(NH_2)COOH$$

The synthesis of *histidine* has been accomplished by reacting 2,4-dithiohydantoin with 2-phenyl-4-ethoxymethyleneoxazolone in the presence of sodium methoxide or diethylamine, reducing the resulting compound with hydrogen in the presence of Raney nickel and hydrolyzing the benzamide ester formed:[226]

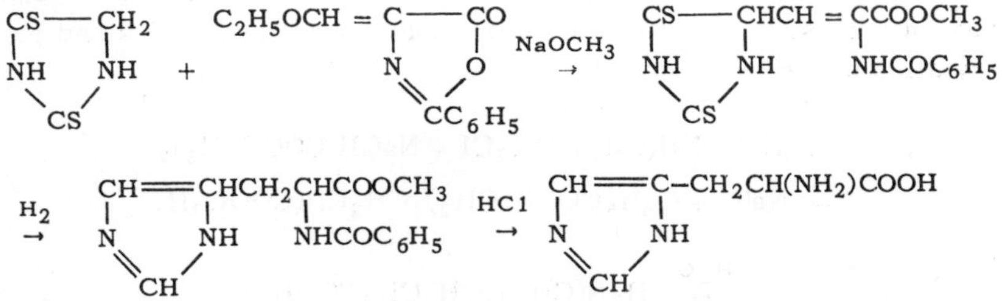

$$\underset{\overset{|}{\underset{NH}{}}\ \ \overset{|}{\underset{NH}{}}}{CS-CH_2} \underset{CS}{\diagdown \diagup} \ + \ \underset{\overset{|}{\underset{N}{}}\ \ \overset{|}{\underset{O}{}}}{C_2H_5OCH=C-CO} \underset{CC_6H_5}{\diagdown \diagup} \ \xrightarrow{NaOCH_3} \ \underset{\overset{|}{\underset{NH}{}}\ \ \overset{|}{\underset{NH}{}}}{CS-CHCH=CCOOCH_3} \underset{CS}{\diagdown \diagup} \ \ \overset{|}{\underset{NHCOC_6H_5}{}}$$

$$\xrightarrow{H_2} \ \underset{\overset{|}{\underset{N}{}}\ \ \ \overset{|}{\underset{NH}{}}}{CH\!=\!CHCH_2CHCOOCH_3} \underset{CH}{\diagdown \diagup} \ \ \overset{|}{\underset{NHCOC_6H_5}{}} \ \xrightarrow{HCl} \ \underset{\overset{|}{\underset{N}{}}\ \ \overset{|}{\underset{NH}{}}}{CH\!=\!C-CH_2CH(NH_2)COOH} \underset{CH}{\diagdown \diagup}$$

β-Amino acids result when ammonia is made to react at 125-135° with α, β-unsaturated acids.[227] *Aspartic acid*, $HOCOCH_2CH(NH_2)COOH$, has been obtained through the reaction of alcoholic ammonia with diethyl fumarate, and saponification of the resulting diacetamidodiketopiperazine with caustic.[228]

The reaction of aldehyde ammonias with malonic acid also results in the formation of β-amino acids, although in some instances pyrimidines and glyoxalidines are formed in this reaction.[229]

Cyclic ketones may be converted to lactams by subjecting their oximes to the Beckmann rearrangement; on hydrolysis with boiling mineral acids, the lactams yield the corresponding amino acid:[84]

$$\overline{CH_2(CH_2)_3CO} \ \rightarrow \ \overline{CH_2(CH_2)_3C\!:\!NOH} \ \rightarrow \ \overline{CH_2(CH_2)_3NHCO}$$

$$\rightarrow \ H_2NCH_2(CH_2)_3COOH$$

This method permits the preparation of δ-, ϵ-, and ζ-amino acids from five-, six-, and seven-membered cyclic ketones.

δ-Amino acids may be obtained through the oxidation of six-membered cyclic amines with potassium permanganate. For example, δ-aminovaleric acid may be obtained from benzoylpiperidine by boiling with hydrochloric acid the benzoyl-aminovaleric acid obtained as the primary product of oxidation:[85]

$$\overline{CH_2(CH_2)_4NCOC_6H_5} \ \xrightarrow{O_2} \ C_6H_5CONH(CH_2)_4COOH$$

$$\xrightarrow{H_2O} \ H_2N(CH_2)_4COOH$$

N-Benzoyl derivatives of cyclic amines, heated with phosphorus pentachloride, undergo ring fissure, giving an open-chain δ-chloro-chloroimide:

$$\overline{CH_2(CH_2)_4NCOC_6H_5} \ \xrightarrow{PCl_5} \ \overline{CH_2(CH_2)_4NC(Cl_2)C_6H_5} \ \rightleftharpoons \ ClCH_2(CH_2)_4N=CClC_6H_5$$

Hydrolysis of the chloroimide gives the benzoylated δ-chloroamine,

$$ClCH_2(CH_2)_4NCOC_6H_5.$$

The chloro derivative may be converted to an amino acid by reaction with potassium cyanide and hydrolysis of the resulting nitrile. *ε-Amino acids* are obtained by this method. The chloro compound may also be converted to a *ζ-amino acid* by reaction with sodio ethyl malonate and subsequent hydrolysis and partial decarboxylation of the resulting product:

$$C_6H_5CONH(CH_2)_4CH_2Cl + NaCH(COOC_2H_5)_2$$
$$\rightarrow NaCl + C_6H_5CONH(CH_2)_4CH_2CH(COOC_2H_5)_2$$
$$\xrightarrow{H_2O} H_2N(CH_2)_4CH_2CH_2COOH$$

Behavior of Amino Acids

Amino acids have the character of internal salts in aqueous solution, although in alcoholic solution they show an acid reaction and can be titrated with alkalies, using phenolphthalein as an indicator.[86] On reaction with alkaline earth hydroxides and carbon dioxide in aqueous solution, amino acids give carbimino carboxylic salts of the type $\overline{NHCH_2COOBaOCO}$.[87] They yield insoluble compounds with picric and picrolonic acids. Acyl chlorides react readily with amino acids giving N-acylated derivatives. The N-formyl derivatives results on heating the amino acids with anhydrous formic acid.

Amino acids in aqueous solution react with formaldehyde, condensation taking place between the methylene group of the aldehyde and the amino group.[88] The acidic nature is brought to evidence as a result of this reaction, and the compound can be determined quantitatively by titration with standard alkali[89] *(Formol titration).*

Copper salts of amino acids are only slightly soluble in water and may be obtained in the crystalline form. This fact is utilized for the isolation of these acids. The copper salts of α- an β-amino acids resemble the cuprammonium compounds: their solutions do not contain cupric ions and therefore give no precipitate of copper hydroxide with alkali hydroxides. The metal can be only partially precipitated with hydrogen sulfide. The nickel and cobalt salts show a similar behavior.

When α-amino acids are heated with acetic anhydride and pyridine, carbon dioxide is eliminated and an α-acetamido ketone is formed:

$$RCH(NH_3)COOH + (CH_3CO)_2O \rightarrow RCH(NHCOCH_3)COCH_3 + CO_2 + H_2O$$

α-Amino acids containing no replaceable hydrogen in the α-position, and alkylamino and β-amino acids undergo simple acetylation.

Guanidino acids are obtained in excellent yield through the reaction of amino acids with S-methylisothiourea in ammoniacal solution.[230] The method is applicable to peptides and proteins. Guanidino acids may also be made by reaction of amino acids with cyanamide, or with cyanogen bromide followed by heating with ammonia.

similar halides, forming esters of the corresponding acids; for this reason the direct use of these halides is not possible for the preparation of aliphatic esters of organic acids.

Esters from Acid Anhydrides

Alcohols react with acid anhydrides to form an ester and the free acid:

$$RCOOCOR + R'OH \rightarrow RCOOR' + RCOOH$$

It is usually sufficient to heat a mixture of equivalent quantities of the alcohol and anhydride to bring about complete esterification. Sodium acetate greatly accelerates the reaction; sulfuric acid also acts as an effective catalyst, apparently forming with the organic acid a mixed anhydride which acts as a vigorous acetylating agent.[33] Zinc chloride also exerts a catalytic effect and is used in the acetylation of cellulose to triacetyl cellulose.

Esters of formic acid may be obtained through the reaction of the mixed anhydride of formic and acetic acids with alcohols. Octyl formate is obtained readily, for example, by adding a little more than the required quantity of the mixed formoacetic anhydride, $CH_3COOCOH$, to capryl alcohol with cooling.

Acetic anhydride reacts readily with phenols in the presence of sodium acetate.[34]

Anhydrides of dibasic acids react with a molecular equivalent of alcohol to give an acid ester:

$$\overline{OCOCH_2CH_2CO} + HOC_2H_5 \rightarrow HOCOCH_2CH_2COOC_2H_5$$

With alkali metal alcoholates the sodium salt of the acid ester is formed. Salts of the acid esters may also be obtained by the partial saponification of the neutral esters with sodium hydroxide.

When acid esters are prepared from dicarboxylic acids of unsymmetrical structure by reaction with a molecular equivalent of alcohol, the carboxyl group possessing the greater acid strength is esterified preferentially. In the inverse reaction, that is, the hydrolysis of neutral esters of dicarboxylic acids of unsymmetrical structure, the carboxylic group of the greater strength is hydrolyzed preferentially.

Acid esters resulting from the intereaction of molecular proportions of an alcohol and a dicarboxylic acid anhydride can, of course, be fully esterified by the usual methods of esterification.

Sodium salts of phenols also react with anhydrides of dicarboxylic acids in inert solvents yielding the sodium salt of the acid phenyl ester:

$$\overline{OCORCO} + NaOC_6H_5 \rightarrow NaOCORCOOC_6H_5$$

The procedure for the preparation of these esters is as follows: To a solution of the phenol in ten times its weight of xylene, the calculated quantity of metallic sodium is added. After all the sodium has disappeared, the anhydride is introduced and the mixture is allowed to stand, whereupon the sodium salt of the acid ester separates out as a solid. The acid may be freed from the solution of the sodium salt by the addition of an excess of mineral acid.

Phenol acid esters of camphoric acid and the guaiacol acid esters of succinic acid have been prepared by this method. Acid esters of *meta*-nitrophenol may also be prepared by this method, but *ortho*- and *para*-nitrophenols and *ortho*-dibromophenol fail to react.

The *Schotten-Baumann* method is applicable to esterification reactions by use of acid anhydrides.

Phenols may be acetylated, for example, by adding acetic anhydride to a solution of the phenol in a somewhat more than the theoretical quantity of aqueous sodium hydroxide. On shaking for a short time, the acetylated phenol separates in an almost pure condition.[35]

The *Deninger-Einhorn* modification is also applicable to acid anhydrides.[36]

The *procedure* is as previously described in connection with acid chlorides: The calculated quantity of the anhydride is added to a thoroughly cooled solution of the alcohol or phenol in about five times its weight of pyridine and the mixture is allowed to stand for several hours. The ester separates out on pouring the mixture carefully and with stirring into an excess of dilute sulfuric acid containing fragments of ice. The ester is taken up in ether, the ethereal solution is washed repeatedly with dilute acid, and the ester is isolated by fractional distillation. The crude ester is occasionally contaminated with small quantities of the organic acid. This is eliminated by washing the ethereal solution with dilute sodium carbonate.

This method is of wide applicability and has been employed for the acylation of a great variety of hydroxy compounds, including phenols and polyhydric alcohols. In acylating α-hydroxy acids the carboxylic hydroxyl group should be protected in order to avoid the formation of non-crystallizable products.

The reaction has been made the basis of the determination of hydroxyl groups. The method employed for this purpose is as follows:

A weighed amount of the compound, usually 1 to 2 grams, and 25 cc of a mixture prepared with 120 grams of acetic anhydride and 800 grams of pyridine are heated in a 200 cc flask on a water bath for fifteen minutes. After cooling, 25 cc of water are added and the mixture is titrated with standard half-normal alkali, using phenolphthalein as an indicator. The success of this method depends on the fact that pyridine is not sufficiently basic to affect the color of phenolphthalein. A check determination should be made with 25 cc of the anhydride-pyridine mixture to be assured that no loss of anhydride takes place in the heating process.

The hydroxyl groups in *sugars* may be effectively acetylated by treatment with acetic anhydride and pyridine, or sodium acetate. Acetylation may be accomplished also by the use of acetic anhydride and catalysts, such as zinc chloride or sulfuric acid, although this method is seldom used. Other acyl groups may be introduced into the sugar molecule by these methods, by substituting other anhydrides for acetic acid.

Cellulose may be acetylated with acetic anhydride or acetyl chloride in the presence of pyridine. In order to avoid hydrolysis of the cellulose, the reaction must be carried out at a low temperature. Degradation of cellulose may also be avoided by carrying out the reaction in solution in a chlorinated acetic acid.[37] Cellulose acetate may also be prepared from hydrocellulose by reaction with acetyl chloride in the presence of zinc- or magnesium acetate, or with acetic anhydride and a little concentrated sulfuric acid.[37] *Hydrocellulose* is prepared by treatment of cellulose with cold, concentrated sodium hydroxide solution (15 to 25%) followed by washing with water.

Cellulose, allowed to stand for a long period with 15% aqueous sodium hydroxide, is converted to alkali cellulose; this compound, freed of excess caustic, reacts with carbon disulfide to form *cellulose xanthate*, a product which dissolves in water to yield a viscous solution. Cellulose may be regenerated in the hydrated form from this solution by coagulation with alcohol or brine.

Mixed anhydrides have been used in esterification reactions. Oleyl and hydrocapryl formates have been prepared from the alcohols by reaction with acetoformic anhydride, $CH_3COOCHO$. The mixed anhydride of carboxylic acids with alkylsulfonic acids, reacting with alcohols, give the ester of the carboxylic acid:

$$ROH + R'COOSO_2R'' \rightarrow ROCOR' + R''SO_2OH$$

The method appears to be of general applicability, and has given satisfactory results even with some sterically hindered acids. The mixed carboxylic-sulfonic anhydrides are formed when the sodium salt of the carboxylic acid is made to react with the sulfonic acid chlorides $R''SO_2Cl$.

Inner anhydrides of hydroxy acids have also been used for the purpose of acylating hydroxyl groups. Thus, alkaloid esters of salicylic acid have been obtained through the reaction of alkaloids or their salts with salicylides or polysalicylides.

Ester Formation with Aromatic Acids – Influence of Substituents

Aromatic acids may be readily esterified, as a rule, with alcohols in the presence of mineral acids or other catalysts. The reaction of benzoic acid with an alcohol proceeds in the cold in the presence of hydrogen chloride. Substituents in the *ortho* position have a retarding influence on the rate of esterification.[38] Among substituents, hydrocarbon radicals have a marked effect, the methyl group has the least influence on the rate, while the effect of other hydrocarbon groups, such as ethyl, *n*-propyl, and phenyl groups, is of approximately the same order of magnitude. The retarding effect of halogens lies in magnitude between that of the methyl radical and the other hydrocarbon groups, with the effect increasing in the order fluorine, chlorine, bromine and iodine. The effect of nitro groups is comparable with that of the halogens, but the effect of hydroxyl groups is considerably less.

There are exceptions to this rule; thus, acetophenoneorthocarboxylic acid and orthophenoxybenzoic acid are more readily esterified than benzoic acid.[39]

The presence of a chlorine atom in the *meta* or *para* position in benzoic acid causes an increase in the rate of the non-catalyzed reaction, and a decrease in the catalyzed reaction,[40] a situation which is comparable with that of the effect of halogen atoms in the α-position in aliphatic acids.

Meyer and Sudborough have found that aromatic acids with two ortho substituents, such as Br, NO_2, CH_3, COOH, etc., are not, as a rule, capable of yielding esters by the usual methods of esterification.[41] This generalization, known as *Victor Meyer's rule*, may be considered of an empirical nature. In accordance with this rule 2,6-dibromobenzoic acid, yields no ester, while the 2,4-dibromo isomer may be esterified to the extent of 90%; 1,4-dinitrophthalic acid fails to yield an ester, while 1,5-dinitrophthalic acid gives a monoester. There are numerous exceptions to the rule. The rule fails to apply to compounds with one or more hydroxyl groups; 3,6-dichloro-, tetrachloro-, tetra-bromo-, tetraiodophthalic acids yield acid esters,[42] a behavior explained by assuming that the acids are converted to anhydrides by the action of hydrogen chloride, and the anhydrides react with the alcohol to form the acid esters. While the formation of neutral esters from these acid esters has been reported, the reaction proceeds very slowly and yields are quite low. It may be added that acids with two substituents in the ortho position may be esterified by heating a mixture of the acid and alcohol to a high temperature under pressure.

When the carboxyl group is separated from the aromatic nucleus by one or more carbon atoms, the rate of esterification is not materially affected by substituents in the *ortho* position in the nucleus. For example, derivatives of phenylacetic acid which contain two substituents in the *ortho* position in the nucleus can be readily esterified.[43] On the other hand, a nitro group in the *ortho* position exerts an appreciable retarding effect in the case of certain derivatives of cinnamic acid.[8]

A lactone ester is obtained when orthocarboxycinnamic acid is esterified with ethyl alcohol in the presence of sulfuric acid or hydrogen chloride:

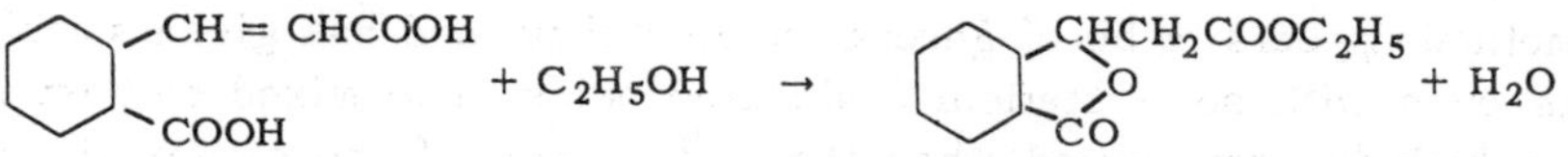

This reaction takes place even in the cold. On hydrolysis of the lactone ester, the original carboxycinnamic acid is regenerated.

Aromatic amino acids do not form esters when they are heated with alcohol in the absence of acids or in the presence of only catalytic quantities of a mineral acid;[14] on the other hand, esterification proceeds well when a mixture of alcohol with the hydrochloride of the amino acid is heated to boiling, and conversions of 65% are possible.[44]

Esters from Metallic Salts

Organic esters may be obtained through the interaction of the silver salt of an organic acid with an alkyl iodide:

$$RCOOAg + IR' \rightarrow RCOOR' + AgI$$

Alkyl bromides, and in some instances, chlorides may also be used in this reaction. The lower alkyl esters of substituted benzoic acids may be obtained readily by this method.[45] The method has also been employed for the preparation of glycols from dibromoparafins by converting these to the corresponding glycol ester and subsequently hydrolyzing the ester. Instead of the silver salt, a suspension of silver oxide in a mixture of the acid and absolute alcohol may be treated with the halide.

Lead or alkali metal salts of acids may be substituted for the silver salt in this reaction. The lead salts may be obtained in a highly reactive form when, immediately after precipitation from an aqueous solution of the alkali metal salt, they are washed successively with water, alcohol and ether and dried at atmospheric temperature. Reaction with alkali metal salts appears to take place more readily in the presence of pyridine or quinoline. Heating in a sealed tube is sometimes necessary when alkali metal salts are employed.

The monoglycol ester of salicylic acid, $HOC_6H_4COOCH_2CH_2OH$, is obtained through the reaction of ethylene chlorhydrin with potassium salicylate.[46] The sodium salt of nipecotinic acid,

$$\text{(structure: cyclohexane ring with NH, and } {-\!H \atop -\!COOH} \text{)}$$

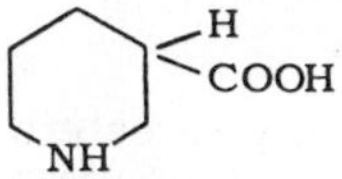

heated at $100°$ for five to six hours with methyl iodide gives methyl nipecotate. [47] The sodium salt of ethyl acid camphorate reacts with allyl iodide in the presence of methyl alcohol to form ethyl allyl camphorate. The reaction fails to occur in the absence of methyl alcohol. [48] The presence of methanol is also necessary in other similar cases. Potassium o-hydroxymethylbenzoate heated with methyl iodide gives phthalide: [49]

$$C_6H_4{\overset{\textstyle COOK}{\underset{\textstyle CH_2OH}{\big\langle}}} + IC_2H_5 \rightarrow C_6H_4{\overset{\textstyle CO}{\underset{\textstyle CH_2}{\big\langle}}}O + KI + C_2H_5OH$$

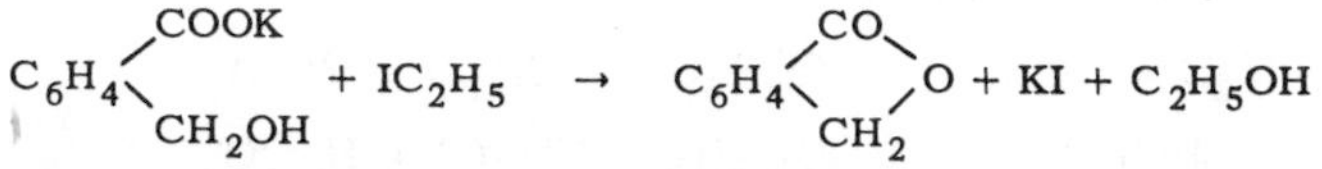

Esters are formed also through the reaction of alkali metal salts of carboxylic acids with alkyl sulfates

$$RCOOK + (CH_3)_2SO_4 \rightarrow RCOOCH_3 + CH_3KSO_4$$

While diethyl sulfate reacts poorly, [50] the reaction proceeds vigorously with dimethyl sulfate. This compound reacts more readily, in effect, than methyl iodide, and is a very satisfactory methylating agent. [51] It is often used in preference to methyl iodide, especially since its use obviates the necessity of carrying out the reaction under pressure. Acids, such as 2,4,6-tribromo- and 2,4,6-trinitrobenzoic, which do not yield esters by direct reaction with alcohols because of steric hindrance, may be converted to their methyl esters by treatment with methyl sulfate. [52]

Esterification by the use of dimethyl sulfate is carried out as follows: The acid is dissolved in an excess of aqueous sodium hydroxide, two molecular equivalents of dimethyl sulfate are added and the mixture is shaken intermittently for half an hour. The unreacted dimethyl sulfate is then decomposed by heating the reaction mixture on the water bath for half an hour. Any free acid is neutralized with caustic after the liquid has been cooled, and the ester is isolated, by filtration if it is solid, and by ether extraction if a liquid.

Aromatic sulfonic acids can also be methylated by heating with methyl sulfate at $150 - 160°$

Glycerine reacts with concentrated sulfuric acid to form a diacid sulfate,

$$HOCH_2CH(OSO_3H)CH_2OSO_3H$$

The reaction is complete within 15 minutes when 1 part of glycerine is mixed with 4 parts of 98.3% sulfuric acid. [53] The diacid sulfate, heated with an organic acid, gives the dicarboxylic ester of glycerine. Glycerine dipalmitate, $HOC_3H_5(OCOC_{15}H_{31})_2$, is obtained, for example, with palmitic acid. [54] Glycerine α-chlorohydrine also gives a diacid sulfate with concentrated sulfuric acid.

Alkyl chlorosulfites react vigorously with the sodium salt of carboxylic acids at $100-150°$ to form the ester of the latter: [155]

$$RCOONa + R'OSOCl \rightarrow RCOOR' + NaCl + SO_2$$

Esters of hindered 2,4,6-trialkylbenzoic acids have been prepared by this method.

Esters by Alcoholysis of Nitriles

Nitriles may be converted directly to esters by reaction with alcohols in the presence of some water and a strong acid:[156]

$$RCN + H_2O + HOR' + HCl \rightarrow RCOOR' + NH_4Cl$$

Esters of a variety of acids have been prepared by this method, including those of 2-hydroxy-3-halobutyric acid. The ethyl ester of glycine has been obtained from methylene aminoacetonitrile:[157]

$$H_2C = NCH_2CN + C_2H_5OH + 2H_2O + 2HCl \rightarrow$$
$$HCl\ H_2NCH_2COOC_2H_5 + NH_4Cl + H_2CO$$

Ester Exchange

When an alcohol is heated with an ester in a sealed tube, an exchange of alkyl residues takes place[55] and an equilibrium is established between the original ester and alcohol, and the new ester and alcohol formed through the exchange:

$$RCOOR' + R''OH \rightleftharpoons RCOOR'' + R'OH$$

The reaction, which is catalyzed by alkaline ethoxides and by other basic substances and acids, takes place readily with saturated and unsaturated aliphatic acids and with aromatic acids. The catalytic effect of alkali metal alkoxides is perhaps explained by the fact that these compounds react with esters to form addition products of the type,

$$RC\begin{cases} ONa \\ OR' \\ OR \end{cases}$$

which give the new ester through cleavage of the alkoxide NaOR. More or less complete replacement of the alkyl group originally present in the ester may be brought about by use of a large excess of the alcohol. Alcoholic caustic may be employed as the catalyst. The alkali metal salt of the acid is formed only to a very slight extent in anhydrous media even when an equivalent of caustic is used.

The procedure is to shake the ester with ten times its weight of the alcohol containing a small amount of potassium- or sodium ethoxide. The reaction proceeds at room temperature with primary alcohols, but heating is necessary with secondary and tertiary alcohols.[56] Ester exchange between glycols or glycerol and esters of monohydric alcohols can also be effected using potassium chromate as a catalyst.[57] Ester exchange between methyl esters of higher fatty acids has been effected by heating at 200-300° in the presence of lead salts.[18] Ester exchange may be brought about by use of an acid catalyst. One to two percent of hydrogen chloride may be employed for the purpose.

A type of ester exchange, known as *reacylation*, involves the reaction of a higher acylated polyhydric compound with the free hydroxy compound to form a lower acylated product. Thus, pyrogallol monoacetate is formed when 2 parts of pyrogallol are heated with 3 parts pyrogallol diacetate at 160° for 1 hour. This method makes possible the preparation of lower acyl derivatives of polyhydric compounds otherwise difficult to obtain.

Ester exchange takes place with particular ease with isopropenyl acetate,

$$CH_2{=}CH(CH_3)OCOCH_3$$

and the compound is an efficient acylating agent.[158] This product is especially useful for the preparation of enol acetates from carbonyl compounds. Vinyl acetate has been prepared, for example, from acetaldehyde, and similar enol acetates have been made from crotonaldehyde, acrolein, and acetophenone. The compound is also useful for the acetylation of hydroxy esters and hydroxy nitriles, tertiary alcohols and other substances which have a tendency to dehydrate under the action of acetic anhydride. Sulfuric acid and *p*-toluenesulfonic acid act as effective catalysts in amounts varying between 0.1 and 0.5%.

Ester exchange in another direction takes place when isopropenyl acetate reacts with carboxylic acids in the presence of a mixture of mercuric acetate and a boron trifluoride-ether complex. Under these conditions isopropenyl esters of the carboxylic acids in question are produced. Isopropenyl crotonate may be prepared by this method from crotonic acid. Vinyl caprylate has been obtained in 72.5% yield by mixing caprylic acid, vinyl acetate and a trace of copper resinate and mercuric acetate, stirring vigorously then allowing to stand at 30° for 72 hours. The ester is recovered by adding sodium acetate and fractionally distilling.[180]

Ester Formation with Diazomethane

Diazomethane reacts with free carboxylic acids forming the methyl ester of the acid:

$$RCOOH + CH_2N_2 \rightarrow RCOOCH_3 + N_2$$

The reaction is quite general and is applicable to all acids.[58] It proceeds at room temperature and is usually carried out in ethereal solution using a slight excess of diazomethane. Other solvents inert toward diazomethane are used when the acid is only slightly soluble in ether. The reaction is complete when the evolution of nitrogen ceases. The yellow color of diazomethane should persist at the end of the reaction, as an indication that a sufficient quantity of this reagent was used. The reaction mixture may be gently warmed if necessary. It should be remembered that diazomethane is a highly poisonous compound.

The reaction is applicable to diazoketones:[159]

$$R'COOH + N_2CHCOR \rightarrow R'COOCH_2COR + N_2$$

The crude diazoketones prepared from acetyl halides and diazomethane may be used in the reaction. The overall yields from benzoyl and β-naphthoyl chlorides are 55% and 72% respectively.[160]

Preparation of Esters from Acetylene[59] and Olefins

Many aliphatic acids combine with acetylene in the presence of the appropriate catalyst forming vinyl esters:

$$HC \vdots CH + RCOOH \rightarrow RCOOCH = CH_2$$

The reaction is similar to the addition of halo acids to acetylene. A second molecule of acid may be added to the vinyl ester formed, giving an ethylidene diester:

$$RCOOCH = CH_2 + RCOOH \rightarrow (RCOO)_2CHCH_3$$

The catalysts usually employed are mercuric salts of strong organic acids. The mercury salt of sulfoacetic acid, $HOCOCH_2SO_2OH$, is a particularly effective catalyst. Other sulfonic acid salts are also good catalysts. The use of boron and fluorine compounds in conjunction with mercuric salts has been proposed.

A certain amount of tarry matter forms during the reaction. Tar formation may be reduced considerably by the addition of oxidizing agents, which prevent the reduction of mercury compounds.

Vinyl esters are the principal product when the reaction is carried out in dilute kerosene or paraffin oil, while ethylidene esters are the major product when the vinyl esters remain long in contact with the acid in excess.

Ester formation through the addition of aliphatic acids at unsaturated bonds is observed also with ethylenic compounds. Zinc chloride is an effective catalyst for the reaction. Esters of the difficulty accessible *tertiary alcohols* have been prepared by this method.[60]

Esters are formed readily under mild conditions through the reaction of an acid with an olefin in the presence of boron trifluoride.[161]

Isopropyl salicylate results through the reaction of salicylic acid with propylene at ordinary temperature in the presence of boron trifluoride. The ester undergoes rearrangement to 2-hydroxy-3-isopropylbenzoic acid when it is warmed. Isopropyl 2-hydroxy-3,5-diisopropylbenzoate results in quantitative yield on prolonged treatment of salicylic acid with propylene in the presence of boron trifluoride.[162]

Esters may be obtained by this reaction from olefins and *p*-nitro- and *o*-chlorobenzoic, phenylacetic and furoic acids. *Ortho* and *para* aminobenzoic acids do not react. Propylene, the butylenes and the amylenes give either secondary or tertiary alcohol esters.[163]

The stepwise formation of esters of polyhydric alcohols is exemplified by the conversion of allyl esters to di- and tri-esters of glycerol.[164] The process involves the addition of hypoiodous acid to the olefinic ester, and reaction of the resulting iodohydroxy ester with the potassium salt of the acids:

$$CH_2{=}CHCH_2OCOR + IOH \rightarrow HOCH_2CHICH_2OCOR$$

$$\xrightarrow{KOCOR} HOCH_2\underset{\displaystyle\;}{C}H(OCOR)CH_2OCOR$$

The resulting hydroxy diester may be converted to the triester by reaction with the acid chloride.

Esters by Oxidation of Carbonyl Compounds and by Rearrangement of Halo Ketones

Treatment of certain carbonyl compounds with peracids results in the formation of esters through the entrance of an oxygen atom between the carbonyl carbon and a group attached to it:[165]

$$RCOR' \xrightarrow{O} RCOOR'$$

The larger group appears as the alcohol component of the ester. Esters have been obtained in 63-73% yield by this method from cycloalkyl and aryl alkyl ketones using perbenzoic acid as the oxidizing agent at room temperature. Cyclic ketones also undergo this reaction giving cyclic esters, from which hydroxy acids may be obtained by hydrolysis.[166]

Certain α-halo ketones undergo rearrangement to esters under the action of sodium alkoxides:[167]

$$R_2CBrCOR' + NaOR'' \rightarrow R_2R'CCOOR'' + NaBr$$

Ethyl trimethylacetate has been obtained in 61% yield by this reaction from methyl α-bromoisopropyl ketone and sodium ethoxide.[168] Ring contraction takes place with α-chlorocyclohexanone, resulting in the formation of cyclopentane carboxylic ester in 53% yield.[169]

Esters from Substituted Acetoacetic Esters

Dialkylacetoacetic esters are cleaved to dialkylacetic ester under the action of a hot absolute ethanolic solution of sodium ethoxide:[170]

$$CH_3COCRR'COOC_2H_5 \rightarrow RR'CHCOOC_2H_5$$

When the treatment is applied to ethyl cyclopentane-2-methyl-2-carboxylic acid, α-methyladipic ester is obtained.[171]

Preparation of Ortho Esters

Ortho esters result through the interaction of alcohols with imino ether hydrochlorides:[61]

$$RC(:NH)OC_2H_5.HCl + 2C_2H_5OH \rightarrow RC(OC_2H_5)_3 + NH_4Cl$$

The reaction proceeds well with some imino ethers and the lower aliphatic alcohols.

A method of wider applicability which often gives satisfactory yields of the ortho ester depends on the reaction of alkyl magnesium halides with orthocarbonic esters:[62]

$$RMgI + C(OC_2H_5)_4 \rightarrow RC(OC_2H_5)_3 + C_2H_5OMgI$$

Ortho esters also result in low yield through the reaction of alkali metal alcoholates with chlorinated hydrocarbon of the type $RCCl_3$:[63]

$$RCCl_3 + 3NaOC_2H_5 \rightarrow RC(OC_2H_5)_3 + 3NaCl$$

Orthoformic esters have been prepared by this reaction from chloroform, and orthoacetic and orthobenzoic esters from 1,1,1-trichloroethylene and benzotrichloride.

Orthoformic esters of the higher alcohols result by alcohol exchange when ethyl orthoformate is heated with higher aliphatic alcohols in the presence of small amounts of hydrochloric acid.[64]

Ortho esters of the type $RCH(OCOR')_2$, derived from the hypothetical ortho aldehyde $RCH(OH)_2$, are obtained through the interaction of acid chlorides or anhydrides with aldehydes.[65]

Ortho esters are generally stable toward alkalies but are readily hydrolyzed with acids. Ethyl orthophenylacetate, $C_6H_5CH_2C(OC_2H_5)_3$, is rapidly converted to ethyl phenylacetate when shaken with water. When vapors of ortho esters are passed over fragments of pumice coated with metallic nickel heated to 250 - 300°, they are usually decomposed to an ether and the normal ester:

$$RC(OC_2H_5)_3 \rightarrow RCOOC_2H_5 + (C_2H_5)_2O$$

Ethyl orthophenylacetate, distilled under 15 to 20 mm pressure, is converted to phenylketene acetal, $C_6H_5CH=C(OC_2H_5)_2$.

Behavior of Esters

Esters are, on the whole, stable compounds. As a rule esters of low or moderately high molecular weight can be distilled under atmospheric pressure without decomposition, while those of a higher molecular weight can only be distilled under reduced pressure.[66] Among the exceptions are certain keto, hydroxy and amino esters. Methyl levomalate decomposes on distillation under vacuum into water and methyl fumarate. Phenol esters of cinnamic acid suffer decarboxylation when distilled, yielding hydrocarbons,[67] while isopropyl benzoate breaks down into propylene and bnezoic acid.[68] β-Bromocinnamic acid can be distilled unchanged under vacuum, but is transformed to the α-bromo isomer when it is distilled under atmospheric pressure.

Esters of higher aliphatic alcohols, heated or distilled under pressure, decompose into an olefinic hydrocarbon and the acid. A similar decomposition takes place with esters of the lower alcohols when they are heated in the presence of oxides of titanium or thorium.[69]

Many unsaturated esters polymerize more or less readily in contact with air.[70] Aliphatic amino esters, particularly those of low molecular weight, gradually decompose on standing.

A characteristic reaction of methyl and ethyl esters is their ability to exchange their alkoxy group with an amino group, when treated with concentrated ammonia, to form amides:

$$RCOOCH_3 + NH_3 \rightarrow RCONH_2 + CH_3OH$$

Esters are reduced to alcohols corresponding to their acid component when acted upon by sodium and alcohol.

Alkali metals react with certain esters in solution in anhydrous ether to form the alkali metal compound of the enolic form of the ester:

$$2RCH_2COOR' + 2K \rightarrow 2RCH{:}C(OK)OR' + H_2$$

These alkali metal enolates are highly reactive and form the intermediates in ester condensation reactions.

The reaction of esters with phosphorus pentachloride leads to the formation of an acid chloride and an organic halide:

$$RCOOC_2H_5 + PCl_5 \rightarrow RCOCl + ClC_2H_5 + POCl_3$$

Acetoxy groups attached to the "reducing" carbon atom in fully acylated reducing sugars can be replaced with chlorine or bromine by reaction with the appropriate hydrogen halide in acetic acid solution or in liquefied form.[72] The α- and β-series of acylated sugars yield the corresponding α- and β-series of halides; of these the α-isomers are the more stable and often are obtained as the product of the reaction of halogen acids with the β-acylated sugars as a result of an intramolecular rearrangement.[73] Halides derived from acetylated glucose and other similar sugars are of importance in organic synthesis, since by their use acetylated sugar residues may be introduced in various types of compounds.[74]

Inner Esters or Lactones

The internal cyclic esters of many hydroxy acids may be prepared by a variety of methods. Such esters are termed *lactones*.

The tendency of hydroxy acids to form lactones varies according to the number of carbon atoms between the carboxyl and the hydroxyl groups. Five-membered rings, i.e., γ-lactones, form with the greatest ease, while six- and seven-membered rings form with some difficulty. Eight- and nine-carbon rings are formed with the greatest difficulty; the tendency to lactone formation increases slightly for carbon chains C_{10} to C_{18}, and then decreases for longer chains.[75]

γ-Lactones

The simplest method of lactone formation, namely, heating the free hydroxy acid, is applicable to the preparation of many lactones. γ-Lactones may be obtained readily by this method, and certain γ-hydroxy acids give lactones even at room temperature.[76] With higher molecular weight acids, distillation under vacuum is required. γ-Lactones may be obtained by this method from the enolic forms of γ-keto acids. α-Angelica lactone results, for example, on slow distillation of levulinic acid:

$$CH_3COCH_2CH_2COOH \rightarrow CH_3\overline{C = CHCH_2COO} + H_2O$$

The β-isomer is obtained when the distillation is carried out rapidly.

γ-Lactones may be prepared from β, γ- and γ, δ-unsaturated acids by heating with sulfuric or hydrobromic acid. It may be assumed that addition of the inorganic acid at the double bond is the first stage of the reaction and is followed by its elimination and the formation of the lactone:[77]

$$HOCOCH_2CH(COOH)CH_2CH = CH_2 + HBr \rightarrow$$
$$HOCOCH_2CH(COOH)CH_2CHBrCH_3$$

$$\rightarrow HOCOCH_2\overline{CHCH_2CH(CH_3)OCO} + HBr$$

γ-Lactones result on long heating of α, β-unsaturated acids with 80 to 100% sulfuric acid. This transformation takes place on short heating with 60% sulfuric acid if a substituent is attached at the β-position:

$$CH_3CH_2C(CH_2CH_3){:}CHCOOH \rightarrow \overline{CH_3CHCH(CH_2CH_3)CH_2COO}$$

Lactone formation also takes place when certain β, γ-unsaturated esters are heated with 50% potassium hydroxide:[78]

$$C_6H_5CH_2C(COOC_2H_5)_2CH = CHCH_3 \xrightarrow{KOH} C_6H_5CH_2\overline{C(COOH)CH_2CH(CH_3)OCO}$$

Double bonds farther removed from the carbonyl group than the γ, δ-position are also capable of forming γ-lactones by a shift in the position of the double bonds. Thus, undecylenic, oleic and erucoic acids may be converted to γ-lactones.

Since β-hydroxy acids yield α, β- or β, γ-unsaturated acids when distilled with sulfuric acid, γ-lactones may result from this treatment of β-hydroxy acids. Hydriodic acid and phosphorus pentoxide also cause γ-lactone formation from these hydroxy acids.

β-Iodo-γ-lactones may be obtained readily from β, γ- and γ, δ-unsaturated acids on treatment with hypoiodous acid:

$$RCH = CHCH_2COOH + IOH \rightarrow RCH(OH)CHICH_2COOH$$

$$\rightarrow \overline{RCHCHICH_2COO} + H_2O$$

γ-Lactones result in yields ranging 5 to 50% upon reduction of esters, amides or chlorides of succinic and glutaric acids with sodium- or aluminum amalgam, sodium and alcohol, or catalytically over nickel.[79]

γ-Halo acids, distilled or boiled with water or treated with alkalies or alkali carbonates in the cold, give γ-lactones. Pyruvic acid, heated with hydrogen chloride, gives a keto γ-lactone by self-condensation:

$$2CH_3COCOOH \rightarrow HOCO\overline{C(CH_3)CH_2COCOO} + H_2O$$

Dimethylfumaryl chloride undergoes molecular rearrangement to form a dichlorolactone, $CH_3\overline{C = C(CH_3)COOC}Cl_2$.[149]

Other Lactones

β-Lactones cannot be prepared directly from β-hydroxy acids, but they may be obtained through the careful decomposition of β-halo acids with sodium hydroxide or carbonate, or silver nitrate.[182] An ethereal suspension of moist silver oxide brings about lactone formation. Aqueous sodium acetate brings about the reaction when the halogen is activated by two adjacent carbonyl groups. The lactone should be removed from the reaction mixture as soon as possible. β-Lactones are formed through the reaction of ketenes with carbonyl compounds at 0 to 20° in the presence of catalysts such as boric acid, boron trifluoride etherate, zinc chloride, etc.[187] Reaction with diphenylketene proceeds in the absence of a catalyst.

An unsaturated β-lactone is obtained when a mixture of α-anisaldehyde oxime, acetoacetic ester and solid phosphoric acid is heated just below 110°.[80]

$$CH_3OC_6H_4CH = NOH + CH_3COCH_2COOC_2H_5$$

$$\rightarrow CH_3OC_6H_4CH = NC = C(CH_3)OCO + H_2O + C_2H_5OH$$

δ-Lactones may be obtained by the methods employed for the preparation of γ-lactones. δ-Lactones result from glutaraldehydes by an intramolecular Cannizzaro reaction, induced by sodium ethoxide, with yields occasionally reaching 90% of theory:[81]

$$(CH_3)_2C(CHO)CH(C_2H_5)CH(CH_3)CHO \rightarrow (CH_3)_2CCH(C_2H_5)CH(CH_3)CH_2OCO$$

An *ϵ-lactone* is formed when 2,6-dimethyloctanol-3-carboxylic-8-acid is distilled:

$$HOCOCH_2CH(CH_3)CH_2CH_2CH[CH(CH_3)_2]OH$$

$$\rightarrow CH_3CHCH_2CH_2CH(C_3H_7)OCOCH_2$$

ϵ-Lactones also result when certain terpene ketones are oxidized with Caro's acid. The first stage of the reaction appears to be the transformation of the keto group to a peroxide group, which subsequently isomerizes to the lactone:[82]

$$(CH_3)_2CHCHCH_2CH_2CH(CH_3)CH_2CO \rightarrow$$

$$(CH_3)_2CHCHCH_2CH_2CH(CH_3)CH_2C\!<\!{}^{O}_{O}$$

$$\rightarrow (CH_3)_2CHCHCH_2CH_2CH(CH_3)CH_2COO$$

A β-keto-δ-lactone is obtained when acetyl chloride is heated in the presence of ferric chloride or strong tertiary bases:[83]

$$4CH_3COCl \xrightarrow{FeCl_3} CH_3C = CHCOCH(COCH_3)COO + 4HCl$$

This compound, which is known as *dehydroacetic acid,* also results when acetoacetic ester is heated strongly or is passed in the vaporized condition over red hot pumice:[84]

$$2CH_3COCH_2COOC_2H_5 \rightarrow CH_3C = CHCOCH(COCH_3)COO + 2C_2H_5OH$$

Dehydroacetic acid also forms when acetic anhydride is boiled with P_2O_5 or when ketene is treated with tertiary bases.[85]

Dehydrobenzoylacetic acid, $C_6H_5\overline{C = CHCOCH(COC_6H_5)COO}$, results when benzoylacetic acid is heated to boiling.

Lactones with 14 to 18 members in the ring may be prepared from cyclic ketones containing 13 to 17 carbons in the ring by oxidation with monopersulfuric acid. The lactone of 14-hydroxytetradecane carboxylic acid is best prepared by heating a very dilute solution of the acid in benzene with benzenesulfonic acid. The lactone of ω-hydroxy undecane acid may be obtained similarly by using *p*-toluene sulfonic acid as a catalyst.[86]

Lactone Formation in the Aromatic Series

Phenolic compounds in which a side chain in the ortho position with respect to the hydroxyl group bears a carboxyl group at the 2-position, yield γ-lactones. The lactone, coumarin

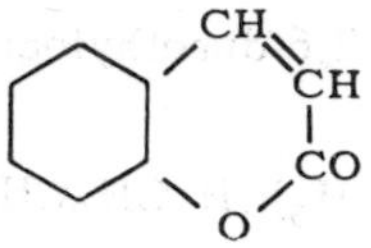

is obtained, for example, from orthohydroxycinnamic acid. These lactones form an important group of oxygen heterocycles, and their modes of formation will be considered in the section on oxygen heterocycles. It may be briefly stated here that condensations leading to the formation of the appropriate type of phenolic acids give rise to such lactones or coumarins. Such condensations take place, for example, when malic acid is heated with phenols in the presence of sulfuric acid or other catalysts; also through the interaction of β-keto esters of the type of ethyl acetoacetate with phenols in the presence of dehydrating agents such as sulfuric acid, phosphorus pentoxide, etc. Perkin's reaction forms the basis of a third important method of formation of these lactones, the basic reaction being the condensation of acid anhydrides with phenolic aldehydes in which the aldehyde group is in the ortho position.

Condensation may take place also between a carbonyl group attached to the aromatic nucleus and a hydroxyl group in the 2-position of a side chain in ortho position, leading to the formation of cyclic esters of which isocourmarin,

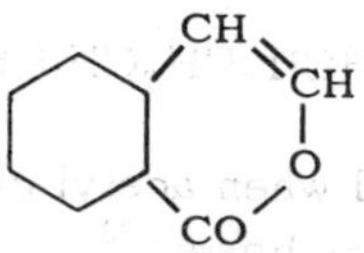

is the simplest representative.

Hydrolysis of Esters

Esters may be hydrolyzed, i.e., broken down into the original acid and alcohol, by reaction with water. Some esters undergo extensive decomposition merely by treatment with cold water. For example, the methyl and ethyl esters of formic, oxalic, tartaric, and especially pyrotartaric acids, are extensively hydrolyzed in contact with cold water.[87] Esters of the lower aliphatic α-amino acids may be completely hydrolyzed by prolonged boiling with an excess of water;[88] β-alkylamino acid esters can also be hydrolyzed in this manner.[89] The majority of esters are hydrolyzed when they are heated with water under pressure at an elevated temperature. Fats, i.e., glycerides of the higher aliphatic acids, are decomposed on the commercial scale by heating with water to 300° in pressure vessels.

Hydrolysis of esters proceeds at lower temperatures when a mineral acid is used as a catalyst. As in the process of esterification, which is also catalyzed by acids, the initial rate of hydrolysis is proportional to the strength and concentration of the acid. Hydrolysis of esters may be brought about effectively by the use of a mixture in equal volumes of concentrated sulfuric acid and water. Completion of the reaction usually is indicated by the fact that no precipitation takes place when an excess of aqueous sodium hydroxide is added to a test portion of the reaction mixture.[90] Esters are known which, contrary to the general rule, are decomposed more readily with moderately concentrated sulfuric acid than with alkalies.[91] Hydrogen chloride is also an effective catalyst, and its use is often preferable, since it can be readily removed by evaporation from the reaction product.[92] The reaction of esters with concentrated hydrogen halides leads to the formation of an acid and an alkyl halide.

The usual procedure followed in decomposing an ester is to treat it with aqueous or alcoholic *alkalies*. The reaction products are the alkali metal salt of the acid and an alcohol:

$$RCOOR' + NaOH \rightarrow RCOONa + R'OH$$

The process is termed saponification; it often proceeds in the cold, but heating is necessary in most cases. Saponification takes place more readily than the hydrolysis of esters with acids. The reaction may be carried out by use of other basic compounds, the nature of the base, and its strength determining the rate at which the reaction proceeds.[93]

Lower alkyl esters of the lower aliphatic acids, and other simple low molecular esters, are readily saponified by heating with an aqueous solution of sodium hydroxide. Careful choice of the concentration of the caustic is important in some instances in order to avoid excessive decomposition. A 25% solution of sodium hydroxide is used for the hydrolysis of diacetosuccinic ester to the corresponding acid, dilute caustic causing decomposition of the acid.[94]

Saponification takes place more readily with alcoholic than with aqueous caustic because of the solubility of esters in alcohol. The use of alcoholic potassium hydroxide presents the advantage that, upon completion of the reaction, the excess hydroxide may be readily removed as the insoluble carbonate by passing a stream of carbon dioxide through the solution.

Neutral esters of dicarboxylic acids and, in particular, esters of some substituted malonic and succinic acids, may be partially saponified to the salt of the acid esters by treatment, in the cold, with half the quantity of alcoholic caustic required for complete saponification.

Inner esters of aliphatic hydroxy acids, i.e., the lactones, are saponified very readily with dilute caustic or even alkali carbonates.

Cellulose acetate may be hydrolyzed with concentrated sulfuric acid and is saponified with alcoholic sodium hydroxide.

Esters the acidic components of which are readily degraded by warm caustic may be saponified by stirring their petroleum solution in the cold with aqueous caustic for 24 hours.[95] Esters of acids of the type of benzalmalonic acid, which are readily decomposed by strong alkalies, may be successfully saponified by a milder base, such as barium hydroxide in 12% aqueous solution.

Acetoacetic ester and other β-keto esters undergo extensive decomposition when subjected to the usual conditions of saponification. These esters may be saponified, and the acid may be obtained in the free state, by proceeding as follows: The ester is shaken with an excess of 2.5% aqueous potassium hydroxide until solution is complete, and the liquid is allowed to stand at room temperature for 24 hours. An excess of sulfuric acid is then added and the acid formed, together with the unconverted ester, is taken up with ether; the ethereal solution is concentrated by evaporation and shaken with an aqueous suspension of barium carbonate, the acid going into solution in the water in the form of the barium salt. The aqueous solution is filtered, acidified with sulfuric acid and extracted with ether; the acid is obtained in the free state on evaporating the ether.

The nitro group in *nitrated esters* may be removed by the action of alkali hydroxides; for this reason, these bases should not be used for the cleavage of esters of this type into their component acid and alcohol.

Nitrile groups in cyano esters are generally attacked during hydrolysis or saponification, but saponification without affecting the nitrile group is possible with some compounds.[96]

Hydrolysis of esters insoluble in water may be effected by the use of *Twitchell reagents*, compounds of unknown structure prepared by sulfonating mixtures of aromatic compounds and oleic or other similar acids. These compounds in emulsified form are employed on the commercial scale for the hydrolysis of fats.[97]

Effect of Structure on Ease of Hydrolysis

Hydrolysis of esters takes place with varying ease depending on the structure of the acid and alcohol. Examples of varying behavior have been cited above. Comprehensive data on the subject is lacking however. Evidence seems to indicate that, at least in the aliphatic series, esters which are formed most readily are also hydrolyzed most readily; thus the ease of hydrolysis decreases in the order: acetate, propionate, isobutyrate and trimethylacetate. Esters of primary alcohols are hydrolyzed more slowly than esters of secondary and tertiary alcohols.

Substituents may exert a marked effect on the rate of hydrolysis of esters; thus, phenylacetic ester is hydrolyzed more rapidly than acetic ester, but the introduction of a second and a third phenyl group causes a considerable decrease in the rate of hydrolysis, and triphenylacetic ester hydrolyzes at an extremely slow rate.[98] Esters of halogenated acetic acids are saponified especially readily, reaction being complete within 10 minutes in the cold in an equivalent of 1/10 molal alcoholic sodium hydroxide solution.[99]

The saponification velocity of dialkyl esters of normal aliphatic dicarboxylic acids decreases with increase in the distance between the carboxyl groups; this decrease is paralleled by a decrease in the dissociation constants of these acids, which are given below:[100]

Acid	Dissociation Constant at 25°	Acid	Dissociation Constant at 25°
Oxalic	about 10	Pimelic	0.0032
Maleic	0.158	Suberic	0.0030
Succinic	0.0065	Azelaic	0.0029
Glutaric	0.0047	Sebacic	0.0029
Adipic	0.0038		

In the aromatic series, esters of acids with two *ortho* substitutents are saponified with difficulty.

While the inner esters, or lactones, of aliphatic hydroxy acids are very easily saponified by dilute caustic or even alkali carbonates, lactones of the aromatic series are saponified less readily and generally require treatment with alcoholic potassium hydroxide.[101] Some acid lactones yield on hydrolysis an unsaturated dicarboxylic acid instead of the expected hydroxydicarboxylic acid; this occurs when the hydroxy group formed is in the β-position with respect to a carboxyl group, as in β-carboxyphenyl-β-hydroxypropionic acid:[102]

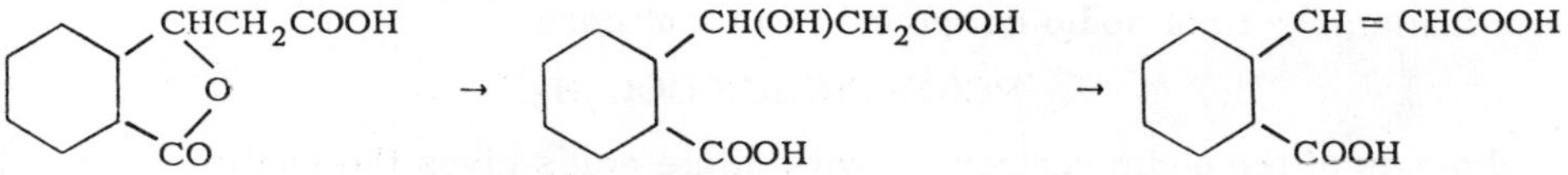

On saponifying pyrrole dicarboxylic esters, the α-carboxy group is first attacked, though 2,4-dimethyl-3,5-dicarbethoxypyrrole forms an exception, the β-carbethoxy group in this compound being hydrolyzed preferentially by concentrated sulfuric acid.[103]

ESTER CONDENSATIONS

Ester condensations involve the interaction of an ester group with a reactive hydrogen in an organic molecule in the presence of sodium, sodium ethoxide or sodamide,(*) resulting in the formation of an acyl compound with cleavage of a molecule of alcohol:[104]

$$RCOOC_2H_5 + HR' \rightarrow RCOR' + C_2H_5OH$$

An intermediate sodium addition compound, NaR′, is first formed which, in turn, yields an addition product with the ester; a molecular rearrangement then ensues and is followed by cleavage of alcohol and the formation of the sodio derivative of the final condensation product.

Many esters take part in such condensations. Thus, condensation products have been made with esters of many of the aliphatic mono and dibasic acids, including formic, orthoformic and oxalic acids, and esters of aromatic acids.

When the compound HR′ contains a methylene group activated by a carbonyl or carboxyl group, the enol form reacts exclusively with sodium, forming a com-

(*) *Sodamide* is dangerous and must be manipulated with care. Violent detonations take place occasionally without apparent cause. Old and corroded pieces are best discarded, but even fresh samples are not free of danger.

pound of the type $RCH = C(ONa)$-. The successive reactions with a carbonyl compound may be represented as follows: [105]

$$R'CH_2COR'' \; \leftrightarrows \; R'CH = C(OH)R'' \; \overset{Na}{\rightarrow} \; R'CH = C(ONa)R''$$

$$RCOOC_2H_5 + R'CH = C(ONa)R'' \; \rightarrow \; RC\overset{\displaystyle ONa}{\underset{\displaystyle OC_2H_5}{-}}OC(R'') = CHR'$$

$$\rightarrow RC\overset{\displaystyle ONa}{\underset{\displaystyle OC_2H_5}{-}}CH(R')COR'' \; \rightarrow \; RC(ONa) = C(R')COR'' + C_2H_5OH$$

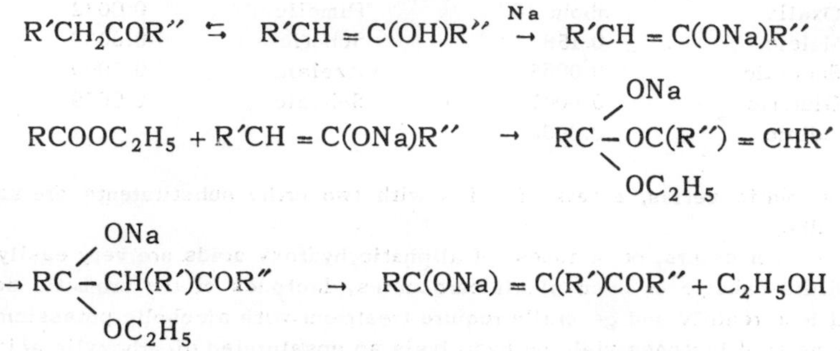

The reactions involved when the methylenic compound is also an ester,

$$R'CH_2COOC_2H_5,$$

are similar; the final sodio compound is in that case

$$RC(ONa):C(R')COOC_2H_5$$

Hydrolysis of the sodio compounds with dilute acids gives the enolic compounds which, as a rule, largely undergo rearrangement to the keto forms,

$$RCOCH(R')COR'' \text{ and } RCOCH(R')COOC_2H_5$$

The final condensation product from acetic ester, when dissolved or suspended in ether or ethyl acetate, spontaneously decomposes to ketene acetal and sodium acetate:

$$CH_3C(ONa)(OC_2H_5)CH_2COOC_2H_5 \; \rightarrow \; CH_2 = C(OC_2H_5)_2 + CH_3COONa$$

The reaction, which takes place also on gentle warming with water, is of secondary character under the usual conditions, but may become the principal one under the proper conditions.

The most important applications of ester condensation involve reactions in which the methylenic compound is an ester[106] or a carbonyl compound. The classic example is the formation of *acetoacetic ester*, $CH_3COCH_2COOC_2H_5$.[107] The addition of the acyl group in these condensations always occurs at the methyl group adjacent to the carbonyl or carboxyl group. This is to be expected from the accepted mechanism of the reaction.

Ester condensations may be effected by use of other catalysts. Sodium hydride, NaH, is an effective catalyst, similar in its action to sodium amide, and has the advantage over the latter that it does not give rise to side reactions.[188] Sodium hydride has proved of great value for the condensation of fatty acid esters. The latter have been successfully acylated with carbonic esters by use of this condensing agent.[189] It must be noted that triphenylmethane adds at the double bond of α, β-unsaturated acids, such as crotonic acid. *Grignard compounds*, RMgHal, have been employed as ester condensing agents.[190] *Diethylaminomagnesium bromide* is also an ester condensing agent.[119] Isobutyric and isovaleric esters do not undergo condensation under the influence of diethylaminomagnesium bromide, but condensation proceeds satisfactorily with diisopropylaminomagnesium bromide.[191] *Boron trifluoride* acts as an effective condensing agent in the self-condensation of acid anhydrides, or in the condensation of anhydrides with ketones. The driving force in this condensation is the tendency toward the formation of a complex between boron trifluoride and the acid resulting from the reaction.[192]

Condensation of Esters with Other Esters

The self-condensation of ethyl acetate to acetoacetic ester[107] takes place with ease, the keto ester forming in good yield, but the self-condensation of other aliphatic esters does not proceed with equal ease.[112] For example, propionic ester gives only 20% yield of α-propionylpropionic ester. Low yields of keto esters are also obtained from *n*-butyric and isovaleric esters.[108] Condensation proceeds well with many of the higher homologs under special conditions; thus, keto esters are obtained with some esters in 74 to 84% yield on slow distillation of the alcohol formed in the reaction. Methoxyacetic ester condenses smoothly to a keto ester.[109]

High molecular fatty esters condense to ethers of β-hydroxy esters under the action of metallic sodium:[110]

$$2RCH_2COOC_2H_5 \cdot \rightarrow RCH_2CH(OC_2H_5)CH(R)COOC_2H_5$$

The free hydroxy acid also forms in small amounts.

Ester condensation may proceed between the molecules of two different as well as identical esters. Sodium ethoxide is to be preferred as a catalyst in effecting condensation between two different esters.

Conversion of various monocarboxylic acids to substituted malonic acids in good yields has been achieved by condensation with carbonic esters using a large excess of the latter and removing the alcohol formed.[207] Carbon dioxide has been made to condense with various esters to substituted malonic half esters, using sodamide as the condensing agent.[208]

Yields of keto esters resulting from the condensation of aliphatic esters with acetic ester are greater the higher the molecular weight of the ester. Yields of condensation products of two different esters are greater the more readily the ester component is saponified.[193]

Esters carrying a single α-hydrogen and esters with a secondary or tertiary β-carbon, such as ethyl isovalerate, $(CH_3)_2CHCH_2COOC_2H_5$, and *tert*-butylacetate, $(CH_3)_3CCH_2COOC_2H_5$, fail to undergo the Claisen condensation in the presence of sodium ethoxide.[194] Condensation with esters of the type

$$RR'CHCOOC_2H_5$$

and with ethyl isovalerate may be effected by using as condensing agent one, or preferably, two molecular equivalents of sodium amide per mole of expected condensation product.[195] The use of sodium amide presents the disadvantage that a certain amount of the amide of the acid is formed in the course of the reaction; amide formation may be reduced to a minimum by making use of esters of high molecular alcohols. Tertiary butyl ester has been acylated with carbonic ester by use of sodium triphenylmethyl.[189]

The yield of condensation product may often be greatly increased, in those cases where the reaction normally proceeds to a limited extent, by distilling off the alcohol formed, thus forcing the reaction in the desired direction.

Formic ester, condensing with other esters, gives formyl esters in moderately good yields:[78]

$$HCOOC_2H_5 + RCH_2COOC_2H_5 \rightarrow OCHCH(R)COOC_2H_5 + C_2H_5OH$$

Formylacetic ester, $OCHCH_2COOC_2H_5$, is unstable and, on standing, changes to ethyl trimesinate, $C_6H_3(COOC_2H_5)_3$. Formylsuccinic ester results in 60 to 70% yield on condensing ethyl formate with diethyl succinate. Phenylacetic ester, reacting in absolute ethereal solution in the presence of sodium, yields formylphenylacetic ester, $OCHCH(C_6H_5)COOC_2H_5$.[111]

The condensation of acetic ester with oxalic ester results in the formation of oxalacetic ester,[113] while benzoylacetic ester results from the condensation of benzoic ester with acetic ester.[114]

α,γ-Dichloracetoacetic ester, $ClCH_2COCHClCOOC_2H_5$, is obtained in good yield as its sodio derivative through the self-condensation of chloracetic ester in the presence of alcohol-free sodium ethoxide in cold, absolute ether. Boiled with dilute sulfuric acid, this compound is converted to α,α'-dichloracetone. Phenylacetic ester yields α,γ-diphenylacetoacetic ester,

$$C_6H_5CH_2COCH(C_6H_5)COOC_2H_5$$

Ethyl trifluoroacetoacetate may be prepared through the condensation of ethyl trifluoroacetate with ethyl acetate in the presence of sodium ethoxide.[196] Trifluoroacetoacetic acid, obtained from the ester by hydrolysis with hydrochloric acid, is characterized by a remarkable stability; it can be distilled under ordinary pressure without decomposition. It yields trifluoroacetone on treatment with sodium hydroxide solution.

Ester condensations may be effected with dicarboxylic esters.[113] *Oxalic ester* condenses with aliphatic esters to form keto dicarboxylic esters:

$$C_2H_5OCOCOOC_2H_5 + RCH_2COOC_2H_5 \rightarrow C_2H_5OCOCOCH(R)COOC_2H_5 + C_2H_5OH$$

The formation of oxalacetic ester has been mentioned above; propionic ester yields α-methyloxalacetic ester,[115] and phenylacetic ester gives α-phenyloxalacetic ester.[116]

γ-Oxalcrotonic ester, $C_2H_5OCOCOCH_2CH{=}CHCOOC_2H_5$, results when oxalic ester is condensed with crotonic ester in the presence of sodium or sodium ethoxide.[117] This compound is notable for its markedly acid character, as shown by the fact that it is capable of decomposing alkali carbonates. It may be observed that, in the enolic form, its structure bears a resemblance to that of phenols. The resemblance to phenols goes beyond the acid character of the enolic hydroxyl group, as the compound is capable of undergoing diazo coupling reactions.[118] Coupling takes place at the carbon atoms designated by asterisks in the formula below; corresponding positions in the molecule of phenol are similarly indicated. The diazo compound obtained is shown at the right:

$$
\begin{array}{ccc}
\overset{\displaystyle OH}{\underset{\displaystyle |}{C_2H_5OCOC}} & \overset{\displaystyle OH}{\underset{\displaystyle |}{C}} & \overset{\displaystyle OH}{\underset{\displaystyle |}{C_2H_5OCOC}} \\
CH^* & CH \quad CH^* & CN = NAr \\
CH & CH \quad CH & CH \\
C_2H_5OCOCH^* & CH^* & C_2H_5OCOCN = NAr
\end{array}
$$

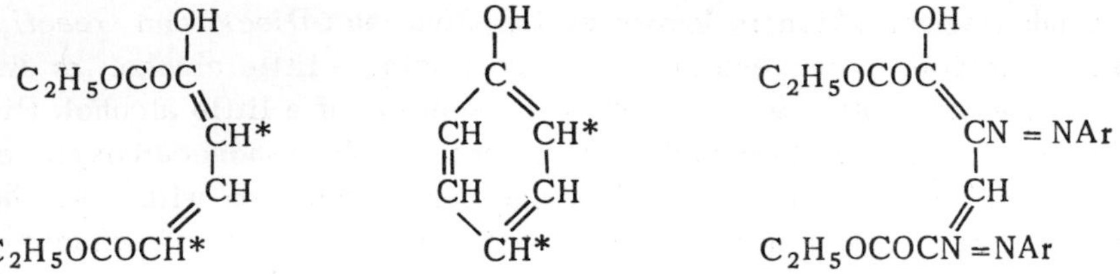

Both ester groups in oxalic ester are capable of taking part in ester condensations. Thus, the condensation of two molecular equivalents of acetic ester with one of oxalic ester leads to the formation of ketipinic ester, [116]

$$C_2H_5OCOCH_2COCOCH_2COOC_2H_5$$

Esters of dibasic acids with two reactive methylene groups condense with oxalic ester to form cyclic diketo esters.[120] 1,2-Diketopentamethylene-3,5-dicarboxylic ester is obtained, for example, from glutaric ester:

$$C_2H_5OCOCOOC_2H_5 + C_2H_5OCOCH_2CH_2CH_2COOC_2H_5$$

$$\rightarrow C_2H_5OCOCH \overset{\displaystyle CO.CO}{\underset{\displaystyle CH_2}{\diagup \diagdown}} CHCOOC_2H_5 + C_2H_5OH$$

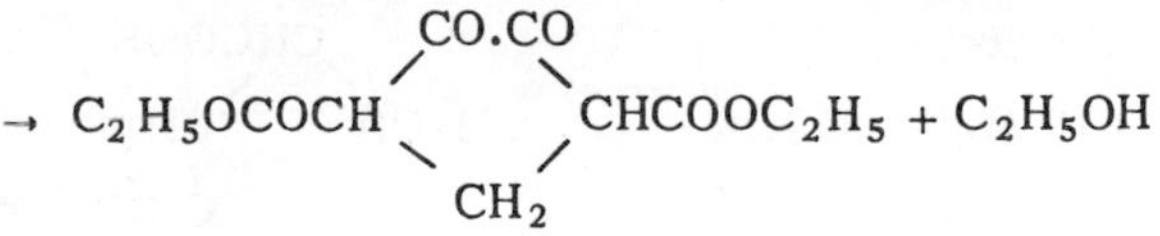

Malonic ester, treated with a half equivalent of sodium at 60-100°, undergoes self-condensation to form triethyl acetonetricarboxylate: [121]

$$2H_2C(COOC_2H_5)_2 \rightarrow C_2H_5OCOCH_2COCH(COOC_2H_5)_2 + C_2H_5OH$$

It is important to carry out the reaction as rapidly as possible. This ester is acidic in character, surpassing in strength acetonedicarboxylic ester; it dissolves in aqueous alkali bicarbonate solutions, and reddens litmus in alcoholic solution. Cold aqueous alkalies convert the ester to malonic acid; boiling acids of moderate concentration decompose it into acetone and carbon dioxide.

Ethyl succinate undergoes self-condensation more readily than esters of monobasic aliphatic acids. It yields succinylsuccinic ester, [122]

$$\overline{C_2H_5OCOCHCH_2COCH(COOC_2H_5)CH_2CO}$$

under the action of metallic sodium. Metallic potassium, sodium ethylate, potassium acetate, etc., also act as catalysts for the reaction.

Aliphatic dicarboxylic esters with 4, 5 and 6 carbon atoms between the carboxyl groups yield cyclic keto esters on condensation with sodium or sodamide.[123] Thus, diethyl adipate gives 2-cyclopentanone-1-carboxylic ester:

$$C_2H_5OCO(CH_2)_4COOC_2H_5 \rightarrow \overline{CO(CH_2)_3CHCOOC_2H_5} + C_2H_5OH$$

This condensation, which is known as the *Bouveault-Dieckmann reaction*, is carried out in boiling benzene or toluene containing a little alcohol, or directly with the ester by heating at 120-140° by the addition of a little alcohol. Pimelic and suberic esters yield cyclohexanone- and cycloheptanonecarboxylic esters respectively. The five- and six-carbon ring compounds form with ease, but the seven-carbon ring is obtained in poor yield. Glutaric, azelaic and sebacic esters do not yield cyclic esters in appreciable amounts.[124] This is in accord with Baeyer's ring tension theory. Dicarboxylic esters showing a tendency to yield cyclic keto esters cannot, of course, be reduced by sodium and alcohol into the corresponding dihydric alcohols.[125] 2,2-Dimethylbutane-1,3,4-tricarboxylic ester gives only 4,4-dimethyl-3-carbethoxycyclopentanone-1-carboxylic ester:

$$
\begin{array}{c}
CH_2COOR \\
|\\
CH_3CCHCH_2COOR \\
|\\
COOR
\end{array}
\quad \rightarrow \quad
\begin{array}{c}
CH_2-CO \\
CH_3{>}C \quad CHCOOR \\
ROCO \quad CH_2
\end{array}
$$

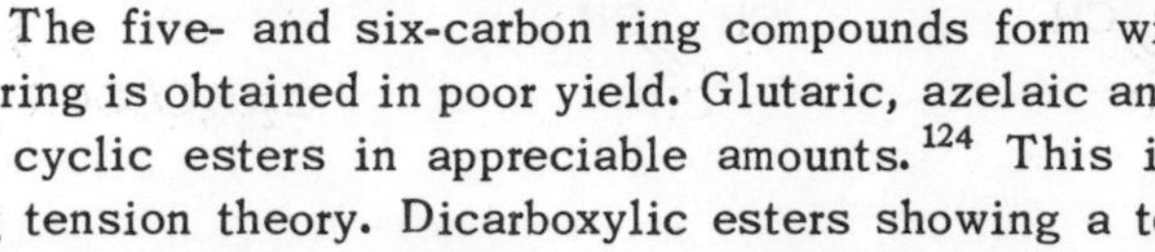

2-Methylpentane-1,3,5-tricarboxylic ester gives 5-methyl-4-carbethoxycyclohexanone-1-carboxylic ester:

$$
\begin{array}{c}
COOR \\
|\\
CHCH_2CH_2COOR \\
|\\
CH_3CHCH_2COOR
\end{array}
\quad \rightarrow \quad
\begin{array}{c}
CHCOOR \\
CH_3CH \quad CH_2 \\
CH_2 \quad CHCOOR \\
CO
\end{array}
$$

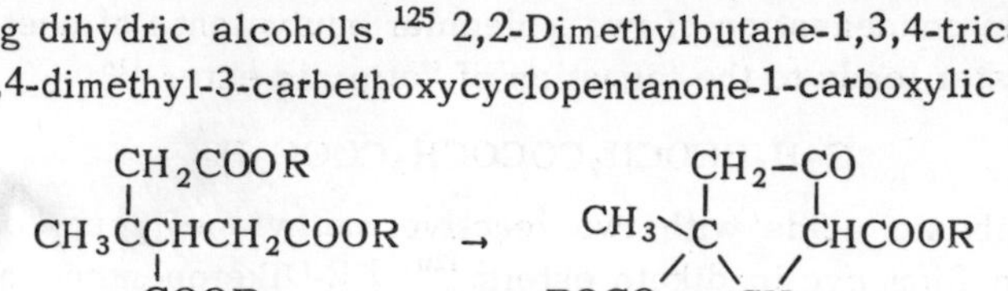

β-Thiopropioacetic ester undergoes internal ester condensation to yield as the main product thiophanon-3-carboxylic-2-ester:[197]

$$
\begin{array}{c}
CH_2CH_2COOR \\
S \\
CH_2COOR
\end{array}
\quad \rightarrow \quad
\begin{array}{c}
CH_2-CH_2 \\
S \quad | \\
ROCOCH - CO
\end{array}
$$

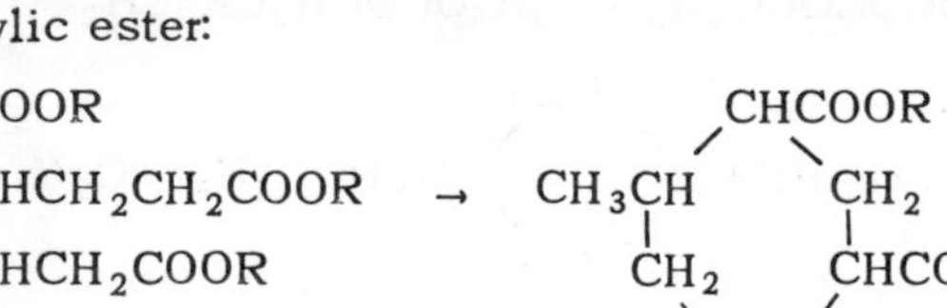

Ethyl o-carbethoxyphenoxyacetate in benzene solution condenses to ethyl coumaranone-2-carboxylate:[198]

$$
\begin{array}{c}
COOC_2H_5 \\
OCH_2COOC_2H_5
\end{array}
\quad \rightarrow \quad
\begin{array}{c}
C{-}OH \\
CCOOC_2H_5 \\
O
\end{array}
+ C_2H_5OH
$$

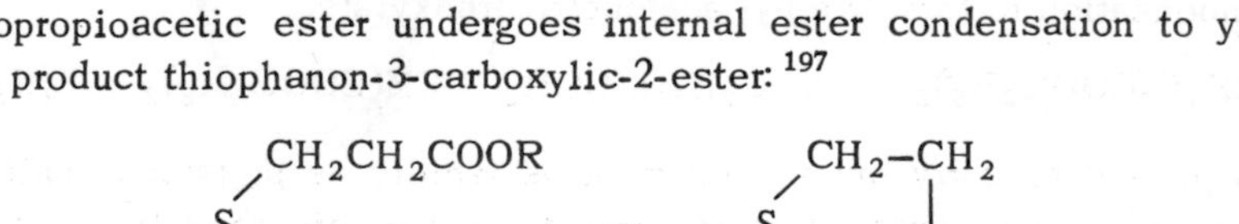

Ester Condensations with Nitriles

Condensation may be brought about between esters and nitriles under the influence of sodium ethoxide or other similar agents. Condensation products have been obtained, for example, from aliphatic nitriles and diethyl carbonate:[126]

$$
RCH_2CN + (C_2H_5O)_2CO \quad \rightarrow \quad RCH(CN)COOC_2H_5 + C_2H_5OH
$$

The cyano ester is obtained only in 10% yield from acetonitrile, but, from many of the other aliphatic nitriles yields of the cyano ester in excess of 40% may be obtained. Condensation products with aliphatic nitriles have also been obtained with oxalic ester; this ester condenses readily with crotono and sorbonitriles.[127] Mono and dioxalsuccinonitriles have been prepared from succinonitrile.[128]

Ester condensation takes place readily with nitriles containing a reactive methylene group, such as cyanoacetic ester, $CNCH_2COOC_2H_5$, or benzyl cyanide, $C_6H_5CH_2CN$. Formic ester yields oxymethylene derivatives, benzyl cyanide, for example, giving $C_6H_5C(CN){:}CHOH$, while other esters give acylated products such as $C_6H_5CH(CN)COCH_3$.[129] Oxalic ester is capable of condensation with one or both ester groups. Cyanophenylpyruvic ester,

$$C_6H_5CH(CN)COCOOC_2H_5$$

and pulvinic dinitrile, $C_6H_4CH(CN)COCOCH(CN)C_6H_5$, may be obtained, for example, with benzyl cyanide.[130]

Succinic ester gives with benzyl cyanide diphenyldicyanoacetonylacetone,

$$C_6H_5CH(CN)COCH_2CH_2COCH(CN)C_6H_5$$ [131]

Paraxylylene cyanide, $CNCH_2C_6H_4CH_2CN$, gives with diethyl oxalate ethyl *p*-(cyanomethyl)-phenylcyanopyruvate,[132] $CNCH_2C_6H_4CH(CN)COCOOC_2H_5$.

Ester Condensations with Ketones

Condensation of esters with ketones may be brought about by use of sodium, sodium ethoxide or sodamide. Addition of the acyl group takes place at a methyl or methylene group adjacent to the carbonyl group. The ease of acylation with a series of esters appears to be related directly to the relative rates of alkaline hydrolysis. Methyl esters, and more especially, phenyl esters are more reactive than the corresponding ethyl esters. In general the effectiveness of the catalyst is proportional to its basic strength. At least an equivalent of the basic condensing agent is consumed in the reaction; two molecular equivalents of sodium amide and sodium hydride are required. Sodium ethoxide induces a smooth reaction and does not cause acyloin formation and for that reason is often the preferred reagent. Metallic sodium and sodium hydride, on the other hand, present the advantage that yields are usually good and the reaction can be carried out more conveniently. In many cases acylations which fail to proceed with sodium ethoxide may be carried out successfully by use of sodium amide and sodium hydride. examples of such reactions are the acylation of ketones with higher homologs of ethyl acetate, and of methylated ketones with methyl or phenyl benzoate.

The *procedure* followed when using *sodium ethoxide* as the condensing agent is as follows: The mixture of sodium ethoxide, ester and the solvent is stirred for fifteen to twenty minutes; it is then cooled in an ice bath and the ketone is added slowly over a period of half to one hour, and cooling in an ice bath and stirring is continued for two to three hours. The mixture is finally allowed to stand at room temperature for twelve to sixteen hours. An alternative procedure is to add the ketone to be acylated to the mixture of ester, sodium ethoxide and solvent in the course of fifteen to thirty minutes, and to heat the whole under reflux for two to five hours. The diketone formed is isolated by cooling the mixture in ice water and agitating with an equal volume of ice water, which dissolves the sodium complex. For complete recovery the organic layer is further extracted with several small portions of ice water. The combined water extract is washed free of organic impurities with small portions of ether and is acidified with excess acetic acid to free the diketone, which is purified by a suitable method. Yields vary in the range 40 to 70% of theory.

The procedure followed when *sodium amide* is employed as the condensing agent is to add the ketone, in the course of 10 to 15 minutes with stirring, to a suspension of sodium amide in ether, then to add the ester after the lapse of about five minutes and to stir and heat the mixture under reflux for two hours. Both ketone and ester may be introduced conveniently in solution in ether. The diketone is recovered by pouring the reaction mixture into a mixture of ice and excess hydrochloric acid with stirring. The diketone remains in the ether layer and is isolated by evaporating off the solvent, and purified by the appropriate method.

Sodium amide is available commercially. It may be prepared from molten sodium and gaseous ammonia. It may be prepared also by adding metallic sodium to an excess of liquid ammonia containing some sodium in solution and a little ferric nitrate. Amide formation is indicated by the appearance of a gray suspension, and the disappearance of the original blue color of the liquid. The excess ammonia is evaporated off and is replaced with an equal volume of ether. The resulting suspension is heated under reflux for a time in order to remove any residual ammonia. The amide prepared in this manner is highly active.[5]

The procedure followed when *sodium hydride* is used as the condensing agent is as follows: The ester mixed with 5% ethanol calculated on the basis of the sodium hydride is added to the hydride; then the ketone dissolved in anhydrous ether is added gradually in the course of 30 to 60 minutes, and the mixture is held at 40 to 50° until at least 80% of the theoretical amount of hydrogen has been evolved. This generally requires about three hours when acylating acetone and three to ten hours with higher ketones. At the end of the reaction the mixture is diluted with ether using about 100 cc to every 0.1 molal equivalent of the reagent, and the unreacted sodium hydride is destroyed by the addition of alcohol. Decomposition of the sodium derivative of the diketone is effected by cooling the mixture to 10° and adding a mixture of ice with a slight excess of hydrochloric acid.

Sodium hydride may take fire in contact with moist air, and due precaution should be observed in handling this reagent. Reactions with sodium hydride are best carried out in an atmosphere of nitrogen.

The purification of many diketones presents difficulties. The work may be greatly simplified by converting the ketones to their copper complexes. The crude ketone is dissolved in an equal volume of methanol, a hot, filtered 10% aqueous solution of copper acetate is added and the mixture is allowed to cool. The copper complex precipitates out, and is filtered, washed with ligroin, and decomposed with an excess of 10% sulfuric acid to regenerate the diketone.

Methyl ketones RCH_2COCH_3 have been converted to β-keto esters

$$RCH_2COCH_2COOC_2H_5$$

in excellent yield by condensation with diethyl carbonate in the presence of sodium hydride.[200]

In ketones of the type CH_3COCH_2R, both the α-methyl and α-methylene groups are acylated, the α-methyl group preferentially. Ethyl benzyl ketone is acylated preferentially at the benzyl group. An α-methylene group $-CHRR'$ has been acylated rarely. *o*-Hydroxyacetone and certain related ketones appear to be acylated more readily than acetophenone itself. Low yields of acylated products are obtained from cyclohexanone and camphor, but better yields are obtained with 3-methyl- and 3,3-dimethylcyclohexanone.

Formic ester condensing with ketones[133] yields in most instances hydroxymethylene ketones RCOC(R′) = CHOH, since the expected isomeric keto aldehydes are usually unstable. The product obtained with acetone is unstable and changes to triacetylbenzene:[134]

$$CH_3COCH_3 + HCOOC_2H_5 \rightarrow CH_3COCH=CHOH + C_2H_5OH$$

$$3CH_3COCH=CHOH \rightarrow$$

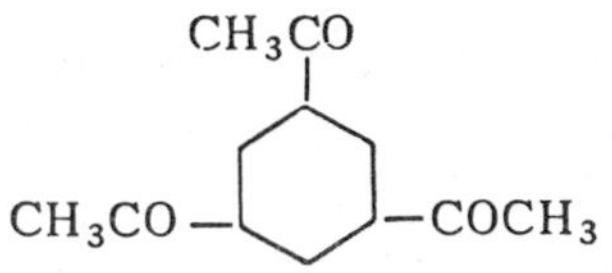

$$+ 3H_2O$$

Other hydroxymethylene ketones also evidence a similar instability.[135] In contrast with other esters, formic ester reacts with the methylene group in methyl ethyl ketone,[183] although methyl *n*-propyl ketone is formylated preferentially at the methyl group, and the methyl group is attacked almost exclusively in methyl isobutyl ketone.

Cyclic ketones, including cyclopentanone, its higher homologs and certain polyhydrophenanthrones or steroidal ketones have been formylated successfully.[184]

2-Hydroxyphenyl benzyl ketone and ethyl formate yield isoflavone in the presence of sodium. Various derivatives of isoflavone have been obtained similarly from analogs of 2-hydroxyphenyl benzyl ketone.

Acetic ester, in common with other aliphatic esters, condenses with acetone and ketones of the general type $RCOCH_3$ to form 1,3-diketones:[136]

$$CH_3COOC_2H_5 + CH_3COCH_3 \rightarrow CH_3COCH_2COCH_3 + C_2H_5OH$$

The reaction, which is of a general character, is applicable to compounds of such diverse type as cinnamic and pyridinecarboxylic esters, and is reversible. It is necessary, therefore, to eliminate the alcohol by distillation as it is formed. Sodium ethoxide is the preferred catalyst for the condensation, since it induces a smooth reaction, and the formation of acyloins is avoided. The acylated ketone may be obtained in yields ranging from 50-70%. Good results have also been obtained by use of sodium amide. Two molecular equivalents of this compound should be employed to one of ester or ketone.[137]

Reaction proceeds well with methyl ketones and with some unsaturated ketones, but it proceeds poorly with ketones in which both hydrocarbon residues attached to the carbonyl group contain two or more carbon atoms. Morgan and Holmes prepared acyl ketones with higher fatty acids, ranging from nonoyl to eikosanoyl, and obtained the products in yields ranging from 27 to 68% of the theoretical.[138] Yields are good with ethyl isovalerate but only fair with esters of many other branched chain acids. Good yields of acylated products may be obtained with the phenyl esters of the latter. Acylation of ω-methoxy- and ω-phenoxyacetophenone with ethyl propionate fails to proceed, but acylation takes place successfully with phenyl propionate.

Oxalic ester condenses with methyl ketones, $RCOCH_3$, to form *α, γ*-diketo esters, $RCOCH_2COCOOC_2H_5$.[139] Acetone gives a mono and a dioxal ester, $C_2H_5OCOCOCH_2COCH_3$ and $C_2H_5OCOCOCH_2COCH_2COCOOC_2H_5$; the latter yields on dehydration diethyl chelidonate,

$$C_2H_5OCOC = CHCOCH = C(O)COOC_2H_5$$ [140]

Both ester groups in oxalic ester are capable of reaction, so that tetraketo compounds, such as oxalyldiacetone, $CH_3COCH_2COCOCH_2COCH_3$, and oxalyldiacetophenone, $C_6H_5COCH_2COCOCH_2COC_6H_5$, may be obtained through the reaction of ethyl oxalate with acetone and acetophenone respectively.[141] It should be pointed out that *α*-keto esters often lose carbon monoxide on heating, a fact which has been utilized in the synthesis of equilenin.[185]

Acylation of ketones with *dicarboxylic esters* other than oxalic acid does not proceed successfully. Diethyl malonate and diethyl succinate undergo aldol type reactions with ketones. Diethyl adipate and diethyl pimalate undergo Dieckmann cyclizations. The condensation of dimethyl glutarate with cyclohexanone has given, however, the acylated product

$$CH_2CH_2CH_2CH_2COCHCO(CH_2)_3COOCH\ ,$$

in 26% yield.

Esters of dibasic acids, reacting with ketones having two potentially reactive methylene groups, give cyclic products; dimethyl cyclopentatrione results, for example, from the reaction of ethyl oxalate and diethyl ketone:[142]

$$CH_3CH_2COCH_2CH_3 + C_2H_5OCOCOOC_2H_5 \rightarrow$$

$$CH_3CHCOCH(CH_3)COCO + 2C_2H_5OH$$

Diacetyl, $CH_3COCOCH_3$, and ethyl oxalate do not, however, give a cyclic compound; the product of condensation is, in this case, bisoxaldiacetyl ethyl ester, $C_2H_5OCOCOCH_2COCOCH_2COCOOC_2H_5$.

Methyl *n*-hexyl ketone is acylated with *ethyl acrylate* or *ethyl crotonate* in the presence of sodium ethoxide. *Ethyl cinnamate* undergoes mainly the Michael reaction with acetone or acetophenone, while phenyl cinnamate acylates these ketones fairly readily. Pyrone derivatives are formed through the reaction of *ethyl phenylpropiolate* with certain ketones in the presence of sodium ethoxide:

$$C_6H_5C \equiv CCOOC_2H_5 + CH_3COCH_3 \rightarrow C_6H_5C \equiv CCOCH_2COCH_3$$

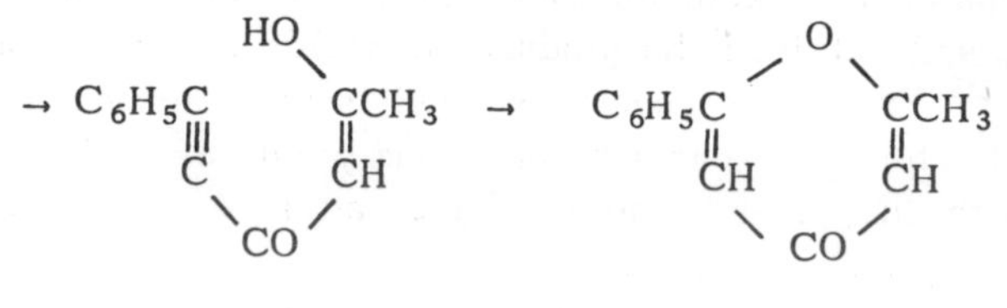

Acetone is benzoylated satisfactorily with *ethyl benzoate* under the action of sodium amide, and with methyl benzoate under the action of sodium hydride. Sodium amide and sodium hydride are also satisfactory for the benzoylation of higher methyl alkyl ketones. Acylation of acetophenone with *ethyl chlorobenzoate* has given only fair yields, and acylation with *ethyl nitrobenzoates* failed. Acylation of ketones with *ethyl phthalate* and *terephthalate* have apparently given low yields.

Acylation of acetone with ethyl furoate and of 2-acetylthiophene with 2-carbethoxythiophene has proceeded satisfactorily.

Intramolecular condensation of esters with a keto group in the δ-, ϵ- and ζ-positions with respect to the ester group takes place with the formation of ring compounds:

$$C_2H_5OCOCH_2CH_2CH_2COCH_3 \rightarrow \overline{COCH_2CH_2CH_2COCH_2} + C_2H_5OH$$

The γ- and ϵ-keto esters form five-membered rings; the δ- and ζ-keto esters form six-membered rings. Cyclization may be effected satisfactorily with sodium ethoxide or methoxide. The reaction has failed with ethyl levulinate, ethyl β-methyllevulinate and with α-acetylglutaric ester,[201]

$$CH_3COCH(COOR)CH_2CH_2COOR.$$

The γ- and ϵ-keto esters form 5-membered rings; δ- and ζ-keto esters form 6-membered rings. Cyclization may be effected satisfactorily with sodium ethoxide or methoxide. The reaction has failed with ethyl levulinate and ethyl β-methyl levulinate.

Aromatic esters of *o*-hydroxyacetophenone and other substituted acetophenones undergo internal acylation on treatment with various basic reagents, including potassium carbonate or hydroxide, sodium ethoxide, etc:

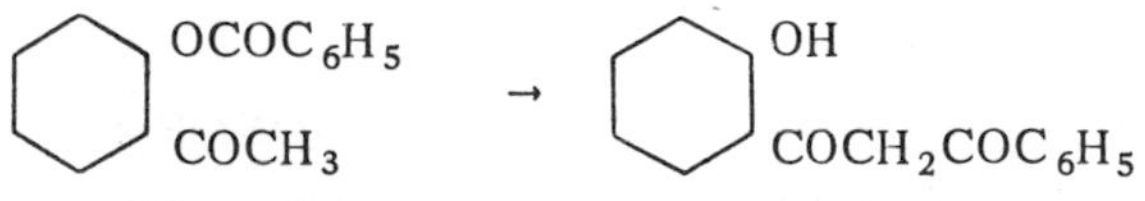

Some of the *o*-hydroxy-β-diketones obtained cyclize to chromones under the action of acids:[186]

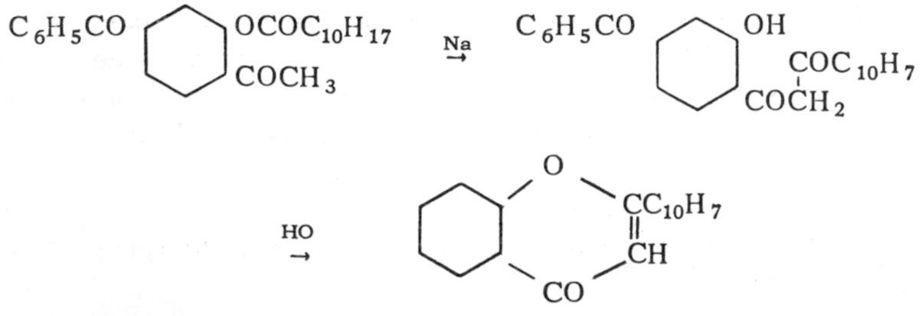

Condensations with Reactive Methylene in Miscellaneous other Compounds

Condensation of esters takes place with reactive methylene groups in types of compounds other than those considered above. Ester condensation takes place with aromatic nitro compounds which contain a methyl group in the *ortho* or *para* position with respect to the nitro group, the acyl group replacing one of the hydrogens in the methyl group.[143] Examples of such compounds are *ortho* and *para* nitrotoluene, 2-nitro-4-tolylic ester, 2-nitro-4-tolunitrile, 1-nitro-2-methylnaphthalene. Condensation takes place also with α- and γ-methylquinolines and with methylene groups situated between two ethylenic linkages in cyclopentadiene, fluorene, indene, etc.[144] Fluorene, for example, gives on condensation with diethyl oxalate the compound

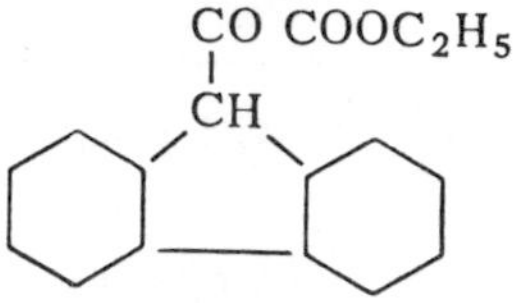

The sodium derivative of phenylacetylene is also capable of giving condensation products with esters; phenylpropiolaldehyde is obtained, for example, with ethyl formate:

$$C_6H_5C \equiv CNa + HCOOC_2H_5 \rightarrow C_6H_5C \equiv CCH(ONa)OC_2H_5$$

$$\xrightarrow{H_2O} C_6H_5C \equiv CCHO$$

Acyloin Condensation with Aliphatic Esters

When the condensation of esters of monobasic aliphatic acids is effected in anhydrous ethereal or benzene solution by use of two equivalents of sodium, two carbonyl groups combine with the formation of a sodio derivative which, on hydrolysis, yields an acyloin:

$$2RCOOC_2H_5 + 4Na \rightarrow RC(ONa) = C(ONa)R + 2C_2H_5ONa$$

$$RC(ONa) = C(ONa)R + 2H_2O \rightarrow RCOCH(OH)R + 2NaOH$$

The reaction proceeds only moderately well with acetic ester, but better yields of the acyloins are obtained from the esters of the higher homologs of acetic acid. Thus butyroin may be prepared in 80% yield from ethyl butyrate.[145]

The presence of acids or compounds containing hydroxyl groups is harmful, especially in the preparation of high molecular weight acids. The reaction is best carried out with sodium powder in suspension in toluene or xylene. The acyloin of the 18-carbon acid is obtained by vigorously shaking the methyl ester of the acid with sodium powder in xylene, then heating at 105 to 110° in a current of nitrogen.[71]

Acyloins are also formed through the reaction of acyl chlorides and sodium followed by hydrolysis.[181]

Formation of Glycidic Esters (Erlenmeyer's Reaction)

α-Halogenated esters, $RCH(X)COOC_2H_5$, condensing with aldehydes or ketones in the presence of sodium ethoxide, give esters of glycidic acids:

$$RCHO + ClCH_2COOC_2H_5 + NaOC_2H_5$$

$$\rightarrow \quad R\overset{\diagup \overset{O}{} \diagdown}{CH.CH}COOC_2H_5 + NaCl + C_2H_5OH$$

$$RCOR' + ClCH_2COOC_2H_5 + NaOC_2H_5$$

$$\rightarrow \quad RR'\overset{\diagup \overset{O}{} \diagdown}{C-CH}COOC_2H_5 + NaCl + C_2H_5OH$$

Sodium amide and metallic sodium can also be used as condensing agents in this reaction.[146]

Behavior of Keto Esters Resulting from Ester Condensation

The free acids derived from β-keto esters, i.e., keto esters resulting from ester condensations, are unstable and decompose into a ketone and carbon dioxide. These esters cannot, therefore, be converted to the corresponding acids except under special conditions. Many β-keto esters release carbon monoxide when subjected to the action of heat. For example, phenyloxalacetic ester, repeatedly distilled under vacuum, gives off carbon monoxide and is thereby converted to phenylmalonic ester:[147]

$$C_2H_5OCOCH(C_6H_5)COCOOC_2H_5 \rightarrow C_6H_5CH(COOC_2H_5)_2 + CO$$

β-Keto esters in solution in acetic acid, acted upon by nitrous gases, are converted to α, β-diketo esters.[148] Diketobutyric ester, $CH_3COCOCOOC_2H_5$, results, for example, from acetoacetic ester.

Acetoacetic ester behaves as a ketone toward sodium hydrosulfite, hydrocyanic acid and hydroxylamine, yielding a bisulfite compound, a cyanohydrin and a ketoxime. With ammonia and amines the ester forms β-aminocrotonic ester:

$$CH_3COCH_2COOC_2H_5 + NH_3 \rightarrow CH_3C(NH_2) = CHCOOC_2H_5 + H_2O$$

With phosphorus pentachloride it yields β-chlorocrotonic ester,

$$CH_3CCl = CHCOOC_2H_5$$

Alkylation of Esters

Esters with a reactive methylene group such as malonic, acetoacetic and cyanoacetic ester yield sodio derivatives by reaction with sodium ethoxide or sodium amide. The sodium in these derivatives may be replaced with alkyl groups by reaction with alkyl halides.[172]

As an example of the *procedure* the alkylation of ethyl malonate with ethylene dibromide may be cited: Two molecular equivalents of ethyl malonate are added with stirring to a cooled suspension of two molecular equivalents of sodium powder in benzene; the mixture is maintained at 20° and stirred until all the sodium dissolves. Two molecular equivalents of ethylene bromide are then added dropwise with cooling, and the mixture is heated to 70° for 10 hours after all the ethylene bromide has been added.[202]

The sodio derivative of diethyl malonate may be prepared by reaction with sodium hydride.

When terpene groups are introduced into the molecule of malonic ester, then the introduction of an alkyl group is rendered difficult due to steric hindrance. Alkylation may be effected successfully by heating with the corresponding alcohol in an autoclave at 140°, or by boiling with a xylene solution of the alcohol.

Trimethylene dibromide, $BrCH_2CH_2CH_2Br$, reacting with sodio ethyl malonate, gives a cyclobutane ester,[203] while ethyl α,α'-dibromo-β,β'-dimethyl glutarate yields an isomeric cyclopropane compound:[204]

$$(CH_3)_2C \begin{matrix} \diagup CHBrCOOC_2H_5 \\ \diagdown CHBrCOOC_2H_5 \end{matrix} + 2NaCH(COOC_2H_5)_2$$

$$(CH_3)_2C \begin{matrix} \diagup CHCOOC_2H_5 \\ | \\ \diagdown CCH(COOC_2H_5)_2 \\ | \\ COOC_2H_5 \end{matrix} + 2NaBr + CH_2(COOC_2H_5)_2$$

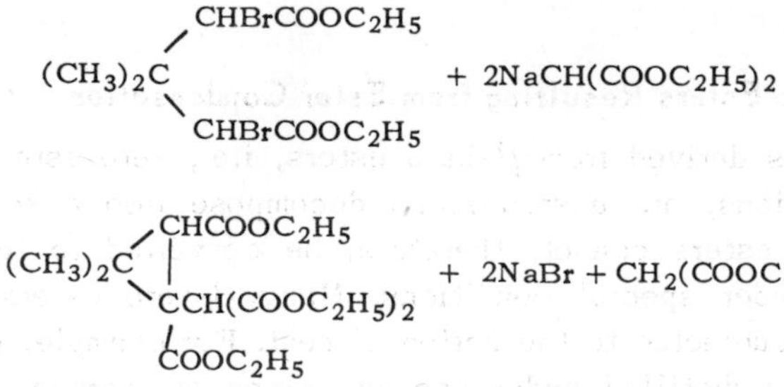

Cyclobutane ring formation takes place when the gem-dimethyl substituent is absent;

$$CH_2 \begin{matrix} \diagup CHBrCOOC_2H_5 \\ \diagdown CHBrCOOC_2H_5 \end{matrix} \xrightarrow{NaCH(COOC_2H_5)_2} \begin{matrix} CH_2 \diagup \overset{CH-COOC_2H_5}{\diagdown}\underset{CH-COOC_2H_5}{C(COOC_2H_5)_2} \diagup \\ \\ CH_2 \diagdown \begin{matrix} CH_2 \\ | \\ CCH(COOC_2H_5)_2 \\ | \\ COOC_2H_5 \end{matrix} \end{matrix}$$

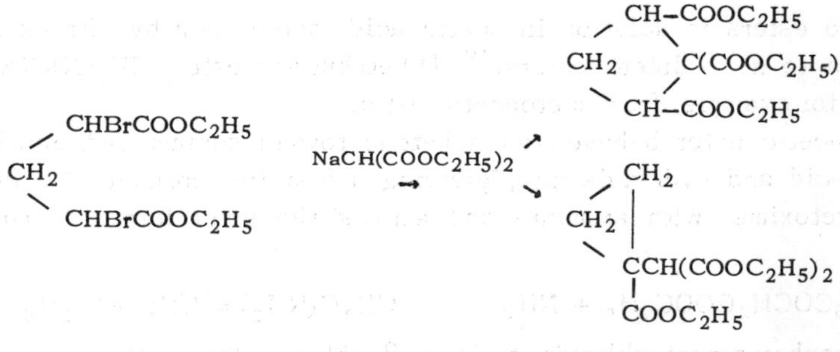

The cyclopropane ester readily changes by internal condensation into the dicyclic ketone

$$CH_2 \begin{matrix} COOC_2H_5 \\ | \\ \diagup C — CO \\ | \quad\quad | \\ \diagdown C — CHCOOC_2H_5 \\ | \\ COOC_2H_5 \end{matrix}$$

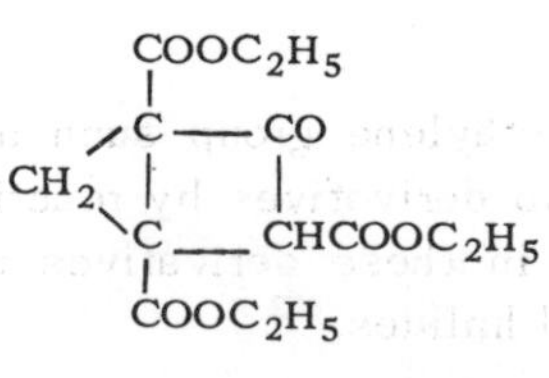

The condensation of α,α'-dibromoadipic ester with sodio malonic ester proceeds smoothly in one direction with the formation of a cyclopentane tetracarboxylic ester:[205]

$$\begin{array}{c} CH_2CHBrCOOC_2H_5 \\ | \\ CH_2CHBrCOOC_2H_5 \end{array} + 2NaCH(COOC_2H_5)_2$$

$$\rightarrow \begin{array}{c} CH_2CH \overset{COOC_2H_5}{\underset{C(COOC_2H_5)_2}{\diagdown}} \\ | \\ CH_2CH \diagdown \\ COOC_2H_5 \end{array} + 2NaBr + CH_2(COOC_2H_5)_2$$

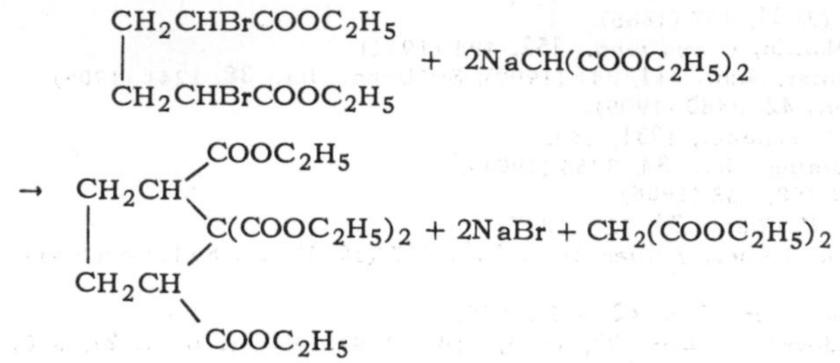

Esters of disubstituted derivatives of acetic acid have been alkylated by treatment with sodium triphenylmethide followed by reaction with an alkyl iodide: [173]

$$RR'CHCOOC_2H_5 \overset{(C_6H_5)_3CNa}{\underset{R''I}{\rightarrow}} RR'R''CCOOC_2H_5$$

References

1. van't Hoff, *Ber.* **10**, 669 (1877); Thomsen, *ibid.*, **10**, 1023 (1877); Urech, *ibid.*, **17**, 2177 (1884); **19**, 1700 (1886); Berthelot, *Bull. soc. chim.*, **31**, 341 (1879); Markownikoff, *Ber.*, **6**, 1177 (1873); Sapper, *Ann.*, **211**, 208 (1882); Preiswerk, *Helv. Chim. Acta*, **2**, 647 (1919); Goldschmidt *et al. Z. physik. Chem.*, **60**, 728 (1907); **81**, 30 (1912); **143**, 139, 278 (1929); Rolf and Hinshelwood, *Trans. Faraday Soc.* **30**, 935 (1934); Williamson and Hinshelwood, *ibid.*, **30**, 1145 (1934).
2. Goldschmidt, *Ber.*, **28**, 3218 (1895); Sudborough and others, *J. Chem. Soc.*, **74**, 81 (1898); **75**, 467 (1899); **84**, 534 (1904); **87**, 1840 (1905).
3. Preiswerk, *Helv. Chim. Acta*, **2**, 647 (1919); Gyr, *Ber.*, **41**, 4308 (1908).
4. Menschutkin, *Ann.*, **195**, 334 (1879); **197**, 193 (1879); *Ber.*, **15**, 1445, 1572 (1882); **21**, R 41 (1888).
5. Sudborough *et al.*, *J. Chem. Soc.*, **93**, 210 (1908); **101**, 236, 317, 1227 (1912).
6. Sudborough et al, *J. Chem. Soc.*, **87**, 1840 (1905); **91**, 1033 (1907); **95**, 315, 975 (1909).
7. Cf. Sudborough, *J. Chem. Soc.*, **101**, 1227 (1912).
8. Sudborough and Lloyd, *J. Chem. Soc.*, **73**, 81 (1898); Sudborough and Roberts, *ibid.*, **87**, 1840 (1905).
9. Fischer and Speier, *Ber.*, **28**, 1150, 3252 (1895); Gyr, *ibid.*, **41**, 4308 (1908).
10. Fischer and Speier, *ibid.*, 3252 (1895).
11. Clemmensen and Heitmann, *Am. Chem. J.*, **42**, 319 (1909).
12. Fischer, *Ber.*, **28**, 3252 (1895); Anschütz, *ibid.*, **16**, 2412 (1883).
13. Aschan, *Ann.*, **271**, 239 (1892).
14. Salkowski, *Ber.*, **28**, 1922 (1895); Curtius and Goebel, *J. prakt. Chem.*, (2) **37**, 150 (1888); Posner, *ibid.*, **38** 2322 (1905).
15. Fischer *et al.*, *Ber.*, **43**, 2027 (1910).
16. Simons, *ibid.*, **26**, R 769 (1893).
17. Phelps and Phelps, *Chem. News.*, **1908**, 97, 112.
18. Grün *et al.*, *Ber.*, **54**, 290 (1921).
19. Menschutkin, *Ann.*, **195**, 334 (1879).
20. Sudborough and Lloyd, *J. Chem. Soc.*, **75**, 467 (1899).
21. Sudborough *et al.*, *ibid.*, **85**, 1840 (1905); **91**, 1033 (1907); **93**, 211 (1908); **95**, 315 (1909).
22. Smith *et al.*, *J. Am. Chem. Soc.*, **61**, 254 (1939); **63**, 605 (1941); **64**, 2362 (1942); **66**, 1496 (1944).
23. Michael and Wolgast, *Ber.*, **42**, 3157 (1909).
24. Schotten and Baumann, *ibid.*, **17**, 2545 (1884); **19**, 3219 (1886); v. Pechmann, *ibid.*, **25**, 1045 (1897); Skraup, *Monatsh.*, **10**, 390 (1891).
25. Panormow, *Ber.*, **24**, R 971 (1891).
26. Brühl, *ibid.*, **36**, 4274 (1903).
27. Houben, *Ber.*, **39**, 173 B (1906). Cf. Kondakow, *J. prakt. Chem.*, (2) **48**, 477 (1893).
28. Deninger, *Ber.*, **28**, 1322 (1895); Einhorn and Hollandt, *Ann.*, **301**, 95 (1898); Ullmann and Nada, *Ber.*, **41**, 1870 (1908).
29. Fischer, *Ann.*, **301**, 101 (1898); *Ber.*, **53**, 1593 (1920); Hess and Messmer, *ibid*, **54**, 499 (1921).
30. Nencki, *J. prakt. Chem.*, (2) **25**, 282 (1882).

31. Seifert, *ibid.*, (2) **31**, 467 (1885).
32. Sabatier and Maihle, *Compt.rend.*, **152**, 494 (1911).
33. Thiele and Winter, *Ann.*, **311**, 341 (1900); Stillichs, *Ber.*, **38**, 1241 (1905).
34. Kaufmann, *Ber.*, **42**, 3480 (1909).
35. Chattaway, *J.Chem.Soc.*, **1931**, 2495.
36. Verley and Bolsing, *Ber.*, **34**, 3354 (1901).
37. *French Patent* 368, 738 (1906).
38. Kellas, *Z.physik.Chem.*, **24**, 221 (1897).
39. Sudborough and Turner, *J.Chem.Soc.*, **101**, 237 (1912). *Cf.* Sudborough and Lloyd, *ibid.*, **75**, 467 (1899).
40. Michael and Oechslin, *Ber.*, **42**, 317 (1909).
41. Meyer and Sudborough, *Ber.*, **27**, 1580, 3146 (1894); Meyer, *ibid.*, **27**, 510, 1586 (1894); **28**, 182, 1254, 3197 (1895); **29**, 831, 1399 (1896); **31**, 504 (1898); Meyer and Wöhler, *ibid.*, **29**, 2569 (1896); Rupp., *ibid.*, **29**, 1625 (1896); Meyer and Kellas, *Z.physik.Chem.*, **24**, 219, 224 (1897); Meyer and Molz, *Ber.*, **30**, 1277 (1897); Rosanoff and Prager, *J.Am.Chem.Soc.*, **30**, 1895 (1908); Prager, *ibid.*, **30**, 1908 (1908).
42. Graebe, *Ber.*, **33**, 2026 (1900).
43. Auwers and Harres, *Z.physik.Chem.*, **143**, 17 (1929).
44. Salkowski, *Ber.*, **28**, 1922 (1895).
45. Bischoff and Hendersen, *ibid.*, **35**, 4090 (1902); Meyer and Jugelewitsch, *ibid.*, **30**, 780 (1897).
46. Kraft, *Ber.*, **36**, 4341 (1903).
47. Ladenburg, *ibid.*, **27**, 2771 (1892).
48. Brühl, *ibid.*, **35**, 3627 (1902).
49. Hjelt, *ibid.*, **37**, 70 (1904).
50. Decker, *ibid.*, **38**, 1144 (1905); Novak, *ibid.*, **45**, 835 (1912).
51. Werner and Seybold, *Ber.*, **37**, 3658 (1904); v. Liebig, *ibid.*, **37**, 4036 (1904); Meyer, *ibid.*, **37**, 4144 (1904); Gräbe, *Ann.*, **340**, 244 (1905).
52. Werner and Seybold, *Ber.*, **37**, 3658 (1902).
53. Grün and Theimer, *ibid.*, **40**, 1792 (1907).
54. Grün, *ibid.*, **38**, 2284 (1905).
55. Friedel and Crafts, *Ann.*, **130**, 198 (1864); **133**, 209 (1864); Grün, *Ber.*, **54**, 294 (1921); Purdie *et al.*, *J.Chem.Soc.*, **53**, 391 (1888); **47**, 855 (1885); **51**, 627 (1887); *Ber.*, **20**, 1554 (1887); Bouis, *J.prakt.Chem.*, (1) **72**, 308 (1857); Claisen, *Ber.*, **20**, 646 (1887); Fischer, *Ber.*, **53**, 1634 (1920); Reimer and Downes, *J.Am.Chem.Soc.*, **43**, 945 (1921); Reid, *Ind.Eng.Chem.*, **29**, 1344 (1937); Sauer *et al.*, *Organic Syntheses*, **20**, 67 (1940); Rehberg and Fischer, *J.Am.Chem.Soc.*, **66**, 1203 (1944); Rehberg, *Organic Syntheses*, **26**, 18 (1946).
56. Reimer and Downes, *J.Am.Chem.Soc.*, **43**, 945 (1921); Pfannl, *Monatsh.*, **31**, 301 (1910); **32**, 513 (1911); Sudborough and Karve, *J.Ind.Inst.Ser.*, **3**, 1 (1919); Dasannacharya and Sudborough, *ibid.*, **4**, 181 (1921); Kolhalker, *J.Chem.Soc.*, **107**, 921 (1915); Shimomura and Cohen, *ibid.*, **121**, 884, 2951 (1922).
57. Fischer, *Ber.*, **53**, 1634 (1920).
58. v. Pechmann, *ibid.*, **28**, 856, 1624 (1895); **30**, 646 (1897); **31**, 501 (1898); Herzig and Wenzel, *Monatsh.*, **22**, 229 (1901); Fischer, *Ann.*, **389**, 205 (1912).
59. Matheson and Skirrow, *U.S. Patent.*, 1,720,184 (1929); Skirrow and Morrison, *U.S. Patents.*, 1,855,366; 1,855,367 (1936); Dykstra, *U.S. Patent.*, 1,849,616 (1932); Strain, *U.S. Patent*, 1,849,647 (1932); Koetschet and Beudet, *U.S. Patent*, 1,304,989; 1,306,964 (1919); Rabald, *U.S. Patent*, 2,011,011 (1935); Weibezahn, *U.S. Patent*, 1,912,608 (1933); Nieuwland and Vogt, *The Chemistry of Acetylene*, p. 129 (1945).
60. Kondakov, *J.prakt.Chem.*, **48**, 477 (1893).
61. Pinner, *Ber.*, **16**, 356 (1883); *Die Iminoäther*, 1892, p.23; Reitter and Hess, *Ber.*, **40**, 3025 (1907); Reitter and Weindel, *ibid.*, **40**, 3358; Staudinger and Rathsam, *Helv.Chim.Acta*, **5**, 651 (1922); McElvain *et al.*, *J.Am.Chem.Soc.*, **59**, 1273 (1937); **64**, 1963 (1942); **68**, 1922 (1946).
62. Limpricht, *Ann.*, **135**, 87 (1865); Tschitschibabin, *Ber.*, **38**, 561 (1905).
63. Williamson and Kory, *Ann.*, **92**, 346 (1854); Staptf, *Z. Für Chemie.*, **1861**, 186; Deutsch, *Ber.*, **12**, 115 (1879); Wichelhaus and Ladenburg, *Ann.*, **152**, 164 (1871); Geuther, *Z. für Chemie*, **1871**, 128; Walter, *J. prakt. Chem.*, (2) **48**, 231 (1893); Driver, *J. Am. Chem. Soc.*, **46**, 2090 (1924); Post and Erickson, *J.Am.Chem.Soc.*, **55**, 3851 (1933).
64. Gerhardt, *Diss.* Bonn, **1910**, p.22.
65. Geuther, *Ann.*, **106**, 249 (1858); Perkin, *ibid.*, **146**, 371 (1868); Geuther and Rubencamp, *ibid.*, **225**, 281 (1884); Wegscheider and Späth, *Monatsh.*, **30**, 830 (1909); Knoevenagel, *Ann.*, **402**, 111 (1914).
66. Fischer, *Ber.*, **34**, 433 (1901).
67. Anschütz, *ibid.*, **18**, 1945 (1885).
68. Linnemann, *Ann.*, **161**, 15 (1872).
69. Mailhe, *Chem. Ztg.*, **37**, 778 (1913).
70. Herb, *Ann.*, **258**, 18 (1890).

71. Hansley, *J.Am.Chem.Soc.*, **57**, 2303 (1935).
72. Fisher and Armstrong, *Ber.*, **34**, 2885 (1901).
73. Fischer and Armstrong, *ibid.*, **34**, 2885 (1901); Schlubach, *ibid.*, **59**, 840 (1926); Brigl, *ibid.*, **59**, 1588 (1926). *Cf.* Hickinbottom, *J. Chem. Soc.*, **1929**, 1680; **1930** 1338.
74. Helferich *et al.*, *Ber.*, **59**, 2658 (1926); *Ann.*, **450**, 225, 229 (1926); **455**, 168 (1927); **466**, 166 (1928).
75. Stoll and Rouvé, *Helv. Chim. Acta*, **18**, 1087 (1935).
76. Hjelt, *Ber.*, **24**, 1236 (1891); **29**, 1858 (1896); Henry, *Z.physik.Chem.*, **10**, 96 (1899); Perkin, *J.Chem.Soc.*, **85**, 660 (1904); Blanc, *Bull.soc.chim.*, (3) **21**, 849 (1899); Bredt, *J.prakt. Chem.*, (2) **84**, 796 (1911); Schischkowski and Reformatski, *J. Russ. Phys.-Chem. Soc.*, **33**, 161 (1901); Buchner and Delbrück *Ann.*, **358**, 32 (1908); Courtot, *Bull. soc. Chim.*, (3) **25**, 219 (1906); Bredt and Pfeil, *Ann.*, **314**, 384 (1901); Sung, *Ann.chim.*, (10) **1**, 343 (1924).
77. Hjelt, *Ber.*, **16**, 334, 335 (1883).
78. Johnson and Hill, *Am.Chem.J.*, **45**, 365 (1911).
79. Blaise, *Compt. rend.*, **136**, 1464 (1908); Blanc, *ibid.*, **141**, 203 (1905); Saytzew, *Ann.*, **171**, 258 (1873); Hjelt, *Ber.*, **16**, 2624 (1883); Eijkman, *Chem. Zentr.*, **1907** I, 1616.
80. Minunni and D'Uso, *Gazz. chim. ital.*, **59**, 32 (1929).
81. Merwein, *Ber.*, **53**, 1829 (1920).
82. Bayer and Villiger, *ibid.*, **32**, 3628 (1899); **33**, 860 (1900); Wallach, *Ann.*, **323**, 331 (1902).
83. Wedekind, *Ann.*, **323**, 253, 347 (1902); **318**, 100 (1901); Diels and Meyerheim, *Ber.*, **40**, 362 (1907).
84. Oppenheim and Precht, *Ber.*, **9**, 324 (1876); Komnenos, *Monatsh.* **31**, 692 (1910).
85. Hurd, *et al.*, *J. Org. Chem.*, **2**, 314 (1937).
86. Stoll and Rouvé, *Parfumerie Moderne*, **29**, 207 (1935); *Helv.Chim.Acta*, **19**, 1079 (1936); Davies, *Trans.Faraday Soc.*, **34**, 252 (1938).
87. Schreimer, *Ann.*, **197**, 7 (1879); Findlay and Hickmans, *J.Chem.Soc.*, **95**, 1004 (1909); Findlay and Turner, *ibid.*, **87**, 747 (1905).
88. Fischer, *Ber.*, **34**, 445 (1901).
89. Morsch, *Monatsh.*, **60**, 61,65,68 (1932).
90. Fischer and Freudenberg, *Ber.*, **45**, 923 (1912).
91. Bischoff and Mintz, *Ibid.*, **23**, 650 (1890); Auwers, *Ann.*, **292**, 180 (1896).
92. Thiele and Winter, *Ann.*, **311**, 346 (1900); Fischer and Bergmann, *Ber.*, **52**, 833 (1919).
93. Reicher, *Ann.*, **228**, 257 (1885); **232**, 103 (1886); Urech, *Ber.*, **20**, 1634 (1887).
94. Pomeranz, *Monatsh*, **10**, 786 (1889); Knorr, *Ber.*, **22**, 169 (1889).
95. Henriques, *Z. angew Chem.*, **8**, 721 (1895); **9**, 221, 423 (1896).
96. Carrick, *J.prakt.Chem.*, (2) **45**, 506 (1892).
97. Twitchell, *J.Am.Chem.Soc.*, **22**, 22 (1899); Grimlund, *Z. angew. Chem.*, **25**, 1326 (1912).
98. Gyr, *Ber.*, **41**, 4308 (1908).
99. Reicher, *Ann.*, **228**, 257, (1885); **232**, 103 (1886); Sudborough and Lloyd, *J.Chem.Soc.*, **75**, 482 (1899).
100. Hjelt, *Ber.*, **31**, 1844 (1898).
101. Benedikt, *Monatsh.*, **11**, 75 (1890).
102. Roth, *Ber.*, **47**, 1597 (1914).
103. Fischer and Walach, *ibid.*, **58**, 2820 (1925).
104. Fehling, *Ann.*, **49**, 192 (1844); Geuther, *Jahresh.*, **1863**, 323; *Zeitschrift für Chemie*, **1866**, 5; Wislicenus, *Ann.*, **186**, 161 (1877); **246**, 306 (1888); *Ber.*, **19**, 3225 (1886); Wislicenus and Böckler, *Ann.*, **285**, 11 (1895); Wislicenus and Silberstein, *Ber.*, **43**, 1826 (1910); Claisen, *ibid.*, **20**, 651, 2178 (1887); **38**, 709 (1905); Scheibler and Ziegener, *ibid.*, **55**, 792 (1922); Scheibler and Marhenkel, *Ann.*, **458**, 4 (1927); Adickes, *Ber.*, **65**, 522 (1932); Fischer and McElvain, *J.Am.Chem.Soc.*, **56**, 1766 (1934); Michael, *Ber.*, **33**, 3735 (1900); **38**, 1922 (1905); Briese and McElvain, *J.Am.Chem.Soc.*, **55**, 1697 (1933); Tingle and Gorsline, *ibid.*, **30**, 1877 (1908).
105. Wislicenus, *Ann.*, **186**, 161 (1877); Claisen and Lawmann, *Ber.*, **20**, 651 (1887); **21**, 1154 (1888); Wislicenus, *Ann.*, **246**, 308, (1888); Claisen, *ibid.*, **297**, 92 (1897); *Ber.*, **36**, 3678 *Ann.*, (1899) (1903); **38**, 709 (1905); Nef, *Ann.*, **298**, 318 (1897); Michael, *J. prakt. Chem;* (2) **60**, 425 (1890); **68**, 492 (1903); *Ber.*, **33**, 3735 (1900); **38**, 1922 (1905); Böeseken, *Rec. trav. chim.*, **15**, 161 (1896); Meyer, *J. prakt. Chem.*, (2) **65**, 528 (1902); Higley, *Am. Chem. J.*, **37**, 299, 316 (1907); Tingle and Gorsline, *ibid.*, **37**, 483 (1907); **40**, 51, 75 (1908); *J. Am. Chem. Soc.*, **30**, 1874 (1908); Scheibler and Marhenkel, *Ann.*, **458**, 1 (1927); Scheibler and Ziegner, *Ber.*, **55**, 792 (1922).
106. Claisen, *Ann.*, **297**, 92 (1897); *Ber.*, **38**, 709 (1905); Michael, *ibid.*, **33**, 3735 (1900); Meyer, *J. prakt. Chem.*, (2) **65**, 528 (1902).
107. Openheim and Precht, *Ber.*, **9**, 323 (1876); Hantzsch, *Ann.*, **222**, 1 (1884); Duisberg, *Ber.*, **15**, 1387 (1882); *Ann.*, **213**, 177 (1882); Feist, *ibid.*, **345**, 60 (1906); **433**, 51 (1923); Scheibler, *ibid.*, **565**, 176 (1950).
108. Hantzsch and Wohlbrück, *Ber.*, **20**, 1320, (1887); Wohlbrück, *ibid.*, **20**, 2332 (1887); McElvain,

J.Am.Chem.Soc., **51**, 3124 (1929); Briese and McElvain, *ibid.*, **55**, 1697 (1900); Dieckmann, *Ber.*, **33**, 2760 (1900).
109. Pratt and Robinson, *J.Chem.Soc.*, **127**, 168 (1925); Briese and McElvain, *J.Am.Chem.Soc.*, **55**, 1697 (1933).
110. Hantzsch, *Ann.*, **249**, 65 (1888).
111. Wislicenus, *Ber.*, **20**, 2930 (1887).
112. Wahl and Doll, *Bull.soc.chim.*, (4) **13**, 265 (1913); Wahl, *Compt. rend.*, **152**, 95 (1911).
113. Wislicenus, *Ber.*, **19**, 3225 (1886); *Ann.*, **246**, 329 (1888); *Ber.*, **20**, 590, 592 (1887); **27**, 1092 (1894); Rassow and Bauer, *J.prakt.Chem.*, (2) **80**, 87 (1909).
114. Claisen and Lowmann, *Ber.*, **20**, 651 (1887).
115. Arnold, *Ann.*, **246**, 329 (1888).
116. Wislicenus, *Ber.*, **20**, 590 (1887).
117. Lapworth, *Proc.Chem.Soc.*, **16**, 132 (1900).
118. Lapworth, *J.Chem.Soc.*, **79**, 1272 (1901); Prager, *Ann.*, **338**, 365, 375 (1905).
119. Hauser and Walker, *J. Am. Chem. Soc.*, **69**, 295 (1947).
120. Dieckmann, *ibid.*, **27**, 965 (1894); **30**, 1470 (1897); **32**, 1933 (1899); Wislicenus and Schwanhäusser, *Ann.*, **297**, 98 (1897); Rimini, *Gaz. chim. ital.*, **26** II, 374 (1896); Herrmann, *Ann.*, **211**, 308 (1882); Baeyer, *Ber.*, **18**, 3457 (1885); Claisen, *Ber.*, **27**, 1353 (1894); *Ann.*, **284**, 245 (1895); Kommppa, *Ann.*, **368**, 137 (1909); Dickens, *et al.*, *J.Chem.Soc.*, **121**, 1496 (1922).
121. Willstätter, *Ber.*, **32**, 1272 (1899); Komnenos, *Monatsh.*, **31**, 421 (1910).
122. Herrmann, *Ann.*, **211**, 306 (1882).
123. Dieckmann, *ibid.*, **317**, 27 (1901); *Ber.*, **27**, 102 (1894).
124. Dieckmann, *Ann.*, **317**, 27 (1901); Haller and Desfontaines, *Compt. rend.*, **136**, 1613 (1903).
125. Bouveault and Blanc, *Bull. soc. chim.*, (3) **31**, 1203 (1904).
126. Wallingford *et al.*, *J. Am. Chem. Soc.*, **64**, 576 (1942). *Cf.* Hauser *et al.*, *ibid.*, **6B**, 672 (1946).
127. Borsche and Manteuffel, *Ann.*, **512**, 97 (1927).
128. Michael, *Am. Chem. J.*, **30**, 156 (1903); Wislicenus and Elvert, *Ber.*, **43**, 228 (1917); Wislicenus and Berg, *ibid.*, **41**, 3757 (1908).
129. Walther and Schickler, *J. prakt. Chem.*, (2) **55**, 305, 331 (1897); Wislicenus, *Ann.*, **291**, 202 (1890); Bodroux, *Bull. soc. chim.*, (4) **7**, 848 (1910); (4) **9**, 726 (1911); Beckt, *Ber.*, **31**, 3160 (1898).
130. Bougault, *J. pharm. chim.*, **10**, 309 (1914); Erlenmeyer, *Ann.*, **271**, 172 (1892); Hessler, *Am. Chem. J.*, **39**, 78 (1908); Gault and Weick, *Bull. soc. chim.*, (4) **31**, 869 (1922); Skinner, *J. Am. Chem. Soc.*, **55**, 2036 (1933).
131. Fleischhauer, *J. prakt. Chem.*, (2) **47**, 375 (1893); Quilico and Paizzi, *Gass. chim. ital.*, **72**, 458 (1942); Bodroux, *Bull. soc. chim.*, (4) **9**, 653 (1911).
132. Wislicenus and Penndorf, *Ber.*, **43**, 1839 (1910).
133. Claisen and Meyerowitz, *Ber.*, **22**, 3273 (1889); Claisen, *ibid.*, **20**, 655, 2192 (1887); Bülow and Sicherer, *ibid.*, **34**, 3891 (1901).
134. Claisen and Meyerowitz, *Ber.*, **22**, 3274 (1889); Claisen and Stylos, *ibid.*, **21**, 1145 (1888).
135. Claisen and Fischer, *Ber.*, **20**, 2191 (1887); Claisen and Meyerowitz, *ibid.*, **22**, 3273 (1889).
136. Claisen, *Ber.*, **20**, 655, 2178 (1887); Ferenczy, *Monatsh.*, **18**, 674 (1897); Claisen and Ehrhardt, *Ber.*, **22**, 1009 (1889); Tscherne, *Monatsh.*, **18**, 674 (1897); Claisen, *Ber.*, **38**, 693 709 (1905); Wild, *Ann.*, **414**, 119 (1907); Couturier, *Compt. rend.*, **150**, 928 (1910); Arndt and Eistert, *Ber.*, **69**, 2381 (1936).
137. Ryan and Dunlea, *Ber.*, **47**, 2423 (1914).
138. Morgan and Holmes, *J. Chem. Soc.*, **127**, 2892 (1925).
139. Claisen *et al.*, *Ber.*, **20**, 2188 (1887); **21**, 1131 (1888); **22**, 1009 (1889); **38**, 695, 709 (1905).
140. Bromme and Claisen, *Ber.*, **21**, 1134 (1888); Claisen, *ibid.*, **24**, 111 (1891).
141. Claisen and Stylos, *Ber.*, **21**, 1142 (1888).
142. Claisen, *ibid.*, **27**, 1353 (1894); Claisen and Ewan, *Ann.*, **284**, 247 (1895); Wislicenus and Mehns, *ibid.*, **436**, 101 (1924).
143. Wislicenus and Mundinger, *Ann.*, **436**, 62 (1924); Mayer and Oppenheimer, *Ber.*, **49**, 2137 (1917); Mayer and Alken, *ibid.*, **55**, 2282 (1922).
144. Thiele, *Ber.*, **33**, 666 (1900); Wislicenus, *ibid.*, **33**, 771 (1900); Stieglitz, *ibid.*, **53**, 1234 (1920); Wislicenus and Weitemeyer, *Ann.*, **436**, 3 (1924); Wislicenus and Hentrich, *ibid.*, **436**, 9 (1924).
145. Bouveault and Locquin, *Bull. soc. chim.*, (3) **35**, 629 (1906); Scheiber and Emden, *Ann.*, **434**, 265 (1923); Feigl, *Ber.*, **58**, 2299 (1925); Corson *et al.*, *J.Am.Chem.Soc.*, **52**, 3988 (1930).
146. Darzens, *Compt. rend.*, **139**, 1214 (1904); Claisen, *Ber.*, **38**, 699, (1905); Rosenmund and Dornsaft, *ibid.*, **52**, 1740 (1919).
147. Wislicenus, *Ber.*, **27**, 1093 (1894); Rassow and Bauer, *J. prakt. Chem.*, (2) **80**, 87 (1909); Souther, *J. Am. Chem. Soc.*, **46**, 1301 (1924).
148. Bouveault and Wahl, *Compt. rend.*, **138**, 1221 (1904); Wahl, *ibid.*, **152**, 95 (1911); Wahl and Doll, *ibid.*, **154**, 1237 (1912); *Bull. soc. chim.*, (4) **13**, 332 (1913).
149. Lutz and Taylor, *J. Am. Chem. Soc.*, **55**, 1589 (1933).
150. Menschutkin, *Ber.*, **21**, R 41 (1888); *Compt. rend.*, **105**, 1016 (1887).

151. Nieuwland et al., J. Am. Chem. Soc., **54**, 2017 (1932); **56**, 2689 (1934); **58**, 271 (1937); Toole and Sowa, ibid., **59**, 1971 (1937); Smith et al., ibid., **62**, 1, 4, 608 (1940); **66**, 715 (1944).
152. Haworth and Perkin, J. Chem. Soc., **93**, 577 (1908).
153. Carter et al., Organic Syntheses, **23**, 13 (1943); Farthing, J. Chem. Soc., **1950**, 3215, Slimowicz and Dezering, J. Am. Chem. Soc., **71**, 1044 (1949).
154. Houben, Ber., **39**, 1742 (1906).
155. Newman and Fones, J. Am. Chem. Soc., **69**, 1046 (1947).
156. Adams and Marvel, J. Am. Chem. Soc., **42**, 310 (1920); Marvel and Tanenbaum, ibid., **44**, 2647 (1922); Bennett and Hock, J. Chem. Soc., **1927**, 475; Adams and Thal, Organic Syntheses, Coll. vol, 1, 270 (1941); Blicke and Feldkamp, J. Am. Chem. Soc., **66**, 1087 (1944); Blicke and Leonard, ibid., **68**, 1934 (1946); Jones et al., ibid., **70**, 2846 (1948); Frank and Reiner, ibid., **72**, 4184 (1950).
157. Marvel, Organic Syntheses, Coll. vol., II, 310 (1943).
158. Chem. Age, **62**, 534 (1950).
159. Plattner and Heusser, Helv. Chim. Acta, **28**, 1047 (1945); Ruggli and Knecht, ibid., **27**, 1113 (1944); Linville and Elderfield, J. Org. Chem., **6**, 271 (1941).
160. Linville and Elderfield, l. c.
161. Nieuwland et al., J. Am. Chem. Soc., **56**, 2689 (1934); Brunel, Ann. chim. phys., (8) **6**, 216 (1905); Wunderley and Sowa, J. Am. Chem. Soc., **59**, 1010 (1937).
162. Nieuwland etal., J. Am. Chem. Soc., **56**, 2054 (1934); J. Org. Chem., **2**, 253 (1937).
163. Dorris and Sowa, J. Am. Chem. Soc., **60**, 358 (1938).
164. Golendejew, Chem. Zentr., **1937**, II, 2670.
165. Friess, J. Am. Chem. Soc., **71**, 14 (1949), Cf. v. Wacek and v. Bezard, Ber., **74**, 845 (1941).
166. Robinson and Smith, J. Chem. Soc., **1937**, 373.
167. Aston et al., J. Am. Chem. Soc., **64**, 301 (1942); Jackman et al., ibid., **70**, 499 (1948); Wagner and Moore, ibid., **72**, 2887 (1940).
168. Aston and Greenburg, J. Am.Chem. Soc., **62**, 2590 (1940).
169. Jackman et al., l. c.
170. Renfrow and Walker, J. Am. Chem. Soc., **70**, 3957 (1948); Finkelstein and Elderfield, J. Org. Chem., **4**, 371 (1939); Elderfield et al., J. Am. Chem. Soc., **70**, 3951 (1948).
171. Cornubert and Borrel, Bull. Soc. Chim., (4) **47**, 305 (1930).
172. Cohen et al., J. Chem. Soc., **1915**, 895, 896; Dox, J. Am. Chem. Soc., **46**, 1708 (1924); Arvin and Adams, ibid., **49**, 2941 (1927); **50**, 1793 (1928); Yohe and Adams, ibid., **50**, 1507 (1928); Kinner and Richter, ibid., **51**, 3132 (1929); Shonle et al., ibid., **52**, 2445 (1930); Karrer et al., Helv. Chim. Acta, **13**, 1296 (1930); Walter and McElvain, J. Am. Chem. Soc., **57**, 1891 (1935); Hiers and Adams, ibid., **48**, 2390 (1936); Levy, Ann. chim., (11) **9**, 66 (1938); Fieser and Gates, J. Am. Chem. Soc., **62**, 2338 (1940); Marvel, Organic Syntheses, **21**, 60, 99 (1941); Coleman et al., J. Am. Chem. Soc., **68**, 1102 (1946).
173. Hudson and Hauser, J. Am. Chem. Soc., **62**, 2457 (1940); **63**, 3161 (1941); Levine et al., ibid., **66**, 1231 (1944).
174. Gomberg and Snow, ibid., **47**, 201 (1925).
175. Schlenk et al., J. Am. Chem. Soc., **74**, 2550 (1952).
176. Fischer, Ber., **53B**, 1621 (1920).
177. Daubert, J. Am. Chem. Soc., **62**, 1713 (1940).
178. Verkade, Fette u. Seifen, **45**, 457 (1938); Daubert, J. Am. Chem. Soc., **62**, 1713 (1940).
179. Bergmann and Carter, Z. physiol. Chem., **191**, 211 (1930).
180. Adelman, J. Org. Chem., **14**, 1057 (1949); Swern and Jordan, Organic Syntheses, **30**, 106 (1950).
181. Klinger and Schmitz, Ber., **24**, 1273 (1891); Basse and Klinger, ibid., **31**, 1218 (1898); Anderlini, Gazz. chim. ital., **25** II, 51, 128 (1895); Zgorova, J. Russ. Phys.-Chem. Soc., **60**, 1199 (1928); Gautier, Compt. rend. **152**, 1100 (1911).
182. Zaugg, Organic Reactions VIII, p. 305 (1954).
183. Royals and Brannock, J. Am. Chem. Soc., **75**, 2050 (1953).
184. Robinson and Rydon, J. Chem. Soc., **1939**, 1394.
185. Bachman, et al., J. Am. Chem. Soc., **62**, 824 (1940).
186. Wheeler et al., J. Chem. Soc., **1950**, 1252; **1952**, 2063.
187. Staudinger, Ann., **356**, 63 (1907); Ber., **41**, 1355 (1908); Staudinger and Bereza, Ann., **380**, 243 (1911).
188. Schlenk et al., Ann., **487**, 135 (1931); Ber., **47**, 1664 (1914); **49**, 608 (1916); Müller et al., Ann., **515**, 97 (1934); Hauser et al., J. Am. Chem. Soc., **59**, 1823 (1937).
189. Hauser et al., J. Am. Chem. Soc., **64**, 2714 (1942).
190. Spielman, and Schmidt, ibid., **59**, 2009 (1937); Conant and Blatt, ibid., **51**, 1227 (1929); Hauser et al., ibid., **70**, 606 (1948); Zouk et al., ibid., **68**, 2404 (1946).
191. Frostick and Hauser, J. Am. Chem. Soc., **71**, 1350 (1949).
192. Meerwein and Pannwitz, J. prakt. Chem., (2) **141**, 123 (1934); Hauser and Adams, J. Am. Chem. Soc., **66**, 345 (1944); **67**, 284 (1945).
193. Hauser et al., J. Am. Chem. Soc., **69**, 119, 1823 (1937).
194. McElvain, ibid., **51**, 3127 (1929); Roberts and McElvain, ibid., **59**, 2007 (1937).

195. Hauser, *J. Am. Chem. Soc.*, **66**, 1230 (1944); Levine *et al.*, *ibid.*, **67**, 1510 (1945). *Cf.* Schlenk *et al.*, *Ann.*, **487**, 135 (1931); Hauser *et al.*, *J. Am. Chem. Soc.*, **59**, 1823 (1937); **60**, 463 (1938).
196. Swarts, *Bull. acad. roy. Belg.*, **12**, 697, 692, 721 (1926); *Bull. soc. chim. Belg.*, **35**, 411 (1926); **36**, 313, 323 (1927).
197. Woodward and Eastman, *J. Am. Chem. Soc.*, **68**, 2229 (1946); Karrer and Schmidt, *Helv. Chim. Acta*, **27**, 116 (1944); Avison *et al.*, *Nature*, **154** II, 459 (1944); Raka *et al.*, *J. Org. Chem.*, **12**, 138 (1947).
198. Friedlaender, *Ber.*, **32**, 1868 (1899); *German patent* 105,200; Auwers, *Ann.*, **393**, 352 (1912).
199. Hauser *et al.*, *J. Am. Chem. Soc.*, **66**, 1230, 1768 (1944); **59**, 1823 (1937).
200. Schechter *et al.*, *J. Am. Chem. Soc.*, **70**, 2287, 3707 (1948); **71**, 3165 (1949).
201. Henecka, *Ber.*, **81**, 197 (1948).
202. Skinner, *J. Am. Chem. Soc.*, **59**, 322 (1937).
203. Perkin, *J. Chem. Soc.*, **51**, 4 (1887).
204. Perkin and Thorpe, *ibid.*, **79**, 729 (1901). *Cf.* Ingold and Thorpe, *ibid.*, **115**, 320 (1919); Ingold and Perkin, *ibid.*, **127**, 2387 (1925).
205. Perkin *et al.*, *J. Chem. Soc.*, **119**, 1393 (1921); **126**, 1492 (1924).
206. Grün *et al.*, *Ber.*, **54**, 290 (1921).
207. Wallingford *et al.*, *J. Am. Chem. Soc.*, **63**, 2056, 2252 (1941). *Cf.* Hauser *et al.*, *ibid.*, **68**, 672 (1946).
208. Breslow *et al.*, *J. Am. Chem. Soc.*, **66**, 1286 (1944).

CHAPTER 8

ALIPHATIC ACID HALIDES, AMIDES AND RELATED COMPOUNDS

ACID HALIDES

Methods of Formation

Acid chlorides are obtained from acids through the replacement of the hydroxyl group with chlorine. This exchange may be accomplished by the use of a number of inorganic chlorine compounds, among others, phosphorus trichloride or pentachloride, thionyl chloride[1] and sulfuryl chloride.

Phosphorus pentachloride is a highly reactive compound and its use offers a general method for the preparation of acid chlorides. The products of the reaction are phosphorus oxychloride and hydrogen chloride, in addition to the acid chloride:

$$RCOOH + PCl_5 \rightarrow RCOCl + POCl_3 + HCl$$

The *procedure* employed is to mix the *dry* acid with an equivalent of phosphorus pentachloride. The reaction proceeds at room temperature, and in many cases it is necessary to apply external cooling or to use an inert solvent in order to moderate the initial reaction. Benzene, chloroform or petroleum ether may be employed for the purpose. The reaction is completed by heating over a water bath. The phosphorus oxychloride formed is then driven off by distilling or by passing a current of carbon dioxide through the mixture heated at 110 - 120°. If the acid chloride is decomposed by heat, it may be isolated by precipitation with dry petroleum ether.[2]

The salt or the anhydride of the acid may also be used in the reaction. The salt is used if the acid cannot be obtained in the dry state. Since phosphorus oxychloride also reacts with the salt, a more complete utilization of the phosphorus pentachloride is achieved when the salt is used in the reaction. Oxalyl chloride is best prepared from oxalic ester.[3] Many acids which react with difficulty with phosphorus pentachloride alone, react more or less readily with this compound in the presence of phosphorus oxychloride.[4]

A few polybasic acids with four- or five-carbon chains between the carboxyl groups, including hemipinic[5] and butanetetracarboxylic[6] acids, give anhydrides when treated with phosphorus pentachloride. Some pyridine carboxylic acids and acids with conjugated double bonds containing negative groups in the 4-position do not form chlorides on treatment with phosphorus pentachloride.[7]

Phenolic hydroxyl groups react with phosphorus pentachloride forming an oxychloride ester, $ROPOCl_2$. This reaction does not take place with phenols in which the hydroxyl group is situated between two substituents in the ortho position.[8] Alcoholic hydroxyl, keto and aldehyde groups as well as amino groups also react with phosphorus pentachloride.

In preparing the chlorides of lower aliphatic acids, it is of advantage to use *phosphorus trichloride,* since this compound is converted in the reaction to the non-volatile phosphorus acid, and the acid chloride may be isolated without difficulty by distillation:

$$3CH_3COOH + PCl_3 \rightarrow 3CH_3COCl + H_3PO_3$$

The use of *thionyl chloride*[1] for the preparation of acid chlorides presents many advantages in a large number of cases. The reaction results in the formation of sulfur dioxide and hydrogen chloride in addition to the acid chloride:

$$RCOOH + SOCl_2 \rightarrow RCOCl + SO_2 + HCl$$

and the isolation of the chloride is, for this reason, a simple matter.

The thionyl chloride must be pure, as the impure product has been known to cause a somewhat explosive decomposition in some instances.[1] The procedure consists in mixing the chloride and acid and heating the mixture, if necessary. The product may be isolated by fractional distillation or, if a solid, by crystallization.

Thionyl chloride leaves intact carbonyl and ester groups. This compound does not react with aliphatic α-keto acids, while with aromatic α-keto acids it yields the chloride of an acid with one carbon less. Complications may arise in the reaction with compounds containing conjugated double bonds. With many dibasic acids thionyl chloride gives only the anhydride. This is the case, for example, with succinic, maleic, glutaric and phthalic acids.[218] Acyl chlorides are obtained with these acids, however, when the reaction is carried out in the presence of zinc chloride.[219] The reaction with thionyl chloride fails with phenolcarboxylic, fumaric, terephthalic, oxalic, tartaric, trichloroacetic and aminoacetic acids.[9] Amino acids may be converted to acyl chlorides with thionyl chloride, providing the amino group is protected with a carbethoxy group.[220]

Malonic ethyl ester chloride, $C_2H_5OCOCH_2COCl$, has been prepared in 68% yield by mixing the potassium salt of the ester acid with 1¼ molecular proportions of thionyl chloride in absolute ether while cooling in a freezing mixture, and subsequently heating on the water bath for two hours.

In preparing malonic acid dichloride, it is necessary to hold the temperature between 40 and 60°.[222]

Phosphorus oxychloride reacting with the sodium salt of carboxylic acids gives acid chlorides:

$$2RCOONa + POCl_3 \rightarrow 2RCOCl + NaPO_3 + NaCl$$

This method is of importance with acids which undergo decomposition with other chlorides of phosphorus. Atropic acid is best obtained, for example, from the sodium salt of the acid and phosphorus oxychloride in benzene solution.[10]

Hydroxyl and carbonyl groups, if present in the molecule of the acid, are attacked by the inorganic chlorides used in the preparation of acyl chlorides.

Such groups may be protected by acylation, although the acyl groups cannot be subsequently removed without also removing the chlorine of the acyl chloride.

The reaction of *phosgene*[11] with carboxylic acids, and of *p-toluenesulfo chloride* or of *sodium chlorosulfonate* with salts of carboxylic acids[12] are also used for the preparation of acid chlorides:

$$RCOOH + COCl_2 \rightarrow RCOCl + HCl + CO_2$$

$$RCOONa + NaOSO_2Cl \rightarrow RCOCl + Na_2SO_4$$

Levulenic acid, treated with an excess of acetyl chloride, undergoes a vigorous reaction, giving levulinic chloride.

Acid chlorides are obtained readily through the reaction of *sulfuryl chloride* with anhydrous salts of organic acids. One molecular equivalent of sulfuryl chloride is used to two of a monobasic acid, and one of a dibasic acid. The reagents are well mixed and subjected to distillation. Best results are obtained with salts of divalent metals.

The chlorides of chloro- and bromomalonic acids have been obtained in quantitative yield by adding the required amount of sulfuryl chloride dropwise to the anhydrous ethereal solution of the acids and evaporating off the ether under vacuum.[223]

Oxalyl chloride is considered a satisfactory reagent for the preparation of the higher olefinic acid chlorides.[224]

Acid chlorides are also obtained through the reaction of an aliphatic acid with hydrogen chloride in the presence of phosphorus pentoxide:

$$3RCOOH + 3HCl + P_2O_5 \rightarrow 3RCOCl + 2H_3PO_4$$

The chlorination of aldehydes also results in the formation of acid chlorides:

$$RCHO + Cl_2 \rightarrow RCOCl + HCl$$

Chlorine adds to carbon dioxide to form phosgene, the dichloride of carbonic acid:

$$CO + Cl_2 \rightarrow COCl_2$$

Amino acids suspended in acetyl chloride and treated with phosphorus pentachloride are converted to the hydrochloride of amino acid chlorides:[13]

$$H_2NCH_2COOH + PCl_5 \rightarrow HCl.H_2NCH_2COCl + POCl_3$$

Amino acid chlorides are highly reactive compounds. Salicylic acid, reacting with phosphorus pentachloride, gives the compound $Cl_2PO.O.C_6H_4COCl$. *o*-Nitro- and *o*-methylsalicylic acids yield chlorides with phosphorus pentachloride, as the phenolic hydroxyl group in these compounds is incapable of reacting with phosphorus pentachloride due to steric hindrance.

Phosphorus bromides react with acids or their salts in the same manner as phosphorus chlorides to form the corresponding acid bromides. A mixture of amorphous phosphorus and bromine reacting with carboxylic acids also gives acid bromides.[14] *Acid iodides* are not formed through the action of phosphorus iodide with acids; acid iodides are obtained, however, when phosphorus iodide is made to react with acid anhydrides or salts of acids. Acyl iodides can also be prepared by the reaction of acid chlorides with calcium iodide.[15] Acetyl iodide may be obtained in 70% yield by conducting through cold acetyl chloride three times its weight of hydriodic acid.[245] The chlorine or bromine in acid chlorides or bromides may be replaced with iodine by heating with potassium iodide.[280]

Acyl fluorides may be prepared through the interaction of fluorosulfonic acid and the free carboxylic acids or their salts; or by distilling a mixture of a salt of the carboxylic [illegible] a salt of fluorosulfonic acid:[16]

$$[illegible] + XFSO_3 \rightarrow RCOF + X_2SO_4$$

Acyl fluorides have also been obtained through the reaction of hydrogen fluoride or alkali metal fluorides with acid anhydrides.[225]

The chlorine atoms in acid chlorides may be replaced with other halogens by various methods.

The *Staudinger and Anthes* method consists in distilling a mixture of the acid chloride with three times the required quantity of hydrogen halide.[17] Acid fluorides cannot be prepared by this method, although they may be prepared through the interaction of acid chlorides with certain metal fluorides. Acetyl fluoride is obtained, for example, from acetyl chloride and arsenic- or antimony trifluorides or zinc fluoride.[18] Benzoyl fluoride results, similarly, through the interaction of benzoyl chloride and zinc- or potassium fluoride.[19] The chlorine in acid chlorides may also be replaced with fluorine by reaction with silver fluoride.[20]

Hydrolysis of Acid Chlorides

The chlorides of aliphatic acids are readily decomposed with water to the corresponding acids. The reaction proceeds vigorously with some of these chlorides. Aromatic acid chlorides are more resistant to the action of water, decomposition proceeding slowly in the cold. Hydrolysis of these chlorides takes place more rapidly on warming with water. Negative substituents in the ortho position in aromatic acid chlorides retard hydrolysis. Thus, 2,4,6-tribromobenzoyl chloride is hydrolyzed only to the extent of 28% when boiled with water for thirty minutes, and is hydrolyzed slowly with boiling aqueous alkalies.[21] Acid chlorides are completely hydrolyzed on boiling with aqueous alkalies for a sufficiently long period.

Syntheses Involving the Use of Acid Chlorides

Acid chlorides are highly reactive compounds and form the starting point of many important syntheses. The *Schotten-Baumann synthesis* consisting in the reaction of acid chlorides with alcohols or amines in the presence of alkalies and the introduction of acyl groups in the molecule of aromatic compounds by the *Friedel-Crafts reaction* are examples of such syntheses. The *Rosenmund aldehyde synthesis*, the *Sonn-Müller reaction* and the formation of ketones or alcohols from acid chloride and organometallic compounds are other examples. These various subjects are considered in their proper places.

The chlorine in acid chlorides may be replaced with other negative groups. The Schotten-Baumann reaction presents an example of such an exchange. The halogen may be replaced with the cyano group by heating the acid chloride in a sealed tube with silver cyanide,[22] although the yields of acyl cyanide obtained by this method are low. A more satisfactory method is based on the reaction of acid chlorides with anhydrous hydrocyanic acid in the presence of pyridine.[23] The chlorine may be replaced with the nitrate group by heating the chloride with silver nitrate. Acyl peroxides are obtained by treating the chloride with sodium peroxide. The chlorine may be replaced with the diazomethane group by reaction of the acid chloride with an excess of diazomethane:[24]

$$RCOCl + 2CH_2N_2 \rightarrow RCOCHN_2 + CH_3Cl + N_2$$

The excess of diazomethane reacts with the hydrogen chloride liberated through the interaction of the diazomethane and the acid chloride almost as rapidly as it is formed. In the absence of a sufficient excess of diazomethane the free hydrochloric acid, acting upon the diazoketone, gives a chloromethyl ketone. The reaction of diazomethane with an acid chloride, leading to the formation of a diazoketone, constitutes one step in the Arndt-Eistert synthesis to be considered presently.

Arndt-Eistert Synthesis

The Arndt-Eistert synthesis[25] involves the formation of a diazoketone from an acid chloride and its conversion to an acid in the presence of the appropriate catalyst:

$$RCOCHN_2 + H_2O \rightarrow RCH_2COOH + N_2$$

The final result is thus the formation of an acid with one carbon atom more than the original acid chloride.

The transformation of a diazoketone to an acid or a derivative thereof was first accomplished by Wolff[26] and is known as the *Wolff rearrangement*. Arndt and Eistert showed that diazoketones, which Wolff prepared through a complicated series of reactions may be obtained readily and in good yield by the addition of an acid chloride slowly to an excess of a cold solution of diazomethane in anhydrous ether or benzene.[27]

The mechanism of the reaction is considered to be similar to that of the Curtius rearrangement, involving the dissociation of the diazo compound to nitrogen and a free radical, the transformation of the unstable radical to a ketene, and finally the hydrolysis of the latter to an acid:[28]

$$RCOCHN_2 \rightarrow N_2 + [RCOCH=] \rightarrow RCH=CO \xrightarrow{H_2O} RCH_2COOH$$

The *procedure* employed in preparing the diazo ketone is to add slowly and with stirring a solution or suspension of one mole of the *dry* acid chloride in anhydrous ether or benzene to a solution of three moles of diazomethane in the same solvent cooled to 0 to 5°. The mixture is allowed to stand at 20 to 25° for one to two hours.

Aromatic acid chlorides react slowly, reaction being complete in two hours or more, in some cases in twelve to twenty-four hours.

The diazo ketone may be isolated by evaporating the solvent at 20 - 30° under reduced pressure. If the product is solid it may be partially purified by washing with a small amount of the solvent. Many diazo ketones have been obtained in the pure form by recrystallization.

When the solution of diazomethane is added to that of the acyl chloride, a chloro ketone is the principal product of the reaction.[226] If the chloro ketone is the desired product, however, the best procedure is to prepare the diazo ketone and submit it to the action of hydrogen chloride:

$$RCOCHN_2 + HCl \rightarrow RCOCH_2Cl + N_2$$

The concentration of the diazomethane in solution may be estimated by titration with benzoic acid by the method originated by Marshall and Acree.[29] It should be noted that diazomethane is *extremely toxic* and its *vapors are explosive*. It may be handled with reasonable safety in cold ethereal solution, though one must always be on guard for a possible accidental explosion.

Conversion of the diazo ketone to the acid is brought about by adding a dioxane solution of the diazo ketone to an aqueous solution of silver nitrate and sodium thiosulfate heated to 60 - 70 °, the silver compound acting as a catalyst.[30] Silver oxide or colloidally dispersed metallic silver are also effective catalysts. Silver oxide is prepared by adding to a 10% aqueous silver nitrate solution just sufficient dilute sodium hydroxide solution to cause complete precipitation of the silver oxide. The oxide is washed by decantation, filtered, and washed again. Powdered copper and platinum also act as catalysts but are seldom used. The transformation does not take place in the absence of a catalyst.

Overall yields of the reaction usually vary between 50 and 80% of theory.

The reaction is applicable to aliphatic or aromatic acid chlorides; it is also applicable to the chlorides of nitrated aromatic acids,[31] lactone acids[32] and unsaturated acids.[33] Since it may be carried out at a moderate temperature, it may be applied to sensitive complex molecules without causing any undesirable decomposition. It is possible to introduce two methylene groups into the molecule of dicarboxylic acids, such as adipic and sebacic acids, in a single operation by the Arndt - Eistert reaction.[34]

Groups reactive toward diazomethane, such as alcoholic or phenolic hydroxyl, reactive methylene, carbonyl groups in aldehydes or α, β-unsaturated ketones, may be expected to interfere in the reaction. However, the reactive methylene in 4-fluorene carboxylic acid chloride[35] and the hydroxyl group in 2-hydroxy-3-naphthoyl chloride do not react appreciably with diazomethane when these compounds are subjected to the Arndt - Eistert synthesis.

The chloride of the acid ester of homocamphoric and mesitoyl chloride fail to react with diazomethane, due apparently to unfavorable steric conditions.[36] Sulfonyl chlorides also fail to react with diazomethane.

Diazoethane and *1-diazopropane* have been employed successfully in the Arndt-Eistert synthesis. The use of these reagents leads to the formation of acids with a methyl or ethyl group in α-position.[227] Rearrangement of the diazoketone may be brought about successfully by heating with a mixture of dimethylaniline and benzyl alcohol at 170 to 180°, giving benzyl esters of the rearranged acids. This method has been applied successfully to diazoketones obtained by the reaction of acyl halides with diazomethane.

Diazoethane was prepared in 75% yield by adding nitrosoethylurethane fairly rapidly to a solution of potassium hydroxide in *n*-propyl alcohol. 1-Diazopropane was prepared similarly in 57% yield from N-nitroso-N-isopropylurethane.

Diazoketones prepared in the first stage of the Arndt-Eistert synthesis may be converted to esters by reaction with alcohol, or to amides by reaction with ammonia or an amine, both reactions requiring a catalyst:

$$RCOCHN_2 + R'OH \rightarrow RCH_2COOR' + N_2$$

$$RCOCHN_2 + R'NH_2 \rightarrow RCH_2CONHR' + N_2$$

These reactions take place in the presence of catalysts which promote the transformation of the diazo ketone to an acid.

Esters are prepared by adding an alcoholic suspension of silver oxide to a hot anhydrous alcoholic solution or suspension of the diazoketone. The silver oxide is added in small portions over a period of one or two hours. The reaction is generally complete within one hour, but occasionally it may be complete only after about twelve hours. Addition of more silver oxide, or removal of the catalyst originally introduced and its replacement with fresh silver oxide may be necessary with the more resistant diazo ketones. A simple test for determining the end of the reaction is to add a few drops of concentrated hydrochloric acid to a test portion withdrawn from the reaction mixture; the reaction is complete if no nitrogen is evolved.[37]

Amides are prepared by conducting a current of gaseous ammonia into a cold solution of the diazo ketone in ethanol containing a small quantity of silver oxide. A more common procedure is to add to a warm solution of the diazo ketone in dioxane 10 - 28% aqueous ammonia to which a little silver nitrate has been added. The mixture is heated for a short time to complete the reaction.[38] *Anilides* are obtained by heating a mixture of the diazo ketone and a solution of aniline in alcohol or dioxane, to which a little aqueous silver nitrate has been added.

The Arndt - Eistert synthesis has been carried out with diazoethane and *p*-nitrobenzoyl chloride, rearrangement of the diazo ketone obtained resulting in the formation of *p*-nitrophenylmethylacetanilide,

$$NO_2C_6H_4CH(CH_3)CONHC_6H_5$$

The reaction has also been extended to diazoacetic ester with which a series of diazo ketones, $RCOC(N_2)COOC_2H_5$, have been prepared and subjected to the Wolff transformation.[39]

Halogenation of Acid Halides; Hell-Volhard-Zelinsky Reaction

While acids are halogenated only at a slow rate, the reaction of acid halides with halogens proceeds quite readily, resulting in the formation of monohalo acid halides. This fact forms the basis of the *Hell-Volhard-Zelinsky reaction,*[40] which consists in the halogenation of acids in the presence of red phosphorus.

The phosphorus first reacts with the halogen to form a phosphorus halide, which then reacts with the acid to convert it to an acid halide; the halogen finally reacts rapidly with the acid halide formed to give the monohalohalide. The halogen invariably enters the α-position with respect to the carboxyl group; it apparently reacts with the enolic isomer of the acyl halide to form a dihalohalide, and a molecule of hydrogen halide is subsequently eliminated to form the monohalohalide:

$$RCH_2COX \rightarrow RCH=C(OH)X \xrightarrow{X_2} RCHXCX_2OH$$
$$\rightarrow RCHXCOX + HX$$

The reaction presents the advantage that it may be carried out under atmospheric pressure.

The *procedure* in preparing the bromo acyl bromide is to add bromine to a mixture of the acid and red phosphorus, at first slowly while the temperature of the mixture is gradually raised to 80°, then more rapidly. The addition is so regulated that the vapors of bromine do not rise in the reflux condenser attached to the reaction vessel. Addition of bromine is continued until the evolution of hydrobromic acid ceases, and finally the vapors of bromine fill and remain in the reflux condenser while the mixture is digested for one half hour. From 5 to 16% of the bromine is carried away with the escaping vapors of hydrogen bromide. The phosphorus is used in slight excess over the amount required in the reaction. The overall reaction may be represented as follows:

$$3RCH_2COOH + P + 11Br \rightarrow 3RCHBrCOBr + HPO_3 + 5HBr$$

It is essential for the success of the reaction that all the reagents used and all parts of the apparatus be quite dry. The phosphorus is first washed free of all acid and is carefully dried; the bromine is dried by shaking with concentrated sulfuric acid.

The bromo acyl bromide, freed of excess bromine, may be converted to the α-bromo acid by hydrolysis, or to an α-bromo ester by reaction with anhydrous alcohol.

Sulfur has also been used as a halogen carrier in this reaction.[41]

The acyl chloride may be brominated successfully. The chloride obtained through the interaction of the acid and phosphorus pentachloride is placed in a sealed tube together with the required quantity of bromine and heated to the requisite temperature.[42] Heating at a comparatively high temperature for several hours may be necessary in some cases. For example, the bromination of hexahydrophthalyl chloride to the dibromo derivative is accomplished by heating at 150° for three hours.

In the preparation of monobromosuccinyl dibromide, reaction proceeds more smoothly when succinic anhydride is used rather than the acid.

Acids with at least one hydrogen atom attached to the α-carbon are halogenated readily by this method,[43] but acids in which α-carbons are fully substituted, such as tetramethyl succinic acid, are not halogenated under the conditions of the reaction.[44]

The conversion of dicarboxylic acids to their monohalo derivatives proceeds with ease, but the introduction of a second halogen atom into the molecule of these acids proceeds slowly, reaction being usually complete only in the course of 10 to 15 hours or longer, dibromination of pimelic acid requiring about 20 hours.[45] Polycarboxylic acids take up as many bromine atoms as there are carboxyl groups in the molecule, providing carbon atoms adjacent to each carboxyl group bear at least one hydrogen atom.

ACID AMIDES AND RELATED COMPOUNDS

Methods of Formation

Amides from Acids and Esters

Among the methods of preparation of *amides* the conversion of the ammonium salt of acids to amides may be considered to involve a direct exchange of the hydroxyl group in the acid with an amino group:

$$RCOON.NH_3 \rightarrow RCONH_2 + H_2O$$

The alkoxy group in esters and the chlorine in acid chlorides may be exchanged with amino groups by reaction with ammonia or amines:

$$RCOOC_2H_5 + NH_3 \rightarrow RCONH_2 + C_2H_5OH$$

$$RCOCl + 2\ NH_3 \rightarrow RCONH_2 + NH_4Cl$$

These reactions form the basis of the more important methods of preparation of acid amides.

Amide formation from *ammonium salts* of acids is brought about by dry-distilling the salt. A considerable portion of the salt dissociates during this operation and escapes transformation. It is a better practice to heat the salt in an autoclave at 230° for five to six hours, and subsequently to distill the charge. The amide may be obtained in a yield ranging from 70 to 80% of the theoretically expected quantity by this method. A mixture of the sodium salt of the acid and ammonium chloride may be used instead of the ammonium salt of the acid.[46] Acetamide is obtained in 90% yield by heating ammonium acetate with glacial acetic acid at 110°.[228] Higher aliphatic amides have been prepared by passing a current of ammonia through the molten acid heated at 160-210°.[229]

Amide formation from ammonium salts and carboxylic acids is an equilibrium reaction, and both the initial rate of transformation and the final equilibrium position vary according to the acid. Amide formation generally begins at a little above 100°, although it proceeds quite slowly at this temperature. The reaction rate increases rapidly with increase in temperature. The percent of amide formed during the first hour and the percent conversion at the equilibrium point for the ammonium salt of various acids at 155° are given in the following table:[47]

Ammonium Salt of:	Percent Conversion to Amide in First Hour at 155°	Percent Conversion at Equilibrium at 155°
Formic acid	57.5	–
Acetic acid	50.9	81.5
Propionic acid	50.9	84.7
Butyric acid	42.5	84.1
isoButyric acid	37.1	84.7
Capric acid	48.2	84.3
Benzoic acid	0.7	–(*)
Phenylacetic acid	36.4	81.5
Anisic acid	3.8	–(*)

(*) Less than 10%.

Monoammonium salts of dibasic acids are converted to cyclic imides when heated. This transformation may also be accomplished by the use of dehydrating agents. The amides and the neutral ammonium salts of these acids can also be converted to cyclic imides.[48] A satisfactory procedure is to heat the amide with three equivalents of acetic anhydride containing 10% sodium acetate at 95° until the reaction is complete, and to pour the liquid into five times its volume of ice water. The precipitated amide is washed free of acid with sodium bicarbonate solution, and is purified by crystallization.[230]

Acid amides have also been obtained in high yield by heating carboxylic acids with urea.[231]

$$RCOOH + CO(NH_2)_2 \rightarrow RCONH_2 + CO_2 + NH_3$$

The reaction begins at 120°.

The reaction of *esters* with ammonia is best carried out with concentrated aqueous ammonia at room temperature. Water and other solvents containing a hydroxyl group catalyze the reaction. The reaction takes place readily with esters that are soluble in water. The amides of lower aliphatic acids are obtained by shaking the esters with concentrated ammonia for 12 to 30 hours. The reaction of the higher fatty acids with ammonia takes place at a much slower rate and does not proceed to completion. The amides of some aromatic acids have been prepared by this method.[49] The amide is obtained in a lower yield when the mixture of ester and aqua ammonia is heated, or when alcoholic ammonia is used.[50] Methyl esters react more readily than ethyl esters. While dimethyl malonate reacts with aqua ammonia to form malonamide, diethyl malonate fails to react at all.[233] Dialkylated malonic esters also resist the action of aqueous or alcoholic ammonia.[51] The ester of trimethylacetic acid fails to yield an amide, while trichloracetic ester reacts with ammonia with great ease to form trichloracetamide. Some acids fail to react in the cold and undergo decomposition when heated with ammonia; examples are methyl β-hydroxy-α-naphthoate and methyl β-methyl cinchoninate. Ethyl benzoylacetate, $C_6H_5COCH_2COOC_2H_5$, reacts with concentrated ammonium hydroxide in the cold to form the corresponding amide in 81% yield; the anilide is obtained in 76% yield by heating the ester at 150° with a xylene solution of aniline.[234] Amides of amino acids have been prepared through the reaction of esters of the acids with methanolic ammonia.[235]

Hydrazine hydrate and hydroxylamine react with esters in the same manner as ammonia.

Amides from Acid Chlorides and Anhydrides

The reaction of *acid chlorides* with ammonia and amines offers the most generally applicable method for the preparation of amides. The chloride used for the purpose need not be isolated in the pure form, although when the chloride has been prepared through the interaction of the acid with phosphorus pentachloride, it is desirable to remove the phosphorus trichloride formed before the crude acid chloride is used in the reaction.[52] A satisfactory procedure is to heat the acid with benzoyl chloride for two to three hours, then to add the amine and an excess of sodium hydroxide solution to the resulting product.

The method of formation of amides from acid chlorides is well adapted for the preparation of amides of the higher fatty acids.[53] The reaction is best carried out in ethereal or benzene solution. An excess of the amine is used to combine with the hydrochloric acid formed, although satisfactory results may be obtained by heating a mixture of equivalent quantities of the acid chloride and amine until hydrogen chloride ceases to be given off.[54]

The reaction with ammonia may be carried out by adding the chloride drop by drop to aqueous ammonia and allowing the mixture to stand overnight. With few exceptions, the amide separates out in the crystalline form. Soluble amides, such as those of acetic, propionic and butyric acids, are isolated by evaporating the solution to dryness and extracting the amide with absolute alcohol; the alcoholic solution is then evaporated to recover the amide.

Anilides may be prepared by adding an excess of an ethereal solution of the aromatic amine to the acid chloride with cooling. The reaction mixture is washed with water and with 6% aqueous hydrochloric acid, the ether layer is separated and the ether is evaporated off to recover the anilide formed.

Amides may be prepared successfully by reaction with amines in the cold from halogenated acid chlorides, since aliphatically bound halogens do not react, in general, with amines at ordinary temperature.[55] Benzoylation of α-amino acids is carried out in aqueous sodium hydroxide solution, the base neutralizing the hydrogen chloride as it is formed during the reaction.[236]

Acid anhydrides reacting with ammonia or amines give amides:

$$(RCO)_2O + 2\ NH_3 \rightarrow RCONH_2 + RCOONH_4$$

The reaction, which usually proceeds with evolution of heat, may be carried out in an indifferent solvent such as ether or benzene.[56] It may also be carried out in water in the presence of a base. Sodium hydroxide is used with aromatic anhydrides and pyridine with aliphatic anhydrides. Dibasic acid anhydrides give with ammonia the half amide of the acid. If the acid is of unsymmetrical structure, the amino group enters the potentially weaker carboxyl group.[57] Reaction of acetic anhydride with α-amino acids in aqueous solution proceeds in the cold.[237] When the reaction is carried out in the presence of pyridine or sodium acetate, decarboxylation takes place, and two acyl groups enter the molecule:[238]

$$RCH(NH_2)COOH + (R'CO)_2O \rightarrow \underset{\displaystyle |\atop \displaystyle COR'}{RCHNHCOR'} + H_2O + CO_2$$

t-Butylphthalimide is obtained by the reaction of phthalic anhydride with *t*-butylurea at 200-240°.[239]

Amides from Nitriles

Nitriles may be partially hydrolyzed to the amide stage by solution in cold concentrated sulfuric or hydrochloric acid, or a mixture of one of these acids with acetic acid.[58] A satisfactory procedure is to saturate a solution of the nitrile in acetic acid with hydrogen chloride, whereby the hydrochloride of the amide is obtained:

$$CH_3CN + CH_3COOH + 2HCl \rightarrow CH_3CONH_2{\cdot}HCl + CH_3COCl$$

The reaction can also be carried out in acetic anhydride solution:[59]

$$CH_3CN + (CH_3CO)_2O + 3\,HCl \rightarrow CH_3CONH_2{\cdot}HCl + 2\,CH_3COCl$$

The amide may be obtained in the crystalline form on carefully diluting the reaction mixture. When sulfuric acid is used as a hydrolyzing agent, the reaction mixture is poured in ice with stirring. Several nitriles containing alkylamino groups have been converted to the corresponding amides by dissolving the nitrile in cold concentrated sulfuric acid and, after standing for a time, pouring onto ice.[240] Hydrolysis to amide by this method may be hastened occasionally by moderate heating for a short period without the formation of any appreciable quantity of acid through the hydrolysis of the amide. Methacrylamide has been prepared in 70% yield by simultaneous hydrolysis and dehydration of acetone cyanohydrin with concentrated sulfuric acid.[241]

Nitriles may also be hydrolyzed to amides by heating with water at 180°.[60]

Nicotinonitrile has been converted to nicotinamide in 73% yield by heating the nitrile at 108° in a sealed tube with concentrated aqueous ammonium hydroxide.[242]

Amides result from nitriles by the action of alkaline *hydrogen peroxide* at 40°:[61]

$$RCN + 2H_2O_2 \rightarrow RCONH_2 + H_2O + O_2$$

A 3% solution of alkaline peroxide is used for the purpose. The mechanism of this reaction is not well understood. Good results are obtained by this method with aromatic nitriles, although substituents in the ortho position with respect to the nitrile group hinder the reaction. Unsatisfactory results are obtained, as a rule, with aliphatic nitriles.[62] Some olefinic nitriles are converted to glycidamides by hydrogen peroxide:[243]

$$RCH = C(C_6H_5)CN \xrightarrow{H_2O_2} RCH\overset{O}{\frown}C(C_6H_5)CONH_2$$

The more resistant nitriles may be converted to an amide by this method by use of an excess of hydrogen peroxide, or of a more concentrated solution of hydrogen peroxide. Even nitriles which resist hydrolysis with acids may be converted to amides by this method. Occasionally hydrolysis by this method proceeds to the acid stage.[63] The method is of little preparative value.

Nitriles heated with aliphatic acids at 200° give secondary amides, while with acid anhydrides they yield tertiary amides of the acid.

Amides have been obtained through the reaction of cyano compounds with olefins in the presence of sulfuric acid, and hydrolysis of the resulting product:[244]

$$(CH_3)_2C = CH_2 + RCN + H_2SO_4 \rightarrow \underset{\displaystyle OSO_3H}{RC} = NC(CH_3)_3 \xrightarrow{H_2O} RCONHC(CH_3)_3$$

Reaction proceeds at room temperature in glacial acetic acid or in dilute ethereal solution. The method has been employed for the preparation of N-alkyl diamides from dinitriles and olefins or alcohols.[244]

Amides by other Methods

Amides may be prepared also by a variety of other methods. They are obtained, for example, through the reaction of fatty acids with alkali thiocyanates[64]

$$2RCOOH + KSCN \rightarrow RCONH_2 + RCOOK + COS$$

The amide may be obtained by this method by heating a mixture of one mole of potassium thiocyanate with two and a half moles of the anhydrous fatty acid for a long period.[65] Aromatic acids yield nitriles when heated with potassium thiocyanate.

Amides result through the reaction of acids with isonitriles. Methyl isocyanide reacting with acetic acid gives methyl formamide:

$$2CH_3COOH + CH_3N = C \rightarrow HCONHCH_3 + (CH_3CO)_2O$$

The oxidation of aldehydes with ammonium persulfate in the presence of lime gives amides.[66] The amide probably results through the oxidation of the additive compound of the aldehyde, $RCH(OH)NH_2$. The procedure best adapted for carrying out the reaction is to shake the aldehyde with a slight excess of aqueous ammonium persulfate containing sufficient lime to neutralize the acid liberated through the decomposition of the persulfate, and to release the ammonia. The mixture is heated to 70° for half an hour, filtered, the residue is washed with ammonia and the combined filtrate and washings are acidified with hydrochloric acid. The amide may be isolated from the resulting liquid by extracting with ether, washing the extract with sodium carbonate solution and finally evaporating off the ether. Amides have been prepared by this method from benzaldehyde, *meta-* and *para*-nitrobenzaldehyde, anisaldehyde, acetaldehyde, propylaldehyde and isovaleraldehyde.

Aromatic amides are obtained by Friedel-Crafts reaction from urea chloride and aromatic compounds:

$$C_6H_6 + ClCONH_2 \xrightarrow{AlCl_3} C_6H_5CONH_2 + HCl$$

Substituted urea chlorides reacting with aromatic compounds in the presence of aluminum chloride give substituted amides:

$$CH_3OC_6H_5 + ClCONHR \rightarrow CH_3OC_6H_4CONHR + HCl$$

Such urea chlorides result from the reaction of hydrogen chloride with isocyanic acid esters:

$$RN = CO + HCl \rightarrow RNHCOCl$$

The Beckmann Transformation

Amides are formed from ketoximes under the action of certain acids. This reaction, which is of little significance in so far as the preparation of simple amides is concerned, is of considerable interest in organic synthesis. It is known as the *Beckmann rearrangement*.

When ketoximes are subjected to the action of certain chlorinated compounds, such as phosphorus pentachloride or acetyl chloride, the hydroxyl group of the oxime becomes replaced with chlorine. The resulting compound undergoes rearrangement, changing to an iminochloride; treated with water, the iminochloride is hydrolyzed and the resulting hydroxy compound in turn undergoes molecular rearrangement, giving rise to an amide: [67]

$$R_1R_2C = NOH + PCl_5 \quad \rightarrow \quad POCl_3 + HCl + R_1R_2C = NCl$$

$$R_1CCl = NR_2 \quad \overset{H_2O}{\rightarrow} \quad RC(OH) = NR_2 \quad \rightarrow \quad RCONHR_2$$

In explanation of the rearrangement of the N-chloroimine, or of the oxime or its esters, the hypothesis has been advanced that these compounds are dipolar in character and an ionic dissociation procedes the rearrangement:

$$^+R_1C(R_2) = NOH^- \quad \rightarrow \quad [R_1N = CR_2]^+OH^-$$

$$\rightarrow \quad R_1N = C(R_2)OH \quad \rightarrow \quad R_1NHCOR_2$$

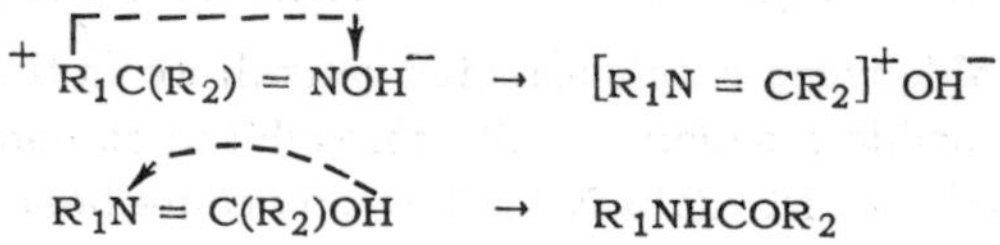

A molecule of the type $R_1C(R_2) = NOX$ may be ionized without appreciable dissociation, particularly in media of low dielectric constant. The dipole structure and the stability of the migrating ions should be favored by polar solvents. [68]

If the group R_2 contains an optically active carbon with which it is joined to the rest of the molecule, the optical activity of this atom is often largely preserved after the transformation. Meisenheimer has demonstrated that the group which stands in the *cis* position with respect to the hydroxyl group exchanges position with the latter: [69]

$$R_2C - R_1 \quad \rightarrow \quad \underset{NR_2}{HOCR_1} \quad \rightarrow \quad \underset{HNR_2}{OCR_1}$$

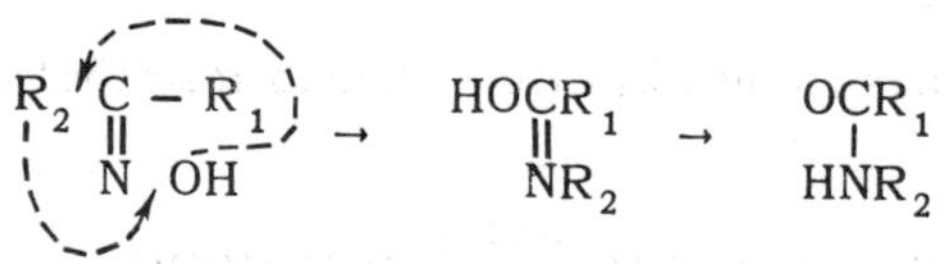

The *procedure* in carrying out the transformation with phosphorus pentachloride is as follows: To a very dilute solution of the oxime in ether, phosphorus pentachloride is added in small portions with agitation and cooling until a large excess of the chloride remains at the bottom of the flask. The solution is then decanted and shaken with ice-water, dried with solid potassium hydroxide, and the ether is finally evaporated off to recover the amide.

The transformation of an oxime to an amide takes place also under the influence of sulfuric, hydrochloric or acetic acids. The so-called "Beckman mixture", which is also an effective catalyst, consists of a solution of hydrogen chloride in a mixture of acetic acid and acetic anhydride. Rearrangement by use of concentrated sulfuric acid is brought about by heating a mixture of the oxime with ten times its weight of the acid over the water bath. Other effective catalysts are aluminum chloride, antimony, tri- and pentachlorides and benzenesulfonyl chloride.

The Beckman transformation takes place with aliphatic, aromatic and heterocyclic ketoximes.

Levulinic oxime, subjected to the transformation, yields succinmethylimide,

$$COCH_2CH_2CONCH_3$$ [70]

Anilides may be prepared from acetophenone and other aromatic ketones without difficulty.

The rearrangement of isomeric α- and γ-benzile monoximes, which may be effected with phosphorus pentachloride, yields different products.[71] The α-isomer gives benzoylbenzimide chloride:

$$\underset{\overset{\|}{NOH}}{C_6H_5CCOC_6H_5} \rightarrow C_6H_5C(Cl) = NCOC_6H_5$$

The γ-isomer yields benzoylformanilide chloride:

$$\underset{\overset{\|}{HON}}{C_6H_5CCOC_6H_5} \rightarrow C_6H_5N = CClCOC_6H_5$$

The various isomeric benzyl dioximes also yield different products when subjected to the transformation. The α-isomer is converted to diphenylhydroxybiazole:[72]

$$\underset{NOH}{C_6H_5\overset{}{C}} \text{———} \underset{HON}{CC_6H_5} \rightarrow C_6H_5C(OH) = NC(:NOH)C_6H_5$$

$$\rightarrow C_6H_5C(OH) = NN = C(OH)C_6H_5$$

Oxanilide results from the β-isomer:

$$\underset{HON}{C_6H_5C} - \underset{NOH}{CC_6H_5} \rightarrow C_6H_5N = C(OH)C(OH) = NC_6H_5$$

The intermediate transformation product of the β-isomer,

$$C_6H_5C(=NOH)NHCOC_6H_5$$

yields 3,5-diphenyl- 1,2,4-oxdiazole,

$$C_6H_5C = NOC(C_6H_5) = N$$ [73]

The transformation product of the γ-isomer is phenylbenzoylpseudourea:

$$\underset{HON}{C_6H_5C} - \underset{NOH}{CC_6H_5} \rightarrow C_6H_5N = C(OH)N = C(OH)C_6H_5$$

Ring formation may take place when certain aromatic ketoximes are subjected to the Beckmann transformation. 2-Substituted benzoxazoles

$$C\,H \underset{O}{\overset{N}{\diamondsuit}} CR$$

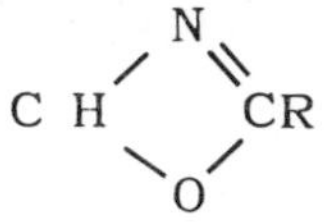

are obtained, for example, from the oximes of orthohydroxy ketones HOC_6H_4COR. [74]

Ring enlargement takes place when certain cyclic ketoximes are subjected to the Beckmann transformation.

Cyclic oximes subjected to the Beckmann transformation give lactams:

$$\overline{CH_2(CH_2)_3C} = NOH \quad \rightarrow \quad \overline{CH_2(CH_2)_3CONH}$$

$$\overline{CH_2(CH_2)_5C} = NOH \quad \rightarrow \quad \overline{CH_2(CH_2)_5CONH}$$

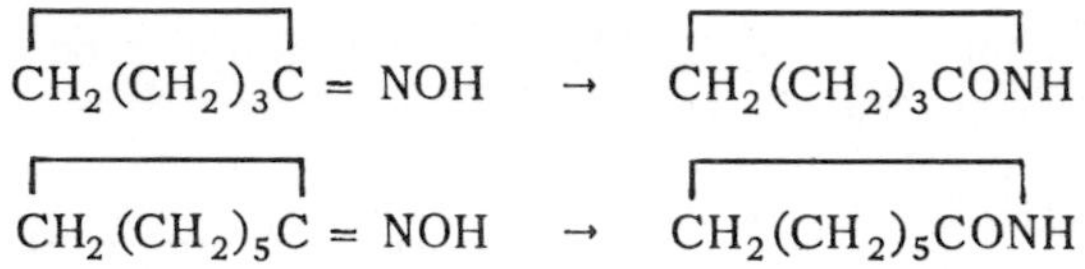

The transformation is best brought about under the action of concentrated sulfuric acid. Isonitrosohydrindone treated with sulfuric acid is transformed to homophthalimide: [75]

$$C_6H_4 \underset{CO}{\overset{CH_2}{\diamondsuit}} C = NOH \quad \rightarrow \quad C_6H_4 \underset{CO\ -\ NH}{\overset{CH_2\ -\ CO}{\diamondsuit}}$$

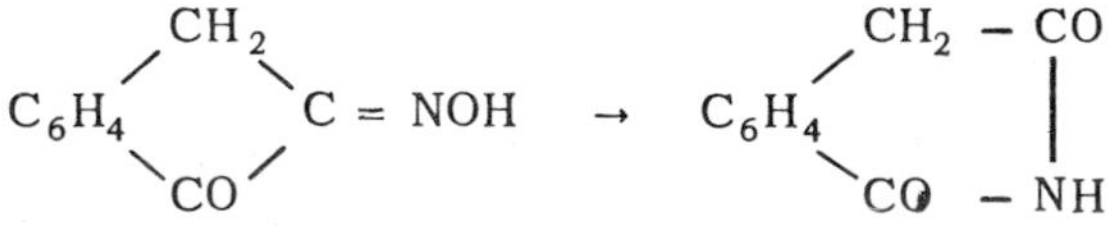

Hydrocarbostyril is obtained from α-hydrindone oxime on treatment with phosphorus pentachloride: [76]

$$C_6H_4 \underset{C(:NOH)}{\overset{CH_2 \longrightarrow}{\diamondsuit}} CH_2 \quad \rightarrow \quad C_6H_4 \underset{NH\ -\ CO}{\overset{CH_2-\ CH_2}{\diamondsuit}}$$

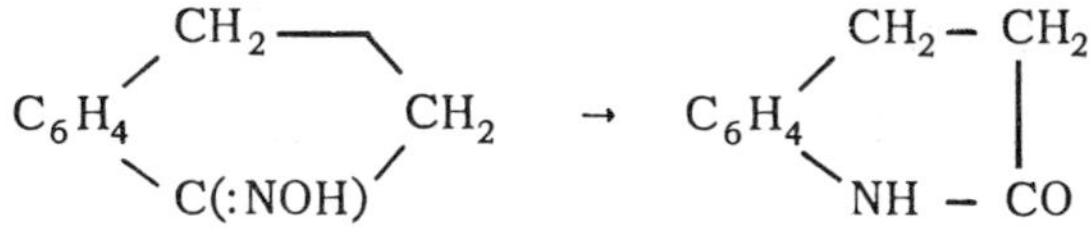

Benzoyleneurea is obtained from a-isatoxime:

$$C_6H_4 \underset{NH}{\overset{CO}{\diamondsuit}} C = NOH \quad \rightarrow \quad C_6H_4 \underset{NH.CO}{\overset{CO.NH}{\diamondsuit}}$$

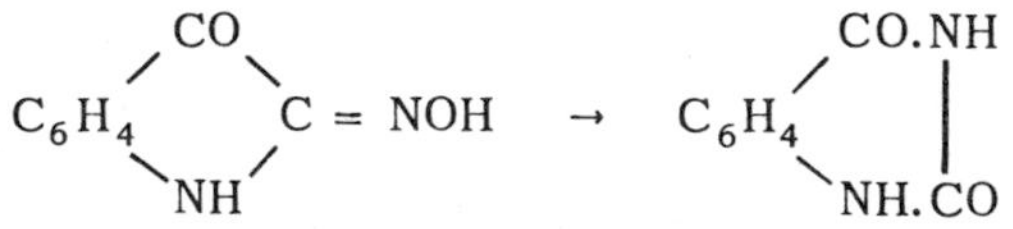

The monoxime of phenanthraquinone yields the imide of 1,1'-diphenyldicarboxylic acid: [77]

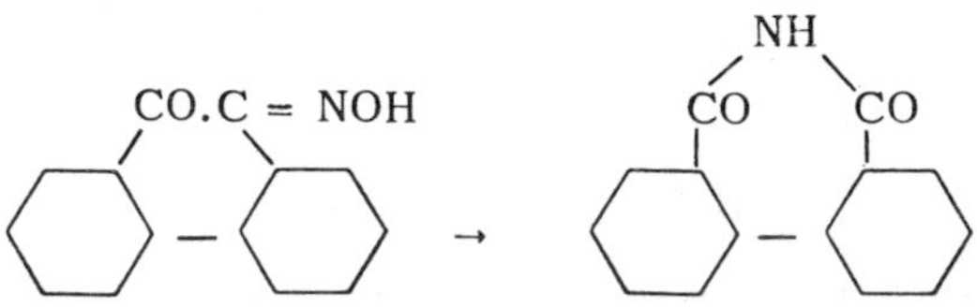

Two cases of the rearrangement of aldoximes to acid amides have been reported. [78] Phthalaldoxime,

$$C_6H_4 \begin{array}{c} CH = N \\ | \\ CO - O \end{array}$$

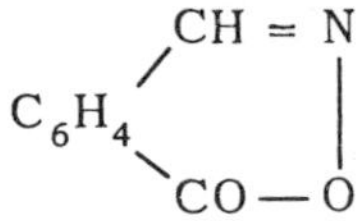

gives phthalimide when subjected to the Beckmann transformation. Cinnamal-doxime is converted to isoquinoline: [80]

$$C_6H_5CH = CHCH = NOH \quad \rightarrow$$

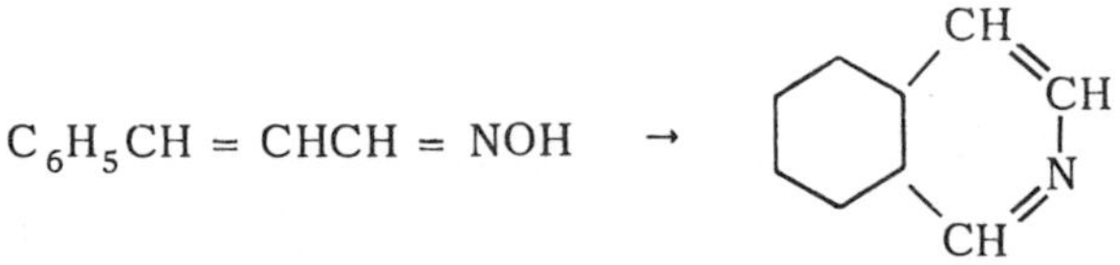

Certain oximes fail to undergo the Beckmann transformation. [79]

Some hydroxamic acids are also capable of undergoing the Beckmann rearrangement. Salicylhydroxamic acid, $C_6H_4(OH)C(OH) = NOH$, gives on treatment with thionyl chloride 2-hydroxybenzoxazole,

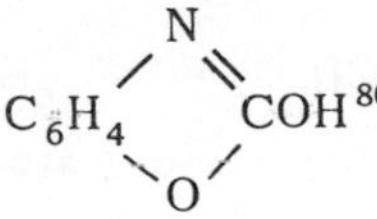

$$C_6H_4 \begin{array}{c} N \\ \diagdown \\ O \end{array} COH \ [80]$$

Phenylhydrazidooxalhydroxamic acid yields 1-phenylurazole: [81]

$$H_2NC(:NOH)CONHNHC_6H_5 \quad \rightarrow \quad \overline{C_6H_5NNHCONHCO} + NH_3$$

Certain amidoximes or their benzenesulfonyl derivatives also undergo the Beckmann rearrangement: [82]

$$RC(:NOH)NH_2 \quad \rightarrow \quad RN = C(OH)NH_2 \quad \rightarrow \quad RNHCONH_2$$

$$RC(=NOH)NH_2 + C_6H_5SO_2Cl \quad \rightarrow \quad RC(=NOSO_2C_6H_5)NH_2HCl$$

$$\rightarrow \quad C_6H_5SO_2OC(=NR)NH_2^+HCl$$

The transformation of amidoximes is brought about by the use of phosphorus trichloride.

Certain ketoximes behave exceptionally when subjected to the conditions inducing the Beckmann transformation. Thus, camphoroxime yields an unsaturated nitrile: [83]

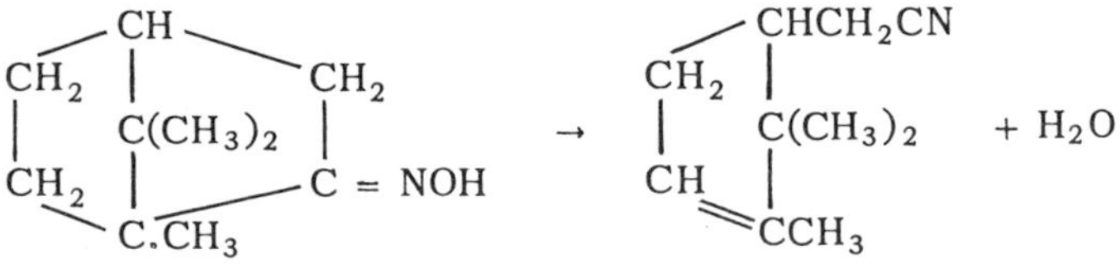

Oximes of α-hydroxy ketones of the type of benzoin undergo cleavage to yield an aldehyde and a nitrile or isonitrile: [84]

$$C_6H_5CH(OH)C(:NOH)C_6H_5 \quad \rightarrow \quad C_6H_5CHO + C_6H_5CN \text{ or } C_6H_5NC + H_2O$$

The monoximes of α-diketones undergo cleavage when treated with benzenesulfonyl chloride in alkaline medium or in pyridine to a nitrile and an acid,[85]

$$C_6H_5C(:NOH)COC_6H_5 \rightarrow C_6H_5CN + C_6H_5COOH$$

although these oximes undergo the normal rearrangement under the influence of phosphorus pentachloride. These abnormal cleavage reactions of α-diketomonoximes and α-hydroxy ketoximes are generally referred to as *Beckmann rearangements of the second order.*[86]

Oximes of certain α,β-unsaturated ketones undergo intramolecular ring closure to form isoxalines when treated with sulfuric acid:[87]

$$C_6H_5CH=CHC(:NOH)C_6H_5 \rightarrow C_6H_5\overline{CHCH_2C(:NO})C_6H_5$$

These oximes undergo the normal rearrangement under the action of phosphorus pentachloride.

Oximes of ketones containing a benzyl group attached to the carbonyl group give, under certain conditions, α-amino ketones or their cyclic condensation products:[88]

$$C_6H_5CH_2C(:NOH)CH_3 \rightarrow C_6H_5CH(NH_2)COCH_3$$

Many unsaturated cyclic ketoximes yield aromatic amines when subjected to the conditions of the Beckmann transformation.[89] Certain 1-aroylanthraquinones undergo dehydration[90] under these conditions.

Tetralone oxime or its acetyl ester, treated with hydrogen chloride in solution in a mixture of acetic acid and acetic anhydride *(Beckmann mixture)*, undergoes rearrangement to α-naphthylamine:[284]

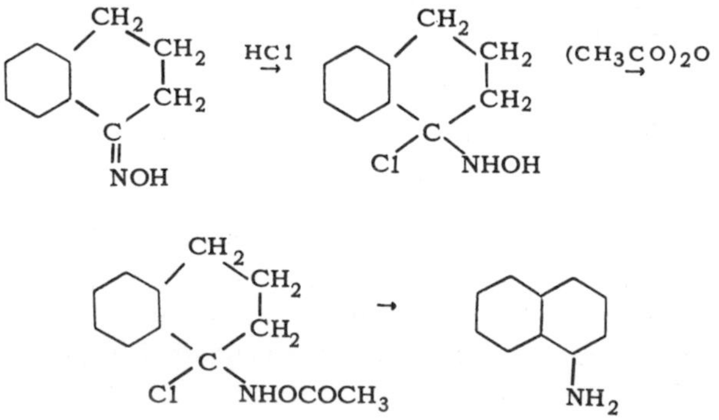

Similar transformations are observed with oximes of 1- or 3-nitro-5-tetralone, chloro-5-tetralone, methoxy-5-tetralone, 1-octanthrone and 9-nitro-1-octanthranone. Oximes of α-tetralones which carry a substituent in ortho position to the keto group undergo the regular Beckmann rearrangement to the lactam. Arylsulfonic and acetic esters of α-tetralone oximes also undergo a normal Beckmann transformation by this treatment.

Properties and Behavior of Amides

Amides are usually crystalline solids, soluble in alcohol and ether. The lower aliphatic amides are soluble in water and may be distilled without decomposition. All are stable toward alkaline permanganate but are attacked by acid permanganate.[91]

Amides are only weakly basic in their reaction, the basicity of the amino group present in the molecule being greatly reduced by the acyl group. They yield salts with strong acids[92] which, however, are quite unstable and are extensively hydrolyzed in aqueous solution. Alkylamides are somewhat stronger bases,[93] and form stable platinum double salts. The bond between the amino group and the acyl carbon is weaker than that between the amino group and the hydrocarbon radical in amines.

Hydrolysis of Amides

Amides may be converted to the salts of the corresponding acids by heating under reflux with a dilute aqueous or alcoholic alkali hydroxide until the evolution of ammonia ceases:

$$RCONH_2 + KOH \rightarrow RCOOK + NH_3$$

Hydrolysis may also be brought about by heating the amide with a dilute acid.[94] Simple and substituted amides are hydrolyzed with equal ease by this method. Acyl amides are somewhat resistant to hydrolysis, but may be converted to the corresponding acid by heating with mineral acids.

The amides of triphenylacetic acid[95] and many trialkylacetic acids[96] as well as aromatic amides with substituents in the ortho position[97] resist hydrolysis by acids. For example, 2,4-dibromobenzamide remains unchanged when heated at 170° with 80% sulfuric acid.

Bouveault's Method

Amides which resist hydrolysis with alkalies or acids can be converted to the corresponding acids, with a few exceptions, by reaction with nitrous acid:[98]

$$RCONH_2 + HNO_2 \rightarrow RCOOH + N_2 + H_2O$$

The procedure is to dissolve the amide in five times its weight of concentrated sulfuric acid and to add with cooling a 20% aqueous solution of about five molecular equivalents of the nitrite, raising the temperature gradually to 100° and maintaining it at this point for a few minutes. In some cases it is of advantage to heat the solution of the amide in sulfuric acid to 120 - 130° and then to add the solution of the nitrite deep below the surface of the liquid.

It is often of advantage to employ the Bouveault's method even if the direct alkali or acid hydrolysis proceeds satisfactorily.

Miscellaneous Reactions of Amides

Amides react with alkali metals to form derivatives in which the metal replaces one hydrogen atom of the amino group. The sodium derivative may be obtained through the interaction of sodamide with the amide in solution in benzene or anhydrous liquid ammonia:

$$RCONH_2 + NaNH_2 \rightarrow RCONHNa + NH_3$$

The metal in these compounds may be replaced by alkyl groups by reaction with alkyl halides or alkyl potassium sulfate:[99]

$$RCONHK + R'OSO_3K \rightarrow RCONHR' + K_2SO_4$$

The substituted amides RCONHR′ can be converted to their alkali metal derivatives and these, in turn, may be alkylated to obtain disubstituted amides $RCONR'_2$.

The dry sodium derivative of an amide reacts with ethyl iodide to form an N-alkyl derivative. If the reaction is carried out in alcoholic solution, imino ethers are formed. The sodium amide apparently first reacts with alcohol forming sodium ethoxide and the free amide; the free amide and alkyl iodide reacting in the presence of sodium ethoxide then yield the imino ether. The silver derivative of benzamide, reacting with ethyl iodide, gives benziminoethyl ether, $C_6H_5C(:NH)OC_2H_5$; the sodium derivative gives the ethylated amide, $C_6H_5CONHC_2H_5$.[100]

Compounds of amides with other metals have also been made.[104] The mercury salts are obtained through the reaction of amides in aqueous solution with mercuric oxide.[101] Silver salts[102] may be obtained by double decomposition from the sodium derivative of the amide and silver nitrate in cold alcoholic solution. The compounds prepared by this method are colored orange-red. Silver compounds may also be prepared through the reaction of freshly precipitated silver oxide with the amide in cold aqueous solution. The products obtained by this method are colorless. The colorless silver derivatives reacting with ethyl iodide give ethyl imino ethers and are probably O-derivatives of the amide:

$$C_6H_5C(:NH)OAg + C_2H_5I \rightarrow C_6H_5C(:NH)OC_2H_5 + AgI$$

The silver derivative of formanilide furnishes on reaction with methyl or ethyl iodides a mixture of alkylaniline, $C_6H_5N(Alk)CHO$, and a formophenyliminoether, $C_6H_5N{=}CHOAlk$. A similar behavior is observed with the silver derivatives of other anilides and nuclearly substituted benzamides.[103] The relative proportions of the O- and N-alkyl derivatives obtained depend on the character of the amide, the experimental conditions and the type of halide employed. Methyl iodide gives a greater proportion of the N-alkyl derivative than ethyl iodide.

Metal derivatives of amides other than those of alkali metals, silver and mercury are also known.[104]

Nitrous acid reacts with amides, $RCONH_2$, to form the corresponding acid with evolution of nitrogen (Bouveault's Method). N-alkyl- or N-arylamides, RCONHR′, react with nitrous acid to form nitroso amides, RCON(NO)R′. Nitroso anilides may be obtained by passing nitrous fumes into a well-colled solution of the anilide in acetic acid.

Substituted ureas, urethanes and other similar compounds also react with nitrous acid to form nitroso derivatives. These nitroso compounds are decomposed on treatment with cold concentrated caustic yielding an alkaline diazotate. Thus nitrosomethylurethane treated at 0° with potassium hydroxide gives the diazotate $CH_3N = NOK$, a white crystalline product which is decomposed with water to diazomethane. Nitroso derivatives of other substituted ureas behave in the same manner, and may serve for the preparation of diazoparaffins.[105] Nitrosoalkylureas may be reduced to alkylhydrazines under appropriate conditions.[106]

Nitric acid converts simple amides to the corresponding acids:

$$RCONH_2 + HNO_3 \rightarrow RCOOH + N_2O + H_2O$$

Certain amides, such as urea, urethane, guanidine, etc., may be nitrated to *nitramides* by the action of highly concentrated nitric acid, but the nitro derivatives formed are decomposed by the unreacted acid even at room temperature. Better results are obtained by use of a mixture of nitric and sulfuric acids. The most satisfactory method appears to be treatment of the amide with ethyl nitrate and concentrated sulfuric acid at a low temperature. Urethane may be successfully converted to nitrourethane, $C_2H_5OCONHNO_2$ by this method.[281]

Nitrourea, $H_2NCONHNO_2$, results when urea nitrate is dissolved in well cooled sulfuric acid with good agitation. *Nitroguanidine*[282] has been prepared by the action of a mixture of sulfuric acid of about 4% SO_3 content and furming nitric acid of 1.5 specific gravity on guanidine. The compound is best prepared, however, by dissolving guanidine nitrate in twice its weight of sulfuric acid of sp.g. 1.84 cooled to below -10°, maintaining the temperature of the mixture at 0° for half an hour and finally pouring it into seven times its weight of ice water with stirring.[294] Guanidine nitrate is prepared in the following manner: One molal equivalent of dicyandiamide and somewhat more than six molal equivalents of dry ammonium nitrate, both preheated to 110° are mixed and rapidly heated to 162 to 165°; a second molal equivalent of dicyandiamide is then introduced at such a rate that the temperature never rises above 165°, and the mixture is maintained at 162 to 165° for a total period of one hour. The guanidine nitrate formed is purified by crystallization first from approximately 25 times its weight of water heated to 80°, then from methanol.

Nitro amides are decomposed by sulfuric acid even on gentle heating; some are decomposed with concentrated sulfuric acid at ordinary temperature.

Nitro amides may be reduced to *nitrosoamides*. Nitroguanidine has been converted to nitrosoguanidine[283] by treatment with zinc and dilute (1:5 by volume) sulfuric acid at 40 to 50°. Reduction is complete within 10 to 15 minutes. Nitrosourethane is obtained on reducing nitrourethane with zinc dust and dilute aqueous acetic acid. Nitrosourea is formed when nitrourea in 20% caustic solution is treated with zinc dust.

The hydrogen atoms of the amino group in amides may be replaced with halogens by reaction with hypochlorous or hypobromous acid.[107] The halogen in the resulting halo amides is loosely combined in these compounds, and for this reason the latter can serve as halogenating agents. All chloro and bromo amides liberate iodine from acidified potassium iodide solution. Halo amides of the type RCONHX yield salts with alkalies.[108]

Amides react with alcohols to form esters, although simultaneously a certain proportion of an amine is also formed through an exchange of the hydroxyl group of the alcohol with the amino group:[109]

$$CH_3CONH_2 + CH_3OH \rightarrow CH_3COOCH_3 + NH_3$$

$$CH_3CONH_2 + CH_3OH \rightarrow CH_3COOH + CH_3NH_2$$

Amides react with phosphorus pentachloride to form an iminochloride:[110]

$$CH_3CONHC_6H_5 + PCl_5 \rightarrow CH_3CCl = NC_6H_5 + POCl_3 + HCl$$

An intermediate dichloro compound, $CH_3CCl_2NHC_6H_5$ in the above example, is apparently formed at first, and yields the chloroimide with loss of a molecule of hydrogen chloride. Simple iminochlorides are unstable and are readily converted to nitriles; substituted chloroimides are comparatively stable.

Substituted benzamides reacting with phosphorus pentachloride give benzonitrile and the chloride of the group attached to nitrogen:

$$C_6H_5CONHR + PCl_5 \rightarrow C_6H_5CN + RCl + POCl_3 + HCl$$

This reaction makes possible the replacement of the NH_2 group in amines with chlorine. The amine is benzoylated by reaction with benzoyl chloride for the purpose and is then subjected to the above reaction.[111] If the nitrogen forms part of a heterocyclic ring, chlorination and ring rupture take place simultaneously, α-pipecoline, $CH_2(CH_2)_3CH(CH_3)N$, giving for example, 1,5-dichlorohexane, $ClCH_2(CH_2)_3CH(CH_3)Cl$.[112]

Cyclic amides heated with phosphorus oxychloride also give chloroimides. This reaction has been applied successfully to purine derivatives. 2,6-Dichloro-8-oxypurine,

$$ClC = NC(Cl) = NC = CNHCONH,$$

is obtained, for example, from uric acid.[113] A third chlorine atom may be introduced using an excess of phosphorus oxychloride, and carefully regulating the temperature to the required value.[114] Uric acid derivatives bearing alkyl groups in the alloxan ring yield an 8-chloro product:[115]

$$CON(CH_3)CONHC = CN(CH_3)CONH \rightarrow CON(CH_3)CONHC = CN(CH_3)C(Cl) = N$$

The exchange of oxygen for chlorine takes place with greater difficulty in the 2,6-dioxypurines.[116] The oxygen in pyrazolones may also be replaced with chlorine by reaction with phosphorus oxychloride.[117]

Heated with phosphorus pentoxide, amides are converted to nitriles of the corresponding acid:

$$CH_3CONH_2 \rightarrow CH_3CN + H_2O$$

Amides condense with chloral to form compounds of the type

$$Cl_3CCH(OH)NHCOR$$

When these are treated with acetic anhydride and sodium hydroxide, they form ether-like anhydro compounds of the general type[118]

$$RCONHCH(CCl_3)OCH(CCl_3)NHCOR$$

Amides have been successfully reduced to primary amines with hydrogen in the presence of a copper-chromium oxide catalyst. The reduction has been carried out by the use of dioxane as a solvent. Secondary amines are formed as the principal byproduct in this reaction.[119]

Urethanes combine with the carbonyl group of aldehydes, giving compounds of the type $CH_3CH(NHCOOC_2H_5)_2$.[214] With chloral, urethane yields chloralurethane, $Cl_3CCH(OH)NHCOOC_2H_5$.[215] Treated with an equivalent of sodium hydroxide and acetic anhydride, this gives anhydrochloralurethane,

$$C_2H_5OCONHCH(CCl_3)OCH(CCl_3)NHCOOC_2H_5$$

Anhydrochloralurethane reacting with the sodio derivative of urethane gives chloraldiurethane, $Cl_3CCH(NHCOOC_2H_5)_2$. Urethane reacts also with the carbonyl group of aldehyde and keto acids.[216]

Hofmann's Reaction

Amides of monobasic acids may be converted to amines containing one less carbon atom by the action of bromine and potassium hydroxide. The amide is first brominated; the bromide changes to an unstable intermediate which rapidly isomerizes to a bromoimide; this last undergoes a transformation similar to the Beckman rearrangement to form an isocyanate, which is finally hydrolyzed in a normal manner to an alkylamine.[120] These changes may be represented schematically as follows:

$$RCONH_2 \rightarrow RCONHBr \rightarrow RC(OH)=NBr$$
$$\rightarrow RN=C(Br)OH \rightarrow HBr + RN=CO$$
$$\rightarrow RNH_2 + CO_2$$

The reaction may be carried out in steps in the following manner. The amide is mixed with a molecular equivalent of bromine and an aqueous solution of potassium hydroxide is added gradually until the color of bromine disappears and the liquid assumes a light yellow color. An excess of caustic is then added and the liquid is subjected to distillation, absorbing the amine which distills over in hydrochloric acid. No secondary or tertiary amines are formed in the reaction, but a considerable quantity of ammonia is formed and is absorbed in the hydrochloric acid together with the amine. The separation of the amine hydrochloride from the ammonium hydrochloride may be effected by evaporating down the hydrochloric acid solution, and extracting the amine hydrochloride with alcohol leaving behind the ammonium chloride.

In the first stage of the reaction a monobromo amide, RCONHBr, is formed. Acetamide monobromide may be isolated as the hydrate, $CH_3CONHBr.H_2O$, by adding a 50% aqueous solution of potassium hydroxide drop by drop, to a mixture of equimolecular amounts of acetamide and bromine until the bromine color is discharged, whereupon the bromo amide separates in the crystalline form. The *aci*-form of the bromide, present as the potassium salt, $RC(OK)=NBr$, gives rise to the unstable intermediate $RN=CBrOK$, and this yields an alkyl carbonate, $RN=C(OK)_2$, by reaction with another molecule of caustic. Hydrolysis of the alkyl carbonate yields the amine RNH_2. If no excess of alkali is used, the unstable intermediate gives rise to an isocyanate:

$$RN=CBrONa \rightarrow RN=CO + NaBr$$

This last transformation takes place very readily in the presence of silver carbonate.

The formation of an isocyanate from the bromo amide may also be explained on the assumption that an unstable radical with a univalent nitrogen is first formed and immediately changes to the isocyanate:

$$CH_3CONHBr \rightarrow HBr + CH_3CON \rightarrow CH_3N = CO$$

There is ample evidence that the group R does not become free during its migration from carbon to nitrogen. For example, optical activity, if originally present in the group, is fully preserved,[121] and the group does not undergo the Walden inversion when the possibility of such inversion exists.

The rate determining step in the Hofmann rearrangement would appear to be the release of the halide ion from the halo amide.[122]

If a mixture of molecular amounts of acetamide and acetomonobromide is heated with alkalies, the isocyanate formed reacts instantaneously with the amide, forming acetylmethylurea:

$$CH_3N = CO + H_2NCOCH_3 \rightarrow CH_3NHCONHCOCH_3$$

Compounds of this type result directly from amides when a mixture of two moles of amide and one of bromine is treated with alkalies.[123] It should be noted that the formation of isocyanates does not account for all the compounds obtained as byproducts in the Hofmann reaction.[124]

The usual procedure employed in carrying out the Hofmann reaction is as follows: One molecular equivalent of finely ground amide is added with stirring to a mixture of one to two molecular equivalents of bromine and six molecular equivalents of 10% aqueous sodium hydroxide solution cooled to 0°. The resulting solution is heated to 70-80° for 15 to 20 minutes and the amine formed is subsequently distilled with steam and collected in a slight excess of dilute hydrochloric acid. The amine is isolated in the form of the hydrochloride by evaporating down the receiver solution and is washed with ether. Amines which are not volatile with steam are isolated from the reaction mixture by extraction with ether and precipitation as the hydrochloride from the ethereal solution by passage of dry hydrogen chloride. Amines which separate as solids may be isolated by filtration and purified by crystallization from an appropriate solvent.

The bromine is used in 10 to 20% excess. The use of a greater excess will generally result in a lowered yield unless the amine formed is stable toward alkali hypobromite. Freshly prepared hypobromite solutions should be used in the reaction, since a marked decrease in the activity of the solution occurs on standing even in the dark.[125]

The use of sodium hypochlorite offers some advantages; in particular the reaction with hypochlorite proceeds at a lower temperature and results in many cases in a better yield of amine.

The Hofmann reaction gives good yields of the amine with the lower aliphatic amides up to caproic amide. The higher amides give increasingly larger quantities of the corresponding nitrile with increasing molecular weight. The formation of nitriles may be explained on the assumption that a more extensive reaction with bromine takes place:[126]

$$RCH_2NH_2 + 2Br_2 \rightarrow RCN + 4HBr$$

The yield of amine from higher amides may be improved sometimes by dissolving the amide in an alkaline solution of potassium hypobromite and conducting superheated steam through the solution.[127]

When the monobrom or monochlor amides of higher molecular weight are treated with sodium methoxide, methoxy derivatives are formed which, on treatment with acid, yield urethanes:[128]

$$BrN = C(R)ONa \rightarrow RN = C(ONa)Br \xrightarrow{NaOCH_3} RN = C(ONa)OCH_3$$

$$\xrightarrow{HCl} CH_3OCONHR$$

The urethanes may be hydrolyzed giving the amine in good yield. Methyl alcoholic alkali may also be used in this reaction instead of sodium methoxide.[129] This offers an effective method for the conversion of the higher amides to amines with one carbon less.

Hypoiodites do not give the Hofmann reaction but this type of transformation is induced by the use of iodoso compounds $RI = O$.[130]

Aldehydes are obtained when aqueous sodium hypochlorite reacts with amides of α-hydroxy acids:[132]

$$RCH(OH)CONH_2 \rightarrow RCH(OH)NH_2 \rightarrow RCHO + NH_3$$

Amides of α, β-unsaturated acids cannot, in general, be successfully subjected to the Hofmann transformation.[131] These amides, subjected to the conditions of the Hofmann reaction, yield aldehydes. They give urethanes in satisfactory yield when treated with methanolic sodium hypochlorite,[133] and hydrolysis of these urethanes also leads to the formation of aldehydes. Poor yields of amine are obtained from β, γ- and γ,δ-unsaturated amides.[134]

α, β-Acetylenic amides, subjected to the conditions of the Hofmann reaction, yield nitriles:[135]

$$RC \equiv CCONH_2 \rightarrow [RC \equiv CNH_2] \rightarrow RCH_2CN$$

Diamides of adipic acid and its higher homologs are converted to diamines.[136]

Succinamide is converted to dihydrouracil, $\overline{COCH_2CH_2NHCONH}$; β-alanine is formed when an excess of alkali is used and the reaction is carried out at a higher temperature. Maleic amide is converted to uracil.[137] Acid glutaramide and its alkylated derivatives are transformed by the Hofmann degradation into pyrolidones

$$R_1R_2\overline{CCH_2CH_2CONHCH_2}$$

The transformation is brought about by adding the salt of the acid glutaramide to a cold solution of potassium hypobromite and heating the mixture slowly to 70 to 75°. The yields of pyrrolidone vary between 20 and 46%. Alicyclic amido acids are readily converted to aminoacids.

Arylaliphatic amides are converted to amines, unless they contain a nuclear hydroxyl, in which case low yields may result due to the halogenation of the ring.[138] Halogenation may be reduced to a minimum by using hypochlorite solution and an excess of alkali.[139]

The Hofmann reaction is applicable to few aromatic amides. With these compounds hydrolysis may occur prior to rearrangement to such an extent that the yield of amine may be seriously lowered. Amides with a substituent which withdraws electrons from the CO-N linkage are particularly susceptible to hydrolysis. A high reaction temperature, in the range 90 to 100°, reduces interference due to hydrolysis to negligible proportions.[122] Methyl, methoxy and other similar groups in the *meta* and *para* positions facilitate, while strongly negative substituents, such as NO_2, CN, etc. retard rearrangement. The reaction has been successfully applied to phthalimide, which gives anthranilic acid:[140]

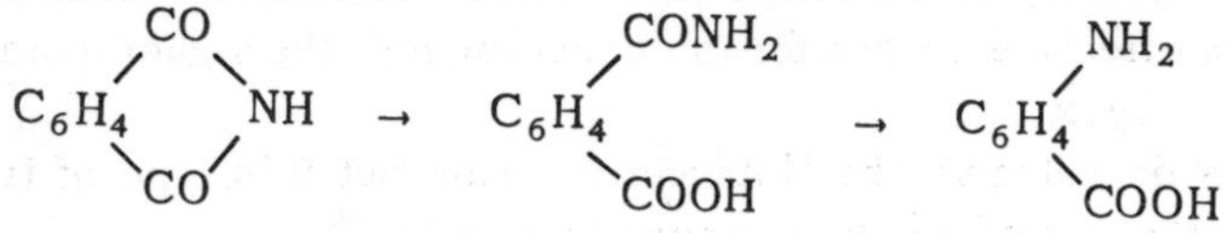

4-Nitrophthalimide,

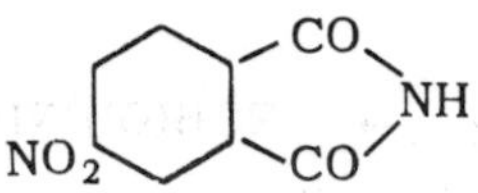

gives 4-nitroanthranilic acid,

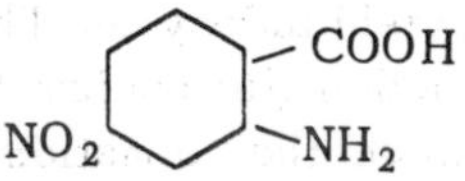

in 70% yield; 3-nitrophthalimide gives 6-nitroanthranilic acid in 80% yield, while 3,4-dimethoxyphthalimide gives a 35% yield of 3,4-dimethoxyanthranilic acid.[141]

The Hofmann reaction has been applied to benzoylbenzoic amide, which gives aminobenzophenone.[142] The reaction has been extended to amines of pyridine carboxylic acids.[143]

The *Weermann degradation*[213] is a modification of the Hofmann degradation applied to α-hydroxy and α-alkoxy amides. The first stage of the reaction is the formation of an isocyanate:

$$RCH(OR')CONH_2 \rightarrow RCH(OR')N=C=O$$

The subsequent reaction leads to the formation of an aldehyde and cyanate if R′ is hydrogen, and to an aldehyde, carbon dioxide, ammonia and an alcohol if R′ is an alkyl group:

$$RCH(OH)N=C=O \xrightarrow{NaOH} RCHO + NaOCN + H_2O$$

$$RCH(OR')N=C=O \xrightarrow{H_2O + NaOH} RCHO + CO_2 + NH_3 + R'OH$$

Polypeptides[144]

Polypeptides are long chain compounds consisting of a number of hydrocarbon groups attached on the one hand to an amino group and on the other to a carbonyl group; the amino group is in turn attached to the carbonyl of the succeeding unit. The simplest possible chain of this type is

$$HOCOCH_2NH[COCH_2NH]_nCOCH_2NH_2$$

Polypeptides may be prepared through the reaction of α-chloro acyl chlorides with amino acids, followed by the conversion of the resulting α-chloro amide to the corresponding amine by reaction with ammonia:

$$ClCH_2COCl + H_2NCH_2COOH \rightarrow HCl + ClCH_2CONHCH_2COOH$$

$$\xrightarrow{NH_3} H_2NCH_2CONHCH_2COOH$$

The chain can be lengthened by repetition of the reaction with the resulting dipeptide.[145] The method is applicable only to simple amino acids.

Another method which makes possible the successive addition of the units of the peptide chain utilizes the reaction of an acid azide with an amino acid:

$$C_6H_5CONHCH_2CON_3 + H_2NCH_2COONa + NaOH$$

$$\rightarrow C_6H_5CONHCH_2CONHCH_2COONa + NaN_3$$

The azide may be prepared from the ester of the acid by conversion, first to the hydrazide by reaction with hydrazine, then to the azide by treatment of the hydrazide with nitrous acid. Conversion of the new acid to its azide and coupling of this with an amino acid increases the chain length by an additional peptide unit. The operation may be repeated only a limited number of times, however.[146]

Direct conversion of a carboxylic acid containing a primary amino group to an acid chloride cannot be carried out without attack upon the amino group. The amino group in such compounds may be protected by conversion to a carbamino group by reaction with chlorocarbonic ester:

$$C_2H_5OCOCl + H_2NCH_2COOH \rightarrow C_2H_5OCONHCH_2COOH + HCl$$

The resulting ethylcarbamino acid may be converted to the corresponding chloride without difficulty. The chloride may be coupled with an amino acid, but since the carbethoxy group cannot be removed without extensive hydrolysis of the molecule, further lengthening of the resulting chain is not possible. The method is of value, however, when used in conjunction with other methods of synthesis of polypeptides.

Benzylcarbamino groups may be converted to amino groups by catalytic reduction.[246] It is, therefore, possible to prepare long chain polypeptides by coupling an amino acid with a benzylcarbamino acid chloride, converting the resulting acid to a chloride or anhydride, and causing this to react with an amino acid. The resulting chain may be further lengthened by freeing the amino group and coupling with a second molecule of benzylcarbamino acid chloride or anhydride.[247] The method may be illustrated by the following series of reactions:

$$2HOCOCH_2CH_2CH(COOH)NH_2 + 2C_6H_5CH_2OCOCl + MgO$$

$$2HOCOCH_2CH_2CH(COOH)NHCOOCH_2C_6H_5 + MgCl_2 + H_2O$$

$$HOCOCH_2CH_2CH(COOH)NHOCOCH_2C_6H_5 + (CH_3CO)_2O \rightarrow$$

$$OCOCH_2CH_2CH(CO)NHCOOCH_2C_6H_5 + 2CH_3COOH$$

$$OCOCH_2CH_2CH(CO)NHCOOCH_2C_6H_5 + H_2NCH(COOC_2H_5)CH_2CH_2COOC_2H_5$$

$$\rightarrow HOCOCH_2CH_2CH(NHCOOCH_2C_6H_5)CONHCH(COOC_2H_5)CH_2CH_2COOC_2H_5$$

$$\xrightarrow{\text{reduction}} HOCOCH_2CH_2CH(NH_2)CONHCH(COOC_2H_5)CH_2CH_2COOC_2H_5$$

Catalytic removal of the carbobenzoxy group is not applicable to cystine peptides, but removal may be effected by reduction with metallic sodium in liquid ammonia,[248] or with phosphonium iodide.[249]

Blocking of one amino group in diamino acids, such as lysine, may be brought about by converting the dibenzylcarbamino acid to the chloride and heating the latter.

The method has been employed in a number of important peptide syntheses. It has been improved by using *p*-bromobenzyl chloroformate in place of benzyl chloroformate.[250]

A modification of the method which does not involve the preparation of either the chloride or ester of the carbobenzylamino acid depends on the reaction of the mixed anhydride of this acid with sulfuric acid,

$$C_6H_5CH_2OCONHCHRCOOSO_3H,$$

with an amino acid or peptide in aqueous solution at pH 9:[251]

$$C_6H_5CH_2OCONHCHRCOOSO_3H + R'NH_2 \rightarrow$$

$$C_6H_5CH_2OCONHCHRCONHR' + H_2SO_4$$

The mixed anhydride is formed in less than one minute at 0° by the action of the dimethylformamide-sulfur trioxide complex on the carbobenzylamino acid:

$$C_6H_5CH_2OCONHCHRCOOH + (CH_3)_2NCHOSO_3 \rightarrow$$

$$C_6H_5CH_2OCONHCHRCOOSO_3H + (CH_3)_2NCHO$$

Mixed anhydrides of carbobenzylamino acids with the half ethyl ester of carbonic acid, $C_6H_5CH_2OCONHCHRCOOCOOC_2H_5$, have been used successfully for the preparation of peptides.[252] Anhydrides of carbobenzylamino acids with diethyl phosphite and diethyl arsenite,

$$C_6H_5CH_2OCONHCHRCOOP(OC_2H_5)_2$$

and

$$C_6H_5CH_2OCONHCHRCOOAs(OC_2H_5)_2,$$

have also been used for the purpose.[253]

Phthalic and phenylthioformyl groups have also been used for the protection of amino groups in peptide synthesis.[254] The phthalic group is introduced by treating the amino acid with phthalic anhydride:

$$H_2NCHR'COOH + C_6H_4 \underset{CO}{\overset{CO}{\diagup\!\!\!\diagdown}} O \xrightarrow[\to]{H_2O} +C_6H_4 \underset{CO}{\overset{CO}{\diagup\!\!\!\diagdown}} NCHRCOOH \xrightarrow{PCl_5}$$

$$C_6H_4 \underset{CO}{\overset{CO}{\diagup\!\!\!\diagdown}} NCHRCOCl \xrightarrow[MgO]{H_2NCHR'COOH} C_6H_4 \underset{CO}{\overset{CO}{\diagup\!\!\!\diagdown}} NCHRCONHCHR'COOH$$

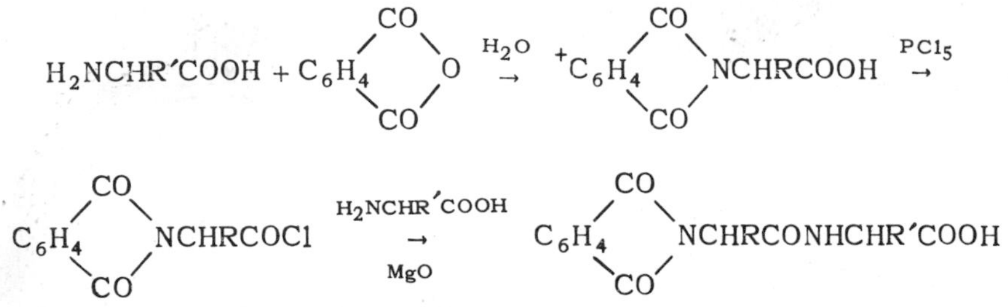

The phthalic group is removed from the final product by treatment with hydrazine:

$$C_6H_4 \underset{CO}{\overset{CO}{\diagup\!\!\!\diagdown}} NCHR\text{-}\cdots + H_2NNH_2 \to C_6H_4 \underset{CO-NH}{\overset{CO-NH}{\diagup\!\!\!\diagdown}} + H_2NCHR\text{-}\cdots$$

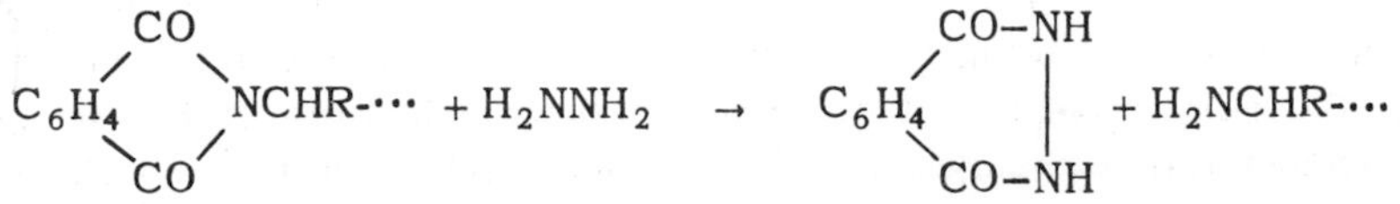

The N-phenylthioformyl derivative of the amino acid is made by the action of phenylthiocarbonyl chloride, C_6H_5SCOCl, on the acid. Removal of the phenylthioformyl group is accomplished by heating with lead acetate in 20% ethanol solution, or with cold tenth normal caustic in the presence of lead hydroxide or carbonate.

The vicinal carboxyl group in N-carbobenzoxydicarboxylic acid may be protected by partial esterification of the anhydride:[255]

$$C_6H_5CH_2OCONHCHCHCO \underset{CH_2CO}{\diagdown\!\!\!\diagup} O + C_2H_5OH \to C_6H_5CH_2OCONHCHCOOC_2H_5 \atop CH_2COOH$$

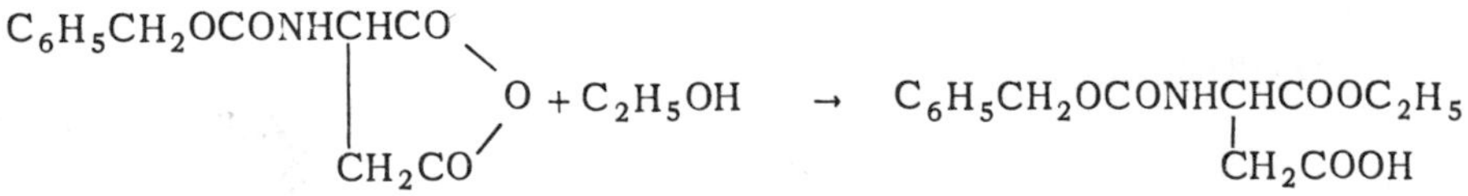

Amino groups may be protected by conversion to p-toluenesulfonamido group. Removal of the sulfonic group is brought about by reductive fission with sodium and liquid ammonia. This method is of considerable importance since optically active amino acids are not racemized by the treatment.[256]

Mixed anhydrides of N-acylated amino acids with oleic or benzoic acids, reacting with esters of amino acids in indifferent media, give peptides.[257] The reaction may also be carried out by shaking the anhydride in ethereal solution with the ester dissolved in aqueous bicarbonate.

Peptides have been synthesized by use of the internal N-carboxylic anhydrides of amino acids.[258] The reaction is carried out in the presence of triethylamine and yields the triethylamine salt of the peptide N-carboxylic acid. The free peptide is obtained on heating the latter:

$$HNCH(R)COOCO + H_2NCH(R')COOC_2H_5 + (C_2H_5)_3N \to$$
$$(C_2H_5)_3N \cdot HOCONHCH(R)CONHCHR'COOC_2H_5 \to$$
$$H_2NCH(R)CONHCHR'COOC_2H_5 + CO_2 + (C_2H_5)_3N$$

A wide variety of di-, tri- and pentapeptides have been prepared by this method.

Acylamino acids condense with amino esters in the presence of phosphorus trichloride to give acylated dipeptide esters.[259] The reaction apparently proceeds with the intermediate formation of a phosphorazo compound, which reacts with the amino acid ester to form the peptide:

$$2C_2H_5OCOCHRNH_2 + PCl_3 \quad \rightarrow \quad 3HCl + \begin{array}{c} C_2H_5OCOCHRN \\ \diagdown \\ \qquad\qquad P \\ \diagup \\ C_2H_5OCOCHRNH \end{array}$$

$$\overset{2CH_3CONHCHR'COOH}{\rightarrow} \quad 2C_2H_5OCOCHRNHCOCHR'NHCOCH_3 + PHO_2$$

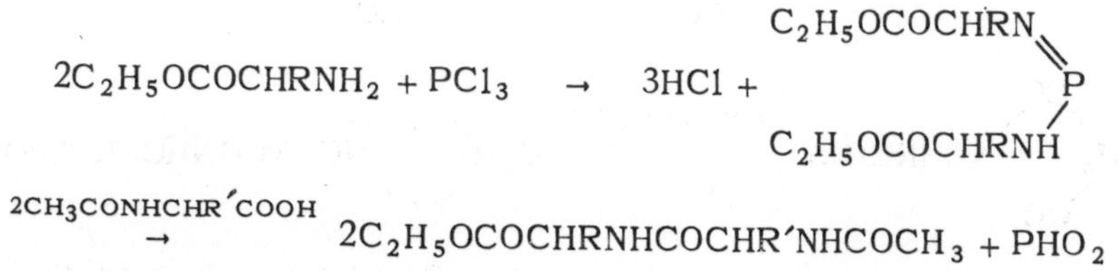

Macromolecular polypeptides have been made from dicarboxylic acids via the carboxyamic acid by making use of the *Lossen rearrangement*.[260] The process involves the polymerization of an inner carboxy anhydride of the amino acid formed through the rearrangement of the thiocyanate resulting by the Lossen rearrangement:

$$\begin{array}{c} COOH \\ \diagup \\ RCH \\ \diagdown \\ COOC_2H_5 \end{array} + H_2NOH \rightarrow C_2H_5OH + \begin{array}{c} COOH \\ \diagup \\ RCH \\ \diagdown \\ CONHOH \end{array} \overset{C_6H_5COCl}{\rightarrow}$$

$$\begin{array}{c} COOH \\ \diagup \\ RCH \\ \diagdown \\ CONHOCOC_6H_5 \end{array} \overset{\text{heated in}}{\underset{\text{benzene or water}}{\rightarrow}} C_6H_5COOH + \begin{array}{c} COOH \\ \diagup \\ RCH \\ \diagdown \\ NCO \end{array} \rightarrow$$

$$\begin{array}{c} CO-O \\ \diagup \quad | \\ RCH \quad | \\ \diagdown \quad | \\ NH-CO \end{array} \quad ; \quad \begin{array}{c} CO-O \\ \diagup \quad | \\ nRCH \quad | \\ \diagdown \quad | \\ NHCO \end{array} \rightarrow (-NHCHRCO-)_n + NCO_2$$

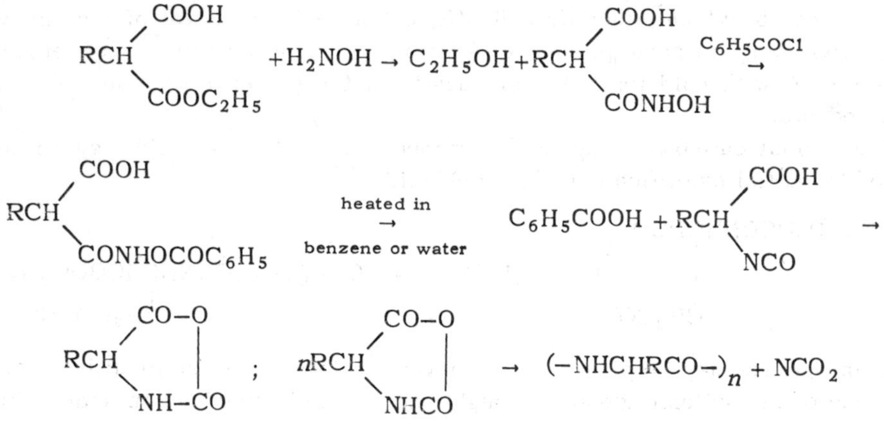

Azlactones react vigorously with amines, the process resulting in rupture of the azlactone ring and coupling of the amino group with a carboxyl group.[261] The compound resulting from the reaction with an amino acid is an N-acylated Δ-α,β-peptide, which gives a peptide on catalytic hydrogenation followed by removal of the acyl radical attached to the nitrogen atom:

$$C_6H_5CH = C \underset{N=C(CH_3)-O}{\overset{\qquad}{\text{------------}}} CO + \overset{COOH}{\underset{|}{H_2NCHCH_2CH_2COOH}} \rightarrow$$

$$\begin{array}{c} COOH \\ | \\ C_6H_5CH = CCONHCHCH_2CH_2COOH \\ | \\ NHCOCH_3 \end{array} \overset{H_2}{\rightarrow} \begin{array}{c} COOH \\ | \\ C_6H_5CH_2CHCONHCHCH_2CH_2COOH \\ | \\ NHCOCH_3 \end{array}$$

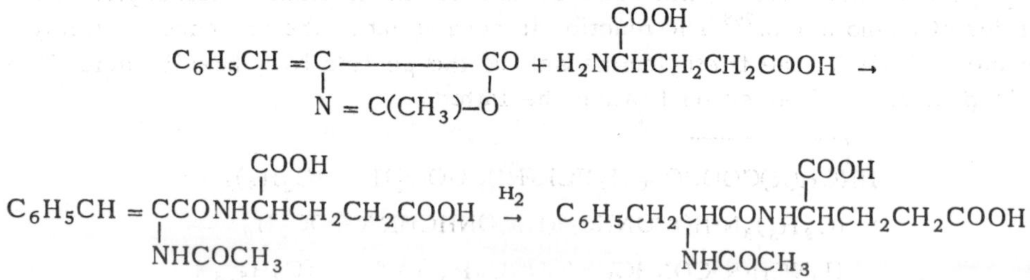

$$\xrightarrow{HCl} C_6H_5CH_2\underset{\displaystyle NH_2}{\underset{|}{C}}HCONH\overset{\displaystyle COOH}{\overset{|}{C}}HCH_2CH_2COOH$$

Dipeptides may be prepared from diketopiperazines by hydrolytic cleavage of the ring:[146]

$$\overline{HNCH_2CONHCH_2CO} + H_2O \rightarrow H_2NCH_2CONHCH_2COOH$$

Diketopiperazines are readily obtained from ∝-chloracetylamino esters by reaction with ammonia:

$$ClCH_2CONHCH_2COOC_2H_5 + 2NH_3 \rightarrow$$

$$\overline{NHCH_2CONHCH_2CO} + NH_4Cl + C_2H_5OH$$

Diketopiperazines are also formed on heating esters of α-amino acids.

Esters of α,β-diamino and ϵ-amino acids give dipeptide esters when they are heated.[262] Higher tripeptide esters are also capable of condensing in this manner. Thus, the tripeptide ester of glycine yields the hexapeptide when heated. This method is of limited applicability, and is restricted to tripeptides of simple monoamino monocarboxylic acids.

Peptides have been prepared by adding tetraethylpyrophosphate to a solution of an acylamino acid and an amino acid in diethyl phosphite:[263]

$$RCONHCHR'COOH + H_2NCHR''COOC_2H_5 \xrightarrow{(C_2H_5O)_2PO}$$

$$RCONHCHR'CONHCHR''COOC_2H_5 + H_2O$$

The reaction of phosphorazo compounds with ester groups leads to the formation of an amide linkage and has been employed for the synthesis of polypeptides:[285]

$$C_2H_5OCOCH(R)N = PNHCH(R)COOC_2H_5 + 2R\underset{\displaystyle NHCOCH_3}{\underset{|}{C}}HCOOH$$

$$\rightarrow 2R\underset{\displaystyle NHCOCH_3}{\underset{|}{C}}HCONHCH(R)COOC_2H_5 + \frac{1}{x}(HPO_2)_x$$

The phosphorazo compound is obtained through the reaction of an amine with phosphorus trichloride:

$$5C_2H_5OCH(R)NH_2 + PCl_3 \rightarrow$$

$$C_2H_5OCH(R)N = PNHCH(R)OC_2H_5 + 3C_2H_5OCH(R)NH_2.HCl$$

Polypeptides are generally soluble in water, but are almost insoluble in alcohol. Many polypeptides in the amorphous condition dissolve in alcohol, but precipitate out in the crystalline form on standing. The higher polypeptides give the biuret reaction. A violet color appears when a dilute aqueous solution of copper sulfate is added to a strongly alkaline solution of a peptide. Polypeptides are amphoteric in character and yield salts with both acids and bases. Acid salts of very high molecular polypeptides are slightly soluble in water. Polypeptides are precipitated by tannin solution. They are degraded into simple amino acids when boiled for about five hours with concentrated hydrochloric acid.

The free amino end group in peptides may be determined with the aid of fluorodinitrobenzene.

Degradation of Peptides

When a dipeptide is subjected to the action of hypobromous acid and the resulting product is hydrolyzed, a breakdown of the molecule takes place with the formation of a nitrile:[147]

$$R_1CH(NH_2)CONHCH(R_2)COOH + 2HOBr$$

$$\rightarrow 2H_2O + HBr + R_1C(:NBr)CONHCH(R_2)COOH$$

$$\xrightarrow{H_2O} R_1CN + HOCONHCH(R_2)COOH + HBr$$

Ring compounds are obtained from tri- and tetrapeptides in addition to the nitrile:

$$RCH(NH_2)CONHCH(R_2)CONHCH(R_3)COOH$$

$$\rightarrow R_1CN + \overline{CONHCH(R_2)CON}CH(R_3)COOH$$

$$\xrightarrow{HOBr} \overline{CON = C(R_2)CON}CH(R_3)COOH$$

$$R_1CH(NH_2)CONHCH(R_2)CONHCH(R_3)CONHCH(R_4)COOH$$

$$\rightarrow R_1CN + \overline{COC(R_2) = NCON}CH(R_3)CONHCH(R_4)COOH$$

The degradation is carried out at 0° by use of 0.4*N* sodium hypobromite containing 0.1*N* excess caustic, generally allowing 20 minutes for the reaction. The excess hypobromite is destroyed with hydrogen peroxide, neutral reaction products are extracted with ether, the aqueous solution is made acid to Congo red and evaporated to dryness under vacuum to recover the products.

1,2,4-Fluorodinitrobenzene (FDNB) has been employed for the determination of the constituting amino acids of a peptide. The protein is treated with 1,2,4-fluorodinitrobenzene and subsequently submitted to complete hydrolysis. Thereafter the N-2,4-dinitrophenyl derivatives of the amino acids are chromatically separated and quantitatively estimated. The method has been applied to the determination of the sequence of amino acids which occupy positions near the terminal acid residues. For this purpose the protein, after treatment with fluorodinitrobenzene, is submitted to partial hydrolysis leading to the liberation of a series of N-2,4-dinitrophenyl peptides. These differ from the other products of hydrolysis in that they are acids which can be extracted from acid solution by organic solvents, and can thus be obtained free from other unsubstituted peptides. The individual compounds in the mixture can be separated chromatographically and identified. From the nature of N-2,4-dinitrophenyl peptides thus isolated the order of amino acid residues in proximity of the α-amino groups in the peptide in question may be determined. [286]

Especially labile peptide bonds may be split during the preparation of DNP-proteins under the usual conditions. [288] The destruction of DNP-amino acids which occurs on hydrolysis of DNP-proteins can be prevented by treating the protein first with xanthydrol. [289]

The terminal group in peptides may be removed by causing the peptide to react with carbon disulfide in the presence of barium hydroxide to obtain the dithiocarbamate, which on acidification yields a thiazolidone with the liberation of the terminal group: [287]

$$\underset{\underset{NH_2}{|}}{RCHCONHR'} + CS_2 \;\rightarrow\; \underset{\underset{NHCSSH}{|}}{RCHCONHR'} \;\rightarrow\; \underset{\underset{NH\quad S}{|\qquad|}}{RCH - CO} + R'NH_2$$
$$\underset{CS}{\diagdown\diagup}$$

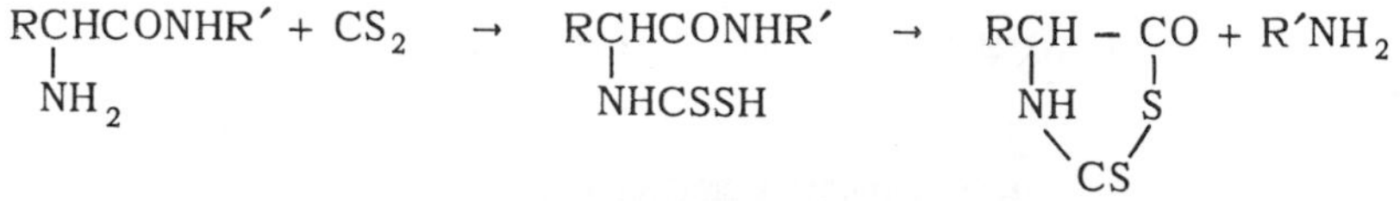

An elegant method of stepwise degradation has been developed which involves the interaction of the peptide with phenyl isothiocyanate and treatment of the resulting N-phenylthiocarbamyl derivative with hydrochloric acid in nitromethane. The N-terminal residue is cleaved by this treatment as a thiohydantoin, which can be hydrolyzed and identified by paper chromatography. The process can be repeated to identify the next residue. [290]

An aspartic acid residue in a protein is released preferentially on boiling with a weak acid, such as acetic or oxalic acid, before any other substance responding to the ninhydrin reaction is released. [291]

Labeled iodine-131 has been employed for the estimation of the amino end grouping in proteins. [264] The protein is made to react with p-iodobenzensulfonyl chloride containing labeled iodine-131. Hydrolysis of the sulfonyl derivative gives an iodosulfonated amino end fragment which can be readily separated and estimated.

The free amino groups of polypeptides can be reductively methylated with formaldehyde and the dimethylamino acid liberated from the terminal group on hydrolysis can be identified by paper chromatography. [292]

N-Thiocarbethoxy derivatives of peptides, subjected to the action of hydrogen chloride and nitromethane, are cleaved into a thiazolid-2,5-dione and the next lower peptide: [265]

$$C_2H_5OCSNHCHRCONHCHR'CO\ldots \quad \overset{HCl + CH_3NO_2}{\rightarrow}$$

$$\underset{\underset{S}{\diagdown\diagup}}{\underset{CO\quad CO}{\underset{|\qquad|}{NH - CHR}}} + HCl.H_2NCHR'CO\ldots + C_2H_5Cl$$

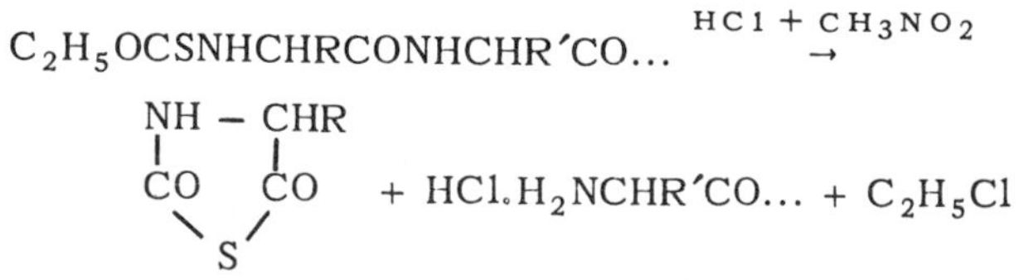

Cleavage of an amino acid group in a peptide may be brought about by reaction with ammonium thiocyanate and acetic anhydride; hydrolysis of the hydantoin derivative formed gives a fragment of peptide possessing a free carboxyl group: [266]

$$\text{---NHCHRCONHCHR'COOH} \xrightarrow{\text{NH}_4\text{SCN}} \text{...NHCHRCON} \begin{array}{c} \text{R'CH} - \text{CO} \\ | \qquad | \\ \text{NH} \\ \diagdown_{\text{CS}}\diagup \end{array}$$

$$\xrightarrow{\text{H}_2\text{O}} \text{-NHCHRCOOH} + \begin{array}{c} \text{R'CH} - \text{CO} \\ | \qquad | \\ \text{NH} \quad \text{NH} \\ \diagdown_{\text{CS}}\diagup \end{array}$$

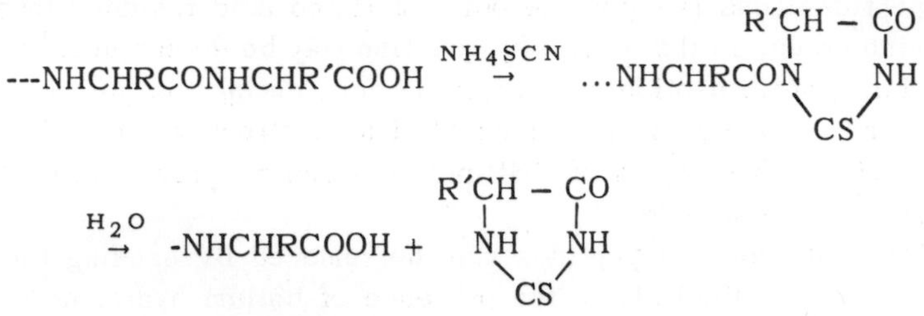

It is possible to obtain high yields of thiohydantoin from simple N-acyl peptides and diphenyl phosphorisothiocyanatidate at room temperature: [293]

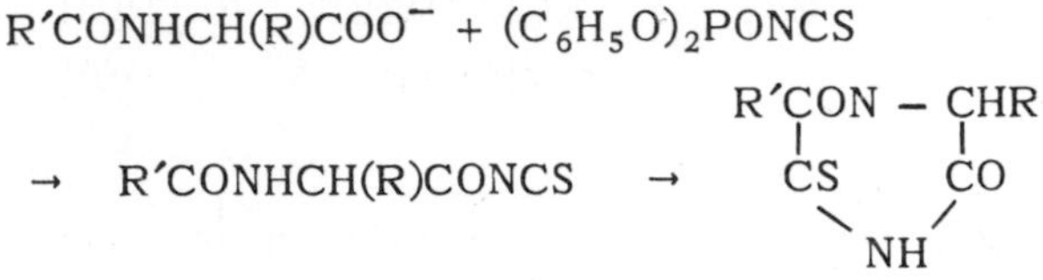

$$\text{R'CONHCH(R)COO}^- + (\text{C}_6\text{H}_5\text{O})_2\text{PONCS}$$

$$\rightarrow \ \text{R'CONHCH(R)CONCS} \ \rightarrow \ \begin{array}{c} \text{R'CON} - \text{CHR} \\ | \qquad | \\ \text{CS} \qquad \text{CO} \\ \diagdown_{\text{NH}}\diagup \end{array}$$

Amide and Imide Chlorides

Amide and imide chlorides, RCCl_2NH_2 and $\text{RCCl} = \text{NH}$, are obtained as unstable intermediates in the reaction of phosphorus pentachloride with an amide:

$$\text{RCONH}_2 \xrightarrow{\text{PCl}_5} \text{RCCl}_2\text{NH}_2 \ \rightarrow \ \text{RCCl} = \text{NH}$$

Imide chlorides, which result from amide chloride by loss of a molecule of hydrogen chloride, in turn, change to nitriles by the loss of a further molecule of this acid.

Imide chlorides may be prepared from nitriles by the addition of hydrogen chloride. Bromoimides and iodoimides are formed similarly by the addition of hydrobromic or hydriodic acid, the reaction proceeding more readily with these acids than with hydrogen chloride. [148]

The instability of imide chlorides is most marked when one or more hydrogen atoms are attached to the α-carbon atom. v. Braun ascribes the structure $\text{RCH} = \text{CClNHR}'$ and $\text{RR''C} = \text{CClNHR}'$ to such compounds. The stability of imide chlorides improves on replacing the hydrogen joined to the nitrogen atom with an alkyl group. The stability of imide chlorides increases also in proportion to the degree of negativity, and the number of negative groups attached to the carbon atom. For example, amides,

$$\text{Cl}_2\text{CHCCl} = \text{NR}$$

are more stable than $\text{ClCH}_2\text{CCl} = \text{NR}$ and these are more stable than $\text{CH}_3\text{CCl} = \text{NR}$. Negative groups attached to the nitrogen of the chlorimide also enhance the stability of the compound.

Thioamides and Selenoamides

Thioamides can be prepared by replacing the oxygen in amides with sulfur by the action of phosphorus pentasulfide. [267] This method fails sometimes, especially when applied to peptides.[268] S-Alkoxythiazoles are formed from acylamido esters when the reaction is carried out under drastic conditions.[269]

Thioformamides are formed through the reaction of potassium dithioformate with an amine:[270]

$$RNH_2 + HCSSK \rightarrow RNHCHS + KHS$$

The reaction proceeds under mild conditions. Other dithio acid salts also undergo the reaction, and the method has been employed for the preparation of thioacylamino acids.[271]

$$RCSSNa + H_2NCHR'COOH \rightarrow RCSNHCHR'COONa + H_2S$$

Amino acids may be thiobenzoylated by reaction with carboxymethyl dithiobenzoate in the presence of caustic:[272]

$$C_6H_5CSSCH_2COOH + H_2NCH_2R \rightarrow C_6H_5CSNHCH_2R + HSCH_2COOH$$

These methods are of little value in the aliphatic series, because aliphatic dithio acids other than dithioformic acid cannot be prepared in good yield.[273]

Thioamides may also be obtained by the reaction of thio esters RCSOR with amines. The reaction is of wide applicability, since both aliphatic and aromatic thio esters may be prepared from imino ethers by the action of hydrogen sulfide.[274]

Thiobenzamides may be prepared by the action of thiobenzoyl chloride, C_6H_5CSCl, on amines. Thiobenzamino acids cannot be prepared by this method, however.[275] Thiobenzoyl chloride is obtained through the reaction of dithiobenzoic acid with oxalyl chloride or thionyl chloride.[276]

Thioamides are obtained by the addition of hydrogen sulfide to nitriles:[149]

$$RCN + H_2S \rightarrow RCSNH_2$$

Alkali metal acid sulfides catalyze the reaction, which proceeds with varying degrees of ease, depending on the character of the nitrile. Good yields of thioamides are obtained, for example, from β-naphthonitrile and benzyl cyanide in the course of 3 to 3½ hours, whereas poor yields of thio amides result from acetonitrile and propionitrile even on 36 hours' heating. The reaction is applicable to cyanhydrins, amino nitriles and their acylated derivatives.

The ease with which thio amides are formed in the aromatic series is markedly influenced by substituents in the aromatic ring. Methoxy and methyl groups in *p*-methoxy and *p*-methylbenzonitrile cause a substantial decrease in the reaction rate in comparison with benzonitrile; on the other hand halogens in the *para* and *meta* positions cause a marked increase in the reaction rate.[150]

The higher aliphatic amides may be prepared through the interaction of ammonium sulfide with the corresponding nitrile in a non-aqueous medium in an autoclave at 150 - 180°.[151]

Seleno amides $RCSeNH_2$ may be obtained through the reaction of hydrogen selenide with ammoniacal solutions of nitriles. The reaction proceeds poorly with the aliphatic nitriles, but takes place quite readily, as a rule, with aromatic nitriles and certain arylaliphatic nitriles.[152] Hydrogen selenide is readily oxidized by atmospheric oxygen and it is, therefore, necessary to carry out the reaction in the absence of air.

AMINO COMPOUNDS RELATED TO ACID AMIDES

Acid Hydrazides

Primary hydrazines may be obtained by the methods employed for the preparation of amides. One of the simplest methods consists in heating the hydrazine salt of the acid:

$$RCOONH_3NH_2 \rightarrow RCONHNH_2 + H_2O$$

Monacylhydrazides are obtained through the reaction of *esters* with hydrazine, *sym*-diacylhydrazides forming simultaneously.

The usual procedure is to treat the methyl or ethyl ester of the acid with hydrazine. For most purposes the commercially available 85% aqueous hydrazine hydrate is preferable to anhydrous hydrazine. The reaction often takes place spontaneously at room temperature with evolution of heat. The reaction proceeds with difficulty with some esters, and heating for several days or under pressure in a sealed tube is occasionally necessary to obtain a good yield. Partial decarboxylation may take place, however, when the reaction is carried out by heating in a sealed tube.

The formation of secondary hydrazides may be reduced to a minimum by dropping the ester into an excess of boiling hydrazine at such a rate that a second layer does not appear.

Aromatic halo compounds are generally unaffected by hydrazine, but halogen atoms activated by *ortho* or *para* nitro groups are replaced with hydrazine. Iodine attached to an aromatic nucleus is sometimes replaced with hydrazine; thus, ethyl *o*-iodobenzoate, reacting with hydrazine, gives the hydrazide

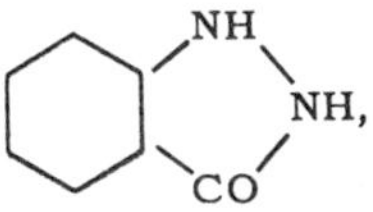

although ethyl *p*-iodobenzoate gives *p*-iodobenzhydrazide.[153] 3,5-Dinitrobenzhydrazide is formed in satisfactory yield from the corresponding ester; 3-nitro-5-aminobenzhydrazide results in 60% yield, when the ester is heated under reflux for 24 hours with a large excess of hydrazine.[154] Ethyl 2-nitro-4-aminobenzoate is obtained from ethyl 2,4-dinitrobenzoate.[155]

Diazoacetic ester reacts with hydrazine to form diazoacetic hydrazide.

Since esters of aromatic acids are much less reactive than those of aliphatic acids, it is often possible to form the hydrazide of an aliphatic group in a compound without affecting any aromatic acid groups which may also be present in the molecule.

Symmetrical diacyl hydrazides result when an excess of the ester is heated with hydrazine. These compounds may also be obtained through the reaction of acid anhydrides with primary hydrazides,[156] and from primary hydrazides and iodine:[157]

$$2RCONHNH_2 + 2I_2 \rightarrow RCONHNHCOR + 4HI + N_2$$

The reaction of hydrazine with *acid chlorides* often results in the formation of a large proportion of secondary hydrazides. The best procedure in carrying out the reaction is to add a well-cooled solution of the acid chloride in ether to a strongly cooled solution of hydrazine hydrate in alcohol with good stirring.[158] The hydrazine should be present in considerable excess. The final solution containing the reaction products may be freed of hydrazine hydrochloride by extraction with water.

Cyclic anhydrides of some dibasic acids can be converted directly to hydrazide acids. For example diphenic anhydride and 4-nitrodiphenic anhydride react with hydrazine to form hydrazide acids.

Primary hydrazides give sodium derivatives with one or two sodium atoms. They yield salts with one or two equivalents of acid. Nitrous acid converts them to azides:

$$RCONHNH_2 + HONO \rightarrow RCON_3 + 2\,H_2O$$

Sym-diacethydrazides heated with acetic anhydride give tri and tetracethydrazides.[159] Monoacyl hydrazides react with aldehydes to form condensation products similar to hydrazones.

Acid Azides

Acid azides, $RCON_3$, may be prepared by the action of nitrous acid on acid hydrazides, or through the interaction of an acid chloride with sodium azide:[160]

$$RCONHNH_2 + HONO \rightarrow RCON_3 + 2H_2O$$

$$RCOCl + NaN_3 \rightarrow RCON_3 + NaCl$$

The usual *procedure* employed in converting hydrazides to azides is as follows: The hydrazide is dissolved in a slight excess of dilute aqueous hydrochloric acid, the solution is covered with a layer of ether and cooled to 0 to 5°. A molecular equivalent of a concentrated sodium nitrite solution is then added with good stirring at such a rate that the temperature does not rise above 10°. Immediately after the addition of sodium nitrite, the ether layer is separated, washed with a little sodium bicarbonate solution and dried. The azide is generally used in ethereal solution.

Alcohol or acetic acid may be used as solvents instead of ether. An alkyl nitrate and dry hydrogen chloride in alcoholic solution may be employed as a source of nitrous acid.[161] Nitrogen trioxide has also been employed for the conversion of hydrazides to azides.[162] Acetic acid may be used in the pure form or mixed with water to a dilution not lower than 50%. The procedure consists in dissolving the hydrazide in acetic acid by the application of heat, then chilling the solution in order to cause the precipitation of the hydrazide in a finely crystalline form, finally adding cracked ice and the required quantity of sodium nitrite. The azide is usually obtained in the form of a crystalline precipitate; if it should fail to precipitate out, it may be thrown out of solution by the addition of water.

A mineral acid may be used in conjunction with acetic acid. The procedure followed in that case is to dissolve the hydrazide in a small volume of acetic acid and to add to the solution first the mineral acid, then the aqueous sodium nitrite. The azide precipitates out at once. A mixture of benzene and acetic acid has been used as a solvent.[163]

If acetic acid alone is employed, secondary hydrazides are more likely to form. Isoxazole-5-carbonyl hydrazide and citraconyl hydrazide yield secondary hydrazides in acetic acid, but give the corresponding azides when a mineral acid is used together with acetic acid. Hippuryl, aspartyl, glutaryl and N-nitrosodiacetyl hydrazides fail to react with sodium nitrite in acetic acid solution, but react to form the azides when a mineral acid is introduced into the solution.

If the hydrazide subjected to reaction is acid sensitive, the compound is mixed with the aqueous solution of sodium nitrite and the acid is gradually added to the mixture.[164] Azides containing in excess of 25% azide nitrogen should not be isolated in the pure form since they are apt to explode violently. Azides of high molecular weight can be safely isolated in the pure form.

Azides may be prepared from *acid chlorides* by stirring a solution of the chloride in a water-miscible organic solvent with a 25% aqueous solution of sodium azide, holding the temperature at or below room temperature. The solvents generally employed are acetone, methanol, ethanol, dioxane and acetic acid. Acetone is usually the preferred solvent. Upon completion of the reaction the azide may be precipitated out by the addition of water.

The reaction may also be carried out by mixing the acid chloride with dry sodium azide. This is the only practicable method for highly reactive chlorides, such as acetyl chloride, and for the preparation of very unstable azides. Many acid chlorides, including those of heterocyclic acids, do not react with dry sodium azide however. With some reactive chlorides, it is difficult to control the reaction. In such cases, the use of a diluent, such as benzene, nitrobenzene and other inert solvents is helpful. The reaction is applicable to half-ester acid chlorides.[165]

Monosubstituted carbonyl azides can be synthesized from isocyanates by reaction with hydrazoic acid:

$$RNCO + HN_3 \rightarrow RNHCON_3$$

The reaction of α, β-olefinic acid hydrazides with nitrous acid often leads to the formation of cyclic products rather than azides.[166] 1-Nitroso-5-phenyl-3-pyrazolone results, for example, from the reaction of cinnanyl hydrazide with nitrous acid:

$$C_6H_5CH = CHCONHNH_2 + HNO_2 \rightarrow \overline{C_6H_5CHCH_2CONHN}NO + H_2O$$

Fumaryl hydrazide yields fumaryl azide, however, on reaction with nitrous acid.[167] Other olefinic azides may be obtained readily through the reaction of sodium azide with olefinic acid chlorides whenever these are available.[168]

α, β-Acetylenic acid esters give pyrazolones with hydrazine:

$$CH_3C \equiv CCOOC_2H_5 + H_2NNH_2 \rightarrow CH_3\overline{C = NNH - COCH_2} + C_2H_5OH$$

Hydrazides are formed from acetylentic acid esters if the acetylenic bonds occupy other than the α, β-position.

Hydroxyl groups in a molecule may interfere with azide formation, although azides containing hydroxyl groups have been prepared. Hydrazides of acids containing a hydroxyl group in the γ-position or other lactone forming position, may, as a rule, be prepared from the corresponding lactones or esters, although lactones of secondary and tertiary hydroxyl groups show considerable resistance, some failing to react altogether.[169]

Amino groups, if present in the molecule of an acid hydrazide, are replaced by hydroxy groups on treatment with nitrous acid. Acylation of the amino group generally affords protection, and the azide may be prepared without difficulty. Acylation prior to conversion to hydrazide is not always practicable, since treatment with hydrazine hydrate may occasionally result in deacylation of the amino group. For example, ethyl 2,6-dibenzamidoisonicotinate gives 2,6-diaminoisonicotinyl hydrazide, and phthalylglycine gives glycyl hydrazide on treatment with hydrazine. Tertiary amino groups, including the nitrogen in the pyrrole ring,[170] are not affected by nitrous acid.

Halo acid hydrazides are conveniently prepared from halo acid halides by reaction with sodium azide.

Diazides may be prepared from dicarboxylic dihydrazides.[171] The formation of hydrazides from esters of disubstituted malonic esters becomes increasingly difficult with increase in the size of the substituents, diethylbis(mesitylmethyl)-malonate failing to react altogether. Succinyl azide may be obtained readily from succinyl chloride and sodium azide.[165]

Esters of phthalic acid reacting with hydrazine give the secondary hydrazide,

$$C_6H_5 \underset{\diagdown}{\overset{\diagup}{ \begin{array}{c} CONH \\ | \\ CONH \end{array}}}$$

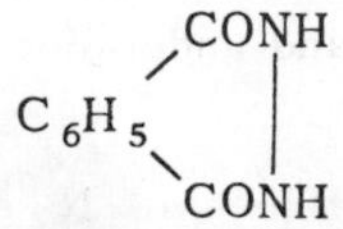

The diazide may be obtained from phthalyl chloride and sodium azide.

Azide hydrazides $N_3CORCONHNH_2$ cannot, in general, be obtained through partial reaction of nitrous acid with a dihydrazide, reaction generally resulting in the formation of a secondary hydrazide. Diphenic acid forms an exception and gives an azide hydrazide,

$$N_3CO \qquad\qquad CONHNH_2$$

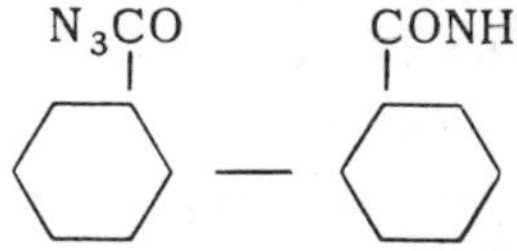

Heterocyclic hydrazides give nitroso derivatives upon treatment with nitrous acid, if they contain reactive methylene groups; 4-isonitrosopyrazolone-3-acetazide is obtained, for example, from pyrazolone-3-acethydrazide.[172]

Unstable azides are formed through the reaction of hydrazoic acid with thiosemicarbazides and with isothiocyanates:

$$RNCS + HN_3 \quad \rightarrow \quad RNHCSN_3$$

Hydroxamyl chlorides reacting with sodium azide give hydroxytetrazoles:[173]

$$RC(=NOH)Cl + NaN_3 \quad \rightarrow \quad \overline{RC = N - N = N}NOH + NaCl$$

Curtius Degradation

Acid azides decompose, when heated, to nitrogen and an isocyanate:[174]

$$RCON_3 \quad \rightarrow \quad RN = CO + N_2$$

Rearrangement proceeds satisfactorily in neutral to strongly acid solution. The fact that it is not necessary to subject the azide to strong acids is an advantageous feature of the reaction.

The transformation is a unimolecular reaction, bearing a resemblance to Hofmann's degradation, and apparently involving the formation of an unstable intermediate with a monovalent nitrogen:

$$\mathrm{RCON}\left\langle\begin{matrix}\mathrm{N}\\ \| \\ \mathrm{N}\end{matrix}\right. \rightarrow \mathrm{N_2 + RCON} \rightarrow \mathrm{RN = CO}$$

When the reaction is carried out in an inert solvent, the isocyanate does not undergo further change, and may be isolated as such. If, on the other hand, water or an alcohol are present in the solvent, symmetrical ureas or urethanes are formed respectively.[175]

Urethanes may result through the addition of alcohols to isocyanates; their formation from azides may also be explained, however, on the assumption that an alkoxy amide is first formed and undergoes molecular rearrangement to yield a urethane:

$$\mathrm{RCON_3 + HOC_2H_5} \rightarrow \mathrm{N_2 + RCONHOC_2H_5}$$
$$\rightarrow \mathrm{RC(OH) = NOC_2H_5} \rightarrow \mathrm{RN = C(OH)OC_2H_5}$$
$$\rightarrow \mathrm{RNHCOOC_2H_5}$$

Urethanes may be prepared by heating the azide with absolute alcohol, while symmetrical ureas are obtained when the azide is heated with a moist inert solvent, such as benzene, chloroform or ether.

Isocyanates, urethane and ureas may all be hydrolyzed to an amine, the last transformation product of *Curtius degradation:*

$$\mathrm{RNCO + H_2O} \rightarrow \mathrm{RNH_2 + CO_2}$$
$$\mathrm{RNHCONHR + H_2O} \rightarrow \mathrm{2\ RNH_2 + CO_2}$$
$$\mathrm{RNHCOOC_2H_5 + H_2O} \rightarrow \mathrm{RNH_2 + CO_2 + C_2H_5OH}$$

The overall result of the reaction is the replacement of a carboxyl group in an acid with an amino group. A primary amine is the product of the reaction, and the position of the amino group in the molecule is fixed unequivocally. The product obtained by the hydrolysis of an isocyanate is not always an amine, certain isocyanates yielding an aldehyde or a ketone. For example, substituted vinyl isocyanates yield aldehydes on hydrolysis:

$$\mathrm{RCH = CHNCO + 2\ H_2O} \rightarrow \mathrm{RCH_2CHO + NH_3 + CO_2}$$

Azides may be transformed directly to amines by heating with a dilute aqueous mineral acid. The method is not always reliable, however, reversion of the azide to the corresponding acid by hydrolysis, and conversion to ureas taking place in many cases.

A satisfactory *procedure* for carrying out the Curtius degradation is to convert the azide to an isocyanate and subsequently to hydrolyze the isocyanate to the amine. The reaction is usually carried out in toluene at about 80°; transformation is generally complete in about one hour. Some azides undergo transformation at much lower temperatures, while others require heating to temperatures up to 150°. Xylene and decalin are satisfactory solvents, especially with axides that require heating to a comparatively high temperature. The solvent does not appear to influence the rate of reaction. The course of the reaction may be followed by determining the unconverted azide. The determination is carried out by hydrolyzing with alkali and precipitating the azide as its silver salt by the addition of silver nitrate to the slightly acidified solution of the resulting alkali metal azide. It should be borne in mind that dry silver azide is an *extremely explosive* compound.

Simple saturated azides rearrange quantitatively to isocyanates, a fact which may be ascertained by measuring the volume of nitrogen evolved. A loss may be incurred in practice with the more volatile isocyanates due to volatilization and entrainment with the escaping nitrogen. Losses due to volatilization may be eliminated by converting the azide to a urethane by reaction with alcohol in a sealed tube at the appropriate temperature and subsequently hydrolyzing the urethane.

Isocyanates resulting from the transformation of azides in the absence of water or alcohols may be isolated as such by fractional distillation. Any residual azide must be removed or destroyed before proceeding with this operation, since otherwise a violent explosion may occur.

The rearrangement of azides in the absence of a liquid diluent is a *highly hazardous operation.*

Isocyanates may be converted to amine hydrochlorides by heating with concentrated hydrochloric acid. The solution of isocyanate in the original solvent in which the transformation of the azide has been carried out may be used directly. The reaction usually proceeds immediately and with vigor, and it is advisable to make use of a reflux condenser with the more volatile isocyanates to prevent possible losses. The amine salt may be isolated by distilling off the solvent and the excess hydrochloric acid. The formation of *sym*-ureas may be largely avoided by using aqueous hydrochloric acid saturated with hydrogen chloride at 0°. Acid hydrolysis preserves the optical activity of groups present in the compound.

Hydrolysis of isocyanates may also be accomplished by use of aqueous or alcoholic alkali. This method is employed with acid-sensitive isocyanates. Carbamates, RNHCOOM, are often formed first in this reaction, acidification causing their rapid decarboxylation and the formation of the amine. Alkaline hydrolysis may bring about loss of optical activity. Isocyanates that are highly resistant to hydrolysis may be converted to amines by dry-distilling in a retort with calcium hydroxide.[176] The amine is often obtained in yields ranging from 50 to 70% of the theoretical.

Urethanes of higher alcohols, such as benzyl alcohol and cholesterol, are generally prepared by heating the isocyanate under reflux with a slight excess of a toluene or xylene solution of the alcohol. The reaction with methanol fails to take place with azides which undergo rearrangement at a temperature above the boiling point of methanol. In such cases the azide remains unchanged, or becomes converted to the methyl ester of the corresponding acid. Succinyldiazide reacting with alcohol gives an imidazole,

$$C_2H_5OCO\overline{NCH_2CH_2NHCO}$$

which is hydrolyzed to ethlenediamine.

The Curtius reaction is applicable to the azide of almost any acid. It has been employed successfully for the preparation of amines from aliphatic, alicyclic, aromatic[177] and heterocyclic acids, both saturated and unsaturated, and from acids containing other functional groups. The method is especially useful for the preparation of amines from higher fatty acids. It is preferable to Hofmann's method for the latter purpose.

Hydroxy azides are converted on heating to ketones through the intermediate formation of a hydroxy isocyanates:[178]

$$R_1R_2C(OH)CON_3 \rightarrow R_1R_2C(OH)NCO \rightarrow R_1R_2CO + HNCO$$

Azides derived from γ-hydroxy acids and other hydroxy acids which yield lactones do not, in general, undergo rearrangement to isocyanates; among the exceptions are *o*-hydroxymethylbenzazide and *o*-hydroxyphenylacetic azide. Nonacylated sugar azides lose hydrazoic acid when heated.

Acylated amino acids undergo rearrangement normally giving acylated amino isocyanates, from which the corresponding amines may be obtained by hydrolysis.

Halogenated acid azides undergo rearrangement normally, but if the halogen is in the α-position, hydrolysis of the isocyanate results in the formation of an aldehyde or ketone.

Azides of cyano acids rearrange normally to cyano isocyanates from which amino acids may be obtained by hydrolysis.

Azides of monosubstituted carbamic acids $RHNCON_3$ undergo rearrangement with difficulty, apparently because these compounds normally exist in a form resembling isoureas, $RN = (OH)N_3$. Disubstituted carbamic azides,

$$R_1R_2NCON_3$$

rearrange in a normal manner. Rearrangement takes place especially readily if one of the groups attached to the amino nitrogen is aromatic. Carbamic azide itself, H_2NCON_3, undergoes rearrangement with difficulty, yielding but a trace of the expected hydrazino compound.

Sulfonamide and sulfide groups and aromatic azo groups do not interfere with the Curtius rearrangement.

Heterocyclic acid azides can, in general, be successfully transformed to the corresponding isocyanate or urethane, but the free amines obtained by hydrolyzing these latter compounds are often inherently unstable.

Amino acids are obtained through the degradation of substituted malonic half-azides which may be prepared from the corresponding half-esters:[179]

$$CH_3CH(COOK)COOC_2H_5 \rightarrow CH_3CH(COOK)CONHNH_2$$

$$\rightarrow CH_3CH(COOK)CON_3 \rightarrow CH_3\overset{\textstyle\ulcorner}{C}HNHCOO\overset{\textstyle\urcorner}{C}O$$

$$\rightarrow CH_3CH(COOC_2H_5)NH_2.HCl$$

Urethanes derived from monosubstituted malonic esters, $RCH(COOC_2H_5)_2$, are rapidly hydrolyzed by mineral acids to aldehydes:

$$C_6H_5CH_2CH(CON_3)_2 \rightarrow C_6H_5CH_2CH(NHCOOC_2H_5)_2$$

$$\rightarrow C_6H_5CH_2CHO$$

The degradation of disubstituted malonic diazides similarly yields ketones.

Suberic azide boiled with water yields N,N′-hexamethyleneurea,

$$CH_2(CH_2)_4CH_2NHCONH$$

N,N′-octamethyleneurea is obtained similarly from sebacic diazide.[180]

Some diazides may be rearranged stepwise. *o*-Isocyanatobenzazide has been obtained, for example, from phthalyl diazide. The remaining acid azide group may also be converted to an isocyano group on longer heating. 1-*p*-Xylyl-1,2,3-triazole-4,5-dicarbonyl diazide and pyridine-2,5-dicarbonyl diazide spontaneously undergo half-rearrangement to isocyano azides.

A modification of the Curtius degradation consists in the direct reaction of hydrazoic acid with a carboxylic acid:[181]

$$RCOOH + HN_3 \rightarrow RNH_2 + CO_2 + N_2$$

Diamines can also be prepared by this method from dibasic acids.

HYDROXAMIC ACIDS

Hydroxamic acids, RC(:NOH)OH or RCONHOH, are the hydroxylamine analogs of acid imides or amides. They are obtained by the general reactions leading to the formation of amides, when hydroxylamine is used instead of ammonia or an amine. They may be obtained, for example, through the interaction of hydroxylamine with an ester:[182]

$$RCOOC_2H_5 + H_2NOH \rightarrow RCONHOH + C_2H_5OH$$

The reaction proceeds rapidly in alcoholic solution at room temperature, especially in the presence of an equimolecular quantity of sodium ethoxide. The reaction may be carried out in aqueous solution in the presence of sodium carbonate.[277] Hydroxamic acids result also through the reaction of hydroxylamine hydrochloride with acid amides:[278]

$$RCONH_2 + H_2NOH.HCl \rightarrow RCONHOH + NH_4Cl$$

Benzamide fails to react.

The reaction of acyl halides with hydroxylamine results in the formation of monohydroxamic acids as well as acylated products.[279] Certain hydroxamic acids have been prepared by this method. Benzhydroxamic acid has been made through the reaction of three parts of benzoyl chloride with one of hydroxylamine hydrochloride.

Hydroxamic acids are obtained very readily when aldehydes are treated with nitrohydroxylamine:

$$CH_3CHO + NO_2NHOH \rightarrow CH_3CONHOH + HNO_2$$

This is known as the *Angeli-Rimini's Reaction.*[183] Benzenesulfonylhydroxylamine may be used in the reaction instead of nitrohydroxylamine.

Hydroxamic acids are formed also by the reaction of aldehydes with hydroxylamine in the presence of hydrogen peroxide:

$$RCHO + H_2NOH \quad \rightarrow \quad RCH(OH)NHOH \xrightarrow{H_2O_2} RC(OH) = NOH$$

Aldoximes may be oxidized to hydroxamic acids with monopersulfuric acid (Caro's acid), $HOSO_2OOH$.[184]

Hydroxamic acids apparently exist in both the possible isomeric forms corresponding to the amide and imide structure

$$\begin{array}{ccccc} 1\,2\,3 & 4 & 5 & 1\,2\,3 & 4 \\ HO.NH.C(R) & = O & \text{and} & HO.N & = C(R).OH \\ & & & 4 & 3 \quad 2\,1 \end{array}$$

According to *Vorlaender's rule* the compound possessing the imide structure should exhibit a strongly acid character, since the unsaturated bonds are in the position 3 and 4 with respect to the two hydrogen atoms. Compounds of both decidedly strong acid character and of nearly neutral reaction are known. Hydroxamic acids of the aromatic series, and oxalhydroxamic acid are strongly acidic, and presumably possess the imide type structure, while those of the aliphatic series react neutral and apparently have the amide type structure.

Lossen Rearrangement

Hydroxamic acids undergo rearrangement when heated with thionyl chloride, forming an isocyanate. The transformation is of the same type as the Hofmann, Curtius and Beckmann rearrangements, and probably involves the formation of an unstable intermediate with a monovalent nitrogen, hydrolysis of the isocyanate finally yielding an amine:[185]

$$C_6H_5C(:NOH)OH \quad \rightarrow \quad H_2O + C_6H_5CON{\textstyle<}$$

$$\rightarrow \quad C_6H_5N = CO \xrightarrow{H_2O} C_6H_5NH_2 + CO_2$$

The rearrangement may be brought about also by the use of acetic anhydride or phosphorus pentoxide. Acylated hydroxamic acids also undergo this transformation. The potassium salt of benzoylbenzhydroxamic acid undergoes the reaction in contact with water at room temperature, yielding diphenylurea.

As in the case of other similar rearrangements involving the formation of an isocyanate, the normal course of the reaction should lead to the formation of symmetrical ureas with water, unsymmetrical ureas with ammonia and urethanes with alcohols. The formation of symmetrical ureas with water is explainable on the assumption that the amine formed by the hydrolysis of a portion of the isocyanate reacts with the unreacted isocyanate:

$$RN:CO + H_2NR \quad \rightarrow \quad RNHCONHR$$

These products are not obtained in every case however. Thus hydroxamic acids derived from phenylacetic and hydrocinnamic acids give ureas with water, but fail to form urethanes with alcohol, while, on the other hand, benzoylcinnamhydroxamic acid readily forms urethanes with alcohols, but does not give a urea with water. Acetyl- and benzoylbenzhydroxamic acids undergo all the expected transformations normally. The two naphthylhydrazidoxalhydroxamic acids yield naphthylurazoles on acetylation.[186] Hydroxamic acids derived from oleic and elaidic acid, heated with an excess of acetic anhydride, apparently yield a mixture of cis- and trans-heptadecenylisocyanates, as shown indirectly by the character of products derived from the mixture of the isomers.

Hydroxamic acids with a hydroxyl group in α-position apparently yield an aldehyde or ketone and cyanic acid when subjected to the conditions of Lossen rearrangement. Carbonyl-, thiocarbonyl-, arylsulfon- and thiobenzhydroxamic acids and their derivatives do not undergo the Lossen rearrangement.

The *Lengfeld - Stieglitz transformation*,[187] which presents a similarity to the Lossen rearrangement, consists in the formation of urethanes from N-bromo amides under the action of methyl alcoholic sodium methylate. The reaction may be illustrated by the formation of methyl carbomethoxy-β-aminopropionate from succinimide bromide:

$$\overline{COCH_2 CH_2 CONBr} \quad \rightarrow \quad \overline{COCH_2 CH_2 C(:NBr)O}$$

$$\rightarrow \quad \overline{COCH_2 CH_2 N:CBrO} \quad \underset{\rightarrow}{NaOCH_3 + CH_3OH}$$

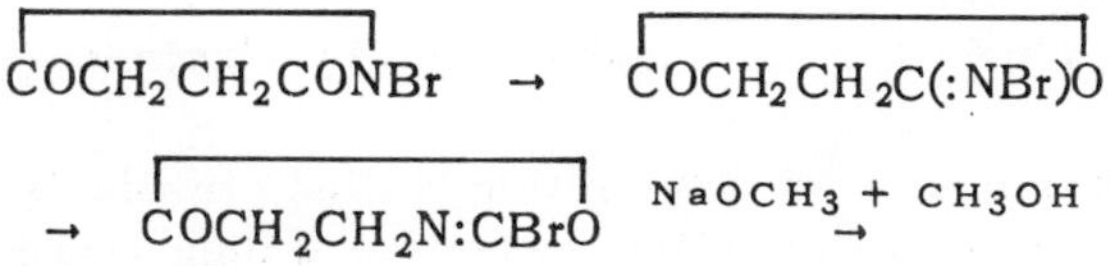

$$CH_3 OCOCH_2 CH_2 N = C(OH)OCH_3 \quad \rightarrow \quad CH_3 OCOCH_2 CH_2 NHCOOCH_3$$

The above mechanism is that proposed by Lengfeld and Stieglitz.

IMINO ETHERS[188]

Imino ethers are the ethers RC(:NH)OR' derived from acid imides RC(:NH)OH. They are obtained in the form of their hydrochloride through the interaction of alcohols with nitriles in the presence of hydrogen chloride. The hydrochloride of an unstable chloro imino ether is apparently formed first which rapidly changes to the imino ether hydrochloride:

$$RCN + C_2 H_5 OH + 2 HCl \quad \rightarrow \quad RC \overset{\nearrow NH_2}{\underset{\searrow Cl}{- OC_2 H_5}} . HCl$$

$$\rightarrow \quad RC(:NH)OC_2 H_5 . HCl + HCl$$

A satisfactory *procedure* for the preparation of imino ether hydrochlorides is as follows: The nitrile is mixed with an equivalent amount of the alcohol, a sufficient quantity of an inert solvent such as ether is added, if necessary, to bring all the nitrile into solution, the whole is cooled and hydrogen chloride is conducted through the solution. After the calculated quantity of hydrogen chloride has been absorbed, the mixture is allowed to remain, first in a freezing mixture, then at room temperature. The compound is obtained in crystalline form by placing the reaction product in a desiccator containing both concentrated sulfuric acid and solid caustic.

The free imino ethers are obtained by adding the powdered imino ether hydrochloride to an excess of 33% potassium carbonate solution with good cooling and vigorous agitation. The imino ether is isolated by extraction with ether, drying the extract with calcium chloride and finally evaporating off the solvent.[189] The free imino ethers may also be prepared by treating the hydrochloride with solid sodium- or potassium hydroxide.

In preparing imino ethers from hydrocyanic acid it is essential to dilute the mixture of alcohol and acid with ether and to cool the solution effectively in a freezing mixture in order to avoid a violent reaction.

Imino ether formation proceeds well with aliphatic nitriles and many of the aromatic nitriles. Certain ortho substituted aromatic nitriles fail to react.[190] Di and trichlor- and bromacetonitriles and dichloronitroacetonitrile do not yield imino ethers, although such ethers are obtained readily from monohaloacetonitriles.[191] Imino ethers may be prepared from cyanamides[192] and thiocyanates.[193]

Imino ethers may be prepared from primary and secondary alcohols and phenols; tertiary alcohols fail to form imino ethers but are converted to unsaturated compounds under the conditions of the reaction. Hydroxy groups situated in the δ-position with respect to the cyano group react with this group to form imino lactones.[194]

Aromatic imino ethers may be prepared also by alkylating the corresponding amides.[195]

Imino ethers are liquids or low-melting solids, insoluble or very slightly soluble in water. Imino ethers of low molecular weight may be distilled under vacuum with partial decomposition; those of high molecular weight and those derived from aromatic nitriles decompose into the original nitrile and alcohol when subjected to distillation. The free imino ethers are not stable and gradually decompose on standing.

Reactions of Imino Ethers

Imino ether hydrochlorides are decomposed by water into esters and ammonium chloride:

$$RC(:NH)OR'.HCl + H_2O \rightarrow RCOOR' + NH_4Cl$$

Alcohols also cause a similar decomposition although more slowly. Formiminoethyl ether hydrochloride, reacting with ethyl alcohol, gives ethyl orthoformate:

$$CH(:NH)OC_2H_5.HCl + 2\ C_2H_5OH \rightarrow CH(OC_2H_5)_3 + NH_4Cl$$

Methyl orthoformate may be obtained similarly from formiminomethyl ether hydrochloride and methanol.

Acetic anhydride reacts with imino ethers to give a secondary amide:

$$CH(:NH)OC_2H_5 + O(COCH_3)_2 \rightarrow CH_3COOC_2H_5 + CH(:NH)OCOCH_3$$
$$\rightarrow CH(OH):NCOCH_3 \rightarrow CHONHCOCH_3$$

Imino ethers are converted to amidines by the action of alcoholic ammonia:[196]

$$RC(:NH)OC_2H_5.HCl + NH_3 \rightarrow RC(:NH)NH_2.HCl + C_2H_5OH$$

Substituted amidines, hydrazidines and amidoximes result respectively when amines, hydrazines and hydroxylamine are used in this reaction instead of ammonia. Hydrazines and hydroxylamine may also replace the imino group in imino ethers to form compounds of the type RC(=NOH)OR′ and RC(=N.NHR″)OR

Aldehydes result when imino ethers are reduced with sodium amalgam and an aqueous acid;[197] amines are obtained, however, when the reduction is carried out electrolytically in 2*N*-sulfuric acid solution.[198]

The free imino ethers, $RC(=NH)OC_2H_5$, react slowly with water forming amidine salts $RC(=NH)NH_2.RCOOH$.[199]

Iminoethers RNHC(=NH)OR′ derived from cyanamides are hydrolyzed to ureas $RNHCONH_2$ on long boiling with aqueous hydrochloric acid.

Imino ethers may be converted to N-substituted amides by heating with alkyl iodides, an addition compound probably forming as an intermediate:[200]

$$RC(=NH)OC_2H_5 + IC_2H_5 \rightarrow RC\begin{matrix} NHC_2H_5 \\ I \\ OC_2H_5 \end{matrix} \rightarrow RCONHC_2H_5 + C_2H_5I$$

This type of transformation takes place when N-alkylated aromatic imino ethers are heated alone:[201]

$$C_6H_5C(:NCH_3)OCH_3 \rightarrow C_6H_5CON(CH_3)_2$$

Thio Imino Ethers

Mercaptans reacting with nitriles in the presence of hydrochloric acid yield the sulfur analogs of imino ethers:

$$RCN + HSR' + HCl \rightarrow RC(=NH)SR'.HCl$$

Thio imino ethers in which both R and R′ are alkyl groups are not known; thio imino ethers have been obtained, however, through the reaction of thiophenols with aliphatic nitriles, and of mercaptans and thiophenols with aromatic nitriles.[202]

AMIDINES

Amidines result through the interaction of ammonia or amines with imide chlorides or thio amides. Amidines also result when certain nitriles are heated with ammonium chloride.[203] Potassium derivatives of amidines are obtained when nitriles are made to react with potassium amide in anhydrous ammoniacal solution.[204] Amidines in the form of their sodium derivatives result also through the reaction of certain nitriles with sodium amide,[205] or with an amine in the presence of metallic sodium.[206] The reaction of a nitrile with an amine in boiling toluene, in the presence of metallic sodium, proceeds very slowly, and is complete only after several days. Trichloracetonitrile reacts with ammonia at room temperature to form an amidine.[207]

Amidines of the fatty acid series have been obtained by heating the amides in a current of hydrogen chloride:

$$2CH_3CONH_2 \xrightarrow{HCl} CH_3C(=NH)NH_2.HCl + CH_3COOH$$

Peralkylated amidines of the aromatic series result through the reaction of

N-alkylimide chlorides with secondary amines, or of N-dialkylamide dichlorides with primary bases

$$RC(:NR')Cl + HN(R'')_2 \rightarrow RC(:NR')N(R'')_2.HCl$$

$$RCCl_2N(R')_2 + H_2NR'' \rightarrow RC(:NR'')N(R')_2.HCl + HCl$$

The amidine may be obtained by heating a mixture of the amide and amine with phosphorus trichloride.[221]

Good yields of amidines are obtained when nitriles are heated with ammonium aryl sulfonates. This reaction takes place even with *o*-substituted aromatic nitriles and with α-naphthylcyanides. Primary and secondary aliphatic amine salts of aryl sulfonates may be used to obtain N-substituted amidines, although aromatic amines do not react.

Amidines are obtained also by heating carboxylic acids with aryl sulfonamides.[217] The amide of the carboxylic acid and the free sulfonic acid appear to be formed first, the interaction of these resulting in the formation of the sulfonated amide, which breaks down to a nitrile and the sulfonic acid. The reaction of the nitrile with the ammonium aryl sulfonate formed in the reaction finally leads to the formation of the amidine sulfonate:

$$RCOOH + R'SO_2NH_2 \rightarrow RCONH_2 + R'SO_2OH$$

$$\rightarrow RCONHSO_2R' \rightarrow RC(=NH)OSO_2R' \rightarrow RCN + R'SO_2OH$$

$$RCN + R'SO_2ONH_4 \rightarrow RC(=NH)NH_2.R'SO_2OH$$

Ketoxime sulfonates afford good yields of substituted amidines when they undergo the Beckmann rearrangement in the presence of ammonia or amines:

$$RCH = NOSO_2R' \rightarrow R'SO_2OCR = NH \xrightarrow{NH_3} RC(=NH)NH_2R'SO_2OH$$

Amidines result through the interaction of ammonia or amines with imino ether hydrochlorides:[196]

$$RC(:NH)OC_2H_5.HCl + NH_3 \rightarrow RC(:NH)NH_2.HCl + C_2H_5OH$$

Amidines are strong mono acid bases and form stable salts even with nitrous acid. They are unstable in the free state and are readily hydrolyzed to the corresponding amide or acid. They form characteristic salts with picric acid which may serve for their identification.

Amidines react with β-keto esters to form pyrimidines; dimethylethoxypyrimidine is obtained, for example, through the reaction of acetamidine with acetoacetic ester:

$$CH_3C(=NH)NH_2 + CH_3COCH_2COOC_2H_5$$

$$\rightarrow CH_3\overline{C = NC(CH_3) = CHC(OC_2H_5) = N} + 2\,H_2O$$

Acetic anhydride eliminates a molecule of ammonia from amidines forming a nitrile.

Hydroxylamine replaces the imine group in amidines forming amidoximes:

$$RC(=NH)NH_2 + H_2NOH \rightarrow RC(=NOH)NH_2 + NH_3$$

Hydrazidines are obtained by the action of hydrazines on imino ethers:

$$RC(:NH)OC_2H_5 + H_2NNHC_6H_5 \rightarrow C_2H_5OH + RC(=NH)NHNHC_6H_5$$

$$\xrightarrow{H_2NNHC_6H_5} RC(=NNHC_6H_5)NHNHC_6H_5$$

Azidines $RC(=NNHR')N = NR'$ are obtained from hydrazidines by oxidation.

Purely aromatic hydrazidines are not known.

Guanidines

Guanidine, $HN = C(NH_2)_2$, may be considered as the amidine of carbonic acid. Representatives of all possible types of guanidine derivatives, with the hydrogens in the mother substance substituted with various groups, have been made.

The principal methods employed for the preparation of guanidines depend upon the reaction of amines with cyanamides; with S-alkyl-isothioureas or O-alkylisoureas; with thioureas in the presence of desulfurizing agents. Several other methods of lesser importance have also been employed for the preparation of guanidines.

The reaction of amines with *cyanamides* may be carried out in aqueous solution or in a suitable organic solvent. The reaction proceeds best in the presence of a salt of the amine, preferably the sulfate or the hydrochloride. Salts of aromatic amines react well in the absence of "free" amine, since they are sufficiently dissociated. The favorable pH range in most instances is around 9. In many cases reaction proceeds at ordinary temperature, though very slowly, and is sometimes allowed to take place at room temperature in order to avoid the formation of excessive amounts of byproducts.

The general reaction may be represented as follows:

$$RR'NCN + HNR''R''' \rightarrow RR'NC(:NH)NR''R'''$$

The reaction of cyanamides with aliphatic and primary aromatic amines usually proceeds with ease and gives guanidines in good yield. The reaction of a second primary amine group attached to an aromatic radical proceeds with some difficulty. Diarylamines and aromatic amines with negative substituents react poorly with cyanamides under usual conditions. Guanidines may be prepared from these amines in good yield by using an excess of cyanamide and carrying out the reaction in the presence of concentrated hydrochloric acid.[295] *Unsym*-diphenylguanidine has been obtained by adding a small amount of concentrated hydrochloric acid to a homogeneous mixture of diphenylamine and free cyanamide.[296] Disubstituted cyanamides undergo the reaction less readily than monosubstituted cyanamides.

Hydroxylamine reacts readily with cyanamide at a low temperature; the reaction with substituted hydroxylamines also proceeds readily as does the reaction with hydrazine.[297]

Among the guanidines prepared through the reaction of amines with cyanamide or substituted cyanamides are monomethylguanidine,[298] *unsym*-diethylguanidine,[299] monocyclohexylguanidine,[300] Monophenylguanidine,[301] *sym*-diphenylguanidine,[302] *unsym*-diphenylguanidine,[303] α-naphthyleneguanidine,[304] mono(chlorophenyl)guanidine,[305] mono(bromophenyl)guanidine,[306] benzamidoguanidine,[307] creatine,[308] N,N-dipropyl-N″-hydroxyguanidine.[309]

Guanidines may be prepared from *dicyandiamide* by reaction with an amine salt. The compound first formed in the temperature range 100 to 120° is a biguanide, which reacts further with the amine salt at 120 to 180°, yielding two molecular equivalents of the guanidine salt:

$$H_2NC(:NH)NHCN + H_2NR.HCl \rightarrow H_2NC(:NH)NHC(:NH)NHR.HCl$$

$$\xrightarrow{H_2NR.HCl} 2H_2NC(:NH)NHR.HCl$$

Guanidines have been prepared from amines and *carbodiimides,*[310]

$$RN = C = NR',$$

which are isomeric with cyanamides. The reaction of aniline with diphenylcarbodiimide proceeds in the cold with generation of heat, although heating is necessary at the end to complete the reaction.[311] The reactivity of carbodiimides is so great that it is possible to prepare guanidines from them by reaction with substituted ureas.[312]

$$C_6H_5N = C = NC_6H_5 + C_6H_5NHCONHC_6H_5 \rightarrow$$

$$C_6H_5N = C(NHC_6H_5)_2 + C_6H_5N = CO$$

The reaction of amines with *thioureas* in the presence of desulfurizing agents (*Hofmann's method*) may be considered as a method related to the preceding, since it may be assumed that a carbodiimide is formed as an intermediate in the reaction. The desulfurizing agents generally employed are silver oxide, lead oxide and lead carbonate. The reaction in the most general case may be represented as follows:

$$RR'NCSNHR'' + HNR'''R'''' + PbO \rightarrow RR'NC(:NR'')NR'''R'''' + PbS + H_2O$$

As an example of the method, the preparation of N,N′,N″-triphenylguanidine from *sym*-diphenylthiourea may be mentioned: Molecular equivalents of the *sym*-diphenylthiourea and aniline are heated in toluene to 100° and an excess of finely divided lead monoxide, PbO, is gradually added with agitation. Heating at 110° is continued for two hours under reflux. The mass is then filtered while hot, the filter cake is extracted with toluene, and the triphenyl guanidine is recovered from the combined filtrate and washings by cooling to crystallization.[313]

Yields seldom exceed 80% because of the formation of byproducts which usually necessitates a careful purification of the guanidine formed from polymeric carbodiimides and other resinous matter.

Iodine has been used as a desulfurizing agent.[314] N,N′,N″-triphenylguanidine has been prepared, for example, from thiocarbanilide, aniline and iodine:[315]

$$SC(NHC_6H_5)_2 + C_6H_5NH_2 + I_2 \rightarrow C_6H_5N = C(NHC_6H_5)_2 + HI + S$$

$$2SC(NHC_6H_5)_2 + C_6H_5NH_2 + I_2$$

$$\rightarrow C_6H_5N = C(NHC_6H_5)_2 + SCNC_6H_5 + 2HI + S$$

The following are some of the guanidines prepared via the thiourea route: monoethylguanidine,[316] N-methyl-N′-propyl-N″-ethylguanidine,[317] N,N′-ditotylguanidine,[318] N-phenyl-N′-amino-N″-phenylguanidine,[319] N-phenyl-N′-phenylamino-N″-phenylguanidine.[320]

The formation of guanidines from thiurets and amines may be considered a related reaction.[321]

$$RN=\overset{S-S}{\overset{|\quad|}{CNHC}}=NH+R_1NH_2 \longrightarrow \begin{cases} RN=C(SH)NHC(:NH)NHR_1+S \\ RN=C(NHR_1)NHCSNH_2+S \end{cases}$$

A method of wide applicability for the preparation of guanidines is that depending on the reaction of amines with the halide or sulfate of S-methylisothioureas or other S-alkylisothioureas (*Rathke's method*). Reaction proceeds best with S-methylisothioureas, less readily with the S-ethyl compounds; it generally begins at room temperature, and yields are close to theoretical. The formation of a mercaptan is an unpleasant feature of the process. The reaction may be represented as follows:

$$RR'NC(SCH_3)=NR''+HNR'''R'''' \rightarrow RR'NC(:NR'')NR'''R''''+CH_3SH$$

As representative of the mode of procedure, the preparation of methylguanidine may be mentioned, which is carried out by warming at 30° under reflux a suspension of 700 gm of S-methylisothiourea sulfate in 700 cc of water with 525 gm of a 33% aqueous solution of methylamine. The reaction is completed by warming the mixture to boiling. The product is isolated by concentrating the solution under vacuum to about 1000 gm and chilling to 5°. On diluting the resulting crystalline mass with 300 cc methanol, filtering and washing with methanol, an 80% yield of methylguanidine sulfate is obtained.[322]

A satisfactory method for the preparation of S-methylisothiourea sulfate consists in alkylating thiourea with dimethyl sulfate. A suspension of one mole of thiourea and half a mole of dimethyl sulfate in 50 cc of water is first gently warmed until the original autogenous reaction is complete, then the mixture is boiled. The S-methylisothiourea is obtained in 90% yield.[323]

When a diamine such as *p*-phenylenediamine is made to react with S-methylisothiourea hydriodide, a substituted monoguanidine alone is usually formed.

Some of the guanidines prepared via the S-alkylisothiourea route are monomethylguanidine,[324] N,N,N'-trimethylguanidine,[316] monophenylguanidine,[325] N,N',N''-tri-*α*-naphthylguanidine,[326] N-phenyl-N'-*o*-carboxyphenylguanidine,[327] pyrrolidineguanidine.[328]

Guanidines have been prepared through the reaction of amines with O-methylisoureas.[329]

Guanidines have been obtained from chloroimines containing the grouping $Cl_2C=N$ by reaction with amines. N,N'-Dimethyl-N,N'-diphenyl-N''-benzoylguanidine,

$$C_6H_5CON=C[N(CH_3)C_6H_5]_2$$

has been made from methylaniline and N'-dichloromethylbenzamide, $C_6H_5CON=CCl_2$.[330] Triamino-guanidine has been made from dichloroformoxime, $Cl_2C=NOH$, and hydrazine.[331] Triphenylguanidine, $(C_6H_5NH)_2C=NC_6H_5$, has been prepared from phenylcyano dichloride, $C_6H_5N=CCl_2$ and aniline.[332] N-Hydroxy-N,N,N'-triphenyl-N''-*p*-totylguanidine has been made from N-*p*-totylhydroxylamine and chloroformic triphenylamidine,

$$ClC(:NC_6H_5)N(C_6H_5)_2.$$ [333]

N,N',N''-Trimethylguanidine has been prepared from methylamine and the diethyl ether of carbonic methylimide, $(C_2H_5O)_2C=NHC_3$.[334]

N,N′,N″-Triallylguanidine is formed on refluxing a ligroin solution of allylamine with S-allylaminotrichloromethylthiol, $C_6H_5NHSCCl_3$.[335] Triphenylguanidine,

$$(C_6H_5NH)_2C = NC_6H_5,$$

has been obtained through the reaction of aniline with carbon tetrachloride.[336] N-Phenyl-N′,N″-naphthalene(1,8)-guanidine results from the reaction of 1,8-diaminonaphthalene with phenyl isothiocyanate. N,N′,N″-triphenylguanidine has been obtained in good yield by fusing sym-diphenylurea with sodium hydroxide.[337]

Replacement of amino groups in guanidines by other amine residues is possible, especially with the hydrazine groups. Anilinoguanidine, $HN = C(NH_2)NHNHC_6H_5$, is formed on heating guanidine carbonate with phenylhydrazine hydrochloride at 180°.[338] Triaminoguanidine, $(H_2NNH)_2C = NNH_2$, is obtained through the reaction of hydrazine hydrate with salts of guanidine.[339] The formation of 4-amino-3,5-dihydrazino-1,2,4-triazolidine,

$$\begin{array}{c} H_2NNHC \!-\!\!-\! NNH_2 \\ \| \quad\quad \| \\ N.N\!=\!CNHNH_2 \end{array}$$

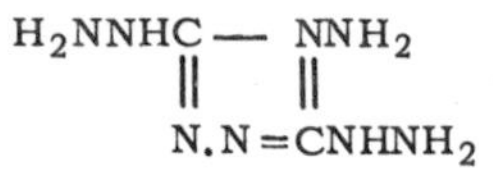

from hydrazine hydrate and guanidine carbonate has been reported.[340] In the reaction of monomethylamine in large excess with cyanogen iodide at 130° N,N′,N″-trimethylguanidine results in 55% yield in consequence of an exchange of the methylamino group for the amino group in the N,N′-dimethylguanidine first formed.[341]

Guanidines not already fully substituted may be *alkylated* under the proper conditions; N,N′,N″-trimethylguanidine has been prepared by methylating N,N′-dimethylguanidine with dimethyl sulfate at 150 to 160° in an autoclave.[342] A picrylguanidine has been obtained by the action of picryl chloride on N,N′-diphenyl-N″-iminobenzylguanidine.[343] Alkylation methods have seldom been used, however, for the preparation of guanidines.

AMIDOXIMES

Amidoximes $RC(=NOH)NH_2$ are obtained through the interaction of hydroxylamine with a nitrile:

$$RCN + H_2NOH \quad \rightarrow \quad RC(=NOH)NH_2$$

The reaction proceeds well with aliphatic nitriles[208] containing fewer than seven carbon atoms and with those having ten to thirteen carbon atoms, and slowly with nitriles containing seven to nine carbon atoms. Chlorinated acetonitriles react readily with hydroxylamine to form amidoximes.[209] The reaction proceeds also with arylsulfonic acetonitriles.[210] Aromatic nitriles react with hydroxylamine at a somewhat higher temperature than most aliphatic nitriles.[211]

Amidoximes also result through the reaction of hydroxylamine with imino ethers or amidines:

$$RC(=NH)OC_2H_5 + H_2NOH \quad \rightarrow \quad RC(=NOH)NH_2 + C_2H_5OH$$
$$RC(:NH)NH_2 + H_2NOH \quad \rightarrow \quad RC(=NOH)NH_2 + NH_3$$

Amidoximes of the aromatic series may also be prepared from thioamides by reaction with hydroxylamine:

$$RCSNH_2 + H_2NOH \rightarrow RC(=NOH)NH_2 + H_2S$$

Amidoximes are crystalline, unstable compounds which readily hydrolyze to the corresponding amide or acid. They react both as acids and bases. Their hydrochlorides are converted to amides by reaction with sodium nitrite:

$$RC(=NOH)NH_2.HCl + NaNO_2 \rightarrow RCONH_2 + NaCl + N_2O + H_2O$$

Reacting with carbon disulfide, they yield dithiocarbamic acids:[212]

$$2RC(=NOH)NH_2 + 3CS_2 \rightarrow$$
$$RC(=NSH)NHCSSH + RC(NH_2) = NSH + 2COS$$

References

1. Heumann and Köchlin, *Ber.*, **16**, 1627 (1883); **28**, 594 (1895); Auwers and Risse, *Ber.*, **64**, 2220 (1931).
2. Gräbe, *Ann.*, **291**, 10 (1896).
3. Fauconnier, *Compt. rend.*, **114**, 123 (1892)
4. v. Pechmann, *Ann.*, **264**, 282 (1891); Pschorr, *Ber.*, **31**, 1295 (1898); Meyer, *Ber.*, **27**, 3154 (1894)
5. Prinz, *J. prakt. Chem.*, (2) **24**, 371 (1881)
6. Auwers and Jakob, *Ber.*, **27**, 1125 (1894)
7. Meyer, *Monatsh.*, **22**, 109 (1901); Riedel, *Ann.*, **361**, 96 (1908); Rinrichsen, *ibid.*, **336**, 195 (1904). *Cf.* Rupe *ibid.*, **369**, 340 (1909).
8. Anschutz, *Ann.*, **228**, 308 (1885); **239**, 314, 333 (1887); **346**, 286 (1906); *Ber.*, **30**, 221 (1897).
9. McMaster and Ahmann, *J. Am. Chem. Soc.*, **50**, 145 (1928)
10. Rupe, *Ann.*, **369**, 331 (1909).
11. Hentschel, *Ber.*, **17**, 1285 (1884)
12. *German Patent* 123,052. *Chem. Zentr.*, *1901* II, 518; *German Patent* 146,690; *Chem Zentr.* **1904** I, 65.
13. Fischer, *Ber.*, **38**, 2914 (1905)
14. Gal, *Ann.*, **129**, 53 (1864)
15. Guthrie, *ibid.*, **103**, 335 (1857); Spindler, *ibid.*, **231**, 272 (1885).
16. Traube and Krahmer, *Ber.*, **52**, 1296 (1919).
17. Staudinger and Anthes, *ibid.*, **46**, 1417, 2162 (1913)
18. Meslans, *Ann. chim. phys.*, (7) **1**, 405 (1894)
19. Meslans and Girardet, *Bull. soc. chim.*, (3) **15**, 878 (1896); Borodine, *Compt. rend.*, **55**, 555 (1863)
20. Gernez, *Bull. soc. chim.*, (3) **5**, 887 (1891); Borodine, *Ann.*, **126**, 60 (1863).
21. Cf. Sudborough, *J. Chem. Soc.*, **65**, 1030 (1894); **67**, 587 (1895); Meyer, *Ber.*, **27**, 3153 (1894).
22. Hübner, *Ann.*, **120**, 334 (1861); Claisen and Shadwell, *Ber.*, **11**, 1565 (1878); Claisen and Moritz, *ibid.*, **13**, 2121 (1880); Moritz, *J. Chem. Soc.*, **39**, 13 (1881).
23. Claisen, *Ber.*, **31**, 1023 (1898).
24. Arndt and Amende, *Ber.*, **61**, 1122 (1928); Bradley and Robinson, *J. Chem. Soc.*, **1928**, 1310; Bradley and Schwarzenbach, *ibid.*, **1928**, 2904; Bradley, Robinson and Schwarzenbach, *ibid.*, **1930**, 797; Clibbens and Nierenstein, *ibid.*, **107**, 1491 (1915).
25. Arndt *et al.*, *Ber.*, **60**, 1364 (1927); **61**, 1122 (1928); Bradley and Robinson, *J. Chem. Soc.*, **1928**, 1310, 1545. Adams, *Organic Reactions*, vol. I p. 38 ff (1942).
26. Wolff, *Ann.*, **394**, 25 (1912).
27. Arndt, Eistert and Partale, *Ber.* **60**, 1364 (1927); Arndt and Amende, *ibid.*, **61**, 1122 (1928); Arndt, Eistert and Amende, *ibid.*, **61**, 1949 (1928); Robinson and Bradley, *J. Chem. Soc.*, **1928**, 1310.
28. Wolff, *Ann.*, **394**, 25 (1912); Eistert, *Ber.*, **68**, 208 (1935); Lane *et al.*, *J. Org. Chem.*, **5**, 276 (1940); **6**, 443 (1941).
29. Marshall and Acree, *Ber.*, **43**, 2323 (1910).
30. Wolff, *Ann.*, **394**, 25 (1912); Arndt and Amende, *Ber.*, **61**, 1122 (1928).
31. Arndt and Eistert, *Ber.*, **68**, 200 (1935).
32. Probrashenski et al., *ibid.*, **68**, 850 (1935); **69**, 1314 (1936).
33. Plentl and Bogert, *J. Org. Chem.*, **6**, 669 (1941).
34. Walker, *J. Chem. Soc.*, **1940**, 1304; Work, *ibid.*, **1940**, 1315.
35. Bachmann and Sheehan, *J. Am. Chem. Soc.*, **62**, 2687 (1940).

36. Krzikalla and Eistert, *J. prakt. Chem.*, (2) **143,** 50 (1935); Cf. Arndt and Scholz, *Ber.*, **66,** 1012 (1933).
37. Eistert, *Ber.*, **69,** 1074 (1936).
38. Arndt and Eistert, *ibid.*, **68,** 200 (1935); Burger and Avakian, *J. Org. Chem.*, **5,** 606 (1940).
39. Staudinger and Mächling, *Ber.*, **49,** 1973 (1916); Staudinger, Becker and Hirzel, *ibid.*, **49,** 1978 (1916); Reichstein and Morsman, *Helv. Chim. Acta,* **17,** 1119, (1934); Schroeter, *Ber.*, **42,** 2346 (1909); **49,** 2704 (1916); Staudinger and Hirzel, *ibid.*, **49,** 2522 (1916).
40. Hell, *Ber.*, **14,** 891 (1881); **21,** 1726 (1888); Volhard, *Ann.*, **242,** 141 (1887); *Ber.* **21,** 1904 (1888); Zelinski, *ibid.*, **20,** 2026 (1887); Auwars and Bernhardi, *ibid.*, **24,** 2216 (1891); Michael, *ibid.*, **34,** 4058 (1901); Hirsch, *Chem. Ztg.* **25,** 437 (1901); Aschan, *Ann.*, **387,** 9 (1912); Aschan, *Ber.*, **45,** 1913 (1912); Auwers and Bernhardi, *ibid.*, **24,** 2209 (1891); Cone and Robinson, *ibid.*, **40,** 2162 (1907).
41. Auger and Béhal, *Bull. soc. chim.*, (3) **2,** 145 (1889); Leperg, *ibid.*, (3) **7,** 359 (1892); Genvresse, *ibid.*, (3) **7,** 364 (1892). *Cf.* Lapworth, *J. Chem. Soc.*, **85,** 32 (1904).
42. Baeyer, *Ann.*, **245,** 175 (1888); *Ber.*, **29,** 328 (1896).
43. Auwers and Meyer, *Ber.*, **23,** 305 (1890); Reformatski, *ibid.*, **23,** 1594 (1890).
44. Marie, *Ann. chim.*, (7) **7,** 222, 225 (1896); Auwers and Bernhardi, *Ber.*, **24,** 2209 (1891).
45. Willstätter, *Ber.*, **28,** 659 (1895).
46. Peterson, *Ann.*, **107,** 331 (1858); Keller, *J. prakt. Chem.*, (2) **31,** 363 (1885); Verley, *Bull. soc. chim.*, (3) **9,** 690 (1893).
47. Menschutkin, *Ber.*, **17,** 846 (1884).
48. Fehling, *Ann.*, **49,** 196 (1844); Laurent, *ibid.*, **41,** 110 (1842). Franchimont and Friedmann, *ibid.*, **25,** 79 (1906); D'Arcet, *Ann. chim.*, (2) **58,** 294 (1835); Piutti and Giustiniani, *Gazz. chim. ital.*, **26** I, 431, 435 (1896); Piutti and Eckstein, *Ber.*, **34,** 3277 (1901).
49. Meyer, *Monatsh.*, **27,** 31 (1906).
50. Meyer, *ibid.*, **27,** 31 (1906); Bülow and List *Ber.*,**35,** 189 (1902); Meyer, *ibid.*, **22,** 24 (1889).
51. Fischer and Dilthey, *Ber.*, **35,** 844 (1902). *Cf.* Meyer, *Monatsh.*, **27,** 31 (1906).
52. Graebe and Rateanu, *Ann.*, **279,** 263 (1894); Aschan, *Ber.*, **31,** 2344 (1898); Schlatter, *J. Am. Chem. Soc.*, **63,** 1735 (1941); Kent and McElvain, *Organic Syntheses,* **25,** 58 (1945); Roe *et al.*, *J. Am. Chem. Soc.*, **71,** 2217 (1949); Horowitz and Geissman, *ibid.*, **72,** 1519 (1950).
53. Aschan, *Ber.*, **31,** 2344 (1898); Kraft and Stauffer, *ibid.*, **15,** 1728 (1882).
54. Franzen, *ibid.*, **42,** 2465 (1909).
55. Beckurts and Otto, *Ber.*, **9,** 1592 (1876).
56. Kaufmann, *ibid.*, **42,** 3480 (1909)
57. Anschütz, *Ann.*, **354,** 121 (1907).
58. Pinner and Fuchs, *Ber.*, **10,** 1061 (1877); Colson, *Bull soc. chim.*, (3) **17,** 57 (1897); *Compt. rend.*, **121,** 1155 (1895); Henle and Schupp, *Ber.*, **38,** 1369 (1905); Maxwell, *ibid.*, **12,** 1764 (1879)
59. Colson, *Compt. rend.*, **121,** 1155 (1895)
60. Engler, *Ann.*, **149,** 305 (1869).
61. Radziszewski, *Ber.*, **18,** 355 (1885); Deinert, *J. prakt. Chem.*, (2) **52,** 431 (1895); Friedländer and Weisberg, *Ber.* **28,** 1841 (1895); Rupe and Majewski, *ibid.*, **33,** 3403 (1900); Dubsky, *J. prakt. Chem.*, (2) **93,** 137 (1916); *Ber.*, **49,** 1045 (1916); McMaster and Langreck, *J. Am. Chem. Soc.*, **39,** 103 (1917); van Peski, *Rec. trav. chim.*, **41,** 687 (1922).
62. Deinart, *J. prakt. Chem.*, (2) **52,** 431 (1895).
63. Oliveri-Mandalâ, *Gazz. chim. ital.*, **52** I, 107 (1922).
64. Lotts, *Ber.*, **5,** 669 (1872); Kekulé, *ibid.*, **6,** 112 (1873); Hemilian, *Ann.*, **176,** 7 (1875); Schulze, *J. prakt. Chem.*, (2) **27,** 514 (1883); West, *J. Am. Chem. Soc.*, **42,** 1662 (1920); Noller, *Organic Syntheses*, Coll. vol II, 586 (1943).
65. Schulze, *J. prakt. Chem.*, (2) **27,** 512 (1883); Hofmann, *Ber.*, **15,** 978 (1882); Schulze, *ibid.*, **16,** 2291 (1883).
66. Pickard and Carter, *J. Chem. Soc.*, **79,** 520 (1901).
67. Stieglitz, *Am. Chem. J.*, **18,** 751 (1896); **29,** 49 (1903); Blatt, *Chem. Revs.*, **12,** 215 (1933); Franklin, *ibid.*, **14,** 219 (1934); Meyer and Warrington, *Ber.*, **20,** 506 (1887); Beckmann, *ibid.*, **19,** 988 (1886); **20,** 2580, 2766 (1887); Wegerhoff, *Ber.*, **21,** 2355 (1888); Beckmann and Wegerhoff, *Ann.*, **252,** 1 (1889); *Ber.*, 22, R 590 (1889); Beckmann and Günther, *Ann.*, **252,** 44 (1889). Hantzsch, *Ber.*, **24,** 4018 (1891); Schroeter, *ibid.*, **42,** 2340 (1909); **44,** 1207 (1911); Wallach, *Ann.*, **312,** 172 (1900); Watson, *Modern Theories of Organic Chemistry,* 2nd ed., p. 198; Watson, *Ann. Reports on Progress of Chem. (Chem. Soc., London),* **36,** 194 (1939); Brynmorfones, *Chem. Revs.*, **35,** 335 (1944); Chapman, *Nature,* **157,** 519 (1946); Chapman, *J. Chem. Soc.* **1934,** 1550; Kenyon and Young, *ibid.*, **1941,** 263; Campbell-Kenyon, *J. Soc. Chem. Ind.*, **49,** 391 (1945).
68. Weiss, *J. Soc. Chem. Ind.*, **1947,** 119.
69. Meisenheimer *et al.*, *Ann.*, **446,** 205 (1926).
70. Bredt and Boeddinghous, *ibid.*, **251,** 318 (1889).
71. Beckmann, *ibid.*, **296,** 279 (1897); Werner and Pignet, *Ber.*, **37,** 4295 (1904).

72. Beckmann and Köster, *Ann.*, **274**, 1 (1893).
73. Angeli and Malagnini, *Ber.*, **27**, R 800 (1894).
74. Auwers and Jordan, *ibid.*, **58**, 26 (1925); Meisenheimer *et al.*, *Ann.*, **446**, 205 (1926); *J. prakt. Chem.*, **119**, 315 (1928).
75. Peters, *Ber.*, **40**, 240 (1907).
76. Kipping, *Ber.*, **27**, R 598 (1894); *Proc. chem. soc.*, **1893**, 240.
77. Wegerhoff, *Ann.*, **252**, 14 (1889); Liebermann, *Ber.*, **45**, 1193 (1912).
78. Hantzsch and Lucas, *Ber.*, **28**, 744 (1895); Comstock, *Am. Chem. J.*, **19**, 485 (1897).
79. Goldschmidt, *Ber.*, **27**, 2795 (1894); **28**, 818 (1895).
80. Marquis, *Compt. rend.*, **143**, 1163 (1906).
81. Thiele and Schleussner, *Ann.*, **295**, 136 (1897).
82. Tiemann, *Ber.*, **24**, 4162 (1891).
83. Béhal, *Bull. soc. Chim.*, (3), **13**, 836 (1895); Tiemann, *Ber.*, **30**, 321 (1897).
84. Werner and Detscheff, *Ber.*, **38**, 69 (1905).
85. Werner and Piguet, *ibid.*, **37**, 4295 (1904); Diels and Stern, *ibid.*, **40**, 1629 (1907).
86. Werner and Piguet, *Ber.*, **37**, 4295 (1904); Werner and Detscheff, *ibid.*, **38**, 69 (1905).
87. Auwers and Seyfried, *Ann.*, **484**, 178 (1930); Auwers and Brink, *ibid.*, **493**, 218 (1932); *J. prakt. Chem.*, (2), **133**, 154 (1932); Blatt, *J. Am. Chem. Soc.*, **53**, 1133 (1931); Blatt and Stone, *ibid.*, **53**, 4134 (1931).
88. Neber *et al.*, *Ber.*, **58**, 1234 (1925); *Ann.*, **449**, 109 (1926); **467**, 52 (1928); **493**, 281 (1932).
89. Semmler, *Ber.*, **25**, 3352 (1892); Wolff, *Ann.*, **322**, 351 (1902); Schroeber *et al.*, *Ber.*, **63**, 1308 (1930).
90. Scholl *et al.*, *Ber.*, **64**, 71, 315, 318, 639 (1931).
91. Colby and Dodge, *Am. Chem. J.*, **13**, 1 (1891); Mathews, *J. Am. Chem. Soc.*, **18**, 679 (1896); **20**, 648 (1898). *Cf.* Gautier, *Z. anal. Chem.*, **1869**, 39; Seldner, *Am. Chem. J.* **17**, 532 (1895).
92. Werner, *Ber.*, **36**, 153 (1903); Dadswell and Kenner, *J. Chem. Soc.*, **1927**, 1104.
93. Wallach, *Ann.*, **214**, 200 (1882); Wallach and Lehmann, *ibid.*, **237**, 239 (1887).
94. Ostwald, *J. prakt. Chem.*, (2) **27**, 1 (1883).
95. Heyl and Meyer, *Ber.*, **28**, 2782 (1895).
96. Haller and Bauer, *Compt. rend.*, **149**, 5 (1909).
97. Sudborough, *J. Chem. Soc.*, **67**, 602 (1895). Cf. Claus, *Ann.*, **265**, 377 (1891); Claus and Beysen, *ibid.*, **266**, 226 (1891); Claus and Beck, *ibid.*, **269**, 212 (1893); Jacobsen, *Ber.*, **22**, 1220 (1889).
98. Bouveault, *Bull. soc. chim.*, (3) **9**, 368 (1892); Friedländer and Weisberg, *Ber.*, **28**, 1841 (1895); Gattermann, *ibid.*, **30**, 1279 (1897); **32**, 1118 (1899); Meyer and Holz, *Ber.*, **30**, 1279 (1898); Graebe and Hönigsberger, *Ann.*, **311**, 274 (1900); Blitz, *Ber.*, **34**, 4127 (1901); Sachs and Goldmann, *ibid.*, **35**, 3325, 3359 (1902); Klages and Margolinsky, *ibid.*, **36**, 4192 (1903). *Cf.* Knoevenagel and Merkin, *ibid.*, **37**, 4091 (1904); Heller and Bauer, *Compt. rend.*, **149**, 5 (1909).
99. Titherly, *J. Chem. Soc.*, **79**, 391 (1901).
100. Stieglitz and Slosson, *Ber.*, **34**, 1614 (1901).
101. Dessaignes, *Ann.*, **82**, 231 (1852); Strecker, *ibid.*, **103**, 324 (1857); Markownikow, *Zeitschrift für Chemie*, **1863**, 534; Tafel and Enoch, *Ber.*, **23**, 1553 (1890); Seliwanow, *ibid.*, **26**, 987 (1893); Fischer and Grutzner, *Arch. Pharm.*, **232**, 329 (1894); Forster, *J. Chem. Soc.*, **73**, 783 (1898); Fürth, *Monatsh*, **23**, 1154 (1902).
102. Titherley, *J. Chem. Soc.*, **71**, 467 (1897).
103. Wheeler and Johnson, *Am. Chem. J.*, **21**, 185 (1899); **23**, 136 (1900); Lander, *J. Chem. Soc.*, **83**, 415 (1903); Lander and Jewson, *ibid.*, **83**, 766 (1903).
104. Rohler, *Z. Elektrochem.*, **16**, 429 (1910).
105. Hantzsch and Lehmann, *Ber.*, **35**, 901 (1902); v. Pechmann, *ibid.*, **31**, 2643 (1898).
106. Bruning, *Ann.*, **253**, 7 (1889).
107. Hofmann, *Ber.*, **15**, 407, 752 (1882).
108. Manguin, *Ann. chim. phys.*, (8) **22**, 305 (1911); Hantzsch and Dollfus, *Ber.*, **35**, 249 (1902); Hoogewerff and van Dorp, *Rec. trav. chim.*, **6**, 373 (1888); **15**, 107 (1896).
109. Baubigny, *Compt. rend.*, **95**, 646 (1882); **103**, 149 (1886); Seifert, *Ber.*, **18**, 1357 (1885); Bonz, *Z. physik. Chem.*, **2**, 882 (1888).
110. Gabriel, *Ber.*, **19**, 1655 (1886); Ruhemann, *ibid.*, **24**, 3975 (1891); Gabriel and Neumann, *ibid.*, **26**, 525 (1893); Angerstein, *ibid.*, **34**, 3956 (1901).
111. v. Braun and Sobecki, *Ber.*, **44**, 1424 (1911).
112. v. Braun and Sobecki, *ibid.*, **44**, 1039 (1911).
113. Fischer and Arch, *ibid.*, **30**, 2208 (1897).
114. Fischer, *ibid.*, **30**, 2220 (1897).
115. Fischer and Arch, *ibid.*, **31**, 1980 (1898); Fischer and Clemin, *ibid.*, **31**, 2622 (1898).
116. Fischer, *Ber.*, **30**, 2406 (1897).
117. Michailis and Lachwitz, *ibid.*, 2106 (1910).
118. Feist, *ibid.*, **45**, 945 (1912); **47**, 1173 (1914).

119. Adkins and Wojcik, *J. Am. Chem. Soc.*, **56**, 247 (1934).
120. Hofmann, *Ber.*, **14**, 2725 (1881); **15**, 407, 752 (1882); **17**, 1406 (1884); **18**, 2734 (1885); **19**, 1822 (1886); Hoogedorft and van Dorp, *Rec. trav. chim.*, **15**, 107 (1896); Graebe and Rostowzew, *Ber.*, **35**, 2747 (1902); Hantzsch, *ibid.*, **35**, 3579 (1902); Mohr, *J. prakt. Chem.*, (2) **73**, 228 (1906); Mauguin, *Ann. chim. phys.*, (8) **22**, 316 (1911). *Cf.* Lapworth and Nichols, *Proc. Chem. Soc. London*, **19**, 22 (1903); Mohr, *J. prakt. Chem.*, (2) **72**, 297 (1905).
121. Wallis and Nagel, *J. Am. Chem. Soc.*, **53**, 2787 (1931); Wallis and Meyer, *ibid.*, **55**, 2598 (1933).
122. Houser and Co-workers, *J. Am. Chem. Soc.*, **59**, 121, 2308 (1937); **61**, 618 (1939).
123. Titherley, *J. Chem. Soc.*, **79**, 398 (1901).
124. Jeffreys, *Am. Chem. J.*, **22**, 14 (1899); Pyman, *J. Chem. Soc.*, **103**, 857 (1913); Stieglitz and Earle, *Am. Chem. J.*, **30**, 412 (1903); Mohr, *J. prakt. Chem.*, (2) **79**, 281 (1909); (2) **80**, 1 (1909); Odenwald, *Ann.*, **418**, 316 (1919).
125. Graebe, *Ber.*, **35**, 2753 (1902). Cf., Graebe and Rostowzer, *ibid.*, **35**, 2747 (1902); Stoermer and Schenk, *ibid.*, **60**, 2575 (1927); Bernstein and Wallis, *J. Org. Chem.*, **7**, 261 (1942).
126. Hofmann, *Ber.*, **17**, 1406, 1920 (1884).
127. Hoogewerff and van Dorp, *Rec. trav. chim.*, **6**, 376 (1887).
128. Lengfeld and Stieglitz, *Am. Chem. J.*, **15**, 504 (1893); **16**, **370** (1894).
129. Lengfeld and Stieglitz, *Am. Chem. J.*, 1. c., Jeffreys, *Ber.*, **30**, 898 (1897); *Am. Chem. J.*, **22**, 14 (1899); Gutt, *Ber.*, **40**, 2063 (1907).
130. Tcherniac, *Ber.*, **36**, 218 (1903).
131. Hofmann, *ibid.*, **21**, 2695 (1888); Willstätter, *ibid.*, **34**, 133 (1901); *Ann.*, **317**, 210 (1901); Pauly, *ibid.*, **322**, 85 (1902). *Cf.* Weerman, *ibid.*, **401**, 1 (1913); *Rec. trav. chim.*, **37**, 1 (1918); **39**, 200 (1920).
132. Weerman, *Rec. trav. chim.*, **37**, 16 (1918).
133. Weerman, *Ann.*, **401**, 1 (1913); *Rec. trav. chim.*, **37**, 2 (1918).
134. Willstätter, *Ann.*, **317**, 243 (1901); Blaise and Blanc, *Bull. soc. chim.*, (3) **21**, 973 (1899); Forster, *J. Chem. Soc.*, **79**, 119 (1901).
135. Rinkes, *Rec. trav. chim.*, **39**, 704 (1920).
136. v. Braun and Scolonina, *Bull. soc. chim.*, (3) **16**, 1878 (1896); v. Braun and Lemke, *Ber.*, **55**, 3529 (1922).
137. Weidel and Roithner, *Monatsh.*, **17**, 183 (1896); Rinkes, *Rec. trav. chim.*, **46**, 268 (1927); Fanchimont and Friedmann, *Rec. trav. chim.*, **25**, 75 (1906).
138. Barger and Walpole, *J. Chem. Soc.*, **95**, 1724 (1909); van Dam, *Rec. trav. chim.*, **18**, 418 (1899); Robinson and Sugasawa, *J. Chem. Soc.*, **1931**, 3166.
139. Buck and Ide, *"Organic Syntheses"*, **2**, 44 (1943); Graebe and Rostowzer, *Ber.*, **35**, 2747 (1902)
140. Hoogewerff and van Dorp, *Ber.*, **10**, 6 (1891); Jeffreys, *ibid.*, **30**, 899 (1897); Gräbe, *ibid.*, **34**, 2111 (1901); **35**, 2748 (1902); Moore *et al.*, *J. Chem. Soc.*, **119**. 1788 (1921).
141. Seidel and Bittner, *Monatsh.*, **23**, 418 (1902); Kahn, *Ber.*, **35**, 471 (1902); Kühn, *ibid.*, **28**, 809 (1895).
142. Graebe and Ullmann, *Ber.*, **27**, 3483 (1894); *Ann.*, **291**, 8 (1896).
143. Kirpal, *Monatsh*, **28**, 439 (1907); **29**, 227 (1908); Meyer, *ibid.*, **15**, 173 (1894); Kirpal and Reiter, *Ber.*, **58**, 699 (1925).
144. Fischer, *Ber.*, **39**, 551 (1906); Oppenheimer, *Handb. d. Biochem d. Mens u T.* **1**, p. 412 ff (1909); Abderhalden, *Neuere Ergebnisse auf dem Gebiete der Speziellen Eiweisschemie;* Fischer, Jena 1909; *Untersuchungen über Aminosäuren, Polypeptide und Proteine*, Vol. II, J. Springer, Berlin, 1923; Schmidt, *The Chemistry of Amino Acids and Proteins*, C. C. Thomas, Springfield, Ill., 1945, pp. 252-333.
145. Fischer, *Ber.*, **36**, 2982 (1903); **37**, 2486 (1904). *Cf.* Fischer, *Ber.*, **36**, 2094 (1903); **37**, 3070 (1904); **38**, 605, 2914 (1905); **39**, 2893 (1906); **40**, 1754 (1907); Fischer and Otto, *Ber.*, **36**, 2106 (1903).
146. Curtius, *Ber.*, **35**, 3226 (1902); *J. prakt. Chem.*, (2) **70**, 57, 73, 89, 109, 137, 158, 195, 223, 230 (1904); Curtius and Benroth, *Ber.*, **37**, 1279 (1904); Mohr, *J. prakt. Chem.*, (2) **81**, 55, 71, 473 (1919); Kaufmann *et al.*, *J. Am. Chem. Soc.*, **74**, 470 (1952); Vaughan and Osato, *ibid.*, **74**, 676 (1952); Holley and Holley, *ibid.*, **74**, 3069 (1952); Boissonnas, *Helv. Chim. Acta*, **34**, 874 (1951).
147. Goldschmidt and Strauss, *Ann.*, **471**, 1 (1929).
148. Biltz, *Ber.*, **25**, 2541 (1892).
149. Cahours, *Compt. rend.*, **27**, 239 (1848); Bernthsen, *Ann.*, **184**, 292 (1877); **192**, 29 (1878); Paradies, *Ber.*, **36**, 4302 (1903); Albert, *ibid.*, **48**, 470 (1915); Kindler, *Ann.*, **431**, 187 (1923); Alin and Johnson, *Rec. trav. chim.*, **50**, 72 (1931).
150. Kindler, *Ann.*, **450**, 1 (1926).
151. Ralston *et al.*, *J. Org. Chem.*, **4**, 68 (1939); Ralston, *U. S. patent* 2,168,847 (1939).
152. Dechend, *Ber.*, **7**, 1273 (1874); Kindler, *Ann.*, **431**, 206 (1923).
153. Sah and Hsü, *Rec. trav. chim.*, **59**, 349 (1940); Kahl, *Chem. Zentr.* **1904** II 1493.
154. Curtius and Riedel, *J. prakt. Chem.*, (2) **76**, 238 (1907).

155. Curtius and Bollenbeck, *ibid.*, (2) **76**, 281 (1907).
156. Stollé, *Ber.*, **32**, 796 (1899); **34**, 681 (1901); Pellizzari, *Atti accad. Lincei* (5) **8, I**, 329 (1899); Autenrieth and Spiess, *Ber.*, **34**, 187 (1901).
157. Curtius, *J. prakt. Chem.*, (2) **50**, 280 (1894).
158. Naegeli and Stefanovich, *Helv. Chim. Acta*, **11**, 609 (1928).
159. Stollé, *Ber.*, **32**, 796 (1899).
160. Curtius and Hille, *J. prakt. Chem.*, (2) **64**, 408, 415 (1901); Curtius and Dellschaft, *ibid.*, (2) **64**, 430 (1901); Naegeli *et al.*, *Helv. Chim. Acta*, **12**, 227, 894 (1929); **15**, 49 (1932); **11**, 609 (1928).
161. Weerman, *Rec. trav. chim.*, **37**, 52 (1917); Graf *et al*, *Ber.*, **64**, 21 (1931); Kermack and Muir, *J. Chem. Soc.*, **1931**, 3089; Toschi, *Gazz. chim. ital.*, **44 I**, 443 (1914).
162. Diels and Loflund, *Ber.*, **47**, 2351 (1914).
163. Schöpf *et al.*, *Ann.*, **497**, 49, 59 (1932).
164. Curtius and Protner, *J. prakt. Chem.*, (2) **58**, 190 (1898); Dimroth, *Ann.*, **364**, 210 (1908); Fischer and Dangschat, *Ber.*, **65**, 1009 (1932); Robinson and Todd, *J. Chem. Soc.*, **1939**, 1743.
165. Curtius and Davidis, *J. prakt. Chem.*, (2) **54**, 66 (1896); Schroeter and Seidler, *ibid.*, (2) **105**, 165 (1923).
166. Muckermann, *Ber.*, **42**, 3449 (1909); Curtius and Blicher, *J. prakt. Chem.*, (2) **107**, 86 (1924); v. Braun, *Ber.*, **67**, 218 (1934).
167. Curtius and Radenhausen, *J. prakt. Chem.*, (2) **52**, 433 (1895).
168. Foster, *J. Chem. Soc.*, **95**, 433 (1909); Jones and Mason, *J. Am. Chem. Soc.*, **49**, 2528 (1927).
169. Teppema, *Rec. trav. chim.*, **42**, 30 (1923).
170. Piccinini and Salmoni, *Gazz. chim. ital.*, **32 I**, 246 (1902); Fischer et al., *Z. Physiol. Chem.*, **132**, 72 (1924); *Ann.*, **481**, 159 (1930); **527**, 115 (1937); **531**, 245 (1937); **540**, 30 (1939).
171. Curtius et al., *J. prakt. Chem.*, (2) **91**, 39 (1915); Lindemann and Schulthers, *Ann.*, **464**, 237 (1928).
172. Curtius and Kufferath, *J. prakt. Chem.*, (2) **64**, 334 (1901).
173. Forster, *J. Chem. Soc.*, **95**, 433 (1909).
174. Curtius, *Ber.*, **27**, 779 (1894); **29**, 1166 (1896); Schroeter, *ibid.*, **42**, 3356 (1909).
175. Curtius 1. c.
176. Naegeli *et al.*, *Helv. Chim. Acta*, **12**, 227 (1929); **15**, 60 (1932).
177. Curtius, *Ber.*, **27**, 781 (1894); *J. prakt. Chem.*, (2) **50**, 295 (1895); (2) **94**, 273 (1917).
178. Curtius, *J. prakt. Chem.*, (2) **94**, 273 (1916); Schroeber, *Chem. Ztg.*, **32**, 933 (1908).
179. Curtius *et al.*, *Ber.*, **46**, 1162 (1913); **55**, 1543 (1922); *J. prakt. Chem.*, (2) **125**, 211 (1930).
180. Steller, *J. prakt. Chem.*, (2) **62**, 222 (1900); Curtius and Clemm, *J. prakt. Chem.*, (2) **62**, 203 (1900).
181. Oesterlin, *Angew. Chem.*, **45**, 536 (1932); Schmidt, *German patent* 500, 435.
182. Hoffman, *Ber.*, **22**, 2854 (1889); Hantzsch, *ibid.*, **27**, 799, 1954 (1894); Nef. *Ann.*, **298**, 212 (1897); *Ber.*, **31**, 2721 (1898); Schroeter, *ibid.*, **31**, 2190 (1898); Jones, *Am. Chem. J.*, **20**, 21 (1898); Biddle, *Ann.*, **310**, 9 (1899); *Am. Chem. J.*, **33**, 63 (1905); Jeanrenaud, *Ber.*, **22**, 1270 (1889); Angeli and Castellena, *Atti accad. Lincei*, (5) **18** I, 221 (1909); Monelli, *ibid.*, (5) **17** II, 74 (1908); Pickard and Neville, *J. Chem. Soc.*, **79**, 847 (1901); Bredt and Perkin, *J. prakt. Chem.*, (2) **197**, 209 (1914); Powell, *J. Am. Chem. Soc.*, **51**, 2436 (1929); Refrow and Hauser, *ibid.*, **59**, 2308 (1937); Bright and Hauser, *ibid.*, **61**, 618 (1939); Inoue, *et al.*, *J. Agr. Chem. Japan*, **16**, 504 (1940); **17**, 411, 491, 771; *C.A.*, **35**, 730 (1941); **36**, 3783, 4803, 4361 (1942).
183. Rimini, *Gazz. chim. ital.*, **31** II, 84 (1901); Angelico and Fanara, *ibid.*, **31** II, 15 (1901); Angeli and Angelico, *ibid.*, **30** I, 593 (1900); **33**, II, 239 (1903); **34**, I, 50 (1904); *Atti. accad. Lincei*, (5) **10**, I, 164 (1901); Angeli and Fanara, *Gazz. chim. ital.*, **31**, II, 26 (1901); Rimini, *Atti accad. Lincei*, (5) **10**, I, 355 (1901).
184. Bamberger and Scheutz, *Ber.*, **34**, 2029 (1901); Bamberger, *ibid.*, **36**, 710 (1903).
185. Lossen, *Ann.*, **161**, 347 (1872); **175**, 313 (1875); **186**, 1 (1877); **252**, 170 (1889); **265**, 176 (1891); **281**, 169 (1894); Rotermund, *ibid.*, **175**, 257 (1875); Rostocki, *ibid.*, **178**, 213 (1875); Piescheli, *ibid.*, **175**, 305 (1875); Jeffreys, *Am. Chem. J.*, **22**, 43 (1899); Bamberger and Destraz, *Ber.*, **35**, 1874 (1902); Marquis, *Compt. rend.*, **143**, 1163 (1906); Weerman, *Rec. trav. chim.*, **26**, 203 (1907); Jones and Sneed, *J. Am. Chem. Soc.*, **39**, 674 (1917); Rinkes, *Rec. trav. chim.*, **39**, 200 (1920); Nicolet and Pelc, *ibid.*, **44**, 1145 (1922); Naegeli and Stefanovitsch, *Helv. Chim. Acta*, **9**, 615 (1928); Yale, *Chem. Revs.*, **33**, 242 (1943).
186. Thiele and Pickard, *Ann.*, **309**, 189 (1899).
187. Lengfeld and Stieglitz, *Am. Chem. J.*, **15**, 215, 504 (1893); Stieglitz, *ibid.*, **18**, 751 (1896); **29**, 49 (1903). Jeffreys, *ibid.*, **22**, 15 (1899); Mauguin, *Ann. chim.*, (8) **22**, 322 (1911).
188. Pinner, *Ber.*, **10**, 1889 (1887); **16**, 352, 1654 (1883); **17**, 184, 2002 (1884); **23**, 2917 (1890); Glock, *ibid.*, **21**, 2650 (1888); Eitner and Wets, *ibid.*, **26**, 2840 (1893); Pinner, *Die Iminöather und ihre Derivate*, 1892.
189. *Cf.* Nef, *Ann.*, **287**, 328 (1895); Pinner, *Ber.*, **28**, 2454 (1895).

190. Pinner, *Ber.*, **23**, 2917 (1890); Yamashita, *Science Reports, Tohoku Imp. Univ. 1st Series*, **18**, 129, 609 (1929).
191. Steinkopf and Malinowski, *Ber.*, **44**, 2898 (1911); Steinkopf, *ibid.*, **42**, 617 (1909).
192. Stieglitz and Mackee, *ibid.*, **23**, 1494 (1899); **33**, 1517 (1900); Basterfield *et al.*, *Can. J. Research*, **17 B**, 390 (1939).
193. Knorr, *Ber.*, **49**, 1735 (1916).
194. Houben and Pfankuch, *ibid.*, **59B**, 1594 (1926).
195. Tafel and Enoch, *ibid.*, **23**, 103 (1890); Lander, *J. Chem. Soc.*, **79**, 691, 701 (1901); **83**, 415 (1903); Bühner, *Ann.*, **333**, 289 (1904).
196. Pinner, *Ber.*, **16**, 359, 1643 (1883); **17**, 179 (1884); Lamb and White, *J. Chem. Soc.*, **1939**, 1253.
197. Henle, *Ber.*, **35**, 3039 (1902).
198. Wenker, *J. Am. Chem. Soc.*, **57**, 3039 (1935).
199. Eschweiler, *Ber.*, **30**, 998 (1897); Hantzsch and Voegelen, *ibid.*, **34**, 3142 (1901); Mackenzie, *J. Chem. Soc.*, **113**, 1 (1918); Rule, *ibid.*, **113**, 3 (1918).
200. Knorr, *Ber.*, **30**, 929 (1897); Wheeler and Johnson, *Am. Chem. J.*, **21**, 185 (1899); Wheeler, *ibid.*, **23**, 135 (1900); Lander, *J. Chem. Soc.*, **83**, 406 (1903); Cf. *ibid.*, **79**, 690 (1901); **81**, 591 (1902); **83**, 320 (1903).
201. Lander, *Proc. Chem. Soc.*, **19**, 45 (1903); *J. Chem. Soc.*, **83**, 320 (1903); *Chem. Zentr.* **1903 I**, 833, 876.
202. Pinner and Klein, *Ber.*, **11**, 1825 (1878); Bernthsen, *Ann.*, **197**, 347 (1879); Pinner, *Die Iminoäther und ihre Derivate*, 1892; Autenrieth and Brüning, *Ber.*, **36**, 3468 (1903); Arnd, *Ann.*, **384**, 222 (1911); Houben and Zivadinovitsch, *Ber.*, **69**, 2352 (1936).
203. Wallach, *Ber.*, **15**, 208 (1882).
204. Cornell, *J. Am. Chem. Soc.*, **50**, 3311 (1928).
205. Kirssanoff and Poliakowa, *Bull. soc. chim.*, (5) **3**, 1600 (1936); Ziegler, *U. S. patent* 2,049,582.
206. Walter, *J. prakt. Chem.*, (2) **50**, 91 (1894); (2) **67**, 445 (1903); Lottermoser, *ibid.*, (2) **54**, 113 (1896); Engelhardt, *ibid.*, (2) **54**, 143 (1896).
207. Dachlauer, *German patent* 671,785 (1939).
208. Lossen, *Ann.*, *Suppl.* **6**, 234 (1868); Lossen and Schifferdecker, *Ann.*, **166**, 295 (1873); Tiemann, *Ber.*, **17**, 126 (1884); **22**, 2391 (1889); Tiemann and Krüger, *ibid.*, **17**, 1685 (1884); Nordmann, *ibid.*, **17**, 2746 (1884); Tiemann, *ibid.*, **18**, 1060 (1885); **24**, 435, 3420, 3648 (1891); Jacoby, *ibid.*, **19**, 1500 (1886); Freund and Lenze, *ibid.*, **24**, 2154 (1891); Freund and Schönfeld, *ibid.*, **24**, 3355 (1891); Nordstedt and Wahlforss, *ibid.*, **25**, R 637 (1892); Forselles and Wahlforss, *ibid.*, **25**, R 636 (1892); Eitner and Wetz, *ibid.*, **26**, 2844 (1893); Tiemann and Sembritzki, *ibid.*, **22**, 2958 (1899).
209. Tiemann and Richter, *Ber.*, **24**, 3676 (1891); Steinkopf and Bohrmann, *ibid.*, **40**, 1641 (1907); Steinkopf and Grunup, *ibid.*, **41**, 3571 (1908).
210. Troeger and Volkmer, *J. prakt. Chem.*, (2) **71**, 236 (1905).
211. Tiemann, *Ber.*, **17**, 128 (1884); **24**, 371 (1891); Pinnow and Sämann, *ibid.*, **29**, 623 (1896).
212. Tiemann, *Ber.*, **24**, 369 (1891).
213. Weerman, *Rec. trav. chim.*, **37**, 16 (1917); Irvine and Pryde, *J. Chem. Soc.*, **125**, 1045 (1924); Humphreys *et al.*, *ibid.*, **1931**, 1298; Haworth *et al.*, *ibid.*, **1933**, 1270; Ault *et al.*, *ibid.*, **1934**, 1722, Micheel Kraft, *Ber.*, **67**, 841 (1934).
214. Nencki, *Ber.*, **7**, 160 (1874); Bischoff, *ibid.*, **7**, 628 (1874); Bischoff and Rainfeld, *ibid.*, **36**, 39 (1903); Conrad and Hock, *ibid.*, **36**, 2206 (1903); Diels and Ochs, *ibid.*, **40**, 4571 (1907); Einhorn, *Ann.*, **361**, 130 (1908); Douris, *Bull. soc. chim.*, (4) **9**, 924 (1911); Maugin, *Ann.*, *chim.*, (8) **22**, 365 (1911); Viguier, *Compt. rend.*, **153**, 1231 (1911); Curtius, *Ber.*, **45**, 1068, 1083 (1912).
215. Moscheles, *Ber.*, **24**, 1803 (1891); Hantzsch, *ibid.*, **27**, 1248 (1894); Diels and Seib, *ibid.*, **42**, 4062 (1909); Diels and Gukassianz, *ibid.*, **43**, 3314 (1910); Feist, *ibid.*, **45**, 945 (1912).
216. Hantzsch, *Ber.*, **27**, 1249 (1894); Simon, *Compt. rend.*, **133**, 535 (1901); **142**, 790, 892 (1906); *Ann. chim.*, (8) **8**, 467 (1906); Curtiss and Stracham, *J. Am. Chem. Soc.*, **33**, 399 (1911).
217. Oxley *et al*, *J. Soc. Chem. Ind.*, **1948**, 349.
218. Meyer, *Monatsh.*, **22**, 437 (1901); McMaster and Alimann, *J. Am. Chem. Soc.*, **50**, 145 (1928); Carré and Libermann, *Compt. rend.*, **199**, 1422 (1934).
219. Kyrides, *J. Am. Chem. Soc.*, **59**, 206 (1937).
220. Fischer, *Ber.*, **36**, 2094 (1903); Michaelis, *Ann.*, **274**, 185 (1893); Herre, *Ber.*, **28**, 594 (1895).
221. Sen and Ray, *J. Chem. Soc.*, **1926**, 646. *Cf.* Druzdov and Bekhli, *J. Gen. Chem. U.S.S.R.*, **14**, 472 (1944).
222. Staudinger and Bereza, *Ber.*, **41**, 4463 (1908).
223. Conrad and Reinbach, *ibid.*, **35**, 1814 (1902).
224. Daubert *et al.*, *J. Am. Chem. Soc.*, **65**, 2143 (1943); Bauer, *Oil and Soap*, **23**, 1 (1946).
225. Mashentoev, *J. Gen. Chem. U.S.S.R.*, **15**, 915 (1945); *C.A.*, **40**, 6443 (1946).
226. Nierenstein, *Nature*, **121**, 940 (1928).
227. Wilds and Meader, *J. Org. Chem.*, **13**, 763 (1948).

228. Coleman and Alvarado, *Organic Syntheses*, Coll. vol. I, 3 (1941).
229. Mitchell and Reid, *J. Am. Chem. Soc.*, **53**, 1879 (1931); Ralston, *et al.*, *J. Org. Chem.*, **8**, 473 (1943).
230. Searle, *U.S. patent* 2,444,536 (1948).
231. Cherubliez and Landolt, *Helv. Chim. Acta*, **29**, 1438 (1946).
232. Gordon *et al.*, *J. Am. Chem. Soc.*, **71**, 1245 (1949).
233. *Cf.* Kohrs and Lang, *J. prakt. Chem.*, **158**, 112 (1941).
234. Abrams and Kipping, *J. Chem. Soc.*, **1934**, 1990; Kibler and Weissberger, *Organic Syntheses*, **25**, 7 (1945).
235. Gang and Rising, *J. Am. Chem. Soc.*, **53**, 3183 (1931).
236. Eck and Marvel, *Organic Syntheses*, Coll. Vol. II, 76 (1943); Ingersoll and Babcock, *ibid.*, 328; *J. Org. Chem.*. **9**, 396 (1944).
237. Herbst and Shemin, *Organic Syntheses*, Coll. Vol. II, 11 (1943).
238. Cleland and Niemann, *J. Am. Chem. Soc.*, **71**, 841 (1949); Dakin and West, *J. Biol. Chem.*, **78**, 91, 757 (1928).
239. Smith and Emerson, *J. Am. Chem. Soc.*, **67**, 1862 (1945); *Organic Syntheses*, **29**, 19 (1949), *Cf.* Tingle and Brenton, *J. Am. Chem. Soc.*, **32**, 116 (1910); Manske, *ibid.*, **51**, 1202(1929).
240. Turner, *J. Am. Chem. Soc.*, **68**, 1607 (1946); Jenkins *et al.*, *ibid.*, **52**, 5202 (1930); Cook and Cox, *J. Chem. Soc.*, **1949**, 2336.
241. Wiley and Waddey, *Organic Syntheses*, **29**, 61 (1949); *J. Org. Chem.*, **13**, 421 (1948).
242. Galat, *J. Am. Chem. Soc.*, **70**, 3945 (1948); Krewson and Couch, *ibid.*, **65**, 2256 (1943).
243. Murray and Cloke, *J. Am. Chem. Soc.*, **56**, 2742 (1934).
244. Ritter and Minieri, *ibid.*, **70**, 4045 (1948); Ritter and Kalish, *ibid.*, **70**, 4048 (1948).
245. Staudinger and Andes, *Ber.*, **46**, 1417 (1913).
246. *Cf.* Rosenmund and Zetzsche, *Ber.*, **54**, 2038 (1921); Freudenberg *et al.*, *ibid.*, **61**, 1735 (1928); Fischer and Baer, *ibid.*, **65**, 337, 345 (1932).
247. Bergmann and Zervas, *Ber.*, **65**, 1192 (1932); Greenberg, *Amino Acids and Proteins*, C.C. Thomas, Springfield, Ill., 1951, p. 178. *Cf.* Bergmann *et al.*, *Ber.*,**65**, 1692 (1932); Kenner and Stedman, *J. Chem. Soc.*, **1952**, 2069; Vaughan and Osato, *J. Am. Chem. Soc.*, **14**, 676 (1952); Wieland and Schäfer, *Ann.*, **576**, 104 (1952); Goldschmidt and Wick, *ibid.*, **575**, 217 (1952).
248. Loring and du Vigneaud, *J. Biol. Chem.*, **111**, 385 (1935).
249. Harington and Mead, *Biochem. J.*, **29**, 1603 (1935).
250. Channing *et al.*, *Nature*, **167**, 487 (1951).
251. Kenner, *Chemistry and Industry*, **1951**, 15. *Cf.* Fischer, *Ber.*, **36**, 2094 (1903); Curtius, *J. Prakt. Chem.*, **70**, 73 (1904); Sheehan and Frank, *J. Am. Chem. Soc.*, **72**, 1312 (1950); Chantrenne, *Biochim. et Biophys. Acta*, **4**, 484 (1950); Wieland *et al*, *Ann.*, **569**, 117, 122 (1950); **572**, 190 (1951); *Angew. Chem.*, **63**, 7 (1951); Coffey *et al.*, *British patent* 642,206.
252. Boisonnais, *Helv. Chim Acta*, **34**, 874 (1951); Vaughan, *J. Am. Chem. Soc.*, **73**, 3547 (1951); Vaughan and Osato, *ibid.*, **73**, 5583 (1951).
253. Anderson *et al.*, *J. Am. Chem. Soc.*, **73**, 501 (1951); Vaughan, *ibid.*, **73**, 1389 (1951).
254. Ing and Manske, *J. Chem. Soc.*, (2) **52**, 446 (1896); Ehrensvärd, *Nature*, **159**, 500 (1947). King and Kidd, *J. Chem. Soc.*, **1949**, 3315; Sheehan and Frank, *J. Am. Chem. Soc.*, **71**, 1856 (1949); Grassmann and Schulte-Uebbing, *Ber.*, **83**, 244 (1950).
255. Waldschmidt-Leitz and Kunstner, *Z. physiol. Chem.*, **171**, 70 (1927).
256. du Vigneaud and Behrens, *J. Biol. Chem.*, **117**, 27 (1937); Wooley, *ibid.*, **172**, 71 (1948). du Vigneaud, *et al.*, *J. Am. Chem. Soc.*, **75**, 4879 (1953); *J. Biol. Chem.*, **205**, 949 (1953).
257. *Cf.* Wieland and Sehring, *Ann.*, **569**, 122 (1950).
258. Bailey, *Nature*, **164**, 889 (1949).
259. Goldschmidt, *Z. anorg. allgem. Chem.*, **62**, 538 (1950); Süs, *Ann.*, **572**, 96 (1951).
260. Hurd and Buess, *J. Am. Chem. Soc.*, **73**, 2409 (1951); Hurd and Bauer, *ibid.*, **73**, 4387 (1951).
261. Bergmann *et al.*, *Ann.*, **449**, 277 (1926); *Z. physiol. Chem.*, **167**, 91 (1927); **175**, 154 (1928); *Ber.*, **62**, 1905 (1929).
262. Fischer and Suzuki, *Ber.*, **38**, 4173 (1905).
263. *Cf.* Anderson *et al.*, *J. Am. Chem. Soc.*, **74**, 5304, 5307, 5309 (1952).
264. Undenfriend and Velick, *J. Biol. Chem.*, **190**, 733 (1951). Velick and Undenfriend, *J. Biol. Chem.*, **203**, 575 (1953).
265. Waley and Watson, *J. Chem. Soc.*, **1951**, 2394; Tibbs, *Nature*, **168**, 910 (1951).
266. Waley and Watson, *l. c.*, Tibbs, *l. c.*; Schlack and Kumpf, *Z. physiol. Chem.*, **154**, 125(1926).
267. Hofmann, *Ber.*, **11**, 338 (1878); Bernthsen, *ibid.*, **11**, 503 (1878); Gatewood and Johnson, *J. Am. Chem. Soc.*, **48**, 2900 (1926).
268. Todd *et al.*, *J. Chem. Soc.*, **1936**, 1557; **1937**, 361; Backes, *Compt. rend.*, **225**, 533 (1947).
269. Myamichi, *J. Pharm. Soc. Japan*, **528**, 103 (1926); *Report to the Committee for Pennicillin Synthesis of the Medical Research Council*, pp. 634, 693.
270. Todd *et al.*, *J. Chem. Soc.*, **1936**, 1557; **1937**, 361; **1946**, 647.
271. Abraham *et al.*, *Report to the Committee for Penicillin Synth.* pp. 43, 74, 438; Cook *et al.*,

ibid., p. 199; Upjohn Co., *ibid.*, 265, 292; Squibb Inst. Med. Res., *ibid.*, pp. 277, 278, 330; Lilly Res. Lab., *ibid.*, pp. 286, 317; Merck Co., Inc., *ibid.*, pp. 289, 307; Brodrick *et al.*, *ibid.*, p. 592.

272. Holmberg, *"The Svedberg Memorial Volume"* (Stockholm 1944); p. 299; *Archiv. Kemi. Mineral. Geol.*, **17A**, 1 (1944); Elliot, *Nature*, **162**, 658 (1948).
273. Levi, *Gazz. chim. ital.*, **54**, 395 (1924); Houben, *Ber.*, **39**, 3227 (1906).
274. Sakurada, *Mem. Coll. Sci. Univ. Kyoto.*, **9**, 237 (1926).
275. Squibb. Inst. for Med. Res., *Report to the Committee for Penicillin Synth.*, p. 301.
276. Staudinger and Siegwart, *Helv. Chim. Acta.*, **3**, 824 (1920).
277. Modeen, *Ber.*, **24**, 3437 (1891).
278. Francesconi and Bastianini, *Gazz. chim. ibal.*, **34**, I, 428 (1904); Hofmann, *Ber.*, **20**, 2204 (1887); **22**, 2854 (1889).
279. Heintz, *Zeitschrift Für Chemie*, **12**, 733 (1869); Hodges, *Ann.*, **182.**,214 (1876), *Cf.* Jones and Hurd, *J. Am. Chem. Soc.*, **43**, 2422 (1921); **49**, 2528 (1927); Jones and Root, *ibid.*, **48**, 181 (1926).
280. Abderhalden and Guggenheim, *Ber.*, **41**, 2853 (1908).
281. Thiele and Lachmann, *Ann.*, **288**, 267 (1895). *Cf.* Thiele and Meyer, *Ber.*, **29**, 961 (1896); Franchimont, *Rec. trav. chim.*, **2**, 96 (1883); **3**, 219 (1884); Franchimont and Umbgrove, *ibid.*, **15**, 196, 211 (1896); **17**, 288 (1898); Degner and v. Pechmann, *Ber.*, **30**, 646 (1897); Heinke, *ibid.*, **31**, 1395 (1898).
282. Thiele, *Ann.*, **270**, 23 (1892); **273**, 133 (1893); Jousselin, *Compt. rend.*, **85**, 548 (1877); **88**, 814, 1086 (1879); Pellizzari, *Gazz. chim. ital.*, **21**, II, 405 (1891); Franchimont, *Rec. trav. chim.*, **10**, 231 (1891).
283. Thiele, *Ann.*, **273**, 133 (1893).
284. Schroeter *et al.*, *Ber.*, **63**, 1308 (1903).
285. Goldschmidt *et al.*, *Ann.*, **580**, 68 (1953); *Ber.*, **86**, 1116 (1953).
286. Sanger, *Biochem. J.*, **45**, 563 (1949); Rice and Sowden, *Can. J. Chem.*, **30**, 575,(1952); Weibull, *Acta. Chem. Scand.*, **7**, 335 (1953); Mellon *et al.*, *J. Am. Chem. Soc.*, **75**, 1675 (1953); Li and Ash, *J. Biol. Chem.*, **203**, 419 (1953); Rovery and Fabre, *Bull. soc. chim., biol.*, **35**, 541 (1953); Bowes and Moss, *Biochem. J.*, **55**, 735 (1953); Schroeder *et al.*, *Proc. Natl. Acad. Sci., U. S.*, **39**, 23 (1953); *J. Am. Chem. Soc.*, **75**, 4612, 4615 (1953); Schramin and Braunitzer, *Z. Naturforsch.*, **86**, 61 (1953); Fraenkel and Singer, *J. Am. Chem. Soc.*, **76**, 180 (1954).
287. Levy, J. *Chem. Soc.*, **1950**, 404; Leonic, *Compt. rend. trav. lab. Carlsberg. sér. chim.*, **26**, 315 (1948); Edman, *Acta Chem. Scand.*, **4**, 253 (1950).
288. Thompson, *Biochim. Biophys. Acta*, **10**, 633 (1953).
289. Dickman and Asplund, *J. Am. Chem. Soc.*, **74**, 5208 (1952).
290. Edman, *Acta Chem. Scand.*, **4**, 277, 283 (1950).
291. Partridge and Davies, *Nature*, **165**, 62 (1950).
292. Ingram, *J. Biol. Chem.*, **202**, 193 (1953).
293. Kenner *et al.*, *J. Chem. Soc.*, **1953**, 673.
294. Ewan and Young, *J. Soc. Chem. Ind.*, **40**, 109 T (1921); Smith *et al.*, *Ind. Eng. Chem.*, **23**, 1124 (1931); Davis and Elderfield, *J. Am. Chem. Soc.*, **55**, 731 (1933); Davis, *Organic Syntheses*, Coll. Vol. I, 302, 399 (1941); Barton *et al.*, *J. Am. Chem. Soc.*, **73**, 2201 (1951); Holstead and Lamberton, *J. Chem. Soc.*, **1952**, 1886; Simkins and Williams, *ibid.*, **1952**, 3086.
295. Bogert and Dox, *J. Am. Chem. Soc.*, **27**, 1127 (1905); Arndt, *Ber.*, **46**, 3522 (1913).
296. Arndt and Rosenau, *Ber.*, **50**, 1248 (1917).
297. Pellizzari and Gaiter, *Gazz. chim. ital.*, **44 II**, 72 (1914); Fantle and Silbermann, *Ann.*, **467**, 274 (1928); *German patent* 689,191 (1940); Lieber and Smith, *Chem. Rev.*, **25**, 213 (1939).
298. Davis, *J. Am. Chem. Soc.*, **44**, 868 (1922); Fromm *et al.*, *Ann.*, **442**, 130 (1925); Tatarinow, *Compt. rend.*, **89**, 608 (1879); Tawildarow, *Ber.*, **5**, 477 (1872).
299. Erlenmeyer, *Ber.*, **14**, 1868 (1881); Tatarinow, l.c..
300. Braun and Randall, *J. Am. Chem. Soc.*, **55**, 2134 (1933).
301. Braun, *ibid.*, **55**, 1280 (1933); Kaempf, *Ber.*, **37**, 1681 (1904); McKee, *Am. Chem. J.*, **26**, 209 (1901); *French patent* 736,174 (1931).
302. *U.S. patents* 1,883,189; 1,884,509; 1,886,087; 1,897,220; *British Patents* 304,360; 478,525; *German patents* 502,045; 684,724; *French patent* 736,174 (1931).
303. Arndt and Rosenau, *Ber.*, **50**, 1248 (1917).
304. King and Wright, *J. Chem. Soc.*, **1939**, 253.
305. *German patent* 172,979.
306. Braun *et al.*, *J. Org. Chem.*, **3**, 146 (1938).
307. Paucksch, *Ber.*, **17**, 2800 (1884).
308. Sullivan and Hess, *J. Am. Chem. Soc.*, **58**, 47 (1936).
309. Braun and Schwarz, *Ber.*, **36**, 3660 (1903).
310. Huhn, *Ber.*, **19**, 2404 (1886); Keller, *ibid.*, **24**, 2398 (1891); Markwald, *Ann.*, **286**, 343 (1895); Schall, *J. prakt. Chem.*, (2) **61**, 440 (1900); Busch *et al.*, *Ber.*, **38**, 4049 (1905); *J. prakt.*

Chem., (2) **74**, 541 (1909); (2) **79**, 513 (1909); Ley and Muller, *Ber.*, **40**, 2950 (1907); Snedker, *J. Soc. Chem. Ind.*, **45**, 352T (1926); Raiford and Daddow, *J. Am. Chem. Soc.*, **53**, 1552 (1931); Sieg and Dehn, *ibid.*, **62**, 3506 (1940).
311. Weith, *Ber.*, **7**, 10 (1874).
312. Weith, *ibid.*, **9**, 810 (1876).
313. Fischer, *ibid.*, **32**, 435 (1899).
314. Hofmann, *Ber.*, **2**, 485 (1869); Losanitsch, *ibid.*, **5**, 156 (1872); Dyer and Johnson, *J. Am. Chem. Soc.*, **54**, 777 (1932).
315. Hofmann, *l.c.*
316. Schenck, *Arch. Pharm.*, **249**, 463 (1911); *Chem. Zentr.*, **1911 II**, 1216.
317. Klinger, *Z. physiol. Chem.*, **155**, 206 (1926); *Chem. Zentr.*, **1926 II**, 1267.
318. *U.S. patent* 1,642,180 (1927) duPont.
319. Busch and Bauer, *Ber.*, **33**, 1058 (1900); Busch and Ulmer, *ibid.*, **35**, 1716 (1902).
320. Marckwald and Wolf, *Ber.*, **25**, 3116 (1892). *Cf.* Schall, *J. prakt. Chem.*, (2) **64**, 261 (1901); Busch, *Ber.*, **38**, 856 (1905); Daddow, *J. Am. Chem. Soc.*, **53**, 1552 (1931).
321. Fromm, *Ann.*, **361**, 302 (1908); **394**, 258 (1912).
322. Phillips and Clarke, *J. Am. Chem. Soc.*, **45**, 1755 (1923).
323. Arndt, *Ber.*, **54**, 2236 (1921).
324. Schenck and Kirchhof, *Z. physiol. Chem.*, **153**, 150; *Chem. Zentr.*, **1925 I**, 643.
325. Schotte *et al.*, *Z. physiol. Chem.*, **174**, 119 (1928); *Chem. Zentr.*, **1928 II**, 1962.
326. Evers, *Ber.*, **21**, 962 (1888).
327. Wheeler *et al.*, *J. Am. Chem. Soc.*, **25**, 787 (1903).
328. *U.S. patent* 1,805,889 (1931); *German patent* 565,881 (1933).
329. Dakin, *J. Biol. Chem.*, **1**, 271 (1906); Davis and Abrams, *Proc. Am. Acad. Arts. Sci.*, **61**, 437 (1926); Englund, *Skand. Arch. Physiol.*, **47**, 15 (1925); *C.A.*, **20**, 1113 (1926); Griess, *Ber.*, **8**, 322 (1875); **15**, 447 (1882).
330. Johnson and Chernoff, *J. Am. Chem. Soc.*, **34**, 164 (1912).
331. Prandtl and Dollfus, *Ber.*, **65**, 754 (1932).
332. Sell and Zierold, *Ber.*, **7**, 1228 (1874). *Cf.* Bly *et al.*, *J. Am. Chem. Soc.*, **44**, 2899 (1922); Busch and Ulmer, *Ber.*, **35**, 1716 (1902).
333. Ley and Winkler, *Ber.*, **47**, 2945 (1914).
334. Schenck, *Arch. Pharm.*, **249**, 463 (1911); *Chem. Zentr.*, **1911 II**, 1216.
335. Connolly and Dyson, *J. Chem. Soc.*, **1937**, 827.
336. Hofmann, *Ann.*, **139**, 107 (1866).
337. Hantschel, *J. prakt. Chem.*, (2) **27**, 498 (1883).
338. Pellizzari, *Gazz. chim. ital.*, **21 I**, 333 (1891).
339. Pellizzari and Gaiter, *ibid.*, **44 II**, 78 (1914); *Chem. Zentr.*, **1914 II**, 1348.
340. Bowles, *Thesis*, Heidelberg (1909). *Cf.* Stollé and Bowles, *Ber.*, **41**, 1099 (1908); Scholl, *ibid.*, **26**, 118 (1893).
341. Schenck, *Z. physiol. Chem.*, **150**, 121 (1925).
342. Schenck, *Arch. Pharm.*, **247**, 466 (1910).
343. Ley, *Ber.*, **41**, 1637 (1908).

CHAPTER 9

ALIPHATIC NITRILES AND RELATED COMPOUNDS

NITRILES

Formation of Nitriles

Nitriles may be prepared by a great variety of reactions; the most important among these depend on the replacement of halogens or other acid radicals in organic compounds with the cyano group by reaction with a metallic cyanide, and the substitution of the diazo group in aromatic compounds with the cyano group.

Preparation of Nitriles by Replacement of Halogens and Other Acid Radicals with the Cyano Group

The halogen in organic halo compounds varies greatly in its mobility, depending on the structure and character of the compound and the position the halogen occupies in the molecule. The reactivity of the halogens in some compounds is so great that reaction with alkali cyanides proceeds in the cold, or at a moderate temperature. Thus, ethylene chlorhydrin reacts with aqueous sodium cyanide at about 50° to form ethylene cyanhydrin:

$$HOCH_2CH_2Cl + NaCN \rightarrow HOCH_2CH_2CN + NaCl$$

In general, negative groups attached to the carbon atom bearing the halogen atom activate the halogen. Thus, phenyl and naphthyl groups attached to CH_2Cl activate the chlorine atom. Carbinol, carbonyl, carboxyl, alkoxy and cyanomethyl groups and the group $>C=CH-$ also cause the activation of the halogen. The bromine atoms in ethylene dibromide are readily replaced with the CN group by reaction with sodium cyanide. Ethylidene dibromide, CH_3CHBr_2, behaves exceptionally; on reaction with an alkali metal cyanide it yields succinonitrile, in low yield, instead of the expected methylmalononitrile.

The more reactive substituted benzyl halides, especially the *p*-methoxy derivative, undergo extensive alcoholysis when the reaction with alkali cyanides is carried out in alcoholic solution.[261] Acetone, acetonitrile, and phenylacetonitrile have been used successfully as solvents for the conversion of such reactive halides to nitriles.[262]

The replacement of halogens in the less reactive compounds can often be accomplished by carrying out the reaction at a sufficiently high temperature. Resort may be had, for this purpose, to the use of high boiling solvents; alternatively, the reaction may be carried out in a sealed tube. Ethylene dichloride, 2,2-dialkyl-1,3-dibromopropanes, methylene halides, halides of the type

$$RCH = CClR'$$

chlorofumaric and α-chlorocrotonic acids are among the unreactive halides.

Bromine in organic compounds is more reactive than chlorine. As a consequence of this difference in reactivity, it is possible to prepare γ-chlorobutyronitrile, $CNCH_2CH_2CH_2Cl$, through the reaction of 1-chloro-3-bromopropane with an alcoholic solution of potassium cyanide used in a slight deficiency.[1] Acetylenic nitriles are best prepared by heating the corresponding iodides with alkali cyanides in aqueous acetone, or with cuprous cyanide in xylene.[263]

Differences are occasionally observed between the results obtained with potassium- and sodium cyanides. Thus, with cetyl bromide and other similar halides, better results are obtained when potassium cyanide is used instead of sodium cyanide.

The use of cuprous cyanide presents an advantage with the less reactive halides. The use of cuprous cyanide offers the further advantage that side reactions arising from the alkaline conditions involved in the use of alkali metal cyanides are avoided. Cyanomethyl ethers, $CNCH_2OR$, may thus, be conveniently prepared from the corresponding chloro compounds by reaction with cuprous cyanide.[2] Some vinyl halides have been converted to cyanides by reaction with cuprous cyanide in the presence of an amine promoter.[264] Acyl cyanides, RCOCN, have been obtained in good yield through the reaction of acid bromides, RCOBr, and cuprous cyanide.[3]

In the reaction of alkyl halides with metallic cyanides the normal as well as the isonitrile may form simultaneously, the proportion of the two depending on the metal cyanide employed. When silver cyanide is used an isonitrile is the major product of the reaction, mercuric and zinc cyanides also yielding a high proportion of the isonitrile. With alkali cyanides, the principal product of the reaction is the normal nitrile.

While cyano compounds are obtained from primary halides, secondary and tertiary halides give olefinic compounds by reaction with alkali cyanides; olefins are also obtained from alicyclic halides.

Acyl chlorides, RCOCl, may be converted to acyl cyanides by reaction with alkali metal cyanides or, preferably, by reaction with hydrocyanic acid in the presence of pyridine or other tertiary bases.[4]

The reaction of hydrocyanic acid with quinoline in the presence of an acid chloride leads to the formation of 1-acyl-cyano-1,2-dihydroquinoline (Reissert's compounds):

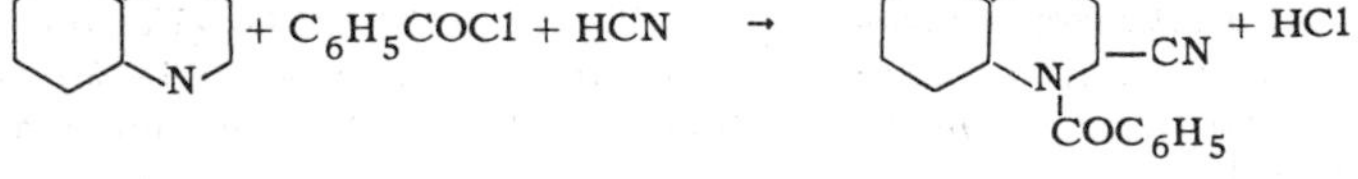

Quinoline cannot, therefore, be used in the above reaction.

Halogen atoms directly attached to an aromatic nucleus are replaced with difficulty by the cyano group. Replacement is possible by heating the halo compound to 200° with an alcoholic solution of an alkali cyanide in the presence of cuprous cyanide, although breakdown of the cyano group takes place under these conditions, with the formation of the ester of the corresponding carboxylic acid. The reaction proceeds well also when nicklous cyanide is used instead of cuprous cyanide.[5] The reaction has been carried out also by heating a mixture of the halide with an alkaline cyanide in the presence of metallic copper, with sand or fullers earth added as diluents. The reaction of an aromatic halide with an alkali metal cyanide usually takes place at 300° in pyridine solution without the use of a catalyst; in the absence of pyridine, heating to 350 - 400° is necessary. There are exceptions, however; thus, *p*-toluene bromide reacts at 200°.

Replacements Involving Other Simultaneous Changes

The replacement of halogens with the cyano group is accompanied in the case of certain compounds by other changes. *α-Chloroethyl methyl ketone* reacting with sodium cyanide gives the epoxy nitrile $CH_3\overset{O}{CH.C}(CH_3)CN$.[6] *1-Chloro-1,2-diphenylethanol* reacting with potassium cyanide gives 1-cyano-1,2-epoxydiphenylethane.[7] *Allyl iodide* in alcoholic solution reacts with potassium cyanide to yield a mixture of β-ethoxypropionitrile and pyrotartaric dinitrile.[8] Potassium dicyanosuccinate, KOCOCH(CN)CH(CN)COOK results from the reaction of potassium cyanide with *ethyl monochloromaleate*. *1,2-Dichloropropylene*, $ClCH_2CCl = CH_2$, gives with an excess of potassium cyanide tricarballylonitrile, $CNCH_2CH(CN)CH_2CN$, while reaction with a deficiency of cyanide results in the formation of β-chlorocrotonic nitrile.

Potassium cyanide causes the severance of the carbon to oxygen bond in α, β-dichloroethyl ether giving chloroacetaldehyde cyanohydrin.[265]

Potassium trichloroacetate reacts with potassium cyanide to form chloroform and carbon dioxide.[9] *1,2-Dichlorodibromoethane*, ClBrCHCHBrCl, reacting with potassium cyanide gives α, β-dichloro-α-bromethylene.[10]

Potassium cyanide reacts with γ-chlorobutyrophenone forming benzoylcyclopropane,[11] $\overline{CH_2CH_2C}HCOC_6H_5$. *Nitrobenzyl chloride* reacting with potassium cyanide gives a certain amount of *o*-dinitrocyanodibenzyl, $NO_2C_6H_4CH(CN)CH_2C_6H_4NO_2$, in addition to *o*-nitrobenzyl cyanide, the normal product of the reaction. Similarly, *o-cyanobenzyl chloride* gives tricyanodibenzyl.[12]

Monochloracetone and potassium cyanide react in aqueous solution to form 2,5-dimethyl-5-hydroxytetrahydrofuran-2,4-dinitrile.[13]

Furfuryl chloride gives with potassium cyanide furfuryl cyanide,

$$\overline{OCH = CHCH = C}CH_2CN$$

and 2-methyl-5-cyanofurane, while *5-methylfurfuryl chloride* gives only the normal product 5-methylfurfuryl cyanide.[14] Tetrahydrofurfuryl chloride behaves normally, although its halogen is more firmly held.[266]

1,3-Dibromo-1,3-dibenzoylpropane, $C_6H_5COCHBrCH_2CHBrCOC_6H_5$, reacts with sodium cyanide in aqueous solution forming the four theoretically possible *2-cyano-2-phenyl-3-bromo-5-benzoyltetrahydrofurans*;[15] 1,4-dibrom-4-dibenzoylbutane yields a cyanodihydropyran derivative.[16]

Acetylchloralurethane reacts with potassium cyanide forming ethyl dichlorocyanovinylcarbamate:[17]

$$Cl_3CCH(OCOCH_3)NHCOOC_2H_5 + 2\ KCN \rightarrow$$
$$Cl_2C = C(CN)NHCOOC_2H_5 + HCN + KCl + CH_3COOK$$

α-Chlorochloralamides yield *β, β*-dichloro-*α*-cyanovinyl derivatives:[18]

$$RCONHCHClCCl_3 + 2KCN \rightarrow RCONHC(CN) = CCl_2 + 2KCl + HCN$$

Chalkone dibromides reacting with a warm alcoholic solution of potassium cyanide give *β*-aroyl-*α*-arylpropionitriles:[19]

$$R_1COCHBrCHBrR_2 + 3KCN + H_2O \rightarrow R_1COCH_2CH(CN)R_2 + 2KBr + HCN + KOCN$$

α-Chloropropanol, $CH_3CHClCH_2OH$, reacts with potassium cyanide giving *β*-hydroxybutyronitrile, $CH_3CH(OH)CH_2CN$.

Unsaturated 1,4-dihalides of the type of *1,4-dichloro-2-butene* reacting with potassium cyanide give largely 1-cyano-1,3-butadienes of the type $CH_2 = CHCH = CHCN$, with some of the expected 1,4-dicyanobutene.

Crotyl halides, $CH_3CH{:}CHCH_2X$, and methyl vinyl carbinyl halides, $CH_3CHXCH = CH_2$, reacting with cuprous cyanide, yield mixtures of isomeric unsaturated nitriles.[267] A similar isomerization is observed in the reaction of sorbyl chloride with potassium cyanide.[268]

1-Chloro-2,3-butadiene, $CH_2 = C = CHCH_2Cl$, subjected to the action of potassium cyanide in methyl alcoholic solution undergoes isomerization giving cyanobutadiene,

$$CH_2 = CHCH = CHCN,$$

a small amount of methoxycyanobutene, $CH_3OCH_2CH = CHCH_2CN$, also forming.[20]

Methyl α-chloroacrylate, $CH_2 = CClCOOCH_3$, reacting with sodium cyanide gives methyl *β*-cyanoacrylate, $CNCH = CHCOOCH_3$. *α*-Chloroacrylonitrile reacts in a similar manner.[21]

Acetylenic halides react with potassium cyanide in methanol solution to form methoxyacrylonitriles:

$$RC \equiv CCl + KCN + CH_3OH \rightarrow RC(OCH_3) = CHCN + KCl$$

These halides fail to react with alkali cyanides in dioxane solution.[22]

Tetrahydrochloroquinone yields 3,6-dihydroxy-2,5-dicyanoquinone on reaction with 85% aqueous methanol solution of potassium cyanide.[23]

Replacement of Sulfo- and Sulfonic Groups by the Cyano Group

Aliphatic nitriles may be obtained by heating alkyl sulfates with an alkali cyanide.[24] The reaction proceeds readily with methyl sulfate, but less readily with ethyl sulfate. Alkyl esters of arylsulfonic acids may also be used in this reaction; this method gives especially high yields of higher alkyl cyanides such as margaric nitrile.

The sulfonic group in aromatic sulfonic acids may be replaced with a cyano group by fusing the alkali metal salt of the sulfonic acid with potassium cyanide, or preferably, with potassium ferrocyanide.[25] Sand may be used as a diluent. The temperature should be carefully regulated, since an excessively high temperature will cause extensive decomposition. The nitrile formed is best distilled off under vacuum as rapidly as it is formed. Distillation may be carried out also under atmospheric pressure by passing a current of an indifferent gas through the reaction vessel. The use of potassium cyanide or ferrocyanide, rather than the sodium salts, is preferable. The yield can reach 40% of the theoretical.

Both sulfonic groups in aromatic disulfonic acids may be replaced with the cyano group by heating with potassium ferrocyanide, though the yield of dinitriles is generally low.[269]

In sulfonated aromatic chloro compounds the chlorine and sulfonic group may be replaced simultaneously by fusion with cyanide, although the reaction fails to proceed with purely chloroaromatic compounds.[26]

Reaction of Alkali Cyanides with γ-Lactones

Certain γ-lactones react with alkali cyanides in the absence of a solvent at elevated temperatures to form γ-cyano acids: [27]

$$H_2C.CH.CHCO.O + KCN \rightarrow CNCH_2.CH.CH.COOK$$

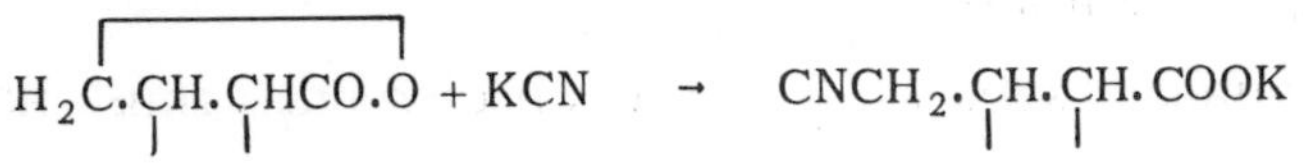

Thus, potassium cyanide and phthalide give homophthalic mononitrile:

$$C_6H_4 \underset{CO}{\overset{CH_2}{<}}O + KCN \rightarrow C_6H_4 \underset{COOK}{\overset{CH_2CN}{<}}$$

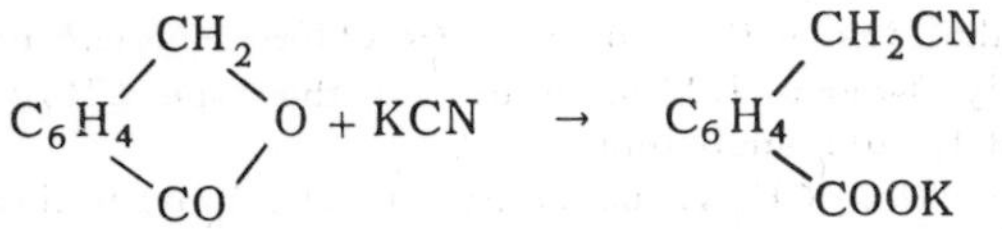

Nitriles from Aromatic Diazo Compounds

Diazo salts react with alkali metal cyanides in the cold to form diazo cyanides:

$$RN = NCl + KCN \rightarrow RN = NCN + KCl$$

The resulting compounds are normal nitriles that exist in the cis and trans isomeric forms,

$$\underset{CNN}{\overset{R-N}{\underset{\parallel}{}}} \quad and \quad \underset{NCN}{\overset{R-N}{\underset{\parallel}{}}}$$

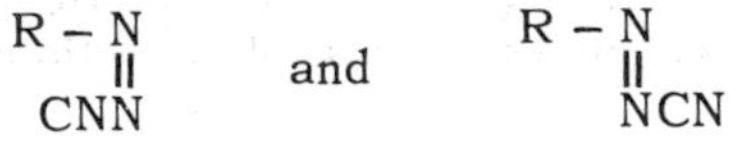

The cis isomer is obtained when the reaction is carried out below zero and is the unstable form; it gradually changes to the trans isomer. The transformation is accelerated by heat, and takes place more readily in solution.

The cis isomer decomposes to a nitrile with evolution of nitrogen when heated in solution in the presence of copper powder:

$$RN = NCN \rightarrow RCN + N_2$$

The trans isomer does not undergo this change.

Cis diazo cyanides form double compounds with cupric cyanide, a fact which undoubtedly plays a part in Sandmeyer's method[28] for the preparation of nitriles from diazonium compounds, which consists in heating a solution of the diazonium salt with potassium cuprocyanide:

$$RN_2Cl + KCNCuCN \rightarrow RCN + N_2 + KCl + CuCN$$

The general procedure is as follows: An aqueous solution of potassium cuprocyanide is heated to 90° and the solution of diazonium chloride is stirred in gradually. After the evolution of nitrogen has ceased, the mixture is heated under reflux for a short period.

The potassium cuprocyanide solution is prepared by dissolving 50 gm of copper sulfate in 200 cc of water on a water bath, and gradually adding a solution of 56 gm of potassium cyanide in 100 cc of water. Cuprous- or nicklous cyanide or potassium copperdiammonio cyanide may be used in place of potassium cuprocyanide. [29]

Other Methods of Formation of Nitriles

α-Hydroxynitriles are obtained readily through the reaction of aldehydes or ketones with hydrocyanic acid in the presence of a base such as sodium hydroxide or ammonia. This subject has been discussed in detail under carbonyl compounds.

One of the most generally applicable methods of preparation of nitriles consists in the dehydration of amides or ammonium salts of carboxylic acids with phosphorus pentoxide. Phosphorus pentachloride is also used occasionally for the purpose. Dehydration may be accomplished in some instances by pyrolysis in the presence of an appropriate catalyst.[270] Nitriles have been obtained in excellent yield by this method from aliphatic and aromatic amides by use of a double salt of aluminum and sodium chlorides, $NaCl.AlCl_3$, as a catalyst.[271]

Other methods of formation of nitriles are the following:

Dehydration of aldoximes, usually brought about by use of acetic anhydride:

$$RCH = NOH + (CH_3CO)_2O \rightarrow RCN + 2CH_3COOH$$

Nitriles are formed in good yield by decarboxylation of oximino acids with warm acetic anhydride:[272]

$$RCH_2C(:NOH)COOH + (CH_3CO)_2O \rightarrow RCH_2CN + CO_2 + 2CH_3COOH$$

Oxamino acids are obtained in good yield by condensing aldehydes with rhodamine under the action of acetic anhydride and sodium acetate, and treating the resulting compound with hydroxylamine in the presence of caustic:

$$RCHO + H_2\overline{CCONHCSS} \rightarrow H_2O + RCH = \overline{CCONHCSS}$$

$$\xrightarrow{NaOH} RCH_2CSCOOH \xrightarrow{H_2NOH} RCH_2C(:NOH)COOH$$

Desulfurization of isothiocyanates[30] with metallic copper in a stream of carbon dioxide or hydrogen, an isonitrile being an intermediate product:

$$C_6H_5N = CS + Cu \rightarrow CuS + C_6H_5N = C \rightarrow C_6H_5CN$$

Desulfurization may be accomplished also with iron powder at 280 - 290°.

Reaction of lead thiocyanate with a carboxylic acid or its zinc salt:

$$RCOOH + Pb(SCN)_2 \rightarrow HSCN + RCOOPbSCN \rightarrow RCN + PbS + CO_2$$

This reaction is generally applicable to aromatic acids.

The reaction of alkyl dichloramines with alkalies:

$$RCH_2NCl_2 + 2\ KOH \rightarrow RCN + 2\ H_2O + 2\ KCl$$

The reaction of phospham with carboxylic acids:

$$2RCOOH + PN_2H \rightarrow 2RCN + H_3PO_4$$

In the reaction of Grignard reagents with cyanogen and with cyanogen halides, iminohalides are formed and converted to nitriles on boiling with water:

$$(CN)_2 + RMgX \rightarrow CNC(NMgX)R$$

$$ClCN + RMgX \rightarrow ClC(:NMgX)R \xrightarrow{H_2O} RCN + ClMgX$$

Reaction of metals with thioureas in high boiling indifferent media at elevated temperatures.

Transformation of isonitriles to nitriles at 200°, a method which is particularly well-adopted for the preparation of aromatic nitriles. The dehydration of an aromatic formamide,[31] which gives an isonitrile as an intermediate, comes under this heading:

$$C_6H_5NHCHO \rightarrow C_6H_5N=C \rightarrow C_6H_5CN$$

Reactions of Nitriles

The cyano group in nitriles is capable of various transformations which are of importance in organic synthesis. Hydrolysis leads to the formation of acids or amides; by reaction with alcohols in the presence of hydrogen chloride in anhydrous media, iminoethers are obtained, while reaction with alcohols in the presence of an inorganic acid and a limited amount of water, leads to the formation of esters. Reaction with amines, proceeds under certain conditions, giving amidines, while reaction with hydroxylamine, which proceeds quite readily in many instances, gives amidoximes. Amines result on reduction of nitriles. Polymeric products of several types have been obtained from various nitriles.

Hydrolysis of Nitriles

Nitriles are hydrolyzed when heated with aqueous mineral acids or bases. The reaction with hydrochloric acid probably proceeds in the following manner:

$$RCN + HCl \rightarrow RCCl=NH \xrightarrow{H_2O} HCl + RC(OH)=NH$$

$$\rightarrow RCONH_2 \xrightarrow{H_2O + HCl} RCOOH + NH_4Cl$$

Alkaline hydrolysis may be assumed to take place *via* the formation of an alkali metal imide:

$$RCN + NaOH \rightarrow RC(OH)=NNa \xrightarrow{H_2O} NaOH + RC(OH)=NH$$

$$\rightarrow RCONH_2 \xrightarrow{NaOH} RCOONa + NH_3$$

Complete hydrolysis of aliphatic nitriles can generally be brought about by heating under reflux with aqueous or alcoholic alkali.[32] Aromatic nitriles can also be hydrolyzed by this method, but these nitriles are more satisfactorily hydrolyzed by heating with aqueous sulfuric or hydrochloric acid. Sulfuric acid has been used in concentrations of 20, 30 or 70%; hydrochloric acid is generally used in a concentration of 20%. *Hydrobromic acid* is a more effective hydrolyzing agent than hydrochloric acid. Thus, *o-dinitrocyanodibenzyl*,

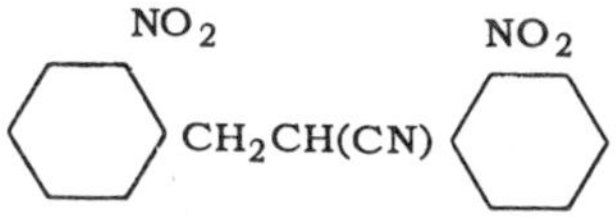

which is not acted upon by boiling hydrochloric acid, is converted to the corresponding acid upon heating for three hours with hydrobromic acid of specific gravity 1.47. Similarly, *tricyanodibenzyl*, $CNC_6H_4CH_2CH(CN)C_6H_4CN$, which is not acted upon by hydrochloric acid, is converted to an imide acid, $HOCOC_6H_4CH_2CHC_6H_4CONHCO$, when boiled with an excess of hydrobromic acid of the same strength.[33]

The use of a mixture of acetic acid and sulfuric acid is of advantage if the nitrile is insoluble in sulfuric acid but dissolves in the mixed acids. *Triphenylacetonitrile* and *α-* and *β-naphthonitriles* may be hydrolyzed successfully by the use of this mixture.[34]

Certain very stable nitriles such as pyrene cyanide, may be saponified by fusion with alkali. Barium hydroxide has been used as a hydrolyzing agent.[35]

For the hydrolysis of *amino nitriles*, heating to 125° for 3 hours with 5 to 7 molecular proportions of 40% sulfuric acid is recommended.[36] The use of sodium hydroxide of less than 5*N* strength in conjunction with ammonia or organic acids or weak inorganic acids has also been recommended for these nitriles.[37] *Alanine nitrile* is converted to alanine when heated at 90 - 95° with barium hydroxide octahydrate. A mixture of β, β′-iminodipropionic acid and its amide is obtained when β, β′-iminodipropionitrile, $NH(CH_2CH_2CN)_2$, is boiled with 30% aqueous sodium hydroxide.[38]

Cinnamaldehyde cyanohydrin, $C_6H_5CH = CHCH(OH)CN$, may be hydrolyzed with cold hydrochloric acid, to the corresponding amide from which the acid may be obtained by careful hydrolysis. Under drastic conditions of hydrolysis γ-benzoylpropionic acid, $C_6H_5COCH_2CH_2COOH$, results.[39] *Acetophenone cyanohydrin* may be converted to atrolactic acid, $CH_3C(C_6H_5)(OH)COOH$, by the action of cold concentrated hydrochloric acid. When heated to boiling with hydrochloric acid and subsequently treated with sodium hydroxide, the cyanohydrin is converted to tropic acid:[40]

$$C_6H_5C(OH)(CN)CH_3 \rightarrow C_6H_5C(=CH_2)COOH \xrightarrow{HCl}$$

$$C_6H_5CH(CH_2Cl)COOH \xrightarrow{NaOH} C_6H_5CH(CH_2OH)COONa$$

Manadelonitrile is converted to mandelamide and mandelic acid on treatment with aqueous hydrochloric acid.[41] The amide condenses in part with the benzaldehyde normally present in the cyanohydrin to form benzalmandelamide.

Hydrolysis of the cyano group in various nitriles does not take place with equal ease, but is influenced by the character of the grouping to which the cyano group is attached.

The ease of hydrolysis of nitriles of the aliphatic series is enhanced when alkoxy groups such as OCH_3, OC_2H_5, etc., are introduced in the molecule in the *α*-position with respect to the cyano group.[42]

Phenylarylacetonitriles cannot be hydrolyzed by boiling with aqueous mineral acids, but are converted to the potassium salt of the corresponding acids by prolonged boiling with alcoholic potassium hydroxide.

Differences are observed in the rates of hydrolysis of various *cyanohydrins*. Cyclohexanone- and cyclopentanone cyanohydrins are readily hydrolyzed, 1,3-dimethylcyclohexanone cyanohydrin less readily, while the cyanohydrin of 1-methyl-2-cyclohexanone cannot be hydrolyzed.

As a general rule, disubstituted *aromatic nitriles* in which both substituents are in the ortho position are hydrolyzed with difficulty or not at all. Thus, 2,4,5,6-tetramethyl-, pentamethyl- and pentachlorobenzonitrile, 2,4,6-trimethyl-1,3-dicyanobenzene and 1,3,5-trimethyltricyanobenzene cannot be hydrolyzed by the usual methods. The presence of negative groups in an aromatic nitrile facilitates hydrolysis of the cyano group. Thus, while great difficulty is experienced in hydrolyzing symmetrical trimethylbenzonitrile, the mono- and dinitro derivatives of this compound may be completely though slowly converted to the corresponding acids.[43] Similarly, when negative groups are introduced into the molecule of isoduric nitrile and the corresponding dinitrile, saponification becomes possible, though only by the use of energetic saponifying agents at high temperatures.[43] The position of the nitro group in the molecule is of importance, however, and nitrodurolnitrile,

$$\begin{array}{cc} H_3C & CH_3 \\ NO_2 \diagdown\!\!\!\!\!\diagup & CN \\ H_3C & CH_3 \end{array}$$

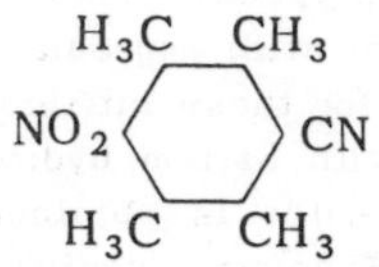

cannot be hydrolyzed to the corresponding acid.[45]

Many aromatic nitriles with substituents in the ortho position yield amides on hydrolysis with sulfuric acid. Amides are obtained, for example, from *2,6-dibromo-3-methyl-*,[33] *2-nitro-4-bromo-6-methyl-*, *2,4-dinitro-*, *2,6-dibromo-*, *2,6-dichloro-*[32] and *2,6-dimethylbenzonitriles.*[47] The acid results when 2,4-dimethylbenzamide is heated at 145 - 150° for half an hour with anhydrous phosphoric acid. Sulfuric acid as well as hydrochloric acid and alcoholic caustic are without action on *2-methoxy-5-acetylbenzonitrile.*[48] The acid results when *2,4-dimethylbenzonitrile* is heated at 220° with alcoholic potassium hydroxide.

Amides result also when *α-dimethylamino-p-methoxybenzylcanide* is hydrolyzed with concentrated sulfuric acid[49] and when *triphenylacetonitrile* is heated with alcoholic potassium hydroxide.[50] *Benzoylphenylacetonitrile* resists hydrolysis under the most drastic conditions.[51]

Benzoyl cyanide is converted to phenylglyoxylic acid, $C_6H_5COCOOH$, by allowing it to remain in contact with cold concentrated hydrochloric acid for several days, then heating for a short period at 70°. Benzoic acid results when the nitrile is boiled with condentrated hydrochloric acid.[52]

The hydrolysis of acetylenic nitriles may result in the hydration of the acetylenic bond. Thus, phenylpropiolic nitrile is converted to benzoylacetamide when heated with sulfuric acid. The triple bond in amyl- and hexylpropiolic nitriles is not affected by sulfuric acid, but the cyano group is converted to an amide group. Alcoholic potassium hydroxide reacts vigorously with acetylenic nitriles forming addition compounds of the type, $RC(OC_2H_5) = CHCN$, which are subsequently converted to the potassium salt of the corresponding acid.[53]

Alkaline hydrolysis of *α*-cyano cyclic ketones results in ring cleavage with the formation of a dibasic acid:[54]

$$\begin{array}{cc} CO\diagdown \\ \quad CHCN \\ \quad | \\ \quad CH_2 \\ CH_2\diagup \end{array} + 2\ KOH + H_2O \quad \rightarrow \quad \begin{array}{c} COOK \\ \diagup \\ \diagdown \\ CH_2CH_2CH_2COOK \end{array} + NH_3$$

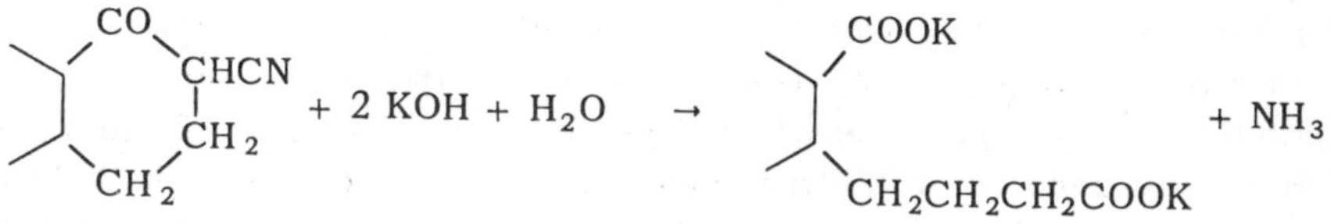

Cyanoacridanes may be hydrolyzed by heating at 160 - 170° in a sealed tube with alcoholic potassium hydroxide. Heating with acids causes the removal of the cyano group as hydrocyanic acid.

Conversion of Nitriles to Amides

The partial hydrolysis of a nitrile to an amide by acid hydrolysis is generally possible under properly controlled conditions. In many cases nitriles may be converted to amides by treatment with cold mineral acids.[55]

Most nitriles which resist hydrolysis by other reagents may be converted to amides on prolonged heating with alcoholic caustic.

Substituted amides may be prepared through the reaction of nitriles and alcohols in the presence of sulfuric acid and subsequent hydrolysis of the product:[273]

$$ROH + H_2SO_4 \rightarrow ROSO_3H \xrightarrow{R'CN} RN = C(R')OSO_3H$$

$$\xrightarrow{H_2O} RNHCOR' + H_2SO_4$$

The yields are generally high. This method makes possible the preparation of otherwise difficulty accessible primary amines containing a tertiary alkyl group.

Conversion of Nitriles to Amides with Hydrogen Peroxide

Nitriles are generally converted to amides when treated with 3% alkaline hydrogen peroxide.[56] Even nitriles which resist hydrolysis with acids, such as α-naphthonitrile and *o*-tolunitrile, are converted to amides by treatment with a somewhat more concentrated solution of hydrogen peroxide.[57]

Cyanogen, which resists hydrolysis by other agents, is converted to oxamide by this treatment. Nitronaphthonitrile readily yields the amide on treatment with alkaline hydrogen peroxide in alcoholic solution, although it is not possible to convert the nitrile to amide by treatment with acids or alkalies. The reaction may best be carried out at 40° The more resistant nitriles may be converted to the amide by use of an excess of hydrogen peroxide, or of a more concentrated solution of the peroxide. Yields are quantitative with some nitriles, but only partial conversions are observed with others.

Acylanthranilic nitriles yield 2-alkyl-4-ketodihydroquinazolines when treated with peroxide; an amide is formed as an intermediate:[58]

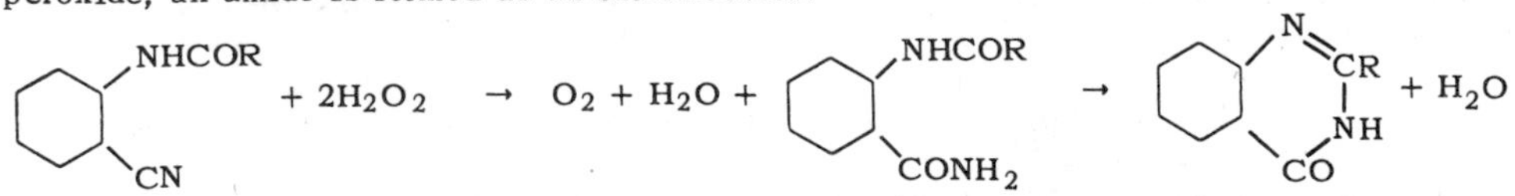

Amides may be converted to the corresponding acids by treatment with hot aqueous nitrous acid *(Bouveault's method)*. The subject has been dealt with in Chapter 8.

Reaction of Nitriles with Alcohols

Alcohols react with nitriles in anhydrous media in the presence of hydrogen chloride to form imino ethers:

$$RCN + R'OH + HCl \rightarrow 2RC(=NH)OR'.HCl$$

Esters may be obtained from nitriles directly by the simultaneous action of an alcohol and a limited amount of water in the presence of a mineral acid:[59]

$$RCN + H_2O + HOR' + HCl \rightarrow RCOOR' + NH_4Cl$$

According to Spiegel,[60] the best proportions of nitrile, alcohol and acid are 1:2:1, though better results are obtained in some instances by use of a larger proportion of alcohol, sometimes as much as ten moles of alcohol to one of nitrile.

The reaction proceeds well with many aliphatic nitriles. Substituents in the ortho position with respect to the cyano group in aromatic nitriles retard or inhibit the reaction. β-Naphthonitrile may be converted to an ester by this method, but α-naphthonitrile cannot be thus esterified.[61]

Esters are also formed from nitriles by reaction with alcohols in the presence of boron trifluoride.[46]

Reaction of Nitriles with Amines

The addition of an amine to the cyano group in a nitrile results in the formation of an amidine:

$$RCN + H_2NR' \rightarrow RC(=NH)NHR'$$

The reaction takes place only in the presence of the hydrochloride of the amine.[62]

The potassium derivatives of amidines result when nitriles are added to a solution of potassium amide in liquid ammonia:[63]

$$RCN + KNH_2 \rightarrow RC(=NH)NHK$$

Amidines result through the reaction of aromatic nitriles with sodium amide.[64]

Guanidine formation from amines and cyanamide and substituted cyanamides is a special case of amidine formation. Cyanamide, for example, reacting with the hydrochloride of an amine, RNH_2, yields the hydrochloride of a monosubstituted guanidine:[65]

$$H_2NCN + RNH_2.HCl \rightarrow H_2NC(=NH)NHR.HCl$$

The reaction proceeds well with aliphatic-, arylaliphatic- and with some aromatic amines such as aniline and its homologs. It proceeds well also with naphthylamines.

Guanidine, $HN = C(NH_2)$, results when cyanamide is heated with an alcoholic solution of ammonium chloride.[66]

Hydroxycyanamide, HONHCN, which results, together with hydroxylamine hydrobromide, from the reaction of *hydroxylamine* with cyanogen bromide at -20°, reacts with hydroxylamine hydrobromide to from dihydroxyguanidine hydrobromide,[67]

$$HN = C(NHOH)_2.HBr.$$

Bis-(phenylhydroxy)guanidine hydrobromide, $HN = C[N(OH)C_6H_5]_2.HBr$, may be obtained similarly from *phenylhydroxylamine* and cyanogen bromide.[68]

Ethylenediamine reacting at room temperature in aqueous solution with an equivalent of cyanogen bromide gives ethyleneguanidine hydrobromide,

$$\overline{CH_2CH_2NHC(=NH)N}HHBr$$

while with a half molecular equivalent of cyanogen bromide it gives diethyleneguanidine hydrobromide,[69]

$$\overline{C = NCH_2CH_2\overline{N}CH_2CH_2NHHBr}$$

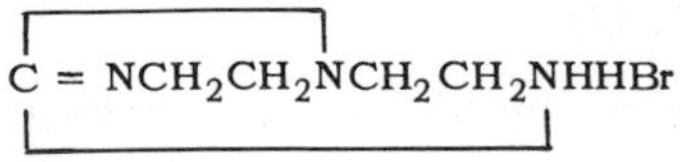

Guanidines are also obtained through the desulfurization of dialkylthioureas with mercuric oxide in the presence of amines:[70]

$$(C_2H_5NH)_2CS + C_2H_5NH_2 + HgO$$

$$\rightarrow \quad C_2H_5N:C(NHC_2H_5)_2 + HgS + H_2O$$

They may also be prepared by the reaction of amines or ammonia with the alkyl halide addition products of thiourea or its N-alkyl derivatives:[71]

$$HN = C(NH_2)SCH_3 \cdot HI + 2(CH_3)_2NH \quad \rightarrow$$

$$HN = C(NH_2)N(CH_3)_2 + HSCH_3 + (CH_3)_2NHHI$$

Biguanides result through the reaction of amines with dicyandiamide:

$$H_2NC(=NH)NHCN + H_2NR \quad \rightarrow \quad H_2NC(=NH)NHC(=NH)NHR$$

Cupric sulfate catalyzes this reaction.[72]

The reaction of dicyandiamide with *o-phenylenediamine* leads to the formation of 2-guanidinobenzimidazole,[73]

$$C_6H_4 \underset{NH}{\overset{N}{<}} CNHC(:NH)NH_2$$

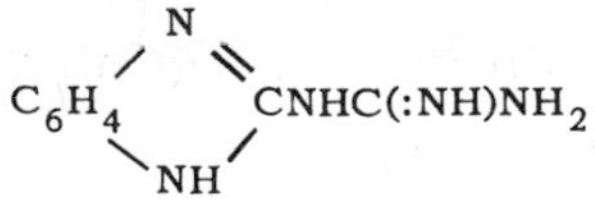

with *o-aminophenol*, guanidinobenzoxazole,[74]

$$C_6H_4 \underset{O}{\overset{N}{<}} CNHC(:NH)NH_2$$

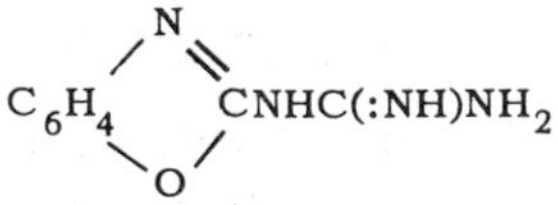

results. *Hydrazine hydrate* gives guanazole, $HN:CNHC(:NH)\overline{NHNH}$, while free hydrazine and hydrazine salts give melamazine.[75] Amidines give with dicyandiamide first an iminobiguanide, and as the end product of diaminotriazine, $H_2NC:N\overline{C(NH_2):NC(R):N}$. The latter may also be obtained through the direct condensation of dicyandiamide with nitriles, RCN.[76]

Hydroxylamine reacts readily with most nitriles to form amidoximes,

$$RC(:NOH)NH_2$$

Hydrazine reacting with nitriles apparently first forms a hydrazidine; this seems to undergo transformation to compounds of the type $RC(:NH)NHNHC(:NH)R$ and $RC(:N.NH_2)NHNHC(:N.NH_2)R$, the latter then condenses to an N-aminotriazoles,

$$RC \underset{N-NH_2}{\overset{N.N}{<}} CR$$

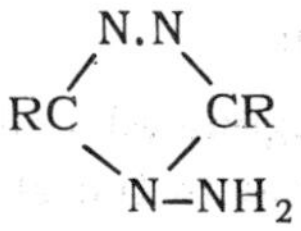

These reactions have been discussed in Chapter 8.

Reaction of Nitriles with Acids

Nitriles react with hydrogen halides to form addition compounds, presumably of the type RC(:NH)X.[77] They may be obtained as insoluble crystalline solids when vapors of hydrogen halides are led through a solution of the nitrile in anhydrous ether.

Aromatic cyanohydrins undergo a complex series of reactions in the presence of hydrogen chloride. The probable course of the reaction appears to be as follows:[78]

$$\text{RCH(OH)CN} \xrightarrow{\text{HCl}} \text{RCH(OH)C(:NH)Cl} \xrightarrow{\text{RCHO}}$$

$$\text{RCH(OH)CCl:NCH(OH)R} \rightarrow \text{RCHCCl:NCH(R)O}$$

$$\rightarrow \text{RC:CHN:C(R)O}$$

$$\text{RCH(OH)CCl:NCH(OH)R} + H_2O \rightarrow \text{HCl} + \text{RCH(OH)C(OH):NCH(OH)R}$$

$$\rightarrow \text{RCH(OH)CON:CHR}$$

$$\text{2RCH(OH)C(:NH)Cl} \rightarrow \text{RCHN:CClCH(R)N:CCl}$$

$$\xrightarrow{H_2O} \text{RCHN:CClCH(R)N:COH} \rightarrow \text{RCHN:CClCH(R)NHCO}$$

$$\rightarrow \text{RC:NCH:C(R)NHCO}$$

Nitriles do not react readily with organic acids, reaction taking place only on heating the mixture of acid and nitrile at a relatively high temperature in a sealed tube. The reaction generally leads to the formation of secondary amides, but an exchange of the nitrile and carboxyl group takes place when an aromatic acid is heated with an aliphatic nitrile.[79]

Anthranilic acid, heated with a nitrile, RCN, under pressure gives a ketodihydroguanazoline,[80]

```
       N = CR
      /     |
  C6H4      |
      \     |
       CO—NH
```

Heated with acid anhydrides, $(R'CO)_2O$, nitriles give tertiary amides,

$$\text{RCON(COR}')_2.$$

Reaction of Nitriles with Halogens

Aliphatic nitriles may be halogenated under appropriate conditions. Acetonitrile does not react with chlorine in the absence of a catalyst, but chlorination proceeds in the presence of a little hydrogen chloride. Chlorination may be carried out in the vapor phase in the temperature range 200 - 400° in the presence of catalysts such as active carbon or carbon impregnated with a halide of copper, zinc or an alkaline earth metal.[81] Propionitrile may be chlorinated in the absence of a catalyst.[82] α-Chloroisobutyronitrile is obtained when chlorine is conducted through isobutyronitrile in direct sunlight at 45 - 65°.[83] Benzonitrile can be chlorinated in direct sunlight to α- and β-hexachlorobenzonitrile and hexachlorochlorobenzonitrile, although reaction takes place quite slowly.[84]

Cyanogen Halides

Halogens react with hydrocyanic acid replacing the hydrogen in the compound with a halogen. Thus, chlorine reacting with hydrocyanic acid in aqueous solution gives cyanogen chloride:

$$HCN + Cl_2 \rightarrow ClCN + HCl$$

Cyanogen chloride can also be obtained through the interaction of chlorine with aqueous alkali cyanides:

$$NaCN + Cl_2 \rightarrow ClCN + NaCl$$

The solution of the cyanide is added gradually to water through which a current of chlorine is conducted. The rate of addition is so regulated that no excess cyanide is present in solution, in order to avoid the occurrence of side reactions. External cooling is applied during the reaction.[85]

Sodium cyanoformimino chloride, CNC(Cl)=NNa, is obtained when a current of chlorine is passed into an aqueous solution of sodium cyanide until the liquid assumes an orange red color.[86] Hydrocyanic acid in alcoholic solution, reacting with chlorine, yields the compounds $ClCH_2CH(NHCOOC_2H_5)_2$ and $Cl_2CHCH(NHCOOC_2H_5)_2$. A similar reaction takes place also with bromine but not with iodine. The imino ether of cyanoformic acid results when a current of chlorine is conducted through an aqueous alcoholic solution of potassium cyanide cooled to -5 to -10°:

$$2KCN + Cl_2 \rightarrow KN{=}CClCN \xrightarrow{C_2H_5OH} HN{=}C(CN)OC_2H_5$$

Further alcoholysis takes place upon the addition of potassium cyanide to the solution of the imino ether, with the formation of diethyl diimino oxalate:

$$HN{:}C(CN)OC_2H_5 + HOC_2H_5 \rightarrow C_2H_5OC({:}NH)C({:}NH)OC_2H_5$$

This compound is hydrolyzed by dilute hydrochloric acid to diethyl oxalate.

Reactions of Cyanogen Halides

Cyanogen chloride reacts with *alkalies* forming a cyanate and a chloride:

$$ClCN + 2NaOH \rightarrow NaOCN + NaCl + H_2O$$

Cyanogen bromide, on the other hand, yields a cyanide, bromide and bromate:

$$3CNBr + 6NaOH \rightarrow 3NaCN + 2NaBr + NaBrO_3 + 3H_2O$$

An identical reaction takes place also with cyanogen iodide.[87]

With alkali metal *sulfides* cyanogen chloride and bromide yield a thiocyanate and a sodium halide:[88]

$$ClCN + Na_2S \rightarrow NaSCN + NaCl$$

Cyanogen bromide reacts with hydrogen sulfide to form hydrocyanic acid, hydro-bromic acid and elemental sulfur.[87]

Cyanogen halides react with primary and secondary amines to form cyan-amides: [90]

$$2RNH_2 + ClCN \rightarrow RNHCN + RNH_2.HCl$$

Aliphatic amines and primary aromatic amines in which the aromatic nucleus does not contain strongly negative substituents such as halogens and nitro groups, react readily. There seems to be no direct relationship, however, between the velocity of reaction and the strength of the base. The velocity increases in the series NH_3, CH_3NH_2, $(CH_3)_2NH$, $(CH_3)_3N$; in the ethylamine series the reactivity increases in the order NH_3, $C_2H_5NH_2$, $(C_2H_5)_3N$ and $(C_2H_5)_2NH$.[91]

Hydroxylamine in alcoholic solution reacts vigorously with cyanogen bromide at room temperature, breakdown of the molecule taking place:

$$2H_2NOH + 2BrCN \rightarrow HCN + N_2 + NH_4Br + HBr + CO_2$$

Hydroxycyanamide results, however, when the reaction is carried out at -20° and, combines with unconverted hydroxylamine, to form dihydroxyguanidine:

$$2HONH_2 + BrCN \rightarrow HONHCN + HONH_2.HBr$$

$$\rightarrow (HONH)_2C = NH.HBr$$

A similar reaction takes place with phenylhydroxylamine at 0°.[92]

Cyanogen bromide reacting with a molecular equivalent of *hydrazine* gives amino-guanazole,

$$\overline{H_2NNC(:NH)NHNHC:NH}$$

Diaminoguanidine is the main product when one molecular equivalent of cyanogen bromide reacts with two of hydrazine.[93] β-Cyanophenylhydrazine, $C_6H_5NH.NHCN$, results through the interaction of phenylhydrazine and cyanogen chloride in cold ethereal solution. It is an unstable compound which polymerizes readily.[94] If the reaction is carried out in aqueous solution, a mixture of α-cyanophenylhydrazine, phenylsemicarbazide and di(phenylamino)guanidine results.[94] α-Cyanophenylhydrazine, reacting in alcoholic solution with cyanogen bromide at 60 - 70°, gives phenyltricyanohydrazide,

$$C_6H_5N(CN)N(CN)_2$$

Diphenylamine in benzene solution does not react with cyanogen chloride, but reaction proceeds vigorously with molten diphenylamine. The main product is tetraphenyl-guanidine when the reaction is carried out below 250°, but a polymer of diphenyl cyana-mide is formed at temperatures above 250°.[95]

o-Phenylenediamine treated with an excess of cyanogen bromide yields a mixture of *o-phenyleneguanidine*,

$$C_6H_4 \underset{NH}{\overset{NH}{\diagup}} C = NH$$

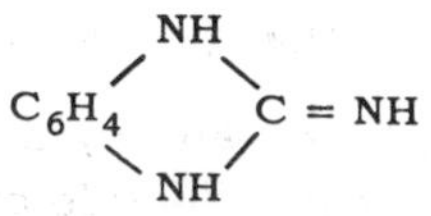

and iminodicarbonyl-*o*-phenyleneguanidine.[96] The hydrobromide of 2-amino-1,2-naphth-imidazole,

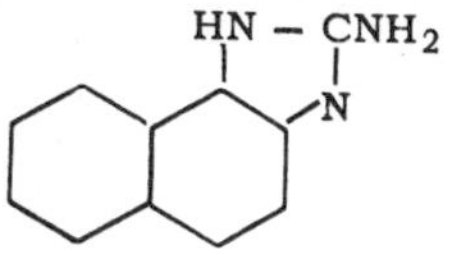

results from the reaction of *1,2-naphthalenediamine* with an aqueous solution of cyanogen bromide.[97]

Cyanogen bromide reacts with a warm aqueous solution of anthranilic acid to form diphenylguanidinedi-*o*-carboxylic acid, $(HOCOC_6H_4NH)_2C{:}NH$, which on boiling with concentrated hydrochloric acid is converted to benzoyleneurea,[98]

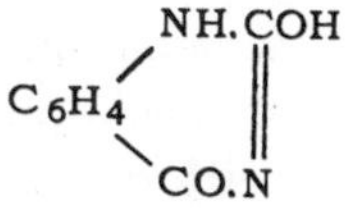

The reaction of *cyanamide* with cyanogen bromide leads to the formation of melanuric acid. With monosodium cyanamide, dicyanimide, $HN(CN)_2$, is obtained.[99] Substituted dicyanimides result similarly through the reaction of cyanogen bromide with the sodium derivative of substituted cyanamides.[100] Dicyanoguanidine results through the reaction of the sodium compound of *dicyandiamide* and cyanogen chloride in an anhydrous medium.[101]

Cyanogen bromide reacts with *tertiary bases* forming a disubstituted cyanamide and a hydrocarbon bromide:

$$R_1R_2NR_3 + BrCN \rightarrow R_1R_2NCN + R_3Br$$

The reaction apparently proceeds in two stages; first a quaternary base is formed by the addition of cyanogen bromide, and this then decomposes to a bromide and the substituted cyanamide.[102] Aliphatic tertiary bases react readily. Reaction is, in general, the more vigorous the smaller the hydrocarbon groups attached to nitrogen. Phenyl groups attached to nitrogen reduce the reactivity of the base. If two or more phenyl groups are attached to the nitrogen, the base fails to react with cyanogen bromide. When a phenyl group is substituted for hydrogen in an aliphatic group attached to the nitrogen, the reactivity of the base decreases.

When unlike radicals are attached to nitrogen then, as a rule, the smallest group is detached from the molecule of the base. This rule holds in the case of normal saturated aliphatic radicals.[103] Alkyl residues attached to nitrogen forming part of a ring may be exchanged by the cyano group under the action of cyanogen bromide. In most instances, a second reaction involving the rupture of the nitrogen ring also takes place:

$$\overline{CH_2(CH_2)_4N}R + BrCN \rightarrow BrCH_2(CH_2)_4N(R)CN$$

The resulting bromo compound reacts with the unconverted cyclic base to form a quaternary compound.[104]

Mercaptides, xanthates and thio acids react with cyanogen halides to form thiocyano derivatives. The reaction may be illustrated by the following examples:

$$R_1R_2NCSSNa + BrCN \rightarrow R_1R_2NCSSCN + NaBr$$

$$(C_2H_5O)_2PSSNa + ClCN \rightarrow (C_2H_5O)_2PSSCN + NaCl$$

Methanol containing some water reacts vigorously with cyanogen chloride, if the concentration of the latter is sufficiently high, giving methyl carbonate.[105] Ethanol reacts on long standing in sunlight, or on heating at 80°, to form urethane, diethyl carbonate and a little ethyl chloride.[106]

Cyanogen chloride reacts with sodium ethoxide in alcoholic solution, or with alcohol containing sodium hydroxide in solution to form ethyl iminocarbonate,[107] $HN = C(OC_2H_5)_2$. Phenyl iminocarbonate results similarly from the reaction of phenol and sodium phenolate with cyanogen chloride.

Cyanogen halides reacting with sodium alcoholates give alkyl cyanurates; similarly, sodium phenolate reacting with cyanogen halides gives phenyl cyanurate.[108]

Cyanamides

Cyanamide, H_2NCN, results through the reaction of ammonia and cyanogen halides. It is obtained also by desulfurizing thiourea with mercuric oxide:[109]

$$H_2NCSNH_2 + HgO \rightarrow H_2NCN + HgS + H_2O$$

Cyanamide results also when urea is heated with metallic sodium[110] or with $SOCl_2$.[111]

Monosubstituted cyanamides are formed through the interaction of primary amines and cyanogen halides. They may also be obtained through the desulfurization of monosubstituted thioureas. Methyl and ethyl cyanamides are obtained by the reaction of diazomethane and diazoethane with cyanamide.[112] Monoalkyl cyanamides are unstable compounds; on evaporation of their aqueous solutions they polymerize to trisubstituted isomelamines. *Disubstituted cyanamides*[113] result through the reaction of secondary amines with cyanogen halides; they are obtained also by the reaction of N-halogenated secondary amines with potassium cyanide:

$$(C_5H_{11})_2NCl + KCN \rightarrow (C_5H_{11})_2NCN + KCl$$

Alkylation of cyanamide by use of dialkyl sulfates also leads to the formation of disubstituted cyanamides. Alkylation may be carried out also conveniently by the reaction of alkyl halides with silver cyanamide. Dialkyl cyanamides do not polymerize readily. Reacting with hydrogen sulfide they yield unsymmetrical thioureas. They readily combine with hydroxylamine.

Carbodiimides, $RN = C = NR$, which are isomeric with disubstituted cyanamides, are little known compounds. Dipropylcarbodiimide, $C_3H_7N = C = NC_3H_7$, has been prepared through the desulfurization of symmetrical dipropylthiourea,[114] a reaction which would seem to be of general applicability.

Reactions of Cyanamides

O-Alkylisoureas[115] result on warming the monohydrochloride of cyanamide with alcohols:

$$H_2NCCl{:}NH + CH_3OH \rightarrow H_2NC(OCH_3){:}NH.HCl$$

The free isourea is obtained by treating the resulting hydrochloride with powdered alkali under ether. O-Alkyl ureas are distinctly basic. O-Methylisourea, for example, is a stronger base than ammonia, though weaker than methylamine. When the chlorides are heated they decompose into urea and an alkyl halide:

$$H_2NC(OCH_3)NH.HCl \rightarrow H_2NCONH_2 + CH_3Cl$$

Decomposition in this direction takes place also, gradually, on heating the compounds to 100° with aqueous hydrochloric acid, although a very small amount of urethane also results in that case.

Guanidine results when cyanamide is heated with an alcoholic solution of ammonium chloride. Substituted guanidines are obtained through the reaction of amine chlorides with cyanamide and substituted cyanamides.

Dicyandiamide, $H_2NC({:}NH)NHCN$, results through the polymerization of cyanamide in alkaline solution. This compound is hydrolyzed to guanylurea when heated with aqueous acids:

$$H_2NC({:}NH)NHCN + H_2O \rightarrow H_2NC({:}NH)NHCONH_2$$

Dicyandiamide is mildly acidic in character, and reacts with an alcoholic solution of sodium ethoxide to form a sodio derivative. The silver salt is soluble in ammonia. Heated with ammonium chloride in the presence of cupric sulfate, dicyandiamide reacts to form biguanide, $H_2NC({:}NH)NHC({:}NH)NH_2$. This compound condenses with ethyl formate to give guanamine,

$$\overline{CH = NC(NH_2) = NC(NH_2) = N}$$

Reaction of Nitriles with Grignard Reagents

Nitriles react with Grignard compounds, normally to form imino compounds, which on hydrolysis give ketones:[116]

$$RCN + R'MgI \rightarrow RR'C = NMgI$$

$$RR'C = NMgI + 2\,H_2O \rightarrow RR'CO + IMgOH + NH_3$$

Aminonitriles, $RCH(NR'_2)CN$, react with Grignard compounds $R''MgX$ in three possible ways, yielding

$$RCH(NR'_2)R'',\ RCH(NR'_2)C(R'') = NMgX \text{ or}$$

$$RCH(NR'_2).CH(NR'_2).R$$

depending on the character of the groups R, R′, R″.[117]

Unsaturated nitriles, in which a double bond is in a conjugated position with respect to the triple bond in CN and which are substituted in the α-position, react with Grignard compounds forming β-substituted saturated nitriles, while nitriles of a similar type with a substituent in the β-position react normally.[118]

Many other cases of exceptional behavior are known and are considered in the chapter dealing with the Grignard reaction.

Phthalonitrile reacts with methylmagnesium iodide to form, after hydrolysis of the metallic complex, the strongly basic 1-amino-3,3-dimethyl-4-isoindole:

$$C_6H_5(CN)_2 \xrightarrow{CH_3MgI} C_6H_4 \begin{array}{c} C(CH_3)_2 \\ \diagdown N \\ C - NH_2 \end{array}$$

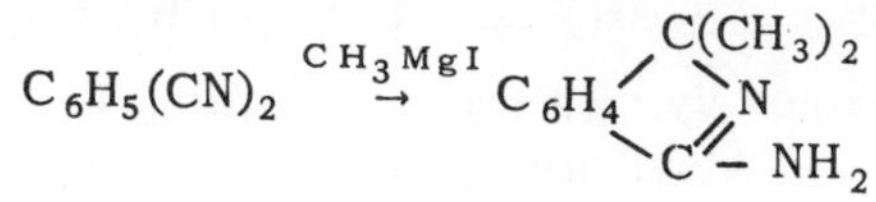

This compound results also through the action of methyllithium with the nitrile.[274] Acetylation of the aminoisoindole followed by hydrolysis yielded dimethylisoindoline. Phthalonitrile reacts in an analogous manner with sodio derivatives of phenylacetonitrile and ethyl cyanoacetate and malonate.[275]

Alkylation of Aliphatic Nitriles

Aliphatic nitriles may be alkylated through the simultaneous action of alkyl halides and sodamide upon the nitriles, yields of α-alkylated nitriles varying between 8.2 to 45.5%.[119] Straight chain nitriles and equimolecular quantities of the lower aliphatic bromides give mainly monoalkylated products. Higher temperatures are necessary for alkylation with higher alkyl bromides. Monoalkylated nitriles may be converted to dialkylated nitriles by the same method.[120]

Compounds containing reactive hydrogen are capable of combining additively with acrylonitrile. Carbon to carbon bonds may be established by this reaction with compounds containing active methylene groups such as ketones and aldehydes, resulting in the formation of saturated nitriles.[276]

Cyclization of Nitriles

Nitriles, RCH_2CN, treated with the sodium compound of a secondary aromatic aliphatic amine, $NaNR_1R_2$, react to form a sodio derivative, $RCH(Na)CN$. The reaction of such sodio compounds with a second molecule of nitrile gives rise to the sodio derivative of the dimeric nitrile, $RCH(CN)C(:NH)CH_2R$. When two cyano groups are present in the molecule, internal condensation may take place resulting in the formation of a cyclic imino nitrile:[121]

$$CNCH_2(CH_2)_nCN \quad \rightarrow \quad CNCH(CH_2)_nC = NH$$

The transformation may be brought about also by use of alkaline earth and magnesium amides. The imino nitriles yield cyclic keto nitriles,

$$CNCH(CH_2)_nCO.$$

Such keto nitriles have been converted to the corresponding cyclic ketones by hydrolysis of the cyano group to a carboxyl group and subsequent decarboxylation.

The best yields of the cyclic nitriles are obtained when the reaction is carried out in dilute solution. The amount of ether used per 10 gm of the dinitrile varies between 2 and 13 liters. Yields approaching the theoretical have been obtained from dicyano compounds with 5, 6 and 7-carbon chains, but 9 to 12 carbon dinitriles give low yields of the cyclic product. High yields have been obtained from dinitriles with 14 to 33 carbon atoms, ranging from 65 to 91%.

Cyclization may take place through the condensation of two molecules of the dicyano compound resulting in the formation of a dicyanodiimino product,[122]

$$\overline{CNCH(CH_2)_nCH_2C(:NH)CH(CN)(CH_2)_nCH_2C:NH}$$

Cyclization of the type under discussion is possible with compounds of the aromatic series.[123] Thus, o-dicyanomethylbenzene, $C_6H_4(CH_2CN)_2$, may be condensed to β-imino-α-cyanhydrindene,

$$C_6H_4 \begin{array}{c} CH_2 \\ \diagup \quad \diagdown \\ \quad \quad C:NH. \\ \diagdown \quad \diagup \\ CH-CN \end{array}$$

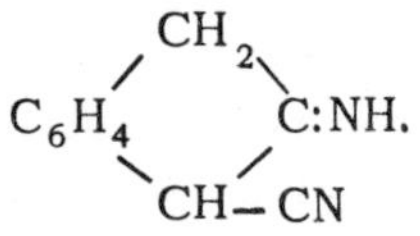

Reduction of Nitriles

Nitriles may be hydrogenated catalytically in the presence of nickel or platinum catalysts.[277] As a rule, primary and secondary amines are formed simultaneously in the process. This fact may be explained on the assumption that an aldimine is first formed; this is reduced to a primary amine which reacts with the unconverted aldimine, forming an aminated secondary amine; reduction of the latter gives a secondary amine:[124]

$$RCN \quad \rightarrow \quad RCH:NH \quad \rightarrow \quad RCH_2NH_2$$

$$RCH:NH + RCH_2NH_2 \quad \rightarrow \quad RCH(NH_2)NHCH_2R$$

$$\rightarrow \quad (RCH_2)_2NH + NH_3$$

If the reduction is carried out in an atmosphere of ammonia, the primary base is formed in greater yield, probably because the reaction between the aldimine and the primary base is repressed by the presence of ammonia.[125] A nearly quantitative yield of the primary base is obtained as the acylated derivative, when the reduction is carried out in the presence of acetic anhydride.[126] Hydrogenation in alkaline medium also results in increased formation of primary amines.[278]

The reduction may be carried out either in the liquid phase or in the gas phase. In many cases reduction proceeds at room temperature, but heating is necessary with some nitriles.

If the hydrogenation of a nitrile is carried out in the presence of a primary or secondary alkylamine, the corresponding N-mono or N-dialkylamine is formed.[279]

Secondary reactions take place when nitriles containing *carbonyl groups* are subjected to catalytic reduction. Thus, α-phenyl-β-benzoylpropionitrile,

$$C_6H_5COCH_2CH(CN)C_6H_5,$$

gives on reduction 2,4-diphenylpyrroline,

$$\overline{C_6H_5C = CHCH(C_6H_5)CH_2NH}$$

in excellent yield.[127] α,β-Diphenyl-β-phenacylpropionitrile,

$$CNCH(C_6H_5)CH(C_6H_5)CH_2COC_6H_5.$$

gives 2,4,5-triphenylpyridine on reduction in the presence of nickel catalyst.[128] Formyl and benzoylphenylacetonitriles are reduced to the corresponding acylaldimines.[129] Reduced at 50 - 70° under 100 - 150 atm pressure, formylphenylacetonitrile is converted to β-phenylpropylamine.[130]

The cyano group in *ketovaleronitrile* and its homologs is reduced in preference to the carbonyl group when the reduction is carried out at 35 - 40° in the presence of Raney nickel; at higher temperatures amino alcohols are obtained, though between 150 and 200° a certain amount of cyclic oxides with the same number of carbon atoms as the original nitriles are also formed.[131]

o-Cyanobenzophenone, hydrogenated at room temperature in the presence of palladium catalyst in acid medium gives 3-methylphthalimidine,

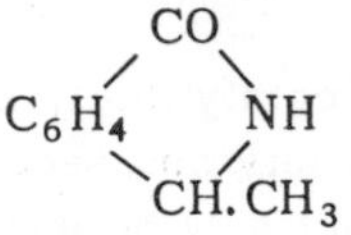
CO
C6H4
NH
CH.CH3

while in neutral medium a compound of unknown structure is formed in addition to 3-methylphthalimidine.

Cyanoacetylurea, $CNCH_2CONHCONH_2$, reduced at 60 - 70° in aqueous solution in the presence of nickel catalyst gives uracil, CONHCH = CHCONH.

Aldehyde and ketone cyanohydrins are reduced only to a limited extent in the presence of nickel, due to the poisoning of the catalyst by the hydrocyanic acid resulting from the dissociation of the cyanohydrin. Good yields of β-hydroxyamines may be obtained by adding a solution of the cyanohydrin drop by drop to a suspension of the catalyst.[132] Many substituted mandelonitriles have been successfully reduced to the corresponding amines in moderate yield by use of platinum oxide as a catalyst.[133] On thus reducing substituted mandelonitriles, alkoxy groups, if present in the molecule, are removed and the benzene ring is hydrogenated.[134]

The *unsaturated bond* in acrylonitrile, its homologs and certain other unsaturated aliphatic nitriles is attacked in preference to the cyano group, and saturated nitriles may be prepared by the selective hydrogenation of these nitriles. Succinonitrile may be prepared, for example, from fumaronitrile and stearonitrile may be obtained from oleonitrile.[135]

α-Carbethoxycinnamonitrile, $C_6H_5CH = C(CN)COOC_2H_5$, is converted to α-carbethoxy-β-phenylpropionaldehyde, $C_6H_5CH_2CH(CHO)COOC_2H_5$, when reduced in the presence of an aqueous suspension of a nickel catalyst. *o*-Nitrobenzylidenecyanoacetic ethyl ester, $NO_2C_6H_4CH = C(CN)COOC_2H_5$, hydrogenated in the presence of a nickel catalyst, is converted to 2-aminoquinoline-3-carboxylic ethyl ester,

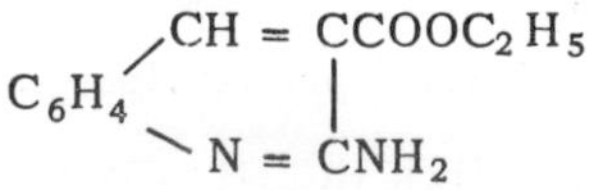
CH = CCOOC2H5
C6H4
N = CNH2

on the other hand, when the reduction is carried out in the presence of platinized asbestos, N-hydroxyaminoquinoline is obtained. *o*-Nitro-*α*-phenylcinnamonitrile, reduced in the presence of platinized silica in ethyl alcohol, gives 2-amino-3-phenylquinoline-1-oxide,

$$C_6H_4\begin{matrix}\diagup CH = C(CN)C_6H_5\\ \diagdown NO_2\end{matrix} \rightarrow C_6H_4\begin{matrix}\diagup CH = CC_6H_5\\ \qquad\qquad | \\ \diagdown NO = CNH_2\end{matrix}$$

The *nitro* group in aromatic nitriles is reduced to an amino group on hydrogenation in the presence of nickel as a catalyst at ordinary temperature. The cyano group may or may not be reduced, depending upon its position with respect to the nitro group. The cyano group is reduced in *p*-nitrobenzyl cyanide; on the other hand, the cyano group is unaffected in *o*-nitrobenzyl cyanide. *Para*- and *meta*-nitrobenzonitriles are reduced to aminoaldimines, $H_2NC_6H_4CH = NH$. These may be hydrolyzed to the corresponding aldehydes.[136] The cyano group in 1,5-, 2,5- and 1,2-nitronaphthonitriles remains intact, while the nitro group is reduced to an amino group.[137]

Aminonitriles may be successfully reduced to the corresponding primary diamines by carrying out the hydrogenation in methanol at 60° under 200 lb hydrogen pressure in the presence of a large amount of ammonia.[138]

Methyl-γ-cyano-γ-phenylbutyrate, $C_6H_5CH(CN)CH_2CH_2COOCH_3$, reduced in alcoholic solution with Raney nickel at 150° under pressure yields 5-phenyl-2-piperidone, $C_6H_5\overline{CHCH_2CH_2COCH_2CH_2}$. Piperidones are obtained also through the reduction of other *γ*-cyano esters.[139]

Pyrrolidine derivatives, $C_6H_5\overline{C(R)CH_2CH_2N(CH_3)CH_2}$, in which R represents hydrogen or the carbethoxy group, result when *γ*-benzylmethylamino-*α*-phenylbutyronitriles, $C_6H_5C(R)(CN)CH_2CH_2N(CH_3)CH_2C_6H_5$, are hydrogenated in the presence of palladium.

Nitriles are reduced smoothly to primary amines with sodium and alcohol (Mendius reaction).[140] Aliphatic nitriles may be reduced with zinc and a mineral acid, although the yields of amine by this method are low. Chromous acetate has also been used to advantage for the conversion of nitriles to the primary amines. The method appears to be of rather wide applicability, although yields are not very satisfactory.[141] Nitriles have also been reduced successfully to amines by the action of Lithium aluminum hydride.[280]

Polymerization of Nitriles

The tendency common to many unsaturated compounds of forming polymeric products is shown by many nitriles. Hydrocyanic acid and cyanogen polymerize readily in alkaline media, the rate of reaction depending on the concentration of the base and the temperature.

Polymers containing a symmetrical triazine ring, $-\overline{C = N\underset{|}{C} = N-\underset{|}{C} = N}$, are obtained from a number of nitriles. This type of polymers are not formed from nitriles in which the cyano group is joined to a carbon bearing at least one hydrogen atom.[142]

Saturated *aliphatic nitriles* do not undergo spontaneous polymerization on standing, even in the presence of substances that may be expected to act as polymerization catalysts. Condensation of aliphatic nitriles to the sodio derivative of dimeric forms is induced by sodium alcoholate,[143] or metallic sodium[144] providing the metal is present in excess: A sodio derivative of the nitrile is first formed and, reacting with a molecule of the nitrile, gives the sodio derivative of the dimeric nitrile:

$$2CH_3CN + 2Na \rightarrow NaCH_2CN + CH_4 + NaCN$$

$$CH_3CN + NaCH_2CN \rightarrow CH_3C(NH_2) = CNaCN$$

The dinitrile, $CH_3C(NH_2) = CHCN$ or $CH_3C(:NH)CH_2CN$, is obtained on hydrolyzing the sodio derivative.

Iminobenzylcyanethyl, $C_6H_5C(:NH)CH(CH_3)CN$, is obtained in the form of its sodio derivative when a mixture of benzonitrile and propionitrile is treated with metallic sodium.[145]

Trimeric forms of aliphatic nitriles are formed through the interaction of metallic sodium with two equivalents of the nitrile.[146] These compounds are derivatives of aminomiazine, $\overline{CH = C(NH_2)N = CH - N = CH}$. Aminodimethylmiazine or cyanethine is obtained, for example, by treatment of acetonitrile with 1/6 its weight of sodium under slight pressure:

$$4CH_3CN + 2Na \rightarrow Na\overline{C = C(NH_2)N = C(CH_3)N = C}CH_3 + CH_4 + NaCN$$

Mixed polymers result through the condensation of two different nitriles under the action of metallic sodium, cyanmethetine being obtained, for example, from a mixture of two molecular equivalents of propionitrile and one of acetonitrile.[147] Mixed polymers may also be obtained with aromatic and aliphatic nitriles. Cyanodiphenylethine, $C_6H_5\overline{C = NC(NH_2) = C(CH_3)C(C_6H_5) = N}$ results, for example, when the sodio derivative of dimeric propionitrile is heated at 150° for 3 hours with an equal weight of benzonitrile.[148]

Aromatic nitriles may be polymerized under appropriate conditions to derivatives of 1,3,5-triazines. Benzonitrile condenses to 2,4,6-triphenyl-1,3,5-triazine, or cyaphenine, $C_6H_5\overline{C = NC(C_6H_5) = N - C(C_6H_5) = N}$, when subjected to the action of chlorosulfonic acid at 0°.[149]

Cyanogen halides, XCN, polymerize under the action of hydrogen halides to symmetrical trihalotriazines, $X\overline{C = NCX = NCX = N}$. Polymerization is accelerated by heat and with increase in the concentration of the halo acid.

Cyanuric chloride results in satisfactory yield when chlorine is conducted for 4 to 5 hours into a well-cooled solution of hydrocyanic acid containing 1% ethyl alcohol, and the resulting solution is allowed to stand for 12 hours in a freezing mixture. The solid polymer is recovered by distilling off the solvent and the unconverted cyanogen chloride.[150] *Cyanuric bromide* results when impure cyanogen bromide is heated to 130 - 140° alone or in ehereal solution; it is obtained also through the condensation of cyanogen bromide in ethereal solution in the presence of bromine or preferably hydrobromic acid.[151]

Reactions of Cyanuric Chloride

The chlorine atoms in cyanuric chloride are reactive and may be replaced with various groups. They may be replaced, for example, by amino or substituted amino groups. One chlorine atom is replaced most readily, the second less readily, while the third with still greater difficulty. In general, monosubstituted amino compounds predominate in the reaction product when amines are made to react with cyanuric chloride at 0°, disubstituted compounds form principally in the temperature range 40 - 60°, and trisubstituted compounds at 90 to 100°. Disubstituted products are also obtained as the principal product when cyanogen chloride is made to react with an excess of the amine.

Cyanuric chloride heated in an autoclave with concentrated *ammonia* gives melamine in nearly quantitative yield.[152] Triethylmelamine is obtained by heating cyanuric chloride at 100° in an autoclave with an ethereal solution of *ethylamine*, while triphenylmelamine results when the chloride is heated at 150° with an ethereal solution of aniline in excess. Other aryl substituted melamines may be prepared in a similar manner by use of the appropriate amine.[153] Hydrazine hydrate reacting with cyanuric chloride in solution in a mixture of alcohol and acetonitrile gives trihydrazinetriazine.[154]

Sodium alcoholates and sodium salts of phenols react with cyanuric chloride forming esters of cyanuric acid. These are converted to the isomeric isocyanuric esters when heated for a long period under reflux. Reaction also takes place with mono- and diamidocyanuric chloride, resulting in the formation of amino cyanuric esters.[155]

Sodium sulfide reacts readily with cyanuric chloride to form sodium thiocyanurate $(NaSCN)_3$.

In contrast to monomeric cyanogen halides, cyanuric halides do not exert an oxidizing action on hydrogen sulfide and sulfurous acid.

Trimethylacetonitrile polymerizes to a dimer,[156] $(CH_3)_3C\overline{C = NC(=N})C(CH_3)_3$. *Malononitrile* polymerizes under the influence of sodium ethoxide and other basic substances giving two types of polymers of the probable structure

$$CNCH_2\overline{C = NC(CH_2CN) = C(CN)C(NH_2) = N}$$

and

$$CNCH_2\overline{C = NC(CH_2CN) = NC(CH_2CN) = N}$$

Dichloroacetonitrile, saturated with hydrochloric acid and heated for several hours at 130 - 140° in a sealed tube, condenses to a trimer. Under the same conditions, *trichloroacetonitrile* also gives a polymer, though very slowly, while *monochloracetonitrile* does not form a polymer.[157] *a-Dichloropropionitrile* polymerizes to trisdichloroethyltriazine,

$$CH_3CCl_2\overline{C = NC(CCl_2CH_3) = NC(CCl_2CH_3) = N}$$

Metallic sodium causes the polymerization of benzonitrile in boiling benzene solution. The product is the sodio derivative of 2,2,4,6-tetraphenyl-1,2-dihydro-

1,3,5-triazine,[158] $(C_6H_5)_2CN = C(C_6H_5)N = C(C_6H_5) = NNa$. Organoalkali compounds, RNa, react with benzonitrile at room temperature forming compounds of the general type[159] $RC(C_6H_5)N = C(C_6H_5)N = C(C_6H_5)NNa$.

Aliphatic acyl chlorides, RCOCl, condense with benzonitrile in the presence of aluminum chloride to diphenylalkyltriazines, $C_6H_5C = NCR = NC(C_6H_5) = N$. Benzylchloride yields the compound[160] $C_6H_5CCl = NC(C_6H_5) = NCOC_6H_5 \cdot AlCl_3$.

Cyanamide polymerizes to a dimer, dicyandiamide, $H_2NC(:NH)NHCN$, in slightly alkaline aqueous solution.[161] Polymerization takes place quantitatively in alkaline solution up to pH 10. The velocity of polymerization is related to the hydrogen ion concentration, reaching a maximum at pH 9.8 and decreasing rapidly above and below this point.[162] Conversion to dicyandiamide proceeds rapidly and nearly quantitatively in the presence of 2 - 4% ammonia.[162] Cyanamide also undergoes polymerization when heated in the absence of any solvent.[163] The trimer of cyanamide, melamine,

$$H_2NC = NC(NH_2) = NC(NH_2) = N$$

is formed on heating cyanamide or dicyanamide in an autoclave at 120 - 125° in an inert atmosphere or in the presence of ammonia.[164] Melamine exists in two isomeric forms, the amino form already given and the imino form,

$$HN = CNHC(:NH)NHC(:NH)NH$$

Trialkyl derivatives of normal or exomelamine result through the reaction of amines with cyanuric chloride or trithiocyanuric esters. Isomelamine derivatives are formed through the polymerization of *alkyl cyanamides*.[165] The derivatives of normal melamine exist in two isomeric forms:

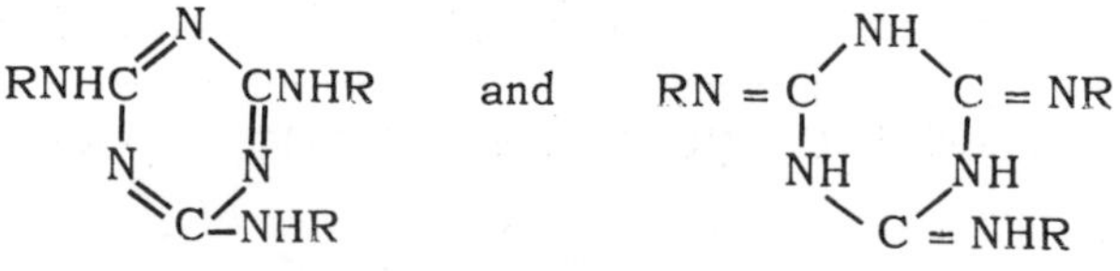

The structure of isomelamine derivatives is assumed to be

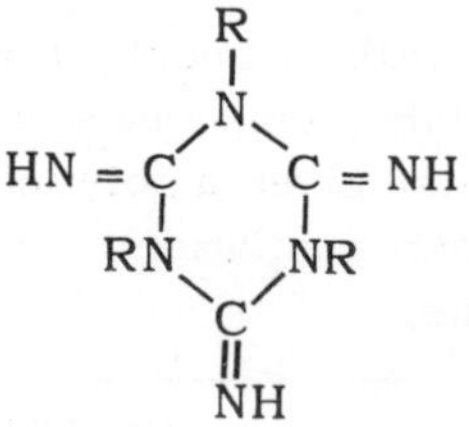

Alkyl and aryl cyanamides polymerize on heating alone or in solution in alcohol or in water.[166]

Ethyl isocyanide, $C_2H_5N = C$, polymerizes on heating to 100 -160° to a trimer which decomposes to propionitrile when heated above 160°. Depolymerization is complete at 240°.[167] Phenyl isocyanide polymerizes to a dimer[168] of the probable formula

$$C_6H_5N \overset{\overset{\displaystyle C}{\|}}{\underset{\underset{\displaystyle C}{\|}}{\diagup\diagdown}} NC_6H_5$$

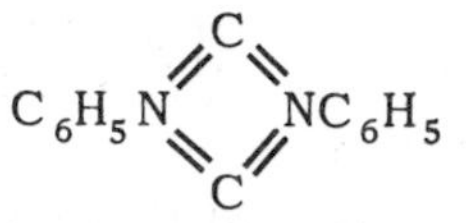

Polymerization of Cyanic Acid, Its Derivatives, and of Fulminic Acid

Vapors of cyanic acid polymerize to cyamelide, $\overline{HN = COC(:NH)OC(:NH)O}$, at temperatures below 15°, and to cyanuric acid, $HO\overline{C = NC(OH) = NC(OH) = N}$, at higher temperatures.[169] Liquid cyanic acid polymerizes at 0° within an hour to a solid consisting principally of cyamelide[170] and a small proportion of cyanuric acid.[171] In ethereal solution, cyanic acid polymerizes largely to cyanuric acid.[172]

Ethyl isocyanate polymerizes readily to ethyl cyanurate,[173] while methyl isocyanate polymerizes to methyl isocyanurate. In the presence of triethylphosphine, methyl isocyanate polymerizes to 3,5-dimethyl-2-methyl-4,6-diketo-1,3,5-oxdi-azine,[174] $CH_3\overline{NCOOC(NCH_3)N(CH_3)C}O$. *Phenyl isocyanate* condenses to a dimer, $C_6H_5\overline{NCON(CO)}C_6H_5$, in the presence of a small amount of triethylphosphine.[175] The condensation also takes place on boiling a pyridine solution of phenylisocyanate.[176] A trimer, triphenyl isocyanurate, results when phenyl isocyanate is heated at 100° with potassium acetate.[177]

Normal cyanuric esters,[178] $RO\overline{C:NC(OR):NC(OR):N}$, result through the reaction of sodium alcoholates with cyanuric chloride or bromide. Boiled under reflux for a long period, normal cyanurates are converted to isocyanuric ester, $\overline{RNCONRCONRCO}$. Isocyanurates also result through the reaction of alkyl sulfates or alkyl halides with sodium cyanurate or of alkyl halides with silver cyanurate. Trimethyl isocyanurate results when cyanuric acid reacts with diazomethane in ethereal solution.

Trialkyl isocyanurates are converted to trialkyl biurets on gently warming with normal caustic:

$$CH_3\overline{NCON(CH_3)CON(CH_3)C}O + H_2O \rightarrow CH_3NHCON(CH_3)CONHCH_3 + CO_2$$

Several polymers of *fulminic acid* are known, among them fulminuric, metafulminuric and isofulminuric acids.[179] Metafulminuric acid results through the polymerization of fulminic acid:

$$3C = NOH \rightarrow -C(=NOH) - C(=NOH) - C(=NOH) -$$

$$\rightarrow HON = C\overline{C(=NOH) - CH = N}O$$

Treated with alkalies, metafulminuric acid yields isonitrosocyanacethydroxamic acid, which is another polymeric form of fulminic acid. Three other polymers also result by this treatment, isofulminuric acid, $H_2NCOC = NON = COH$, hydroxyisonitrosoisoxazoloneimide, $HN = CC(=NOH)C(OH) = NO$, and aminoisonitrosoisoxazolone, $H_2NC = NOCOC = NOH$. Fulminuric acid results when mercuric fulminate is dissolved in aqueous potassium chloride and the solution is heated to boiling.

A polymeric compound, trifulmin,[180] is obtained when a half-molal equivalent of aqueous sodium carbonate is added drop by drop and with continuous stirring to a solution of methylnitrolic acid $HC(=NOH)NO_2$, cooled with ice. The compound is insoluble in all solvents in the cold, and is very explosive. Treated carefully with hydrochloric acid, it gives formyl chloride oxime, $HCCl = NOH$. The polymer is regarded as trimolecular formonitrile oxide, $(HC \equiv N = O)_3$.

ISOCYANIC, THIOCYANIC AND ISOTHIOCYANIC ESTERS; FULMINIC ACID

Isocyanic Esters

Normal cyanic esters are not known,[181] and where their formation is expected, isocyanic esters, RNCO, are obtained. Isocyanic esters were first prepared by distilling alkyl sulfuric salts with potassium cyanate. They are obtained readily through the reaction of alkyl halides with silver cyanate:

$$C_3H_7I + AgNCO \rightarrow C_3H_7NCO + AgI$$

They may be prepared conveniently by conducting phosgene over the heated chlorides of amines and treating the resulting carbamic chloride with lime:[182]

$$CH_3NH_2.HCl + COCl_2 \rightarrow CH_3NHCOCl + 2HCl$$
$$2CH_3NHCOCl + Ca(OH)_2 \rightarrow 2CH_3N = CO + CaCl_2 + 2H_2O$$

The only side reaction of any significance in this process is the formation of disubstituted ureas by reaction of the isocyanate with the free amine. This is largely eliminated by using a salt of the amine and by effective agitation. Lower diisocyanates have not been made successfully by this reaction because it has not been found possible to avoid intramolecular urea formation.

The use of the carbamate salt was found to be preferable to the chloride in the preparation of hexamethylene isocyanate.[281]

Isocyanates have been prepared in good yield by the gas phase reaction of amines with phosgene at 180 to 400° in the presence of a catalyst such as bleached clay impregnated with barium chloride, zinc chloride or sodium sulfate.[282] This method is not suitable for the preparation of isocyanates of very high boiling point.

Carbamates may be decomposed to an isocyanate and an alcohol. Carbamyl chlorides and fluorides as well as certain ureas may also be decomposed to isocyanates.[283]

Isocyanates are formed as intermediates in the Hofmann reaction[284] and the Curtius transformation. They may be obtained by heating acid chlorides, RCOCl, and sodium azide in diisoamyl ether. The acid azide first formed in the reaction decomposes rapidly yielding an isocyanate:[183]

$$RCOCl + NaN_3 \rightarrow RNCO + NaCl + N_2$$

The Hofmann rearrangement is useful only for the preparation of those isocyanates which do not react readily with water, since an aqueous medium is required.

Isocyanates are unstable and polymerize on standing, especially in the presence of certain impurities. They are highly reactive compounds. Reaction with amines leads to the formation of substituted ureas:

$$C_2H_5N=CO + H_2NR \rightarrow C_2H_5NHCONHR$$

With alcohols they give carbamic esters:

$$C_2H_5N=CO + C_2H_5OH \rightarrow C_2H_5NHCOOC_2H_5$$

Alkalies decompose them to an amine:

$$CH_3N=CO + 2\ NaOH \rightarrow CH_3NH_2 + Na_2CO_3$$

Heated with water they form dialkyl ureas:

$$C_2H_5N=CO + H_2O \rightarrow C_2H_5NH_2 + CO_2$$

$$C_2H_5N=CO + C_2H_5NH_2 \rightarrow C_2H_5NHCONHC_2H_5$$

With hydrogen halides haloformamides result:[184]

$$RN=CO + HCl \rightarrow RNHCOCl$$

Phenylcarbamyl fluoride, C_6H_5NHCOF, results in quantitative yield through the interaction of hydrogen fluoride with phenyl isocyanate in the cold. Other aromatic isocyanates react similarly.

Hydrocyanic acid reacts with isocyanates to form aminoformyl cyanides:[185]

$$RN=CO + HCN \rightarrow RNHCOCN$$

Cyanoformanilide, resulting from the reaction of hydrocyanic acid with phenyl isocyanate, reacts with a second molecule of isocyanate to give 1,3-diphenylparabanic acid-4-imide, $\overline{C_6H_5NCON(C_6H_5)COC}=NH$, reaction with a third molecule of isocyanate forming phenylureidoparabanic acid.[186]

Carbon dioxide combines with methyl isocyanate in alcoholic solution in the presence of triethylphosphine to form 3,5-dimethyl-2,4,6-triketo-1,3,5-oxdiazine,[187]

$$\overline{CH_3NCON(CH_3)COOCO}$$

Organic acids react at a moderate temperature with phenyl isocyanate forming the anhydride of the acid and diphenylurea:

$$2C_6H_5N=CO + 2RCOOH \rightarrow C_6H_5NHCONHC_6H_5 + (RCO)_2O + CO_2$$

At higher temperatures the acid anhydride reacts with the diphenylurea formed, giving the anilide of the acid:

$$C_6H_5NHCONHC_6H_5 + (RCO)_2O \quad \rightarrow \quad 2RCONHC_6H_5 + CO_2$$

With dibasic acids, $R(COOH)_2$, the phenyl imide,

$$R\underset{CO}{\overset{CO}{\diagup\diagdown}}NC_6H_5$$

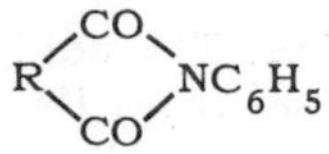

may result.[188] The dianilides of malonic, sebacic and azelaic acids are obtained when the acids are heated at 170° with phenyl isocyanate. Cyanacetic acid reacts with phenyl isocyanate in the cold, forming cyanacetanilide, $CNCH_2CONHC_6H_5$. Other a-cyano acids react similarly.[189]

Phenyl isocyanate reacts with diethyl malonate in the presence of a trace of alkali to form methanetricarboxylic diethyl ester anilide,[190] $C_6H_5NHCOCH(COOC_2H_5)_2$; with sodio ethyl cyanoacetate, the sodio derivative of cyanomalonic ester anilide results.[191]

Phenyl isocyanate in chloroform solution reacts with chlorine forming a very unstable dichloride, $C_6H_5OCNCl_2$. Bromine reacts in a similar manner forming a dibromide.[192]

The reaction of phenyl isocyanate with diazomethane in alcoholic solution results in the formation of a cyclic amide:[285]

$$C_6H_5NCO + 2CH_2N_2 \quad \rightarrow \quad \begin{array}{c} C_6H_5 - N \underline{\hspace{1cm}} CO \ + 2N_2 \\ | \qquad\qquad | \\ CH_2 - CH_2 \end{array}$$

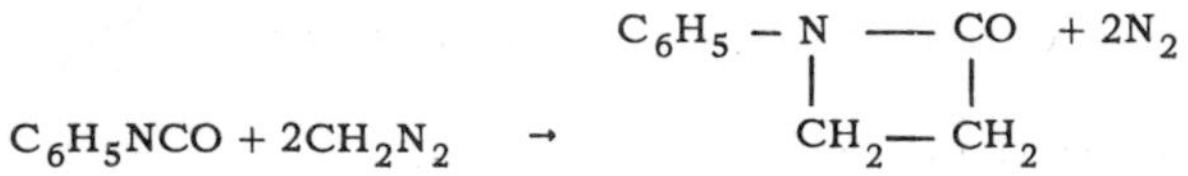

Hydrolysis with sodium hydroxide, followed by acidification converts the product to N-phenyl-β-alanine.

Isocyanates give amides on treatment with organomagnesium halides and hydrolysis of the product formed:

$$RN = CO + RMgX \quad \rightarrow \quad RN(MgX)COR' \xrightarrow{H_2O} RNHCOR'$$

Phenyl isocyanate reacting with an excess of phenylmagnesium bromide, gives o-phenyl-benzohydroxylanilines:[286]

$$C_6H_5NCO \quad \xrightarrow{C_6H_5MgBr} \quad \underset{-C_6H_5}{\overset{C_6H_5NHCHC_6H_5}{\bigcirc}}$$

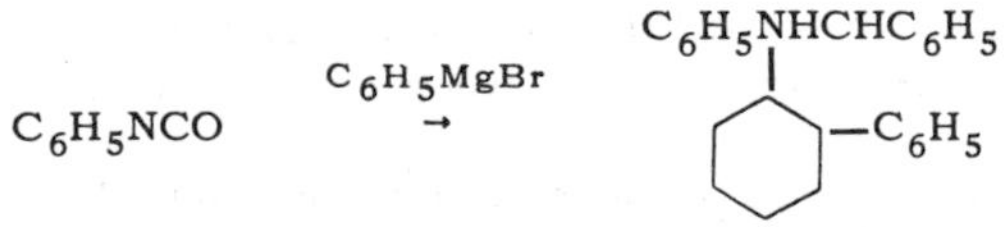

Formation of Ureas from Isocyanic Esters

Primary and secondary amines react smoothly with isocyanic esters to form ureas:[193]

$$RN = CO + H_2NR' \quad \rightarrow \quad RNHCONHR'$$

The reaction may be carried out by warming equimolecular quantities of the amine and isocyanate in an inert solvent, such as petroleum ether. Moisture must be carefully excluded from the reaction mixture.[194]

Primary aliphatic amines react with isocyanates about nine times as fast as ammonia, and the latter reacts about twice as rapidly as aniline.

Salts of *amino acids* react with phenyl isocyanate forming ureidoacid salts. The free acids do not react readily as a rule.[195]

Phenyl isocyanate reacts with a concentrated aqueous solution of *hydroxylamine* in excess to form anilinoformylhydroxylamine,[196] $C_6H_5NHCONHOH$. N-Benzoylhydroxylamine, on the other hand, gives the urethane derivative, $C_6H_5CONOCONHC_6H_5$.[287] With *methylhydrazine* in ethereal solution, 2-methyl-4-phenylsemicarbazide,

$$C_6H_5NHCON(CH_3)NH_2,$$

is obtained,[197] and with *phenylhydrazine*, 1,4-diphenylsemicarbazide. *Amides* and *amidines* also react with phenyl isocyanate giving substituted ureas.[198] Benxamidoxime gives ω-phenylureidobenzoxime,[199] $C_6H_5NHCONHC(C_6H_5) = NOH$, while benzanilide yields benzenyldiphenylamidine:[200]

$$C_6H_5CONHC_6H_5 + C_6H_5NCO \rightarrow C_6H_5C(=NC_6H_5)NHC_6H_5 + CO_2$$

Guanidine thiocyanate and phenyl isocyanate react in the presence of sodium ethoxide to form N,N′-dianilinoformylguanidine,[201] $(C_6H_5NHCONH)_2C = NH$.

Isocyanates react with ureas to form biurets. ω, ω′-Diphenylbiuret,

$$C_6H_5NHCONHCONHC_6H_5$$

results, for example, by the reaction of phenylurea with phenyl isocyanate.[202]

Formation of Urethanes from Isocyanic Esters

The reaction of isocyanic esters with alcohols results in the formation of urethanes:

$$RNCO + HOR' \rightarrow RNHCOOR'$$

Alcohols react with isocyanates less readily than amines. Primary alcohols react about three times as fast as secondary alcohols and about two-hundred times as readily as tertiary alcohols.[288] Some tertiary alcohols are dehydrated on reaction with isocyanates. Aromatic and benzyl isocyanates are the most reactive, primary aliphatic isocyanates are less reactive, and secondary aliphatic and alicyclic isocyanates are the least reactive. Bulky substituents in ortho position in aromatic isocyanates cause a marked decrease in reactivity.

The reaction between phenyl isocyanate with *methyl alcohol* proceeds with evolution of heat. Other *aliphatic alcohols* also react well with phenyl isocyanate.[203] Ethylene glycol gives the dicarbanilic ester of ethylene glycol, while glycerine forms a trisphenylcarbamate.[204]

The hydroxyl group in esters of *α-hydroxyacids* also enters in reaction with phenyl isocyanate.[205] Such esters yield compounds of the type $C_6H_5NHCOOC(R_1R_2)CONHC_6H_5$.

Monohydroxybenzoic acids react with phenyl isocyanate to form the amides

$$HOC_6H_4CONHC_6H_5$$

exclusively.[289] Triphenylcarbinol does not react with isocyanates.

The reaction of mercaptans with isocyanates is similar to that of alcohols and results in the formation of thiourethanes:

$$RNCO + HSR' \rightarrow RNHCOSR'$$

Ethyl mercaptan, heated with phenyl isocyanate in a sealed tube at 100°, gives thiocarbanilic S-ethyl ester.[206] Phenyl mercaptan reacts with phenyl isocyanate on prolonged heating at 100° in a sealed tube to form thiocarbanilic S-phenyl ester.[207]

N-Acyl urethanes[208] are obtained through the reaction of alcohols with acyl isocyanates.

Polymerization of Isocyanates

Most aromatic isocyanates dimerize in the presence of triethylphosphine

$$2C_6H_5NCO \quad \rightarrow \quad C_6H_5N\begin{matrix} CO \\ \diagup \quad \diagdown \\ \diagdown \quad \diagup \\ CO \end{matrix}NC_6H_5$$

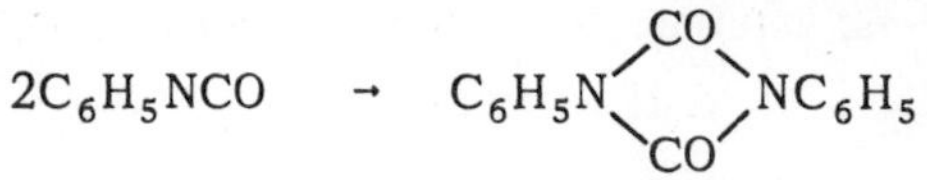

Dimerization may be brought about also by heating the isocyanate with pyridine.[290] Ethyl isocyanate is converted to a trimer when brought into contact with triethylphosphine.[291] Trimers are formed from both aromatic and aliphatic isocyanates under the action of various salts such as calcium and potassium acetates, sodium formate and carbonate. Polymerization is brought about also by triethylamine, oxalic acid, peroxides and aluminum chloride.

Thiocyanic and Isothiocyanic Esters

Normal thiocyanates, RSCN, are obtained by heating alkyl halides or salts of monoalkyl sulfates with dry potassium thiocyanate. They may be obtained in good yield by shaking a concentrated aqueous solution of potassium thiocyanate with alkyl sulfates or sulfonates.[209] Copper powder, sodium bromide or iodide may be used as catalysts.

Allyl chloride and, in general, compounds that contain the grouping, $C_2 = CHCH_2Cl$, react with sodium thiocyanate to form thiocyano derivatives:[210]

$$CH_2 = CHCH_2Cl + NaSCN \quad \rightarrow \quad CH_2 = CHCH_2SCN + NaCl$$

The reaction of *ethylene chlorhydrin* with sodium thiocyanate leads to the formation of β-hydroxyethyl thiocyanate, $HOCH_2CH_2SCN$, which may be converted by internal rearrangement to mercaptooxazoline,[211] $\overline{OCH_2CH_2N} = CSH$; ethoxy-1-mercaptodihydroimidazole, $HOCH_2CH_2\overline{NCH_2CH_2NHCS}$, results through the condensation of two molecules of the compound.[212]

Ammonium thiocyanate reacts with *chloracetone* in alcoholic solution to form thiopropionine thiocyanate in 30% yield:[213]

$$CH_3COCH_2Cl + 2 NH_4SCN \quad \rightarrow \quad CNSCH_2C(CH_3) = NH.HSCN + NH_4Cl + H_2O$$

Thiocyanoacetone results, however, through the reaction of chloracetone with barium thiocyanate or with aqueous solutions of alkali thiocyanates.[214] The compound gradually cyclizes in aqueous solution, rapidly in hydrochloric acid solution, probably to

$$CH_3\overline{C = CHSCONH} \quad [215]$$

Potassium thiocyanate reacts with *chloracetic acid* to form isothiocyanoacetic acid,[216] $S = C = NCH_2COOH$. In common with other compounds in which a thiocyano group is present in α-position with respect to a carboxyl or carbonyl group, thiocyanoacetic acid may be condensed to a thiazole derivative, 3,4-dioxotetrahydrothiazole, $\overline{SCH_2CONHCO}$. Chloracetic acid, heated with an aqueous solution of ammonium thiocyanate yields rhodanic acid, $\overline{SCH_2CONHCS}$.

Certain 2,3-dihalides or tertiary halides react with alkali metal thiocyanates to form only thiocyanogen polymers.

Thiocyanates may be obtained also by the reaction of cyanogen halides with metallic mercaptides RSM or organic sulfides RSR'.

Thiocyano compounds are formed through the addition of thiocyanogen to unsaturated compounds. Hydrogen atoms in certain aromatic bodies are replaceable with the thiocyano group by reaction with thiocyanogen. The subject is considered in a later section in this chapter.

Aromatic thiocyano compounds may be prepared by replacing diazo groups with the thiocyano group by reaction with cuprous thiocyanate. They may be formed also from sulfenyl compounds by reacting these with alkali metal cyanides:

$$RSSO_3Na + NaCN \rightarrow RSCN + Na_2SO_3$$
$$RSCl + NaCN \rightarrow RSCN + NaCl$$

Thiocyanates are converted on heating to isothiocyanates, RN : C : S. Zinc chloride and certain other metallic salts act as catalysts in this transformation. Methyl thiocyanate is converted largely to methyl isothiocyanate on heating for several hours at 180 - 185°. Allyl thiocyanate is converted to allyl isothiocyanate after a single distillation.

The thiocyano group does not exert an activating influence on hydrogen atoms bound to adjacent carbon atoms.

Hydrogen bromide reacts with ethyl thiocyanate forming thioformamide dibromide, $C_2H_5SCBr_2NH_2$.

Thio acids react with normal thiocyanates to form acylated thiocarbamic esters:[217]

$$RSCN + HSCOCH_3 \rightarrow RSCSNHCOCH_3$$

Phenyl thiocyanate and certain other thiocyanates react with thio acids forming esters of these acids:

$$C_6H_5SCN + HSCOC_6H_5 \rightarrow C_6H_5SCOC_6H_5 + HNCS$$

Benzyl thiocyanate gives 2-thio-4-phenylthiazoline, $C_6H_5\overline{CHCH_2N = C(SH)S}$, with thioacetic acid.[218]

Isothiocyanates result when alkyl dithiocarbamates are treated with a boiling aqueous solution of a heavy metal salt:[219]

$$C_2H_5NHCSSHNH_2C_2H_5 + HgCl_2 \rightarrow$$
$$CS = NC_2H_5 + HgS + C_2H_5NH_2.HCl + HCl$$

Alkyl dithiocarbamates are obtained through the reaction of primary amines with carbon disulfide in cold ethereal solution:

$$CS_2 + 2\ C_2H_5NH_2 \rightarrow C_2H_5NHCSSHH_2NC_2H_5$$

The reaction may be carried out in such a manner as to utilize the entire quantity of the amine. The operation is carried out in aqueous solution and equivalent quantities of carbon disulfide and caustic are added successively with cooling. The solution is then diluted and boiled with an equivalent of basic lead acetate.[220]

Isothiocyanates are also formed when the carbalkoxy derivative of dithiocarbamates are decomposed by heat:

$$RNHCSSCOOR \rightarrow RNCS + COS + ROH$$

Isothiocyanates may be obtained by oxidizing dithiocarbamic salts with iodine and treating the resulting thiuramdisulfides with sodium ethoxide and iodine:[221]

$$2RNHCSSH.H_2NR + I_2 \rightarrow RNHCSSSCSNHR + 2RNH_2.HI$$

$$RNHCSSSCSNHR + 2NaOC_2H_5 \rightarrow$$

$$2C_2H_5OH + RN = C(SNa)SSC(SNa) = NR$$

$$\xrightarrow{I_2} 2RN = CS + 2NaI + 2S$$

Isothiocyanic esters result when isocyanic esters are heated with phosphorus pentasulfide;[222] they are obtained also by the addition of sulfur to an isonitrile.[223]

Isothiocyanates are formed through the reaction of amines with thiophosgene:

$$RNH_2 + Cl_2CS \rightarrow RNCS + 2HCl$$

Aromatic isothiocyanates have been made by the action of iodine on *sym*-diaryl thioureas:

$$(ArNH)_2S \xrightarrow{I_2} ArNCS$$

This transformation has been brought about also under the action of phosphorus pentoxide, acetic anhydride, hydrogen chloride, etc.

Isothiocyanates result through the reaction of thiocyanic acid with certain unsaturated compounds, by addition at the multiple bond. The isothiocyano group attaches itself to the carbon atom bearing the greater number of substituents. Olefins with activated double bonds, such as dicyclopentadiene, styrene and mesityl oxide give isothiocyanates in good yield. Lower olefins yield a mixture of thiocyanate and isothiocyanate, while higher olefins give these compounds in low yield. Isothiocyanates are formed exclusively from tertiary olefins with 6 to 9 carbon atoms.

Acyl isothiocyanates result through the reaction of organic acid chlorides with lead thiocyanate:[224]

$$2RCOCl + Pb(SCN)_2 \rightarrow PbCl_2 + 2RCOSCN \rightarrow 2RCONCS$$

Isothiocyanates dissolve in sulfuric acid with evolution of heat and the formation of an amine and carbon sulfoxide:

$$C_2H_5NCS + H_2O \rightarrow C_2H_5NH_2 + COS$$

On heating with water they are converted to dialkyl thioureas:[225]

$$2RN = CS + H_2O \rightarrow (RNH)_2CS + COS$$

Thiol acids react with isothiocyanates, forming principally acid amides and carbon disulfide:

$$RN = CS + HSCOC_6H_5 \rightarrow RNHCOC_6H_5 + CS_2$$

Reduction with nascent hydrogen leads to the formation of an amine and thioformaldehyde, the latter polymerizing to its trimer:

$$C_2H_5N = C = S + 2H_2 \rightarrow C_2H_5NH_2 + H_2CS$$

Reacting with *amines*, isothiocyanates give substituted thioureas.[226] Primary alkyl hydrazines give semicarbazides in which the CSNHR group occupies the α-position; γ-substituted phenylhydrazines also give α-compounds, but those with *o*- and *m*-substitutents in the phenyl group give the β-compounds.

Guanidine carbonate, reacting with phenyl isothiocyanate at 100° in the presence of some alcohol, gives phenylguanylthiourea, $C_6H_5NHCSNHC(=NH)NH_2$, and thiocarbanilic O-ethyl ester,[227] $C_6H_5NHCSOC_2H_5$.

The reaction of *γ-chlorobutylamine* with phenyl isothiocyanate leads to the formation of the cyclic compound,[228] $CH_3CH(CH_2)_3NHC(S) = NC_6H_5$.

Isatin gives with phenyl isothiocyanate the compound[229]

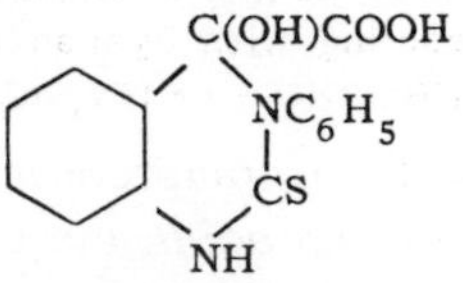

The reaction of isothiocyanates with *alcohols* is similar to that of isocyanates, the reaction product being thiocarbamic esters:[230]

$$RN = CS + HOR' \rightarrow RNHCSOR'$$

Phenol, hydroquinone, pyrogallol and aromatic alcohols such as benzyl alcohol do not react with isothiocyanates.[231] Acyl isothiocyanates, RCONCS, react with alcohols to form acylthiocarbamates,[232] RCONHCSOR'.

Thioglycolic acid, $HSCH_2COOH$, reacts with phenyl isothiocyanate to form phenylrhodanic acid, $C_6H_5NCSSCH_2CO$. Methylphenylrhodanic acid,

$$C_6H_5NCSSCH(CH_3)CO$$

similarly results from phenyl isothiocyanate and thiolactic acid.[233]

Phenyl isothiocyanate reacts with diethyl malonate forming

$$C_6H_5N = C(SNa)CH(COOC_2H_5)_2$$

which changes to $C_6H_5NHCSCH(COOC_2H_5)_2$ on treatment with acids. Allyl isothiocyanate reacts in a similar manner.[234]

Isothiocyanates in chloroform solution react with chlorine forming isocyanodichlorides,[235] $RN = CCl_2$. These compounds react with amines to form guanidines. The reaction of phenyl isothiocyanate with bromine, carried out in chloroform solution containing a little water, leads to the formation of phenylphenyliminodisulfazolidone,[236] $C_6H_5N = CSSCONC_6H_5$.

Formation of Ureas and Thioureas from Amine Salts of Cyanic and Thiocyanic Acids

Cyanates of primary and secondary amines isomerize to substituted ureas:

$$RNH_2HCNO \rightarrow RNHCONH_2$$

The reaction is quite general, although it takes place with varying degrees of ease, depending on the nature of the amine.

Cyanates of *amino acids* may be transformed to carboxylated ureas. α-Carboxy ureas may be dehydrated to hydantoins:[237]

$$HOCOCH_2NHCONH_2 \rightarrow \overline{COCH_2NHCONH}$$

Cyanates of *α-amino ketones* are transformed to imidazolone derivatives:

$$RCOCH(R_2)NH_2.HOCN \rightarrow R_1\overline{C = C(R_2)NHC(OH) = N}$$

Potassium cyanate reacts with salts of *hydroxylamine* to form hydroxyurea, isohydroxyurea and other compounds.[238] Reacting with cyanamide in aqueous solution, potassium cyanate gives monocyanurea, $CNNHCONH_2$ or $HN = CNHCONH_2$.[239]

Thioureas are obtained through the transformation of amine salts of thiocyanic acid. Thiocyanic acid salts of *α-amino acids* are transformed to thiohydantoins.[240] Thiocyanates of *α-amino ketones* yield mercaptoimidazole derivatives.[241]

Other Reactions Involving Cyanic and Thiocyanic Acids

Allophanic esters are formed through the reaction of alcohols with cyanic acid:

$$HNCO + HOC_2H_5 \rightarrow H_2NCOOC_2H_5$$

$$HNCO + H_2NCOOC_2H_5 \rightarrow H_2NCONHCOOC_2H_5$$

Thiocyanic acid reacts with hydrogen chloride to form chlorothiocarbamide,[242] H_2NCSCl.

Cyanic acid reacting with hydrazoic acid gives carbamic azide,[243] $HOC(=NH)N_3$.

Thiocyanic acid reacts with thio acids to form the amide of the corresponding oxy acid:[244]

$$HSCN + C_6H_5COSH \rightarrow C_6H_5CONH_2 + CS_2$$

Inorganic acid chlorides such as PCl_3, $POCl_3$ react with metal thiocyanates yielding isothiocyano derivatives such as $P(N = CS)_3$. Silicon tetrachloride would appear to give the normal thiocyanate, $Si(SCN)_4$.[245]

Thiocyanation by Means of Thiocyanogen

Thiocyanogen, CNS.SCN, has the characteristics of a pseudohalogen, and like halogens is capable of reacting with unsaturated compounds forming addition compounds. Thiocyanogen is less reactive in this respect than bromine,[246] though more reactive than iodine. Its reactivity is greatly influenced by the solvent used. The reaction proceeds vigorously, for example, when nitromethane is used as a solvent. Reactivity is also enhanced by radiation and by catalysts such as ferric thiocyanate. The latter is formed when iron powder is added to the thiocyanogen solution.[247]

A number of satisfactory procedures have been developed for carrying out the reaction. The thiocyanogen may be prepared, for example, through the reaction of lead thiocyanate in ethereal suspension with bromine; or through the oxidation of thiocyanic acid with manganese dioxide or lead tetraacetate in non-aqueous media. The use of *nascent* thiocyanogen may be of advantage. The procedure is to dissolve the required quantity of sodium bromide and the compound to be thiocyanated in 96% acetic acid, to cool the solution in ice, and to add the calculated quantity of bromine dissolved in the same solvent, drop by drop.[248] More satisfactory results were obtained with isoprene and dimethyl butadiene by the use of nascent than of preformed thiocyanogen.

Thiocyanogen resulting from the decomposition of cupric thiocyanate may also be used for the purpose.[249] The reaction may be carried out in the absence of an organic solvent with a slurry or paste of the thiocyanate with water. The procedure can be further simplified by the use of a mixture of copper sulfate and sodium thiocyanate. Thioxoles are obtained by this method from certain aromatic polyhydroxy compounds:

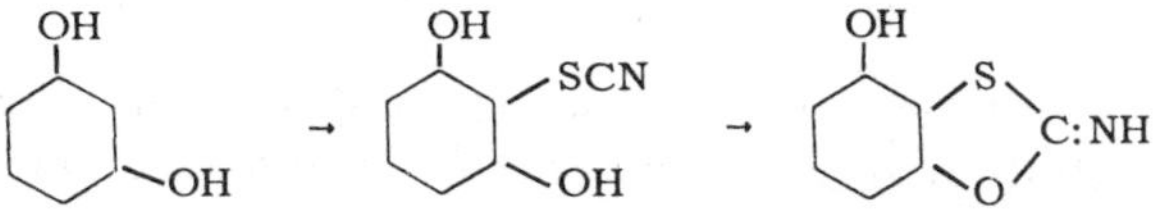

Thiocyanogen may be generated also by the electrolysis of inorganic thiocyanates. Acetone, aniline, phenetidine, toluidines and naphthylamines have been thiocyanated by use of thiocyanogen generated electrolytically. Ethyl acetate, methanol and dilute sulfuric acid have been used as solvents.[250]

Thiocyanogen is capable of yielding addition products with the following in acetic acid solution in the absence of radiation: ethylene, butylene, phenylacetylene, tolan, anethole, safrole, allyl alcohol, oleic acid, elaidic acid, erucic acid, brassidic acid, ricinelaidic acid, acetoacetic ester, acetyldibenzoylmethane, ethyl α, β-diacetylsuccinate, phenylacetic ester, antipyrene and pinene. No addition compounds are obtained under the same conditions from: acetylene, styrene, stilbene, crotonic acid, fumaric acid, maleic acid, cinnamic acid and methyl cinnamate, cinnamaldehyde, α_2, β- and α-diacetylsuccinic ester, and behenolic acid. Acetylene, styrene and stilbene take up thiocyanogen on irradiation. Styryl methyl ketone gives a substitution product, $C_6H_5CH = C(SCN)COCH_3$; a monosubstitution product is also obtained from carvone.[251] Butadiene reacts with thiocyanogen giving 2,4-thiocyanobutadiene in 80% yield.[292] Isoprene and dimethylbutadiene give well-defined crystalline dithiocyano compounds.[293]

Reaction with aliphatic and substituted aliphatic amines leads to the formation of thiocyanoamines, the polymer of thiocyanogen forming simultaneously. Thiocyanobenzylamine, $C_6H_5CH_2NHSCN$, and benzylsulfocyanamine, $C_6H_5CH_2N(SCN)_2$ result, for example, from the reaction of thiocyanogen with benzylamine.

Substitution in the aromatic ring takes place when thiocyanogen reacts with aromatic amines and phenols.[252] The SCN group enters the ring in the para position with respect to the amino group, and if this position is not available, it enters the ortho position, though very much more slowly. If both para and ortho positions are occupied rhodanation fails to take place.[253] Hydroxy groups in certain positions in the nucleus may prevent the reaction. Thus, while thiocyanated compounds may be obtained from pyrocatechol, rhodanation fails to occur with hydroquinone, resorcinol and phlorglucinol.[254]

Thiocyanogen is capable of replacing bromine or iodine in certain organic compounds. Thus, the reaction of thiocyanogen with dibromoethylene results in the formation of dithiocyanoethylene, and dibromothiocyano and dibromodithiocyanoethane.[294]

Dilute solutions of thiocyanogen in carbon tetrochloride may be kept almost unchanged in the dark. Decomposition proceeds at a moderate rate when the solutions are exposed to light, and more rapidly when they are heated to boiling. A 0.1 *N* solution for example, when boiled for 3 hours, retains only 24% of the original thiocyanogen.

Fulminic Acid

Fulminic acid,[255] C:NOH, may be considered the oxime of carbon monoxide. It may also be considered a derivative of isonitrile, obtained by the replacement of the hydrogen by a hydroxyl group. The accepted structure of the compound was first proposed by Nef.[256]

The usual method of preparation of fulminic acid is by the reaction of nitric acid with ethyl alcohol in the presence of mercuric nitrate.[257] The reaction is assumed to proceed in the following manner:

$$CH_3CH_2OH \quad \rightarrow \quad CH_3CHO \quad \rightarrow \quad CH(:NOH)CHO$$
$$\rightarrow \quad CH(:NOH)COOH \quad \rightarrow \quad NO_2C(:NOH)COOH$$
$$\rightarrow \quad NO_2CH:NOH \quad \rightarrow \quad C:NOH + HNO_2$$

Fulminic acid results also in moderate yield by warming a solution of methyl nitrol and silver nitrate in dilute nitric acid.[258] It is formed very readily by heating a solution of formamidoxime and silver nitrate in nitric acid solution:[259]

$$HC(:NOH)NH_2 \quad \rightarrow \quad C:NOH + NH_3$$

Fulminic acid has not been isolated in the free state.[260] Its existence in solution and in the vapor form at a low temperature ($-5°$) has been demonstrated, however. It rapidly polymerizes in ethereal solution to metafulminic acid.

Methylnitrolic acid results through the reaction of fulminic acid with nascent nitrous acid:[89]

$$C:NOH + HNO_2 \quad \rightarrow \quad NO_2CH:NOH$$

On reduction with ferrous salts or with an arsenite, fulminic acid is converted to hydrocyanic acid:

$$C:NOH \quad \overset{H_2}{\rightarrow} \quad H_2C:NOH \quad \rightarrow \quad HCN + H_2O$$

Reaction with hydrazoic acid leads to the formation of N-hydroxy tetrazole:[44]

$$C:NOH + N_3H \quad \rightarrow \quad \overset{H}{\underset{N_3}{\diagdown \diagup}}C:NOH \quad \rightarrow \quad \overline{HC:NN:NNOH}$$

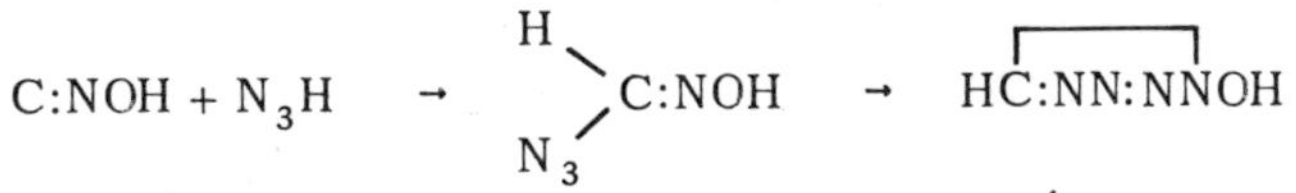

Hydrogen sulfide first forms thioformhydroxamic acid, which decomposes to thiocyanic acid and water:

$$C:NOH + H_2S \quad \rightarrow \quad HSCH = NOH \quad \rightarrow \quad HSCN + H_2O$$

Treated with hydrochloric acid, mercuric fulminate decomposes to formic acid and hydroxylamine:[37]

$$(CNO)_2Hg + 4\ HCl \quad \rightarrow \quad HgCl_2 + 2\ ClCH = NOH \quad \overset{H_2O}{\rightarrow} \quad HCOOH + H_2NOH.HCl$$

Bromine reacts with mercuric fulminate to form, first the unstable bromoformonitrile oxide, and finally dibromofuroxane:

$$(C:NO)_2Hg + 2\ Br_2 \quad \rightarrow \quad (Br_2C:NO)_2Hg$$

$$\rightarrow \quad HgBr_2 + 2\ BrC\underset{O}{\overset{}{=}}N \quad \rightarrow \quad \overline{BrC:NON - CBr}_{O}$$

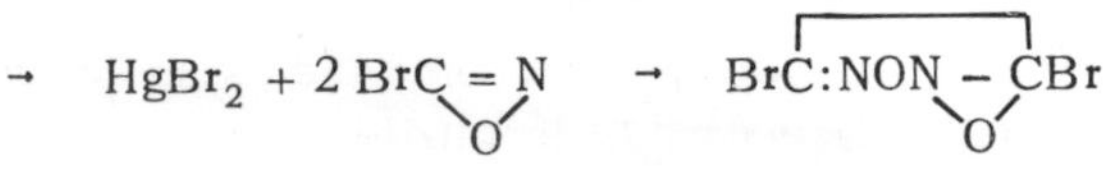

Acetyl chloride reacts with silver fulminate to form acetyl isocyanate:

$$CNOAg + CH_3COCl \rightarrow CH_3COCCl{:}NOAg$$

$$\rightarrow AgCl + CH_3CO\overline{C{:}NO} \rightarrow CH_3CON{:}CO$$

References

1. Gabriel, *Ber.*, **23,** 1771 (1890); **42,** 1252 *footnote,* (1909).
2. Bruson and McCleary, *U. S. patent,* 2,169,578 (1939); Henze *et al.*, *J. Am. Chem. Soc.*, **56,** 1350 (1934); **71,** 2122 (1949); *J. Org. Chem.*, **4,** 234 (1939); Henry, *Bull. soc. chim.*, (2) **44,** 458 (1885).
3. Tchelizeff and Schmidt, *J. Soc. Chim. Russe,* **61,** 1995 (1929); Hurd *et al. J. Am. Chem. Soc.*, **66,** 2013 (1944); Oakwood and Weisgerber, *Org. Syntheses,* **24,** 14 (1944).
4. Claisen, *Ber.*, **31,** 1024 (1898); Marsh and Stephen, *J. Chem. Soc.*, **127,** 1635 (1925); Mauthner, *Ber.*, **41,** 920 (1908); **42,** 188 (1909); Blackstock, *J. Am. Chem. Soc.*, **34,** 1080 (1912); Meyer and Nicolaus, *J. prakt. Chem.*, (2) **82,** 521 (1910).
5. Rosenmund and Struck, *Ber.*, **52,** 1749 (1919); Koelsch, *J. Am. Chem. Soc.*, **58,** 1328 (1936); Newman, *ibid.*, **59,** 2472 (1837); Koelsch and Whitney, *J. Org. Chem.*, **6,** 795 (1941); Burger and Bryant, *ibid.*, **6,** 119 (1941); McElvain and Goese, *J. Am. Chem. Soc.*, **63,** 2283 (1941); Helberger and Rebay, *Ann.*, **531,** 280 (1937); Slebodzinski, *J. prakt. Chem.*, (2) **143,** 115 (1935) Waldmann and Oblath, *Ber.*, **71,** 366 (1938).
6. Favrel and Prevost, *Bull. soc. chim.*, (4) **49,** 243 (1931); Richard, *Compt. rend.*, **199,** 71 (1934).
7. Richard, *Compt. rend.*, **198,** 943 (1934); Kohler and Brown, *J. Am. Chem. Soc.*, **55,** 4299 (1933); Justoni, *Gazz. chim. ital.*, **69,** 378 (1939); *C.A.*, **33,** 8574 (1939); Delbaere, *Bull. soc. chim. Belg.*, **51,** 1 (1942).
8. Claus, *Ber.*, **5,** 612 (1872); *Ann.*, **191,** 37 (1878); Rinne, *Ber.*, **6,** 389 (1873); Euler, *ibid.*, **28,** 2952 (1895); Pomeranz, *Ann.*, **351,** 354 (1907).
9. Claus, *Ber.*, **9,** 225 (1876); Bourgoin, *Compt. rend.*, **94,** 448 (1882).
10. Chavanne, *Bull. soc. chim. Belg.* **28,** 240 (1914). *Cf.* Franke, *Monatsh.*, **34,** 1913 (1913).
11. Allen and Ball, *J. Am. Chem. Soc.*, **59,** 686 (1937).
12. Posner, *Ber.*, **27,** 2492 (1894).
13. Justoni, *Gazz. chim. ital.*, **71,** 41 (1941); Glutz, *J. prakt. Chem.*, (2) **1,** 141 (1870); Hantzsch, *Ber.*, **23,** 1472, 1816 (1890); Obrégia, *Ann.*, **266,** 336 (1891); Matthews and Hodgkinson, *Ber.*, **15,** 2679 (1882); James, *Ann.*, **231,** 245 (1885).
14. Reichstein and Zschokke, *Helv. Chim. Acta,* **15,** 1124 (1932); Reichstein, *Ber.*, **63,** 749 (1930); Runde, *et al.*, *J. Am. Chem. Soc.*, **52,** 1284 (1930); Scott and Johnson, *ibid.*, **54,** 2549 (1932); Sherman and Amstutz, *J. Am. Chem. Soc.*, **72,** 2195 (1950).
15. Fuson, *et. al.*, *J. Am. Chem. Soc.*, **53,** 4187 (1931); **60,** 2404 (1938).
16. Fuson, *et. al.*, *J. Am. Chem. Soc.*, **54,** 313 (1932); **51,** 1536 (1929); **52,** 4074 (1930).
17. Diels and Sieb, *Ber.*, **42,** 4062 (1909); Diels and Gukassianz, *ibid.*, **43,** 3314 (1910).
18. Hirwe and Rana, *J. Indian Chem. Soc.*, **17,** 481 (1940).
19. Dudwadimoth and Wheeler, *Proc. Indian Acad. Sci.*, **2,** 438 (1935).
20. Coffmann, *J. Am. Chem. Soc.*, **57,** 1981 (1935).
21. Chattaway and Irving, *J. Chem. Soc.*, **1929,** 1038.
22. Moureu and Lazennec, *Bull. soc. chim.*, (3) **35,** 520 (1906); McCuster and Vogt, *J. Am. Chem. Soc.*, **59,** 1307 (1937).
23. Richter, *Ber.*, **44,** 3472 (1911).
24. Auger, *Compt. rend.*, **145,** 1287 (1907); Walden, *Ber.*, **40,** 3215 (1907); Linnemann, *Ann.*, **148,** 251 (1868).
25. Merz and Hühlhäuser, *Ber.*, **3,** 710 (1870); Wahl, *et. al.*, *Bull. soc. chim.*, (5) **6,** 536 (1939); Craig, *J. Am. Chem. Soc.*, **55,** 2854 (1933); Camps, *Arch. Pharm.*, **240,** 366 (1902); Merz, *Zeitschrift für Chemie,* **11,** 33 (1868); Meyer, *Ann.*, **15,** 273 (1870); Werner *et al.*, *Ann.*, **321,** 323, 328 (1902); McKee and Strauss, *Chem. Met. Eng.*, **24,** 638, 697 (1921); Bradbrook and Linstead, *J. Chem. Soc.*, 1936, 1739; Fieser, *J. Am. Chem. Soc.*, **54,** 4110 (1932); Oliveri-Mandalà, *Atti accad. Lincei,* (5) **21,** I, 77 (1912).
26. Barth and Senhoffer, *Ann.*, **174,** 242 (1874); Limpricht, *ibid.*, **180,** 88, 92 (1875).
27. Leuchs and Möbis, *Ber.*, 42, 1229 (1909); Price and Kaplan, *J. Am. Chem. Soc.*, **66,** 477 (1944). *Cf.* Bawman, *Ber.*, **20,** 890 (1887); Rodionow, *et al.* ibid., **66,** 1623 (1933).
28. Sandmeyer, *Ber.*, **17,** 2633, 2650, 2653 (1884); **18,** 1492 (1885); Gattermann, *ibid.*, **23,** 1218 (1890).
29. Korczynski and Fondrich, *Compt. rend.*, **183,** 421 (1926); *British patent,* 326,149 (1930).
30. Schwarz, *Ber.*, **15,** 2508 (1882); *German patent* 259,363; 259,364 (1913).
31. Hofmann, *Ber.*, **1,** 39 (1867).

32. Claus, *Ann.*, **266**, 224, 377 (1891); **262**, 211 (1892); Sudborough, *J. Chem. Soc.*, **67**, 602 (1895).
33. Claus and Herbabny, *Ann.*, **265**, 370 (1891).
34. Fischer, *ibid.*, **194**, 261 (1878); Besemfelder, *ibid.*, **266**, 187 (1891); Rabe, *Ber.*, **31**, 1898 (1898).
35. Leuchs, *Ber.*, **42**, 1232 (1909).
36. Cocker and Lapworth, *J. Chem. Soc.*, **1931**, 1395.
37. Scholl, *Ber.*, **27**, 2816 (1894); Nef, *Ann.*, **280**, 305,308,313 (1894).
38. Hanslik, *U. S. patent* 2,377,147.
39. Fittig, *Ann.*, **299**, 23 (1898); *Ber.*, **28**, 1724 (1895); **29**, 2582 (1896); Matsmoto, *ibid.*, **8**, 1145 (1875).
40. Schenk, *Ausfuhrliches Lehrbuch der Organischen Chemie*, II, p. 444.
41. Tiemann and Friedländer, *Ber.*, **14**, 1967 (1881); Winckler, *Ann.*, **4**, 246 (1832); **18**, 311 (1836); Liebig, *ibid.*, **18**, 321 (1836).
42. Sulokilpi, *Z. physik. Chem.*, **86**, 641 (1914).
43. Küster and Stallberg, *Ann.*, **278**, 207 (1894).
44. Palazzo, *Atti accad. Lincei.*, (5) **19 I**, 218 (1910).
45. Cain, *Ber.*, **28**, 967 (1895).
46. Kenna and Sowa, *J. Am. Chem. Soc.*, **60**, 124 (1938).
47. Berger, *Rec. trav. chim.*, **46**, 600 (1927).
48. Bogert and Curtin, *J. Am. Chem. Soc.*, **45**, 2165 (1923).
49. Knoevenagel and Mercklin, *Ber.*, **37**, 4091 (1904); Sachs, *ibid.*, **35**, 3325 (1902); Klager, *ibid.*, **36**, 4192 (1903).
50. Fischer, *Ann.*, **194**, 261 (1878); Meyer, *Ber.*, **28**, 2782 (1895).
51. Wislicenus, *et al.*, *Ann.*, **436**, 90 (1924).
52. Claisen, *Ber.*, **10**, 430, 845, 1663 (1877).
53. Moureu and Lazennec, *Bull. soc. chim.*, (3) **36**, 525 (1906).
54. Johnson and Shelberg, *J. Am. Chem. Soc.*, **67**, 1754 (1945); Lapworth, *J. Chem. Soc.*, **77**, 1053 (1900).
55. Tiemann and Stephan, *Ber.*, **15**, 2035 (1882); Cordier, *Bull. soc. chim.*, (5) **6**, 1299 (1939); Tiemann and Friedländer, *Ber.*, **14**, 1967 (1881).
56. Radziszewski, *Ber.*, **18**, 355 a (1885); Dinert, *J. prakt. Chem.*, (2) **52**, 431 (1895); McMaster and Langreck, *J. Am. Chem. Soc.*, **39**, 103 (1917).
57. Friedländer and Weisberg, *Ber.*, **28**, 1841 (1895).
58. Bogert and Hand, *J. Am. Chem. Soc.*, **24**, 1031 (1902).
59. Beckurtz and Otto, *Ber.*, **9**, 1590 (1876).
60. Szydlowsky and Spiegel, *ibid.*, **51**, 297 (1918).
61. Pfeiffer *et al. ibid.*, **44**, 1113 (1911); **48**, 1777 (1915); *J. prakt. Chem.*, (2) **109**, 191 (1925); **411**, 72 (1916); **465**, 20 (1928).
62. Bernthsen, *Ber.*, **9**, 429 (1876); **10**, 1235, 1238 (1877); *Ann.*, **184**, 329 (1877); **192**, 1 (1878); Blochmann, *Ber.*, **20**, 1856 (1887).
63. Cornell, *J. Am. Chem. Soc.*, **50**, 3311 (1928).
64. Kirssanoff and Poliakowa, *Bull. soc. chim.*, (5) **3**, 1600 (1936).
65. Erlenmeyer, *Ann.*, **146**, 259 (1870); *Ber.*, **14**, 1868 (1881); Tartarinow, *Compt. rend.*, **89**, 608 (1879); Bischoff, *J. Biol. Chem.*, **80**, 345 (1928); Braun and Randall, *J. Am. Chem. Soc.*, **56**, 2134 (1934).
66. Erlenmeyer, *Ann.*, **146**, 259 (1868).
67. Wieland, *Ber.*, **38**, 1445 (1905).
68. Wieland, *ibid.*, **37**, 1536 (1904).
69. Pierron, *Ann. chim. phys.*, (9) **11**, 361 (1919).
70. Hofmann, *Ber.*, **2**, 601 (1869); Schenck, *Arch. Pharm.*, **250**, 311 (1912).
71. Wheeler and Jamieson, *J. Biol. Chem.*, **4**, 111 (1908); *Chem. Zentr.* **1908** I, 1467.
72. Smolka and Reiedreich, *Monatsh.*, **9**, 227 (1888); Bamberger and Seeberger, *Ber.*, **25**, 525 (1892); Bentel, *Ann.*, **310**, 335 (1900); Lumière and Perrin, *Bull. soc. chim.*, (3) **33**, 205 (1905).
73. Pellizzari, *Gazz. chim. ital.*, **51 I**, 89, 140 (1921); Ziegelbauer, *Ber.*, **9**, 1524 (1876); *Montash.*, **17**, 653 (1896).
74. Smith *et al.*, *J. Am. Chem. Soc.*, **51**, 2522 (1929).
75. Hofmann and Ernart, *Ber.*, **45**, 2731 (1912); Stollé and Krauch, *J. prakt. Chem.*, (2) **88**, 306 (1913).
76. Ostrogovich, *Rend. Accad. Lincei*, (5) **20**, 182, 249 (1911); Ostrogovich and Gherghiu, *Gazz. chim. ital.*, **60**, 648 (1930).
77. Hantzsch, *Ber.*, **64**, 667 (1931).
78. Ingham, *J. Chem. Soc.*, **1927**, 692. *Cf.* Fischer, *Ber.*, **29**, 205 (1896); Minovici, *ibid.*, **32**, 2206 (1899).
79. Colby and Dodge, *Am. Chem. J.*, **13**, 1 (1891); Mathews, *J. Am. Chem. Soc.*, **18**, 679 (1896); **20**, 648 (1898); Gauthier, *Z. anal. Chem.*, **1869**, 127. Miller, *J. Am. Chem. Soc.*, **16**, 443 (1894).

80. Bogert and Gotthelf, *J. Am. Chem. Soc.*, **22**, 129, 522 (1900); Gotthelf, *ibid.*, **23**, 611 (1901).
81. Foster, *British patent* 567,289 (1945).
82. Otto, *Ann.*, **116**, 196 (1860).
83. *U. S. patents* 2,174,756; 2,175,810; 2,283,237.
84. van der Linden, *Rec. trav. chim.*, **53**, 45 (1934).
85. Held, *Bull. soc. chim.*, (3) **17**, 287 (1897); Hantzsch and May, *Ber.*, **28**, 2466 (1895).
86. MacAfee, *U. S. patent* 2,129,700 (1938).
87. Chattaway and Wadmore, *J. Chem. Soc.*, **81**, 199 (1902).
88. Gutman, *Ber.*, **42**, 3628 (1909).
89. Palazzo, *Rend. Accad. Lincei*, (5) **16** I, 550 (1907).
90. Gloëz and Cannizzaro, *Compt. rend.*, **32**, 62 (1851); Schenk, *Arch. Pharm.*, **247**, 490 (1906); Oberhauser, *Ber.*, **62**, 1436 (1929); Gloëz, *ibid.*, **3**, 265 (1870); Henke, *Ann.*, **106**, 268 (1858); Kaess and Grusskiewicz, *Ber.*, **35**, 3598 (1902); Wallach, *ibid.*, **32**, 1872 (1899); MacKee, *Am. Chem. J.*, **36**, 208 (1906); Braun *et al.*, *Ann.*, **449**, 249 (1926).
91. Griffith, *et al.*, *Trans. Faraday Soc.*, **34**, 316 (1938).
92. Wieland, *Ber.*, **37**, 1536 (1904).
93. Stollè and Hofmann, *Ber.*, **37**, 4524 (1904); Pellizzari *et al.*, *ibid.*, **38**, 283 (1905); *Gazz. chim. ital.*, **35**, I, 291 (1905); **37 II**, 317, 437 (1907); **41 I**, 54 (1911); **44 II**, 72 (1914).
94. Pellizzari *et al.*, *Gazz. chim. ital.*, **37 I**, 611 (1907); **48 II**, 151 (1918); **53**, 661 (1923); **54**, 451 (1924).
95. Weith, *Ber.*, **7**, 10, 843 (1874).
96. Pierron, *Ann. chim. phys.*, (8) **15**, 145 (1908).
97. Grippa and Maffei, *Gazz. chim, ital.*, **71**, 418 (1941).
98. König, *J. prakt. Chem.*, (2) **69**, 38 (1904).
99. Madelung and Kern, *Ann.*, **427**, 1 (1922).
100. Biechler, *Compt. rend.*, **200**, 141 (1935); **202**, 667 (1936).
101. Kaiser and Thurston, *U. S. patent* 2,371,100 (1945).
102. v. Braun, *Ber.*, **33**, 1438 (1900); **40**, 3914, 3933 (1907); v. Braun and Röver, *ibid.*, **36**, 1196 (1903).
103. Braun, *Ber.*, **33**, 1438 (1900); *Ann.*, **382**, 1 (1911).
104. Braun *et al.*, *Ber.*, **47**, 3025 (1914); **51**, 255 (1918); **55**, 3318 (1922).
105. Eschevarria, *Ann.*, **79**, 110 (1851).
106. Wurtz, *ibid.*, **79**, 280 (1851); Mulder, *Rec. trav. chim.*, **5**, 65 (1886).
107. Nef, *Ann.*, **287**, 310 (1895).
108. Hantzsch and May, *Ber.*, **28**, 2466 (1895); Gloëz, *Compt. rend.*, **44**, 482 (1857); *Ann.*, **102**, 355 (1857); Gal, *ibid.*, **137**, 127 (1866); Hofmann and Olshansen, *Ber.*, **3**, 269 (1890); Mulder and Ponomaref, *ibid.*, **15**, 515 (1882); Ponomarew, *Ber.*, **18**, 3264 (1885); Hantzsch and Bauer, *ibid.*, **38**, 1007 (1905); Mulder, *Rec. trav. chim.*, **1**, 63, 191 (1882); **2**, 133 (1883); **3**, 287 (1884); *Ber.*, **15**, 70 (1882); Klason, *J. prakt. Chem.*, (2) **33**, 131 (1886); Hofmann, *Ber.*, **19**, 2082 (1886); Nef., *Ann.*, **287**, 319,321 (1895).
109. Baumann, *Ber.*, **6**, 1376 (1873); Volhard, *J. prakt Chem.*, (2) **9**, 25 (1874); Drechsel, *ibid.*, (2) **11**, 286 (1875); (2) **21**, 78 (1880); Prätorius-Seidler, *ibid.*, (2) **21**, 129 (1880); Traube, *Ber.*, **18**, 461 (1885); Walther, *J. prakt. Chem.*, (2) **54**, 510 (1896); Hantzsch and Wolvekampf, *Ann.*, **331**, 282 (1904); Witerstein and Küng, *Helv. Chim. Acta*, **59**, 143 (1909).
110. Fenton, *J. Chem. Soc.*, **41**, 262 (1882); Emich, *Monatsh.*, **10**, 321 (1889).
111. Moureu, *Bull. soc. chim.*, (3) **11**, 1069 (1894).
112. Cahours and Gloëz, *Ann.*, **90**, 95 (1854); Hofmann, *Ber.*, **3**, 265 (1870); Baumann, *ibid.*, **6**, 1372 (1873); Glaësson, *ibid.*, **18** Ref 499 (1885); Kaess and Gruszkiewicz, *ibid.*, **35**, 3600 (1902); McKee, *Am. Chem. J.*, **36**, 211 (1906); Palazzo and Scels, *Gazz. chim. ital.*, **38** I, 676 (1908); Baum, *Ber.*, **41**, 524, 525 (1908).
113. Fileti and Schiff, *Ber.*, **10**, 427 (1877); Berg, *Bull. soc. chim.*, (3) **7**, 547 (1892); *Compt. rend.*, **114**, 484 (1892); **116**, 327 (1893); *Ann. chim.*, (7) **3**, 352 (1894); Chancel, *Compt. rend.*, **116**, 329 (1893); Brahl, *Z. physik. Chem.*, **16**, 218 (1895); Wallach, *Ber.*, **32**, 1872 (1899); Jackson and Fuller, *Am. Chem. J.*, **23**, 494 (1900); v. Braun, *Ber.*, **33**, 1438 (1900); **40**, 3938 (1907); **42**, 2042 (1909); v. Braun and Röver, *ibid.*, **36**, 1196 (1903); v. Braun and Schwarz, *ibid.*, **36**, 3660 (1903); McKee, *Am. Chem. J.*, **36**, 208 (1906); Traube and Engelhardt, *Ber.*, **44**, 3149 (1911); Diels and Gollmann, *ibid.*, **44**, 3160 3165 (1911).
114. Chancel, *Compt. rend.*, **116**, 329 (1893), Brühl, *Z. physik. Chem.*, **79**, 31 (1912); Eisenlohr, *ibid.*, **79**, 137, 145 (1912).
115. Stieglitz and McKee, *Ber.*, **33**, 807, 1517 (1900); McKee, *Am. Chem. J.*, **26**, 243 (1901); **42**, 29 (1909); Bruce, *J. Am. Chem. Soc.*, **26**, 422, 455, 457 (1904); Stieglitz and Noble, *Ber.*, **38**, 2243 (1905).
116. Blaise, *Compt. rend.*, **132**, 38 (1901); **133**, 299 (1901); Thomas and Couder, *Bull. soc. chim.*, (4) **23**, 288 (1918); Ralston and Christensen, *Ind. Eng. Chem.*, **29**, 195 (1937).
117. Bruilants, *Bull. Acad. roy. Belg.*, **10**, 166 (1924); **11**, 261 (1925); *Bull. soc. chim. Belg.*, **33**, 467 (1924); **35**, 139 (1926); Stevens, *et al.*, *J. Chem. Soc.*, **1931**, 2568; **1932**, 2607; Christiaen, *Bull. soc. chim. Bel.*, **33**, 483 (1924).

118. Maxim and Aldea, *Bull. soc. chim.*, (5) **2**, 582, (1935); Kohler and Reimer, *Am. Chem. J.*, **33**, 333 (1905); Birch and Robinson, *J. Chem. Soc.*, **1943**, 501; Hook and Robinson, *ibid.*, **1945**, 153; Fuson, *et al.*, *J. Am. Chem. Soc.*, **60**, 1447 (1938).
119. Ziegler and Ohlinger, *Ann.*, **495**, 84 (1932); Kirsanov and Poliakova, *Bull. soc. chim.*, (5) **3**, 1601 (1936); Bergstrom and Agostino, *J. Am. Chem. Soc.*, **67**, 2152 (1945).
120. *German patent* 473,329.
121. Ziegler *et al.*, *Ber.*, **67 A**, 139 (1934); *Ann.*, **504**, 94 416 (1933); **513**, 43 (1934); **528**, 114 (1937); Thorpe, *J. Chem. Soc.*, **95**, 1905 (1909); *German patents* 591,269; 620,904; 628,904; 652,862; *U. S. patent* 2,068,586 (1937).
122. Ziegler and Aurnhammer, *Ann.*, **513**, 43 (1934).
123. Moore and Thorpe, *J. Chem. Soc.*, **93**, 165 (1908); Ziegler and Lüttringhaus, *Ann.*, **511**, 1 (1934); Kenner and Turner, *J. Chem. Soc.*, **99**, 2101 (1911); Kenner, *ibid.*, **103**, 614 (1913).
124. Sabatier and Senderens, *Compt. rend.*, **140**, 482 (1905); Paul and Gerum, *Ber.*, **42**, 1553 (1909); Frébault, *Compt. rend.*, **140**, 1036 (1905); Rupe *et al.*, *Helv. Chim. Acta*, **6**, 880 (1923); **8**, 838, 848 (1925); **13**, 457 (1930); **19**, 591 (1936).
125. Schwoegler and Adkins, *J. Am. Chem. Soc.*, **61**, 3499 (1939); Rentenauer and Paquot, *Ind. Corps Gras*, **2**, 336 (1947); *C.A.* **41**, 6526 (1947); *Compt. rend.*, **224**, 478 (1947).
126. Carothers and Jones, *J. Am. Chem. Soc.*, **47**, 3051 (1925); Carothers, Bickford and Hurwitz, *ibid.*, **49**, 2912 (1927).
127. Rogers, *J. Chem. Soc.*, **1943**, 590.
128. Rupe and Stern, *Helv. Chim. Acta*, **10**, 859 (1927).
129. Rupe *et al.*, *ibid.*, **8**, 338 (1925); **10**, 299 (1927); **10**, 846 (1927); *Bull. soc. chim.*, (4) **41**, 769 (1927).
130. Keller, *Helv. Chim. Acta*, **20**, 436 (1937).
131. Wiley and Adkins, *J. Am. Chem. Soc.*, **60**, 914 (1938).
132. Kinder, *Ber deut. pharm. Ges.* **269**, 74 (1931).
133. Buck, *J. Am. Chem. Soc.*, **55**, 2593, 3388 (1933).
134. Hahn *et al.*, *Ber.*, **72 B**, 1291 (1939).
135. Reppe and Hoffmann, *German patent* 552,987 (1932).
136. Hartung, *J. Am. Chem. Soc.*, **50**, 3370 (1928); Kindler, *Arch. Pharm.*, **265**, 389 (1927); **269**, 70 (1931); Paul and Gerum, *Ber.*, **42**, 1558 (1909).
137. Rupe and Metzger, *Helv. Chim. Acta*, **8**, 838 (1925).
138. Huber, *J. Am. Chem. Soc.*, **66**, 876 (1944).
139. Koelsch, *ibid.*, **65**, 2093, 2459 (1943); Koelsch and Stratton, *ibid.*, **66**, 1883 (1944); Bloom *et al.*, *ibid.*, **67**, 539 (1945); **68**, 1607 (1946); Case *et al.*, *ibid.*, **68**, 1905 (1946); King and Acheson; *J. Chem. Soc.*, **1946**, 683.
140. Ladenburg, *Ber.*, **18**, 2956 (1885); **19**, 780 (1886); Kraft *et al.*, *Ber.*, **22**, 811 (1889); **23**, 2360 (1890); **33**, 3580 (1900); Renenauer and Paquot, *Compt. rend.*, **224**, 478 (1938); Teunissen, *Rev. trav. chim.*, **46**, 208 (1927).
141. Graf, *J. prakt. Chem.*, (2) **140**, 39 (1934).
142. Meyer, *ibid.*, (2) **37**, 396 (1886).
143. Schwarze, *J. prakt Chem.*, (2) **42**, 1 (1890); Holtzwart, *ibid.*, (2) **39**, 230 (1889); Adkins and Whitman, *J. Am. Chem. Soc.*, **64**, 152 (1942).
144. Moir, *J. Chem. Soc.*, **81**, 100 (1902); Bouveault and Hanriot, *Bull soc. chim.*, (3) **1**, 548 (1889); Adkinson and Whitman, *J. Am. Chem. Soc.*, **64**, 150 (1942).
145. Meyer, *J. prakt. Chem.*, (2) **38**, 337 (1887); (2) **39**, 188 (1889); (2) **52**, 113 (1895); (2) **92**, 174 (1915); Sonn, *Ber.*, **51**, 821 (1918).
146. Meyer, *J. prakt. Chem.*, (2) **22**, 262 (1880); (2) **27**, 152 (1883); (2) **37**, 396 (1888); (2) **39**, 188 (1889); Troeger, *ibid.*, (2) **37**, 407 (1888); Wache, *ibid.*, (2) **39**, 245 (1889); Frankland and Kolbe, *Ann.*, **65**, 269 (1848); Bayer, *Ber.*, **2**, 319 (1869); **4**, 176 (1871); Adkins and Whitman, *J. Am. Chem. Soc.*, **64**, 150 (1942).
147. Riess and Meyer, *J. prakt. Chem.*, (2) **31**, 112 (1885).
148. Meyer, *ibid.*, (2) **39**, 188 (1889).
149. Cook and Jones, *J. Chem. Soc.*, **1941**, 278.
150. Klason, *J. prakt. Chem.* (2) **34**, 154 (1886).
151. Eghis, *Ber.*, **2**, 159 (1869); Ponomarew, *ibid.*, **18**, 3261 (1885).
152. Gloëz and Cannizzaro, *Compt. rend.*, **32**, 62 (1857); Hofmann, *Ber.*, **18**, 2765 (1885).
153. Klason, *J. prakt. Chem.*, (2) **33**, 290 (1886); Hofmann, *Ber.*, **18**, 2755 (1885); Fries, *ibid.*, **19**, 2057 (1886).
154. Troeger, *J. prakt. Chem.*, (2) **37**, 407 (1888).
155. Hofmann, *Ber.*, **19**, 2061 (1886); Otto, *ibid.*, **20**, 2236 (1887).
156. Freund and Lenze, *Ber.*, **24**, 2161 (1891); Butlerow, *Ann.*, **170**, 154 (1873).
157. Weddige and Korner, *J. prakt. Chem.*, (2) **31**, 176 (1885).
158. Lottermoser, *ibid.*, (2) **54**, 113 (1896); Cook and Jones, *J. Chem. Soc.*, **1941**, 278.
159. Anker and Cook, *ibid.*, **1941**, 323.
160. Kraft *et al.*, *Ber.*, **22**, 803 (1889); **23**, 2382, 2389 (1890); **25**, 2263 (1892).
161. Beilstein and Gautier, *Ann.*, **108**, 99 (1858); **123**, 241 (1862); Haag, ibid., **122**, 22 (1862);

Baumann, *Ber.*, **6**, 1373 (1883); Drechsel, *J. prakt. Chem.*, (2) **11**, 298 (1875); Grube and Krüger, *Z. physik. Chem.*, **86**, 65 (1913); Grube and Nitsche, *Z. angew. Chem.*, **127**, 368 (1914); Werner, *J. Chem. Soc.*, **107**, 715 (1915).
162. Buchanan and Barsky, *J. Am. Chem. Soc.*, **52**, 195 (1930).
163. Drechsel, *J. prakt. Chem.*, (2) **9**, 284 (1877).
164. Drechsel, *ibid.*, (2) **11**, 302 (1875); (2) **33**, 331 (1876); Gloëz and Cannizzaro, *Compt. rend.*, **32**, 63 (1851); *Ann.*, **78**, 229 (1851); Lemoult, *Ann. chim. phys.*, (7), **16**, 409 (1899); Smolka and Friedreich, *Monatsh.*, **10**, 91, 93 (1889); *British patents* 466,957; 502,148; 513,383; 524,349; *French patent* 817,895; Widmer, *U. S. patent* 2,265,215.
165. Hofmann, *Ber.*, **2**, 603 (1869); **3**, 264 (1870); **18**, 2755, 2781 (1885); Baumann, *ibid.*, **6**, 1673 (1873); Klason, *ibid.*, **18**, Ref. 498 (1885); *J. prakt. Chem.*, (2) **33**, 290 (1886); Freund and Schwarz, *Ber.*, **29**, 2498 (1896); Diels, *ibid.*, **32**, 692,698,700,702 (1899); Palazzo and Scelsi, *Gazz. chim. ital.*, **38 I**, 677 (1908); Diels and Gollman, *Ber.*, **44**, 3160, 3164 (1911).
166. Baumann, *Ber.*, **6**, 1372 (1873); **41**, 524, 525 (1908); Hofmann, *ibid.*, **2**, 602 (1869); **3**, 264 (1870); **18**, 2784, 3223 (1885); Arndt, *Ann.*, **384**, 350 (1911); Heller and Bauer, *J. prakt. Chem.*, (2) **65**, 374 (1902); Strakosch, *Ber.*, **5**, 695 (1872).
167. Guillemard, *Compt. rend.*, **144**, 142 (1907); *Bull. soc. chim.*, (4) **1**, 272 (1907); *Ann. chim. phys.*, (8) **14**, 349 (1908); Nef, *Ann.*, **286**, 296 (1894); Wade, *J. Chem. Soc.*, **81**, 1603 (1902).
168. Esafax, *J. Gen. Chem., (U.S.S.R.)*, **14**, 299 (1944).
169. Troost and Hautefeuille, *Compt. rend.*, **67**, 1345 (1868).
170. Troost and Hautefeuille, *ibid.*, **69**, 49 (1869); Hantzsch, *Ber.*, **38**, 1013 (1905); *Z. physik. Chem.*, **61**, 281 (1908); Hantzsch and Stuer, *Ber.*, **38**, 1042 (1905); Stuer, *ibid.*, **38**, 2326 (1905).
171. Senier and Walsch, *J. Chem. Soc.*, **81**, 290 (1902); Kroustein, *Ber.*, **35**, 4150 (1902).
172. Krason, *J. prakt. Chem.*, (2) **33**, 129 (1886).
173. Hofmann and Olshausen, *Ber.*, **3**, 269 (1870); Hofmann, *Jahresb.*, **1861**, 515, 1862, 335; *Ann.*, **103**, 353 (1852); **115**, 275 (1860); *Ber.*, **3**, 765 (1870).
174. Slotta and Tschesche, *Ber.*, **60**, 295 (1927); Hofmann, *ibid.*, **3**, 765 (1870).
175. Hofmann, *Ann.*, Spl. **1**, 57, *Ber.*, **3**, 765 (1870); **4**, 246 (1870).
176. Snope, *J. Chem. Soc.*, **49**, 254 (1886).
177. Hofmann, *Ber.*, **18**, 765 (1885); Michael, *ibid.*, **38**, 30 (1905); Frentzel, *ibid.*, **21**, 413 (1888).
178. Hofmann and Olshausen, *Ber.*, **3**, 272 (1870); Ponomarew, *ibid.*, **18**, 3266, 3270 (1885); Hofmann, *ibid.*, **18**, 2796, 2800 (1885); Krapirvin and Zelinsky, *ibid.*, **22** Ref. 251 (1889); Lemoult, *Ann. chim.*, (7) **16**, 356 (1899); Fischer, *Ber.*, **30**, 2616 Anm. (1897); **31**, 3273 (1898); Fischer and Frank, *ibid.*, **30**, 2616 (1897); Palazzo and Scelsi, *Gazz. chim. ital.*, **38 I**, 664 (1908).
179. Wieland and Hess, *Ber.*, **42**, 1346 (1909); Wieland and Baumann, *Ann.*, **392**, 196 (1912).
180. Wieland, *Ber.*, **42**, 803, 808 (1909).
181. Cloëz, *Ann.*, **102**, 354 (1857); Gal , *ibid.*, **137**, 128 (1865); Hofmann and Olshausen, *Ber.*, **3**, 269 (1870); Ponomarew, *ibid.*, **15**, 515 (1882); Mulder, *Rec. trav. chim.*, **1**, 191 (1882); **2**, 133 (1883); **3**, 287 (1884); Nef. *Ann.*, **287**, 310 (1895); Hantzsch and Mai, *Ber.*, **28**, 2466 (1895).
182. Gattermann and Schmidt, *Ann.*, **244**, 35 (1888); Turping, *Ber.*, **21**, 2486 (1888); *French patent* 809,233 (1937); *Brit. patents* 462,182 (1937); 483,308 (1938); *U.S. patents* 2,261,156 (1941); 2,311,046; 2,319,057 (1943); 2,362,648; 2,340,757 (1944).
183. Schrötter, *Ber.*, **42**, 2336, 3356 (1909).
184. Lengfeld and Stieglitz, *Am. Chem. J.*, **16**, 71 (1894); **17**, 98 (1895); Stieglitz, *ibid.*, **21**, 101 (1899); Gattermann, *Ann.*, **244**, 29 (1888); Hentschel, *Ber.*, **18**, 1178 (1885); Buckley *et al.*, *J. Chem. Soc.*, **1945**, 864.
185. Slotta and Tschesche, *Ber.*, **60**, 1021 (1927).
186. Wiekmann and Kämmerer, *ibid.*, **38**, 2980 (1905); **40**, 3737 (1907).
187. Slotta and Tschesche, *ibid.*, **60**, 295 (1927).
188. Lambling, *Bull. soc. chim.*, **17**, 356 (1897); Haller, *Compt. rend.*, **114**, 1326 (1892); **115**, 19 (1892); **116**, 121 (1893).
189. Haller, *Compt. rend.*, **121**, 189 (1895); Haller and Blanc, *ibid.*, **132**, 384 (1901).
190. Dieckmann *et al.*, *Ber.*, **37**, 4628, 4635 (1904). *Cf.* Michael, *ibid.*, **38**, 22 (1905).
191. Michael and Cobb, *Ann.*, **363**, 78 (1908).
192. Gumpert, *J. prakt. Chem.*, (2) **32**, 294 (1885).
193. Degner and Pechmann, *Ber.*, **30**, 650 (1897); Scholl and Holdermann, *Ann.*, **345**, 382 (1906).
194. Neuberg and Manasse, *Ber.*, **38**, 2359 (1905); French and Wirtel, *Am. Chem. J.*, **48**, 1736 (1926).
195. Kaufmann *et al.*, *Ber.*, **70**, 2519 (1937); Paal, *ibid.*, **27**, 974 (1894).
196. Kjellin, *Ber.*, **26**, 2384 (1893); Beck and Hase, *Ann.*, **355**, 50 (1907).
197. Kjellin, *Ber.*, **26**, 2383 (1893); Beckmann, *Ann.*, **365**, 212 (1891); Busch *et al.*, *Ber.*, **37**, 2324 (1904).
198. Kühn, *Ber.*, **17**, 2882 (1884).

199. Krüger, *ibid.*, **18**, 1059 (1885).
200. Kühn, *ibid.*, **18**, 1476 (1885).
201. Michael, *J. prakt. Chem.*, (2) **49**, 42 (1894).
202. Kühn and Henschel, *Ber.*, **21**, 504 (1888); Johnson and Bristol, *Am. Chem. J.*, **30**, 174 (1903).
203. Knoevenagel and Schürenberg, *Ann.*, **297**, 148 (1897); Orndorff and Richmond, *Am. Chem. J.*, **22**, 465 (1899); Lambling, *Bull. soc. chim.*, (3) **19**, 771, 777 (1898); Bloch, *ibid.*, (3) **31**, 49 (1904).
204. Snape, *Ber.*, **18**, 2430 (1885); Tessmer, *ibid.*, **18**, 968 (1885).
205. Lambling, *Bull. soc. chim.*, (3) **27**, 441, 606, 871 (1902).
206. Goldschmidt and Meissler, *Ber.*, **23**, 272 (1890).
207. Snape, *ibid.*, **18**, 2432 (1885); Rivier, *Bull. soc. chim.*, (4) **1**, 736 (1907).
208. Kretzschmar and Salmon, *J. prakt. Chem.*, (2) **9**, 299 (1874); Franchimont and Klobbie, *Rec. trav. chim.*, **8**, 292 (1889); Andreocci, *Ber.*, **25** Ref. 640 (1892); Hantzsch, *ibid.*, **27**, 1250 (1894); Young and Clark, *J. Chem. Soc.*, **73**, 361 (1898); Diels, *Ber.*, **36**, 739, 745 (1903); **42**, 1853 (1909); Diels and Nawiasky, *ibid.*, **37**, 3679, 3680 (1904); Ruhemann and Priestley, *J. Chem. Soc.*, **95**, 449 (1909).
209. Kaufler and Pomeranz, *Monatsh.*, **22**, 495 (1901); Walden, *Ber.*, **40**, 3214, 4301 (1907).
210. *French patent* 850,218 (1939).
211. Sergnéeff and Kolytscheff, *J. Gen. Chem. (U.S.S.R.)*, **7**, 1390 (1937).
212. Kolytscheff and Kondratief, *ibid.*, **7**, 2600 (1937).
213. Schmidt and Striewsky, *Ber.*, **73 B**, 286 (1940).
214. Tscherniac, *ibid.*, **16**, 349 (1883); *J. Chem. Soc.*, **115**, 1071 (1919).
215. Hantzsch, *Ber.*, **60**, 2537 (1927); Tscherniac, *ibid.*, **61**, 574 (1928).
216. Beckurts and Frerichs, *J. prakt. Chem.*, (2) **66**, 172 (1902).
217. Chanlaroff, *Ber.*, **15**, 1987 (1882); Wheeler and Merriam, *J. Am. Chem. Soc.*, **23**, 283 (1901).
218. Dains and Krober, *J. Am. Chem. Soc.*, **61**, 1830 (1939).
219. Rudnew, *Ber.*, **12**, 1023 (1879); Hecht, *ibid.*, **23**, 282 (1890); Hofmann, *ibid.*, **1**, 170 (1868); Anschütz, *Ann.*, **371**, 201 (1909).
220. Delépine, *Bull. soc. chim.*, (4) **3**, 641 (1908).
221. v. Braun, *Ber.*, **35**, 818, 829 (1902); Schneider and Kaufmann, *Ann.*, **392**, 4 (1912).
222. Michael and Palmer, *Ber.*, **18**, Ref. 72 (1885).
223. Nef, *Ann.*, **280**, 296 (1894).
224. Miguel, *Ann. chim.*, (5) **11**, 295 (1877); Dixon *et al.*, *J. Chem. Soc.*, **67**, 565 (1895); **67**, 1040 (1895); **69**, 855, 1593 (1896); **85**, 807 (1904); **89**, 892 (1906); **87**, 486 (1905); **93**, 684, 2148 (1908); Doran, *ibid.*, **87**, 331 (1909); Hawthorne, *ibid.*, **89**, 556 (1906).
225. Gadamer, *Arch. Pharm.*, **237**, 103 (1899).
226. Andreasch, *Monatsh.*, **2**, 277 (1865); Nef, *Ann.*, **265**, 113 (1891); Dixon, *J. Chem. Soc.*, **67**, 557 (1895); Gebhardt, *Ber.*, **17**, 3038 (1884).
227. Bamberger, *Ber.*, **13**, 1581 (1880); **14**, 2638 (1881); **15**, 2165 (1882); Cramer, *ibid.*, **34**, 2602 (1901); Michael, *J. prakt. Chem.*, (2) **49**, 42 (1894).
228. Luchmann, *Ber.*, **29**, 1430 (1896).
229. Reissert and Schaaf, *ibid.*, **59**, 2494 (1926).
230. Orndorff and Richmond, *Am. Chem. J.*, **22**, 458 (1899); Bamberger, *Ber.*, **15**, 2164 (1882); Fromm, *ibid.*, **42**, 1957 (1909).
231. Orndorff and Richmond, *Am. Chem. J.*, **22**, 470 (1899); Rivier, *Bull. soc. chim.*, (3) **35**, 841 (1906); Schneider and Wrede, *Ber.*, **47**, 2083 (1914).
232. Wheeler and Johnson, *Am. Chem. J.*, **24**, 199 (1900).
233. Andreasch and Zipser, *Monatsh.*, **24**, 500 (1904); **25**, 178 (1905).
234. Michael, *J. prakt. Chem.*, (2) **35**, 450 (1887); Ruhemann, *J. Chem. Soc.*, **93**, 621 (1908).
235. Sell and Zierold, *Ber.*, **7**, 1227 (1874); Nef, *Ann.*, **270**, 284 (1892); Helmers, *Ber.*, **20**, 786 (1887); Bly *et al.*, *J. Am. Chem. Soc.*, **44**, 2896 (1922).
236. Helmers, *Ber.*, **20**, 786 (1887); Hantzsch and Wolvekamp, *Ann.*, **331**, 279 (1904); Proskauer and Sell, *Ber.*, **9**, 1262 (1876); Friedmann and Gattermann, *ibid.*, **25**, 3526 (1892); Gattermann, *J. prakt. Chem.*, (2) **59**, 575 (1899).
237. Urech, *Ann.*, **165**, 99 (1873); Schwebel, *Ber.*, **10**, 2045 (1877).
238. Dressler and Stein, *Ann.*, **150**, 242 (1869); Hantzsch and Sauer, *ibid.*, **299**, 99 (1898); Fransesconi and Parrozzani, *Gazz. chim. ital.*, **31 II**, 334 (1901).
239. Hallwachs, *Ann.*, **153**, 293 (1870); Baumann, *Ber.*, **8**, 708 (1875); Ulpiana, *Gazz. chim. ital.*, **38 II**, 385, 392 (1908).
240. Biltz and Slotta, *J. prakt. Chem.*, (2) **113**, 233 (1926).
241. Ochiai and Susumu, *Ber.*, **39**, 1147 (1936); Wohl and Markwald, *ibid.*, **22**, 568 (1889); **25**, 2395 (1892); Gabriel and Pinkus, *ibid.*, **26**, 2206 (1893).
242. Battegay and Hégazi, *Helv. Chim, Acta*, **16**, 999 (1933).
243. Hantzsch and Vogt, *Ann.*, **314**, 361 (1901).
244. Wheeler and Merriam, *J. Am. Chem. Soc.*, **24**, 439 (1902).
245. Miguel, *Ann. chim.*, (5) **11**, 341 (1877); Dixon, *J. Chem. Soc.*, **79**, 541 (1901); **85**, 350 (1904);

Reynolds, *ibid.*, **89**, 397 (1906); Dixon and Taylor, *ibid.*, **93**, 2153 (1908); **97**, 935 (1910); Cocksedge, *ibid.*, **93**, 2177 (1908).
246. Kaufmann and Liepe, *Ber.*, **33**, 139 (1923); Challenger, Smith and Paton, *J. Chem. Soc.*, **123**, 1055 (1923); Challenger and Bott, *ibid.*, **127**, 1039 (1925); Söderback, *Ann.*, **443**, 142 (1925).
247. Kaufmann and Thomas, *Ber.*, **56**, 2520 (1923).
248. *U.S. patent* 1,765,678; *German patents* 491,225; 492,885.
249. Kaufmann and Küchler, *Ber.*, **67**, 944 (1934); Brewster and Dains, *J. Am. Chem. Soc.*, **58**, 1364 (1936).
250. Fichter and Schönmann, *Helv. Chim. Acta*, **19**, 1411 (1936).
251. Challenger and Bott, *J. Chem. Soc.*, **127**, 1039 (1925).
252. Brus and Mesnard, *Bull. soc. chim.*, (5) **6**, 471, 1603 (1939); Jones and Fleck, *J. Am. Chem. Soc.*, **50**, 2018 (1928).
253. Likhocherstoff and Petroff, *J. Gen. Chem., (U.S.S.R.)* **3**, 759 (1934).
254. Maschek, *Monatsh.*, **63**, 216 (1933).
255. Wohler, *Ber.*, **43**, 754 (1910); Wieland, *ibid.*, **43**, 3362 (1910).
256. Holleman, *Rec. trav. chim.*, **10**, 65 (1891); *Ber.*, **26**, 1403 (1893); Scholl, *ibid.*, **23**, 3505 (1890); **24**, 581 (1891); **27**, 2816 (1894); **32**, 3492 (1899); Nef, *Ann.*, **280**, 303 (1894); Lev and Kissel, *Ber.*, **32**, 1365 (1899); Jovitschitsch, *Ann.*, **347**, 233 (1906); **350**, 390 (1906); Grigorowitsch, *J. Russ. Phys.-Chem. Soc.*, **37**, 1113 (1906); Palazzo, *Atti accad. Lincei*, (5) **16 I**, 546 (1907).
257. Wöhler and Theodorovits, *Ber.*, **38**, 1345 (1905); **43**, 755 (1910); Wieland, *ibid.*, **40**, 421 (1907); **43**, 3363 (1910).
258. Wieland, *Ber.*, **40**, 419 (1907). *Cf.* Wieland and Hess, *ibid.*, **42**, 4176, 4181 (1909).
259. Wieland, *Ber.*, **42**, 821 (1909).
260. Scholvien, *J. prakt. Chem.*, (2) **30**, 90 (1884); **32**, 461 (1885); Nef, *Ann.*, **280**, 315, 338 (1894); Palazzo and Tamburello, *Gazz. chim. ital.*, **37 I**, 23 (1907); Wieland and Hess, *Ber.*, **42**, 1347, 1352 (1902); Palazzo, *Gazz. chim. ital.*, **39 II**, 252 (1909).
261. Hewett and Martin, *J. Chem. Soc.*, **1940**, 1396; Quelet, *Bull. soc. chim.*, (5) **7**, 205 (1940).
262. Hewett and Martin, *l. c.;* Wittig and Petri, *Ann.*, **513**, 39 (1934); Hewett, *J. Chem. Soc.*, **1940**, 293.
263. Newman and Wotiz, *J. Am. Chem. Soc.*, **71**, 1292 (1949).
264. Koelsch, *ibid.*, **58**, 1328 (1936).
265. Houben and Pfankuch, *Ber.*, **59**, 2400 (1926).
266. Barger *et al.*, *J. Chem. Soc.*, **1937**, 720.
267. Lane *et al.*, *J. Am. Chem. Soc.*, **66**, 545 (1944).
268. Reichstein and Trivelli, *Helv. Chim. Acta*, **15**, 254 (1932).
269. Nölting, *Ber.*, **8**, 1113 (1875); Barth and Senhofer, *Ann.*, **174**, 236 (1874); *Ber.*, **8**, 1481 (1875); Korner and Mooselise, *Gazz. chim. ital.*, **6**, 139 (1876); *Ber.*, **9**, 584 (1876); Meyer and Michler, *ibid.*, **8**, 673 (1875); Garrick and Fittig, *Ann.*, **174**, 124 (1874); Ebert and Merz, *Ber.*, **9**, 604 (1876).
270. Mitchell and Reid, *J. Am. Chem. Soc.*, **53**, 1879 (1931); Ralston *et al.*, *ibid.*, **59**, 986 (1937); *U. S. patent* 2,061,314 (1936); Rentenauer and Paquot, *Inds. Corps. gras.*, **2**, 336 (1946); **3**, 174 (1947); *C. A.* **41**, 6526 (1947); **43**, 4629 (1949); *Compt. rend.*, **224**, 478 (1947). *Cf.* Weidel and Ciamician, *Ber.*, **13**, 65 (1880); I. G. Farbenind, *British patent* 416,631 (1934); *French patents* 781,444; 785,622 (1935); Nicodemus and Wolf, *U. S. patent* 2,177,619 (1939); Mailhe, *Bull. soc. chim.*, (4) **27**, 266 (1920); *Ann. chim.*, (9) **13**, 183 (1920).
271. Norris and Klemka, *J. Am. Chem. Soc.*, **62**, 1432 (1940).
272. Julian and Sturgis, *ibid.*, **57**, 1126 (1935); Campbell and McKail, *J. Chem. Soc.*, **1948**, 1251.
273. Plaut and Ritter, *J. Am. Chem. Soc.*, **73**, 4076 (1951).
274. Barrett *et al.*, *J. Chem. Soc.*, **1939**, 1809; **1940**, 1079.
275. Barrett *et al.*, *ibid.*, **1940**, 1076.
276. Bruson, *Organic Reactions*, **5**, 79 (1949).
277. Rupe and Glenz, *Helv. Chim. Acta*, **5**, 937 (1922); Winans and Adkins, *J. Am. Chem. Soc.*, **54**, 306 (1932); Schwoezler and Adkins, *ibid.*, **61**, 3499 (1939). *Cf.* Adkins and Billica, *ibid.*, **70**, 695 (1948).
278. Rentenauer and Paquot, *Inds. Corps. gras.*, **2**, 336 (1946); *C. A.*, **43**, 4629 (1949); Young and Christensen, *U. S. patent* 2,287,219 (1942); Adkins and Billica, *J. Am. Chem. Soc.*, **70**, 695 (1948).
279. Briggs and Bishop, *Ind. Eng. Chem.*, **38**, 1084 (1946); Kindler and Hess, *Arch. Pharm.*, **271**, 439 (1933).
280. Nystrom and Brown, *J. Am. Chem. Soc.*, **70**, 3738 (1948); Crowe and Nord, *J. Org. Chem.*, **15**, 81 (1940); Herz, *J. Am. Chem. Soc.*, **72**, 4999 (1950); Amundson and Nelson, *ibid.*, **73**, 242 (1951); Brown, *Organic Reactions*, **6**, 469 (1951).
281. Shriner *et al.*, *Organic Syntheses;* Coll. Vol. II, 453 (1943). *Cf.* Pinner, *Plastics* (London), **11**, 206 (1947).
282. Modersohn, *O. P. B. Report* No. 707.

283. *BIOS Final Report* No. 719; Interview with Prof. Otto Bayer-Chabrier, *Compt. rend.*, **214,** 362 (1942); Raiford and Shelton, *J. Org. Chem.*, **4,** 207, (1939).
284. Pyman, *J. Chem. Soc.*, **103,** 852 (1913). *Cf.* Cagniant and Buu-Hoi, *Bull. soc. chim.*, (5) **10,** 349 (1943); Montagne and Guilmart, *ibid.*, (5) **12,** 836 (1945).
285. Sheehan and Izzo, *J. Am. Chem. Soc.*, **70,** 1985 (1948).
286. Gilman *et al.*, *ibid.*, **51,** 2252 (1929).
287. Marquis, *Compt. rend.*, **143,** 1165 (1906).
288. Davis and Farnum, *J. Am. Chem. Soc.*, **56,** 883 (1934).
289. Humnicki, *Roczniki Chem.*, **11,** 674 (1931); *C. A.*, **26,** 5556 (1932).
290. Raiford and Freyermuth, *J. Org. Chem.*, **8,** 230 (1943).
291. Hofmann, *Ber.*, **3,** 765 (1870).
292. Muller and Freytag, *J. prakt. Chem.*, (2) **146,** 58 (1928).
293. Bruson and Calvert, *J. Am. Chem. Soc.*, **50,** 1735 (1928).
294. Soderback, *Ann.*, **443,** 142 (1925).

CHAPTER 10

ALIPHATIC AMINES AND RELATED COMPOUNDS

AMINES

Methods of Formation

Among the more important methods of preparation of amines are those dependent on the replacement of halogens in alkyl halides with the amino group and the similar replacement of hydroxy groups and acidic radicals. Other methods of importance depend upon the reduction of nitrogenated compounds such as nitro compounds, aldimines, hydrazines, oximes and nitriles.

Formation of Amines by Replacement of Halogens

The halogen in alkyl halides may be replaced with an amino group by heating a mixture of the halide and alcoholic or aqueous ammonia in a sealed tube to a sufficiently high temperature.[1] In general, primary, secondary and tertiary amines are formed simultaneously in the reaction:

$$RCl + 2NH_3 \rightarrow RNH_2 + NH_4Cl$$

$$RCl + RNH_2 + NH_3 \rightarrow R_2NH + NH_4Cl$$

$$RCl + R_2NH + NH_3 \rightarrow R_3N + NH_4Cl$$

The higher alkyl halides yield the primary amine. The method fails with halides containing 20 or more carbon atoms. Good yields of the primary amines may be obtained from alkyl bromides by reaction with liquid ammonia.[243] With benzyl, α-naphthyl and anthranylylmethyl chloride the tertiary and secondary amines predominate, the former being obtained in greater amount than the latter.[2] By substituting an alkyl amine for ammonia in the reaction, mixed secondary and tertiary amines are obtained.[3] The hydrogen chloride formed in the reaction combines with the free amine inhibiting the reaction. This difficulty may be partly overcome by carrying out the reaction in the presence of an alkali carbonate, bicarbonate, or other reagent capable of reacting with the acid formed.

Homologs of methylaniline may be prepared by heating an alkyl halide with a large excess of the arylamine, the excess of the latter being removed by precipitation with aqueous zinc chloride.[4]

Secondary and especially tertiary alkyl halides give olefins in addition to amines.[226] Cyclohexyl halides give cyclohexane with ammonia, but form a mixture of a cyclohexyl arylamine and cyclohexene with aromatic amines.[227]

β, γ-Dibromobutane reacts with alcoholic ammonia at 110° to give β-bromo-2, 3-butene as the principal product and a small quantity of β-γ-diaminobutane,[228] though arylamines give mainly the diaminobutane.[229]

Aliphatic dibromides with bromines at 1,4 and 1,5 positions generally yield cyclic amines with ammonia and amines:

$$CH_3CHBr.CH_2CH_2CHBrCH_3 + H_2NAr$$

$$\rightarrow \quad CH_3\overline{CHCH_2CH_2CH(NAr)}CH_3.HBr + HBr$$

With ammonia, quaternary nitrogen spiranes may be the main product:[244]

$$2Br(CH_2)_5Br + NH_3 \quad \rightarrow \quad CH_2 \begin{array}{c} CH_2-CH_2 \\ \diagup \quad \diagdown \\ \diagdown \quad \diagup \\ CH_2-CH_2 \end{array} N \begin{array}{c} CH_2-CH_2 \\ \diagup \quad \diagdown \\ \diagdown \quad \diagup \\ CH_2-CH_2 \end{array} CH_2.Br + 3HBr$$

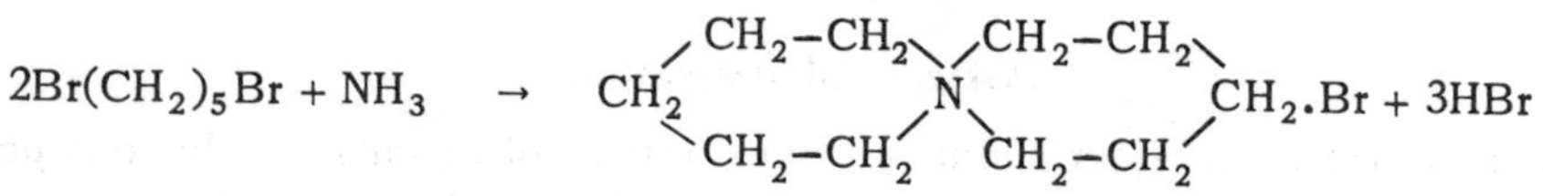

The reaction may be carried out to advantage in solution in *liquid ammonia*. It proceeds at room temperature with some halides in sealed tubes, but it is usually necessary to heat under pressure to 100° or higher. The reaction again results in the formation of primary, secondary and tertiary amines,[3] although a greater proportion of the primary amine is obtained when it is carried out in anhydrous ammonia than in aqueous or alcoholic ammonia. The proportions of primary and secondary amines obtained by this method from various halides were as follows:

Halide	Primary Amine, % of total	Secondary Amine, % of total
$C_5H_{11}Br$	10	80
$C_8H_{11}Br$	45	43
$C_{12}H_{25}Br$	90	little
$C_6H_5CH_2Cl$	53	39
α-$C_{10}H_7CH_2Cl$	72	20
α-$C_{14}H_9CH_2Cl$	70	26

The replacement of halogens in alkyl halides with an amino group has also been accomplished by carrying out the reaction in anhydrous ammonia in the presence of sodium.[5] The reaction of alkyl halides with sodamide in anhydrous ammonia results in the formation of primary amines and a very small amount of an ethylenic hydrocarbon:

$$C_2H_5I + NaNH_2 \quad \rightarrow \quad C_2H_5NH_2 + NaI$$

$$C_2H_5I + NaNH_2 \quad \rightarrow \quad C_2H_4 + NH_3 + NaI$$

Hydroxy, carbonyl and alkoxy groups have an activating influence on the halogen in alkyl halides, and chloro and bromohydrins react readily with ammonia to form amino alcohols.[6] α-Halo ketones react similarly, though secondary reactions may take place with such compounds. Thus, ω-bromoacetophenone gives 2,6-diphenyldihydropyracine,

$$C_6H_5\overline{C = CHNHCH = CH(C_6H_5)}NH$$

which, however, is converted to ω-aminoacetophenone hydrochloride on treatment with hydrochloric acid. The reactivity of halogens in α-halo ketones increases in the order Cl, Br, I, while that of halonitrobenzenes increases in the order I, Cl, Br.[7] The halogen in α-halo ethers, ROCHClR′, is of greater activity than that in halohydrins and halo ketones. These compounds react readily with aliphatic and aromatic amines to yield methoxy alkylamine derivatives:

$$2RNH_2 + ClCH_2OCH_3 \rightarrow RNHCH_2OCH_3 + RNH_2.HCl$$

The reaction may be carried out in an inert solvent.[8]

A *phenyl* group attached to the carbon atom to which the halogen is attached also activates the halogen. The activating effect of the nitrophenyl group is still greater, a nitro group in the *meta* position exerting a stronger activating effect than one in the *para* position.[9] The *vinyl* group exerts an effect similar to that of a phenyl group; Thus, the β-chlorine in β-chloroallyl chloride is quite reactive:

$$2RNH_2 + ClCH_2CH = CHCl \rightarrow RNH_2.HCl + RNHCH_2CH = CHCl$$
$$\rightarrow RNHCH_2C \equiv CH$$

The halogen in halo purines is readily replaced by the amino group by reaction with ammonia at a comparatively high temperature; 8-bromocafein for example, is converted to the corresponding amino compound by heating to 130° with alcoholic ammonia.[10]

The halogen in acid halides is readily replaceable by amino groups, yielding amides, the reaction of chloroformic esters giving carbamic esters:

$$RNH_2 + ClCOOR' \rightarrow RNHCOOR' + HCl$$

If the radical R′ is a β- or γ-chloroalkyl group, then treatment of the resulting amide with caustic results in the formation of ring amides:

$$RNHCOOCH_2CH_2Cl + NaOH \rightarrow \overline{RNCOOCH_2CH_2} + NaCl + H_2O$$

Decarboxylation of this ring compound leads to the formation of a hydroxy amine:

$$\overline{RNCOOCH_2CH_2} + 2NaOH \rightarrow RNHCH_2CH_2OH + Na_2CO_3$$

The hydroxy amines are obtained in good yield, and the reaction offers the basis for the preparation of this type of amines.[11]

The reaction of cyanogen halides with amines results in the formation of cyanamides.

Secondary amines have been prepared in the pure form by alkylating an alkyl benzylamine with an alkyl halide and removing the benzyl group from the tertiary amine formed by catalytic hydrogenolysis:[245]

$$RNHCH_2C_6H_5 + R'X \rightarrow XH + RR'NCH_2C_6H_5 \xrightarrow{H_2} RR'NH + C_6H_5CH_3$$

The alkylbenzylamine is obtained through the reaction of a primary alkyl amine with benzaldehyde and reduction of the aldimine formed.

A modification of the procedure of amination of halides utilized *hexamethylenetetramine* in the presence of alcohol. This compound forms a molecular complex with alkyl iodides; heated with alcoholic hydrochloric acid, these complexes give a primary amine hydrochloride:

$$C_6H_{12}N_4RI + 3HCl + 12C_2H_5OH$$
$$\rightarrow RNH_2.HCl + 6CH_2(OC_2H_5)_2 + 2NH_4Cl + NH_4I$$

The reaction proceeds well with all alkyl halides, although the reaction velocity decreases with increasing molecular weight of the halide. The normal straight chain halides react more readily than branched chain halides.[12] The reaction has been applied to the preparation of amino ketones from compounds such as ω-chloro- and ω-bromoacetophenone, β-methoxy-ω-chloracetophenone, ω-chloracetopyrocatechine acetate, ω-iodopyrocatechine diacetate, ω-bromacetoveratrol, chlor- and iodacetates. These halides form definitely crystalline complexes with hexamethylene tetramine, which readily yield the amino ketones on mixing with 38% alcoholic hydrochloric acid and allowing the mixture to stand at room temperature for three days.[13] Halo acetones give poor yields of the amino ketone by this method. The molecular complexes between the halides and hexamethylenetetramine are obtained readily when the reaction is carried out in chloroform. Iodides react most readily and chlorides least readily. The addition compounds are soluble in water, slightly soluble in alcohol and insoluble in most indifferent organic solvents.

Halogen atoms attached to *aromatic nuclei* are generally of low reactivity and are replaced with difficulty by amino groups. The reaction generally proceeds well in the presence of copper bronze or cuprous iodide.[14] Many nitrated halo benzenes react readily, however, in the absence of a catalyst, to form well-defined crystalline compounds. These halobenzenes yield the primary amine as the main product.[225]

Acidic groups in alkyl esters of inorganic acids may also be replaced with amino groups by heating with ammonia or amines. Thus, salts of acid sulfuric esters react with primary and secondary amines to form alkylated derivatives of the amines:[15]

$$(C_2H_5)_2NH + CH_3OSO_3K \rightarrow (C_2H_5)_2NCH_3.HOSO_3K$$

Dimethyl sulfate reacts at 0° with ammonia to form methylamine.[16]

The acid group in nitric esters may also be replaced by amino groups by reaction with ammonia or amines. This method is particularly well adapted for the preparation of higher amines.[17]

Gabriel's Synthesis[18]

Gabriel's synthesis may be regarded as an extension of the method depending upon the replacement of a halogen atom with an amino group by reaction with ammonia. The reaction of the alkali metal derivative of phthalimide with organic halogen compounds forms the basis of this synthesis:

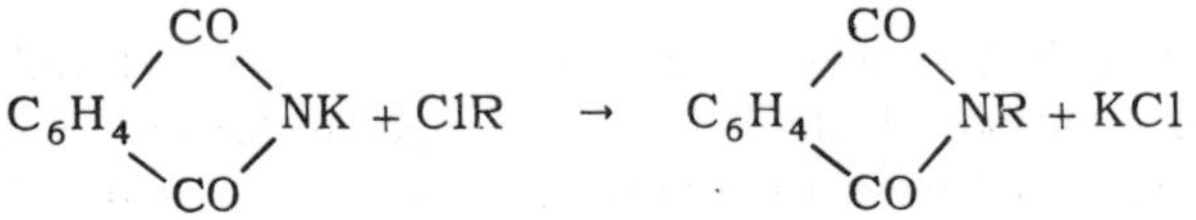

Hydrolysis of the substituted phthalimide obtained gives the amino compound.

The reaction between the alkali metal phthalimide and organic halides proceeds more or less readily, depending upon the nature of the halide. Iodo compounds, and many of the bromo compounds react readily. Compounds having a reactive chlorine also react readily, while those with more tightly bound chlorine require heating to a comparatively high temperature. The synthesis is of wide applicability and can be carried out successfully with a large variety of halogenated compounds.

Substituted phthalimides have been made through the reaction of phthalimide and the halo compound in the presence of sodium carbonate: [19]

$$2C_6H_4 \diagup\!\!\!\begin{matrix}CO\\\\CO\end{matrix}\!\!\!\diagdown NH + 2ClR + Na_2CO_3 \rightarrow$$

$$2C_6H_4 \diagup\!\!\!\begin{matrix}CO\\\\CO\end{matrix}\!\!\!\diagdown NR + 2NaCl + CO_2 + H_2O$$

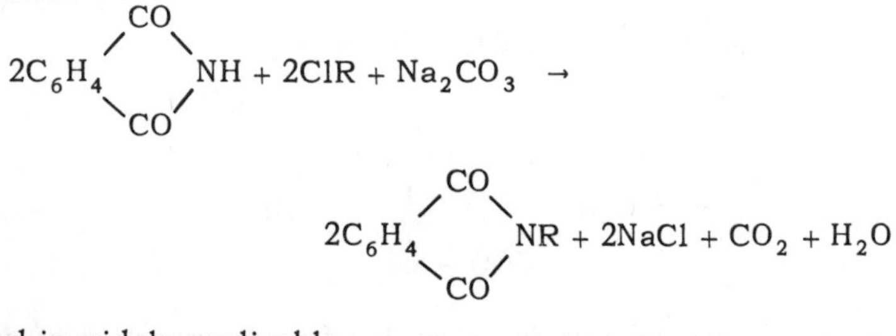

This method is widely applicable.

The *procedure* followed in hydrolyzing the substituted phthalimide is to heat the compound with 20% hydrochloric or hydrobromic acid. Cleavage is occasionally brought about simply by boiling the compound with the acid, but heating to 180 - 190° in a sealed tube is required in many cases. Another method consists in heating the imide with 10% potassium hydroxide,[20] and decomposing the resulting potassium salt of the amide by heating with an acid:

$$C_6H_4 \diagup\!\!\!\begin{matrix}CO\\\\CO\end{matrix}\!\!\!\diagdown NR + KOH \rightarrow C_6H_4 \diagup\!\!\!\begin{matrix}CONHR\\\\COOK\end{matrix}$$

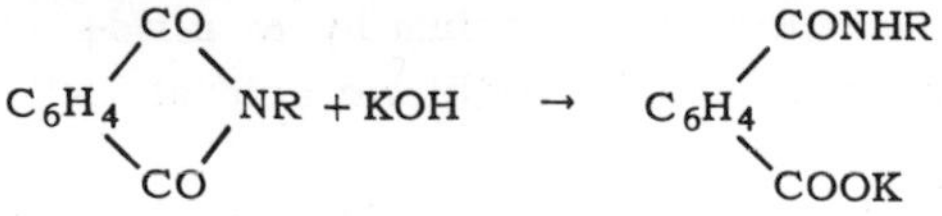

$$\rightarrow \quad C_6H_4(COOH)_2 + RNH_2 \cdot HCl + KCl$$

There is a possibility, however, that heating with a mineral acid may cause the regeneration of the substituted phthalimide.[21]

Potassium phthalimide may be prepared through the reaction of phthalimide with potassium hydroxide in alcoholic solution.[20]

Gabriel's synthesis has been applied to a variety of halo compounds; among these are the following:

Halo compounds with no other functional groups:[22] Methyl iodide, methylene iodide, several monobromoaliphatic hydrocarbons, ethylene chloride, allyl bromide, trimethylene bromide, pentamethylene chloride, benzyl chloride, o-, m- and p-xylyl bromides, o- and m-xylylene bromide, styryl bromide, mesityl bromide, ω-dibromo- and ω-dichloromesitylenes.

Halonitriles:[23] γ-Chloro- and γ-bromobutyronitriles, ϵ-chlorocapronitrile.

Hydroxy halo compounds:[24] chlorohydrins, dichlorhydrin, 1-hydroxy-2-chloropropane, 1,2-dibromopropanol, β-bromophenetol, β-bromethyl cresol ether, bromethyl xylenol ether.

Halo aldehydes, acetals and ketones:[25] Chloracetone, Sym-dichloroacetone, bromacetophenone, brompropiophenone, desyl bromide, $C_6H_5COCHBrC_6H_5$, desyl chloride.

Halo esters and ethers:[26] Chloracetic ester, α-bromobutyric ester, β, β′-diiodoethyl ether, bromomalonic ester.

Nitrated halo compounds:[27] o-, m- and p-Nitrobenzyl chlorides, picryl chloride.

Dihalo compounds, such as ethylene dibromide, yield diphthalimides as

well as halo phthalimides. Reacting with potassium hydroxide, halo alkyl phthalimides may yield ring compounds; thus, β-bromethyl phthalimide yields a hydro-
oxethyl phthalamic acid:

$$C_6H_4\begin{array}{c} CO \\ \diagup \\ \diagdown \\ CO \end{array}NCH_2CH_2Br + KOH \quad \rightarrow \quad C_6H_4\begin{array}{c} CONHCH_2CH_2Br \\ \diagup \\ \diagdown \\ COOK \end{array}$$

$$\rightarrow \quad C_6H_4\begin{array}{c} CONH-CH_2 \\ \diagup \quad | \\ \diagdown \quad | \\ COO-CH_2 \end{array} + KBr$$

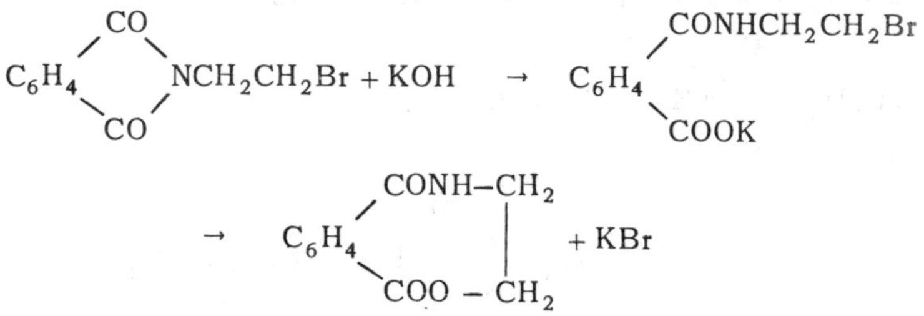

The stability of halo phthalimides resulting from the reaction of dihalo compounds with potassium phthalimide makes possible the replacement of the
halogen with other substituents and the formation, of variously substituted
amines. Thus, bromomethyl or bromethyl phthalimide treated with sodium mercaptide yield a mercaptomethyl or mercaptoethylphthalimide, hydrolysis of which
gives the mercapto amines. [28]

Amino mercaptans result when halo alkyl phthalimides are treated for an hour
at 100° in a pressure bottle with potassium hydrosulfide, and the resulting product is heated with concentrated hydrochloric acid at 180 - 200° under pressure
for three hours. [29]

The halogen in alkyl phthalimides can also be replaced by the amino group
by direct reaction with amines, hydrolysis of the resulting product leading
to the formation of alkylenediamines. [30] γ-Aminoethylpiperidine has been obtained by this method from bromethylphthalimide and piperidine.

Halo alkyl phthalimides reacting with sodio malonic ester yield the esters of
the corresponding malono substituted phthalimide, such as

$$C_6H_4\begin{array}{c} CO \\ \diagup \\ \diagdown \\ CO \end{array}NCH_2CH_2CH(COOC_2H_5)_2$$

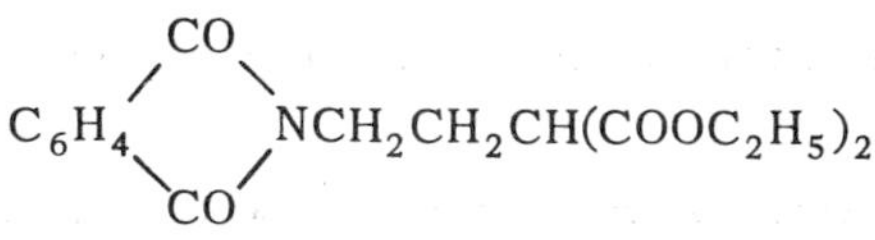

from which amino acids may be obtained by hydrolysis and partial decarboxylation. [31]

When α-chloro acid chlorides are made to react with potassium phthalimide,
the chlorine attached to the methylene group is replaced with the phthalimino-
group, yielding α-phthalimino acid chlorides, such as

$$C_6H_4\begin{array}{c} CO \\ \diagup \\ \diagdown \\ CO \end{array}NCH_2COCl$$

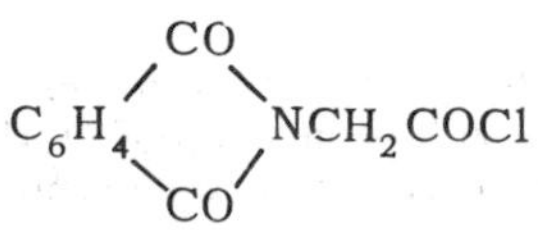

The reaction of such derivatives with sodiomalonic ester leads to the formation
of acylmalonic esters of the type of

$$C_6H_4 \underset{CO}{\overset{CO}{\diagup\diagdown}} NCH_2COCH(COOC_2H_5)_2$$

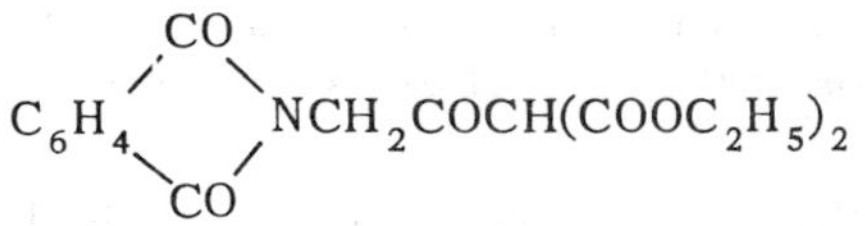

The halogen in phthalimido-α-haloamides, such as

$$C_6H_4 \underset{CO}{\overset{CO}{\diagup\diagdown}} NCH_2CHBrCOOH$$

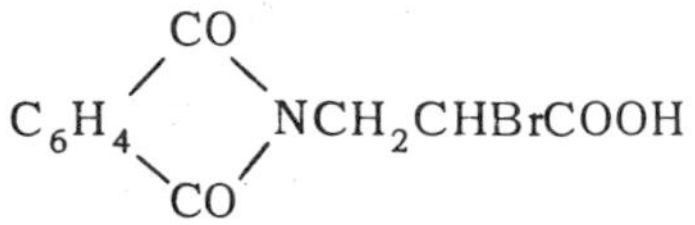

may be replaced by hydroxyl, sulfhydryl and other groups. Hydrolysis of the resulting compounds yields the corresponding hydroxy, mercapto etc., acids. Phthalic anhydride reacts with allyl isothiocyanate to form allyl phthalimide:[32]

$$C_6H_4 \underset{CO}{\overset{CO}{\diagup\diagdown}} O + SCNC_3H_5 \rightarrow C_6H_4 \underset{CO}{\overset{CO}{\diagup\diagdown}} NC_3H_5 + COS$$

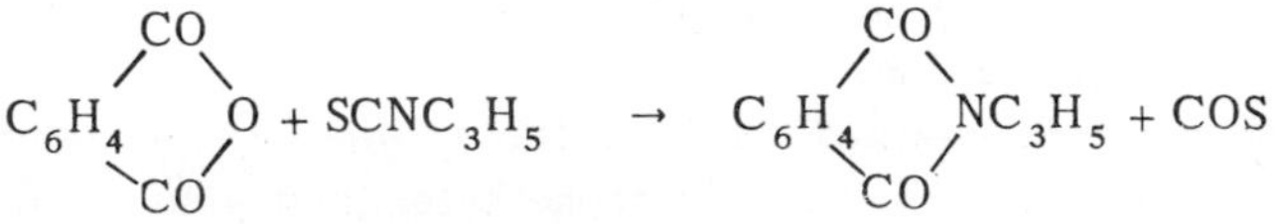

Secondary fatty aromatic amines may be prepared by a method resembling Gabriel's synthesis. Aliphatic amides of the type of CH_3CONHR yield alkali metal derivatives $CH_3C(OM) = NR$; reacting with alkyl iodides, these compounds are converted to N-alkyl derivatives, CH_3CONRR'. On hydrolysis these are converted to alkyl aromatic amines, $R_1R'NH$.[33] Acetanilide and its homologs, formyl derivatives of primary amines and arylsulfonyl derivatives have been used in carrying out the reaction.

A satisfactory procedure, when making use of formanilide, is to mix this with the alkyl halide, preferably the bromide, and to add a molecular equivalent of alcoholic potassium hydroxide. Upon completion of the reaction, the precipitated solid is filtered off, the alkylated formanilide is isolated by distillation and is hydrolyzed by use of an acid or an alkali.[34]

Replacement of Hydroxyl Groups by Amino Groups

Alcoholic hydroxyl groups may be replaced with amino groups by heating a mixture of the alcohol, ammonia and zinc chloride to 250 - 260°, although the method is of slight preparative value.[35] The reaction often takes place readily in the aromatic series, and the method is employed commercially for the preparation of alkylated aromatic amines. Thus methyl aniline is obtained on heating a mixture of 55 parts of aniline hydrochloride and 16 parts of methyl alcohol at 180°. Dimethylaniline is similarly obtained by heating a mixture of 80 parts of aniline, 78 parts of methyl alcohol and 8 parts of sulfuric acid to 235°. Mixtures of copper powder and sodium bromide or copper halides and sodium halides are effective catalysts for the reaction.[36]

The replacement of alcoholic hydroxyl groups in primary and secondary alcohols may be accomplished catalytically by passing a mixture of the vapors of the alcohol and ammonia over an appropriate catalyst heated above 400°.[37] Thoria and alumina are satisfactory catalysts. Silica, boron trioxide, tungsten trioxide, titanium dioxide and aluminum silicate have also been used as catalysts. The alcohol is first converted to the corresponding aldehyde, and this, reacting with the amine gives an aldimine; reduction of the latter with the hydrogen resulting from the dehydrogenation of the alcohol gives the amine:

$$RCH_2OH \rightarrow RCHO \xrightarrow{R'NH_2} H_2O + RCH = NR'$$

$$\xrightarrow{H_2} RCH_2NHR'$$

Primary, secondary and tertiary amines are formed simultaneously. Methanol is quantitatively converted by this method to a mixture of mono, di and trimethylamines.[38] The proportion of one or other of the products may be increased by the proper choice of conditions. The method is of general applicability and the yields are often quantitative, although the best conditions vary and should be determined for each case individually.

Cyclohexanol heated with aniline in an autoclave at 170° in the presence of nickel gives cyclohexylaniline.

Methylamine may be obtained through the interaction of formaldehyde with ammonium chloride at 104°.[39] Di- and trimethylamines also result from the reaction.[40]

Methylamine in 33% aqueous solution, reacting with methyl acetoacetate gives β-methylaminopropene-α-carboxylic methyl ester,

$$CH_3C(NHCH_3) = CHCOOCH_3$$

in high yield.[41]

Reductive Amination of Carbonyl Compounds

The simultaneous action of ammonia and hydrogen on carbonyl compounds at elevated temperatures and in the presence of a hydrogenating catalyst gives primary amines:[246]

$$RR'CO + NH_3 + H_2 \rightarrow RR'CHNH_2 + H_2O$$

The reaction is preferably carried out in ethanolic solution in the presence of Raney nickel under pressure ranging from 20 to 150 atm and at temperatures in the range 40 to 150°. Secondary and tertiary amines have been prepared by this reaction by use of simple primary and secondary amines.[247]

Leuckart Reaction (Wallach Reaction)

Certain aldehydes and ketones heated with an excess of ammonium formate are converted to amines.[42] The mechanism of the reaction appears to be as follows:

$$HCOONH_4 \rightarrow HCOOH + NH_3$$

$$RCOR' + NH_3 \rightarrow RC(OH)(NH_2)R'$$

$$\xrightarrow{HCOOH} RCH(NH_2)R' + CO_2 + H_2O$$

$$RCH(NH_2)R' + HCOOH \rightarrow RCH(NHCOH)R'$$

Dialkylammonium formates react to form tertiary amines without the formation of an intermediate formyl derivative.

Good yields of amines have been obtained from 3-phenyl 2-butanone, propio, benzo and *p*-methyl caprophenones on 7 to 9 hours' heating. Reaction proceeds slowly with laurophenone and 8-pentadecanone, while *p*-methyl laurophenone does not react.

Tertiary amines with a methyl group are obtained through the reaction of secondary amines with formaldehyde in the presence of formic acid. Dimethylamino derivatives may be prepared by this method from amino acids such as glycine, alanine and α-aminoisobutyric acid, though some complicated amino acids yield only degradation and condensation products.

Preparation of Amines through the Reduction of Nitro compounds, Azomethines, Amides and Nitriles

Amines are obtained through the reduction of *nitro compounds* with tin and hydrochloric acid, alkylhydroxylamines forming as intermediates:

$$CH_3NO_2 + 4H \rightarrow H_2O + CH_3NHOH$$

$$\xrightarrow{2H} CH_3NH_2 + H_2O$$

The isomeric nitrous esters are not reduced by this treatment but are hydrolyzed. On the other hand, when a mixture of a nitrous ester with hydrogen is passed over heated finely divided nickel, an amine is obtained probably following a rearrangement of the ester to a nitro compound.

The reduction of *azomethines*, RCH = NR′, leads to the formation of amines:

$$RCH = NR' \rightarrow RCH\ NHR'$$

Reduction may be brought about electrolytically,[43] by use of zinc dust and alkali,[44] with sodium and absolute alcohol,[45] with formic acid,[46] or catalylically.[248]

Phenylhydrazones[46] and *oximes*[47] also yield amines on reduction:

$$CH_3CH = NNHC_6H_5 + 4H \rightarrow CH_3CH_2NH_2 + C_6H_5NH_2$$

$$(CH_3)_2C{:}NOH + 4H \rightarrow (CH_3)_2CHNH_2 + H_2O$$

Oximes are best reduced with sodium amalgam and glacial acetic acid. The reduction of both types of compounds may be effectively carried out electrolytically or catalytically by use of finely divided nickel or copper.[48]

Amines are formed through the reduction of amides with sodium in boiling amyl alcohol[49] and from thioamides by reduction with aluminum amalgam in alcoholic or ethereal solution:[50]

$$CH_3CONH_2 + 4H \rightarrow CH_3CH_2NH_2 + H_2O$$

$$CH_3CSNH_2 + 4H \rightarrow CH_3CH_2NH_2 + H_2S$$

Some secondary amines are also formed.

Amines are obtained through the reduction of nitriles with sodium and alcohol,[51] or catalytically.[52] This subject has been dealt with in the chapter on nitriles.

Other Methods of Formation of Amines

Amines are obtained by the hydrolysis of isonitriles, by heating with water or dilute acids:

$$C_2H_5N = C + 2 H_2O \rightarrow C_2H_5NH_2 + HCOOH$$

Isocyanates and isothiocyanates also yield amines on hydrolysis with alkalies:

$$CH_3N = CO + 2KOH \rightarrow CH_3NH_2 + K_2CO_3$$

$$CH_3N = CS + 3KOH \rightarrow CH_3NH_2 + K_2CO_3 + KSH$$

The reaction may be made use of for the replacement of an alcoholic hydroxyl group with an amino group. For this purpose the alcohol is converted to the corresponding iodide, this is heated with silver cyanate, and the reaction product is mixed with powdered sodium hydroxide, and subjected to distillation in an oil bath.[52]

Secondary amines are obtained by treating azomethines with an alkyl iodide and hydrolyzing the resulting addition compound with water or alcohol.[53]

Secondary amines are also obtained through the decomposition of dialkylated p-nitroso anilines by heating with potassium hydroxide:[54]

$$NOC_6H_4N(CH_3)_2 + KOH \rightarrow NOC_6H_4OK + (CH_3)_2NH$$

Disubstituted nitro anilines are obtained by the alkylation of nitrosoaniline.

Amino acids may be converted to amines by decarboxylation brought about by distilling the compound with baryta.

The Beckann transformation, the Hofmann and Curtius degradations which give rise to substituted amides or urethanes may serve as the basis for the preparation of amines. These reactions have been dealt with in Chapter 8.

Primary amines RNH_2 may be converted to methylated tertiary amines $RN(CH_3)_2$ by treatment with formic acid and formaldehyde.[249] The yield does not generally exceed 80%, but the final product is not contaminated with primary and secondary amines.

Chlorides of primary alkyl amines reacting with formaldehyde and 2-methylfuran give the hydrochloride of alkyl-5-methylfurfuryl amine:[250]

$$RNH_2HCl + CH_2O + \ \text{(furan)} \ CH_3 \rightarrow RNHCH_2 \cdot \text{(furan)} \ CH_3HCl + H_2O$$

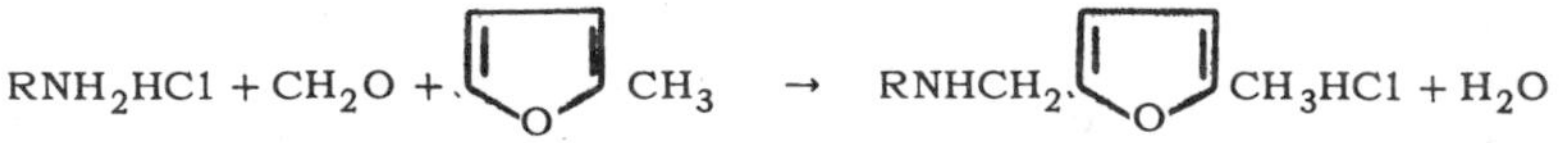

Amines may be prepared, further, by the Lossen rearrangement of hydroxamic acids, dealt with in Chapter 8; by the reaction of hydrazoic acid with ketones, and through the interaction of Grignard reagents with o-methylhydroxylamine or with Schiff bases.

Imines

Imines of the type $RCH = NR'$ are obtained through the reaction of primary amines with aldehydes:[251]

$$RCHO + H_2N R' \rightarrow RCH = NR' + H_2O$$

This reaction takes place most readily with aromatic aldehydes and amines.

Cyclic imines of the type $\overline{RCHCH(R')NH}$ are formed by heating the internal salt of the sulfate ester of the corresponding amino alcohol: [252]

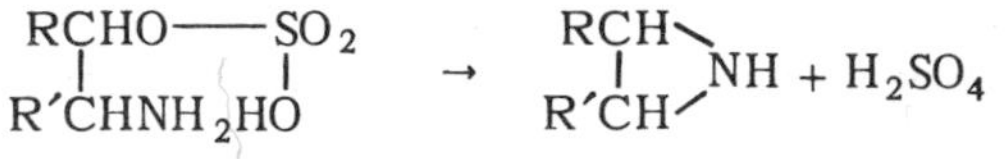

$$\begin{array}{c} RCHO\!\!-\!\!SO_2 \\ | \qquad | \\ R'CHNH_2HO \end{array} \rightarrow \begin{array}{c} RCH\!\!\diagdown \\ | \qquad \quad NH + H_2SO_4 \\ R'CH\!\!\diagup \end{array}$$

Ethyleneimine, $H_2\overline{CCH_2N}H$, has been obtained in 37% yield by this method; 2, 2-dimethyleneimine in 51% and N-ethylethyleneimine in 70% yield. Aryl substituted, 1,2-amino alcohols fail to undergo this reaction, but are instead dehydrated to vinylamines.

Cyclic imines of this type may be obtained through the reaction of aryl alkyl ketoximes with aliphatic or aromatic Grignard reagents and subsequent decomposition of the resulting complex with water. [253]

$$\begin{array}{ccccc} & & R' & & R' \\ & & | & & | \\ RCCH & \xrightarrow{R'MgX} & R\!-\!C\!-\!CH & \xrightarrow{H_2O} & R\!-\!C\!-\!CH \\ \| & & \diagdown\diagup & & \diagdown\diagup \\ NOH & & NMgBr & & NH \end{array}$$

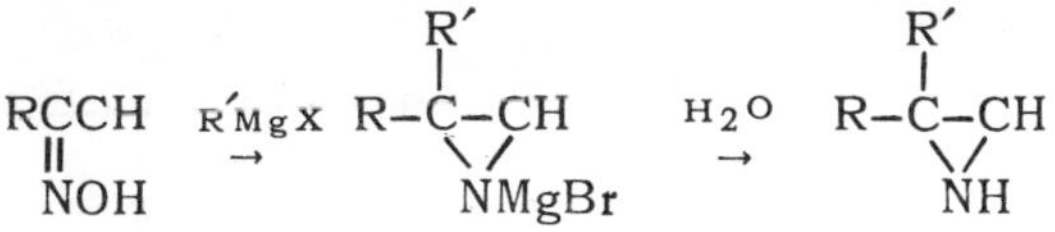

The yields range between 20 and 60%

Carbodiimides [269]

Carbodiimides, $RN = C = NR'$, are obtained from disubstituted thioureas by treatment with mercuric oxide: [270]

$$RNHCSNHR' + HgO \rightarrow RN = C = NR' + HgS + H_2O$$

In many instances the reaction proceeds at room temperature in ethereal solution. The reaction may be carried out in boiling acetone or benzene, though the latter solvent gives rise to sulfur containing byproducts which may not be easily removed by distillation. An excess of the metallic oxide is generally used. Good yields have been obtained with aliphatic thioureas by using two- to fivefold excess of the oxide,[271] though with aromatic thioureas an excess of only 50% of oxide is recommended in order to minimize the formation of ureas.[272] The reaction is generally complete within a few hours in the cold, and within about half an hour in boiling acetone. In some instances higher temperatures and longer reaction times are required. Highly satisfactory results have been obtained with an aqueous suspension of freshly precipitated mercuric oxide.[273] Carbodiimides have been prepared from thioureas by the action of sodium hypochlorite;[274] the products are contaminated, however, and purification is sometimes troublesome.

Symmetrical and unsymmetrical aromatic carbodiimides have been prepared through the reaction of azomethines with nitroso compounds:

$$ArN = CH_2 + ONAr' \quad \rightarrow \quad ArN \underset{CH_2}{\overset{O}{\diagdown \diagup}} NAr' \quad \rightarrow \quad ArN = C = NAr' + H_2O$$

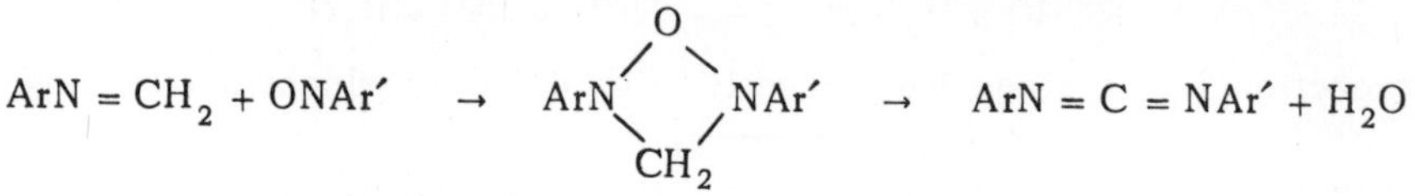

Carbodiimides are highly reactive, unstable bodies that undergo polymerization more or less readily. In the aliphatic seriee, an increase in the length of the alkyl chain has a slight stabilizing effect, and branching of the chain generally has a marked stabilizing effect. Carbodiimides react with acids to form acyl ureas, usually in excellent yield:

$$RN = C = NR + HOCOR'' \quad \rightarrow \quad RNHCON(R')COR''$$

They are recommended for this reason as reagents for the characterization of carboxylic acids. [275] Di-p-dimethylaminophenylcarbodiimide is considered the most suitable reagent for this purpose.

Disubstituted ureas are formed from carbodiimides quantitatively by reaction with oxalic acid: [276]

$$RN = C = NR' + (COOH)_2 \quad \rightarrow \quad RNHCONHR' + CO + CO_2$$

The reaction provides a method for the estimation of carbodiimides. Reaction with amines gives guanidines.

Carbodiimides have found application in the preparation of nucleotides. [277]

Quaternary Ammonium Compounds

Tertiary amines react with alkyl halides more or less readily to form quaternary ammonium halides: [55]

$$RR'R''N + R'''I \quad \rightarrow \quad RR'R''R'''NI$$

The reaction is carried out by simply mixing the amine and halide with or without the use of an inert solvent. The reaction takes place rapidly and vigorously, with evolution of heat in some cases, but in others it is necessary to allow the mixture of the amine and halide to stand for as long as a week. Heating the mixture in a sealed tube may be necessary with the less reactive halides and amines. The addition of a 10% aqueous solution of sodium carbonate favors the reaction in many cases. Iodides react the most readily among the halides and are commonly used, while chlorides are the least reactive.

Trimethylamine and methyl chloride react with evolution of heat, while trimethylamine and ethyl chloride do not react even when heated under 50 atmospheres pressure. [56] There are marked differences in the reactivity of various alkyl iodides; thus, ethyl iodide reacts with dimethyl aniline more readily than n-propyl iodide, while methyl iodide reacts considerably more rapidly than ethyl iodide, and allyl iodide reacts more readily than methyl iodide. [57] The reaction proceeds at different rates in different solvents; thus, triethylamine and ethyl iodide combine more than seven hundred times as rapidly in benzyl alcohol as in hexane. Quaternary ammonium salt formation proceeds most readily in strongly polar solvents.

Ability to form quaternary ammonium compounds is not confined to halides of hydrocarbons, and compounds such as iodoacetic acid and ω-bromoacetophenone are capable of giving quaternary ammonium compounds with certain tertiary amines and quinoline.

Bromides or chlorides of quaternary ammonium compounds may be prepared from the iodides by heating with bromides or chlorides of silver or lead.

Quaternary ammonium iodides form intensely colored tri, penta and ennea iodides with elemental iodine.[58]

The ease of formation of quaternary ammonium compounds is determined by the character of the tertiary amine as well as that of the halide. The same quaternary compound may form with varying ease depending on the choice of the tertiary base and the alkyl halide. Thus, methyl propylphenylbenzyl ammonium iodide results with evolution of heat through the interaction of methyl propyl aniline and benzyl iodide, while the reaction of methyl benzyl aniline with propyl iodide proceeds incompletely on heating under pressure at 100°.

Ortho substituents in aromatic amines greatly retard the reaction,[59] dimethyl aniline reacting much more readily than dimethyl-*o*-toluidine, although methyl groups in the *meta* and especially the *para* position seem to have an accelerating effect. Diethyl and benzyl methyl aniline react much more slowly than dimethyl aniline. Quinoline is far less reactive than isoquinoline or pyridine, while methyltetrahydroquinoline reacts almost as rapidly as isoquinoline.[60] Tertiary diamines of the diphenylmethane series with *o*-substituents in both nuclei do not react appreciably, while those with an *o*-substituent in only one ring are capable of adding methyl iodide on both amino groups.[61] Ring formation appears to decrease the effect of steric hindrance, dimethyltetrahydro-α-naphthylamine reacting more readily than dimethyl-*o*-toluidine. That other factors also influence the reactivity of the amine is apparent from the fact that 3-dimethylamino-1,2-xylol and 2-dimethylamino-1,4-xylol are capable of yielding quaternary ammonium compounds.[62]

Tetraphenyl, methyl triphenyl and diphenyl dimethyl ammonium compounds do not seem to be capable of existence.[63] Tertiary aromatic amines in which the amino group is attached to a short side chain also fail to give quaternary ammonium compounds. Cinnamyl ammonium compounds are the first in the ascending series to yield stable quaternary compounds.[64]

The behavior of ditertiary bases of the type, $RR'N(CH_2)_nNRR'$, varies according to the character of the groups R and R′, and according to the chain length. If R is a phenyl and R′ an ethyl group and *n* is 2, the compound fails to add benzyl bromide, while if *n* is 3, the compound adds one benzyl group. If R is a phenyl group, R′ a methyl group and *n* is 3, a diquaternary compound forms rapidly with benzyl bromide.[65] In the methylenediamine series, the quaternary compounds with the lower aliphatic substituents are unstable; a crystalline compound, $(C_3H_7)_2N(CH_3)(I)CH_2N(CH_3)(I)(C_3H_7)_2$, is obtained in anhydrous ether by the reaction of tetraphenylmethylenediamine with methyl iodide.

N,N′-Dimethyldiethyl-*p*, *p*′-diaminodiphenylmethane,

$$CH_3N(C_2H_5)C_6H_4CH_2C_6H_4N(C_2H_5)CH_3$$

adds two molecules of methyl iodide. Ethyl, propyl, and isobutyl iodides react with two molecules of the compound to form a complex which, on conversion to the salt of another acid, excepting the perchlorate, decomposes to the normal monoquaternary compound.[66]

Alkylated hydrazines containing a tertiary nitrogen, such as $C_6H_5N(C_2H_5)NH_2$, $C_6H_5N(CH_3)NH_2$, add a molecule of alkyl halide to form quaternary ammonium compounds, termed azonium compounds.[254]

Phenazine gives with alkyl halides and dialkyl sulfates quaternary phenazonium salts of the type,

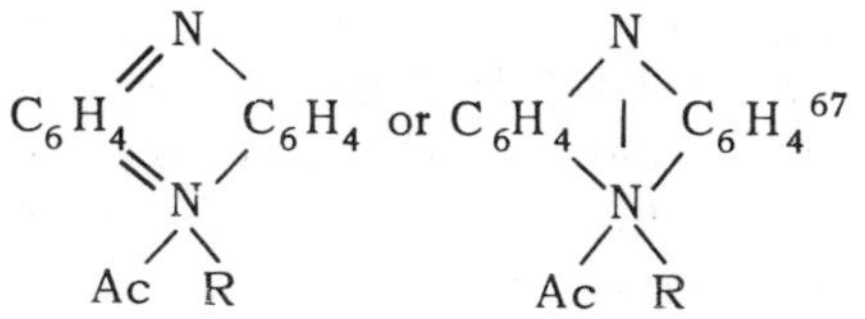

N-Phenyl phenazonium salts are prepared indirectly through the deamination of aposafranine,

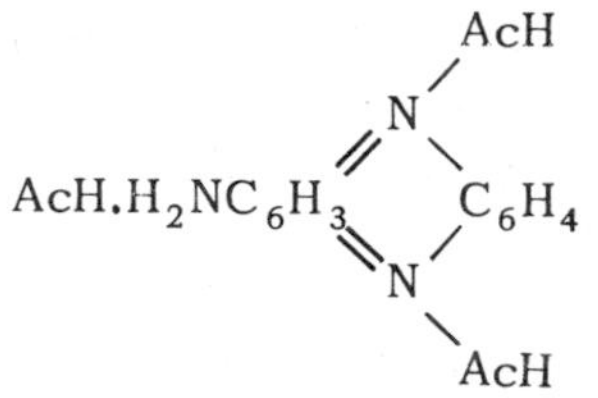

by diazotization followed by decomposition of the diazo compound.[68]

Quaternary ammonium compounds may be obtained also through the reaction of *dimethyl sulfate* with tertiary bases. Such compounds have been obtained with tertiary bases in which one hydrocarbon group is phenyl another a methyl or ethyl, and the third *n*-propyl, isopropyl, butyl, isobutyl and allyl. The quaternary compound results readily in quantitative yield in ethereal or benzol solution.[69] *Nitric esters* react very slowly with tertiary bases and are not suited for the preparation of quaternary ammonium compounds.

Picrates of methylated quaternary ammonium bases result readily through the reaction of tertiary bases with trinitroanisole:

$$RR'R''N + CH_3OC_6H_2(NO_2)_3 \rightarrow RR'R''N(CH_3)OC_6H_2(NO_2)_3$$

Quaternary ammonium hydroxides may be prepared by treating aqueous solutions of the halides of these bases with silver oxide.[70] Treatment of aqueous solutions of quaternary ammonium compounds with alkalies may result in the breakdown of the base to a tertiary amine. In other instances, the quaternary salt may remain unaffected by the alkali. The hydroxide may also be obtained by treating a methyl alcoholic solution of the chloride of the base with potassium hydroxide, potassium chloride precipitating out and leaving the quaternary hydroxide in solution.[71] Another method involves the conversion of the quaternary ammonium salt to the acid ferrocyanide, which is then converted to the sulfate by treatment with copper sulfate; the sulfate is finally converted to the free base with barium hydroxide.[72] The solution of quaternary salt thus prepared is practically free of other impurities. The sulfates of some quaternary bases are obtained directly from tertiary bases and dimethyl sulfate. These may be isolated from their aqueous solution by the addition of concentrated alkali. The free hydroxide may be liberated, as before, by boiling with baryta water.[73]

Quaternary ammonium hydroxides are, in general, strong bases readily soluble in water. They combine directly with the carbon dioxide of the air. Tetraalkylammonium hydroxides are approximately of the same strength as alkali hydroxides.[74]

Schlenk and Holtz have prepared compounds of pentavalent nitrogen in which all five valences are satisfied by hydrocarbon groups, by the reaction of halides of the quaternary ammonium compounds with sodium triphenylmethane and with benzyl sodium:[75]

$$(C_6H_5)_3CNa + ClN(CH_3)_4 \rightarrow (C_6H_5)_3C.N(CH_3)_4 + NaCl$$

$$C_6H_5CH_2Na + ClN(CH_3)_4 \rightarrow C_6H_5CH_2N(CH_3)_4 + NaCl$$

These compounds, in solution in anhydrous pyridine, conduct the electric current. They are completely hydrolyzed in water to a quaternary ammonium compound and a hydrocarbon:

$$C_6H_5CH_2N(CH_3)_4 + H_2O \rightarrow C_6H_5CH_3 + HON(CH_3)_4$$

The reaction of the sodium derivative of diphenylamine, $(C_6H_5)_2NNa$, with tetramethylammonium chloride leads to the formation of the compound,

$$(C_6H_5)_2N.N(CH_3)_4.$$

The reaction of trimethylamine in aqueous solution with benzene sulfonyl chloride gives another type of quaternary ammonium compound, phenyl sulfuryltrimethylammonium chloride,[76] $C_6H_5SO_2N(CH_3)_3Cl$. The *p*-toluol- and α- and β-naphthalene analogs of this are obtained from trimethylamine, *p*-toluol and α- and β-naphthalenesulfonyl chlorides. Other tertiary amines do not give this reaction.

Pyrolysis of Quaternary Ammonium Compounds

Quaternary ammonium hydroxides are decomposed on heating to tertiary amines, and an olefin hydrocarbon, except when the ejected residue is a methyl group. Dimethyltetrahydroquinolinium hydroxide yields methyl alcohol and methyl tetrahydroquinoline; and methylethyl and methyl-*n*-propylpiperidinium hydroxides yield methyl piperidine.[77] Ring fissure takes place in some instances with cyclic quaternary ammonium hydroxides. Thus, dimethyl pyrrolidinium hydroxide gives butadiene on pyrolysis.[78] The ring in benzyl and isoamyl piperidines may be ruptured by a repeated cycle of methylation followed by pyrolysis of the quaternary base.[79]

Quaternary ammonium salts also decompose when heated, to give a tertiary amine, with the ejection of an alkyl group as an olefin, unless the ejected residue is a methyl group.[80] The ease with which alkyl groups are severed from the compound is dependent upon the character of the group. The ease with which some of the radicals are eliminated is, in descending order, as follows: allyl, benzyl, ethyl, isopropyl, isoamyl, methyl.[81]

When the quaternary iodide $C_6H_5N(CH_3)_3I$ is heated, the methyl groups migrate one by one, as the temperature rises, and enter the aromatic ring. The final product is (trimethylphenyl)-ammonium iodide

$$C_6H_5N(CH_3)_3I \rightarrow CH_3C_6H_4N(CH_3)_2.HI \rightarrow$$
$$(CH_3)_2C_6H_3NHCH_3.HI \rightarrow (CH_3)_3C_6H_2NH_2HI$$

Separation of Amines

Many of the methods of preparation of amines lead to the formation of mixtures of primary, secondary, and tertiary amines. Several methods have been employed for the separation of the various individual amines from these mixtures.

One method consists in treating the mixture with diethyl oxalate, thereby converting the primary amine to a dioxamide, and the secondary amine to an ester amide:

$$C_2H_5OCOCOOC_2H_5 + 2CH_3NH_2 \rightarrow CH_3NHCOCONHCH_3 + 2C_2H_5OH$$

$$C_2H_5OCOCOOC_2H_5 + (CH_3)_2NH \rightarrow C_2H_5OCOCON(CH_3)_2 + C_2H_5OH$$

The tertiary amine remains unaffected and may be isolated by distillation.[82] In the example given, the dioxamide is soluble in water, while the ester amide is insoluble and may be separated by filtration.

Another method[83] makes use of the reaction of benzenesulfonyl chloride, $C_6H_5SO_2Cl$, with amines in the presence of alkalies. Tertiary amines fail to react with this compound, while primary and secondary amines give compounds of the type $C_6H_5SO_2NHR$, $C_6H_5SO_2NRR'$, the former soluble in aqueous alkalies, the latter insoluble. Dibenzenesulfon alkyl amides, $(C_6H_5SO_2)_2NR$, are formed also from primary amines. These may be converted to ether-insoluble sodio derivatives by heating with sodium ethoxide. Some primary bases yield small quantities of insoluble matter, especially when a fairly large excess of alkali is used.[84] Some bases of the terpene group, such as dihydrocarvylamine and dihydroeucocarvylamine, react with benzenesulfonyl chloride to form amides insoluble in alkali.[85] Primary alkylamines and hydroaromatic amines containing seven or more carbon atoms also yield caustic-insoluble products. Weakly basic aryl amines, such as diphenylamine or nitrated aromatic bases, and acid amides fail to react with benzenesulfonyl chloride.

The varying behavior of primary and secondary amines on the one hand, and tertiary bases on the other, toward carbon disulfide is also made use of for the separation of these bases. Primary and secondary bases react with this reagent, forming salts of alkyl dithiocarbamic acids, while tertiary bases remain unchanged and may be isolated by distillation. When the residual solution of dithiocarbamates is boiled with mercuric chloride or ferric chloride, a portion of the thiocarbamate resulting from the primary amine is attacked and appears as an isothiocyanate.[86]

The differences in behavior of primary, secondary and tertiary amines toward nitrous acid may also be made use of for the separation of amines. The primary amine is converted to an alcohol by nitrous acid, the secondary to a nitrosoamine insoluble in aqueous hydrochloric acid; the tertiary amine remains unchanged and may be isolated. The nitrosoamine may be converted to the original amine by heating with concentrated hydrochloric acid:

$$(CH_3)_2NNO + 2\ HCl \rightarrow (CH_3)_2NH.HCl + NOCl$$

Properties of Amines

Lower aliphatic amines are gases at ordinary temperature while higher molecular weight amines are liquids. Aliphatic amines, except those of the highest molecular weight, are soluble in water. Most amines form hydrates with water; some of these hydrates can be dehydrated only by treatment with potassium hydroxide or by distillation over anhydrous barium hydroxide.[87] Salts of amines are generally soluble in alcohol. Many amines yield double salts with platinum-, gold-, and mercuric halides. The picrates, picrolonates and salts with other aromatic polynitro compounds are characteristic and may serve for the identification of amines.

Aliphatic amines are strongly basic and react alkaline to litmus. They combine with the carbon dioxide of the air. The lower aliphatic amines are more basic than ammonia, their basicity increasing, as a rule, with increase in the number of aliphatic groups attached to nitrogen.[87] Aliphatic diamines are strongly basic and their basicity increases with increase in the number of carbon atoms between the amino groups.

The substitution of a phenyl or other negative group for a hydrogen atom attached to nitrogen causes a decrease in basicity, so that it is impossible to titrate aromatic amines by use of the common indicators. The salts of aromatic amines show an acid reaction in aqueous solution. As the number of aryl groups introduced is increased, the basicity continues to decrease and diphenylamine hydrochloride is extensively hydrolyzed in aqueous solution, while triphenylamine reacts neutral and is incapable of forming salts. The latter forms an *addition* compound with perchloric acid and a fluoride of the base is also known. Aromatic groups containing halogens, nitro or other negative groups as substituents, cause a greater decrease in basicity, although mononitroanilines are still sufficiently basic to form salts that are largely hydrolyzed in water.

Characterization of Amines

The varying behavior of primary, secondary and tertiary bases toward *nitrous acid* may be used to advantage for the characterization of these different classes of amines. Nitrous acid reacts with primary aliphatic amines to form an alcohol:

$$RNH_2 + HONO \rightarrow ROH + H_2O + N_2$$

Nitrosoamines are formed as intermediates but these are stable only at low temperatures.[88] Molecular rearrangements take place occasionally resulting in the formation of secondary or tertiary alcohols.[89] Secondary amines give nitrosoamines, RR′NNO, on reaction with nitrous acid. The reaction may be carried out by adding the theoretical quantity of aqueous sodium nitrite to the solution of the hydrochloride of the amine in water. Diisopropylamine gives a nitrite, $(C_3H_7)_2NH.NNO_2$, on reaction with nitrous acid.

Nitrosoamines derived from mixed aromatic aliphatic amines may undergo molecular rearrangement, if allowed to remain long in contact with aqueous hydrochloric acid, yielding *p*-nitrosophenylamines.[90]

Dialkylanilines treated with nitrous acid yield *p*-nitrosoanilines, unless the *para* position is occupied by a substituent. The presence of *ortho* substituents in the molecule hinders the formation of *p*-nitrosoamines.[91] Dialkylanilines containing a tertiary alkyl group fail to give a *para* nitroso derivative.[92]

Cyclobutanemethylamine, $\overline{CH_2CH_2CH_2CH}CH_2NH_2$, undergoes ring enlargement when treated with nitrous acid while at the same time the amino group is replaced with a hydroxyl group, forming cyclopentanol, $\overline{CH_2(CH_2)_3CH}OH$. This behavoir is shown also by other cyclic amines of the type

$$\overline{CH_2(CH_2)_nCH_2CH}CH_2NH_2$$

where n = 1-4, Ring enlargement does not always take place quantitatively, and a certain amount of the alcohol corresponding to the original amine also forms.[93] In some instances dehydration of the cyclic amine occurs, resulting in the formation of an unsaturated cyclic hydrocarbon,[94] and in other cases ring rupture may take place giving an open chain unsaturated hydrocarbon.[95]

Amines of various types behave differently toward *sulfomonoperacid (Caro's acid).* Primary amines are transformed by this reagent to hydroxamic acids:[96]

$$RCH_2NH_2 \rightarrow RCH_2NHOH \rightarrow RCH=NOH$$
$$\rightarrow RC(OH){:}NOH$$

Hydroxamic acids are readily recognized by the red coloration they produce when treated with iron chloride. Amines of the type, $RR'CHNH_2$, are oxidized to ketoximes, RR′C:NOH, while those of the type, $RR'R''CNH_2$, yield nitro derivatives, hydroxylamino and nitroso derivatives forming as intermediates.[97] Primary aromatic amines are oxidized smoothly to nitroso compounds by treatment with Caro's acid. Amino groups may also be converted to nitroso groups by oxidation with *peracetic acid,* aqueous *sodium peroxide* or acidified *sodium persulfate* in the presence of a little silver nitrate.[98]

Hydrogen peroxide reacting with primary arylamines converts these to aldehydes:[99]

$$CH_3CH_2NH_2 \rightarrow CH_3CHO$$

With secondary amines, dialkyl hydroxylamines result, while tertiary amines yield trialkylamino oxyhydrates,[100] $RR'R''N(OH)_2$.

Potassium permanganate attacks all amines readily in alkaline solution.

Oxidation takes place less readily in acid solution and, depending on the type of amine employed, aldehydes, acids or other degradation products result.[101]

Ozone also has been employed for the oxidative degradation of amines.[102]

Primary amines reacting with chloroform in the presence of potassium hydroxide give *carbylamines*.

Primary and secondary amines react with methyl magnesium halides to form derivatives of the type RNHMgHal and R_1R_2NMgHal. This reaction offers a means for the quantitative determination of primary and secondary amines (*Zerewitinoff's method*). Tertiary amines react partially with Grignard reagents to form addition compounds

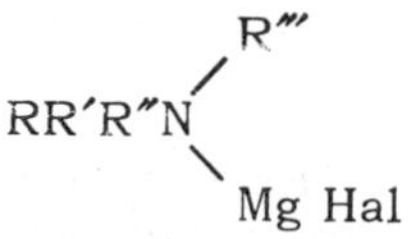

$$RR'R''N \overset{\displaystyle R'''}{\underset{\displaystyle Mg\ Hal}{<}} \qquad 100$$

Acylation of Amines

Acylated derivatives of amines serve well for the purpose of the identification of amines.

Amines are readily acylated by reaction with acid chlorides:

$$2RNH_2 + ClCOR' \rightarrow RNHCOR' + RNH_2.HCl$$

Many acylated amines are insoluble in water and their separation from the amine hydrochlorides, therefore, presents no problem. The separation of water-soluble amides from the amine hydrochloride may be effected by the proper choice of the solvent in which the reaction is carried out.

The Schotten-Baumann method is applicable to the preparation of acylated amines if the acid chloride is stable toward dilute alkalies. This holds true of aromatic acid chlorides, sulfonyl chlorides and furoyl chloride. A suspension or solution of the amine in 10% aqueous sodium hydroxide is treated with one and a quarter to one and one-half molecular equivalents of the acid chloride, and the mixture is well agitated during the addition of the chloride. The excess of chloride is destroyed by gentle heating and the acylated amine is filtered and purified by crystallization. Barium hydroxide may be substituted for the potassium hydroxide used in the reaction for the benzoylation of sensitive amines.[103] *l*-Aspartic acid may be successfully benzoylated in aqueous solution in the presence of sodium bicarbonate.

Primary amines may be acylated conveniently by treatment with the acid anhydride. The reaction is usually carried out by adding the anhydride to a suspension or solution of the amine in five times its weight of water. Lower acetylated amines may be readily isolated in the pure form by fractionally distilling the reaction mixture, and collecting the fraction boiling above 200°. It is preferable to use aqueous acetic acid as the reaction medium with amines of high molecular weight. The amine or its hydrochloride is dissolved in aqueous acetic acid, sodium acetate is added, and the anhydride is introduced without cooling the solution. It is often desirable to heat the mjxture finally to 60°. This method does not work satisfactorily with arylamines containing negative substituents in the aromatic nucleus.

If acetylation of an amine is carried out in the absence of a diluent, a certain amount of diacetylated amine results, together with the mono acetylated product. The presence of substituents such as CH_3, NO_2, Cl and Br in the *ortho* position in aromatic amines favors the formation of diacetyl derivatives.[104] The presence of negative substituents such as NO_2 and to a lesser degree Br or Cl, in the nucleus of an aromatic amine, on the other hand, causes a marked decrease in the reaction rate. The effect is greater the greater number of such substituents. As an example, 2,4,6-tribromoaniline fails to react with acetic anhydride, although a small quantity of sulfuric acid acts as a catalyst causing the formation of the acetanilide in good yield within ten minutes.[105]

In the acylation of phenylethanolamine, $C_6H_5CH(OH)CH_2NH_2$, the amine group is first attacked.[255]

Tertiary amines form molecular compounds with acid chlorides which are decomposed by water. Pyridine combines, for example, with one molecular proportion of acetyl chloride.[106] Addition compounds have also been reported with oxalyl chloride, benzoyl chloride and aryl sulfonyl chlorides.[107]

Acylation of amines with *inorganic chlorides* generally proceeds in a satisfactory manner. In the reaction with diethylamine two chlorine atoms in sulfur monochloride, sulfur dichloride, thionyl chloride, sulfuryl chloride and phosphorus oxychloride are replaced with the diethylamino group. Thionyl chloride also yields an imide, thionyl ethyl imine, $SONC_2H_5$, and phosphorus oxychloride gives a dichloro compound, diethylaminodichlorophosphine oxide,

$$POCl_2N(C_2H_5)_2$$

and a triamino product. Nitrosyl chloride gives nitrosodiethylamine. Only one of the chlorine atoms in PCl_3, $PSCl_3$, BCl_3 and $SiCl_4$ is replaced by the diethylamino group.

Primary aliphatic *nitramines* $RNHNO_2$ are obtained indirectly from acyl nitramines. Methyl nitramine, CH_3NHNO_2, has been prepared from oxaldinitramide by decomposition with aqueous ammonia.[266]

$$CH_3N(NO_2)COCON(NO_2)CH_3 + 2NH_3 \rightarrow 2CH_3NHNO_2 + H_2NCOCONH_2$$

Aliphatic disubstituted nitramines may be prepared from the sodio or silver derivative of primary nitramines by reaction with an alkyl iodide or bromide. Two isomeric alkylated nitramines exist.

Nitramide, H_2NNO_2 is formed when the dipotassium compound of nitrocarbamic acid, $KOCONKNO_2$, is treated with a mixture of ice and sulfuric acid.[267] Nitrates of amines have been converted to nitramines by the action of acetic anhydride.[268] The dipotassium derivative of nitrocarbamic acid is formed when nitrourethane is treated at 0° with aqueous potassium hydroxide.

Degradative Reactions

A number of reactions are known, leading to the breakdown of the molecular structure of certain types of amines, which have played an important role in the determination of the structure of complex nitrogenous bases. Among these are the Hofmann degradation, v. Braun's cyanogen bromide and acylchloride methods and miscellaneous other reactions.

Hofmann's Degradation

Hofmann's degradation[108] involves the transformation of an amine to a methylated quaternary ammonium iodide by treatment with methyl iodide, conversion of this to a quaternary ammonium base and the pyrolysis of the latter:

$$\overline{CH_2(CH_2)_3CH_2N}CH_3 + CH_3I \rightarrow \overline{CH_2(CH_2)_3CH_2N}(CH_3)_2I$$

$$\rightarrow \overline{CH_2(CH_2)_3CH_2N}(CH_3)_2OH \rightarrow CH_2 = CH(CH_2)_2CH_2N(CH_3)_2$$

Repetition of the process leads, in the case of the example given, to the formation of piperylene:

$$CH_2 = CH(CH_2)_2CH_2N(CH_3)_2 + CH_3I \rightarrow CH_2 = CH(CH_2)_2CH_2N(CH_3)_3I$$
$$\rightarrow CH_2 = CHCH_2CH = CH_2$$

The method is applicable to primary and secondary bases which, however, are first transformed to methylated bases in the process by reaction with methyl iodide. The nature of the base is revealed by an analysis of the reaction product for combined hydriodic acid, providing an excess of methyl iodide is used and the reaction is carried to completion. The conversion of the quaternary iodide to the corresponding hydroxide is brought about by treatment with moist silver oxide.

An alkyl group higher than the methyl group is released in preference to the latter; if more than one such group is attached to the nitrogen, each can be removed in turn by repetition of the process of methylation, conversion to hydroxide and pyrolysis.

The method is applicable to all fully hydrogenated cyclic bases. Repeated application of the method finally leads to the formation of trimethylamine and a nitrogen-free product. The tetrahydroquinoline ring cannot be ruptured by the Hofmann method.[109]

v. Braun's Cyanogen Bromide Method of Degradation

Tertiary amines combine with cyanogen bromide forming a labile addition compound. These addition products break down yielding an alkyl bromide and a disubstituted cyanamide:[110]

$$RR'R''N + BrCN \rightarrow RR'R''N\begin{matrix} \diagup Br \\ \diagdown CN \end{matrix} \rightarrow RR'NCN + R''Br$$

The disubstituted cyanamide formed may be converted to a secondary amine by hydrolysis of the cyano group to a carboxyl group and subsequent decarboxylation:

$$RR'NCN \rightarrow RR'NCOOH \rightarrow RR'NH + CO_2$$

The reaction of cyanogen bromide with tertiary bases often takes place quite vigorously. The reaction velocity decreases with increasing length of the carbon chains of the hydrocarbon groups attached to nitrogen. The introduction of unsaturated groups or groups with branched chain does not appear to affect the reaction velocity. A phenyl radical attached to the nitrogen of the amine causes a marked decrease in the reaction velocity.[111]

When unlike radicals are attached to the nitrogen of the base, then, as a rule, the smallest group is detached from the molecule. The allyl group is removed in preference to normal aliphatic saturated hydrocarbons. The benzyl group is more readily removed than the groups methyl, ethyl, propyl and phenyl; methyl and ethyl groups are removed in preference to the phenyl group. The α- and β-naphthyl groups are removed in preference to the methyl group, the α-naphthyl group in preference to the β-naphthyl group.[112] The bond strength between the nitrogen of the amine and the hydrocarbon group increases in the series $C_6H_5(CH_2)_n$ with increase in the aliphatic chain length, the phenylethyl and phenylpropyl groups forming exceptions.

Compounds of the type, R_2NCH_2CN and $R_2NCH_2COOC_2H_5$, react with cyanogen bromide to form two disubstituted cyanamides, R_2NCH_2CN giving R_2NCN and

$$RN(CN)CH_2CN$$

Aromatic aminoacetonitriles are not cleaved by reaction with cyanogen bromide, but yield p-bromo derivatives, $C_6H_5N(CH_3)CH_2CN$ giving, for example,

$$BrC_6H_4N(CH_3)CH_2CN$$

The reaction is not applicable to methyldiphenyl- and triphenylamines.

The reaction of cyanogen bromide with N-substituted cyclic bases may lead either to the formation of a cyclic cyanamide with detachment of the substituent, or it may result in ring cleavage

$$\overline{CH_2(CH_2)_3CH_2N}R + BrCN \nearrow \overline{CH_2(CH_2)_3CH_2N}CN + RBr$$

$$\searrow BrCH_2(CH_2)_3CH_2N(R)CN$$

Cyclic cyanamides are obtained in general if R is of low molecular weight. Ring rupture takes place with most N-alkylated piperidines and quinolines, but not with N-benzyl and N-allyl derivatives.[112] The method has been applied to the determination of the stability of heterocyclic systems containing a nitrogen atom in the ring.[113]

v. Braun's Acylation Method

When acylated amines, RCONR′R″, in which R is a phenyl, substituted phenyl or naphthyl group, are heated with a molecular equivalent of phosphorus pentachloride, they are converted to amide chlorides:

$$RCONR'R'' + PCl_5 \rightarrow RCCl_2NR'R'' + POCl_3$$

If R′ and R″ are alkyl groups, the dichloride changes to a chloroimide, and on further heating, the latter is converted to a nitrile:[114]

$$RCCl_2NR'R'' \rightarrow R''Cl + RCCl = NR' \rightarrow RCN + R'Cl$$

If one of the groups R′ and R″ is an alkyl radical while the other is aromatic, the alkyl group is removed and the aromatic group remains attached to nitrogen. Acylated hydroaromatic amines such as piperidine, tetrahydroquinoline, 7-methylindole, etc., heated with phosphorus pentachloride undergo ring cleavage;[115] in the process chlorinated imide chlorides or dichlorohydrocarbons are formed:

$$C_6H_5CO\overline{NCH_2(CH_2)_3CH_2} \xrightarrow{PCl_5} \begin{cases} C_6H_5CCl{:}NCH_2(CH_2)_3CH_2Cl \\ C_6H_5CN + ClCH_2(CH_2)_3CH_2Cl \end{cases}$$

The proportion of one or other product may be increased by the proper choice of conditions. A chlorinated amine results through the hydrolysis of the chlorochlorimide:[116]

$$C_6H_5CCl = NCH_2(CH_2)_3CH_2Cl + 2H_2O$$
$$\rightarrow C_6H_5COOH + H_2NCH_2(CH_2)_3CH_2Cl.HCl$$

Other Degratative Reactions of Amines

Pyrrole and its homologs subjected to the action of hydroxylamine undergo ring fissure:

$$\overline{CH{:}CHCH = CHNH} + 2H_2NOH \rightarrow HON{:}CHCH_2CH_2CH = NOH + NH_3$$

This reaction takes place also with N-alkyl pyrroles, N-amyl pyrroles forming an exception.[117]

Certain hydroxy amines decompose on heating to a carbonyl compound and an amine, ephedrine, yielding, for example, propiophenone and methylamine:

$$C_6H_5CH(OH)CH(CH_3)NHCH_3 \rightarrow C_6H_5COCH_2CH_3 + CH_3NH_2$$

The process is termed the *hydramine degradation.*

The reaction of tertiary amines with sodium hypobromite results in the formation of dialkyl chloro amines.[118]

Hypochlorous acid or chlorine in aqueous solution react with aliphatic tertiary amines, or cyclic amines such as tropidine, forming a chlorinated secondary amine:[119]

$$RR'R''N \xrightarrow{Cl_2} RR'R''NCl \rightarrow RR'NCl$$

A similar reaction takes place with tetranitromethane, which yields a nitroso secondary amine:

$$(RCH_2)_3N + C(NO_2)_4 \rightarrow (RCH_2)_2NNO + RCHO + HC(NO_2)_3$$

The reaction with aliphatic amines is best carried out in acetic acid solution, and that with dialkylarylamines in pyridine.[120] A similar reaction takes place with nitric acid and dialkylarylamines under suitable conditions.

The amino group in aliphatic amines may be replaced with chlorine by reaction with nitrosyl chloride: [121]

$$RNH_2 + NOCl \quad \rightarrow \quad RCl + N_2 + H_2O$$

Halogenation of Amines

Monochloroamines result on heating the hydrochlorides of primary and secondary amines in ethereal solution with sodium hypochlorite. The mono- or dichloro derivatives are formed depending on the proportion of hypochlorite used: [256]

$$RNH_2 + NaOCl \quad \rightarrow \quad RNHCl + NaOH$$

$$RNH_2 + 2NaOCl \quad \rightarrow \quad RNCl_2 + 2NaOH$$

Dichloroamines are obtained by distilling a mixture of the hydrochloride of a secondary amine with calcium hypochlorite and water. [122]

Chloro compounds of secondary amines are more stable than those of primary amines. The reaction of potassium hydroxide with the chloro compounds of secondary aliphatic amines in which the two groups attached to nitrogen are different leads to the formation of two aldimines which, on hydrolysis, give the corresponding aldehydes:

$$
\begin{array}{ccc}
& \underset{(CH_3)_2CHCH_2CH_2}{\overset{CH_3CH}{\underset{\|}{\underset{N}{\vert}}}} & \rightarrow \quad CH_3CHO + (CH_3)_2CHCH_2CH_2NH_2 \\
\underset{(CH_3)_2CHCH_2CH_2}{\overset{CH_3CH_2}{\underset{\vert}{\underset{NCl}{\vert}}}} \quad \overset{KOH}{\underset{\searrow}{\nearrow}} & & \\
& \underset{(CH_3)_2CHCH_2CH}{\overset{CH_3CH_2}{\underset{\|}{\underset{N}{\vert}}}} & \rightarrow \quad (CH_3)_2CHCH_2CHO + CH_3CH_2NH_2
\end{array}
$$

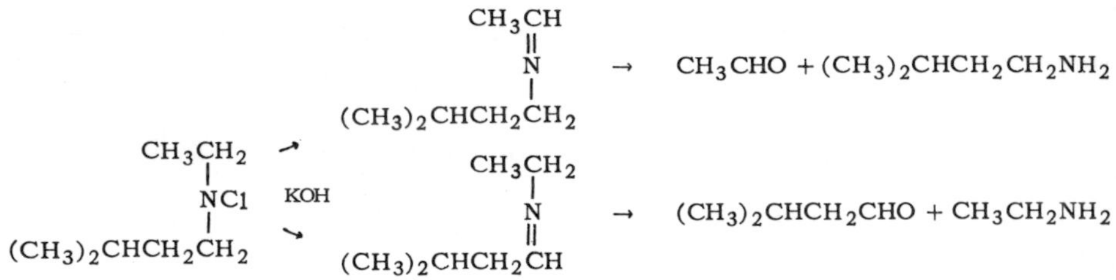

Tertiary amines form addition compounds with bromine and iodine. [123]

Hydrogen atoms attached to nitrogen in primary and secondary amines may be replaced with chlorine by reaction with dichlorourea, $ClNHCONHCl$. [124] One or both hydrogen atoms of primary amines may thus be replaced with chlorine. Chlorocarbamic acid may be substituted for dichlorourea in this reaction. [125]

The amino group in primary amines may be replaced with chlorine by reaction with nitrosyl chloride: [257]

$$RNH_2 + NOCl \quad \rightarrow \quad RCl + N_2 + H_2O$$

The reaction is carried out by conducting nitric oxide, NO, and chlorine simultaneously into the solution of the amine in the appropriate solvent.

Stieglitz Rearrangement

N-Halo amines of the type $RR'R''CNHHal$, undergo rearrangement to $RR'C = NR$ under the influence of bases. [258] The dihalo amines $RR'R''CN(Hal)_2$ undergo a similar rearrangement on simple heating. It has been noted that an aromatic group migrates to the nitrogen atom in preference to an aliphatic group. This transformation is known as the Stieglitz rearrangement. The formation of 9-substituted phenanthridines from 9-substituted 9-chloraminofluorenes,

may be looked upon as a special case of the Stieglitz rearrangement.[259]

HYDRAZINES, HYDROXYLAMINES, PHOSPHINES AND ARSINES

Alkyl Hydrazines

Alkylated hydrazines result through the reaction of hydrazine with alkyl iodides. The reaction of methyl iodide with hydrazine in the cold results in the formation of methyl hydrazine, together with as-dimethyl hydrazine. On heating hydrazine with an excess of methyl iodide in the presence of alkali, trimethylhydrazonium iodide, $H_2NN(CH_3)_3I$, is obtained.[126] Symmetrical dialkyl hydrazines may be prepared from diformylhydrazine by treatment of the lead or alkali metal derivatives of the latter with alkyl iodides or sulfates, and subsequent hydrolysis of the dialkylformylhydrazine formed.[127]

Monoalkyl hydrazines are obtained on heating an aqueous solution of a hydrazine salt with alkyl sulfuric acids.[128]

The reduction of alkyl nitrosamines with zinc dust and acetic acid results in the formation of asymmetrical alkyl hydrazines:[129]

$$(CH_3)_2NNO + 4H \rightarrow (CH_3)_2NNH_2 + H_2O$$

This reduction may also be carried out electrolytically. Similarly, the nitroso derivatives of alkyl ureas, reduced with hydrogen, yield hydrazino ureas which, on hydrolysis, give alkyl hydrazines:[130]

$$CH_3NHCONHCH_3 \xrightarrow{HONO} CH_3NHCON(NO)CH_3$$

$$\xrightarrow{H_2} CH_3NHCON(NH_2)CH_3 \xrightarrow{H_2O} CH_3NHNH_2 + CO_2 + CH_3NH_2$$

Alkyl iodo derivatives of *n*-alkylpyrazoles decompose on boiling with potassium hydroxide solution with the formation of *sym*-dialkyl hydrazines:[131]

$$CH_3\overline{NCH = CHCH = N}(CH_3)I \rightarrow CH_3NHNHCH_3$$

Monoalkyl hydrazines reduce Fehling's solution in the cold. Reduction takes place with dialkyl hydrazines on warming. This serves to distinguish these compounds from amines, since the latter do not cause the reduction of Fehling's solution.

Aliphatic azoxy compounds $RN = N \rightarrow OR$ have been prepared by oxidation of the corresponding azo compounds.[264]

Azo compounds may be prepared through the oxidation of hydrazines. Azopropane has been obtained by oxidizing di-n-propylhydrazine in ethereal solution with mercuric oxide.[265]

Alkyl Hydroxylamines

The alkylation of hydroxylamine with alkyl iodides results in the formation of N-dialkyl hydroxylamines, but prolonged action yields the trialkylhydroxylammonium iodides.[132] Trimethylhydroxylammonium iodide, $HON(CH_3)_3I$, is obtained directly through the reaction of methyl iodide with hydroxylamine.[133] O,N-Dialkylhydroxylamines, RNHOR, may be prepared through the alkylation of carbethoxyhydroxamic acids, $C_2H_5OCONHOH$, and subsequent hydrolysis. O,N-alkylhydroxylamines are also obtained, together with more highly alkylated products, through the reaction of alkyl halides with O-alkyl hydroxylamines.[134]

O-Substituted hydroxylamines may be prepared from benzaldoxime by alkylation, followed by hydrolysis:[135]

$$C_6H_5CH = NOH \xrightarrow{RI} C_6H_5CH = NOR$$

$$\xrightarrow{H_2O} C_6H_5CHO + H_2NOR$$

N-Monosubstituted hydroxylamines result through the alkylation of the isomeric syn-benzaldoximes and subsequent hydrolysis:[135]

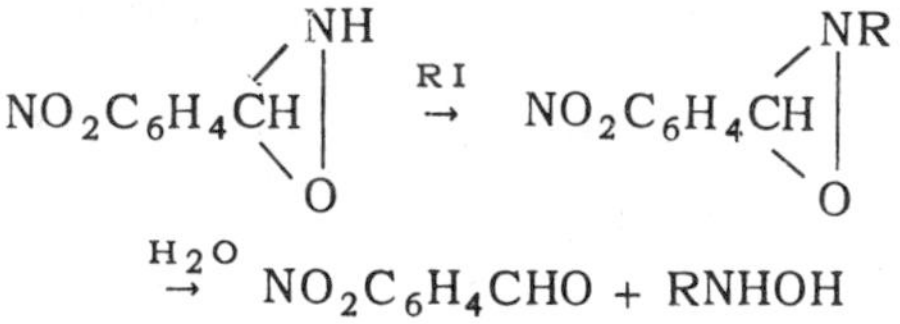

$$NO_2C_6H_4CH \underset{O}{\overset{NH}{<}} \xrightarrow{RI} NO_2C_6H_4CH \underset{O}{\overset{NR}{<}}$$

$$\xrightarrow{H_2O} NO_2C_6H_4CHO + RNHOH$$

O-Substituted hydroxylamines may also be obtained through the hydrolysis of the alkyl esters of benzhydroxamic acids:[136]

$$C_6H_5C(NH_2){:}NOR \xrightarrow{H_2O} C_6H_5COOH + H_2NOR + NH_3$$

N-Substituted hydroxylamines result from the oxidation of amines with Caro's acid. This method succeeds well with secondary amines,[137] but the monosubstituted hydroxylamines resulting from primary amines are further oxidized to aldoximes, hydroxamic acids, etc.[138]

N-Substituted hydroxylamines are obtained as intermediates in the reduction of nitro paraffins with stannous chloride or, preferably, with zinc dust and water.[139] The reduction may also be effected electrolytically.[140] Neutral reducing agents such as aluminum amalgam, sodium amalgam to which aluminum sulfate has been added, and under certain circumstances, zinc dust and glacial acetic acid also give hydroxylamines.

Nitro compounds in which the nitro group is not attached to a tertiary carbon, are reduced to oximes when treated with stannous chloride and fuming hydrochloric acid in the cold.[260] Nitro and isonitroso compounds are converted to oximes by various reducing agents. Phenylisonitrosomethane gives benzaldehyde on treatment with sodium amalgam, aluminum amalgam, or zinc dust.[261]

N-Alkylated hydroxylamines may be prepared from alkyl nitrites and nitro paraffins[141] by reaction with zinc alkyls, decomposition of the alkyl zinc hydroxylamine formed giving the substituted hydroxylamine:

$$C_2H_5ONO + 2Zn(C_2H_5)_2 \rightarrow (C_2H_5)_2NOZnC_2H_5 + C_2H_5ZnOC_2H_5$$

$$(C_2H_5)_2NOZnC_2H_5 \rightarrow (C_2H_5)_2NOH$$

$$CH_3CH_2NO_2 \rightarrow CH_3CH = NOOH$$

$$\xrightarrow{2Zn(C_2H_5)_2} CH_3CH(C_2H_5)N(C_2H_5)OZnC_2H_5 + C_2H_6 + ZnO$$

$$CH_3CH(C_2H_5)N(C_2H_5)OZnC_2H_5 \rightarrow CH_3CH(C_2H_5)N(C_2H_5)OH$$

The reaction of nitrosodiphenylamine with zinc alkyls can also be utilized for the preparation of N-alkylated hydroxylamines:[142]

$$(C_6H_5)_2NNO \xrightarrow{Zn(C_2H_5)_2} (C_2H_5)_2NOZnN(C_6H_5)_2$$

$$\rightarrow (C_2H_5)_2NOH$$

Alkyl magnesium halides reacting with nitrogen dioxide yield halomagnesium derivatives of N-substituted hydroxylamines. From these the substituted hydroxylamines are obtained by hydrolysis:[143]

$$2NO_2 + 4\ C_2H_5MgI \rightarrow 2(C_2H_5)_2NOMgI + MgO + 2MgI_2$$

$$(C_2H_5)_2NOMgI \xrightarrow{H_2O} (C_2H_5)_2NOH$$

Trialkylaminoxides

Trialkylaminoxides are obtained in the hydrated form, $R_3N(OH)_2$, through the oxidation of trialkylamines with hydrogen peroxide. Their iodides, $R_3N(OH)I$, are formed by the reaction of alkyl iodides with hydroxylamine or with N-substituted hydroxylamines.[137] The free oxides, R_3NO, are obtained by heating the hydrates carefully.

Trimethylaminoxide reacting with methyl iodide gives trimethylmethoxyammonium iodide:

$$(CH_3)_3NO + CH_3I \rightarrow (CH_3)_3N(OCH_3)I$$

Hydrogen chloride yields a hydroxy chloro compound with trimethylaminoxide, and the reaction of this with sodium methoxide results in the formation of trimethylmethoxyammonium hydroxide:

$$(CH_3)_3NO + HCl \rightarrow (CH_3)_3N(OH)Cl$$

$$\xrightarrow{NaOCH_3} (CH_3)_3N(OH)OCH_3$$

The hydroxide obtained from the iodide resulting through the reaction of methyl iodide with trimethylaminoxide differs from this in its properties, showing that the two bonds of nitrogen attached to oxygen in trimethylamine oxide are not equivalent.[145]

Trialkyl aminoxides with unlike substituents have been resolved into optical isomers.[146]

Phosphines

Alkylated phosphines are obtained by heating phosphonium iodide at 150° with alkyl iodides in the presence of metallic oxides, preferably zinc oxide. Mono and dialkyl phosphines are obtained by this method:[147]

$$2PH_4I + 2C_2H_5I + ZnO \rightarrow 2P(C_2H_5)H_2.HI + ZnI_2 + H_2O$$

$$PH_4I + 2C_2H_5I + ZnO \rightarrow P(C_2H_5)_2H.HI + ZnI_2 + H_2O$$

The primary phosphonium iodides are decomposed by water, but the secondary compounds require treatment with caustic.

On heating phosphonium iodide with alkyl iodides at 150 - 180° in the absence of metallic oxides, tertiary and quaternary phosphonium iodides are obtained:

$$PH_4I + 3CH_3I \rightarrow P(CH_3)_3HI + 3HI$$

$$P(CH_3)_3.HI + CH_3I \rightarrow P(CH_3)_4I + HI$$

Tertiary phosphines also result through the action of alkyl halides on calcium phosphide, and through the reaction of zinc alkyls with phosphorus trichloride.

Monoalkyl phosphines are obtained on heating monoalkyl phosphinous acids:

$$3C_5H_{11}P(OH)_2 \rightarrow C_5H_{11}PH_2 + 2C_5H_{11}PO_3H_2.$$

Alkyl phosphinous acids are obtained in turn through the interaction of mercury alkyls with phosphorus trichloride, followed by hydrolysis:

$$PCl_3 + (C_2H_5)_2Hg \rightarrow C_2H_5PCl_2 + C_2H_5HgCl$$

$$C_2H_5PCl_2 + 2H_2O \rightarrow C_2H_5P(OH)_2 + 2HCl$$

Phosphines with unlike substituents may be prepared by metathesis from alkyl chlorophosphines and organomagnesium halides:[148]

$$C_2H_5PCl_2 + 2RMgBr \rightarrow C_2H_5PR_2 + MgBr_2 + MgCl_2$$

Arsines

Trisubstituted arsines result through the interaction of arsenic trichloride and zinc alkyls, or of sodium arsenide and alkyl iodides:

$$2AsCl_3 + 3Zn(CH_3)_2 \rightarrow 2As(CH_3)_3 + 3ZnCl_2$$

$$AsNa_3 + 3C_2H_5I \rightarrow As(C_2H_5)_3 + 3NaI$$

ALIPHATIC DIAZO COMPOUNDS

Primary aromatic amines reacting with nitrous acid generally yield an alcohol through the replacement of the amino group by a hydroxy group, and while aliphatic diazo compounds, such as diazomethane, are known, these are prepared by indirect methods. Diazo compounds may be prepared from certain classes of aliphatic amino compounds by reaction with nitrous acid.[149] The ethyl ester of aminoacetic acid, for example, reacts with nitrous acid to form diazoacetic ester, $N_2CHCOOC_2H_5$. Other α-amino acid esters react similarly.

As a general rule, amino compounds in which the amino group forms part of an aliphatic molecular segment, give diazo compounds only when the complex H_2NCH- is combined to a pair of atoms containing a multiple bond, but containing no free hydroxyl groups. In particular, diazo compounds are obtained when the groupings, $OS.\overset{|}{C}H.NH_2$ or $X:\overset{|}{C}.\overset{|}{C}H.NH_2$, are present in the compound, X in the latter representing an atom of oxygen or the groupings, RN= or RR′C=.[150] Diazo compounds may be obtained, for example, from α-amino fatty esters, and less readily from α-amino acid amides, nitriles,[151] and α-amino ketones.[152] Esters of β- and γ-amino acids do not yield diazo compounds, but are converted to the corresponding hydroxy esters on treatment with nitrous acid.[153] The most stable diazo derivatives are obtained from those compounds which fulfill the requirements for the formation of diazo derivatives, and in which the amino group is attached to a CH_2 group.

Polypeptide esters containing the grouping, H_2NCH_2CO-, also yield crystalline diazo esters.[154]

Aminoguanidine reacting with nitrous acid gives carbaminoiminoazoimide,[155] $H_2NC(:NH)N:N:N$. When the reaction is carried out in the presence of perchloric acid, the perchlorate of a base, $C_2N_{10}H_7OH$, is obtained which seems to possess the character of a true diazo compound.[157]

Aminomethanedisulfonic acid, $(HSO_3)_2CHNH_2$, also gives a diazo compound, $(HSO_3)_2C:N:N$.[157]

Methods of Preparation

A general method for the preparation of aliphatic diazo compounds depends upon the reduction of alkylnitramines:[158]

$$CH_3N:NOONa \quad \rightarrow \quad CH_3N:NONa \quad \rightarrow \quad CH_2:N\vdots N$$

Diazo hydrocarbons also result through the reaction of an alkyl nitrate and an alkali with nitrosohydrazines:[159]

$$CH_3N(NO)NH_2 \quad \rightarrow \quad CH_3N = NONa \quad \rightarrow \quad CH_2:N\vdots N$$

Aliphatic diazo compounds may also be prepared through the oxidation of aldehyde- and ketone hydrazones with mercuric oxide:[160]

$$RCH:NNH_2 \xrightarrow{HgO} RCH:N\vdots N$$

The simplest aliphatic diazo compounds may be readily obtained through the reaction of alkalies with nitrosourethanes:[161]

$$CH_3N(NO)COOC_2H_5 + 2KOH \quad \rightarrow \quad CH_2:N\vdots N + K_2CO_3 + C_2H_5OH + H_2O$$

They may be prepared similarly also from nitrosoureas.[162] Diazo paraffins result through the decomposition of nitroso-β-alkylaminoisobutyl methyl ketones.[163] Nitroso ketones are obtained fairly easily through the condensation of monoalkyl amines and mesityl oxide and subsequent nitrosation of the resulting alkyl amino ketone. This method is generally applicable. The yields of diazo compounds are satisfactory with the lower members of the aliphatic series, but decrease with increase in molecular weight, so that the diazo compounds of hexane and octane are obtained in yields of only 23% and 16% of the theoretical. Vinyl diazomethane is obtained in 41% yield by this method.

Diazomethane is a yellow gas at ordinary temperature and is *extremely poisonous*. It is explosive both in the gaseous and liquid form. Its solutions explode when heated to 200°.

Diphenyldiazomethane, $(C_6H_5)_2C:N\vdots N$, and its derivatives are quite stable. Phenyldiazomethane and its derivatives are unstable.

Monoacyl diazomethanes, such as diazoacetophenone and phenylbenzoyldiazomethane, may be distilled with steam or under vacuum. They are soluble in water and most organic solvents.

The ethyl ester of azodicarboxylic acid, HOCON:NCOOH, is obtained on oxidation of hydrazine dicarboxylic acid ester. The alkali metal salt of the acid may be obtained on saponifying the ester with caustic.[164] The ester acts as a mild oxidizing agent.

Azoformamidine, $H_2NC(:NH)N:NC(:NH)NH_2$, is obtained in the form of the nitrate on oxidizing aminoguanidine with nitric acid. It is converted to azodicarbamide, $H_2NCON:NCONH_2$, by boiling water.

Aliphatic diazo compounds differ in character from the corresponding aromatic compounds. They possess the structural formula, $RCH:N_2$,[165] and in general do not yield compounds corresponding to aromatic diazonium salts, although a potassium methyl diazotate, $CH_3N:NOK$, and some aliphatic diazocyanides and sulfites are known.

Aliphatic diazonium alkali metal salts are formed as intermediates in the reaction of alkalies with nitroso alkyl urethanes:[166]

$$CH_3N(NO)COOC_2H_5 + 3KOH$$
$$\rightarrow CH_3N:NOK + H_2O + K_2CO_3 + C_2H_5OH$$

Ethyl diazo sulfonate is formed on oxidation of potassium ethyl hydrazine sulfonate with mercuric oxide and potassium hydroxide:[167]

$$C_2H_5NHNHSO_3K \rightarrow C_2H_5N:NSO_3K$$

Acetophenone azocyanide results through the reaction of diazoacetophenone with hydrogen cyanide:[168]

$$C_6H_5COCH:N\vdots N + HCN \rightarrow C_6H_5COCH_2N:NCN$$

Diazoacetic ester reacts with aqueous alkali sulfites to form a diazo sulfite:[169]

$$ROCOCH:N\vdots N + K_2SO_3 + H_2O \rightarrow ROCOCH_2N:NSO_3K + KOH$$

Diazoacetic ester is gradually converted to a true diazonium salt, $\overline{N_2CHCOO}$, when it is treated with dilute aqueous alkalies.[170] The free diazoacetic acid is unstable and decomposes rapidly.

Reactions of Aliphatic Diazo Compounds

Aliphatic diazo compounds reacting with an *acid* in non-aqueous media yield an ester:[171]

$$C_2H_5OCOCH = N_2 + CH_3COOH \rightarrow C_2H_5OCOCH_2OCOCH_3 + N_2$$

Reaction proceeds explosively when diazoacetic ester is dropped into concentrated hydrochloric acid. Reaction also proceeds with violence when diazoacetic ester is added to sulfuric acid. In water acidified with a little mineral acid regular evolution of nitrogen takes place on boiling, with the formation of glycolic ester.

When the reaction of aqueous mineral acids with diazoacetic ester is carried out in the presence of a salt of the acid, it proceeds partly in another direction, resulting in the replacement of the diazo group with the anion of the acid:

$$C_2H_5OCOCHN_2 + HCl \rightarrow C_2H_5OCOCH_2Cl + N_2$$

The greater the concentration of the salt, the greater is the extent to which this second reaction takes place.

Concentrated aqueous hydrogen fluoride converts ethyl diazoacetate to ethyl diglycolate,[172] $O(CH_2COOC_2H_5)_2$.

Alkoxy acetic esters are produced when diazoacetic ester is boiled with alcohols. The ester of anilinoacetic acid, $C_6H_5NHCH_2COOC_2H_5$, results from the reaction of aniline with diazoacetic ester.

Diazomethane reacts with *hydrocyanic acid* to form acetonitrile and carbylamine, $CH_3N{:}C$.[173] With phenols, phenol ethers are obtained:

$$CH_2N_2 + C_6H_5OH \rightarrow C_6H_5OCH_3 + N_2$$

Diazomethane fails to react with aliphatic mercaptans but reacts readily with thiophenols.[174] Reaction with cold water in the presence of an acid leads to the formation of methanol:

$$CH_2N_2 + H_2O \rightarrow CH_3OH + N_2$$

Diazomethane is an energetic methylating agent for acids, and presents the advantage that it may be used at low temperatures.[175] Weakly acidic compounds are not methylated in ethereal solution because of the neutralizing tendency of the ether.

Diazomethane reacts with the ammonium and amine salts of acids to form the methyl ester of the acid.[230] Methyl esters of γ-hydroxy acids, which readily form lactones on excessive heating, are readily obtained by treatment with diazomethane.[231]

Aliphatic monohydric *alcohols* other than methanol do not react with diazomethane, and it is possible to keep an alcoholic solution of diazomethane for several days with little change. On the other hand, polyhydric unsaturated alcohols, and alcohols containing a halogen or acyl, cyano and α-carbonyl groups react more or less readily with diazomethane. Ethylene glycol does not react with diazomethane, though its monoacetate reacts readily to form acetyl glycolmonomethyl ether.[176]

Diazomethane reacting with *amines* yields methylated amines:

$$CH_3C_6H_4NH_2 + CH_2N_2 \quad \rightarrow \quad CH_3C_6H_4NHCH_3 + N_2$$

Diazoacetoacetic ester reacts with ammonia in solution in aqueous ammonium acetate to form the ethyl ester of 5-methyltriazole-4-carboxylic acid,[177]

$$C_2H_5OCO-\overset{\Gamma}{C} = C(CH_3)NHN = N$$

A similar reaction also takes place with hydroxylamine.[178] Diazoacetic ester is converted to the potassium salt of 1,6-dihydro-1,2,4,5-tetrazine-3,6-dicarboxylic acid, the so-called *pseudo* diazoacetic acid, under the action of cold concentrated aqueous potassium hydroxide:[263]

$$2N_2CHCOOC_2H_5 + 2KOH \quad \rightarrow \quad KOCOC\overset{\displaystyle N-NH}{\underset{\displaystyle N=N}{\Big\rangle}}CHCOOK + 2C_2H_5OH$$

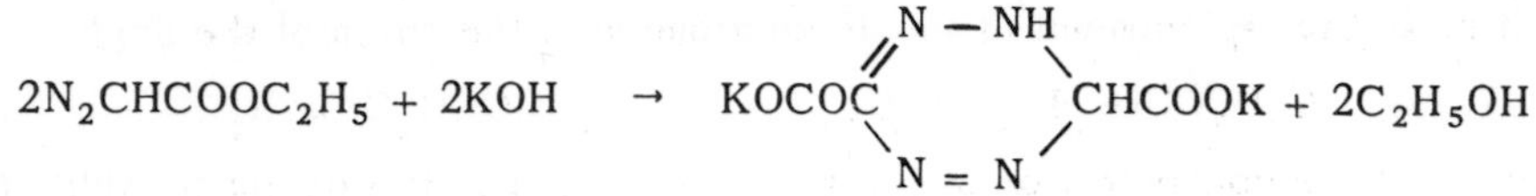

Liquid ammonia also brings about the transformation to the *pseudo* diazoacetic salt. Heat causes the isomerization of the latter to the salt of bisdiazoacetic acid,

$$HOCOC = N \cdot N = C(COOH)NH \cdot NH$$

Bromine and iodine react with diazo compounds in ethereal solution replacing the diazo group:[179]

$$C_2H_5OCOCHN_2 + Br_2 \quad \rightarrow \quad C_2H_5OCOCHBr_2 + N_2$$

With a mixture of bromine and chlorine, a 50% yield of chlorobromacetic ester is obtained.[180]

Acid chlorides react with aliphatic diazo compounds to form diazoketones[181]

$$C_6H_5COCl + 2N_2CHCOOC_2H_5 \quad \rightarrow$$

$$C_6H_5COC(N_2)COOC_2H_5 + ClCH_2COOC_2H_5 + N_2$$

Phosgene gives with diazoacetic ester diazomalonic ester acid chloride,[182]

$$C_2H_5OCOC(N_2)COCl$$

Diphenyldiazomethane yields with thiophosgene α, α-diphenyl- β-dichloroethyl sulfide,

$$(C_6H_5)_2C \overset{\displaystyle \frown}{\underset{\displaystyle S}{\diagup}} CCl_2 \quad ^{224}$$

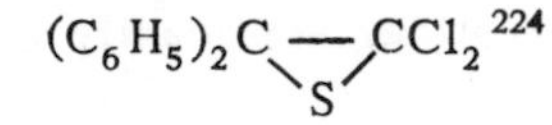

Simple diazo ketones result through the reaction of acyl halides with diazoalkanes:[183]

$$RCOCl + 2CH_2N_2 \quad \rightarrow \quad RCOCHN_2 + CH_3Cl + N_2$$

The procedure is to add one equivalent of the acyl halide slowly to the ethereal solution of 2.5 to 3 molal equivalents of the diazoalkane cooled to 0°, and to allow the mixture to stand for a sufficiently long period for complete reaction. Yields are practically quantitative. Bisdiazoketones have been made by this method from dicarboxylic acid chlorides.

Hydrogen chloride reacts with diazoketones to form chloro ketones.[184] With naphthoquinone derivatives methyl substituted products result:

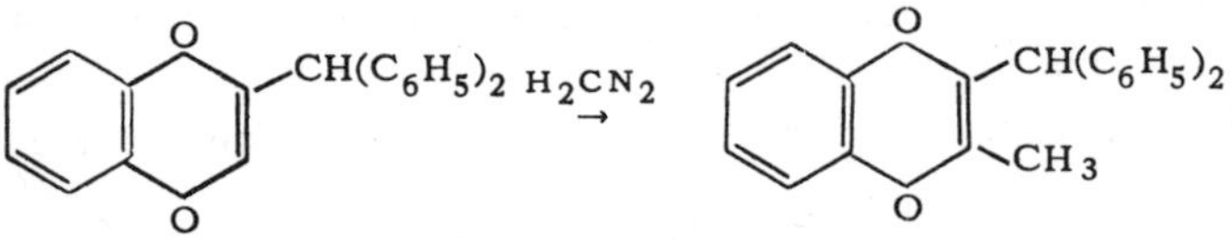

α-Pyrone derivatives containing a negative substituent undergo a similar nuclear methylation in the 6-position.[144]

Diphenyldiazomethane in solution in carbon disulfide, reacting in the cold with sulfur dioxide, gives tetraphenylethylenesulfone,

$$(C_6H_5)_2C \underset{SO_2}{\overset{}{\underset{\diagdown \diagup}{\quad}}} C(C_6H_5)_2 \quad [224]$$

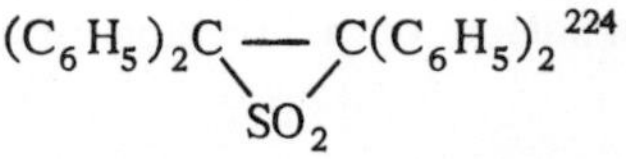

Diazomethane reacting with *aldehydes* generally gives methyl ketones or the next homolog of the aldehyde, but in some instances the isomeric ethylene oxides are formed:[222]

$$RCHO + CH_2N_2 \rightarrow RCH\overset{O-N}{\underset{CH_2-N}{\diagup \| }} \rightarrow$$

$$N_2 + RCH\overset{O}{\underset{CH_2}{\diagup \diagdown}} \quad \overset{RCOCH_3 \text{ or } RCH_2CHO}{\underset{RCH\overset{O}{\diagdown}CH_2}{}}$$

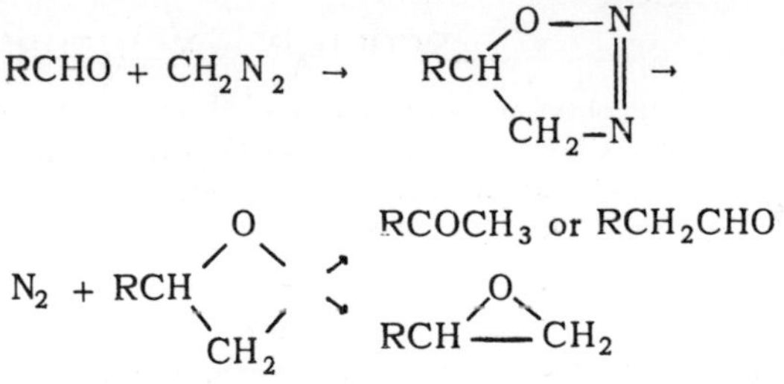

If R is a *negative* group, as in chloral or o-nitrobenzaldehyde, the oxide is formed almost exclusively. On the other hand, if R is a *positive* group the formation of oxide is suppressed, and the methyl ketone, or the homologous aldehyde is obtained. Catalytic influences bring about the formation of the latter. In the presence of a large amount of methanol, the aldehyde formed gives an ethylene oxide derivative:

$$CH_2\overset{O}{\underset{O}{\diagup \diagdown}}C_6H_3CHO \rightarrow CH_2\overset{O}{\underset{O}{\diagup \diagdown}}C_6H_3CH_2CHO \rightarrow$$

$$CH_2\overset{O}{\underset{O}{\diagup \diagdown}}C_6H_3CH_2CH{-}CH_2\overset{O}{\diagup \diagdown}$$

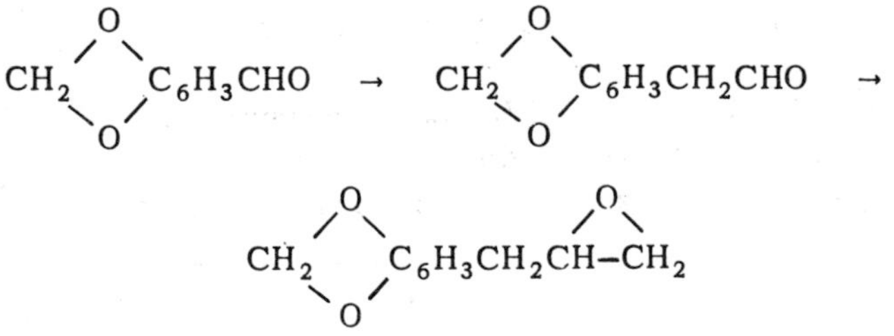

Many aldehydes fail to react with diazomethane in the absence of methanol or react only very slowly.

Benzaldehyde and m-nitrobenzaldehyde give acetophenone and m-nitroacetophenone; isobutyraldehyde gives methyl isobutyl ketone.[185] Piperonal and o-nitropiperonal also yield a ketone with diazoethane, but react abnormally with diazomethane.[186]

Aldehydes and ketones which form hydrates and carbonyl compounds with negative groups generally yield ethylene oxides. Chloral gives 1,1,1-trichloropropylene-2,3-oxide. Chloro and trichloroacetone react similarly. o-Nitrobenzaldehyde gives o-nitrophenylethylene oxide. Oxides are obtained also from piperonal, mesoxalic ester, alloxan and phenanthraquinone.[187]

Diazoacetic ester reacts with benzaldehyde to form benzoylacetic ester,

$$C_6H_5COCH_2COOC_2H_5.\text{[188]}$$

Other aldehydes generally fail to react with diazoacetic ester, unless they bear negative substituents.[223] Chloral yields trichloroacetonecarboxylic ester,

$$Cl_3CCOCH_2COOC_2H_5.\text{[262]}$$

Diazomethane, in general, does not react with ketones. When reaction takes place, it results in the formation of a homolog of the ketone or an ethylene oxide:

$$RCOR' \quad \longrightarrow \quad \overset{\displaystyle O}{\overset{\displaystyle \diagup\diagdown}{RR'C-CH_2}}$$

$$\searrow \quad RCOCH_2R' \text{ or } RCH_2COR'$$

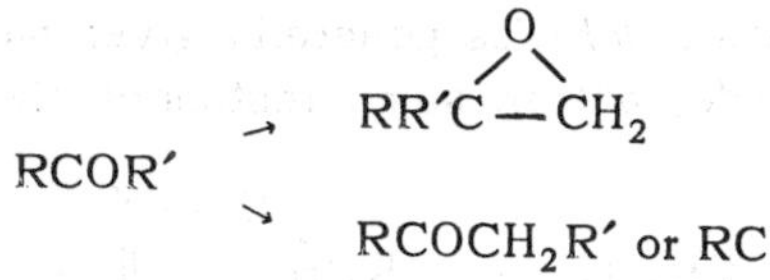

The proportion of oxide obtained with acetone[189] is about 40%, with chloroacetone 65%, and trichloroacetone, Cl_3CCOCH_3, 90%. α-Hydroxy ketones and their ethers give oxides chiefly; in the sugar series, ketones give ethylene oxide derivatives in good yield.[232] Mesoxalic esters, ROCOCOCOOR, and alloxan,

$$\overline{HN-CONHCOCOCO}$$

give oxides exclusively.

Where keto-enol equilibrium is present, the reaction with diazomethane results exclusively in the formation of the enol ester, if the enolic form is more acidic, and the C-methyl derivative in the reverse case. Methyl benzoylacetate gives exclusively the enol ether; acetoacetic ester yields largely the enol ether, with small amounts of the oxide.[233] Methyl pyruvate gives exclusively the oxide. Ketones of the general formula, RSO_2CH_2COR', yield the enol methyl ether, although there is no indication that enolization takes place.[234]

Trimethyl sufone, $\overline{CH_2SO_2CH_2SO_2CH_2SO_2}$, and cyanuric acid, $\overline{HNCONHCONHCO}$, give exclusively the C- and N-methylated derivatives.

a-Diketones react with diazomethane forming methylene ethers:[280]

$$RCOCOR' + CH_2N_2 \quad \rightarrow \quad \overline{RC = C(R')OCH_2O} + N_2$$

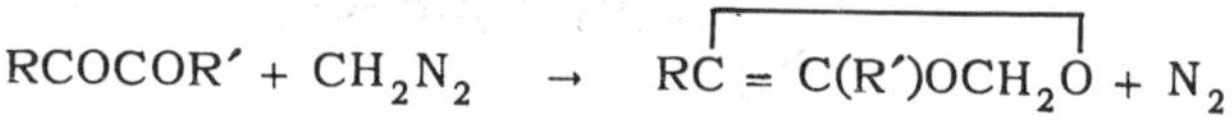

Some cyclic dicarbonyl compounds including camphorquinone undergo ring enlargement.[281]

Cyclic ketones react with diazomethane only in the presence of methanol. Homologous ring ketones result with *ring enlargement*, together with some oxides. Cyclopentanone and cyclohexanone give both cycloheptanone and cyclooctanone, while cycloheptanone yields only cyclooctanone.[190, 236, 235]

All cyclic ketones do not undergo ring enlargement with equal ease. The yield of cyclic ketone from cyclohexanone is 63% of the theoretical, but drops to 45% for cyclooctanone, and to about 20% for cyclononanone and cyclodecanone. The reactivity is at a minimum with ring ketones which are most difficult to prepare by the usual ring closure methods. Ring expansion again becomes the predominant reaction for cyclic ketones with 15 or more carbon atoms, in agreement with Ziegler's results concerning the formation of cyclic ketones.[237]

This method of ring enlargement is applicable to cyclic aromatic ketones. Thus, fluorenone reacting with diazomethane gives 9-methoxyphenanthrone;[238] similarly, methyl 1,3-indenedione-2-carboxylate gives methyl 1,4-dihydroxy-2-naphthoate.

Heterocyclic ketones also undergo ring enlargement on treatment with diazomethane.[282] Thus, isatin gives 2,3-diketoquinoline and the isomeric 3,4-dihydroxyquinoline or its desmotrope:

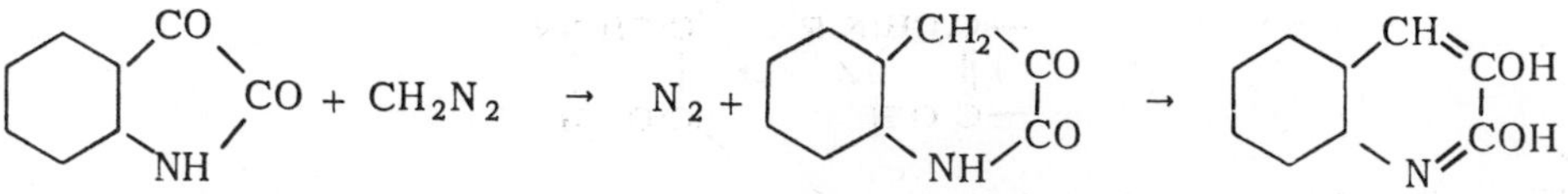

Halo and methylisatins react in a similar manner. Oxindole and dioxindole are not acted upon by ethereal diazomethane solution, while dimethylisatol and dimethylisatinone are normally methylated.[191] Coumarandione does not undergo ring enlargement but gives a methylene ether,

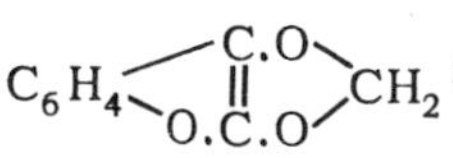

$$C_6H_4 \underset{O.C.O}{\overset{C.O}{\diagup}} CH_2 \quad [239]$$

thiocoumarandione behaves similarly.

Ortho quinones and ortho quinoneimines react with diazomethane to form five-membered heterocyclic ring compounds:[192]

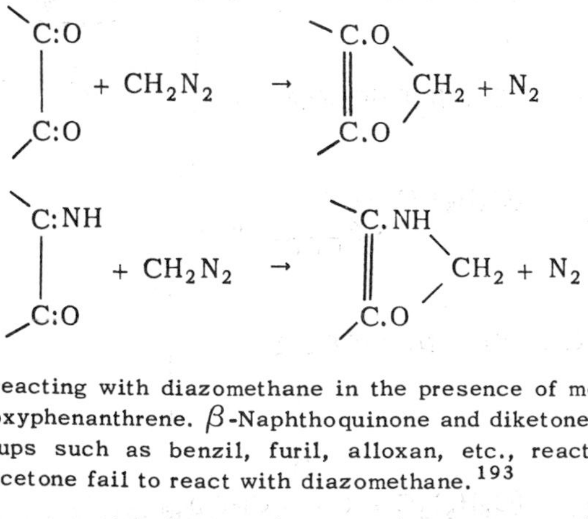

Phenanthraquinone reacting with diazomethane in the presence of methanol gives the methyl ether of dihydroxyphenanthrene. β-Naphthoquinone and diketones with especially reactive carbonyl groups such as benzil, furil, alloxan, etc., react in like manner. Diacetyl and acetonylacetone fail to react with diazomethane.[193]

Ortho hydroxyanils react with diazomethane in the presence of methyl alcohol to form coumaran derivatives:

$$\begin{array}{c} \diagdown CCH = NR \\ \| \\ {}_{\diagup}COH \end{array} \rightarrow \begin{array}{cc} \diagdown C = CH & NR \\ | & | \\ {}_{\diagup}C{:}O \rightarrow H \end{array} \xrightarrow{CH_2N_2} \begin{array}{c} \diagdown C \text{---} CHNHR \\ \| \diagdown \diagup CH_2 \\ N{:}N \\ {}_{\diagup}C{:}O \end{array}$$

$$\rightarrow \begin{array}{c} \diagdown C \text{---} CHNHR \\ \| \quad | \\ {}_{\diagup}C \diagdown \diagup CH_2 \\ O \end{array} + N_2$$

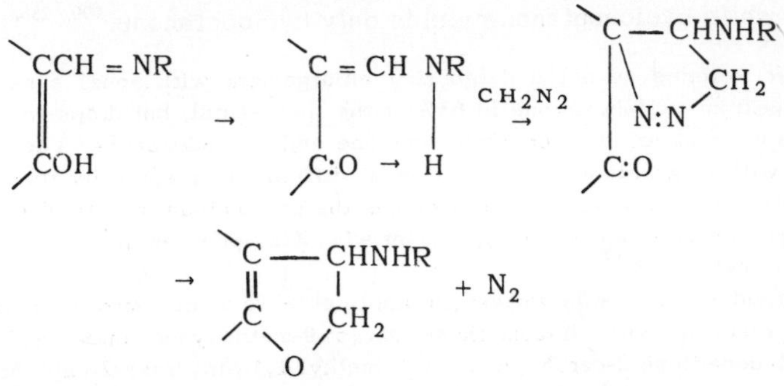

This reaction does not take place in ethereal solution in the absence of methyl alcohol. This fact is ascribed to the formation of a chelated ring

$$\begin{array}{cc} -C.CH{:}N.R & \diagdown C{:}CH.NR \\ \| \quad \swarrow \quad \text{or} & | \quad | \\ -C\ O\ H & {}_{\diagup}C{:}O \rightarrow H \end{array}$$

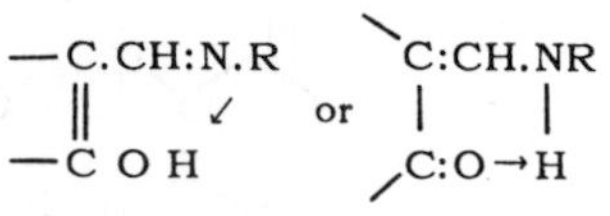

When alcohol is present, the chelate ring is destroyed forming a keto compound,

$$\begin{array}{c} \diagdown C{:}CHNHR \\ | \\ {}_{\diagup}CO \end{array}$$

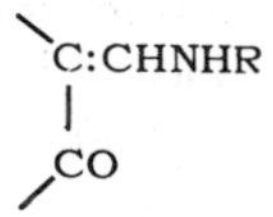

which reacts with diazomethane.

Aliphatic diazo compounds react energetically with *ketenes*, $RR_2C{:}CO$. Addition takes place either at the C–C double bond, or more readily at the carbonyl group. Unstable addition products are first formed and change to derivatives of cyclopropanol or ethylene oxide with cleavage of nitrogen:[194]

$$(C_6H_5)_2C = CO + N_2CHCOOR \rightarrow \left[\begin{array}{c} (C_6H_5)_2\ C \text{---} CO \\ | \quad \diagdown CHCOOR \\ N = N \diagup \end{array} \right]$$

$$\rightarrow \begin{array}{c} (C_6H_5)_2C \text{---} COH \\ \diagdown \quad \diagup\!\!/ \\ C.COOR \end{array} + N_2$$

$$(C_6H_5)_2C = CO + N_2CHCOOR \rightarrow \left[\begin{array}{c} (C_6H_5)_2C = C \text{---} O \\ | \quad | \\ N \quad CHCOOR \\ \diagdown_N \diagup \end{array} \right]$$

$$\rightarrow \quad (C_6H_5)_2C = C \overset{O}{\overset{\diagup \diagdown}{\text{---}}} CHCOOR + N_2$$

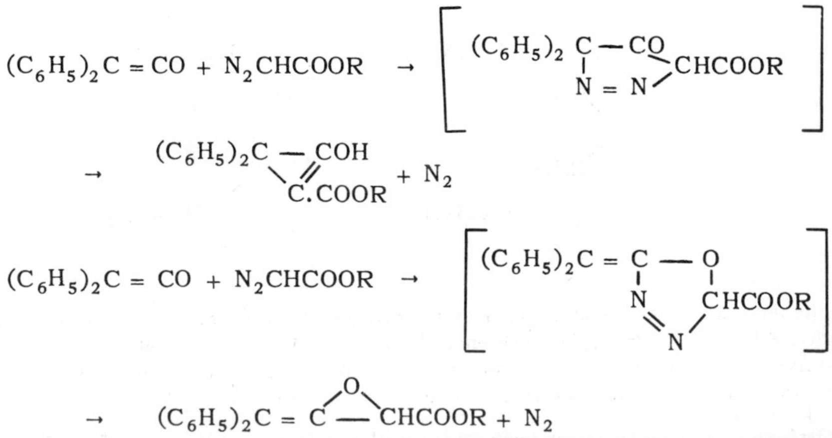

While ketones do not react with many aliphatic diazo compounds, thioketones, such as thiobenzophenone, react with diphenyldiazomethane with the formation of phenyl ethylene sulfides: [195]

$$(C_6H_5)_2CS + N_2C(C_6H_5)_2 \rightarrow (C_6H_5)_2\underset{\underset{S.N:N}{|\quad\quad|}}{C\!-\!C}(C_6H_5)_2$$

$$(C_6H_5)_2\underset{S}{C\!-\!C}(C_6H_5)_2 + N_2$$

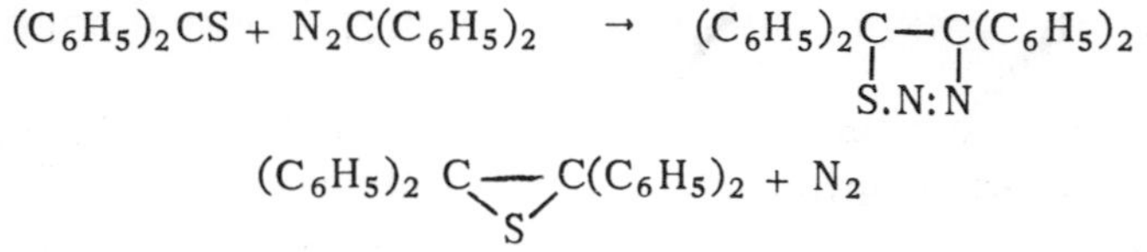

These sulfides lose sulfur on heating and are thereby converted to ethylene derivatives:

$$(C_6H_5)_2\underset{S}{C\!-\!C}(C_6H_5)_2 \rightarrow (C_6H_5)_2C = C(C_6H_5)_2 + S$$

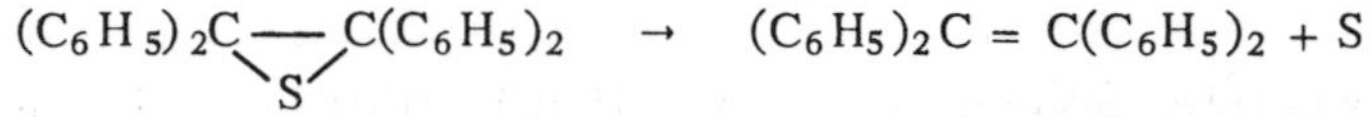

Thiobenzophenone reacts with diazomethane to give

$$(C_6H_5)_2\underset{\underset{\underset{CH_2}{\diagdown\quad\diagup}}{S\quad\quad S}}{C\!-\!-\!-\!-\!C}(C_6H_5)_2$$

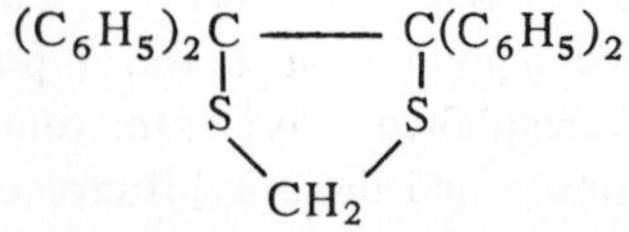

Diphenylenediazomethane and phenyldiazomethane react readily in this manner, but diazoacetic ester and phenylbenzoyldiazomethane react slowly, while diazomalonic ester and benzoyldiazoacetic ester do not react. Thiobenzoic ester, thiobenzanilide and thiourea do not react with diazo compounds.

Phenyl isothiocyanate reacts with diazomethane to form phenylaminothiodiazole, $C_6H_5NH\overline{C = CHN = N}S$. In contrast to other thiodiazoles, this compound is stable. [196]

Aliphatic diazo compounds add at *double* and *triple bonds*. Ethylene, tolan and stilbene do not react with diazomethane, though acetylene combines with the compound readily forming pyrazole: [197]

$$HC\!:\!CH + H_2CN_2 \rightarrow \overline{CH = CHNHN = CH}$$

Reaction with ethylenic compounds produces pyrazoline derivatives.

Diazomethane and diazoacetic ester combine with *unsaturated carboxylic acids* to form pyrazoline carboxylic acids: [198]

$$RCH = CHCOOC_2H_5 + N_2CHCOOC_2H_5$$

$$\rightarrow \overline{RCH\!-\!CH(COOC_2H_5)NHN = CCOOC_2H_5}$$

The addition of diazomethane to α, β-unsaturated esters and ketones proceeds so that the methylene group becomes attached to the β-carbon atom, ethyl acrylate giving, for example, $CH_2CH = \overline{NNHCHCOOC_2H_5}$ [240]. Diphenyldiazomethane and diethyl furmarate yield the compound

$$C_2H_5OCOCHC(COOC_2H_5) = \overline{NNHC(C_6H_5)_2}$$

These compounds lose nitrogen when heated and give cyclopropane derivatives:

$$\overline{RCHCH(COOC_2H_5)} = NNHCCOOC_2H_5 \quad \rightarrow \quad \overline{RCHCH(COOC_2H_5)CHCOOC_2H_5}$$

The reaction of tetrolic ester, $CH_3C\dot{:}CCOOC_2H_5$, with diazoacetic ester results in the formation of 4-methylpyrazole-3,5-dicarboxylic diethyl ester,[199]

$$\overline{C_2H_5OCOC:C(CH_3)C(COOC_2H_5):NNH.}$$

Conjugated dienes in general add diazomethane at 1,2-positions, butadiene

giving, for example, 5-vinylpyrazoline, $CH_2:CH\overline{CHCHNHN:CHCH_2}$ and 5,5'-bi-

pyrazoline, $\overline{CH_2CH:NNHCH}\overline{CHCHNHN:CHCH_2}$.[241] Conjugated systems bearing negative groups add diazo compounds at 1 and 4 positions with a shift of the double bond, isodehydroapocamphoric ethyl ester resulting, for example, through the reaction of diethyl muconate and dimethyldiazomethane:[200]

$$C_2H_5OCOCH = CHCH = CHCOOC_2H_5 + N_2C(CH_3)_2$$

$$\rightarrow \quad C_2H_5OCO\overline{CHC(CH_3)_2CH(COOC_2H_5)CH} = CH + N_2$$

Diazo compounds add at enolic double bonds. For example, malonic ester reacting with diazoacetic ester gives 4-hydroxypyrazole-3,5-dicarboxylic ester,

$$C_2H_5OCO\overline{C:C(OH)C(COOC_2H_5):NNH}$$

in 25% yield.[201] Quinones also yield pyrazoline derivatives.[202]

Diazoacetic ester reacts with *aromatic hydrocarbons* on heating to form bicyclic systems.[203] Norcaradiene carboxylic ester is obtained, for example, by reaction with benzene:

$$C_6H_6 + N_2CHCOOC_2H_5 \quad \rightarrow \quad
\begin{array}{c}
CH = CH.CH \\
| \qquad\qquad | \qquad\diagdown \\
\qquad\qquad\qquad CHCOOC_2H_5 + N_2 \\
| \qquad\qquad | \qquad\diagup \\
CH = CH.CH
\end{array}$$

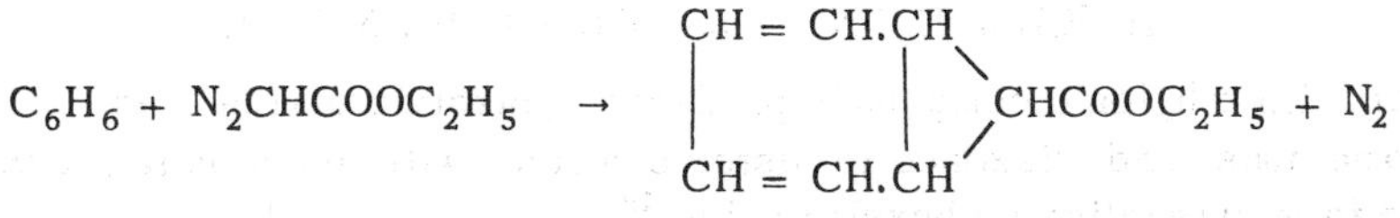

These compounds are oxidized to *trans*-1,2,3-cyclopropane tricarboxylic acid.

The reaction of diazoacetic ester with pyrrole or N-methylpyrrole in the presence of copper leads to the formation of α-acetic acid derivatives:[204]

$$\underset{NH}{\boxed{}} + N_2CHCOOC_2H_5 \quad \rightarrow \quad \underset{NH}{\boxed{}}-CH_2COOC_2H_5 \quad + N_2$$

2,4-Dimethylpyrrole and *benzoylphenyldiazomethane*, $C_6H_5COC(N_2)C_6H_5$, yield

the diphenylacetyl derivative, $HNC(CH_3) = CHC(CH_3) = \overline{CCOCH(C_6H_5)_2}$, presumably through the intermediate transformation of the diazo ketone to diphenylketene. Indole also reacts with diazoacetic ester, but in this case the acetic ester group enters the β-position giving indolyl-β-acetic ester.[205]

Diazomethane reacts with carbodianil, $C_6H_5N{:}C{:}C{:}NC_6H_5$, to form 1-phenyl-5-carbiminotriazole; carbodinaphthylimides react similarly, while the C:N bond in oximes is unreactive toward diazomethane.[206]

Nitroso compounds yield nitrones with diazo compounds:

$$RNO + R_2CN_2 \rightarrow \overline{RNON{:}NCR_2} \rightarrow RNO = CR_2$$

Nitrosoamines and nitrous esters do not give this reaction. Carbonyl substituted diazo compounds react less readily than diazo hydrocarbons.[207]

Diazomethane is capable of adding at the multiple bond of the cyano group; with cyanoformic ester triazole carboxylic ester,[208]

$$\overline{CH = C(COOC_2H_5)N = NNH}$$

is formed. Reacting with cyanogen in ethereal solution at -10°, diazomethane gives 1,2,3-triazole-1-nitrile.[209]

The reaction of diazomethane with o-nitrobenzaldehyde leads to the formation of nitraldin:[210]

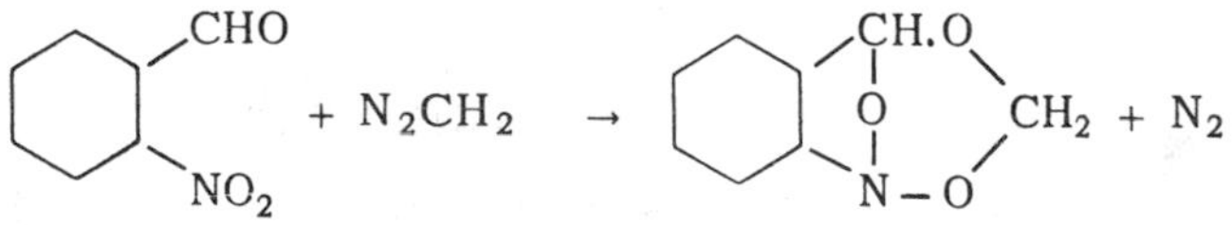

Diazomethane causes the cleavage of the acetyl group from its esters:[211]

$$HOCOC_6H_4OCOCH_3 \xrightarrow{N_2CH_2} HOCOC_6H_4OCH_3$$

Acetyl groups combined with amino groups are not thus replaced, although spirohydantoins form an exception.[212]

The heterocyclic azlactone ring is ruptured very readily by a methanolic solution of diazomethane, the process appearing to be a simple methanolysis, in which the diazomethane takes no part:

$$C_6H_5CH{:}\overline{CN{:}C(C_6H_5)OCO} \xrightarrow{CH_3OH} C_6H_5CH{:}C(COOCH_3)NHCOC_6H_5$$

Chlorophyll, phaeophorbid and other chlorophyll derivatives are similarly cleaved.[213]

ω-Diazo-o-nitroacetophenone treated with excess acetic acid is converted to N-hydroxyisatin:[214]

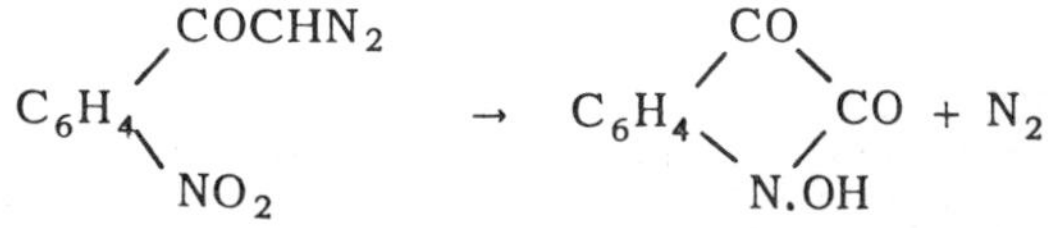

An exceptional behavior is shown by 3-methoxy-2-diazoacetonaphthalene;

treated with hydrogen chloride, this compound is transformed to β-benzocoumaranone:[215]

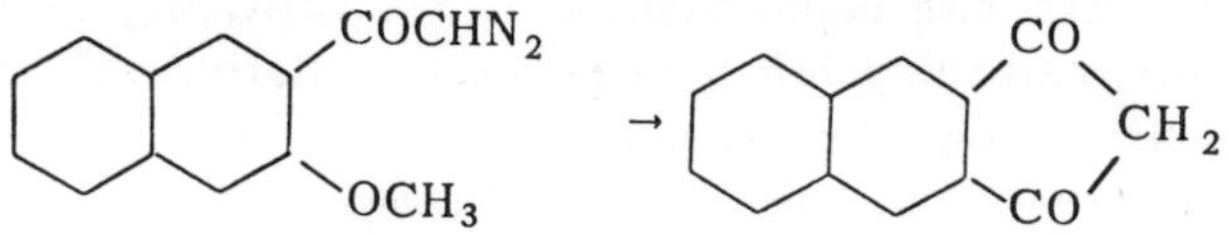

Reactions of Hydrazoic Acid

Hydrazoic acid reacts with hydrocyanic acid and cyanogen to form tetrazoles:[216]

$$HCN + HN_3 \rightarrow HN{:}CHN_3 \rightarrow \overline{CH{:}NN{:}NNH}$$

$$CNCN + HN_3 \rightarrow CN\overline{C{:}NNHN{:}N}$$

$$\xrightarrow{HN_3} \overline{N{:}NNHN = C}.\overline{C = NNHN = N}$$

Dicyandiamide gives 5-aminotetrazole in quantitative yield.[218] Methyl isocyanide gives 1-methyltetrazole:[217]

$$CH_3N{:}C + HN_3 \rightarrow CH_3\overline{NN{:}NN{:}CH}$$

Fulminic acid reacting at -12 to -5° with hydrazoic acid gives 1-hydroxytetrazole:[219]

$$HON = C + HN_3 \rightarrow HON{:}CHN_3 \rightarrow HO\overline{NN = NN = CH}$$

Nitriles, RCN, yield 5-aminotetrazoles:[220]

$$RCN \xrightarrow{HN_3} RN = C = NH \xrightarrow{HN_3} H_2NC({:}NR)N_3$$

$$\rightarrow H_2N\overline{C{:}NN{:}NNR}$$

Hydrazoic acid reacts with propiolic acid to form 1,2,3-triazole-4-carboxylic acid:[221]

$$CH{\vdots}CCOOH + HN_3 \rightarrow HOCO\overline{C = CHNHN = N}$$

References

1. Hofmann, *Ann.*, **73**, 91 (1850); **74**, 159 (1850); **78**, 253 (1851); **79**, 16 (1851); Malbot, *Ann. chim.*, (6) **13**, 451 (1888); Garner and Tyrer, *J. Chem. Soc.*, **109**, 174 (1916). Forgher, *J. Chem. Soc.*, **117**, 1351 (1920); Marvel *et al.*, *J. Am. Chem. Soc.*, **49**, 2299 (1927).
2. v. Braun *et al.*, *Ber.*, **70**, 979 (1937).
3. Brander, *Rec. trav. chim.*, **37**, 67 (1917).
4. Hickinbottom, *J. Chem. Soc.*, **1930**, 992; **1933**, 946.

5. Kraus and White, *J. Am. Chem. Soc.*, **45**, 768 (1923); White, *ibid.*, **45**, 779 (1923); White and Knight, *ibid.*, **45**, 1780 (1923); Kraus and Kawamura, *ibid.*, **45**, 2756 (1923); Dean and Berchet, *ibid.*, **52**, 2823 (1930).
6. Forneau and Pugel, *Bull soc. chim.*, (4) **31**, 424 (1922). Cf. Kötz and Merkel, *J. prakt. Chem.*, (2) **113**, 49 (1926).
7. Matheson and Humphries, *J. Chem. Soc.*, **1931**, 2514; Baker, *ibid.*, **1931**, 2416; **1932**, 1148.
8. Merck, *German patent* 273,323; Wernert and Brode, *J. Am. Chem. Soc.*, **54**, 4365 (1932).
9. Peacock, *J. Chem. Soc.*, **127**, 2177 (1925); *J. Phys. Chem.*, **30**, 673 (1926).
10. Fischer, *Ber.*, **32**, 459 (1899).
11. Adams and Segur, *J. Am. Chem. Soc.*, **45**, 785 (1923); Pierce and Adams, *ibid.*, **45**, 790 (1923); Nemirowsky, *J. prakt. Chem.*, (2) **31**, 173 (1885); Otto, *ibid.*, (2) **44**, 20 (1891); Johnson and Langley, *Am. Chem. J.*, **44**, 352 (1910); Dox and Yoder, *J. Am. Chem. Soc.*, **45**, 723 (1923).
12. Wohl, *Ber.*, **19**, 1840 (1886); Delépine, *Compt. rend.*, **120**, 501 (1895); **124**, 292 (1897); *Bull. soc. chim.*, (3) **17**, 290 (1897); Sommelet, *Compt. rend.*, **157**, 737 (1913); Grieswald, *Ber.*, **45**, 2571 (1912); Delépine and Jaffeux, *Bull. soc. chim.*, (4) **31**, 108 (1922).
13. Mannich and Hahn, *Ber.*, **44**, 1542 (1911); *German patent* 264,263.
14. Ullmann, *Ber.*, **38**, 2120 (1905); Wohl, *ibid.*, **39**, 1951 (1906); Goldberg, *ibid.*, **39**, 1691 (1906); **40**, 4541 (1907); *German patents* 185,663; 187,870; 202,170.
15. Ullmann and Wenner, *Ber.*, **33**, 2476 (1900); Eschweiler, *ibid.*, **38**, 880 (1905); Ullmann, *Ann.*, **327**, 104 (1903); Ullmann and Wenner, *ibid.*, **327**, 120 (1903); Földi, *Ber.*, **55**, 1535 (1922); Ferns and Lapworth, *J. Chem. Soc.*, **101**, 281 (1921).
16. Passon, *Ber.*, **24**, 1678 (1891).
17. Wallach and Schulze, *ibid.*, **14**, 421 (1881).
18. Gabriel *et al.*, *Ber.*, **20**, 2224 (1887); **21**, 566, 2669 (1888); **20**, 2869 (1887); **23**, 1771 (1890); **24**, 3104 (1891); **25**, 3056 (1892); **26**, 2197 (1893); **35**, 3805 (1902); Seitz, *ibid.*, **24**, 2624 (1891); Lohmann, *ibid.*, **24**, 2631 (1891); Neumann, *ibid.*, **23**, 994 (1890).
19. Ing and Manske, *J. Chem. Soc.*, **1926**, 2348; Putokin, *C. A.* **24**, 3756 (1930).
20. Posner, *Ber.*, **26**, 1858 (1893).
21. Michels, *ibid.*, **25**, 3048 (1892); Posner, *ibid.*, **26**, 1858 (1893).
22. Graebe and Pictet, *Ber.*, **17**, 1174 (1884); Neumann, *ibid.*, **23**, 994 (1890); Gabriel, *ibid.*, **20**, 2224 (1887); **21**, 566 (1888); **22**, 1137 (1889); **24**, 3104 (1891); **42**, 4051 (1910); Seitz, *ibid.*, **24**, 2624 (1891); Reissert, *ibid.*, **26**, 2138 (1893); Gabriel and Weiner, *ibid.*, **21**, 2669 (1888); Marckwald, *ibid.*, **37**, 1047 (1904); v. Braun, *ibid.*, **37**, 3584 (1904); Strassmann, *ibid.*, **21**, 576 (1888); Brömme, *ibid.*, **21**, 2700 (1888); Posner, *ibid.*, **26**, 1856 (1893); Lustig, *ibid.*, **28**, 2986 (1895); Landau, *ibid.*, **25**, 3011 (1892); Hopkins, *J. Am. Chem. Soc.*, **45**, 541 (1923).
23. Gabriel, *Ber.*, **20**, 2224 (1887); **22**, 3337 (1889); **23**, 1771 (1890); **42**, 1252, *Anm.*, (1909); Albert, *ibid.*, **42**, 557 (1901); Reinglass, *ibid.*, **24**, 2418 (1891); Ehrlich, *ibid.*, **34**, 3366 (1901); Günther, *ibid.*, **23**, 1058 (1890); Banse, *ibid.*, **27**, 2165 (1894).
24. Dersin, *Ber.*, **54**, 3158 (1921); Goedeckemeyer, *ibid.*, **21**, 2684 (1888); Gabriel and Pinkus, *ibid.*, **26**, 2198 (1893); Gabriel, *ibid.*, **22**, 224 (1889); **47**, 3028 (1914); Gabriel and Posner, *ibid.*, **27**, 1042 (1894); Posner, *ibid.*, **32**, 1242 (1899); Posner and Rohde, *ibid.*, **42**, 3241 (1909); Gabriel and Michels, *ibid.*, **25**, 3056 (1892); Gabriel and Ohle, *Ber.*, **50**, 804 (1917); Philipps and Seka, *Ann.*, **435**, 88 (1923); Schreiber, *Ber.*, **24**, 170 (1891); Lohmann, *ibid.*, **24**, 2633 (1891); Schrader, *ibid.*, **29**, 2399 (1896).
25. Gabriel and Colman, *Ber.*, **35**, 3805 (1902); Alexander, *Monatsh.*, **25**, 1074 (1905); Posner and Rohde, *Ber.*, **42** 3241 (1909); Schmidt, *ibid.*, **22**, 3249 (1889); Neumann, *ibid.*, **23**, 994 (1890); McKenzie and Barrow, *J. Chem. Soc.*, **103**, 1331 (1913); Ryan, *Ber.*, **31**, 2133 (1898); Rüdenburg, *ibid.*, **46**, 3555 (1913); Bargellini and Settimj, *Gazz. chim. ital.*, **53**, 601 (1923).
26. Goedeckemeyer, *Ber.*, **21**, 2684 (1888); Gabriel and Pinkus, *ibid.*, **26**, 2198 (1893); Gabriel and Kroseberg, *ibid.*, **22**, 426 (1889); Gabriel and Colman, *ibid.*, **33**, 983, 994 (1900); Gabriel, *ibid.*, **38**, 3413 (1905); Sörensen, *Compt. rend. des trav. lab, Carlsberg, Ser. chim.*, **6**, 1-63 (1903).
27. Gabriel, *Ber.*, **20**, 2224 (1887); Gabriel and Hendess, *ibid.*, **20**, 2869 (1887); Salkowski, *ibid.*, **22**, 2142 (1889); Hafner, *ibid.*, **23**, 337 (1890); Schmidt, *ibid.*, **22**, 3249 (1889).
28. Schneider, *et. al.*, *Ann.*, **386**, 332 (1912).
29. Gabriel, *Ber.*, **22**, 1138 (1889); **24**, 1110 (1891); Gabriel and Lauer, *ibid.*, **23**, 88 (1890).
30. Gabriel, *Ber.*, **22**, 2223 (1889); **24**, 1120 (1891); Ristenpart, *ibid.*, **29**, 2526 (1896); Fränkel, *ibid.*, **30**, 2497 (1897); Hirsch, *ibid.*, **23**, 964 (1890); Baringer, *ibid.*, **23**, 1003 (1890); Goldenring, *ibid.*, **23**, 1168 (1890); Newmann, *ibid.*, **24**, 2191 (1891); Gabriel and Lauer, *ibid.*, **23**, 89 (1890); Schmidt, *ibid.*, **22**, 3256 (1889); Schreiber, *ibid.*, **24**, 189 (1891); Lohmann, *ibid.*, **24**, 2631 (1891); Schrader, *ibid.*, **29**, 2401 (1896); Diefenbach, *ibid.*, **27**, 928 (1894), Gabriel and Michels, *ibid.*, **25**, 3056 (1892).
31. Aschan, *Ber.*, **24**, 2450 (1891); Manasse, *ibid.*, **35**, 1367 (1902).
32. Key, *Ber.*, **26**, 2848 (1893).

33. Hepp, *Ber.*, **10**, 328 (1877); Paul and Otten, *ibid.*, **23**, 2587 (1890); Hickinbottom, *J. Chem. Soc.*, **1933**, 946.
34. Tiherley, *J. Chem. Soc.*, **79**, 399 (1901).
35. Merz and Gasiorowski, *Ber.*, **17**, 623, 640 (1884).
36. Hill and Donleavy, *J. Ind. Eng. Chem.*, **13**, 504 (1921); Johnson, Hill and Donleavy, *ibid.*, **12**, 636 (1920).
37. Brown and Rist, *J. Phys. Chem.*, **28**, 1067 (1924); Morgan and Pratt, *Brit. Patent* 396,760; Opotzki and Dranowski *Chem. Zentr.*, **1938 II**, 2256, *Ukrainski chemitschri Shurnal* **11**, 446 (1938); Guyot and Fournier, *Compt. rend.*, **189**, 927 (1929); *Bull soc. chim.*, (4) **47**, 203 (1930); Winans and Adkins, *J. Am. Chem. Soc.*, **54**, 306 (1932).
38. Briner and Gandillon, *Helv. Chim. Acta*, **14**, 1283 (1931).
39. Brochet and Cambier, *Bull. soc. chim.*, (3) **13**, 533 (1895); Gilmann and Blatt, *Organic Syntheses*, Coll. vol. 1, p 347 (1941); Sharp and Salomon, *J. Chem. Soc.*, **1931**, 1477.
40. Werner, *J. Chem. Soc.*, **111**, 850 (1917).
41. Korschun and Roll, *Bull. soc. chim.*, (4) **33**, 1106 (1923).
42. Leuckart *et al.*, *Ber.*, **18**, 2341 (1885); **19**, 2128 (1886); **20**, 104 (1887); **22**, 1409, 1851 (1889); Wallach *et al.*, *ibid.*, **24**, 3992 (1891); *Ann.*, **269**, 347 (1892); **276**, 306 (1893); **300**, 283 (1898); **312**, 188 (1900); **343**, 54 (1905); Sommelet and Ferrand, *Bull. soc. chim.*, (4) **25**, 457 (1919); (4) **35**, 446 (1924); Clark, Gillespie and Weisshaus, *J. Am. Chem. Soc.*, **55**, 4571 (1933); Ingrsoll *et al.*, *ibid.*, **58**, 1180 (1936); Johns and Burch, *ibid.*, **60**, 919 (1938); Novelli, *ibid.*, **61**, 520 (1939); Read *et al.*, *J. Chem. Soc.*, **1926**, 2217; **1934**, 231; Blatt, *Organic Syntheses*, Coll. vol. II, p. 28, 503 (1943); Crossley and Moore, *J. Org. Chem.*, **9**, 529 (1944); Doeuvre and Courtois, *Bull. soc. chim.*, (5) **11**, 545 (1944); Goodson *et al.*, *J. Am. Chem. Soc.*, **68**, 2174 (1946); Borrows *et al.*, *J. Chem. Soc.*, **1947**, 197; Alexander and Wildman, *J. Am. Chem. Soc.*, **70**, 1187 (1948); Staple and Wagner, *J. Org. Chem.*, **14**, 559 (1949); *Mechanism.* Pollard and Young, *J. Org. Chem.*, **16**, 661 (1951).
43. Law, *J. Chem. Soc.*, **101**, 154 (1912).
44. Morgan, *British Patent* 102,834.
45. Stoermer and v. Lepel, *Ber.*, **29**, 2110 (1896).
46. Tafel, *Ber.*, **19**, 1925 (1886); **20**, 505 (1887); **22**, 1854 (1889); Wallach, Hüttner and Altenburg, *Ann.*, **343**, 54 (1905); Ishizaka, *Ber.*, **47**, 2456 (1914).
47. Goldschmidt, *Ber.*, **19**, 3232 (1886); **20**, 728 (1887); Noyes, *Am. Chem. J.*, **15**, 539 (1893); Kann and Tafel, *Ber.*, **27**, 2307 *Anm.* (1894); Menschutkin, *Chem. Zentr.* **1898** I. 702.
48. Mailhe, *Compt. rend.*, **141**, 113 (1905).
49. Guerbet, *J. Pharm. Chim.*, (6) **10**, 160 (1899), *Compt rend.*, **129**, 61 (1899); *Bull. soc. chim.*, (3) **21**, 778 (1899).
50. Kindler, *Ann.*, **431**, 190 (1923).
51. Ladenburg, *Ber.*, **18**, 2957 (1885); **19**, 783 (1886); Tafel, *ibid.*, **22**, 1854 (1889).
52. Meyer *et al. Ber.*, **10**, 131 (1877); v. Braun *et al.*, *ibid.*, **56**, 1988 (1923); Mendius, *Ann.*, **121**, 129 (1862).
53. Decker and Becker, *Ann.*, **395**, 362 (1913); Hamilton and Robinson, *J. Chem. Soc.*, **109**, 1033 (1916).
54. Baeyer and Caro, *Ber.*, **7**, 964 (1877); Menschutkin, *J. Russ. Phys.-Chem. Soc.*, **30**, 251 (1898).
55. Schigern Komatsu, *Mem. Coll. Sci. Kyoto Imp. Univ.*, **3**, 371 (1912); Wedekind, *Ann.*, **318**, 90 (1901); Menschutkin, *Ber.*, **28**, 1398 (1895); *Z. physik. Chem.*, **17**, 193, 233 (1895); Fawcett and Gibson, *J. Chem. Soc.*, **1934**, 396; Macovski, *Bull. soc. chim.*, (5) **3**, 498 (1936); Westphal *et al.*, *Ber.*, **73B**, 1002, 1109 (1940); Niederl *et al.*, *J. Am. Chem. Soc.*, **63**, 1476, 3534 (1941); **66**, 840, 844 (1944); Lawrence *et al.*, *J. Am. Pharm. Assoc. Sci. Ed.*, **36**, 353 (1947); *U.S. patents* 2,048,885 (1936); 2,152,047 (1939); 2,191,922 (1940); 2,317,999 (1943); *French patent* 842,299 (1939).
56. Vincent and Chappius, *Compt. rend.*, **102**, 436 (1886).
57. Preston and Jones, *J. Chem. Soc.*, **101**, 1931 (1912).
58. Weltzien, *Ann.*, **91**, 33 (1854); **99**, 1 (1856); Müller, *ibid.*, **108**, 1 (1858); Dobbin and Masson, *J. Chem. Soc.*, **49**, 846 (1886); Geuther, *Ann.*, **240**, 66 (1887); Strömholm, *J. prakt. Chem.*, (2) **67**, 345 (1903).
59. Fischer and Windaus, *Ber.*, **33**, 345, 1967 (1900); Hofmann, *ibid.*, **18**, 1824 (1885); **5**, 718 (1872).
60. Thomas, *J. Chem. Soc.*, **103**, 595 (1913). *Cf.* Menschutkin, *Ber.*, **28**, 1398 (1895); **30**, 2775, 2966 (1897); **38**, 2465 (1905); Wedekind, *Ann.*, **318**, 90 (1901); *Ber.*, **32**, 511 (1899).
61. v. Braun *et al.*, *Ber.*, **46**, 3473 (1913); **49**, 1101 (1916); **50**, 1651 (1917).
62. v. Braun *et al.*, *Ber.*, **51**, 282 (1918).
63. Menschutkin, *Z. physik. Chem.*, **17**, 227 (1895); Wedekind, *Ann.*, **318**, 90 (1901).
64. Emde, *Arch. Pharm.*, **249**, 93 (1911).
65. Wedekind and Meyer, *Ber.*, **42**, 303 (1909).
66. Wedekind and Goost, *ibid.*, **52**, 446 (1919).
67. Kehrmann *et al. ibid.*, **46**, 343, 2804, 2820 (1913); **47**, 279, 1886 (1914); **48**, 1932 (1915); **49**, 1207 (1916); *Helv. Chim. Acta*, **1**, 275 (1918).

68. Kehrmann *et al.*, *Ber.*, **29**, 2316, 2968 (1896); **30**, 2620 (1897); **47**, 1886 (1914); *Ann.*, **322**, 67 (1902); *Helv. Chim. Acta*, **1**, 275 (1918).
69. Ullmann, *Ann.*, **327**, 111 (1907).
70. Walker and Johnson, *J. Chem. Soc.*, **87**, 956 (1905).
71. Crichton, *ibid.*, **91**, 1793 (1907).
72. Nölting, *Ber.*, **24**, 563 (1891).
73. v. Braun and Anton, *ibid.*, **64**, 2865 (1931).
74. Walker and Johnston, *J. Chem. Soc.*, **87**, 961 (1905); Bredig, *Z. physik. Chem.*, **13**, 300 (1894).
75. Schlenk and Holtz, *Ber.*, **49**, 604 (1916); **50**, 274, 276 (1917).
76. Vorländer and Nolte, *ibid.*, **46**, 3212 (1913); Kaufmann and Vorländer, *ibid.*, **43**, 2735 (1910).
77. Feer and Koenigs, *ibid.*, **18**, 2393 (1885); Hofmann, *ibid.*, **14**, 660 (1881); v. Braun, *ibid.*, **42**, 2532 (1909).
78. Willstätter, *Ann.*, **317**, 230 (1901); Willstätter and Waser, *Ber.*, **44**, 3455 (1911).
79. Schotten, *Ber.*, **15**, 421 (1882).
80. Hofmann, *Ann.*, **78**, 268 (1851); Lawson and Collie, *J. Chem. Soc.*, **53**, 624 (1888); Meyer and Lecco, *Ann.*, **180**, 184 (1876); Lossen, *ibid.*, **181**, 377 (1876).
81 v. Braun, *Ann.*, **382**, 5 (1911). *Cf.* Ingold *et al.*, *J. Chem. Soc.*, **1927**, 997; **1928**, 3125; **1929**, 2357; **1933**, 66, 69, 523, 526.
82. Hofmann, *Ber.*, **3**, 109, 776 (1870); **8**, 760 (1875); Wallach, *Ann.*, **184**, 64 (1877).
83. Hinsberg and Kessler, *Ber.*, **38**, 908 (1905); Mulder, *Rec. trav. chim.*, **25**, 104 (1906).
84. Solonina, *J. Russ. Phys.-Chem. Soc.*, **29**, 405 (1897); **31**, 540 (1899).
85. Willstätter and Lessing., *Ber.*, **33**, 557 (1900).
86. Hofmann, *ibid.*, **8**, 105, 461 (1875); **14**, 2754 (1881); **15**, 985, 1290 (1882); Weith, *ibid.*, **8**, 461 (1875); Grodzki, *ibid.*, **14**, 2754 (1881). *Cf. U.S. patent* 1,782,112 (1925).
87. Ostwald, *J. prakt. Chem.*, (2) **33**, 352, (1886); Vörlander, *Ann.*, **345**, 256 (1906); *Z. physik. Chem.*, **77**, 385 (1911); Moore and Winmill, *J. Chem. Soc.*, **101**, 1635 (1912).
88. Neogi, *J. Chem. Soc.*, **105**, 1270 (1914).
89. Freund and Schönfeld, *Ber.*, **24**, 3350 (1891); Erdmann, *ibid.*, **26**, 2440 (1893). Wallach, *Ann.*, **353**, 331 (1907); Crichton, *J. Chem. Soc.*, **91**, 1793 (1907).
90. Fischer and Diepolder, *Ann.*, **286**, 163 (1895).
91. v. Braun *et al.*, *Ber.*, **51**, 282 (1918); Friedländer, *Monatsh.*, **19**, 627 (1898); Houben, *Ber.*, **42**, 3188 (1909).
92. Hickinbottom, *J. Chem. Soc.*, **1933**, 946.
93. Demjanoff and Luschnitcoff, *J. Russ. Phys.-Chem. Soc.*, **35**, 26 (1903); Demjanoff, *Ber.*, **40**, 4961 (1907); Wallach, *Ann.*, **353**, 325 (1907); Ruzicka and Brugge, *Helv. Chim. Acta*, **9**, 399 (1926).
94. Ruzicka and Brugge, *l. c.*
95. Kischner, *J. Russ. Phys.-Chem. Soc.*, **37**, 304 (1905).
96. Bamberger, *Ber.*, **35**, 4293 (1902). *Cf.* Bamberger and Seligman, *ibid.*, **35**, 4299 (1902).
97. Bamberger and Seligmann, *ibid.*, **36**, 685 (1903).
98. D'Ans and Kneip, *Ber.*, **48**, 1144 (1915); Witt and Kopetschni, *ibid.*, **45**, 1134 (1912); Meisenheimer and Hesse, *ibid.*, **52**, 1162 (1919); Fischer and Trost, *ibid.*, **26**, 3083 (1893).
99. *Biochem. Z.* **71**, 169.
100. Dunstan and Goulding, *J. Chem. Soc.*, **75**, 1004 (1899); Bamberger *et al.*, *Ber.*, **32**, 342, 1882 (1899); **34**, 16 (1901); **39**, 4285 (1906); Sudborough and Hibbert, *J. Chem. Soc.*, **95**, 477 (1909). Hibbert and Wise, *ibid.*, **101**, 341 (1912). *Cf.* Meisenheimer, *Ber.*, **52**, 1671 (1919).
101. Wallach and Claisen, *Ber.*, **8**, 1237 (1875); Vorländer, *Ann.*, **345**, 251 (1906); deHaas, *Rec. trav. chim.*, **14**, 166 (1895); Vorlaender, *Ber.*, **34**, 1637 (1901); Ginzberg, *ibid.*, **36**, 2703 (1903).
102. Strecker *et al.*, *Ber.*, **53**, 2112 (1920); **54**, 2701 (1921).
103. Etard and Vila, *Compt. rend.*, **135**, 699 (1902); Biehringer and Busch, *Ber.*, **36**, 139 (1903).
104. Sudborough, *J. Chem. Soc.*, **79**, 534 (1901).
105. Smith and Orton, *ibid.*, **93**, 1242 (1908); Orton, *ibid.*, **81**, 495 (1902).
106. Dennstedt and Zimmermann, *Ber.*, **19**, 75 (1886); Freudenberg and Peters, *ibid.*, **52**, 1463 (1919).
107. Freudenberg and Peters, *l. c.*, Dehn, *J. Am. Chem. Soc.*, **34**, 1399 (1912); Dehn and Ball, *ibid.*, **36**, 2091 (1914); Vorländer and Nolte, *Ber.*, **46**, 3212 (1913).
108. Hofmann, *Ber.*, **14**, 494, 661 (1881); Ladenburg, *ibid.*, **16**, 2058 (1883); etc; Merling, *ibid.*, **17**, 2139 (1884); **19**, 2628 (1886); *Ann.*, **264**, 310 (1891); *Ber.*, **19**, 2629 (1886); Howard and Roser, *ibid.*, **19**, 1596 (1886); Eykman, *ibid.*, **25**, 3071 (1892); Willstätter, *ibid.*, **33**, 365 (1900), etc.; Merling, *ibid.*, **24**, 3108 (1891); *Ann.*, **264**, 314 (1891); Knorr and Schneider, *Ber.*, **39**, 1414 (1906), etc.; Pschorr and Einbeck, *ibid.*, **40**, 1908 (1907); Pschorr, *ibid.*, **40**, 1984 (1907), etc.; Braun, *ibid.*, **42**, 2532 (1909); Polonovski, *Bull. soc. chim.*, (4) **23**, 335 (1918).
109. v. Braun, *Ber.*, **42**, 2533 (1909).
110. v. Braun, *ibid.*, **33**, 1438, 2728, 2734 (1900); **36**, 2286, 2651 (1903); v. Braun and Schwarz, *ibid.*, **35**, 1279 (1902); v. Braun, *ibid.*, **40**, 3933 (1907); **43**, 3209 (1910). Migrdichian, *The Chemistry of Organic Cyanogen Compounds*, (1947) p. 107.

111. v. Braun and Schwarz, *Ber.*, **35**, 1280 (1902).
112. v. Braun et al., *Ber.*, **33**, 1438, 2734 (1900); **35**, 1265 (1923); **40**, 3914 (1907); **42**, 2035, 2219 (1909); **43**, 1353, 3209 (1910); **56**, 2165 (1923); *Ann.*, **382**, 1 (1911); **445**, 201 (1925); Scholl and Nörr, *Ber.*, **33**, 1550 (1900).
113. v. Braun, *Ber.*, **40**, 3916 (1907); **49**, 2624 (1916); **42**, 2221 (1909); **49**, 2629 (1916).
114. v. Braun *et al.*, *Ber.*, **37**, 2812, 2915, 3210, 3583, 4581, 4723 (1904); **44**, 1464 (1911); Wallach, *Ann.*, **184**, 1 (1876); Pechmann, *Ber.*, **33**, 611 (1900); Ley and Holzweissig, *ibid.*, **36**, 19 (1903).
115. v. Braun *et al.*, *Ber.*, **37**, 2818, 2915, 3583, 4581, 4723 (1904); **38**, 179 (1905); **42**, 1429 (1909); **39**, 4119, 4365 (1906).
116. v. Braun, *Ber.*, **37**, 2915 (1904).
117. Ciamician and Dennstedt, *ibid.*, **17**, 533 (1884).
118. Meisenheimer, *ibid.*, **46**, 1148 (1913).
119. Willstätter and Iglauer, *ibid.*, **33**, 1636 (1900); Meisenheimer, *ibid.*, **46**, 1148 (1913).
120. Schmidt *et al.*, *Ber.*, **53**, 1537 (1920); **54**, 1414 (1921).
121. Solonia, *J. Russ. Phys.-Chem. Soc.*, **30**, 431 (1898).
122. Wurtz, *Ann.*, **76**, 319, 327 (1850); Tcherniac, *Ber.*, **9**, 143 (1876); **32**, 3582 (1899). *Cf.* Palomaa, *ibid.*, **32**, 3343 (1899); Köhler, *ibid.*, **12**, 770 (1879); Hofmann, *ibid.*, **15**, 767 (1882); **16**, 558 (1883); Raschig, *Ann.*, **230**, 222 (1885); Pierson and Heumann, *Ber.*, **16**, 1047 (1883); Berg, *Compt. rend.*, **110**, 862 (1890); **114**, 483, 1379 (1892); **116**, 327, 887 (1893), *Bull. soc. chim.*, (3) **3**, 685 (1890); **17**, 297 (1897); *Ann. chim.*, (7) **3**, 289 (1894).
123. Cain, *Ber.*, **38**, 2715 (1905); Norris, *ibid.*, **38**, 3904 (1905).
124. Datta, *J. Am. Chem. Soc.*, **34**, 1613 (1912).
125. Datta and Gupta, *ibid.*, **36**, 386 (1914).
126. Harries, *Ber.*, **31**, 56 (1889).
127. Harries, *ibid.*, **27**, 2279 (1894); Harries and Haga, *ibid.*, **31**, 62 (1898); Knorr and Köhler, *ibid.*, **39**, 3261 (1906); Thiele, *ibid.*, **42**, 2576 (1909).
128. Stollé, *Ber.*, **34**, 3268 (1901); *J. prakt. Chem.*, (2) **66**, 334 (1902).
129. Fischer, *Ann.*, **199**, 308 (1879); Renouf, *Ber.*, **13**, 2171 (1880); Thiele and Meyer, *ibid.*, **29**, 961 (1896); v. Pechmann, *ibid.*, **28**, 859 (1895); Backer, *Rec. trav. chim.*, **31**, 142 (1912).
130. Fischer, *Ann.*, **199**, 283 (1879); *Ber.*, **17**, 284 (1884); v. Bruning, *Ann.*, **253**, 5 (1889).
131. Knorr *et al.*, *Ber.*, **39**, 3257 (1906); **42**, 3523 (1909).
132. Dunstan and Goulding, *J. Chem. Soc.*, **75**, 802 (1899); Hantzsch and Hilland, *Ber.*, **31**, 2065 (1898); Lachman, *ibid.*, **33**, 1025 (1900).
133. Dunstan and Goulding, *Chem. News*, **69**, 308 (1894); **73**, 196 (1896); *J. Chem. Soc.*, **69**, 839 (1896); **75**, 792 (1899); Hantzsch and Hilland, *Ber.*, **31**, 2061 (1898).
134. Lossen, *Ann.*, **252**, 230 (1889).
135. Dittrich, *Ber.*, **23**, 599, 3597 (1890); Goldschmidt and Kjellin, *ibid.*, **24**, 2552 (1891); Kjellin, *ibid.*, **26** 2377 (1893); **27**, 587 (1894); 30 1891 (1897); Brühl, *ibid.*, **27**, 805 (1894); **26**, 2514 (1893).
136. Lossen and Zanni, *Ann.*, **182**, 223 (1876); Gürke, *ibid.*, **205**, 273 (1880); Lossen, *ibid.*, **252**, 222 (1889).
137. Mamlock and Wolffenstein, *Ber.*, **34**, 2499 (1901).
138. Bamberger and Seligman, *ibid.*, **36**, 701 (1903).
139. Bamberger, *ibid.*, **27**, 1350 (1894); Majert, *Ann.*, **362**, 204 (1909).
140. Pierron, *Bull. soc. chim.*, (3) **21**, 780 (1899).
141. Bewad, *J. prakt. Chem.*, (2) **63**, 94, 193 (1901); *Ber.*, **40**, 3065 (1907); Lachman, *ibid.*, **33**, 1030 (1900); Mamlock and Wolfenstein, *ibid.*, **34**, 2499 (1901); Dunstan and Goulding, *J. Chem. Soc.*, **79**, 641 (1901).
142. Lachman, *Ber.*, **33**, 1022 (1900).
143. Wieland, *ibid.*, **36**, 2315 (1903).
144. Fried and Ederfeld, *J. Org. Chem.*, **6**, 577 (1941).
145. Meisenheimer, *Ann.*, **397**, 273 (1913).
146. Meisenheimer, et al., *Ber.*, **41**, 3966 (1908) *Ann.*, **385**, 117 (1911); **428**, 252 (1922); **449**, 188 (1926).
147. Hofmann, *Ber.*, **4**, 430 (1871).
148. Meisenheimer *et al.*, *Ann.*, **449**, 213 (1926).
149. Curtius, *Z. angew. Chem.*, **24**, 2 (1911); Curtius and Muller, *Ber.*, **37**, 1264 (1904). *Cf.* Angeli, *ibid.*, **26**, 1715 (1893).
150. Curtius and Müller, *Ber.*, **37**, 1264 (1904); Angeli, *ibid.*, **37**, 2080 (1904); *Gazz. chim. ital.*, **23** II, 345 (1893); Curtius, *Ber.*, **31**, 2491 (1898); v. Pechmann and Manck, *ibid.*, **28**, 2377 (1895).
151. Curtius, *Ber.*, **17**, 953 (1884); **31**, 2491 (1898).
152. Angeli, *ibid.*, **26**, 1715 (1893); Schiff, *ibid.*, **14**, 1375 (1881).
153. Curtius and Müller, *Ber.*, **37**, 1261 (1904); Curtius, *ibid.*, **16**, 2230 (1883); *J. prakt. Chem.*, (2) **38**, 401 (1888).
154. Curtius, *Ber.*, **37**, 1295 (1904).

155. Thiele, *Ann.*, **270,** 1 (1892); Thiele and Osborne, *Ber.*, **30,** 2867 (1897); *Ann.*, **305,** 64 (1899).
156. Hofmann and Roth, *Ber.*, **43,** 682 (1910).
157. v. Pechmann and Manck, *ibid.*, **28,** 2374 (1895); v. Pechmann, *ibid.*, **29,** 2161 (1896).
158. Thiele and Meyer, *Ber.*, **29,** 961 (1896); Hantzsch and Lehmann, *ibid.*, **35,** 901 (1902).
159. Thiele, *Ann.*, **376,** 252 (1910).
160. Curtius and Thun, *J. prakt. Chem.*, (2) **44,** 161 (1891); Staudinger and Kupfer, *Ber.*, **44,** 2197 (1911); Staudinger, *ibid.*, **49,** 1889 (1916); Curtius and Pflug, *J. prakt. Chem.*, (2) **44,**537 (1891); Curtius and Lublin, *Ber.*, **33,** 2466 (1900); Staudinger, *et al.*, *ibid.*, **49,** 1932 (1916).
161. v. Pechmann, *Ber.*, **27,** 1888 (1894).
162. Werner, *J. Chem. Soc.*, **115,** 1093 (1919); Arndt and Amende, *Z. angew. Chem.*, **43,** 444 (1930); Arndt and Scholz, *ibid.*, **46,** 47 (1933); *Organic Syntheses*, **15,** 3 (1935).
163. Jones and Kenner, *J. Chem. Soc.*, **1933,** 363; Adamson and Kenner, *ibid.*, **1935,** 286; **1937,** 1551.
164. Thiele, *Ann.*, **271,** 130 (1892); Angeli, *Rend. accad. Lincei* (5)**19 II,**34 (1910); Hantzsch and Lifschitz, *Ber.*, **45,** 3021 (1912). Curtius and Heidenreich, *ibid.*, **27,** 774 (1894); *J.prakt. Chem.*, (2) **52,** 460, 478 (1895); Diels and Fritzsche, *Ber.*, **44,** 3018 (1911); Stollé, *ibid.*, **45,** 289 (1912).
165. Sidgwick, *J. Chem. Soc.*, **192?,** 1108; Sidgwick, Sutton and Thomas, *ibid.*, **1933,** 406; Lindemann *et al.*, *Ber.*, **63,** 702 (1930).
166. Hantzsch and Lehmann, *Ber.*, **35,** 901 (1902).
167. Fischer, *Ann.*, **199,** 303 (1879).
168. Wolff, *Ann.*, **394,** 41 (1902).
169. v. Pechmann, *Ber.*, **28,** 1848, 2374 (1895).
170. Curtius, *J. prakt. Chem.*, (2) **38,** 409 (1888).
171. Curtius, *ibid.*, (2) **38,** 413 (1888); v. Pechmann. *Ber.*, **28,** 857 (1895).
172. Curtius, *J. prakt. Chem.*, (2) **38,** 431 (1888).
173. v. Pechmann, *Ber.*, **28,** 857 (1895).
174. Müller and Freytag, *J. prakt. Chem.*, (2) **146,** 56 (1936).
175. v. Pechmann and Degener, *Ber.*, **30,** 646 (1897); Blitz, *ibid.*, **53,** 2327 (1920).
176. Meerwein and Hinz, *Ann.*, **484,** 1 (1930); Nierenstein, *Ber.*, **60,** 1820 (1927).
177. Wolff, *Ann.*, **325,** 153 (1902); **394,** 26, 48 (1912).
178. Wolff, *ibid.*, **325,** 163 (1902).
179. v. Pechmann, *Ber.*, **27,** 1889 (1894).
180. Taylor and Forscey, *J. Chem. Soc.*, **1930,** 2272.
181. Staudinger *et al.*, *Ber.*, **49,** 1978, 1928 (1916).
182. Staudinger *et al. ibid.*, **49,** 1978 (1916).
183. Arndt and Amende, *Ber.*, **61,** 1122 (1928); Bradley and Schwarzenbach, *J. Chem. Soc.*, **1928,** 2904; Arndt and Eistert, *Ber.*, **68,** 200 (1935); Haberland and Kleinert, *ibid.*, **71,** 470 (1938); Ruggli and Reichwein, *Helv. Chim. Acta*, **20,** 905, 913 (1937); Dornow, *Ber.*, **73,** 185 (1940); Walker, *J. Chem. Soc.*, **1940,** 1304; Newman and Beal, *J. Am. Chem. Soc.*, **71,** 1506 (1949); Smith, *Chem. Revs.*, **23,** 193 (1938); Bachmann and Struve, *Organic Reactions*, vol. 1, p. 38 (1942); Eistert, *Newer Methods of Preparative Organic Chemistry*, Intersc. Publ., 1948, pp. 513-570.
184. Clibbens and Nierenstein, *J. Chem. Soc.*, **107,** 1491 (1915); Staudinger *et al.*, *Ber.*, **49,** 1939, 1975 (1916); Nierenstein *et al.*, *J. Am. Chem. Soc.*, **46,** 2551, 2556 (1924); **47,** 1728 (1925); Bradley and Robinson, *ibid.*, **52,** 1558 (1930).
185. Schlotterbeck, *Ber.*, **40,** 481 (1907); **42,** 2559 (1909); Arndt and Eistert, *ibid.*, **61,** 1118 (1928).
186. Mosettig and Czadek, *Monatsh.*, **57,** 291 (1931).
187. Arndt *et al.*, *Z. angew. Chem.*, **40,** 1099 (1927); Arndt, Eistert and Ender, *Ber.*, **62,** 44, 1271 (1929); **61,** 1118 (1928); **68,** 197 (1935); *Monatsh.*, **59,** 202 (1932); Mosettig, *Ber.*, **61,** 1391 (1928).
188. Curtius and Buchner, *Ber.*, **18,** 2371 (1885); Schlotterbeck, *ibid.*, **40,** 3000 (1907); **42,** 2565 (1909).
189. Meerwein and Burneleit, *Ber.*, **61,** 1840 (1928).
190. Mosettig and Burger, *J. Am. Chem. Soc.*, **52,** 3456 (1930); Kohler et al., *ibid.*, **61,** 1057 (1939); Adamson and Kenner, *J. Chem. Soc.*, **1939,** 181.
191. Heller, *Ber.*, **52,** 742 (1919); **59,** 704 (1926).
192. Arndt *et al.*, *Monatsh.*, **59,** 202 (1932); Fieser and Hartwell, *J. Am. Chem. Soc.*, **57,** 1479 (1935); Schönberg and Mustafa, *J. Chem. Soc.*, **1946,** 746.
193. Bietz and Paetzold, *Ann.*, **433,** 64 (1923).
194. Staudinger *et al.*, *Ber.*, **49,** 1939, 1959 (1916); *Helv. Chim. Acta*, **4,** 3 (1921).
195. Staudinger and Siegwart, *Helv. Chim. Acta*, **3,** 833, 840 (1920).
196. v. Pechmann, *Ber.*, **29,** 2588 (1896).
197. Buchner, *Ann.*, **273,** 226 (1893); **284,** 197 (1894); *Ber.*, **22,** 842 (1889); **27,** 868, 877 (1894); **34,** 347 (1901); v. Pechmann, *ibid.*, **27,** 1890 (1894); **31,** 1898, 2950 (1898); **33,** 3597 (1900); Staudinger and Gaule, *ibid.*, **49,** 1951 (1916); v. Auwers *et al.*, *Ann.*, **470,** 284 (1929); **496,** 27 (1932); *Ber.*, **66,** 1198 (1933); Gotkis and Cloke, *J. Am. Chem. Soc.*, **56,**

2710 (1934); Müller and Roser, *J. prakt. Chem.*, (2) **133**, 291 (1932); v. Auwers and Ungemach, *ibid.*, **66**, 1905 (1933); Fischer and Staff, *Z. physik. Chem.*, **234**, 97 (1935); Fischer and Medick, *Ann.*, **517**, 245 (1935); Wieland and Probst, *ibid.*, **530**, 274 (1937); Smith and Pings, *J. Org. Chem.*, **2**, 23 (1937).

198. Buchner *et al.*, *Ann.*, **273**, 239, 245 (1893); *Ber.*, **27**, 873, 1888 (1894); **46**, 764, 2108, 2684 (1913); Pechmann *et al.*, *Ber.*, **27**, 1890 (1894); **33**, 3590, 3597 (1900); Darapsky, *ibid.*, **43**, 1108 (1910); **45**, 799 (1912); Staudinger *et al.*, *ibid.*, **49**, 1928, 1956 (1916); Ziegler and Schnell, *Ann.*, **437**, 243 (1924); Guhre and Sankaran, *Ber.*, **70**, 1688 (1937); Auwers and König, *Ann.*, **496**, 27 (1932).

199. Buchner and Fritsch, *Ber.*, **26**, 257 (1893); Feist, *Ann.*, **345**, 114 (1906); Auwers and Ungermach, *Ber.*, **66**, 1205 (1933).

200. Guha and Sankaran, *Ber.*, **70**, 2109 (1937). Müller and Roser, *J. prakt. Chem.*, (2) **133**, 291 (1932). *Cf.* von der Heide, *Ber.*, **37**, 2101 (1904); Staudinger *et al.*, *Helv. Chim. Acta*, **7**, 390 (1924).

201. Wolff, *Ann.*, **325**, 135 (1902); **394**, 26 (1912); Dimroth *et al.*, *ibid.*, **335**, 29, 107 (1904); **373**, 239 (1910); *Ber.*, **43**, 2900 (1910); Bertho and Nüssel, *Ann.*, **457**, 278 (1927).

202. v. Pechmann and Seel, *Ber.*, **32**, 2294 (1899); Fieser and Peters, *J. Am. Chem. Soc.*, **53**, 4080 (1931).

203. Buchner, et al., *Ber.*, **18**, 2377 (1885); **33**, 3455 (1900); **34**, 982 (1901); **36**, 3502 (1903); **37**, 931 (1904); *Ann.*, **358**, 1 (1907); **377**, 259 (1910); *Ber.*, **53**, 865 (1920); Ebel *et al.*, *Helv. Chim. Acta*, **12**, 19 (1929).

204. Nenitzescu and Solomonika, *Ber.*, **64**, 1924, 1930 (1931); Puccinini, *Rend. accad. Lincei*, (5) **8 I**, 314 (1899).

205. Jackson and Manske, *Can. J. Research*, **13B**, 170 (1935).

206. Rotter, *Monatsh.*, **47**, 353 (1926); Rotter and Schaudy, *ibid.*, **58**, 245 (1931); Werner, *J. Chem. Soc.*, **115**, 1168 (1919).

207. Staudinger and Miescher, *Helv. Chim. Acta*, **2**, 554 (1919); v. Pechmann, *Ber.*, **28**, 886 (1895).

208. Peratoner and Azzarello, *Gazz. chim. ital.*, **38 I**, 76 (1908); Oliveri-Mandalà, *ibid.*, **40 I**, 120 (1910).

209. Peratoner and Azzarello, *Gazz. chim. ital.*, **38 I**, 84, 94 (1910).

210. Arndt and Partale, *Ber.*, **60**, 446 (1927).

211. Herzig and Tichatschek, *ibid.*, **39**, 268, 1557 (1906).

212. Biltz, *ibid.*, **64**, 1146 (1931).

213. Fischer and Hofmann; *Helv. Chim. Acta*, **245**, 139 (1937).

214. Arndt *et al.*, *Ber.*, **60**, 1364 (1927).

215. Haberland and Klemert, *ibid.*, **71**, 470 (1938).

216. Oliveri-Mandalà and Passalaqua, *Gazz. chim. ital.*, **41 II**, 431 (1911); **43 II**, 465 (1913); Lifschitz, *Ber.*, **48**, 415 (1915).

217. Oliveri-Mandalà, *Rend. accad. Lincei*, (5) **19 I**, 229 (1910).

218. *German patent* 426,343 (1928).

219. Palazzio, *Gazz. chim. ital.*, **43 I**, 569 (1913).

220. Braun and Keller, *Ber.*, **65**, 1677 (1932).

221. Oliveri-Mandalà and Coppola, *Gazz. chim. ital.*, **40 II**, 441 (1910).

222. Meyer, *Monatsh.*, **26**, 1300 (1905); *Ber.*, **40**, 847 (1907); Schlotterbeck, *ibid.*, **40**, 479 (1907); **42**, 2559 (1907); Arndt *et al.*, *ibid.*, **60**, 1364 (1927); **61**, 1107, 1118, 1122, 1948 (1928); **68**, 196 (1935); *Z. angew. Chem.*, **40**, 1099 (1927); Mosettig, *ibid.*, **61**, 1391 (1928); Meerwein and Burneleit, *ibid.*, **60**, 1840 (1927); Bradley and Robinson, *J. Chem. Soc.*, **131**, 1310 (1928).

223. Curtius and Buchner, *Ber.*, **18**, 2371 (1885); Schlotterbeck, *ibid.*, **40**, 3000 (1907); **42**, 2565 (1909); Dieckmann, *ibid.*, **43**, 1024 (1910).

224. Staudinger and Pfenninger, *Ber.*, **49**, 1946 (1916).

225. Turpin, *J. Chem. Soc.*, **59**, 714 (1891).

226. Jahn, *Ber.*, **15**, 1288 (1882); Nef, *Ann.*, **309**, 164 (1899); Hofmann, *Ber.*, **7**, 513 (1874); Hickinbottom, *J. Chem. Soc.*, **1933**, 946.

227. Hickinbottom, *J. Chem. Soc.*, **1932**, 2650.

228. Morgan and Hickinbottom, *J. Soc. Chem. Ind*, **43**, 310 T (1924).

229. Morgan and Hickinbottom, *J. Chem. Soc.*, **123**, 97 (1923).

230. Frankel and Katchalski, *J. Am. Chem. Soc.*, **65**, 1670 (1943); **66**, 763 (1944).

231. Soffer and Hunt., *ibid.*, **67**, 692 (1945).

232. Wolfram *et al.*, *ibid.*, **63**, 632 (1941).

233. Arndt *et al.*, *Ber.*, **71**, 1640 (1938); **74**, 1460 (1941).

234. Arndt et al., *Monatsh.*, **59**, 209 (1932); *Ann.*, **499**, 243 (1932).

235. Giraitis and Bullock, *J. Am. Chem. Soc.*, **59**, 951 (1937); Kohler *et al.*, *ibid.*, **61**, 1057 (1939); Robinson and Smith, *J. Chem. Soc.*, **1937**, 371; Adamson and Kenner, *ibid.*, **1939**, 181; Barbier, *Helv. Chim. Acta*, **23**, 523 (1940); Steadman, *J. Am. Chem. Soc.*, **62**, 1606 (1940); Audrat-i-Khuda and Ghosh, *J. Indian Chem. Soc.*, **17**, 19 (1940).

236. Mosetig and Burger, *J. Am. Chem. Soc.*, **52**, 3456 (1930).
237. Ziegler and Aurnhammer, *Ann.*, **513**, 43 (1934); Ruzicka *et al.*, *Helv. Chim. Acta*, **9**, 499 (1926).
238. Schultz *et al.*, *J. Am. Chem. Soc.*, **62**, 2902 (1940); Cook and Schoental, *J. Chem. Soc.*, **1945**, 288.
239. Schonberg *et al.*, *J. Chem. Soc.*, **1941**, 348.
240. v. Auwers *et al.*, *Ann.*, **470**, 284 (1929); **496**, 27, 252 (1932); *Ber.*, **66**, 1206 (1933); Smith *et al.*, *J. Org. Chem.*, **2**, 23 (1937); *J. Am. Chem. Soc.*, **65**, 159, 165 (1943). *Cf.*, Hüttel, *Ber.*, **74**, 1680 (1941).
241. Guha and Sankaran, *Ber.*, **70**, 2109 (1937); Guha and Hazra, *J. Indian Inst. Sci.*, **22 A**, 263 (1939).
242. *Cf.* Staudinger and Siegwart, *Helv. Chim. Acta*, **3**, 840 (1920).
243. v. Braun, *Ber.*, **70**, 987 (1937).
244. v. Braun, *ibid.*, **70**, 979 (1937).
245. Birkofer, *ibid.*, **75B**, 429 (1942); Buck and Baltzly, *J. Am. Chem. Soc.*, **63**, 1964 (1941).
246. Borrows *et al.*, *J. Chem. Soc.*, **1947**, 197; Schwoegler and Adkins, *J. Am. Chem. Soc.*, **61**, 3499 (1939); Winans, *ibid.*, **61**, 3566 (1939); Haskelberg, *ibid.*, **70**, 2811 (1948); Rohrmann and Schonle, *ibid.*, **66**, 1516 (1944).
247. Skita *et al.*, *Ber.*, **61B**, 1452, 1682 (1928); **62B**, 1142 (1929); **63B**, 34 (1930); *Monatsh.*, **53**, 753 (1929).
248. Lutz *et al.*, *J. Org. Chem.*, **12**, 760 (1947); Cromwell *et al.*, *J. Am. Chem. Soc.*, **65**, 313 (1943), **67**, 1658 (1945).
249. Clark *et al.*, *J. Am. Chem. Soc.*, **55**, 4571 (1933); Kirby, *U. S. patent* 2,366,534 (1945).
250. Holdren and Hixon, *J. Am. Chem. Soc.*, **68**, 1198 (1946).
251. Bigelow and Eatough, *Organic Syntheses*, Coll. vol., I, 80 (1941).
252. Leighton *et al.*, *J. Am. Chem. Soc.*, **69**, 1580 (1947); Campbell *et al.*, *Organic Syntheses*, **27**, 12 (1947); Allen *et al.*, *Organic Syntheses*, **30**, 38 (1950). *Cf.*, Bestian, *Ann.*, **566**, 210 (1950).
253. Campbell *et al.*, *J. Org. Chem.*, **8**, 103 (1943); **9**, 184 (1944).
254. Harries, *Ber.*, **27**, 696 (1894), Fischer, *Ann.*, **190**, 102 (1877).
255. Emerson, *Chem. Revs.*, **45**, 261 (1949).
256. Coleman, *J. Am. Chem. Soc.*, **55**, 3001 (1933); Jackson *et al.*, *ibid.*, **69**, 1539 (1947); Klages *et al.*, *Ann.*, **547**, 25 (1941).
257. Solonina, *J. Russ. Phys.-Chem. Soc.*, **30**, 431 (1898); *Chem. Zentr.*, **1898I**, 887; Tilden, *Chem. News*, **29**, 183 (1873); *Chem. Zentr.*, **1874**, 370.
258. Vosburgh, *J. Am. Chem. Soc.*, **38**, 2081 (1916); Stieglitz *et al.*, *ibid.*, **36**, 272 (1914); **38**, 2046, 2718, 2727, (1916); *J. Org. Chem.*, **1**, 31 (1936); Porter, *Molecular Rearrangements*, (1928); Pinck and Hilbert, *J. Am. Chem. Soc.*, **59**, 8 (1937).
259. Pinck and Hilbert, *l. c.*
260. Konowalow, *Chem. Zentr.*, **1899 I**, 597; v. Braun *et al.*, *Ber.*, **44**, 2533 (1911); **45**, 384 (1912).
261. Hantzsch and Schultze, *Ber.*, **29**, 2252 (1896); Bamberger and Frei, *ibid.*, **35**, 1085 (1902); Wislicenus and Endres, *ibid.*, **35**, 1759 (1902), Meyer and Constam, *Ann.*, **214**, 328 (1882); Wieland and Hess, *Ber.*, **42**, 4182 (1909).
262. Comstock and Koenigs, *Ber.*, **18**, 2379 (1885); **40**, 3000 (1907).
263. Curtius *et al.*, *Ber.*, **41**, 3161 (1908).
264. Langley *et al.*, *J. Chem. Soc.*, **1952**, 4191; **1951**, 2309; Aston and Parker, *J. Am. Chem. Soc.*, **56**, 1387 (1934).
265. Langley *et al.*, *J. Chem. Soc.*, **1952**, 4195. *Cf.* Thiele, *Ber.*, **42**, 2578 (1909).
266. Franchimont, *Rec. trav. chim.*, **13**, 322 (1894).
267. Thiele and Lachmann, *Ann.*, **288**, 267 (1895).
268. Bamberger, *Ber.*, **28**, 399, 535 (1895).
269. Khorana, *Chem. Revs.*, **53**, 145 (1953).
270. Weith, *Ber.*, **6**, 1395 (1873); **7**, 10, 1306 (1874).
271. Schmidt *et al.*, *ibid.*, **71**, 1933 (1938).
272. Zetzsche and Nerger, *ibid.*, **73 B**, 467 (1940).
273. Schmidt and Striewsky, *ibid.*, **74**, 1288 (1941).
274. Schmidt *et al.*, *Ann.*, **571**, 83 (1951).
275. Zetzsche *et al.*, *Ber.*, **71 B**, 1512, 1516, 2095 (1938); **72 B**, 363, 1477, 1599, 1735, 2095 (1939); **73 B**, 50, 465, 467, 1114 (1940); **74 B**, 183, 1022 (1941); **75 B**, 100 (1942).
276. Zetzsche and Fredrich, *Ber.*, **72 B**, 1477 (1939).
277. Todd *et al.*, *J. Chem. Soc.*, **1952**, 1234, etc.

CHAPTER 11

ALIPHATIC HALOGEN COMPOUNDS

Methods of Formation

Halogenated hydrocarbons may be obtained through the halogenation of hydrocarbons or through the replacement of the hydroxyl group in alcohols, or the oxygen of carbonyl groups with halogens. Halogenated hydrocarbons are also obtained through the reaction of halogens and hydrogen halides with unsaturated hydrocarbons.

The halogenation of saturated hydrocarbons and the replacement of hydroxyl groups with halogens is discussed in Chapters 1 and 2 dealing with saturated hydrocarbons and alcohols; the substitution of the oxygen of carbonyl groups is considered in Chapter 5; and the halogenation of acids in Chapter 6. The halogenation of unsaturated hydrocarbons and the reaction of these hydrocarbons with hydrogen halides is taken up in Chapters 17 and 19.

The chlorination of saturated aliphatic hydrocarbons is facilitated by sunlight and may be accelerated by the use of halogen carriers such as iodine, antinony pentachloride or aluminum chloride.[1] Undesirable reactions are avoided by carrying out the reaction under diminished pressure.[2] Rupture of carbon to carbon bonds may result if the reaction becomes too energetic,[3] and carbon tetrachloride and perchlorobenzene are then the products of the reaction, depending on the starting materials. Iron is also an effective catalyst[4] and when used in carrying out the bromination of hydrocarbons causes the replacement of one hydrogen atom from each carbon atom in the chain with a bromine atom.

Mono- and polyhalo hydrocarbons are formed when halogenation is carried out in the sunlight, or in the liquid phase in the presence of iodine. The individual halo hydrocarbons formed may be isolated by fractional distillation or, in the case of solid compounds, by fractional crystallization. The formation of polyhalo compounds may be largely avoided by carrying out the reaction in the vapor phase. In the chlorination of long chain hydrocarbons the methylene groups are attacked in preference to the terminal methyl groups.[5]

Monoalkyl halides are best prepared from the corresponding alcohols by replacement of the alcoholic hydroxyl group with a halogen atom by reaction with hydrogen halides or, preferably, with phosphorus trihalides. Reaction with hydrogen halides requires long heating,[6] while reaction with phosphorus trihalides takes place rapidly and vigorously. The reaction does not take place quantitatively in either case, however, phosphorus trihalides yielding esters of phosphoric acid as byproducts. The phosphorus halide method is suitable for the preparation of bromides and iodides.

A series of chlorinated propanes are obtained through the condensation of polychloroethylene with chloroform or carbon tetrachloride in the presence of aluminum chloride:[7]

$$Cl_2C = CHCl + HCCl_3 \xrightarrow{AlCl_3} Cl_2CHCHClCCl_3$$

Solvents suitable for carrying out chlorination reactions are carbon tetrachloride, chloroform and other organic halides, glacial acetic acid, phosphorus oxychloride, nitrobenzene, sulfuric acid and occasionally water. Chloroform is converted to carbon tetrachloride in the course of the reaction, especially if the liquid is exposed to light.

Carboxyl groups in aliphatic compounds may be replaced with chlorine by treating the silver salt of the acid with chlorine:[133]

$$RCOOAg + Cl_2 \rightarrow RCl + AgCl + CO_2$$

The carboxyl group may be similarly replaced with a bromine atom. The procedure is useful as a step in the synthesis of ω-bromoesters.[134]

Phosphorus pentachloride may serve as a chlorinating agent to replace hydrogen atoms in aromatic bodies. The compound dissociates extensively at higher temperatures giving rise to elemental chlorine. Dissociation is complete at 300°.

Phosphorus pentachloride has been employed for the purpose of replacing amino groups with chlorine:[135]

$$RNHCOC_6H_5 + PCl_5 \rightarrow RCl + C_6H_5CN + HCl + POCl_3$$

Many bromination reactions proceed readily at room temperature and under atmospheric pressure when vapors of bromine are led into the compound to be brominated.

A satisfactory procedure is to lead a current of carbon dioxide into bromine contained in a flask, and to conduct the bromine-charged gas into the compound to be brominated. Acetone and cyclohexanone can be effectively monobrominated by this procedure.[136]

While *nitromethane* is not attacked by bromine, sodium nitromethane, $NaCH_2NO_2$, reacts readily with the halogen to form bromonitromethane. This compound is obtained more conveniently by treating nitromethane in baryta water with bromine.

Bromination reactions may be carried out in indifferent solvents. Ether, chloroform, tetrachloroethane, sulfuryl chloride, carbon disulfide, glacial acetic acid, and formic acid have been used for the purpose. When ether is used as the solvent, the reaction should be carried out at 0°. Water and aqueous solutions of hydrogen chloride and bromide and concentrated sulfuric acid may also be used as solvents in bromination reactions. Alcohol is attacked to some extent by bromine.

Commercial bromine may be purified by fractionally distilling the halogen after it has been repeatedly shaken with water, then with concentrated sulfuric acid. Further purification may be effected by distillation over precipitated manganese dioxide or mercuric oxide, and drying the distillate by shaking with sulfuric acid or by the addition of phosphorus pentoxide.

Bromination of benzoylpiperidine with phosphorus pentabromide leads to the formation of 1,5-dibromopentane:[135]

$$C_5H_{10}NCOC_6H_5 + PBr_5 \rightarrow Br(CH_2)_5Br + C_6H_5CN + POBr_3$$

1,4-Dibromobutane is similarly obtained from benzoyltetrahydropyrrole.

Compounds containing the group CH_3CO or $CH_3CH(OH)$ yield iodoform when treated with a freshly prepared solution of iodine in caustic.[137] Triiodo compounds are formed as intermediates in this reaction. Alkali hypoiodites in the nascent state serve as the active agent in the electrolytic preparation of iodoform on the commercial scale.

Hexaiodoacetone, I_3CCOCI_3, results from the reaction of iodine with acetone dicarboxylic acid, $HOCOCH_2COCH_2COOH$.[138]

Halogen Exchange

Aliphatic mono- and polybromo compounds may be obtained through the reaction of the chlorides with aluminum bromide.[8] This exchange can also be accomplished by heating the chloro compound with bromine in the presence of iron.[9] Conversely, bromides can be converted to the corresponding chlorides by reaction with antimony pentachloride:[10]

$$2C_2H_5Br + SbCl_5 \rightarrow 2C_2H_5Cl + Br_2 + SbCl_3$$

Treatment of α-chloro esters with bromine results in the replacement of chlorine with bromine, and substitution of a β-hydrogen with halogen:

$$RCH_2CHClOR' + Br_2 \rightarrow RCHBrCHBrOR' + HCl$$

This reaction forms the second stage of the Boord synthesis of olefins.

The interchange of one halogen in an organic body with another may be effected by reaction with the proper metallic halide. The replacement of chlorine or bromine with iodine may be brought about by heating the alkyl halides with potassium iodide in methyl alcoholic solution,[11] or with sodium iodide in acetone solution.[141] This method is suitable for the preparation of alkyl iodides, α-iodo ketones, aliphatic iodo acids, benzyl and substituted benzyl iodides. It fails with compounds such as aryl halides, in which the halogen is unreactive. Applied to dihalo compounds in which the halogens are attached to adjacent carbon atoms, the method leads to the formation of unsaturated monoiodo compounds.

Alkyl iodides may be converted to alkyl bromides by reaction with copper bromide,[12] and to chlorides by reaction with mercuric or copper chlorides.[13] When methylene iodide is covered with water, and bromine in great excess is added gradually, considerable heat is evolved and methylene bromide is formed.

An exchange of halogens takes place when alkyl bromides are made to react with lead- or mercury iodides, with separation of some elemental iodine and the formation of unsaturated hydrocarbons or halo derivatives. The latter result from polybromo compounds.[13]

The results obtained in these exchange reactions are greatly influenced by the choice of the solvent. Water, methanol, ethanol, acetone and glacial acetic acid have been used for the purpose. The use of acetone presents an advantage in cases where esterification may take place if alcohols or acetic acid are employed as solvents. Bromine is replaced more readily than chlorine. Primarily-bound halogens undergo reaction more readily than secondarily-bound halogens, and the latter more readily than tertiarily-bound halogens. Halogen atoms joined to an aromatic ring can be replaced only if they have been activated by other substituents in the ring. A mixture of various halides are obtained in all these exchange reactions.

Chlorine or bromine in an organic body may be replaced with iodine by reacting the compound with hydriodic acid or heavy metal iodides. In many cases the reaction proceeds at room temperature. The addition of amorphous phosphorus accelerates the reaction. Occasionally the reaction results in the replacement of a halogen atom with hydrogen.[139] Exchange can take place in both directions when halides of zinc, cadmium, thallium, bismuth, iron and nickel are used.[140]

Methyl iodide is formed in quantitative yield through the interaction of sodium iodide and methyl chloride in alcoholic solution. Methylene iodide may be obtained similarly from methylene chloride.[142] The halogen in glycol chlorohydrin, propargyl bromide and benzoyl-ε-chloroamylamine, $C_6H_5CONH(CH_2)_5Cl$, may also be exchanged for iodine under these conditions.[143]

An indirect method of introducing iodine into an organic molecule consists in treating an alkyl magnesium halide with iodine:[15]

$$RMgCl + I_2 \rightarrow RI + MgICl$$

The bromine in aliphatic bromides can generally be replaced with fluorine by reaction with antimony trifluoride.[14] Ethyl or propyl fluorides result through the reaction of the corresponding iodides with silver fluoride at room temperature. The reaction proceeds with alkyl bromides and chlorides only when heated in a sealed tube.

Halogenated derivatives of unsaturated compounds cannot, in general, be obtained by the direct action of halogens, since the normal reaction products of halogens with such compounds are saturated halides. Unsaturated halides may be obtained, however, by the careful treatment of saturated poly halo compounds with alcoholic potassium hydroxide or with silver oxide:

$$ClCH_2CH_2Cl + KOH \rightarrow CH_2 = CHCl + KCl + H_2O$$

Haloethylenes result also by heating polyhalogenated aliphatic hydrocarbons with zinc or iron filings in the presence of water.

If the reaction of dihalo compounds with potassium hydroxide is carried out under vigorous conditions, both halogen atoms may be removed from the molecule, with the formation of an acetylenic hydrocarbon.

A few halogenated olefin hydrocarbons have been prepared from unsaturated acids by conversion of the latter to their dihalo derivatives by reaction with the halogen, and subsequently treating these with an alkali carbonate. Chloroprolylene has been prepared, for example, from crotonic acid:

$$CH_3CH = CHCOOH \rightarrow CH_3CHClCHClCOOH \xrightarrow{Na_2CO_3} CH_3CH = CHCl$$

The halogen in the resulting halide is joined to a carbon atom with a double bond.

Unsaturated halides in which the halogen is attached to a saturated carbon atom may be prepared by replacing the hydroxyl group in the corresponding unsaturated alcohol with a halogen atom by reaction with a phosphorus halide:

$$3CH_2 = CHCH_2OH + PBr_3 \rightarrow 3CH_2 = CHCH_2Br + P(OH)_3$$

Fluorination

Most organic compounds react violently with fluorine. The reaction is especially vigorous with organic vapors and may often result in ignition or explosion. Reaction in the liquid phase may be moderated by use of an inert solvent, while vapor phase reactions may be controlled by dilution with an inert gas such as nitrogen. The product of the reaction always consists of a mixture of fluorinated compounds, and consequently the method is of little preparative value.

The most satisfactory *procedure* in carrying out the reaction between the vapors of an organic compound and fluorine consists in bringing the mixture of the vapors with fluorine diluted with nitrogen in contact with copper gauze.[16] The reaction of gaseous fluorine with liquid hydrocarbons is best carried out by bringing the gas into contact with the surface of the liquid. The liquid may be diluted with carbon tetrachloride, and the reaction may be carried out at 0° in a copper or nickel vessel. If the liquid is of low volatility, fluorine can be passed through the liquid without the danger of fire, although partial carbonization may take place. Carbonization may be largely avoided by fluorinating thin films of the liquid with gaseous fluorine distributed by means of a metal screen.

The fluorination of methane results in the formation of a mixture consisting of CH_3F, CH_2F_2, CHF_3, CF_4, C_2F_6 and C_3F_8. The fluorination of difluoroethane, CH_3CHF_2, results in the formation $CH_2F.CHF_2$, CHF_2CHF_2 and CF_4.[17] The compounds

$$CH_3CHF_2CH_3,\ (CF_3)_2CO,\ F_3COF,\ F_2CO \text{ and } CF_4$$

result from the direct fluorination of acetone.

The yields of fluorocarbons diminishes as one ascends a homologous series, and the method is not convenient for use with fluorocarbons greater than C_{10}.

The cyano group, CN, would appear to resist fluorination.[144] Iodine pentafluoride, IF_5, reacts with cyanogen iodide, however, forming diazotrifluoromethane, $F_3CN = NCF_3$.[145] and fluorination of silver cyanide in admixture with Ag_2O and $KMnO_4$ results in the formation of F_3NO. Aliphatic compounds containing a carbonyl group may undergo cleavage under the action of fluorine.[146]

Fowler's Method

Hydrocarbons may be fluorinated by the action of the higher fluorides of certain metals at elevated temperatures. Silver difluoride, AgF_2, and cobalt trifluoride CoF_3 have been used for the process, which is carried out in two stages consisting of the fluorination of the metal to a higher stage, and reaction of the higher fluoride with the hydrocarbon.

The procedure, when using cobalt trifluoride, is to fluorinate cobalt difluoride, CoF_2, at 250° in a nickel reactor agitated with a horizontal coaxial stirrer, and then to pass the vapors of the hydrocarbon diluted with nitrogen over the cobalt trifluoride at temperatures ranging 150 to 350°. The optimum temperature would appear to be 300 to 350°. For complete fluorination two passages through the catalyst bed seems to be necessary. Too rapid exhaustion of the cobalt trifluoride should be avoided.[159]

Simon's Process[160]

This is an electrolytic process applicable to substances that dissolve in anhydrous liquid hydrogen fluoride giving highly conducting solutions. Such solutions are obtained with many compounds containing oxygen, nitrogen and sulfur. Steel cathodes and nickel anodes are employed; the cells are constructed of copper, nickel or iron. Electrolysis is carried out under a low potential.

Fluorination by Replacement of Halogens and Amino or Hydroxy Groups

One of the most generally applicable methods for the preparation of fluoro compounds is based on the replacement of chlorine or bromine in halo compounds with fluorine. Elementary fluorine is capable of replacing other halogens in certain halo compounds, though this reaction is not of preparative importance. In a number of instances the replacement of a halogen by fluorine may be brought about by reaction with *hydrogen fluoride*.[*] Reaction proceeds most readily with compounds of the type RCX_3.[18] Heating at or above $110°$ under pressure is necessary in many cases.

The three chlorine atoms in *benzotrichloride* are readily replaced with fluorine by reaction with hydrogen fluoride.[20] With few exceptions, nuclear substituents, in the case of aromatic compounds, do not have an adverse effect; a chlorine atom in the ortho or para position, and a cyano group[21] inhibit the reaction. Two trichloromethyl groups in ortho and para position in the benzene nucleus are converted simultaneously to trifluoromethyl groups. Symmetrical $C_6H_3(CF_3)_3$ is obtained from the corresponding chloro derivative.

Hexafluoro-*o*-xylene, $C_6H_4(CF_3)_2$, may be prepared by first converting the pentachloro compound resulting from the direct chlorination of *o*-xylene to the pentafluoro derivative, chlorinating this to chloro pentafluoro-*o*-xylene, and finally exchanging the chlorine in this with a fluorine atom.

Trichloromethyl benzal chloride may be converted to the corresponding fluoro compound by reaction with hydrogen fluoride, but the method is not applicable to benzal chloride, since hydrogen fluoride causes the formation of resinous products from this compound.

Halogenated side-chains composed of more than one carbon atom attached to an aromatic system resist complete fluorination even when a fluorine carrier is employed. The Cl_3C group in *p*-trichloromethylheptachloroisopropyl benzene is converted to F_3C, but the group $CCl(CCl_3)_2$ requires treatment with hydrogen fluoride and antimony pentachloride under pressure for transformation into the heptafluoro group.[147] Chlorine atoms attached to a carbon atom separated from the nucleus by a CF_2 group are replaced with difficulty. *Phenyl pentachloroethane* subjected to the action of hydrogen fluoride at an elevated temperature yields a mixture of 2-phenyl-1,1,2,2-tetrafluoro-1-chloroethane and phenyl-1,1,1-trichloro-2,2-difluoroethane. *Diphenyltetrachloroethane* reacting with hydrogen fluoride at $50-60°$ gives diphenyldifluorodichloroethane, although other compounds of this type are incapable of reaction with hydrogen fluoride in the absence of catalysts.

The chlorine atoms in a trichloromethyl group attached to sulfur in compounds of the type of $C_6H_5SCCl_3$ are all replaceable with fluorine.[22]

Fluorination of the methyl group in toluidines may be accomplished by chlorinating the corresponding phthalimide,

$$C_6H_4 \begin{array}{c} O \\ / \quad \backslash \\ \quad \quad \quad NC_6H_4CH_3 \\ \backslash \quad / \\ O \end{array}$$

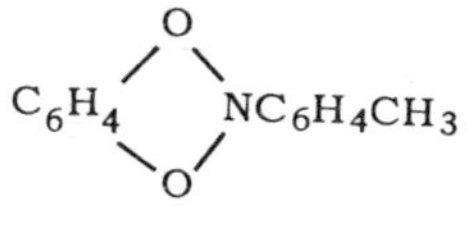

replacing the chlorine atoms with fluorine by reaction with hydrogen fluoride, and finally decomposing the fluorophthalimide by use of hydrazine:

---

[*]Serious hazards are involved in the use of hydrogen fluoride. The vapors of the compound, in the concentrated form, cause severe and extremely painful burns on short contact. Injury makes its appearance hours after exposure to the compound. The anhydrous liquid and concentrated solutions of hydrogen fluoride rapidly destroy the skin. Injury permeates deep in the flesh and healing is extremely slow. As a measure of protection, affected areas should be washed immediately with a suspension of calcium hydroxide, and a glycerolmagnesium oxide paste, or a magnesium stearate ointment should then be applied. Injection of a calcium gluconatelactobionate relieves the pain in such burns and accelerates the healing process.[19]

$$C_6H_4 \begin{array}{c} CO \\ \diagup \quad \diagdown \\ \diagdown \quad \diagup \\ CO \end{array} NC_6H_4CF_3 \xrightarrow{H_2NNH_2} H_2NC_6H_4CF_3$$

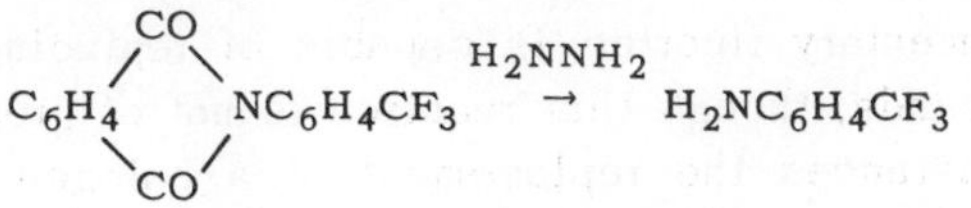

A small excess of hydrogen fluoride is used in carrying out the halogen exchange. Methylene chloride is a suitable solvent. It is important, however, to maintain fully anhydrous conditions.[23]

Aliphatic trichloromethyl compounds of the type of Cl_3CCH_3 may be converted to fluorides by reaction with hydrogen fluoride, although all chlorine atoms cannot, apparently, be replaced by this method. The chlorine atoms in ethylidene chloride, CH_3CHCl_2, are also replaceable by fluorine by reaction with hydrogen fluoride.

The halogen in acid halides, RCOX, is readily replaceable with fluorine by this method. Reaction proceeds vigorously when the acid halide is added to liquid hydrogen fluoride. The yields are generally in the range 50 - 90% of theory.

The exchange of other halogens by fluorine through the action of *hydrogen fluoride* often proceeds readily in the presence of a *catalyst*. Antimony trifluoride is an effective catalyst, particularly in the presence of a small amount of a pentavalent antimony compound.[24] Good results are obtained by the addition of 5% antimony pentafluoride or elemental bromine. Exchange generally takes place readily with compounds containing at least two halogen atoms bound to the same carbon atom. *Antimony chlorofluorides* are very effective cretalysts and are used in present commercial practice.

This catalyst is prepared by heating antimony trichloride with hydrogen fluoride and chlorine at 100° under pressure. The analysis of the product indicates that it is a mixture of the compounds SbF_2Cl_3 and SbF_3Cl_2. The properly prepared catalyst melts at 40° and has a fluorine content between 10 and 20%. Catalysts containing less than 10% fluorine give very uncertain results.

In carrying out the exchange reaction, a certain amount of chlorine is introduced with the hydrogen fluoride in order to maintain part of the antimony in the pentavalent condition. The proportion of the trivalent compound should be between 10 and 30% for best results. The quantity of hydrogen fluoride introduced is so regulated that the proportion of the fluorine in the catalyst remains at the desired level.

In the commercial preparation of dichlorodifluoromethane, the alkyl chloride and hydrogen fluoride are introduced at the bottom of the reaction vessel and bubble up through the liquid catalyst. Emerging at the top, the vapors enter a scrubber containing the alkyl halide used in the process. Insufficiently fluorinated products and antimony compounds carried over with the vapors are absorbed here and returned to the reaction chamber. The pressure is so regulated that the catalyst remains in the liquid condition, while the products vaporize and are removed. The hydrogen chloride formed in the reaction is absorbed with water and with a suspension of calcium hydroxide; then the vapors are dried by passage through concentrated sulfuric acid and are liquified and purified by fractional distillation.

In a few instances the reaction between a chloro or bromo compound and hydrogen fluoride in the presence of a catalyst proceeds at room temperature, but, in general, good results are secured only on heating to 60 - 100°. Occasionally heating to 120° is necessary; in that case a pressure of 2.7 atm must be maintained in the reaction vessel in order to keep the catalyst in the liquid condition. When alkyl bromides are used in the reaction, it is the preferred practice to convert the antimony trifluoride to antimony bromofluoride. Water rapidly inhibits the reaction.

Complete exchange of chlorine atoms in a trichloromethyl group by reaction with hydrogen fluoride in the presence of a catalyst is possible in the case of aryl trichloromethyl and a few aliphatic compounds. Thus, the trichloromethyl group in 1,1,1,2-tetrachloroethane is converted to a trifluoro group at 160.[25] Alkyl halides which contain any of the halogens in any proportion can be fluorinated by this method. The method is applicable also to unsaturated halides, although in this case addition of hydrogen fluoride at the unsaturated bonds takes place, giving rise to saturated halides.[26]

The following generalizations have been formulated in regard to the exchange of fluorine for chlorine in various types of chloro compounds by reaction with hydrogen fluoride in the presence of catalysts: The chlorine in the groups $ClCH_2$- and -CHCl- is not replaceable; the groups Cl_2CH- react slowly and are converted to FClCH-, and with greater difficulty to F_2CH-; Cl_3C- groups are the most reactive and are converted to FCl_2C- and F_2ClC- and rarely to F_3C-. The presence of fluorine in an aliphatic halide diminishes the reactivity of a halogen attached to an adjacent carbon atom, and in some cases inhibits the reaction entirely. A similar deactivating effect is observed in the aromatic series of *o*-fluorobenzotrichloride. Phenyldichlorotrifluoroethane is converted to the corresponding pentafluoro compound by this method. Side reactions and decomposition proceed in proportion to the hydrogen content of the molecule. Side reactions assume importance also when halogen and hydrogen atoms are attached to the same carbon atom in the compound.

The replacement of other halogens with fluorine by reaction with hydrogen fluoride has been accomplished by *vapor phase catalysis*. Thus, carbon tetrachloride reacts with hydrogen fluoride at 250° over a catalyst consisting of charcoal impregnated with cupric chloride, giving trichlorofluoromethane in 82% yield. The reaction proceeds at 150° with a catalyst consisting of charcoal impregnated with ferric chloride. Working at 300°, chloroform has been similarly converted to a mixture of 60% dichlorofluoromethane and 10% dichlorodifluoromethane over a charcoal catalyst. Copper- and iron chloride catalysts supported on corundum have been used in the temperature range 250 - 450°. Hexachloroethane, treated in the vapor phase with fluorine in contact with copper gauze, gives *sym*-tetrachlorodifluoroethane.

Halogen Exchange by Reaction with Metallic Fluorides

Exchange of chlorine or bromine atoms with fluorine may be brought about by heating the organic chloro or bromo compound with various metallic fluorides. *Antimony trifluoride* may be used effectively for the purpose in many instances. The reaction of benzotrichloride with this compound proceeds so vigorously that control is difficult;[27] reaction with benzal chloride proceeds with even greater vigor, although it is possible to obtain benzal fluoride in 40% yield by careful manipulation.[28] Diphenyldichloroethane is transformed to the corresponding difluoroderivative by heating with antimony trifluoride at 140° until the mixture completely liquifies.[29] Halides of the type $RR'CX_2$ and RCX_3 are transformed to the corresponding fluorides on long heating with antimony trifluoride under a reflux condenser.[30] Hexachloropropene heated under reflux with antimony trifluoride is transformed to the trifluoride $Cl_2C = CClCF_3$;[31] similarly, the allyl compound $F_2C = CClCF_2Cl$, heated overnight at 180 - 200° under pressure with an excess of antimony trifluoride is transformed to $F_2C = CClCF_3$. Trifluoroethers, such as F_3COCH_3, have been obtained through the reaction of trichloromethyl ethers with antimony trifluoride.[32]

The reaction of antimony trichloride with organic halides is accelerated by pentavalent antimony salts. The addition of bromine or chlorine also has an accelerating effect.

Potassium fluoride has been used for the replacement of chlorine in acyl chlorides by fluorine. Thus, acetyl fluoride has been prepared by heating a mixture of acetic acid and benzoyl chloride with potassium fluoride.[33] Formyl fluoride has been prepared in a similar manner. The reaction is at first retarded and finally ceases to proceed when applied to higher homologs of acetic acid, apparently because of the formation of an insoluble coating on the particles of potassium fluoride.

The halogen in compounds containing groupings -CHX- and CH_2X- may be replaced with fluorine by reaction with potassium fluoride in suitable solvents at elevated temperatures under pressure. Fluoracetamide may be prepared from chloracetamide by reaction with potassium fluoride in xylene solution under atmospheric pressure.[34] It is possible also to exchange halogens in organic compounds containing the grouping -CHX- or $-CH_2X$ with fluorine by heating with potassium fluoride in solution in certain polyhydroxy compounds under atmospheric pressure to a temperature of at least 140°. Suitable solvents are ethylene glycol, glycerol, diethylene glycol, and polyethylene glycol. Fair yields of the fluorinated compound are obtained by this method.[35]

Silver- and *mercury fluorides* have been used to effect the exchange reaction. All exchange reactions that may be brought about by other reagents may be accomplished by use of these compounds; in addition, a number of exchange reactions may be affected by these reagents which cannot be successfully carried out with other reagents.

Silver fluoride can be used in solution or as a fine powder mixed with cupric fluoride.[36] Acetonitrile and anhydrous hydrogen fluoride are the preferred solvents.[37] The reagent should be completely dry. The silver fluoride required for the reaction may be prepared directly in the hydrogen fluoride used as a solvent by dissolving silver carbonate in this liquid.[38] Since silver fluoride reacts with the silver halide formed to give an inactive complex AgF.AgX, only half of the silver fluoride is available for the reaction.

ω-Difluoroacetophenone has been obtained in 40% yield through the reaction of the corresponding chloro compound with anhydrous silver fluoride in hydrogen fluoride.[39] With trichloroacetophenone, ω-dichlorofluoroacetophenone and a small amount of ω-chlorodifluoroacetophenone is obtained. Allyl fluoride results on gently heating a mixture of allyl chloride and silver fluoride.[40] In the reaction with higher alkyl bromides, olefins are formed through the elimination of hydrogen bromide.[41]

Mercurous fluoride has been used to effect the exchange of other halogens with fluorine. This method works satisfactorily with iodo compounds.[42] Thus iodoform reacting with mercurous fluoride is converted to fluoroform. Bromo compounds react poorly, while chloro compounds fail to react. Ethylene bromide and ethylidene bromide are converted to vinyl bromide when heated with mercurous fluoride. Other polyhalo compounds also yield olefins. Partly fluorinated acetic acid derivatives such as $Cl_2CFCOOH$, $ClCF_2COOH$, ICHFCOOH, $Br_2CFCOOH$ and $BrCF_2COOH$ have been prepared by an interchange reaction between the halogenated acids and mercurous fluoride.[43] The reactivity of mercurous fluoride can be enhanced by the addition of iodine.[44]

Mercuric fluoride reacts with organic iodides or bromides very much more readily than mercurous fluoride. The reaction is often violent, although it can be controlled readily. The reaction can be carried out successfully in solvents such as hydrocarbons or fluorinated hydrocarbons. Alcohols, esters, and ethers retard the reaction, while ketones inhibit it entirely. Mercuric fluoride is rapidly decomposed by water and by compounds which readily yield water.

Mercuric fluoride is among the best reagents for the conversion of organic bromo compounds to the corresponding fluoro compounds. The reaction proceeds rapidly with the lower alkyl bromides, and gives the fluorides in quantitative yield. Ethylene bromide and ethylidene bromide yield chiefly $BrCH_2CH_2F$ and CH_3CHF_2 respectively, with small amounts of FCH_2CH_2F and CH_3CHFBr, butadiene and butyl fluoride. Difluoromethyl bromide is converted to fluoroform,[41] while difluoroethyl iodide F_2CHCH_2I and difluoroethyl dibromide, $F_2CHCHBr_2$, are converted respectively to trifluoro and tetrafluoroethane. 1,1,2-Trifluoroethane results from 1,1-difluoro-2-bromoethane.[45] Acetylene tetrabromide is converted stepwise to acetylene tetrafluoride. Methylene chloride and chloroform do not react with mercuric fluoride and can therefore be used as solvents in carrying out the reaction of other halides with the reagent. Vinyl halides are also unreactive toward mercuric fluoride.

Mercurous fluoride is difficult to prepare in the anhydrous condition required for these exchange reactions. A mixture of mercuric oxide and anhydrous hydrogen fluoride may be used instead of mercuric fluoride for many of these reactions.

The general *procedure* is as follows: Mercuric oxide is added with stirring to the organic halide or its solution in an inert solvent in a nickel flask cooled externally. Dry hydrogen fluoride is then led into the liquid at a rate to maintain the desired temperature. The reaction is complete when the red color of mercuric oxide disappears. The optimum temperature varies according to the nature of the halide, some reacting best at temperatures well below zero, while others may require heating to temperatures up to a maximum of 50°. The yields are generally good.[45]

Methylene chloride and chloroform, which are unreactive toward mercuric fluoride, are converted by this method to methylene fluoride and chlorodifluoromethane, respectively. The halogen in the groups CH_2Br, $CHCl_2$ and CCl_2 and halogen atoms in haloesters may be replaced with fluorine following this procedure. Olefin formation through the elimination of hydrogen halide has not been observed in exchange reactions carried out by this method.

In the case of most resistant halo compounds, replacement with fluorine is effected by use of the more vigorous reagents, antimony pentafluoride, bromine trifluoride, and iodine pentafluoride.[148]

Replacement of Amino Groups by Fluorine

Halo compounds in which the halogen is joined to an aromatic nucleus cannot be replaced with fluorine by reaction with hydrogen fluoride or with any of the other reagents usually employed for the purpose. Aromatic fluorides in which the fluorine atom is joined to the aromatic nucleus can be prepared only through the decomposition of aromatic diazonium fluorides.

The arylamine is dissolved in hydrogen fluoride, the solution is cooled to 0 to 5°, and diazotation is effected with sodium nitrite or nitrous fumes:

$$C_6H_5NH_2 + HNO_2 + HF \rightarrow C_6H_5N_2F + 2H_2O$$

The diazonium fluoride thus obtained is decomposed by warming the solution to 30 to 40°. After the evolution of nitrogen has ceased and the hydrogen fluoride has been distilled off, the aryl fluoride remaining behind is treated with anhydrous potassium fluoride and is purified by distillation.[46]

Replacement of the diazo group by fluorine may be effected conveniently by heating the diazonium fluoborates ArN_2BF_4, which are crystalline compounds slightly soluble in water.[161]

Replacement of Hydroxy Groups by Fluorine

The substitution of alcoholic hydroxyl groups with fluorine by reaction with hydrogen fluoride is of little preparative value. Ethyl fluoride results in 36% yield when ethyl alcohol is heated under pressure at 140 to 190° with hydrogen fluoride.[47] Lower alkyl fluorides have been obtained in good yield through the reaction of the corresponding alcohols with hydrogen fluoride in the presence of catalysts, such as antimony chlorofluoride or beryllium difluoride.[21]

Miscellaneous other Methods

Hydrogen fluoride reacts with certain sulfur compounds containing the -SH group, replacing this group by a fluorine atom. An example is the formation of acetyl fluoride from thioacetic acid, a reaction which takes place quite vigorously:

$$CH_3COSH + HF \rightarrow CH_3COF + H_2S$$

The preparation of fluorine derivatives of oxygenated compound by halogen exchange is often accompanied by the formation of water, which causes a retardation of the reaction or an alteration of its course. A number of oxygenated fluorine compounds have been prepared by special methods.

Trifluoroacetic acid has been obtained in 90% yield through the oxidation of

$$F_3CCCl = CCl_2$$

by alkaline permanganate,[149] or by hydrolysis of trifluoro trichloroethane, F_3CCCl_3, with fuming sulfuric acid in the presence of mercury salts.[150] Trifluoroacetic acid may be converted to its anhydride by treatment with phosphoric oxide,[151] or by reacting its silver salt with iodine.[152] Hexafluoroethane results in excellent yield by electrolysis of sodium trifluoroacetate.[48]

Difluoro- and chlorodifluoroacetic acids have been prepared by the alkaline permanganate oxidation of 1,1-dichloro-3,3-difluoropropylene, $F_2CHCH = CCl_2$ and 1,1,3-trichloro-3,3-difluoropropylene, $F_2CClCH = CCl_2$.[153]

Trifluoroethanol, F_3CCH_2OH, may be prepared by the catalytic reduction of trifluoroacetic acid, its anhydride or amide.[154] Trifluoroisopropyl alcohol, $F_3CCH(OH)CH_3$, may be prepared through the reduction of trifluoroacetone, F_3CCOCH_3.[155] Both these compounds are acidic in nature and liberate carbon dioxide from carbonates and bicarbonates.

Perfluoroadipic acid is formed by the permanganate oxidation of perfluorocyclohexene which is in turn obtained by the action of aqueous alkali on undecafluorocyclohexane. The acid may also be prepared by the careful fluorination of benzene to perfluorocyclohexene with CoF_3 or MnF_3 and subsequent oxidation.

Trifluoroacetaldehyde, F_3CCHO, has been prepared by the oxidative nitration of trifluoropropane, $F_3CCH_2CH_3$, or by the reduction of trifluoroacetic acid with lithium aluminum hydride.

Fluoroketones have been prepared through the hydrolysis of fluoroacetoacetates by sulfuric acid.[49]

Trifluoromethyl-β-diketones have been obtained by acylating ketones with trifluoroacetic ester in the presence of sodium ethoxide:[162]

$$F_3CCOOC_2H_5 + H_3CCOCH_3 \xrightarrow{NaOC_2H_5} F_3CCOCH_2COCH_3 + C_2H_5OH$$

Some of the heterocyclic β-diketones prepared by this method from trifluoroacetic ester or heptafluoropropionic ester and a heterocyclic ketone form remarkable complexes with certain metals and have found use in the separation of some new synthetic elements.

Fluorinated ethylamines have been obtained by heating F_2CHCH_2I with concentrated aqua ammonia in a sealed tube at 130°.[50]

Tetrafluoreethylene, $F_2C = CF_2$, is obtained in yields of up to 95% by heating F_2CHCl to an elevated temperature. A remarkable polymeric body, polytetrafluroethylene, is prepared on the industrial scale from this compound by a technique of emulsion polymerization in aqueous medium, using persulfates or organic peroxides as catalysts. Trifluoromethylacetylene, $F_3CC \equiv CH$, has been prepared through the addition of trifluoromethyl iodide to acetylene and subsequent dehydroiodination of the resulting compound.

Fluorinated compounds are formed through the addition of hydrogen fluoride at multiple bonds. Many fluoro compounds have been obtained by this method. The subject is considered under unsaturated compounds.

Properties and Behavior of Halogenated Hydrocarbons

Saturated chlorinated or brominated hydrocarbons are stable compounds. Iodinated compounds are somewhat unstable and assume a red color when exposed to light, due to partial liberation of iodine. Unsymmetrical halo compounds have a lower specific gravity than the corresponding symmetrical compounds. Unsymmetrical halo compounds boil at a lower temperature than the corresponding symmetrical product. For example, ethylidene chloride, CH_3CHCl_2, boils at a lower temperature than ethylene dichloride, $ClCH_2CH_2Cl$. A method has been evolved for the approximate calculation of the boiling point of a given compound.[51]

Monohaloethylenes and the unsymmetrical dichloro- and dibromoethylenes, $CH_2 = CCl_2$, $CH_2 = CBr_2$, show a tendency to polymerize.[52] Dibromoethylene is spontaneously oxidized to bromoacetyl bromide:[53]

$$CH_2 = CBr_2 \xrightarrow{O_2} \overset{\displaystyle O}{CH_2\!-\!\!-\!CBr_2} \rightarrow BrCH_2COBr$$

Chlorobromoethylene, $CH_2 = CBrCl$, also undergoes spontaneous oxidation, yielding a mixture of chloroacetyl bromide and bromoacetyl chloride.[54] The spontaneous oxidation of trichloroethylene, $ClCH = CCl_2$, results in the formation of phosgene, carbon monoxide and hydrogen chloride,[55] while tribromoethylene yields dibromoacetyl bromide.

Symmetrical dihaloethylenes exist in two isomeric forms. 2-Bromo-2-butene,

$$CH_3CBr = CHCH_3$$

has been demonstrated to exist in two isomeric forms,[56] the *cis*,

$$\begin{array}{c} CH_3-CB \\ \| \\ CH_3-CH \end{array} \quad \text{and } \textit{trans}, \quad \begin{array}{c} CH_3-CBr \\ \| \\ HC-CH_3 \end{array}$$

The elimination of hydrogen halide takes place appreciably more readily from the latter than from the former.[57]

Certain unsaturated aliphatic iodo compounds are capable of forming dichloro iodo addition products of the type of $ICH = CHICl_2$. Such addition compounds are obtained, for example, from diiodoethylene, $ICH = CHI$, and chloroiodoethylene, $ClCH = CHI$. These addition compounds resemble aromatic dichloroiodo compounds, such as $C_6H_5ICl_2$, which are obtained by the addition of chlorine to aromatic iodo compounds. Dichloroiodo compounds may also be prepared from some saturated alkyl iodides, such as methyl and ethyl iodides, by carrying out the reaction at a very low temperature, but these are extremely unstable compounds,[58] methyl iododichloride decomposing, for example, at $-28°$ to methyl chloride and iodine monochloride.

Halides of acetylene have unusual properties. Monochloroacetylene is a very unstable gas. Decomposition of this compound can be prevented only by dilution with a sufficiently large proportion of hydrogen. It decomposes violently within a short time when isolated in the pure form with the separation of carbon;[59] it reacts with ammoniacal copper chloride to form a yellowish red precipitate, and with ammoniacal silver nitrate to yield a white precipitate. Both of these compounds are highly explosive. Bromoacetylene $BrC \vdots CH$ is spontaneously combustible, although it will not burn when diluted with much air. Its solutions phosphoresce in the dark for days, emanating some ozone. Its vapors are toxic. Bromoacetylene polymerizes to insoluble products when exposed to light, a little tribromobenzene forming simultaneously. The halo derivatives of mono substituted acetylenes have a sweetish odor and are toxic. Nef regarded dihalo-acetylenes as derivatives of acetylidene, $H_2C = C$, comparing them with hydrocyanic acid and isonitrile. Like the latter, they are extremely toxic.

Aliphatic bodies with a single fluorine atom in their molecule tend to be unstable, and monofluoroparaffins with more than five carbon atoms in the chain spontaneously lose hydrogen fluoride. Two or more fluorine atoms attached to a carbon atom strengthen the carbon to fluorine bonds and also stabilize a halogen atom attached to an adjacent carbon atom, though exerting the reverse effect on a hydrogen atom similarly situated. The effect of a di- or trifluorinated carbon atom on an adjacent carbonyl or hydroxyl group is to increase the acidic character of the latter.

Trifluoroacetic anhydride reacts violently with pyridine giving solid products which have not been identified. The bromine and iodine atoms in the compounds $F_3CCOOBr$ and F_3COOI possess a *positive* character. These compounds are formed by the action of the halogen on the silver salt of trifluoroacetic acid.

Polyfluoroamines, such as $F_3CCH_2NH_2$, yield stable diazo compounds with nitrous acid. Treatment of the diazo compound with a halogen results in the replacement of the diazo group with two halogen atoms; treatment with a hydrogen halide in its replacement with a halogen and a hydrogen atom.

Pyrolysis of a quaternary ammonium fluoride generally results in the elimination of the most electronegative group as a fluoride, benzyltrimethylammonium fluoride giving benzyl fluoride in 60% yield.

Isomerization of Halo Compounds

Many halogenated compounds undergo molecular rearrangement when heated to a sufficiently high temperature. For example, propyl bromide heated to 280° for a prolonged period yields isopropyl bromide, probably *via* the intermediate formation of propylene and hydrogen bromide:[60]

$$CH_3CH_2CH_2Br \quad \rightarrow \quad CH_3CH = CH_2 + HBr \quad \rightarrow \quad CH_3CHBrCH_3$$

In a similar manner, isobutyl bromide, $(CH_3)_2CHCH_2Br$, yields *tert*-butyl bromide,[61] $(CH_3)_3CBr$. The reaction is reversible and a condition of equilibrium is reached when the mixture contains about 80% *tert*-butyl bromide, completion of the process requiring about 3 hours at 140°. A trace of zinc bromide accelerates the reaction markedly, while *iso*- and *tert*-butyl alcohols and diisobutene, which normally are present as impurities in isobutyl bromide, retard the reaction.[62] Isomerization is also greatly accelerated by aluminum bromide, this reagent inducing the change even at room temperature. Thus, propyl bromide containing 4% aluminum bromide is completely converted to the secondary bromide on standing one day at room temperature. Complete isomerization takes place on five minutes' boiling in the presence of 10% aluminum bromide.[63] Butyl bromide is unaffected on boiling in the presence of iron bromide.[64]

Migration of an alkyl group may take place during the isomerization of halo compounds containing a quaternary carbon.[65] For example, the halides of 2-dimethylpropanol are converted on boiling under atmospheric pressure to halo-2-methyl-2-butanol:

$$(CH_3)_3CCH_2Br \rightarrow (CH_3)_2CBrCH_2CH_3$$

Isomerization of halides may be brought about also by passing the vapors of the halo compound over the chlorides of barium or thorium at 250°. Tertiary amyl- and butyl bromides are obtained in 60 and 75% yield respectively from the isobromides by this method; isopropyl bromide is obtained from *n*-propyl bromide in 25% yield.[66] Ethylene- and propylene dibromides may be isomerized by heating in a sealed tube at 300 and 200° respectively.

Reactivity of Halogens in Halo Compounds

Halogens in halo compounds may be replaced with various other groups by reaction with the proper reagent. They may be replaced with a hydroxyl group, for example, by reaction with aqueous caustic:

$$RCl + NaOH \rightarrow ROH + NaCl$$

The ease with which such reactions take place varies according to the character of the compound. Differences are observed in the reactivity of the halides of the saturated series,[67] for example, in the reaction with sodium ethoxide. Taking the reaction rate for ethyl chloride as one, the approximate rate for other aliphatic chlorides are as follows: methy 15.7, *n*-propyl 0.4, *n*-butyl 0.4, *n*-heptyl 0.3, *n*-octy 10.3, cetyl 0.3, isobutyl 0.1. There is, thus, a slight dedecrease in reactivity as the chain length is increased. Greater differences in reactivity are observed with brominated compounds.[68] Thus, the approximate reaction rates for the same reaction, taking the rate for ethyl bromide as one, are for methyl bromide 18, *n*-propyl 0.3, isobutyl 0.03, *tert*-amyl 4×10^{-6}. For the reaction between alkyl bromides and silver nitrate the approximate reaction rates for various alkyl bromides are for methyl 0.8, propyl 0.5, isobutyl 0.08, *tert*-amyl 0.01, again taking the rate for ethyl bromide as one.

Among the monochlorides of the aliphatic series the secondary chlorides are less reactive toward potassium iodide in acetone solution than the primary, but more reactive than the tertiary halides.[69] Iodides are the most reactive among monohalides derived from the same hydrocarbon, while chlorides are the least reactive. For example, ethyl iodide reacts readily with an alcoholic solution of silver nitrate, but the bromide reacts only on warming, and the chloride fails to react even on long boiling. Like the corresponding bromide and chloride, methyl iodide is much more reactive than ethyl iodide, reacting about ten times as rapidly as the latter in most cases. Great variations are observed in the reaction of the same halide with various reagents.

The accumulation of halogen atoms on the same carbon atom in simple aliphatic compounds, as in chloroform and carbon tetrachloride, causes a marked decrease in reactivity, while the presence of halogens on adjacent carbon atoms enhances the reactivity. Thus, ethylene dibromide, $BrCH_2CH_2Br$ is more reactive than ethyl bromide, and the latter is more reactive than ethylidene dibromide, CH_3CHBr_2.

Trimethylene bromide, $BrCH_2CH_2CH_2Br$, reacts readily with sodium carbonate to form glycol, and yields a dinitrile with potassium cyanide. β, β-Dialkyl derivatives of this compound, $BrCH_2C(R)_2CH_2Br$, are unreactive toward these reagents, but the β-phenyl-β-methyl derivative reacts with aqueous sodium carbonate to form a glycol.

The reactivity of the halogen attached to a methylene group, CH_2Cl, is enhanced if the following groups are joined to the methylene:

$$RC : C,\ RC \equiv C,\ C_6H_5,\ ROCO,\ CN,\ H_2NCO,\ RCO \text{ and } RO.$$

Certain other negative groups, such as SCN and NO_2, also exert an activating influence, although to a far smaller extent.

In accordance with the foregoing, the bromine in allyl bromide,

$$CH_2 = CHCH\ Br$$

is of enhanced activity. The interposition of a methylene group between the vinyl and chloromethyl groups diminishes the activity of the bromine, but the interposition of any additional methylene groups brings about little or no change. Thus, while the bromine in allyl bromide is more reactive than that in 4-butene bromide, $CH_2 = CHCH_2CH_2Br$, the halogen in the latter is no more reactive than that in 5-pentene bromide, $CH_2 = CHCH_2CH_2CH_2Br$. In effect, the reactivity of the halogen in the last named differs little from that of the halogen in propylene and pentylene bromides. This rule holds also in regard to the influence of a double bond forming part of a benzenoid ring. Thus, benzyl chloride, $C_6H_5CH_2Cl$, resembles allyl chloride in its reactivity, but the chlorine in β-phenylethyl chloride, $C_6H_5CH_2CH_2Cl$, is much less reactive.

Halogen atoms combined with a vinyl group are far less reactive than the chlorine in a methyl group joined to a vinyl group. Thus, chlorine in vinyl chloride $CH_2 = CHCl$ is much less reactive than that in allyl chloride,

$$CH_2 = CHCH_2Cl$$

The reaction constants of some unsaturated halo compounds with potassium iodide are given below:[70]

	K		*K*
$CH_2 = CHCH_2Cl$	0.052	$CH_2 = CHCH_2CH_2Br$	0.628
$CH_2 = CHCH_2CH_2Cl$	0.0075	$CH = CHCH_2CH_2CH_2Br$	0.814
$CH_2 = CHCH_2CH_2CH_2Cl$	0.0078	$CH_3CH = CHBr$	0.00017
$CH_2 = CHCH_2Br$	126.0	$CH_3CH = CHCH_2Br$	519.0

The constant *K* is calculated by the equation

$$K = \frac{1}{0.4343(9bt)} \log \frac{10 - Z}{10(1 - Z)}$$

in which Z = amount of KI disappearing in time t, and b = initial concentration of KI, expressed in moles/liter.

The relative reactivity of chlorine in various chloro compounds, with the reactivity of allyl chloride, $CH_2 = CHCH_2Cl$, taken as 1 are given below:[156]

	Relative Reactivity
$ClCH = CHCH_3$	0.0
$CH_2 = CClCH_2Cl$	0.72
$CH_2 = CBrCH_2Cl$	0.87
$CH_2 = CHCH_2Cl$	1.00
$CH_2 = C(CH_3)CH_2Cl$	1.58
$ClCH = CHCH_2Cl$, high boiling isomer	2.90
$ClCH = CHCH_2Cl$, low boiling isomer	8.58
$ClCH = C(CH_3)CH_2Cl$, high boiling isomer	8.45
$ClCH = C(CH_3)CH_2Cl$, low boiling isomer	32.8
$Cl_2C = C(CH_3)CH_2Cl$	33.0

The ease with which various unsaturated chlorinated compounds react with different reagents does not necessarily range in the same order.[32] Thus, while reactivity with potassium hydroxide decreases in the order

$$C_6H_5CCl = CHCl > C_6H_5CCl = CH_2 > C_6H_5CH = CCl_2 > C_6H_5CH = CHCl$$

that with pyridine ranges in the order

$$C_6H_5CCl = CHCl > C_6H_5CH = CHCl > C_6H_5CCl = CH_2 > C_6H_5CH = CCl_2$$

and that with aqueous silver nitrate in the order

$$C_6H_5CCl = CH_2 > C_6H_5CCl = CHCl > C_6H_5CH = CHCl > C_6H_5CH = CCl_2$$

A halogen atom in the γ-position with respect to an activating group is generally more reactive than one at the β-position.[71]

The reaction rate of sodium ethoxide with allyl halides is about sixty times the rate of the reaction with the corresponding propyl halides.[72] The reaction of allyl iodide with metallic mercury proceeds so much more rapidly in comparison with other iodides that it is possible to make use of this reaction for the separation of allyl iodide from other iodides.[73]

The reaction between allyl iodide, $CH_2=CHCH_2I$, and sodio acetoacetic ester proceeds with such vigor that the mixture begins to boil within half a minute, and the reaction is complete within less than one minute.[74] Propyl iodide reacts with the same sodio derivative with slight spontaneous heating, and the reaction is complete only after two to three hours heating.

Allyl bromide reacts with tertiary amines with marked evolution of heat to form quaternary ammonium bromides such as $(C_2H_5)_3(C_3H_5)NBr$.

Allyl halides reacting with Grignard reagents, RMgI, yield alkenes with a terminal double bond, $RCH_2CH = CH_2$.

Vinyl bromide fails to react with potassium cyanide or silver cyanide on long heating;[75] it fails to react also with moist silver acetate at 100°, with sodiomalonic ester at 170 to 180°, and with alcoholic ammonia at 150°.[76] Reaction with potassium hydroxide results in the formation of acetylene. Alpha and beta bromopropenes, $BrCH=CHCH_3$ and $CH_2 = CBrCH_3$, heated with triethylamine are converted to allylene, $CH \equiv CCH_3$.

The activating influence of the vinyl group comes to evidence also in hydroxy compounds, hydroxyl groups joined to a methylene adjacent to a vinyl group being readily replaceable by halogens. The effect is exerted also on hydrogen atoms attached to a methylene group adjacent to a vinyl group, and hydrogen atoms thus activated are readily replaced with bromine by reaction with N-bromosuccinimide *(Wohl-Ziegler's method)*.

Replacement reactions of chlorinated compound proceeds at considerably lower temperatures in the presence of some alkali metal iodide.[157]

The halogen in propargyl halides of the type $CH \equiv CCH_2X$ are active, and react with sodium thiocyanate, for example, to give a thiocyano derivative

$$CH \equiv CCH_2SCN$$

The iodide reacts with metallic mercury to form an iodomercury compound,

$$CH \equiv CCH_2HgI$$

The isomeric iodoallylenes, $IC \equiv CR$, do not react in this manner.

Halogens in compounds in which the sum of halogen atoms and of the carbon bonds attached to a single carbon atom is four appear to be more reactive than those in which this sum is three. Thus the halogen in compounds bearing the groups $C = CH_2X$, $CCHX_2$ is less reactive than in those bearing the groups $C \equiv CX$, $C = CX_2$ and CCX_3.[77] In compounds of the type of allyl chloride, the accumulation of halogens on the "saturated" carbon atom seems to increase the reactivity of the halogen. Thus, the chlorine in $C_6H_5CCl_3$ is more reactive than that in $C_6H_5CHCl_2$; the chlorine in this compound is in turn more reactive than that in $C_6H_5CH_2Cl$.

The reactivity of halogens is enhanced also by *carbonyl, carboxyl,* and *aryl groups.* The effect of these as well as other activating groups may be modified by other groups in combination with them. For example, the chlorine in chloroacetone, CH_3COCH_2Cl is more reactive than that in ω-chloroacetophenone, $C_6H_5COCH_2Cl$.

Differences in the reactivity of benzyl and naphthylmethyl bromides due to substituents have been brought to evidence by determinations of their hydrolysis constants, the results of which were as follows:[78]

	K		*K*
α-$C_{10}H_7CH_2Br$	270	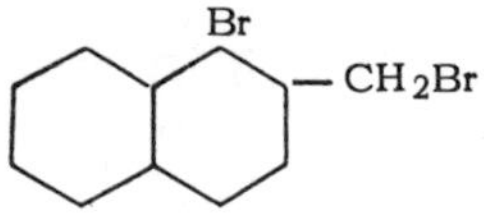	59
β-$C_{10}H_7CH_2Br$	210		
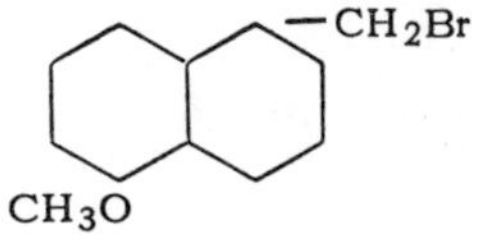	485	$C_6H_5CH_2Br$	125
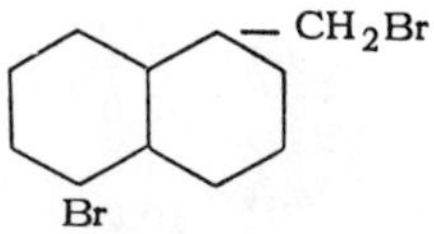	129	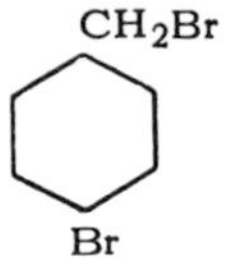	71
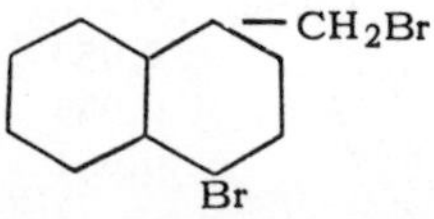	137	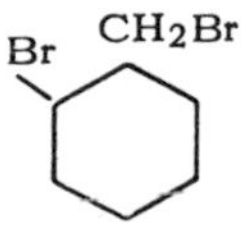	39

The effect of substituents joined to CH_2Cl on the reactivity of the chlorine in this group increases in the order C_2H_5, C_2H_5OCO and C_6H_5CO.[79]

Differences in the reactivity of the chlorine in β-chloroethyl and γ-chloropropylphenyl sulfides and their nitrated derivatives have also been established quantitatively by determination of the relative velocities of their reaction with potassium iodide in acetone solution at 55°:[80]

	Relative Reactivity		Relative Reactivity
$C_6H_5SC_2H_4Cl$	1	p-$NO_2C_6H_4SC_2H_4Cl$	2.62
o-$NO_2C_6H_4SC_2H_4Cl$	1.98		
		$C_6H_4SC_3H_6Cl$	3.52
m-$NO_2C_6H_4SC_2H_4Cl$	2.09	p-$NO_2C_6H_4SC_3H_6Cl$	9.19

These compounds range in respect to their reactivity toward alcoholic sodium hydroxide, in descending order, as follows:

p-$NO_2C_6H_4S\ C_2H_4Cl$, o-$NO_2C_6H_4SC_2H_4Cl$ m-$NO_2C_6H_4SC_2H_4Cl$,

$C_6H_5S\ C_2H_4Cl$, $C_6H_5SC_3H_6Cl$ p-$NO_2C_6H_4SC_3H_6Cl$.

The velocity constants of various chlorinated compounds for the reaction with pyridine in absolute alcoholic solution is given below:[81]

	K		K
$C_2H_5CH_2Br$	0.0179	$(CH_3)_3COCOCH_2Br$	0.934
$CH_2=CHCH_2Br$	1.253	$C_6H_5OCOCH_2Br$	1.927
$C_6H_5CH_2Br$	5.118	$C_6H_5CH_2OCOCH_2Br$	1.211
$C_6H_5CH{:}CHCH_2Br$	0.472	$CH_2=CHCH_2OCOCH_2Br$	0.768
$HOCOCH_2Br$	0.666	$C_2H_5OCOCH_2CH_2Br$	0.0277
CH_3OCOCH_2Br	0.919	$(C_2H_5O)_2CHCH_2Br$	0.012
$C_2H_5OCOCH_2Br$	1.004	H_2NCOCH_2Cl	0.01115
n-$C_3H_7OCOCH_2Br$	0.752	$C_6H_5NHCOCH_2Cl$	0.0264
iso-$C_3H_7OCOCH_2Br$	1.048	$C_6H_5NHCOCH_2Br$	1.533
$C_2H_5CH_2CH_2OCOCH_2Br$	0.770	$C_6H_5COCH_2Br$	7.269

The reaction constant is calculated by the equation

$$K = \frac{1}{C_o t} \times \frac{C_t}{C_o - C_t}$$

In the table below are given the velocity constants for the reaction with the vapors of sodium:[82]

	Velocity Constant (cc/mole sec x 10^7)		Velocity Constant (cc/mole sec x 10^7)
C_2H_5Br	0.5	$C_6H_5CH=CHCH_2Cl$	7.8
C_2H_5I	20.0	$C_6H_5CH=CHCH_2Br$	43.0
$CH_2=CHBr$	0.23	$C_6H_5CH_2Cl$	5.3
$CH_2=CHI$	2.5	$CNCl$	10.7
$C_6H_5CH_2CH_2Cl$	2.6	$CNBr$	12.0
$C_6H_5CH_2CH_2Br$	3.8	$CNCH_2Cl$	7.2
$C_6H_5CH=CHCl$	0.96	$CNCH_2CH_2Cl$	0.059
$C_6H_5CH=CHBr$	1.14	$ClCH_2CH_2Cl$	0.095
$CH_3CH_2CH_2Cl$	0.01	$HOCH_2CH_2Cl$	0.051
$CH_2=CHCH_2Cl$	0.35		

The reactivity of the halogen in the following decreases in the order named, in reactions of the type[83]

$$-CCl + HOCH_3 \rightarrow -COCH_3 \text{ and } -CCl + HOCOCH_3 \rightarrow -COCOCH_3:$$

$$(CH_3OC_6H_4)_2C(Cl)C_6H_5,\ (C_6H_5CH=CHCH=CH)_2CCl_2,\ C_6H_5COCl,$$

$$(C_6H_5)_3CCl,\ (C_6H_5CH=CH)_2CCl_2,\ (p\text{-}ClC_6H_4CH=CH)_2CCl_2,\ (C_6H_5)_2CCl_2,$$

$$p\text{-}Cl\,C_6H_4CH=CHC(Cl_2)C_6H_4Cl\text{-}p$$

$$(C_2H_5)_2CCl,\ (C_6H_5)_2CHCl,\ C_6H_5CCl_3,\ C_6H_5CH_2Cl,\ CH_2=CHCH_2Cl,$$

$$(C_2H_5OCO)_2CHCl,\ (C_2H_5OCO)_2CCl_2.$$

The bromine atoms in the dibromide of phenylpropenyl,

$$C_6H_5CHBrCHBrCH_3,$$

and of its derivatives may be readily removed; these compounds may be converted to ketones by treatment with two molecular equivalents of sodium ethoxide. The corresponding dibromallyl compound, $C_6H_5CH_2CHBrCH_2Br$, and its analogs cannot be converted thus to ketones.

Phenacyl halides and β-halo ethers fail to give a precipitate with alcoholic silver nitrate.[84]

The influence of the nitro groups on the reactivity of halogens in fatty acids is less marked than that of CO or COOH groups. Thus, while compounds ofthe type $RCOC(R)ClCOOC_2H_5$, or $RCCl(COOC_2H_5)_2$ are reduced with hydrazine with removal of chlorine, those of the type $NO_2C(R)ClCOOC_2H_5$ and

$$NO_2CCl_2COOC_2H_5$$

do not yield their chlorine under the action of hydrazine, although the corresponding bromine compounds yield their bromine.[85]

The difluoromethylene group, F_2C, enhances the stability of other halogen atoms in close proximity; it deactivates α-halogens. The deactivating influence extends in some measure to the β-position, but the γ-position is practically unaffected.[158]

Reactivity of Halogens in Aromatic Compounds

Halogens directly attached to an aromatic nucleus are, in general, quite unreactive. For example, chloro and bromobenzene do not react with alcoholic silver nitrate even at 100 to 150°. They are unaffected by alcoholic ammonia or sodium hydroxide at these temperatures. It is notable, however, that many aromatic halo compounds are capable of forming organomagnesium compounds with magnesium.

The introduction of substituents may induce a marked activation of a halogen atom attached to the aromatic nucleus. Thus, *nitro* groups in the *ortho* and *para* position with respect to the halogen atom bring about activation of the halogen. In general, substituents in these positions which are *meta* directing may exert an activating influence, though the activating influence exerted by nitro groups far surpasses that of any other group. The introduction of nitro groups in the *meta* position generally causes very slight change in the reactivity of the halogen. Examples are offered by the relative inertness of the chlorine in meta-nitro and 3,5-dinitrochlorobenzene. This rule does not strictly hold, however; the chlorine in *m*-nitrochlorobenzene, for example, is reactive and is readily exchanged for the sulfonic group by reaction with alkali bisulfites in alcoholic solution.[86] The difference in the effect of *o*- and *p*-nitro groups as contrasted with that of a meta group is shown by the behavior of 1,2,4,6-tetrachloro-3,5-dinitrobenzene toward ammonia, amines and sodium ethoxide. These reagents replace the chlorine atoms at 2,4 and 6 positions, but not that at position 1.

The difference in the effect of groups in the *ortho* and *para* positions as compared with the group in the *meta* position follows from the principle of *vinylogy.*[87] *Ortho* and *para* nitrochlorobenzenes are vinylogs of nitrosyl chloride, $ClNO_2$, which has a very reactive halogen, whereas *m*-nitrochlorobenzene is not a vinylog of this compound. The effect of an *ortho* nitro group is greater than that of a *para* nitro group.

An increase in the number of nitro substituents in aromatic halo compounds increases the reactivity of the halogen; thus the chlorine in 2,4,6-trinitrochlorobenzene is more reactive than that in 2,4-dinitrochlorobenzene, and the halogen in the latter compound is more reactive than that in nitrochlorobenzene.

The halogen in 3-nitro-4-bromobenzonitrile is more reactive than that in *o*-nitrophenyl bromide. The bromine in 4-methyl-3-nitro-6-bromobenzonitrile is less reactive than that in 4-methyl-1,2-nitro-6-bromobenzonitrile.[88]

The halogen in 2,4-dinitrochloro- and bromobenzene is very reactive and may be replaced with a hydroxyl group merely by treatment with warm, dilute alkali, and with aryloxy groups by treatment with metallic phenolates. The halogen in these compounds may be further replaced with the group $NHNH_2$ by treatment with hydrazine, and with the SCN group by reaction with alkali thiocyanates. The compound is capable of reaction with alkali sulfides and hydrosulfides. The labile halogen can, further, be replaced by the malonic ester and acetoacetic ester residues by reaction with sodio malonic or sodio acetoacetic ester.[89]

In some cases a nitro group rather than a halogen atom is replaced; this occurs, for example, with *sym*-dinitrochlorobenzene and 1-chloro-3,4-6-trinitrochlorobenzene.

The chlorine in 1-chloro-2,4-dinitronaphthalene is more reactive toward sodium methoxide than that in 1-chloro-2,4-dinitrobenzene. The introduction of a nitro group in the 5-position in 1-chloro-2,4-dinitronaphthalene increases the reactivity of the halogen considerably.[90] The bromine in α-bromo-β-naphthol is sufficiently reactive to give di-β-naphthol sulfide, $HOC_{10}H_6SC_{10}H_6OH$, with sodium sulfide in quantitative yield.[91]

The activating effect of nitro groups is manifested in aromatic nitro compounds other than halides. Thus, nitrated phenyl alkyl ethers in which the nitro groups are in the *ortho* or *para* position with respect to the alkoxy group, are decomposed to the alkali metal salt of the corresponding nitrophenols when heated with aqueous alkali. The alkoxy group can also be replaced with the hydrazino group by reaction with hydrazine, and with amino groups by reaction with amines.[92] The amino group in nitrated anilines can be replaced with a hydroxyl group by reaction with aqueous alkali, or with substituted amino groups by heating with amines, providing the nitro group is in the *ortho* or *para* position.

In certain *para* halo substituted phenols, as for example, 6-bromothymol, the halogen is replaced with a nitro group on nitration. The halogen is not eliminated from the molecule however, but migrates to the *ortho* position with respect to the phenolic hydroxyl group.[93]

Reactivity of Halogens in Miscellaneous other Compounds

Two halogen atoms in tetrachloroquinone occupying the *ortho* position with respect to each carbonyl group are reactive and may be replaced with various other groups.

Halogen atoms occupying certain positions in heterocyclic compounds are active. Thus, halogens in the α-position in furans and in quinoline are active but not in pyridine.[94] A halogen in position 1 in isoquinoline is reactive. Chlorine atoms in positions 2 and 6 in purine are reactive and may be easily replaced with a hydroxyl, ethoxy and amino group; a chlorine atom in position 8 in this compound may be replaced with a hydroxyl group by treatment with fuming hydrochloric acid but not with alkalies.[95]

The chlorine in triphenylmethyl chloride, $(C_6H_5)_3CCl$, is very reactive, while that in diphenylcarbamic chloride, $(C_6H_5)_2NCOCl$, is far less reactive due to the deactivating influence of the nitrogenous group attached to the carbonyl group.[96]

The degree of reactivity of bromine in cyanuric bromide lies between that of acyl and alkyl bromides, and is comparable to that of bromine atoms in tribromopropane.[97]

Formation of Olefins from Halo Compounds

Saturated halo compounds in which the carbon atom adjacent to that combined with the halogen bears at least one hydrogen atom, may be converted to olefins by the removal of a molecule of hydrogen halide. This may be accomplished in various ways. In many instances it is sufficient to heat the halo compound with alcoholic caustic. This method is applicable to all iodo compounds and to many brominated hydrocarbons. The intensity of reaction varies according to the halo compound.[98] Sodium ethoxide or hydrazine hydrate[99] may also be used to bring about the removal of the elements of hydrogen halide and the formation of an olefin. In the reaction with alcoholic caustic or sodium ethoxide, dialkyl ethers are formed in addition to the olefin.[100]

A high concentration of alkali favors the formation of olefins. Concentrated alcoholic potassium hydroxide is more effective for the production of olefins than aqueous alkali. A large proportion of ethers are apt to form with some halides; thus, *n*-propyl bromide gives on treatment with alcoholic caustic, 20% propylene and 60% *n*-propyl ether, while isopropyl bromide gives 75% propylene.[101]

The hydrogen is generally removed from that carbon atom which bears the least number of hydrogen atoms. Thus, tertiary amyl iodide, $C_2H_5CI(CH_3)_2$, gives trimethylethylene, $(CH_3)_2C = CHCH_3$ in 94% yield, and a small amount of methylbutene, $C_2H_5C(CH_3) = CH_2$. Tertiary butyl iodide yields butylene by reaction with AgI, AgCN, NH_3 or AgOCN and sodio acetoacetic or sodiomalonic esters, although the normal exchange reaction is observed with normal and isobutyl iodides.

In some instances elimination of hydrogen halide from a halogen compound is brought about simply by heating. The reaction is accelerated by anhydrous metal chlorides.[102]

Occasionally elimination of the elements of hydrogen halide from the molecules of two compounds is observed giving rise to an unsaturated product. Thus, fluorene and benzophenone dichloride reacting at 320 to 330° give diphenyldiphenyleneethylene in 50 to 60% yield:

$$\begin{matrix} C_6H_4 \\ | \\ C_6H_4 \end{matrix} \!\!> CH_2 + Cl_2C(C_6H_5)_2 \rightarrow \begin{matrix} C_6H_4 \\ | \\ C_6H_4 \end{matrix} \!\!> C = C(C_6H_5)_2 + 2HCl$$

The removal of hydrogen halide from a halo compound is easier the fewer the number of hydrogen atoms attached to the carbon atom bearing the halogen. Thus, tertiary halides are converted to olefins on heating with pyridine or a tertiary aromatic base.[103] The position of the double bond in unsaturated compounds obtained by the action of quinoline on cyclohexylmethyl halides is uncertain, since quinoline salts seem to cause a shift in the unsaturated linkage.[104]

Olefinic compounds are formed from chlorides by heating these with *lead oxide* to 220 - 225°.

Olefins may be prepared also from dihalo compounds in which the halogen atoms are attached to adjacent carbon atoms, by heating the compound with zinc dust and acetic acid or alcohol, or with metallic sodium or magnesium.[105] The use of zinc filings and alcohol may cause the polymerization of the olefins formed; in such cases the use of magnesium in suspension in ether generally gives satisfactory results.[106]

Unsaturated compounds are obtained from dibromides or dichlorides in which the halogen atoms are attached to adjacent carbon atoms by treatment with sodium iodide in acetone solution.[107]

Dihalides resulting from the replacement of the carbonyl oxygen in ketones are often very unstable, and give off hydrogen halide on distillation to form olefins.

Where the possibility of the formation of two stereoisomeric unsaturate compounds is possible, only the stable form results on removal of two halogens from the dihalide.

Acetylenic hydrocarbons may be prepared from dibromoethylenes of the general type AlKCBr = CHBr, by heating with zinc and alcohol.[108] Sodium and moist ether have been employed for the preparation of acetylenic hydrocarbons from the corresponding dichlorides.[109]

Replacement of Halogens with Various Groups

The halogen in alkyl halides may be replaced with various acidic groups or with the hydroxyl group, generally by reaction of the halide with the alkali metal derivative of the acid or with caustic.

Normal chlorides generally react with alkalies with difficulty; bromides and especially iodides react more readily. The halogen in secondary and tertiary halides is more reactive; the latter are so reactive that it is sufficient to reflux them with water to cause their hydrolysis.[110] Triarylmethyl halides are also smoothly converted to the corresponding alcohol.

If the halide shows a tendency to yield an olefin on treatment with alkalies, or alkaline-earth hydroxides, the alcohol corresponding to the halide may be obtained by heating the latter with an aqueous suspension of lead oxide or silver oxide. The alcohol may also be obtained by carrying out the hydrolysis with caustic in a feebly alkaline solution. Chlorine in α-chloro acids is readily replaced with a hydroxyl group by heating with aqueous alkalies. β-Chloro acids yield an unsaturated acid under a similar treatment.

Occasionally it is of advantage to convert the halide first to the corresponding acetate by reaction with potassium- or silver acetate, and to hydrolyze the acetate subsequently. This is particularly desirable in preparing glycols from alkyl dibromides.

Isobutyl aldehyde results through the hydrolysis of isobutylene dibromide, a compound which is obtained in 65 to 75% yield by the action of bromine on tertiary amyl alcohol:[111]

$$(CH_3)_2CBrCH_2Br + H_2O \rightarrow (CH_3)_2CHCHO + 2HBr$$

Chloral reacts readily with sodium hydroxide yielding chloroform and sodium formate:

$$Cl_3CCHO + NaOH \rightarrow Cl_3CH + HCOONa$$

Aromatic halides react with difficulty with caustic, unless the halogen is activated by nitro groups attached to the aromatic nucleus.[112] These halides are converted to the corresponding phenol by heating with crystalline sodium acetate and copper bronze to about 220 - 250° in a sealed tube.[113]

The reaction of alkyl halides, RX, with silver nitrite generally results in the formation of a nitrated hydrocarbon, RNO_2, and an alkyl nitrite, RONO. The relative proportions of the two compounds obtained depend on the nature of the alkyl halide.[114] The chain length of the hydrocarbon radical does not seem to be a factor, but primary halides give nitro compounds in greater yield than secondary and tertiary halides. The normal halides give higher yields of the nitro compound than the branched chain halides. The reaction proceeds smoothly with methyl, ethyl, propyl and isopropyl iodides. Side reactions take place with higher molecular weight iodides and yields are lower.

Benzotrichloride condenses readily with phenol to form bis-(p-hydroxyphenyl)-phenylmethyl chloride, a compound which on hydrolysis gives benzaurin:[115]

$$C_6H_5CCl_3 + 2C_6H_5OH \rightarrow C_6H_5CCl(C_6H_4OH)_2 + 2HCl$$

A similar reaction takes place with dimethyl aniline, resulting in the formation of malachite green.

Attempted replacement of a halogen atom by various negative groups results in some exceptional cases in the substitution of the halogen by a hydrogen atom:[116]

$$(C_6H_5)_2CBrCOC_6H_5 \xrightarrow{HBr} (C_6H_5)_2CHCOC_6H_5$$

The halogen attached to the hydrocarbon group reacts in such cases as a *positive* atom, and the hydrogen in the resulting product is more or less reactive.

The replacement of halogens in organic compounds with *amino* groups has been considered in connection with amino compounds. The reaction of alkali metal derivatives of *acetoacetic ester* and of other compounds with a reactive methylene group has been dealt with in connection with the reaction of carbonyl compounds.

Alkali metal derivatives of polynuclear aromatic hydrocarbons such as naphthalene, anthracene, etc., reacting with alkyl halides yield dialkyl substituted hydrocarbons.[117] Isoamyl and isobutyl chlorides react especially well.

Alkyl halides are more susceptible to attack by nitric acid than non-halogenated hydrocarbons. Halonitro compounds or oxidation products result from primary or secondary halo hydrocarbons, according to their structure. Tertiary halides readily liberate a molecule of hydrogen halide, and the resulting olefinic compounds may yield nitrated products.[118]

Typical of the behavior of some alkyl halides toward fuming sulfuric acid is that of isoamyl chloride which yields hydroxyamylsulfonic acid, $HOC_5H_{10}SO_3H$.[119]

Alkyl halides may be reduced to the corresponding hydrocarbons with zinc and hydrochloric or acetic acid, or with sodium amalgam and water. The lower alkyl iodides are readily converted to the corresponding halogen-free hydrocarbon by reduction with a zinc-copper couple in the presence of some alcohol.[120]

Alkyl halides may also be reduced catalytically. The reduction may be carried out in alcoholic or aqueous medium in the presence of a platinum or palladium catalyst. Hydrogen under pressure is passed in until the calculated quantity has been absorbed.[121] Nickel has also been used occasionally as a catalyst.

Benzotrichloride, $C_6H_5CCl_3$, is reduced in the presence of colloidal palladium to tetrachloro- α,β-diphenylethane, $C_6H_5CCl_2CCl_2C_6H_5$. Benzal chloride yields some toluene and α,β-dichloro- α,β-diphenylethane,[122] $C_6H_5CHClCHClC_6H_5$.

Wurtz Reaction

The hydrocarbon radicals of an organic halide RX may be joined together by heating with metallic sodium:

$$2RI + 2Na \rightarrow R-R + 2NaI.$$

Other metals, among them lithium, calcium, magnesium, aluminum and copper are also capable of bringing about the reaction.[123] Metallic zinc was used in carrying out the earliest example of this type of reaction.[124] The reaction proceeds well, as a rule, with metallic sodium.

The *procedure* is as follows: Clean sodium, in 50% excess over the theoretically required quantity, is placed in dry ether in a flask provided with a reflux condenser and cooled in a mixture of ice and water. The alkyl halide is added slowly and, after the initial vigorous reaction has subsided, the mixture is heated to refluxing temperature. After the completion of the reaction, the clear solution is decanted from the unreacted sodium and the precipitated sodium halide and is distilled. The distillate is heated under reflux with metallic sodium and is then fractionally distilled.

Petroleum ether and other hydrocarbons may also be used as solvents instead of ether. Benzene and toluene cause a decrease in the rate of reaction, while ether has an accelerating effect. The reaction may be accelerated by the addition of one or two drops of acetonitrile or ethyl acetate.

The yields are often low and the product is apt to be contaminated with unsaturated hydrocarbons and products of reduction of the alkyl halide.[125]

The reaction proceeds especially well with the higher molecular iodides. Optically active compounds may be obtained from optically active halides. When a mixture of dissimilar halides RX, R′X is used three compounds, RR′, RR and R′R′ are formed simultaneously. The reaction fails with the tertiary halides. The reaction is applicable to α-halo acids, and to a mixture of an α-acid and an alkyl halide, although it proceeds badly in the latter case.[126] Better results are obtained in such cases by use of metallic silver, instead of sodium.

Mixed aralkyl hydrocarbons may be prepared by the Wurtz reaction (*Wurtz-Tollens-Fittig synthesis*):[123]

The procedure followed is the same as in the preparation of purely aliphatic hydrocarbons. The alkyl halide is used in 50% excess over the theoretically required amount. The reaction is usually complete within a few hours. Should reaction proceed slowly with sodium wire or pellets, powdered sodium or, preferably, powdered potassium may be employed.

On occasions reaction may be delayed for a considerable period, only to proceed with much vigor when it once gets under way, control becoming difficult. In such cases a little ethyl acetate or acetonitrile is introduced initially to promote the reaction, the halide mixture being then added gradually. The liquid generally begins to boil soon after reaction sets in; the halide mixture is then added at such a rate that the liquid continues to boil briskly. The liquid is heated toward the end in order to complete the reaction. Occasionally reaction proceeds very slowly and is complete only after several days heating. The method seldom fails however in the preparation of normal alkyl benzenes, and lack of success may be traced generally to faulty procedure.

The reaction has been applied to the synthesis of alkylated benzene derivatives from monobromo compounds. Ethyl and propyl derivatives are obtained in reasonably good yield, but some of the higher homologs are often formed in mediocre yield. It is possible to introduce two alkyl groups into the aromatic nucleus, the second in the *para* position with respect to the first, though the yields of the di-substituted derivative are generally low. The replacement of a second halogen in the *ortho* position, and especially one in the *meta* position proceeds only to a very limited extent. Brominated hydrocarbons give better results than chlorinated compounds. Iodo compounds react most readily, although they do not always give the best yields. The synthesis succeeds especially well with high molecular primary halides.[127]

The reaction of purely aromatic halides, ArX, with sodium to form hydrocarbons, Ar.Ar., proceeds poorly, giving only low yields of the hydrocarbon.[128]

The removal of halogen atoms from aromatic halo compounds with the resulting union of two carbon atoms may be accomplished by use of copper bronze (*Ullmann's reaction*). Better results may be obtained by this method than with sodium, providing an active bronze is used. Most commercial bronzes have been shown to be inactive.[129]

Unsymmetrical compounds cannot always be obtained by use of copper bronze.[130] Very high molecular halides also fail to react with copper bronze; reaction proceeds with such compounds when silver is used instead of copper.[131]

Precipitated copper powder is a more effective reagent than copper bronze. Iodine compounds react more readily than other halides. Sand may be used as a diluent.[132]

Catalytic Removal of Halogens with Hydrogen

Chlorine and other halogens may be removed from an organic halide by reaction with nascent hydrogen in the presence of palladium catalyst to produce coupling of the residues. Hydrazine is used as a source of hydrogen in the reaction.

The *procedure* is as follows: The halo compound in solution in methanol, ethanol or dioxane is made alkaline, the catalyst and hydrazine are added, and the mixture is boiled at atmospheric pressure, or heated in an autoclave. Palladium deposited on calcium carbonate is used as a catalyst.

Biphenyl has been obtained in 80% yield from bromobenzene by this method, and benzidine and biphenyl-*p,p*′-dicarboxylic acid in 60% and 40% yields from *p*-bromoaniline and *p*-bromobenzoic acid respectively. ω-Bromostyrene gives diphenylbutadiene in about 50% yield.

Dihalo aromatic compounds yield polyphenyls and the method offers the possibility of synthesizing complex chains from more or less readily accessible simple units.

Condensation may take place within the molecule. Thus 2,2′-diiododibenzyl gives dihydrophenanthrene in about 30% yield.

As a general rule, the condensation reaction assumes prominence in inverse ratio to the ease with which halogens are removable.[128]

References

1. Mouneyrat, *J. Russ. Chem. Soc.*, **32,** 390 (1900); *Chem. Zentr.* **1900 II.** 720; Schorlemmer, *Ann.* **161,** 263 (1872). *Cf* Markownikow, *J. prakt. Chem.*, (2) **59,** 562 (1899).
2. Strauss, *Germ. Patent* 267, 204; *Chem. Zentr.* **1913** II, 2013, *Germ. Patent* 266, 119.
3. Krafft and Merz, *Ber.* **8,** 1296 (1875); Kraft, *ibid.* **10,** 801 (1877); Tolloczko *Chem. Zentr.* **1913** II, 99; Hartmann, *Ber.*, **24,** 101 (1891).
4. Schorlemmer, *Ann.* **225,** 196 (1884); Schenfelen, *ibid,* **231,** 158 (1885).
5. Schorlemmer, *Ann.*, **188,** 249 (1877) *Cf.* Michael, *Ber.*, **34,** 4037 (1901); **39,** 2138 (1906).
6. Cain, *Z. physik. Chem.*, **12,** 751 (1893).
7. Prins, *J. prakt. Chem.* (2) **89,** 414, 425 (1914).
8. Pauret, *Compt. rend.*, **130,** 1191 (1900); *Bull. soc. chim.*, (3) **25,** 191, 293 (1901).
9. Meyer and Petrenko — Kritschenko, *Ber.*, **25,** 3306 (1892).
10. Lossner, *J. prakt. Chem.*, (2) **13,** 421 (1876).
11. van Bomburg, *Ber.*, **16,** 392 (1883); Henry, *Bull. Soc. Chim.*, (3) **19,** 348 (1890); Finkelstein, *Ber.*, **43,** 1528 (1910). *Cf* Wohl, *ibid.*, **39,** 1951 (1906).
12. Oppenheim, *Ber.*, **3,** 442 (1870).
13. Wildermann, *Z. physik. Chem.*, **9,** 12 (1892).
14. Swarts, *Bull. Acad. roy. Belg.* (3) **37,** 357 (1899); *ibid.* **1901,** 383.

15. Bodroux, *Compt. rend.*, **135**, 1350 (1902).
16. Dimroth and Bockemuller, *Ber.*, **64**, 516 (1931); Miller *et al.*, *J. Am. Chem. Soc.*, **59**, 198 (1937); Calfee *et al.*, *ibid.*, **59**, 2072 (1937); **61**, 3552 (1939); **62**, 267 (1940); Fukuhara *et al.*, *ibid.*, **60**, 427 (1933); **62**, 1171 (1940); **63**, 788, 2792 (1941).
17. Bigelow, *Chem. Revs.*, **40**, 51 (1947).
18. German patent 670, 140 (I.G.) *C.A.*, **33**, 2911 (1938).
19. Fredenhagen, *Angew. Chem.*, **52**, 289 (1939).
20. Simons and Lewis, *J. Am. Chem. Soc.*, **60**, 492 (1938); *German patent* 575,593.
21. Scherer, *Angew. Chem.*, **52**, 457 (1939).
22. *British patent* 465,885; *Frencb patents* 820,795; 805,704; 820,796.
23. *French patent* 820,796.
24. Daudt and Youker, *U.S. patent* 2,005,705 (1935); Midgley *et al.*, *U.S. patents* 1,838,847; 1,930,129; 2,007,208.
25. *U.S. patent* 2,230,925.
26. *U.S. patents*, 2,005,705; 2,005,706; 2,005,707; 2,005,708,; 2,005,709; 2,005,711; 2,005,713; 2,024,095; 2,062,743; 2,058,453.
27. Swarts, *Bull. Acad. roy. Belg.*, **35**, 375 (1898); 1920, 389.
28. van Howe, *ibid.*, **1913**, 1074.
29. Henne and Leicester, *J. Am. Chem. Soc.*, **60**, 864 (1938).
30. Henne *et al*, *ibid.*, **58**, 889 (1936); **59**, 2434 (1937); **61**, 938 (1939).
31. Henne *et al*, *ibid.*, **63**, 3478 (1941).
32. Booth and Burchfield, *ibid.*, **57**, 2070 (1935).
33. Nesmejanov and Kahn, *Ber.*, **67**, 370 (1934).
34. Davis and Dick, *J. Chem. Soc.*, **1932**, 483, 2042; Buckley *et al.*, *ibid.*, **1945**, 864; McCombie and Saunders, *Nature*, **158**, 382 (1946); Bradley, *U.S. patent*, 2,403,576 (1946).
35. Hoffmann, *J. Am. Chem. Soc.*, **70**, 2596 (1948).
36. Ruff, *Ber.*, **69**, 299 (1936).
37. Meslans, *Compt. rend.*, **111**, 882 (1890); *Ann. chim.*, (7) **1**, 374 (1894); Helferich and Gootz, *Ber.*, **62**, 2505 (1929); Fredenhagen, *Z. Elekrochem.*, **37**, 684 (1931).
38. Fredenhagen, *Z. Elektrochem.*, **37**, 684 (1931).
39. Simmons and Herman, *J. Am. Chem. Soc.*, **65**, 2064 (1943).
40. Meslans, *Compt. rend.*, **111**, 882 (1890); *Ann. chim.*, (7) **1**, 374 (1894).
41. Henne, *J. Am. Chem. Soc.*, **59**, 1200 (1937).
42. Henne and Renoll, *ibid.*, **58**, 887 (1936); Swarts, *Bull. Acad. roy. Belg.*, (3) **31**, 675 (1896).
43. Swarts, *Bull. Acad. roy. Belg.*, **1907**, 339; **1898**, 319; **1903**, 597; *Chem. Zentr.* **1903**, I, 13.
44. Swarts, *ibid.*, **22**, 781 (1936); *Bull. soc. chim. Belg.*, **46**, 10 (1937).
45. Henne, *J. Am. Chem. Soc.*, **60**, 1569 (1938).
46. *German patent* 600,706.
47. Meslans, *Compt. rend.*, **115**, 1080 (1892); **117**, 853 (1894); *Ann. chim.*, (7) **1**, 346 (1894).
48. Swarts, *Bull. soc. chim. Belg.*, **42**, 102 (1933).
49. Swarts, *Bull. Acad. roy. Belg.*, **1926**, 689, 721.
50. Swarts, *ibid.*, **1904**, 762.
51. Kinney, *J. Am. Chem. Soc.*, **60**, 3032 (1938); *Ind. Eng. Chem.*, **32**, 559 (1940); *J, Org. Chem.*, **6**, 220 (1941); **7**, 111 (1942).
52. Anschütz, *Ber.*, **12**, 2076 (1879) Ostromysslenski, *J. Russ, Phys.-Chem. Soc.*, **44**, 204 (1912).
53. Biltz, *Ber.*, **46**, 143 (1913).
54. Biltz, *ibid.*, **35**, 3527 (1902).
55. Erdmann, *J. prakt. Chem.*, (2) **85**, 78 (1912).
56. Wislicenus, *Ann.*, **313**, 207 (1900). *Cf. Z. phyzik. Chem.*, **21**, 387 (1896).
57. Vande Walle, *Bull. soc. chim. Belg.*, **27**, 209 (1913); Chavanne and Vos, *Compt. rend.*, **158**, 1582 (1914); *Chem. Ztg.* **37**, 622, Chavanne. *Bull. soc. chim. Belg.*, **28**, 240 (1914).
58. Thiele and Peter, *Ber.*, **38**, 2842 (1905).
59. Meyer, **Ann.**, **175**, 138 (1875).
60. Aronstein, *Ber.*, **14**, 607 (1881); **16**, 391 (1883).
61. Eltekow, *ibid.*, **6**, 1258 (1873); **8**, 1244 (1875); Faworsky, *Ann.*, **354**, 325 (1907); Michael *et al.*, *ibid.*, **379**, 263 (1911); **393**, 81 (1912); *J. Am. Chem. Soc.*, **38**, 653 (1916); Brunel, *ibid.*, **39**, 1978 (1917); *Ann.*, **384**, 245 (1911).
62. Michael *et al.*, *J, Am. Chem. Soc.*, **38**, 653 (1916).
63. Gustavson, *Ber.*, **16**, 958 (1883).
64. Meyer and Müller, *J. prakt. Chem.*, (2) **46**, 182 (1892).
65. Tissier, *Ann. chim.*, (6) **29**, 359, 361, 364 (1893).
66. Sabatier and Mailhe, *Compt rend.*, **156**, 659 (1913).
67. Segaller, *J. Chem. Soc.*, **105**, 106 (1914). *Cf.* Burke and Donnan, *ibid.*, **85**, 555 (1904); Brussof, *Z. physik. Chem.*, **34**, 129 (1900); Haywood, *J. Chem. Soc.*, **121**, 1904 (1922); Menschutkin and Wassilieff, *Z. physik. Chem.*, **5**, 589 (1890); Wislicenus, *Ann.*, **212**, 244 (1882); Preston and Jones, *J. Chem. Soc.*, **101**, 1930 (1912).
68. Dostrovsky and Hughes, *J. Chem. Soc.*, **1946**, 157.

69. Connant *et al.*, *J. Am. Chem. Soc.*, **47**, 476, 488 (1925).
70. Juvala, *Ber.*, **63**, 1989 (1930).
71. Paul, *ibid.*, **24**, 4253 (1891); Dixon, *J. Chem. Soc.*, **61**, 550 (1892).
72. Conrad and Bruckner, *Z. physik. Chem.*, **4**, 631 (1889).
73. Linnemann, *Ann.*, spl. **3**, 262 (1865).
74. Wislicenus, *ibid.*, **212**, 244 (1882).
75. Baumann, *ibid.*, **163**, 311 (1872).
76. Kutscherow, *Ber.*, **14**, 1532 (1881).
77. Petrenko — Kritchenko *et al.*, *J. Gen. Chem. U.S.S.R.*, **61**, 1777 (1929); *Bull. soc. chim.*, (4) **50**, 70 (1931).
78. Shoesmith and Rubli, *J. Chem. Soc.*, **131**, 3098 (1927).
79. Conant and Kirner, *J. Am. Chem. Soc.*, **46**, 232 (1924).
80. Bennett and Berry, *J. Chem. Soc.*, **131**, 1676 (1927).
81. Wislicenus, *Ann.*, **212**, 239 (1882); Hecht, *et al.*, *Z. physik. Chem.*, **4**, 273 (1889); Menschutkin, *ibid.*, **5**, 589 (1890); Burke and Donnan, *J. Chem. Soc.*, **85**, 555 (1904); *Z. physik. Chem*; **69**, 148 (1909); Slator, *J. Chem. Soc.*, **85**, 1286 (1904); **87**, 482 (1905); Slator and Twiss, *ibid.*, **95**, 93 (1909); Senter, *ibid.*, **91**, 460 (1907); **95**, 1827 (1909); Clarke, *ibid.*, **97**, 416 (1910).
82. Evans and Walker, *Trans. Faraday Soc.*, **40**, 384 (1945).
83. Strauss and Hussy, *Ber.*, **42**, 2168 (1909).
84. Lapworth, *Proc. Chem. Soc.*, **19**, 23 (1903).
85. Macbeth and Trail, *J. Chem. Soc.*, **127**, 892 (1925).
86. Kirner, *J. Am. Chem. Soc.*, **48**, 2745 (1926); Fuson, *et al.*, *ibid.*, **60**, 2404 (1938).
87. Fuson, *Chem. Revs.*, **16**, 1 (1935).
88. Borsche *et al.*, *Ber.*, **49**, 2222 (1916).
89. Borsche, *Ann.*, **386**, 356 (1911); **379**, 152 (1911); **402**, 81 (1913).
90. Talen, *Rec. trav. chim.*, **47**, 329 (1928); *Bull. soc. chim.*, (4) **44**, 1394 (1928).
91. Ringeissen, *Compt. rend.*, **198**, 2180 (1934).
92. Giua and Cherchi, *Gazz. chim. ital.*, **49**, (2), 152 (1919). *Cf.* Ullmann and Nádai, *Ber.*, **41**, 1870 (1908).
93. Robertson *et al.*, *J. Chem. Soc.*, **93**, 793 (1908); **101**, 1961 (1912); **105**, 1885 (1914).
94. Fischer, Ber., **32**, 1298 (1899); **35**, 3674 (1902); Troger and Meinecke, *J. prakt. Chem.*, (2) **106**, 203 (1923).
95. Fischer, *Ber.*, **30**, 2220, 2226 (1897).
96. Fischer, *Triphenylchlormethan in seinen chemishen Wirkungen als Säure chloride.* Dissert, Dresden (1905); Nicolaus, *Zur Kentnis des Diphenylcarbaminesaure chloride*, Dissert Borna, Leipzig (1907); Meyer, *J. prakt. Chem.*, (2) **82**, 521 (1910).
97. v. Meyer and Näke, *J. prakt. Chem.*, (2) **82**, 521 (1910).
98. Hecht *et al.*, *Z. physik. Chem.*, **4**, 273, 631 (1889); Wildermann and Disinmann, *ibid.*, **8**, 661 (1891).
99. Rothenburg, *Ber.*, **26**, 866 (1893).
100. Brusson, *J. Russ. Phys.-Chem. Soc.*, **32**, 7 (1900); *Chem. Zentr.*, **1901** I, 1063; *Z. physik. Chem.*, **8**, 661 (1891); Nef, *Ann.*, **309**, 128 (1899); **318**, 2 (1901); Burke and Donnan, *J. Chem. Soc.*, **85**, 558 (1904).
101. Nef, *Ann.*, **309**, 126 (1899).
102. Sabatier and Mailhe, *Compt. rend.*, **141**, 238 (1905); *Germ. Patent* 255,519 (1913).
103. Klages, *Ber.*, **37**, 1451 (1904); Baeyer, *Ann.*, **278**, 94, 107 (1894); Markovnikoff, *ibid.*, **302**, 27 (1898).
104. Faworski and Borgmann, *Ber.*, **40**, 4870 (1907).
105. Linnemann, *Ber.*, **10**, 1113 (1877); Michael, *ibid.*, **34**, 4217 (1901); Michael and Schulthess, *J. prakt. Chem.*, (2) **43**, 589 (1891).
106. v. Braun *et al.*, *Ber.*, **54**, 618 (1921); **56**, 1563 (1923).
107. Finkelstein, *Ber.*, **43**, 1530 (1910); Biilmann, *Rec. trav. chim.*, **36**, 313 (1917); **37**, 245 (1917).
108. Lespieau, *Bull. soc. chim.*, (4) **29**, 532 (1921).
109. Kunckell *et al.*, *Ber.*, **33**, 2656, 3261 (1900).
110. Michael and Leupold, *Ann.*, **379**, 287 (1911).
111. Whitmore *et al.*, *J. Am. Chem. Soc.*, **55**, 1136 (1933).
112. Meyer and Bergius, *Ber.*, **47**, 3155 (1914).
113. Rosenmund and Harns, *ibid.*, **53**, 2226 (1920).
114. Meyer, *Ann.*, **171**, 1 (1874); Reynolds and Adkins, *J. Am. Chem. Soc.*, **51**, 279 (1929). *Cf.* Kohler, *ibid.*, **38**, 898 (1916); Keppler and Meyer, *Ber.*, **25**, 1709 (1892); Braun and Sobecki, *ibid.*, **44**, 2528 (1911); Meyer and Locher, *ibid.*, **7**, 1510 (1874); **9**, 539 (1876); *Ann.*, **180**, 140 (1876).
115. Döbner, *Ann.*, **217**, 227 (1883).
116. Willstätter and Hottenroth, *Ber.*, **37**, 1776 (1904); Howk and McElvain, *J. Am. Chem. Soc.*, **54**, 282 (1932); Macbeth *et al.*, *J. Chem. Soc.*, **121**, 892, 904, 1116, 2169 (1922); Schiff,

Ber., **13**, 1406 (1880); Kohler, *Am. Chem. J.*, **41**, 417 (1909); Woodward and Fuson, *J. Am. Chem. Soc.*, **55**, 3472 (1933); Kohler and Tischler, *ibid.*, **54**, 1594 (1932); Meyer, *Ann.*, **380**, 212 (1911); Backes *et al.*, *J. Chem. Soc.*, **119**, 359 (1921); Kröhnke and Timmler, *Ber.*, **69**, 614 (1936); Seliwanow, *ibid.*, **25**, 3617 (1892); Stieglitz, *Am. Chem. J.*, **18**, 758 (1896); Henderson and Macbeth, *J. Chem. Soc.*, **121**, 892 (1922).
117. Hugel and Lerer, *Compt. rend.*, **195**, 249 (1932).
118. Konowalow, *J. Russ. Phys.-Chem. Soc.*, **36**, 220 (1904); *Chem. Zentr.*, **1904 I**, (1478).
119. Worstall, *J. Am. Chem. Soc.*, **25**, 932 (1903).
120. Gladstone and Tribe, *J. Chem. Soc.*, **26**, 445, 678, 961 (1873); Campbell and Parker, *ibid.*, **103**, 1292 (1915).
121. Busch and Stöve, *Ber.*, **49**, 1063 (1916); Rosenmund and Zetsche, *ibid.*, **51**, 578 (1918); Kelber, *ibid.*, **50**, 305 (1917); **54**, 2255 (1921).
122. Borsche and Heimbürger, *Ber.*, **48**, 452 (1915).
123. Fittig *et al.*, *Ann.*, **131**, 303 (1864); **144**, 277 (1867); **149**, 324 (1869); Spencer and Price, *J. Chem. Soc.*, **97**, 388 (1910); Lal and Dutt, *J. Indian Chem. Soc.*, **9**, 565 (1932); Kalischen. *J. Russ. Phys.-Chem. Soc.*, **46**, 447 (1914); Rupe and Burgin, *Ber.*, **44**, 1219 (1911); Ray and Dutt, *J. Indian Chem. Soc.*, **5**, 103 (1928); Hückel *et al.*, *J. prakt. Chem.*, (2) **142**, 208 (1935); Defreu, *Ber.*, **28**, 2649 (1895); Thöel and Tripke, *ibid.*, **28**, 2459 (1895); Auwers, *Ann.*, **419**, 111 (1919); Körner, *ibid.*, **216**, 223 (1882); Klages, *ibid.*, **40**, 2368 (1907); Stenzl and Fichter, *Helv. Chim. Acta*, **17**, 669 (1934); Wooster, *Chem. Revs.*, **11**, 1 (1932); Gilman and Wright, *J. Am. Chem. Soc.*, **55**, 2893 (1933).
124. Schorlemmer, *Ann.*, **144**, 184 (1867); **161**, 277 (1872); Young and Fortey, *J. Chem. Soc.*, **77**, 1126 (1900); Hell and Hägle, *Ber.*, **22**, 502 (1889).
125. Zander, *Ann.*, **214**, 167 (1882); Young and Fortey, *J. Chem. Soc.*, **77**, 1126 (1900); Faillebin, *Bull. soc. chim.*, (4) **35**, 160 (1924).
126. Schneider, *Jahresb.*, **1869**, 528; Zincke, *Ber.*, **2**, 738 (1869); Borsche and Fittig, *Ann.*, **133**, 119 (1815).
127. Schweinitz, *Ber.*, **19**, 641 (1886); Kraft and Gottig, *ibid.*, **21**, 3184 (1888).
128. Fittig, *Ann.*, **121**, 363 (1862); **132**, 201 (1864); Ullmann, *ibid.*, **332**, 40 (1904); Wibaut *et al.*, *Rec. trav. chim.*, **62**, 31 (1943).
129. Ullmann *et al.*, *Ann.*, **332**, 41 (1904); *Ber.*, **34**, 2176 (1901).
130. Meyer and Freitag, *Ber.*, **54**, 356 (1921); Späth and Gibian. *Monatsh.*, **55**, 342 (1930); Kenner and Shaw, *J. Chem. Soc.*, **1931**, 769. *Cf.* van Alphen, *Rec. trav. chim.*, **51**, 453 (1932).
131. Pummerer and Bittner, *Ber.*, **57**, 85 (1924).
132. Rule and Parsell, *J. Chem. Soc.*, **1935**, 571; Ullmann and Bielecki, *Ber.*, **34**, 2176 (1901); Yuan and Isao, *J. Chinese Chem. Soc.*, **3**, 358 (1935).
133. Kleinberg, *Chem. Revs.*, **40**, 381 (1947); Cason and Way, *J. Org. Chem.*, **1950**, 100; Barkovsky, *Ann. chim.*, (11) **19**, 491 (1944); Oldam, *J. Chem. Soc.*, **1950**, 100.
134. Hunsdiecker and Hunsdiecker, *Ber.*, **75**, 291 (1942); *U. S. patent* 2,176,181 (1939); Allen and Wilson, *Organic Syntheses*, **26**, 53 (1946).
135. Braun, *Organic Syntheses*, Coll. Vol. I, 428 (1941); Braun and Dobecki, *Ber.*, **44**, 1464 (1911); Suida and Drahowzal, *ibid.*, **75**, 991 (1942).
136. Schall and Matthaipoulos, *Ber.*, **29**, 1555 (1896); Kotz, *Ann.*, **358**, 195 (1908); Kotz and Steinhorst, *ibid.*, **379**, 15, 21 (1911).
137. Lieben, *Ann. Suppl.*, **7**, 218, 377 (1870); Pieroni and Tonnioli, *Gazz. chim. ital.*, **43** II, 620 (1913); *Chem. Zentr.*, **1914** I, 522; Pieroni, *Gazz. chim. ital.*; **42** I, 534 (1912); *Chem. Zentr.*, **1912 II**, 321.
138. Lederer, *German patent* 95,440.
139. Friedlander and Weinberg, *Ber.*, **18**, 1531 (1885); Knorr, *Ann.*, **236**, 99 (1886).
140. Brix, *Ann.*, **225**, 146 (1884); Köhnlein, *ibid.*, **225**, 171 (1884); Spindler, *ibid.*, **231**, 257 (1885); Kerez, *ibid.*, **231**, 285 (1885).
141. Diehls and Reinbeck, *Ber.*, **43**, 1274 (1910); Finkelstein, *ibid.*, **43**, 1528 (1910); Knoll and Co., *German patent* 230,172; *Chem. Ztg.*, **35**, Ref. 79 (1911).
142. Henry, *Bull. acad. roy. Belg.*, (3) **19**, 348 (1891); *Ber.*, **24**, Ref. 74 (1891).
143. Henry, *Bull. acad. roy. Belg.*, (3) **18**, 182 (1891); *Ber.*, **24**, Ref. 75 (1891); *ibid.* **17**, 1132 (1884); v. Braun and Steindorff, *ibid.*, **38**, 174 (1905).
144. Griess and Ruff, *Ber.*, **69**, 604 (1936). *Cf.* Cuculo and Bigelow, *J. Am. Chem. Soc.*, **74**, 710 (1952).
145. Ruff and Willenberg, *Ber.*, **73**, 724 (1940).
146. Bigelow and Fukuhara, *J. Am. Chem. Soc.*, **63**, 788 (1914).
147. McBee and Pierce, *Ind. Eng. Chem.*, **39**, 399 (1947).
148. Klein and Ruff, *Z. anorg. allgem. Chem.*, **193**, 176 (1930).
149. Henne and Trott, *J. Am. Chem. Soc.*, **69**, 1820 (1947).
150. *U.S. patent* 2,396,076.
151. Swarts, *Bull. acad. roy. Belg.*, **6**, 399 (1920).
152. Swarts, *Anales reale soc. espan. fis. y quim (Madrid)*, **27**, 683 (1929).

153. Alderson *et al.*, *J. Am. Chem. Soc.*, **67**, 918 (1945).
154. Ramler and Simons, *ibid.*, **65**, 389 (1943).
155. Swarts, *Bull. soc. chem. Belg.*, **38**, 99 (1929).
156. Hatch *et al.*, *J. Am. Chem. Soc.*, **70**, 1093 (1948).
157. Wehl, *Ber.*, **39**, 1951 (1906).
158. Haekl and Henne, *J. Am. Chem. Soc.*, **63**, 2692 (1914); Henne and Whaley, *ibid.*, **64**, 1157 (1942); Henne and Hinkamp, *ibid.*, **67**, 1195 (1945). *Cf.* Elmore *et al.*, *ibid.*, **62**, 3340 (1940).
159. Fowler *et al.*, *Ind. Eng. Chem.*, **39**, 292, 343, 380, 399 (1947); *U.S. patent* 2,533,132 (1944); *U.S. Atomic Energy Commission Rep. MDDG*-898, June 30, 1943; Cady *et al.*, *Ind. Eng. Chem.*, **39**, 236 (1937); Bigelow *et al.*, *ibid.*, **39**, 360 (1947); Barbour *et al.*, *J, Appl. Chem.*, **2**, 127 (1952).
160. Simons, *Fluorine Chemistry*, N.Y. 1950; *Chem. Eng. News*, **30**, 4514 (1952).
161. Roe, *Organic Reactions*, V, 123 (1949).
162. Hazeldine *et al.*, *J. Chem. Soc.*, **1951**, 609.

CHAPTER 12

GRIGNARD REACTION

Many organic halides, RX, react with metallic magnesium under suitable conditions forming organomagnesium complexes of the type RMgX. These complexes have the ability to combine with carbonyl groups to form addition compounds.(*)

$$R'COR'' + RMgX \rightarrow$$ 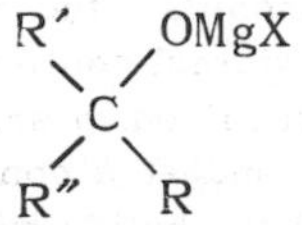

On treating the resulting magnesium complex with dilute acids an alcohol is formed:

$$RR'R''COMgX + HCl \rightarrow RR'R''COH + ClMgX$$

This is representative of a large number of other reactions, involving organomagnesium halides, characterized by the addition of the organic and halomagnesium halides at a multiple bond. The reaction with nitriles and esters may be cited as other examples:

$$R'CN + RMgX \rightarrow R'C(R) = NMgX \rightarrow R'COR$$

$$R'COOR'' + RMgX \rightarrow R'C(R)_2OMgX \rightarrow R'C(R)_2OH$$

These reactions are indicative of the high reactivity of organomagnesium complexes, which has come to evidence in a large variety of other reactions. For this reason these complexes have been of incalculable value in organic synthesis. The great importance of the method lies in the fact that it permits

---

(*)The Grignard reaction had its origin in an observation of Barbier[1] that in the *Friedel-Ladenburg* reaction, involving the introduction of alkyl groups into a carbonyl group by use of zinc alkyl, magnesium could be substituted for zinc. Barbier also noted that it was not necessary to prepare the alkylmagnesium compound separately, and that a mixture of alkyl halide and metallic magnesium gave the desired result:

$$(CH_3)_2C = CHCH_2CH_2COCH_3 + CH_3I + Mg \rightarrow (CH_3)_2C = CHCH_2CH_2C(CH_3)_2OMgI$$

$$\rightarrow (CH_3)_2C = CHCH_2CH_2C(OH)(CH_3)_2$$

Grignard[2] correctly explained the nature of the reaction and showed that an organomagnesium halide, CH_3MgI, was formed as an intermediate, which reacted with the carbonyl compound to form the now well-known complex.

the formation of new carbon-to-carbon bonds and makes possible many complex syntheses.

Organomagnesium halides will also be referred to as Grignard reagents or compounds.

Preparation of Organomagnesium Compounds

The *general procedure* followed in preparing an organomagnesium halide is as follows:

The required quantity of magnesium in the form of turnings, 3 mm long and 0.6 mm thick, is placed in a dry flask provided with a sealed stirrer and a reflux condenser; the air is displaced with a current of dry nitrogen, a little ether and a crystal of iodine are added, then a small amount of the halide is introduced to initiate the reaction. If reaction fails to proceed spontaneously, the mixture is heated to 45°, although more frequently it is necessary to apply external cooling in order to moderate the reaction. After the initial vigorous reaction has subsided to some extent, the halide, mixed with 1 to 3 volumes of ether, is added slowly and at a constant rate, while the liquid in the flask is stirred. After the addition of all the halide mixture, the flask is heated until the reaction is complete.[3]

It is important that both the reflux condenser and the dropping funnel used for the introduction of the halide-ether mixture, be protected from atmospheric moisture by means of calcium chloride tubes. The magnesium turnings must be clean and, in particular, free from any oily matter. Commercial magnesium in the form of turnings or of coarse powder may be used. The quality of magnesium employed may greatly affect the yields obtained. The magnesium should be stored dry and, if desirable, it may be washed with pure, dry ether by decantation. The impurities present in the metal remain as a dark powder after the completion of the reaction. The metal is used in an amount corresponding to the halide or in slight excess. The ether must be anhydrous and free from alcohol. Commercial alcohol-free ether distilled over phosphorus pentoxide is satisfactory. The ether may also be dried by storing it over sodium wire. The halide must be in a very pure form and free from acids, water or alcohol.

It is important that the halide be added slowly in order to avoid the presence of any large excess of unreacted halide and thus to prevent the reaction

$$RMgX + XR \rightarrow R.R + MgX_2$$

which proceeds quite readily when iodides are employed.[4] This reaction is favored if an excessive amount of iodine is used for initiation of the reaction.

Proportions of the organomagnesium halide and the hydrocarbon, R.R, formed from various halides are given below:[5]

	Proportion of:	
	RMgX,%	R.R,%
n-Butyl iodide	—	9.2
Hexadecyl iodide	64.4	29.6
Dodecyl iodide	64.8	29.2
Dodecyl chloride	91.0	4.7
n-$C_{14}H_{29}I$	64.0	29.6
n-$C_{18}H_{37}I$	66.5	27.8
Benzyl chloride	87.5	9.4
α-Naphthylmethyl chloride	—	high
Benzyl iodide	62.0	38.0

Aryl iodides give an appreciable quantity of diphenyl or its homologs; allyl bromide and iodide and cinnamyl halides also give hydrocarbons R.R, though in lesser amount.

The coupling reaction has been reduced to a minimum by proceeding in dilute solution, and in such a way as to use up the magnesium compound as rapidly as it is formed.[400]

Another possible side reaction is the formation of a saturated and an unsaturated hydrocarbon through a disproportionation reaction,

$$2C_nH_{2n} + IX + Mg \rightarrow C_nH_{2n+2} + C_nH_{2n} + MgX_2$$

which apparently takes place via the intermediate appearance of free radicals and is favored by higher temperatures. These side reactions may be avoided almost completely by using the chlorides.[6] High yields may be obtained from the chloro compounds when water and oxygen are completely excluded from the reaction mixture.

The reaction of the organic halide, RX, with an atomic proportion of magnesium leads to the formation of an organomagnesium compound, R_2Mg:

$$2RX + 2Mg \rightarrow R_2Mg + MgX_2$$

The organomagnesium compound, R_2Mg, may be assumed to result also through the interaction of two molecules of the organomagnesium halide:[7]

$$2RMgX \rightarrow R_2Mg + MgX_2$$

This reaction is apparently reversible and proceeds to an equilibrium point (*Schlenk equilibrium*).[430] The amount of dialkyl magnesium formed increases with increase in the length of the alkyl chain. The proportion of the organomagnesium halide, RMgX, remaining unchanged in solution when the pure halides are dissolved in anhydrous pure ether are given below for a number of halides:

	% Mg as RMgX		% Mg as RMgX
CH_3MgI	87	$CH_3CH_2CH_2MgBr$	24
C_2H_5MgI	43	$CH_3CH_2CH_2MgCl$	17
C_2H_5MgBr	41	C_6H_5MgI	38
$CH_3CH_2CH_2MgI$	24	C_6H_5MgBr	30

The equilibrium is influenced by heat, the amount of R_2Mg increasing with rising temperature.

Secondary and tertiary alkyl halides react abnormally; for example, isopropyl iodide yields propylene, propane and 2,3-dimethylbutane:

$$2(CH_3)_2CHI + Mg \rightarrow CH_3CH{=}CH_2 + CH_3CH_2CH_3 + MgI_2$$

$$2(CH_3)_2CHI + Mg \rightarrow (CH_3)_2CHCH(CH_3)_2 + MgI_2$$

$$2(CH_3)_2CHI + Mg \rightarrow CH_3CH{=}CH_2 + MgI_2 + H_2$$

tert-Butyl and -amyl chlorides react similarly.[8]

tert-Alkylmagnesium chlorides have been prepared successfully, however, by carrying out the reaction in dilute ethereal solution and introducing the halide-ether mixture very slowly to the reaction flask containing the required quantity of freshly turned magnesium and internally coated with a very thin deposit of iodine. The reaction may be initiated by the addition of a few drops of ethyl or *n*-butyl bromide if necessary.[431]

Organomagnesium halides are attacked by atmospheric oxygen, and while it is true that a dry current of air is without effect on the reaction of butyl bromide with magnesium,[9] it is none the less preferable to carry out the reaction in an inert atmosphere,[10] especially when long boiling is required.

The reaction between magnesium and an organic halide is promoted by various compounds. Among these are tertiary amines,[11] $AlCl_3$, $AlBr_3$, nickel chloride,[12] β-bromoethyl ether, iodoform, acetic ester, alkyl sulfides, diethyl selenide, dimethyl telluride, 1,4-dioxane, 1,4-dithion, 1,4-thioxane, *p*-chlorobenzene, diphenyl- and diisoamyl sulfoxide, ethyl propyl sulfide, pentamethylene ether and tribenzyl-phosphine oxide. All these compounds combine with organomagnesium halides to form complexes.[13]

Retardation of the reaction is occasionally caused by the fact that the organomagnesium halide formed is insoluble in the solvent used and coats the surface of the granules of magnesium. In such cases the reaction may be accelerated by the addition of an organic halide which forms a readily soluble organomagnesium compound. A magnesium compound has been obtained, for example, in 36% yield from 4-bromoveratrol, and in 80-82% yield from pentamethylbromobenzene by use of this method.

Ethyl bromide may be used effectively for the purpose. The best yields are obtained when 1 or 2 moles of ethyl bromide are used for each mole of Grignard reagent to be prepared. The metal is used in 25% excess and for every gram molecule of RX and ethyl bromide, 1 liter of ether is taken.[14]

The magnesium may be activated by various methods. Iodine is added to the reaction mixture for this purpose. Activation may also be brought about by alloying the magnesium with sodium or with copper. The most effective method consists in the use of special catalysts of which the best is that proposed by Gilman.

Gilman's Catalyst is prepared in the following manner: Five grams of a 100-200 mesh magnesium-copper alloy powder containing 12.75% copper are ground in a mortar with 1 gram iodine; the mixture is heated to 300° over a free flame under vacuum until the iodine disappears completely. The operation requires about 10 minutes. Care should be exercised to prevent the melting of the powder. After cooling, the powder is exposed to atmospheric air for 15 to 20 minutes and is stored in a sealed container.[15]

A small amount of the activator, generally 0.25-0.5 gm, is added to approximately 15% of the halide in 25% ethereal solution. The activator is heated in a test tube over a burner and the powder is added, while still warm, to the halide solution. As soon as the original vigorous reaction subsides, the liquid is added to the mixture of magnesium with a small portion of the halide, and the remaining halide is introduced gradually.

An *activator* may also be prepared by treating magnesium with iodine under benzene. Five grams of magnesium and some iodine are covered with 100 cc of benzene, 5 cc of ether are added drop by drop while the mixture is stirred. Stirring is continued for 10 minutes, then the benzene and ether are distilled off on a water bath, and the residue is heated at 150-160° for five minutes and cooled. The material should be stored out of contact with atmospheric moisture. The activator is heated, before use, until a slight amount of iodine vapors appears and is then cooled for 4 minutes while protected from atmospheric moisture.

A small portion of ethyl orthosilicate, $(C_2H_5O)_4Si$, is claimed to be an excellent activator giving good results even in the absence of ethyl ether.[432]

The solvent employed has a marked effect on the reaction rate. With many halides, yields of the organomagnesium compound are higher in ether than either in benzene or in petroleum ether. This is the case, for example, with *n*-butyl and phenyl bromides, benzyl chloride, *o*-bromotoluene, β-bromostyrene and ethyl iodide. Cyclohexyl bromide, on the other hand, gives a higher yield of the magnesium compound in toluene solution.[16] The reaction often proceeds with difficulty in solvents other than ether, although reaction may be accelerated considerably by adding small amounts of a tertiary amine. Yields are satisfactory, as a rule, when the reaction is carried out in di-*n*-butyl ether and methyl ethers of higher alcohols, 1,3-dioxane and N-alkylmorpholines.[17] The optimum concentration of the reagent in ethyl ether generally lies between 30 and 40%; for the *n*-butylmagnesium bromide, it is 55%, and for the *n*-butylmagnesium chloride, about 70%.[18]

Ether combines with organomagnesium halides, and it is impossible to isolate the complex free of ether by evaporation of the solvent, except by heating the residual mass at 150° for a long period. The reagent thus freed of ether becomes insoluble in ether, however, and cannot be used for synthetic purposes.[7] The structure

$$[(C_2H_5)_2O]_2 ::: Mg(R)X$$

has been assigned to the organomagnesium halide-ether complex.[19]

The organomagnesium halide may be precipitated from its ethereal solution by the addition of dioxane, but the precipitate carries dioxane of constitution. Magnesium alkyls are not thus precipitated but remain in solution.[20]

Grignard compounds may be prepared through the direct reaction of organic halides with finely divided metallic magnesium in the absence of a solvent. Reaction proceeds slowly, however, and long heating at an elevated temperature is necessary.[21] Thus, phenylmagnesium chloride results on heating 4 parts chlorobenzene and 1 part magnesium in an autoclave at 160-170°.[22] This compound may be prepared also by heating chlorobenzene with magnesium under a reflux condenser.[23] This method is not of general applicability largely because the organomagnesium compound decomposes at the temperature at which the reaction proceeds, and is of little preparative value, especially since the complex obtained must still be brought into solution before it can be employed for synthetic purposes.

Iodo compounds react with magnesium most readily, although they do not give the best yield because side reactions take place to a greater extent with iodides than with other halides.[24] The reaction proceeds readily with bromides and yields are generally high.[25] The best yields of the organomagnesium halide are obtained from primary alkyl halides. The reaction velocity of normal alkyl bromides and iodides decreases with increasing molecular weight.[26] Secondary and, more particularly, tertiary halides give organomagnesium halides in low yield. Thus, a 20 to 30% yield of the magnesium complex is obtained with *tert*-butyl bromide, with the greater portion of the halide converted to butylene.[27] Bromopentamethylene benzene, 4-bromoveratrol, *p*-dibromobenzene and *p*-bromobenzyl bromide react poorly with magnesium.[28]

The yields of halomagnesium compounds obtained from various organic bromides under identical experimental conditions are given below:[29]

Bromide	Yield of Organo Magnesium Halide (%)	Bromide	Yield of Organo Magnesium Halide (%)
ethyl	93	*tert*-amyl	24
n-propyl	92	*n*-hexyl	92
isopropyl	84	*n*-heptyl	89
n-butyl	94	*n*-octyl	88
isobutyl	87	bromobenzene	95
sec-butyl	78	*o*-bromotoluene	93
tert-butyl	25	*m*-bromotoluene	88
n-amyl	89	*p*-bromotoluene	87
isoamyl	88	α-bromonaphthalene	95
sec-butyl	67	β-bromonaphthalene	84

Mesityl bromide reacts rapidly in ethereal solution, while triphenyl bromobenzene reacts only in boiling toluene, giving the magnesium complex in 84% yield.[30]

9-Bromoanthracene, 2-bromofluorene and bromopyran do not form organomagnesium halides. 9,10-Dibromoanthracene fails to react with magnesium in ether, although it reacts well in a mixture of benzene and butyl ether, yielding a monobromomagnesium derivative.[31] γ-Tetrahydrofurylpropyl chloride forms a halomagnesium complex.

Halo compounds containing a free *hydroxyl* group or an enolizable carbonyl group are incapable of giving a magnesium complex.

Among *halo ketones*, bromocamphor reacts normally;[32] δ-aceto-*n*-butylmagnesium iodide rapidly undergoes ring closure however:[33]

$$CH_3CO(CH_2)_3CH_2I + Mg \rightarrow CH_3CO(CH_2)_3CH_2MgI$$

$$\rightarrow CH_3\overline{C(OMgI)(CH_2)_3CH_2} \rightarrow CH_3\overline{C(OH)(CH_2)_3CH_2}$$

2-Chloroethyl-N-diethylamine fails to form a halomagnesium complex, but such complexes may be obtained from 3-chloropropyl- or 5-chloropentyldialkyl amines and from chloroalkylmethylaniline.[34]

Halo ethers in which the halogen is in the vicinity of oxygen, as in

$$ClCH_2OCH_3$$

do not form halomagnesium complexes.[35] If the halogen is further removed from the oxygen, then alcohol may be split off according to the equation:[36]

$$BrCH_2CH(R)OC_2H_5 + Mg \rightarrow BrMgCH_2CH(R)OC_2H_5$$

$$\rightarrow CH_2{=}CHR + C_2H_5OMgBr$$

Halomagnesium complexes have been obtained, however, from certain halo ethers,[37] such as $CH_3O(CH_2)_3MgI$, $C_5H_{11}O(CH_2)_3MgI$, $C_5H_{11}O(CH_2)_4MgBr$, $C_5H_{11}O(CH_2)_5MgBr$.

Unsaturated halogen compounds may be converted to halomagnesium complexes only under special conditions. Allylmagnesium bromide may be obtained in 90% yield by adding a 0.5 molar equivalent of allyl bromide in 7.5 molar equivalents of ether to 3 atomic equivalents of magnesium covered with 25 cc of ether while the ether is gently boiled.[38]

Vinyl bromide, reacting with metallic magnesium, gives mainly acetylene. Good yields of the vinylmagnesium halides may be obtained by allowing the bromide and magnesium to react in the presence of a carbonyl compound.[39] Substituted vinyl bromides, such as $C_5H_{11}CBr{=}CH_2$ and $C_5H_{11}CH{=}CHBr$, give low yields of the magnesium compound which, however, are incapable of the normal reactions of such compounds.[40] Vinyl halides with aromatic substituents give better yields of the magnesium complex.[41] An anomalous reaction takes place with cinnamyl halides:[42]

$$C_6H_5CH{=}CHCH_2X + Mg \rightarrow C_6H_5CH{=}CHCH_2MgX$$
$$\rightarrow C_6H_5C(MgX){=}CHCH_3$$

Magnesium reacts with disubstituted vinyl bromides only when both substituents are identical.[43] Better yields of the magnesium compound is obtained by use of magnesium-copper alloys in the form of wire.

Among dihalo unsaturated compounds, 1,4-dibromo-2-butene gives butadiene.[44]

In the reaction of *polyhalo compounds* with magnesium, elimination of halogens with the formation of olefins is often observed. Olefin formation by this process is observed with dihalo compounds in which the halogens are attached to adjacent carbon atoms. Methylene iodide, CH_2I_2, seems to react with two atoms of magnesium;[45] ethylene dibromide gives only ethylene, while 1,3-dibromopropane gives trimethylene, $\overline{CH_2CH_2CH_2}$, with a small amount of hexamethylene dimagnesium dibromide, $BrMg(CH_2)_6MgBr$.[46] Partial conversion to a dimagnesium compound takes place occasionally. For example, dibromo compounds,

$$BrCH_2(CH_2)_nCH_2Br$$

with values of *n* ranging from 2 to 5, give dimagnesium compounds in 50% yield.[47] The formation of unsaturated compounds is avoided by using the halo compound in four- to fivefold excess.

Iodobenzene, *p*-iodotoluene, *m*-bromoaniline, *p*-bromophenol and α-bromonaphthalene react with magnesium powder at their boiling point forming the respective organomagnesium halides. Aryl chlorides and all lower alkyl chlorides up to the butyl derivatives react only when heated to about 270° in a sealed tube for several hours. Alkyl chlorides higher in the series than the butyl derivatives react when heated with magnesium powder at their boiling point for a few minutes.

Halogenated benzene derivatives generally react with difficulty or not at all with magnesium. *p*-Methoxybromobenzene and *p*-methoxybenzyl bromide react with activated magnesium.[48] 4-Bromoveratrol reacts under special conditions while *o*- and *p*-nitrobenzene fail to react;[49] methoxybenzyl chloride[50] and nitrated bromo-naphthalenes[51] also fail to react, and *p*-chloro and *p*-bromophenyl ether react slowly.[52]

Among *halo esters*, p- and *m*-bromobenzoic esters fail to react with magnesium. The reactivity of the halogen is not influenced by a carboxyl group attached to a side chain. A halogen attached to the side chain, as in $BrCH_2C_6H_4COOC_2H_5$, is reactive.[53]

Among *halo aromatic amines*, *o*-iodo- and *o*-bromodimethylaniline react with magnesium quite readily, while *p*-bromodimethylaniline reacts very poorly.[54]

There is resistance to the entrance of more than one magnesium atom into the nucleus of aromatic polyhalocompounds.[55] Tribromotoluene does not react with magnesium.

Phenyldimagnesium bromide, $BrMgC_6H_4MgBr$, may be obtained in 40% yield through the reaction of bromophenylmagnesium bromide with magnesium in the presence of two molecular equivalents of ethyl bromide. The dimagnesium compounds corresponding to 4,4′-dihalodiphenyls are also obtained in 40% yield by this method. The yield is raised to 72% when magnesium iodide is added to the reaction mixture.[56]

3-Bromo- and 3,5-dibromopyridine do not react with an activated magnesium-copper alloy; a partial reaction takes place with 2-bromopyridine in the presence of some ethyl bromide.[57] 2-Chloromethylbenzofuran reacts with magnesium to form the chloromagnesium salt of *o*-allenylphenol, $ClMgOC_6H_4CH{=}C{=}CH_2$.[433]

Organomagnesium Compounds of Acetylene and Other Compounds with Reactive Hydrogen

Acetylene reacting with an ethereal solution of ethylmagnesium bromide yields acetylene dimagnesium bromide:[58]

$$HC \equiv CH + 2C_2H_5MgBr \rightarrow BrMgC \equiv CMgBr + 2C_2H_6$$

The compound is prepared in the following manner:[59] Pure, dry gaseous acetylene is passed at a slow rate for 24 hours through a solution of ethylmagnesium bromide prepared by the reaction of 19.2 gm magnesium ribbon with 88 gm of ethyl bromide dissolved in 230 cc of ether. The reaction product separates as a turbid, viscous layer.

Acetylene monomagnesium bromide is prepared from the dimagnesium compound by conducting acetylene under 0.5 atmosphere positive pressure at 15 to 20°C for 9 to 10 hours through a solution of the magnesium compound:[60]

$$BrMgC \equiv CMgBr + HC \equiv CH \rightarrow 2HC \equiv CMgBr$$

The monomagnesium compound is obtained in 76 to 85% yield. The compound has also been prepared through the reaction of acetylene with phenylmagnesium bromide.[401]

Acetylenic hydrocarbons of the type $RC \equiv CH$ may also be converted to their halomagnesium derivatives by reaction with ethylmagnesium bromide. Vinylacetylene, $CH_2{=}CHC \equiv CH$, can thus be converted to the corresponding halomagnesium compound.[61] Such acetylenic organomagnesium halides react in the normal manner of Grignard reagents, but are stable toward ammonia.[62]

The reaction of Grignard reagents with acetylenic ketones results in the formation of ethylenic ketones:[402]

$$RCOC \equiv CR' \xrightarrow{CH_3MgI} RCOCH = C(CH_3)R'$$

Indene reacts with organomagnesium compounds in the manner of acetylene and monosubstituted acetylene derivates, yielding indene magnesium bromide:

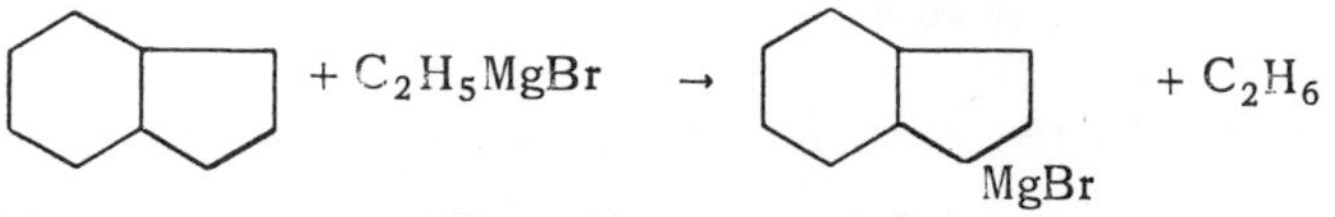

Fluorene and *cyclopentadiene* react similarly.[63]

The preparation of *halomagnesium pyrrole* may be carried out simply through the reaction of pyrrole with a mixture of the halo alkyl and magnesium in absolute ether; the reaction is complete within one-half hour. *Indole-* and *carbazolemagnesium halides* can also be prepared by this method.[64]

Acetomesitylene yields a halomagnesium compound, apparently through an indirect replacement of a hydrogen atom in the acetyl group:

$$(CH_3)_3C_6H_2COCH_3 + RMgBr \rightarrow (CH_3)_3C_6H_2COCH_2MgBr + RH$$

Similar substitution reactions are occasionally observed in the aromatic series. For example, anisol heated at 250° with ethylmagnesium bromide yields $CH_3OC_6H_4MgBr$.[65] Toluene similarly yields $CH_3C_6H_4MgBr$.[66]

Organomagnesium fluorides are generally prepared with great difficulty. *n*-Amylmagnesium fluoride has been obtained by allowing *n*-amyl fluoride to react with magnesium for a week,[67] while phenylmagnesium fluoride has been prepared by allowing phenyl fluoride to remain in contact with magnesium-copper alloy for a period of 18 months at room temperature.[68]

Grignard reagents of perfluoroalkyl compounds containing another halogen have been prepared by carrying out the reaction at a low temperature in carefully chosen solvents and under rigidly controlled conditions.[434] Perfluoroalkyl Grignard reagents are highly sensitive to heat.

Evaluation of Grignard Reagents

Two methods are available for the quantitative evaluation of Grignard reagents:

1. A gas analytical method[69] similar to Zerevitinov's method, which utilizes the formation of a gaseous hydrocarbon by the reaction:

$$2RMgX + H_2SO_4 \rightarrow 2RH + MgSO_4 + MgX_2$$

This method is applicable, of course, only if the hydrocarbon formed in the reaction is a gas.

2. Gilman's volumetric method[70] which is carried out in the following manner:

An aliquot part of the solution of organomagnesium halide, about 20 cc, measured with an accuracy of 0.1 cc, is poured slowly into 50 cc of distilled water. The cylinder is washed with distilled water, and the washings are combined with the main mixture.

Twenty cubic centimeters of 0.25N sulfuric acid are added and the mixture is heated to complete the reaction. The liquid is then cooled and the excess of sulfuric acid is titrated with standard sodium hydroxide solution, using methyl orange as an indicator. The amount of halomagnesium compound is calculated on the basis of the equation:

$$2RMgX + H_2SO_4 \rightarrow 2RH + MgSO_4 + MgX_2$$

The values obtained by this method are usually a little high.

As an alternative method, the inorganic chloride formed may be determined by titration with standard silver nitrate solution.

Qualitative Test for the Detection of Organomagnesium Halides

Gilman and Schulze[71] have developed a qualitative method for the detection of organomagnesium halides, which may be used for determining the end point of reactions carried out with these compounds. The test is carried out in the following manner:

One-half to one cubic centimeter of the solution to be tested is added to an equal volume of a 1% solution of Michler's ketone in benzene and the reaction product is hydrolyzed by slowly adding 1 cc of water, while the mixture is shaken slowly. A few drops of a 0.2% solution of iodine in acetic acid is then added whereupon a characteristic blue-green color appears if an organomagnesium halide is present. Very minute quantities of the reagent can be detected by this method. An excess of Michler's ketone solution is used if amines are present in the solution to be tested.[72]

Acid halides give a color reaction with Michler's ketone.

Stability of Grignard Reagents

In common with most organometallic compounds, organomagnesium halides are sensitive to oxygen. They may be regarded as completely stable, however, when protected from moisture and atmospheric oxygen.[73] Organomagnesium halides are stable also toward light. The concentration of the organomagnesium halide may suffer some decrease in a highly concentrated solution.

The strength of the bond between the organic radical and magnesium in organomagnesium halides has been determined for a number of radicals by making use of the reaction of iodine with such compounds, and taking the rate of generation of RH as an inverse measure of bond strength.[74] Bond strength decreases in the order

$$\text{iso-}C_4H_9 > CH_3 > n\text{-}C_4H_9 > sec\text{-}C_4H_9 > n\text{-}C_3H_7 > C_2H_5 > \text{iso-}C_3H_7$$

When acetylene dimagnesium bromide in ethereal solution is kept for three or four weeks, it is converted to a crystalline product of low reactivity, melting at a comparatively high temperature. The compound is probably magnesium carbide, C_2Mg.

Warning! Work with small quantities of solutions of organomagnesium halides in ether presents no particular danger, but large quantities of such solutions may be a great source of danger, if carelessly handled. For example, the addition of water to a supposedly though not really exhausted solution of the reagent, may be fraught with serious danger.

Procedure in Carrying out Grignard Reaction

The Grignard reaction is carried out in the following manner:

The compound dissolved in ether is added to the solution of the organomagnesium halide at such a rate that the solution boils continuously. If the compound is insoluble in ether, it may be dissolved in benzene, petroleum ether, etc. Solid compounds may be added to an ethereal solution of the organomagnesium halide in the form of a powder. If there is a possibility of reduction, any temporary excess of the organomagnesium halide is avoided, by gradually adding the solution of the Grignard reagent to the solution of the compound. The reaction generally proceeds quite rapidly in most cases.

The magnesium complex resulting from the reaction is then decomposed, carrying out the operation with great care in order to assure the success of the preparation and to avoid danger. Rapid dilution and cooling by the addition of water and ice generally accomplishes the desired result. Decomposition with water results in the formation of magnesium hydroxide. The formation of this compound may be avoided by adding dilute hydrochloric or sulfuric acid to the diluted, cooled reaction mixture. It is preferable to pour the reaction mixture on ice, and then to add the acid.

If the reaction product is sensitive to acids and likely to polymerize when decomposition is carried out with an acid, ammonium chloride may be used in place of the acid.

The success of the Grignard reaction often depends upon the rapidity with which the operation is carried out.

The ether, as well as other reagents must be quite dry. The ether is best kept dry by storing it over metallic sodium. The reaction often proceeds only when ether dried over phosphorus pentoxide is employed,[76] though it has been carried out successfully in some cases with moist ether, using an excess of the reagent.[77]

If it becomes necessary to employ a high-boiling solvent as the reaction medium, the ether used in the preparation of the organomagnesium halide is removed as much as possible by distillation under vacuum at 100-105°, and the desired solvent is added. Benzene and ethers of higher alcohols are suitable solvents. Among the latter, methyl benzyl, methyl cyclohexyl, amyl and butyl ethers are often employed.[75]

The use of rubber stoppers should be strictly avoided, since rubber inhibits the reaction. Glass, or new, paraffin coated cork stoppers are satisfactory.[78]

The rate of reaction is proportional to the concentration of the organomagnesium halide in the solution. The optimum concentration of the reagent appears to be 30-40%, although occasionally concentrations as high as 70% are employed.[18]

High molecular products may be formed and may separate out in the course of the reaction; if they are liquids, sufficient benzene is added to bring them into solution. Solids, if they appear, are not readily brought into solution and may cause considerable difficulty.

The reaction occasionally proceeds only to the point of the formation of an intermediate product. In that case, it is necessary to raise the temperature in order to complete the reaction. This is accomplished by removing a portion of the ether by distillation, adding a higher boiling inert solvent, and then heating the mixture to its boiling temperature.

In rare instances an unsaturated compound results from the reaction of an organomagnesium halide with ketones, alcohols, etc.

$$RR'CO + R''CH_2CH_2MgI \rightarrow R''CH{=}CH_2 + RR'CHOMgI$$

Reaction Velocity

The speed of the reaction of organomagnesium halides with various compounds depends on the character of the reacting compounds. The reaction of benzaldehyde with the following is complete within five minutes: methylmagnesium iodide, *n*-butyl-, cyclohexyl-, and tolylmagnesium bromides, and with benzylmagnesium chloride. The reaction proceeds equally rapidly also between *n*-butyl- and phenylmagnesium bromides and benzalacetone, acetophenone, phenyl isocyanate and ethyl cinnamate. On the other hand, the reaction between these same magnesium compounds and *o*-nitrotoluene, nitrocymol, 2-nitro-*p*-xylene, 2,3-chloronitrobenzene and *α*-nitronaphthalene requires from 0.2 to 1.5 hours for its completion.

The time required for the completion of the reaction of azobenzole with various halomagnesium compounds is given below:

			Time in hours				Time in hours
methylmagnesium		iodide	6	*n*-butylmagnesium		bromide	1.5
ethyl	"	"	0.6	isobutyl	"	"	4.0
n-propyl	"	"	2.5	cyclohexyl	"	chloride	0.25
n-butyl	"	"	2.5	phenyl	"	bromide	168.0
"	"	chloride	0.25	*o*-totyl	"	"	33.0
sec-butyl	"	bromide	0.25	benzyl	"	chloride	1.2
tert-butyl	"	chloride	0.25	styryl	"	bromide	4.0

The reactivity of various functional groups toward phenylmagnesium bromide decreases in the following order: [79]

$$CHO,\ COCH_3,\ NCO,\ COF,\ CO,\ C_6H_5,\ COCl,\ COBr,\ COOC_2H_5,\ CN.$$

Steric hindrance is occasionally encountered in Grignard reactions. Thus, the halomagnesium compound derived from (*β*-chloroethyl) methylaniline,

$$C_6H_5N\ (CH_3)C_2H_4MgCl$$

fails to yield addition compounds with ketones, although it reacts normally with aldehydes. [80]

Reaction of Grignard Reagents with Carbonyl Compounds

Organomagnesium halides react with aldehydes and ketones normally to form organomagnesium complexes:

$$RR'CO + R''MgX \rightarrow RR'C(R'')OMgX$$

The reaction apparently proceeds via the formation of loose addition compounds, $RR'CO :: R''MgX$, in which the magnesium and oxygen are joined by their residual valencies.

On treatment with water or dilute acids, the resulting organomagnesium complexes are converted to carbinols:

$$RR'C(R'')OMgX \xrightarrow{H_2O} RR'C(R'')OH$$

Secondary alcohols are thus obtained from aldehydes other than formaldehyde, and tertiary alcohols from ketones.

Aliphatic, fatty aromatic, and purely aromatic aldehydes are all capable of undergoing the reaction.

The reaction of organomagnesium compounds with aldehydes may take a different course when the aldehyde is present in excess. The aldehyde then reacts with the resulting halomagnesium carbinol giving rise to a ketone. Thus, propiophenone results from ethylmagnesium bromide and benzaldehyde:

$$C_6H_5CHO + C_2H_5MgBr \rightarrow C_6H_5CH(C_2H_5)OMgBr$$

$$C_6H_5CH(C_2H_5)OMgBr + C_6H_5CHO \rightarrow C_6H_5COC_2H_5 + C_6H_5CH_2OMgBr$$

This is similar to a Cannizzaro reaction. Acetophenone results by this reaction from benzaldehyde and methylmagnesium bromide, and benzophenone from benzaldehyde and phenylmagnesium bromide. A similar reaction takes place with aliphatic aldehydes when they are present in excess. The reaction is further complicated through the condensation of the resulting ketone with the aldehyde.[81] A Tichtchenko type of reaction may take place with certain aldehydes:[435]

$$2HOCH_3C(CH_3)_2CHO \xrightarrow{CH_3MgI} HOCH_2C(CH_3)_2COOCH_2C(CH_3)_2CH_2OH$$

The reaction of formaldehyde with Grignard compounds in general proceeds normally, to form the halomagnesium derivative of primary alcohols. The reaction proceeds quite rapidly when gaseous formaldehyde is led into the solution of the Grignard reagent.[82] When polymers of formaldehyde are used, it is best to carry out the reaction in a high boiling solvent, such as di-*n*-butyl ether methylal,[83] and the reaction mixture should be heated for about a day. The reaction is facilitated in this case by the addition of aluminum chloride.[84] The ethers of the expected alcohols are obtained when formaldehyde acetals are employed in the reaction.[85]

In the reaction of ketones with Grignard reagents, a certain amount of ketone is converted to a secondary alcohol by reduction. Other side reactions are enolization of the ketone and the formation of condensation products. These reactions take place almost exclusively when sterically hindered ketones are treated with highly branched Grignard reagents.[403] Ketols, $RCH_2C(OH)R'CH(R)COR'$, are formed with certain ketones, RCH_2COR', under the action of Grignard reagents. Ketol formation has been observed with cyclohexanone to the extent of 36%; with methyl tertiary butyl ketone and with methyl isopropyl ketones to the extent of 43% and 70%, respectively. Monochloroacetone gives the secondary alcohol $(CH_3)_2CHCH(OH)CH_3$ with methylmagnesium bromide, apparently via the oxide $(CH_3)_2C\underset{O}{\diagdown\!\diagup}CH_2$.[436]

In the treatment of the product of reaction of Grignard reagents with carbonyl compounds, the use of mineral acids should be avoided, since removal of traces of acid is difficult, and these may cause dehydration of the carbinol formed.

Low yields of some 1,2-diols are obtained from α-hydroxy ketones, unless the hydroxyl group is protected by acetylation.[404]

Pyrrolemagnesium halides react with acetaldehyde forming first pyrrole 2-methylcarbinol, which immediately changes to the ether:

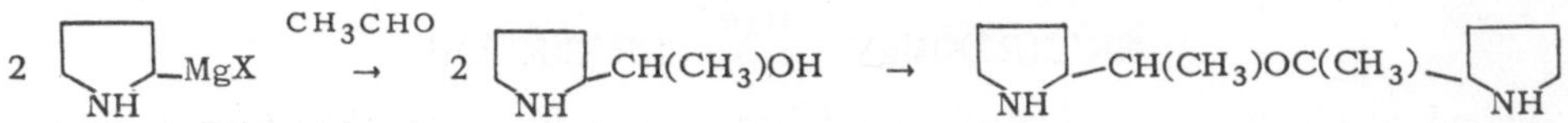

Two molecular proportions of a pyrrolemagnesium halide, reacting with one of aldehyde yield dipyrryl-2,2′-methylmethene, which readily changes to the corresponding methene,

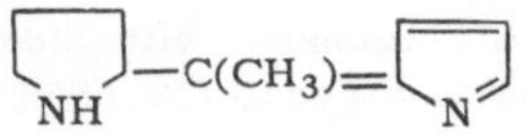

86

The reaction of benzylmagnesium chloride with formaldehyde proceeds in an abnormal manner and results in the formation of *o*-tolylmethyl alcohol:[87]

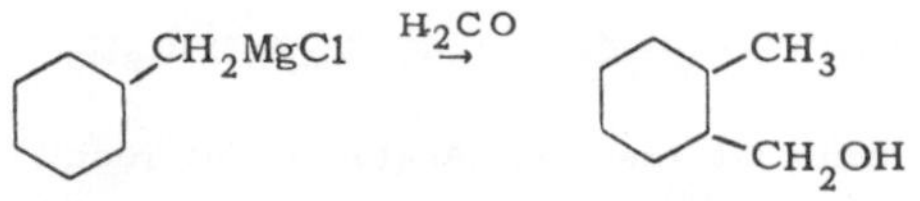

Ortho, *meta* and *para* methylbenzyl halides react normally, but mesitylmagnesium bromide reacts in the same manner as benzylmagnesium chloride.[88] A similar abnormal reaction takes place also with cinnamylmagnesium, sorbylmagnesium and α-naphthylmethylmagnesium chlorides, the last named yielding α-methyl-β-naphthylcarbinol.[89]

The oxygen in the carbonyl group of some aldehydes may be replaced with two alkyl groups. Thus, dimethyl- and diethylaminobenzaldehyde, which undergo the normal reaction at a low temperature, react as follows at a higher temperature:

$$R_2NC_6H_4CHO \xrightarrow{CH_3MgBr} R_2NC_6H_4CH(CH_3)OMgBr$$

$$\xrightarrow{CH_3MgBr} R_2NC_6H_4CH(CH_3)_2$$

Dimethylaminocinnamaldehyde reacts similarly.

Aliphatic, aryl aliphatic and purely aromatic ketones all are capable of undergoing the normal Grignard reaction.

δ-Acetobutyryl iodide in ethereal solution, reacting with magnesium, gives the iodomagnesium compound of methyl cyclopentanol.

In some cases a reduction of the ketone to a secondary alcohol takes place, without the addition of a hydrocarbon radical to the molecule of the ketone.

It is noteworthy that when *optically active sec*-octyl bromide is made to react with magnesium and the resulting complex is allowed to react with acetone, an optically inactive addition compound is obtained. Complete racemization is observed also when optically active methylphenyl bromide is put through this succession of reactions.[90] The reaction of organomagnesium halides with ketones in which an asymmetric carbon atom is present in the α-position, results in the formation of only one of two possible diastereomeric forms. Different isomeric forms result, however, depending on whether the ketone $RR'R''COR'''$ is made to react with the magnesium compound of $R''''MgX$, or the ketone $RR'R''COR''''$ with the magnesium compound $R'''MgX$. If the center of symmetry in the original compound is separated from the center of symmetry in the resulting compound by a non-asymmetric carbon atom, then both diastereomeric forms are obtained simultaneously in varying quantities.[91]

Acetylenic Grignard reagents, reacting with carbonyl compounds, give triply unsaturated alcohols; but a second reaction is also possible, involving a molecular rearrangement, and leading to the formation of a glycol:[92]

$$CH_3COC_2H_5 + HC\equiv CMgBr \rightarrow C_2H_5C(CH_3)(C\equiv CH)OMgBr$$

$$\rightarrow BrMgC\equiv C(CH_3)(C_2H_5)OH \xrightarrow{CH_3COC_2H_5} BrMgOC(CH_3)(C_2H_5)C\equiv C(CH_3)(C_2H_5)OH$$

$$\xrightarrow{H_2O} HOC(CH_3)(C_2H_5)C\equiv CC(CH_3)(C_2H_5)OH$$

Dimagnesium compounds, reacting with two molecular proportions of a carbonyl compound, give halomagnesium glycols. For example, acetylene dimagnesium dibromide reacting with acetaldehyde gives the bromomagnesium derivative of 3-hexyne-2,5-diol, $CH_3CH(OH)C\equiv CCH(OH)CH_3$. Analogous compounds may be obtained from chloral, benzaldehyde and acetophenone.[93] Benzil gives the compound

$$C_6H_5COC(OH)(C_6H_5)C\equiv CC(OH)(C_6H_5)COC_6H_5$$ [94]

With aldehydes yields of the order of 44 to 70%, and with ketones yields of 52-65% are obtained.[95]

Esters of halohydroxy acids are obtained through the reaction of a ketone with dichloroacetic ester in the presence of a 2% magnesium amalgam (*Darzen's procedure*):[96]

$$(CH_3)_2CO + Cl_2CHCOOC_2H_5 \xrightarrow{Mg} (CH_3)_2C(OMgCl)CHClCOOC_2H_5$$

$$\rightarrow (CH_3)_2C(OH)CH(Cl)COOC_2H_5$$

Calcium and zinc amalgams can also be used successfully in this reaction.

Of the two carbonyl groups in aliphatic diketones, only one reacts with Grignard reagents, the second becoming immediately enolized.[97] Thus, the reaction between benzoylacetophenone and phenylmagnesium bromide proceeds in the following manner:

$$C_6H_5COCH_2COC_6H_5 \xrightarrow{C_6H_5MgBr} (C_6H_5)_2C(OMgBr)CH = C(C_6H_5)OMgBr$$

Hydrolysis of the product results in the formation of acetophenone and benzophenone. Since phenylhydrazones are not acted upon by Grignard reagents, it is possible to protect one carbonyl group in a diketone by conversion to phenylhydrazone; the remaining carbonyl group can then be converted to a carbinol group, and a keto alcohol obtained on hydrolysis of the resulting phenylhydrazone alcohol:[98]

$$CH_3COC(CH_3) = NN(CH_3)C_6H_5 \xrightarrow{RMgX} CH_3C(OH)(R)C(CH_3) = NN(CH_3)C_6H_5$$

$$\rightarrow CH_3C(OH)(R)COCH_3$$

Both carbonyl groups in 2-*p*-methylbenzoyl-1-cyclopentanone,

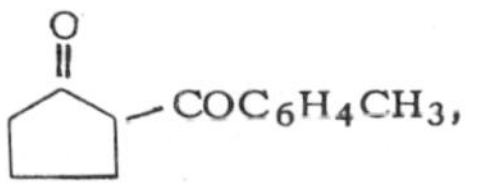

are capable of reacting with Grignard compounds. Two unsaturated ketones are formed, for example, with ethylmagnesium bromide:

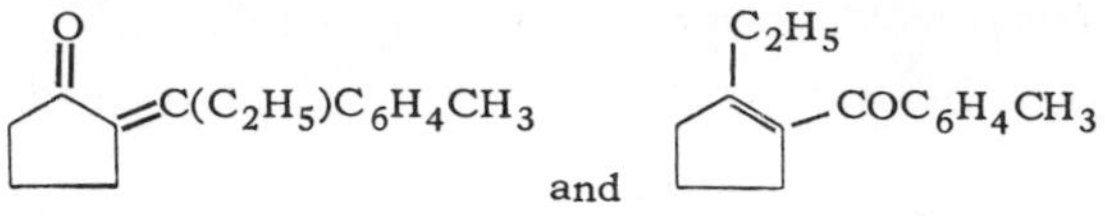

2-*o*-*p*-dimethylethylbenzoyl-1-cyclopentanone yields only the ketone

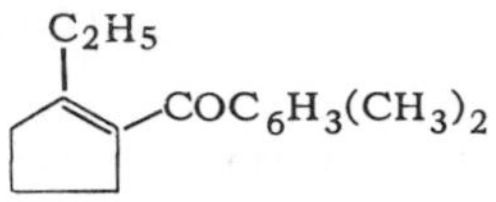

since the carbonyl in the benzoyl group is sterically protected by the methyl groups in *ortho* position.[99]

Replacement of the methoxy group in mesityl *o*-methoxyphenyl ketone with a phenyl group has been observed in the reaction of this ketone with phenylmagnesium bromide.[405]

Two of the carbonyl groups in *triketones* appear to be capable of undergoing the normal Grignard reaction:[100]

$$CH_3COCOCOCH_3 \xrightarrow{CH_3MgI} (CH_3)_2C(OH)COC(OH)(CH_3)_2$$

In cyclic nitrogen compounds with several keto groups, only one carbonyl group generally reacts.

α-Naphthylnaphthoquinone reacts with two molecules of phenylmagnesium bromide giving as the end product 1,4-dihydroxy-1,4-diphenyldihydronaphthalene. 2,3-Dimethyl-1,4-naphthoquinone is largely reduced by phenylmagnesium bromide to hydroquinone, although some 1,4- and 1,2-addition also takes place.[101] 2-Methyl-1,4-naphthoquinone and 2-methoxynaphthoquinone behave similarly. In β-Naphthoquinone only one carbonyl is reactive, while in *phenanthraquinone* and *acenaphthoquinone* both carbonyl groups react to yield dihydroxy derivatives.

Anthraquinone reacts with organomagnesium halides to form alkyl- or arylhydroxyanthrone and dialkyl- or diaryldihydroanthraquinone.[414] Diolefins are obtained readily from the dialkylated compounds by cleavage of two molecules of water. Such diolefins are not stable and are obtained in the form of polymeric products.[102] Simultaneously a little of the hydroquinone is reduced to anthrahydroquinone and to anthracene.

The reaction of organomagnesium halides with anthraquinone derivatives proceeds in a satisfactory manner only if no trace of metallic magnesium is present in the solution of the Grignard reagent. Under the proper conditions, diols may be obtained in yields ranging from 70 to 90%.

Olefin Formation

The reaction of organomagnesium compounds with aldehydes or ketones occasionally results in the formation of unsaturated compounds. An increase in temperature and an excess of the Grignard reagent favor this reaction. In many cases, olefin formation occurs only when the carbinol is first isolated and subjected to the action of dehydrating agents, although isolation of the carbinol offers great difficulties in some instances.[103] Olefin formation is favored when the carbon atom bearing the hydroxyl group carries substituents. Secondary alcoholates yield olefins more readily than primary alcoholates, while with tertiary alcoholates olefin formation is quite general especially when aromatic radicals are attached to the carbon atom bearing the alcoholic hydroxyl group.[104] *p*-Propenylphenol, $HOC_6H_4CH = CHCH_3$, is obtained through the reaction of *p*-hydroxybenzaldehyde with ethylmagnesium bromide.[105] Anisaldehyde also yields an unsaturated compound.

Unsaturated aldehydes also show a tendency toward cleavage of water with the formation of diolefins. Thus, highly arylated fulvenes may be obtained conveniently through the reaction of arylated cyclopentadienones with methyl-, ethyl- and benzylmagnesium bromides, and subsequent elimination of water:[106]

$$C_6H_5C = C(CH_3)C(CH_3) = C(C_6H_5)CO + RCH_2MgX$$

$$\rightarrow C_6H_5C = C(CH_3)C(CH_3) = C(C_6H_5)C(CH_2R)OMgX$$

$$\rightarrow C_6H_5C = C(CH_3)C(CH_3){:}C(C_6H_5)C = CHR$$

Allene derivatives are obtained when cleavage can only proceed in the direction of formation of such compounds.[107]

Anthrones react with organomagnesium halides to form dihydroanthranols:

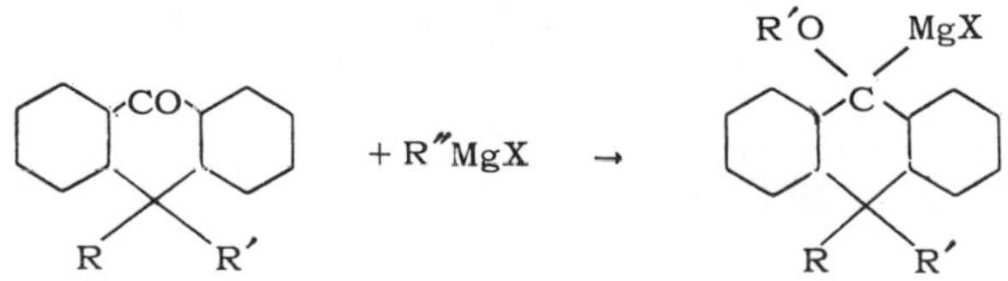

If R is hydrogen or the benzyl radical, it is generally eliminated with the formation of a substituted anthracene,[102]

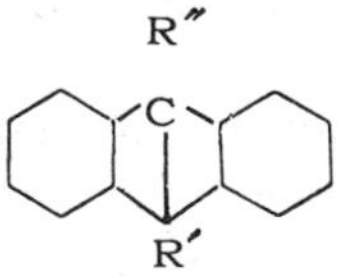

The reaction is inhibited if a chlorine atom is present at positions 1 or 2.[108] If a chlorine atom is present at 4 or 5 positions, the *meso* hydrogen atom is immobilized, and no anthracene derivatives are obtained. If, however, both R and R′ are hydrogen, loss of hydrogen occurs if a chlorine atom is present at 4 or 5 positions; on the other hand, if chlorine is present at both 4 and 5 positions, then both hydrogen atoms are immobilized.[109]

Reaction with Halo and Amino Carbonyl Compounds

Halo aldehydes react normally with organomagnesium halides, giving a halomagnesium derivative of a halohydrin; hydrolysis gives the halohydrin:

$$RCHClCHO + R'MgX \rightarrow RCHClCH(R')OMgX \rightarrow RCHCl = CH(OH)R'$$

The halohydrin formed reacts with a further molecule of the magnesium compound as follows:

$$XMgOCHR'CH(R)Cl + R'MgX \quad \rightarrow \quad ClMgX + XMgOCHR'CHRR'$$

$$\xrightarrow{H_2O} \quad HOCHR'CHRR'$$

Asymmetric stilbenes may be prepared by this method using different halomagnesium compounds in the two steps:[110]

$$ClCH_2CHO + RMgX \quad \rightarrow \quad Cl\overset{\cdot}{C}H_2CH(R)OMgX$$

$$\xrightarrow{R'MgX} \quad R'CH_2CH(R)OMgX \quad \rightarrow \quad R'CH = CHR$$

α-*Chloroisobutyraldehyde* behaves in an exceptional manner. Reacting with methylmagnesium bromide, it gives dimethylisopropylcarbinol in 53% yield. The formation of this compound is explained by the following series of transformations:

$$(CH_3)_2CClCHO + CH_3MgBr \quad \rightarrow \quad (CH_3)_2CClCH(CH_3)OMgBr$$

$$\rightarrow (CH_3)_2C\overset{O}{\overbrace{\qquad}}CHCH_3 \quad \xrightarrow{CH_3MgBr} \quad (CH_3)_2C(OMgBr)CH(CH_3)_2$$

$$\rightarrow (CH_3)_2C(OH)CH(CH_3)_2$$

The halomagnesium compound resulting from the reaction of α-*chlorocyclohexylformaldehyde* with a Grignard reagent undergoes transformation yielding an aldehyde or a ketone, the former with aromatic Grignard reagents, the latter with aliphatic reagents:[111]

$$\overline{CH_2(CH_2)_3CH(Cl)}CHCHO \quad \xrightarrow{RMgX}$$

$$\overline{CH_2(CH_2)_3CHCl}CHCH(R)OH \quad \rightarrow \quad \left[\overline{CH_2(CH_2)_3CH.}CHCH(R)O\right] \rightarrow$$

$$\overline{CH_2(CH_2)_3CH_2}CHCHO \quad or \quad \overline{CH_2(CH_2)_3CH_2}CHCOR$$

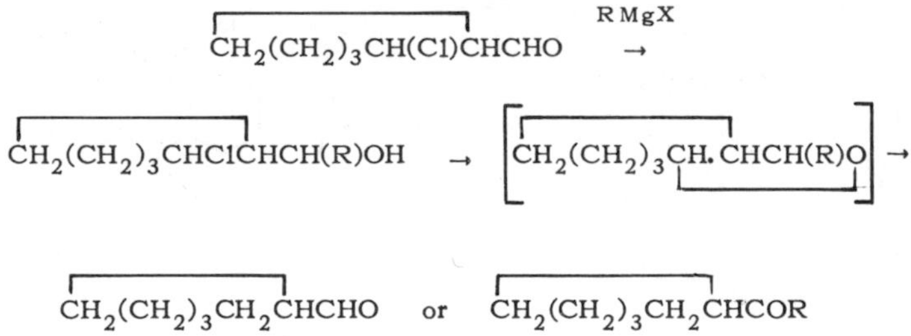

Halo ketones also generally react in a normal manner with Grignard reagents. The primary reaction may be followed, however, by cleavage of hydrogen halide; a migration of an alkyl or aryl group may also take place, resulting in the formation of a halogen-free ketone:

$$RCHClCOR' \quad \xrightarrow{R''MgX} \quad RCHClC(OMgX)R'R''$$

$$\rightarrow RCH\overset{O}{\overbrace{\qquad}}CR'R'' \quad \rightarrow \quad RCH(R'')COR'$$

The end result is replacement of the halo group with the group R'' in the organomagnesium halide.[112] The resulting ketone may also react with the organomagnesium halide giving a tertiary carbinol. Tetramethylethyl alcohol may result, for example, through the reaction of methylmagnesium iodide with 3-bromo-

3-methyl-2-butanone. Direct replacement of the halogen with the organic group in the Grignard reagent takes place if the halogen in the halo ketone is activated by a neighboring aromatic group.

Only the keto function in *bromanil* reacts with ethylmagnesium iodide, yielding

$$
\begin{array}{ccc}
CH_3 & & CH_3 \\
& C_6Br_4 & \\
HO & & OH
\end{array}
$$

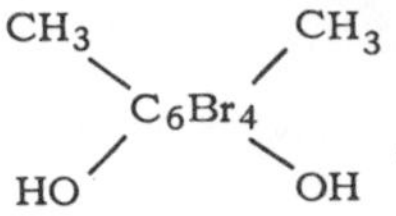

In *2,3-dichloro-1,4-naphthoquinone* one chlorine atom is replaced by a methyl group. Phenylmagnesium iodide reacts more energetically and replaces three halogens with phenyl groups in chlor and bromanil. Both chlorine atoms are replaceable in 2,4-dichloro and 1,4-dichloronaphthoquinone, but the chlorine atoms in 2,3-dichloronaphthoquinone are retained.[113]

Amino ketones react normally with Grignard reagents, although it is necessary to use an excess of the reagent.

The reaction of 1-acetyl-2-methylindolizine proceeds in the following manner:[114]

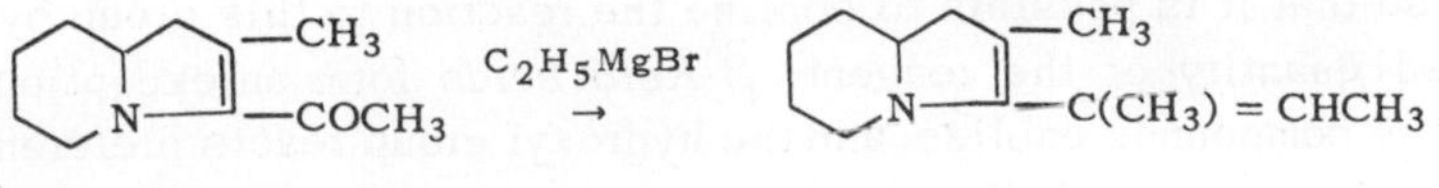

Replacement of the acetyl group also takes place, and results in the formation of some 2-methylindolizinemagnesium bromide.

Reaction with Aldehyde and Keto Esters

The aldehyde group in aldehyde acid esters is first attacked by organomagnesium halides. Advantage has been taken of this fact in the synthesis of chaulmoogric and hydrocarpic acids from β-oxododecane-α-carboxylic methyl ester. The latter is obtained from erucaic acid ozonide by aldehyde cleavage.

The aldehyde acid reacting with cyclopentylmagnesium bromide gives μ-cyclopentyl-μ-hydroxydodecane carboxylic methyl ester, $\overline{CH_2(CH_2)_3CHCH}(OH)(CH_2)_{11}COOCH_3$. On replacing the hydroxyl group with hydrogen, dihydrochaulmoogric ester is obtained.[115]

η-Cyclopentyl-i-hydroxydecane-α-carboxylic methyl ester,

$$
\overline{CH_2(CH_2)_3CHCH_2}CH(OH)(CH_2)_8COOCH_3
$$

results through the reaction of the aldehyde acid with cyclopentylmethylmagnesium bromide. Dihydrohydnocapric ester is obtained on replacing the hydroxyl group with hydrogen.[115]

Phthalic aldehyde ester reacts with methyl magnesium iodide in the following manner:[116]

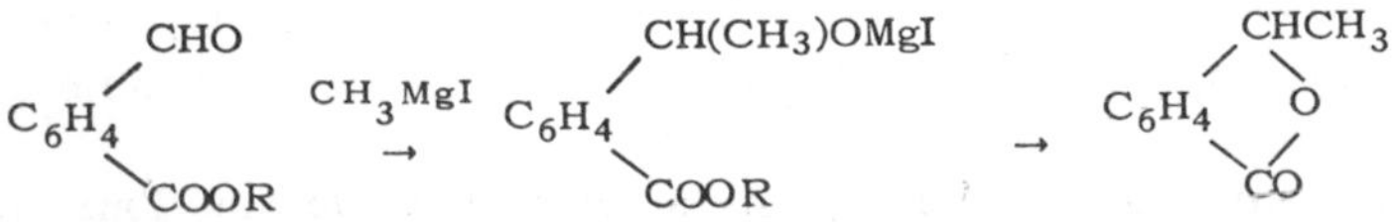

β-Camphoraldehyde ester reacts with Grignard compounds to form substituted β-campholides:[117]

$$C_8H_{14}\!\!\begin{array}{l}\diagup COOCH_3\\ \diagdown CHO\end{array} \quad \xrightarrow{\;R\,Mg\,X\;} \quad C_8H_{14}\!\!\begin{array}{c}\diagup CO\diagdown\\ \;\;\;\;\;\;\;O\\ \diagdown CHR\diagup\end{array}$$

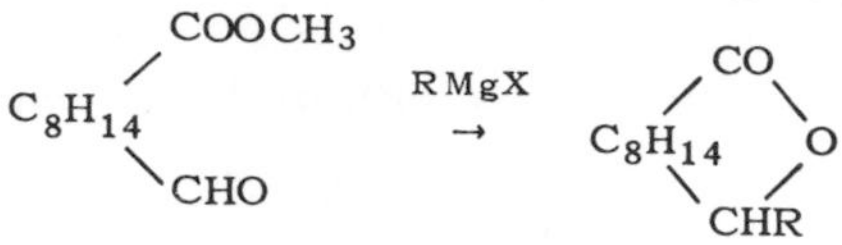

In some cases, the principal reaction may be the transformation to a β-campholide:

$$C_8H_{14}\!\!\begin{array}{l}\diagup COOCH\\ \diagdown CHO\end{array} + CH_3CH_2CH_2MgBr \;\rightarrow\; CH_2\!=\!CHCH_3 + C_8H_{14}\!\!\begin{array}{l}\diagup COOCH_3\\ \diagdown CH_2OMgBr\end{array}$$

$$\rightarrow\; C_8H_{14}\!\!\begin{array}{c}\diagup CO\diagdown\\ \;\;\;\;\;\;\;O\\ \diagdown CH_2\diagup\end{array} + CH_3OMgBr$$

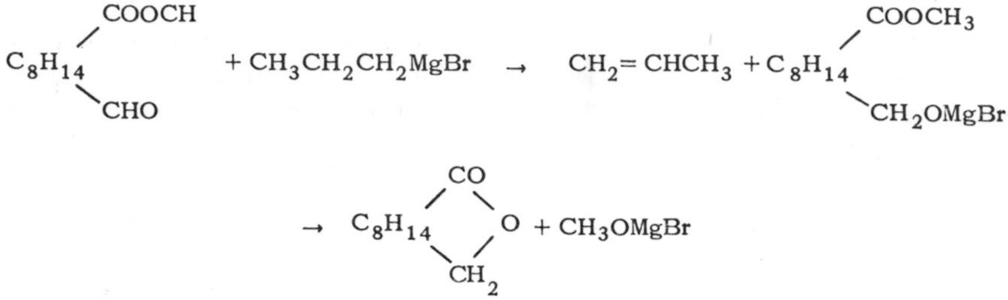

The keto group in *keto acid* esters is attacked first by organomagnesium halides, so that it is possible to confine the reaction to this group by use of the calculated quantity of the reagent. β-*Keto acids* form an exception, however, since these compounds enolize, and the hydroxyl group reacts preferentially with the magnesium compound. For this reason a single product can be obtained from acetoacetic ester and its homologs.

An exception is presented by *mesoxalic ester*, $C_2H_5OCOCOCOOC_2H_5$, which gives tetramethyldihydroxyacetone with methylmagnesium iodide, and diethylhydroxypyruvic ester, $(C_2H_5)_2CH(OH)COCOOC_2H_5$, with ethylmagnesium bromide.[118]

Reaction with Unsaturated Carbonyl Compounds

Unsaturated carbonyl compounds in which the unsaturated bonds are at a distance from the carbonyl group react in a normal manner with organomagnesium halides. If the unsaturated bonds are conjugated with the double bond between the oxygen and carbon in the carbonyl group, then a 1,4-addition may take place as follows:

$$-\underset{|}{C}=\underset{|}{C}C=O + RMgX \quad \rightarrow \quad -\underset{|}{C}(R)C=\underset{|}{C}OMgX$$

Hydrolysis leads to the formation of an unsaturated alcohol, which undergoes rearrangement to a saturated carbonyl compound:

$$-\underset{|}{C}(R)C=\underset{|}{C}OH \quad \rightarrow \quad -\underset{|}{C}(R)\underset{|}{C}H\underset{|}{C}O$$

The normal Grignard reaction always proceeds simultaneously, however, yielding the unsaturated alcohol, $-\underset{|}{C}=\underset{|}{C}\underset{|}{C}(R)OH$. The proportion of the resulting two

compounds is determined by the velocity at which the two reactions proceed.

Addition at the C–C double bond takes place only when an activating functional group is present in the vicinity of the double bond. The activating group itself may be unreactive toward organomagnesium halides. Addition takes place, for example, with styryltoluylsulfone:[119]

$$C_6H_5CH = CHSO_2C_6H_4CH_3 + C_6H_5MgBr \rightarrow C_6H_5CH(C_6H_5)CH(MgBr)SO_2C_6H_4CH_3$$

$$\xrightarrow{H_2O} (C_6H_5)_2CHCH_2SO_2C_6H_4CH_3$$

α, β-Unsaturated aldehydes generally give 1,2-addition products, but in a few cases,1,4-addition also takes place simultaneously.[120]

1,2-Addition is the prevailing reaction with aliphatic α,β-unsaturated ketones, especially when the β-carbon atom bears two alkyl groups. The presence of a small proportion of cuprous chloride in the reaction mixture would seem to favor the formation of the 1,4-addition product.[437]

Butylideneacetone, $CH_3(CH_2)_2CH = CHCOCH_3$, reacting with ethylmagnesium bromide gives a mixture of 60% of an unsaturated alcohol, and 40% of a saturated ketone. The compounds $CH_3CH = C(CH_3)COCH_3$ and $CH_3(CH_2)_2CH = C(CH_3)COCH_3$ also yield some saturated ketone, while hydroxymethylenemethylheptenone,

$$CH_3C(CH_3) = CHCH_2CH_2COCH = CHOH,$$

yields the 1,4-addition product.[121] Unsaturated ketones with aromatic substituents undergo 1,4-addition unless a large group, such as a phenyl group, is attached to the β-carbon atom.[122] 1,4-Additions involving an aromatic ring have been reported.[438]

Ketenes, $R_2C = CO$, generally react with organomagnesium halides to form saturated ketones or unsaturated alsohols:[123]

$$(C_6H_4)_2C{:}CO + C_6H_5MgBr \nearrow (C_6H_5)_2C(MgBr)COC_6H_5 \rightarrow (C_6H_5)_2CHCOC_6H_5$$

$$\searrow (C_6H_5)_2C = C(OMgBr)C_6H_5 \rightarrow (C_6H_5)_2C = C(OH)C_6H_5$$

Ketene, $CH_2 = CO$, gives only a small yield of acetone with methylmagnesium iodide. Diphenylketene does not give a diol with acetylenedimagnesium dibromide.

Carbonyl compounds with *acetylenic bonds* do not undergo 1,4-addition with organomagnesium halides.

Unsaturated cyclic ketones undergo both 1,2- and 1,4-addition. The latter reaction takes place when a hydrogen atom is attached to the α-carbon atom. The proportion of 1,2- and 1,4-addition products varies according to the organomagnesium halide used.

Δ^2-Cyclohexenone gives 38% of the 1,2-product and 15% of the 1,4-product with methylmagnesium halides, and 52% of the 1,2-product and 24% of the 1,4-product with ethylmagnesium halides. Isopropylmagnesium halides yield 10% of the 1,2- and 44% of the 1,4-product, while *tert*-butylmagnesium halides yield 70% of the 1,4-product and none of the 1,2-addition compound.[124]

1,4-Addition is observed with phenyl diphenylstyryl ketone:[406]

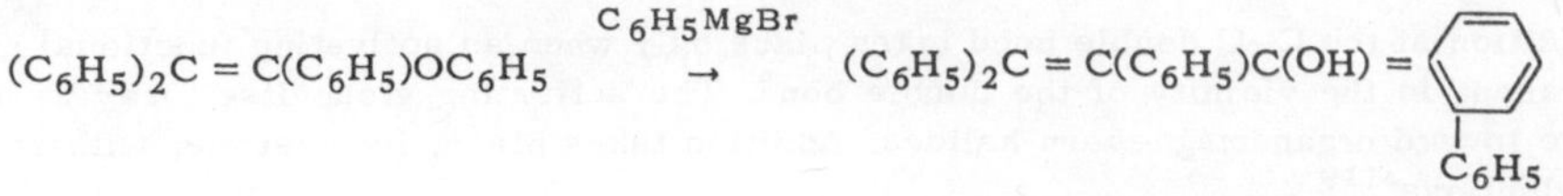

A similar addition takes place with naphthoquinone,[407] 6,13-pentacenequinone,[408] 7-ethoxyperinaphthindone-9,[409] mesityl 2-benzofuryl ketone,[410] mesitoyl-5-mesityl-2-methyl-4-phenylfuran,[411] with alkyl mesitoates, mesityl phenyl ketone and mesityl 1-naphthyl ketone.[412]

The ketones, $\overline{CH = CHC(R)(CHCl_2)CH = CH - CO}$, in which R is an alkyl group, give the alcohol on reaction with Grignard reagents of the type $R'CH_2MgI$,[125] while ketones of the type

$$\overline{CH = CHCH = CHC(CHCl_2)(R)CO}$$

yield the ketones $\overline{CH_2CH(CH_2R)CH = CH(CHCl_2)CO}$.[99]

Dimethylpyrone reacts with Grignard reagents normally giving pyranoles:

$$\overline{CH = C(CH_3)OC(CH_3) = CHCO} \xrightarrow{RMgX} \overline{CH = C(CH_3)OC(CH_3) = CHC(R)OMgX}$$

$$\xrightarrow{H_2O} \overline{CH = C(CH_3)OC(CH_3) = CHC(R)OH}$$

These compounds are unstable in the free state and change to open chain unsaturated diketones although their perchlorates are stable.[126]

1,6-Addition of organomagnesium halides is observed with certain aromatic compounds.[413] Thus, 1,6-addition takes place when *fuchsone* reacts with methylmagnesium iodide:

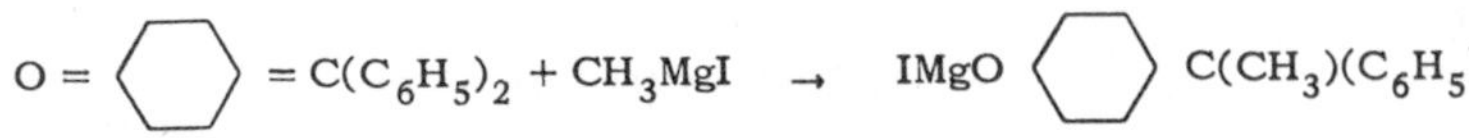

Anthrafuchsone undergoes only 1,2-addition. Phenylmagnesium bromide gives the 1,2-addition product with both fuchsone and anthrafuchsone. *Methylanthrone* undergoes 1,6-addition with methyl, ethyl and phenylmagnesium bromide:[127]

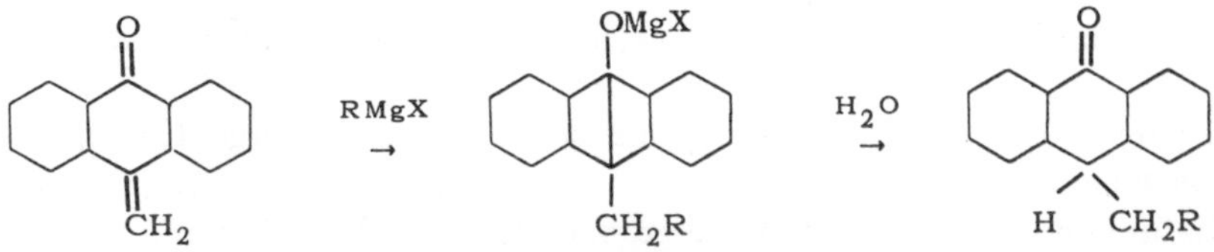

Benzalanthrone,

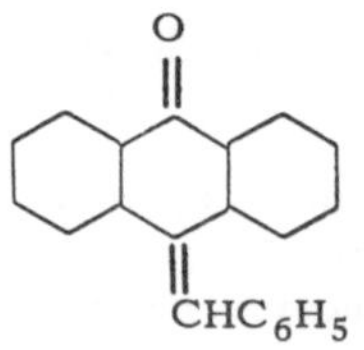

undergoes 1,2-addition.[128]

1,6-Additions involving aromatic rings have been observed.[439]

Quinones react with Grignard reagents in general to give only small yields of readily isolable and identifiable products.

Enolization Induced by Organomagnesium Halides

Grignard reagents cause the enolization of certain ketones. The effect is the more pronounced the higher the temperature, and increases with increasing magnitude of the organic group in the halomagnesium compound.[129] Primary organomagnesium halides induce enolization to the extent of 6 to 8.5%, the secondary 13.5 – 16% and the tertiary to the extent of at least 20%.[130] The extent of enolization brought about by *tert*-butylmagnesium chloride in various ketones is given below:

	Extent of Enolization, %		Extent of Enolization, %
dibutyl ketone	20	thujone	41
carvone	20	*p*-methylcyclohexanone	46
dibenzyl ketone	24	butyrone	49
acetone	30	cyclohexanone	50.5
acetophenone	31	menthone	51
cyclopentanone	32.5	mesityl oxide	60

Pulegone is enolized to the extent of 24-27% by methyl magnesium bromide, and 100% by isopropylmagnesium bromide. The degree of enolization varies also with the halide employed. In a series of experiments the degree of enolization of camphor induced by chlorides was found to be 28.2%, while bromides and iodides caused the enolization of 24% and 14.8% of the compound respectively.[131] The order of effectiveness of various halides may be the reverse of this in other instances.[130] The solvent employed also plays an important part; thus, while camphor was found to be enolyzed to the extent of 3.6% in amyl ether, the degree of enolization under the action of the same reagent was found to be 45.7% in ether and 32.5% in benzene.

Enolization induced by Grignard reagents generally proceeds slowly. The enol may be isolated as the acetate, and the latter subsequently reconverted to the enol by hydrolysis with water or oxalic acid. Mineral acids, alkalies and bromine revert the enol to the corresponding ketone.

The halomagnesium compounds resulting from the reaction of enols with organomagnesium halides are capable of undergoing the usual reactions of Grignard reagents. The reaction between the enolate of phenylacetic acid and aldehydes proceeds as follows:

$$C_6H_5CH(MgX)COONa + RCHO \rightarrow C_6H_5CH(COONa).CH(R)OMgX$$

Excellent yields are obtained in this reaction by proceeding in the following manner: To 0.2 gram atom of metallic magnesium are added a trace of iodine dissolved in 5 to 10 cc of ether, and 0.115 mole of phenyl acetate dissolved in 150 cc of ether; then a solution of 0.2 mole of isopropyl chloride in 50 cc of ether is introduced dropwise and the mixture heated until the evolution of gas ceases. Finally 0.115 mole of the aldehyde is added slowly and the mixture is heated for three hours.

Reaction with Acetals

Acetals react with organomagnesium halides to form ethers according to the scheme:[132]

$$RCH(OR')_2 + R''MgX \rightarrow RCH(R'')OR' + R'OMgX$$

This reaction offers a general method of preparation of *ethers*. Ethers of primary alcohols result from acetals of formaldehyde, those of secondary alcohols from acetals of other aldehydes. Ketone acetals yield ethers of tertiary alcohols.

The reaction of acetals with *bromomagnesium acetylides* leads to the formation of mono- and diethers of thrice-unsaturated alcohols:[133]

$$H_2C(OC_2H_5)_2 + C_4H_9C \equiv CMgBr \rightarrow$$

$$C_4H_9C \equiv CCH_2OC_2H_5 + C_2H_5OMgBr$$

$$2H_2C(OC_3H_7)_2 + BrMgC \equiv CMgBr \rightarrow$$

$$C_3H_7OCH_2C \equiv CCH_2OC_3H_7 + 2C_3H_7OMgBr$$

Ethoxy acetals yield glycol diethers with Grignard reagents:

$$C_2H_5OCH_2CH(OC_2H_5)_2 + R'MgX \rightarrow$$

$$C_2H_5OCH_2CH(R')OC_2H_5 + C_2H_5OMgX$$

Heated with sulfuric acid, these glycol ethers are converted to aldehydes, RCH_2CHO.[134]

Halo acetals reacting with arylmagnesium halides yield aromatic substituted chlorinated ethers:

$$ClCH_2CH(OC_2H_5)_2 + RMgX \rightarrow ClCH_2CH(R)OC_2H_5 + C_2H_5OMgX$$

These ethers are capable of reacting with a second molecule of arylmagnesium halide to form diarylethyl ethers:

$$ClCH_2CH(R)OC_2H_5 + RMgX \rightarrow RCH_2CH(R)OC_2H_5 + ClMgX$$

When such arylethers are boiled with dilute sulfuric acid, stilbene derivatives are obtained:[135]

$$RCH_2CH(R)OC_2H_5 \qquad RCH = CHR + C_2H_5OH$$

Unsymmetrical stilbenes are obtained by using a different arylmagnesium halide in the second stage of the reaction. Stilbenes result also directly from chloroacetaldehyde and two molecular equivalents of arylmagnesium halide:

$$ClCH_2CHO + 2RMgX \rightarrow RCH = CHR + HOMgX + ClMgX$$

Reaction with Esters

Carboxylic acid esters react with organomagnesium halides normally to form the halomagnesium derivative of a tertiary alcohol:

$$RCOOC_2H_5 + 2R'MgBr \rightarrow C_2H_5OMgBr + R(R')_2COMgBr$$

$$\rightarrow R(R')_2COH$$

The tertiary alcohols(*) formed are occasionally unstable and undergo transformation to an unsaturated hydrocarbon with cleavage of alcohol.[136]

The velocity of the reaction of dihalomagnesium compounds with esters decreases with the degree of branching of the alkyl chains in the ester. For example, the reaction velocities of *n*-butyl, *sec*-butyl and *tert*-butyl benzoic esters with ethylmagnesium bromide are in the ratio 400:40:1; of dipropylcarbinol and diisopropylcarbinol benzoates, 13:1, and of methylbutylcarbinol and methyl-*tert*-butylcarbinol benzoates, 7:1. The ratio for ethyl, methyl and 2,4,6-trimethyl benzoates is 1000:30:1, and that for ethyl valerate and ethyl trimethylacetate 28:1. The reaction velocity increases with an increase in the strength of the acid; thus, ethylmagnesium bromide reacts with *o*-chlorbenzoic ester twenty-four times as rapidly as with *o*-methylbenzoic ester.[138]

Carbonic esters first yield carboxylic esters, generally in excellent yield, and these on further reaction yield tertiary alcoholates with three identical organic groups:[139]

$$(C_2H_5O)_2CO + RMgX \rightarrow (C_2H_5O)_2C(R)OMgX \xrightarrow{H_2O} RCOOC_2H_5 + C_2H_5OH + HOMgX$$

$$(C_2H_5O)_2C(R)OMgX + 2RMgX \rightarrow 2C_2H_5OMgX + R_3COMgX \xrightarrow{H_2O} (R)_3COH$$

Formic esters yield secondary alcohols; when the ester is present in excess, the reaction leads to the formation of an aldehyde. The normal reaction does not always yield the expected alcohols, but occasionally gives rise to their formic esters. Halomagnesium compounds of *indole*, reacting at a low temperature with formic esters, yield N-formylindole, which is converted on heating to indyl-β-aldehyde.[140] The reaction of decylenedimagnesium bromide with formic esters yields a microcrystalline compound resulting from a condensation polymerization, and represented by the formula $[-(CH_2)_{10}-CH(OH)-]_x$.[141]

Dicarboxylic esters such as those of oxalic, iso and terephthalic acids, react with four molecular proportions of organomagnesium halides forming derivatives of tertiary glycols,[142] although the hydroxy esters may be obtained by using an ethereal solution of an alkyl iodide in conjunction with metallic magnesium.[139] Phthalic esters behave in a different and characteristic manner.[143] With phenylmagnesium bromide, *o*-benzoylbenzoic ester is first formed and reacts with another molecule of the reagent to give dibenzoylbenzene and diphenylphthalide:

$$C_6H_4(COOR)_2 \rightarrow C_6H_4 \begin{smallmatrix} COC_6H_5 \\ \\ COOR \end{smallmatrix} \nearrow \begin{smallmatrix} C_6H_4(COC_6H_5)_2 \\ \\ C_6H_4 \begin{smallmatrix} C(C_6H_5)_2 \\ \\ O \\ \\ CO \end{smallmatrix} \end{smallmatrix}$$

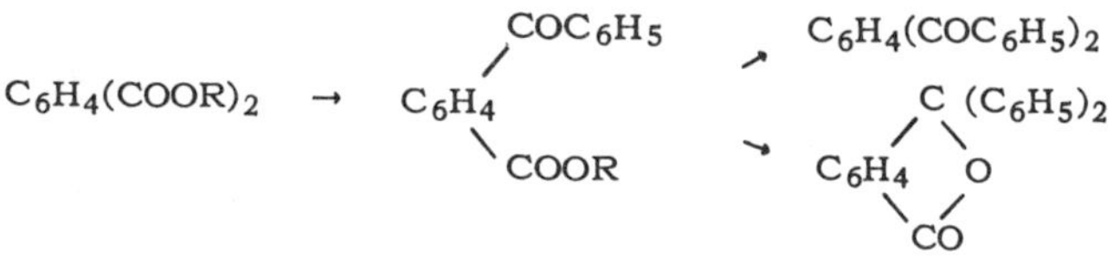

(*) Tertiary alcohols are oxidized to a ketone by chromic acid:

$$RCH_2C(OH)(CH_3)_2 \xrightarrow{O} RCOOH + CH_3COCH_3 + H_2O$$

This reaction is of importance in the determination of the structure of these compounds.[137]

The latter reacts normally to yield tetraphenylxylyleneglycol, $C_6H_4[C(OH)(C_6H_5)_2]_2$, or its dehydration product tetraphenylphthalan,

$$C_6H_4 \begin{array}{c} C=(C_6H_5)_2 \\ \diagup \qquad \diagdown \\ \qquad \qquad O \\ \diagdown \qquad \diagup \\ C=(C_6H_5)_2 \end{array}$$

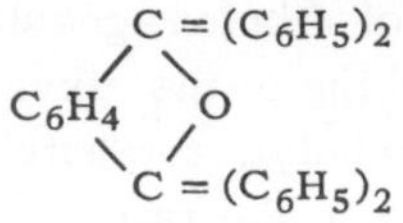

and a greater proportion of a phthalan derivative,

$$C_6H_4 \begin{array}{c} C=(C_6H_5)_2 \\ \diagup \qquad \diagdown \\ \qquad \qquad O \\ \diagdown \qquad \diagup \\ C=(OH)C_6H_5 \end{array}$$

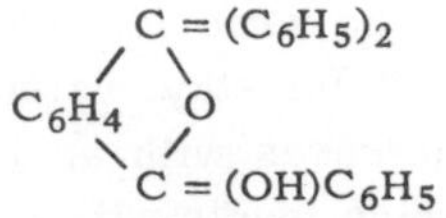

With halomagnesium compounds of *indole*, *oxalic esters* yield N,N′-oxalyldiindole, N-β-(indylglyoxyl)-indole and β-indylglyoxylic ester.[144]

Ethoxyacetic ester, $C_2H_5OCH_2COOC_2H_5$, reacts normally with organomagnesium halides to form monoethers of a glycol, $C_2H_5OCH_2C(OH)(R)_2$. Heated with 25% aqueous sulfuric acid, or hydrochloric acid, these ethers are transformed to aldehydes,

$$OCHCH(R)_2 .$$

This transformation occasionally takes place in the course of the reaction with the organomagnesium halide.[145]

Ortho esters reacting with organomagnesium halides first form acetals, usually in good yield:[146]

$$RC(OC_2H_5)_3 + R'MgX \quad \rightarrow \quad RR'C(OC_2H_5)_2 + C_2H_5OMgX$$

The reaction is quite general. The *procedure* followed in carrying it out is as follows:

Equimolecular quantities of the ortho ester and organomagnesium halide in ethereal solution are mixed and the ether is then distilled off. Reaction proceeds vigorously during the distillation with evolution of heat. The acetal separates as an oil on the addition of acidulated water.[147]

Ethoxy groups in ethyl orthoformate may be replaced stepwise with phenyl groups by reaction with phenylmagnesium bromide. The compounds

$$C_6H_5CH(OC_2H_5)_2, \quad (C_6H_5)_2CHOC_2H_5 \quad \text{and} \quad (C_6H_5)_3CH$$

have all been prepared by this method.[148] Carboxylic ortho esters may be obtained through the reaction of organomagnesium halides with *orthocarbonic esters*.[149]

Phenylacetic ester reacts in the enolic form with isopropylmagnesium bromide, and the final reaction product is α,β-diphenylacetoacetic ester:

$$C_6H_5CH = C(OH)OC_2H_5 + C_3H_7MgX \quad \rightarrow$$

$$C_3H_8 + C_6H_5CH = C(OMgX)OC_2H_5$$

$$\rightarrow \quad C_6H_5CH(MgX)COOC_2H_5$$

$$\underset{\rightarrow}{C_6H_5CH_2COOC_2H_5} \qquad C_6H_5CH_2COCH(C_6H_5)COOC_2H_5$$

Esters of p-chlorophenylacetic, diphenylacetic, malonic and cyanopropionic acids react in a similar manner. Phenylacetic ester reacts normally with methyl-, ethyl-, n-propyl-, n-butyl- and phenylmagnesium halides.

The first stage in the reaction of esters or salts of carboxylic acids with organomagnesium halides presumably is the formation of a ketone, although suspension of the reaction at this stage and isolation of the ketone is often difficult, if not impossible. In some instances *ketone formation* takes place in a clear-cut manner:

$$RCOOC_2H_5 + R'MgX \rightarrow RCOR + C_2H_5OMgX$$

Ketone formation is observed, for example, with Grignard reagents derived from secondary and tertiary alkyl halides, and less frequently with those derived from primary halides.[150] Thus, methyl isobutyl ketone is obtained through the reaction of isobutylmagnesium bromide with sodium acetate; methyl isoamyl ketone and acetophenone result similarly through the reaction of isoamylmagnesium bromide with sodium acetate, and diethyl ketone results from the reaction of ethylmagnesium bromide with sodium propionate. Pyrylmagnesium halides and diortho substituted arylmagnesium halides display a special tendency toward ketone formation. α,β-Unsaturated esters show a tendency to form ketones regardless of the nature of the Grignard reagent with which they are reacted. Ketone formation with such esters is often accompanied by 1,4-addition.

Many ketones are capable of undergoing enolization under the influence of Grignard reagents; self-condensation of the *Claisen type* may occur when the esters are susceptible to enolate addition at the carbonyl double bond.[440]

Examples of symmetrical ketone formation in reactions of esters with Grignard reagents in high boiling solvents are known.[441]

One of the products of the reaction of an ester with a Grignard reagent is sometimes an ether of the expected alcohol, which undoubtedly forms by a Williamson type of reaction between the corresponding halo compound and the Grignard complex:

$$RR'_2CX + RR'_2COMgX \rightarrow (RR'_2C)_2O + MgX_2$$

Heated with butylmagnesium chloride to 85 - 100°, *ethyl acetate* yields acetone:

$$CH_3COOC_2H_5 + C_4H_9MgCl \rightarrow CH_3COCl + C_4H_9MgOC_2H_5$$

$$2CH_3COCl + 2C_4H_9MgOC_2H_5 \rightarrow (CH_3)_2CO + MgCO_3 + MgCl_2 + C_4H_9 \cdot C_4H_9 + C_2H_4 + C_2H_6$$

Mesityl oxide and phorone are formed simultaneously. Higher fatty acid esters react similarly yielding the corresponding ketones.[151] *Laurone* results from lauric ester and *palmitone* from palmitic ester, while oenanthic ester yields dihexyl ketone. Benzoic ester gives benzhydrol by a secondary reduction.

The reaction of organomagnesium halides with substituted acetoacetic esters results in the formation of tertiary alcohol esters, which on hydrolysis give methyl ketones:

$$CH_3COCR'R''COOR \xrightarrow{R'''MgX} CH_3C(OH)R'''CRR'COOR$$

$$\xrightarrow{H_2O} CH_3COR''' + R'R''CHCOOH + ROH$$

Halo esters react preferentially with their ester group. Occasionally the halogen may be subsequently exchanged against the organic residue of the magnesium compound. The chlorine atom in *chlorocarbonic esters*, ClCOOR, reacts first with Grignard reagents, yielding carboxylic esters; with an excess of the reagents tertiary alcohols are obtained.

The reaction of *α-chloroisobutyric ester* with methylmagnesium iodide results in the formation of pentamethyl ethanol.[152] The formation of this compound is explained by the following series of reactions:

$$(CH_3)_2CClCOOR + 2CH_3MgI \rightarrow (CH_3)_2CClC(OMgI)(CH_3)_2$$

$$\rightarrow (CH_3)_2C\overset{O}{\text{—}}C(CH_3)_2 \xrightarrow{CH_3MgI} (CH_3)_2C(OMgBr)C(CH_3)_3$$

$$\xrightarrow{H_2O} (CH_3)_2C(OH)C(CH_3)_3$$

Hydroxy esters yield glycols with magnesium compounds. While the reaction of *α-hydroxynaphthoic ester* with methylmagnesium iodide gives 1-hydroxy-naphthyl-2-isopropylene,

$$C_{10}H_6\begin{matrix} / OH \\ \backslash C(:CH_2)CH_3 \end{matrix}$$

the reaction with phenylmagnesium iodide yields 2-diphenylmethylene-1-naphthoquinone,

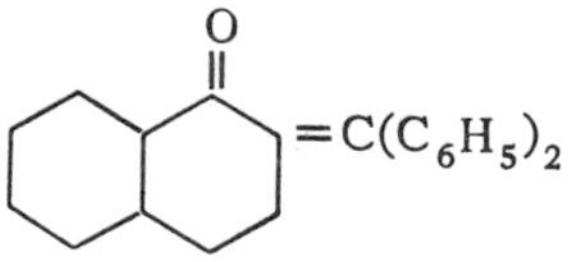

A similar product is obtained with α-naphthylmagnesium iodide.

Aldehyde and *keto esters* also give glycols. The carbonyl group in the latter reacts preferentially with the reagents.

The oxido group in *glycidic esters*, $RR'C\overset{O}{\text{—}}CHCOOR$, reacts preferentially with organomagnesium halides, diphenylglycidic ester giving α-hydroxy-β,β-diphenylbutyric ester, $(C_6H_5)_2C(CH_3)CH(OH)COOC_2H_5$, with methylmagnesium iodide.[153]

Amino esters react normally with Grignard reagents, although since the amino group consumes an equivalent of the reagent, a molecular excess of the latter must be used in the reaction:

$$H_2NCH_2COOR + 3R'MgX \rightarrow R'H + ROMgX + XMgNHCH_2C(R')_2OMgX$$

$$\xrightarrow{\text{dil. acid}} H_2NCH_2C(R')_2OH$$

Benzoylated amines, sulfamic derivatives and peptide esters also react in a similar manner,[154] while diethyl oxamic ester, $(C_2H_5)_2NCOCOOC_2H_5$, reacts normally. Oxamic ester yields triphenylcarbinol with phenylmagnesium bromide, according to the scheme:[155]

$$H_2NCOCOOC_2H_5 \xrightarrow{C_6H_5MgBr} H_2NCOC(C_6H_5)_2OMgBr \rightarrow NCC(C_6H_5)_2OMgBr$$

$$\xrightarrow{C_6H_5MgBr} (C_6H_5)_3COMgBr \xrightarrow{H_2O} (C_6H_5)_3COH$$

Substituted amides are obtained through the reaction of aminomagnesium halides with esters:[272]

$$RCOOC_2H_5 + R'NHMgX \rightarrow RCONHR' + C_2H_5OMgX$$

Reactions with Lactones

Lactones react with organomagnesium halides in the manner of the corresponding hydroxy acid ester:

$$\overline{OCH_2CH_2CH_2CO} + RMgX \rightarrow XMgOCH_2CH_2CH_2COR$$

$$\xrightarrow{RMgX} XMgOCH_2CH_2CH_2C(R)_2OMgX \xrightarrow{H_2O} HOCH_2CH_2CH_2C(R)_2OH$$

The reaction of *phthalides* with organomagnesium halides generally results in the formation of half-acetals:

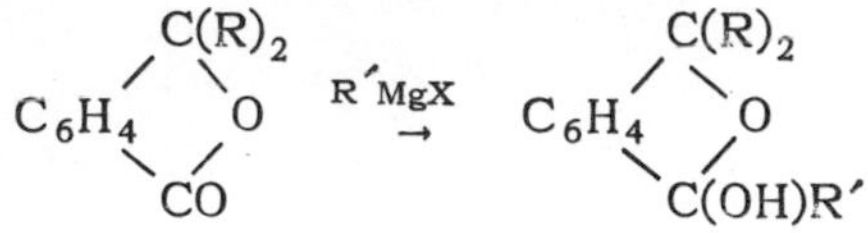

Benzalphthalenes are obtained from arylphthalides and benzylmagnesium chloride:[156]

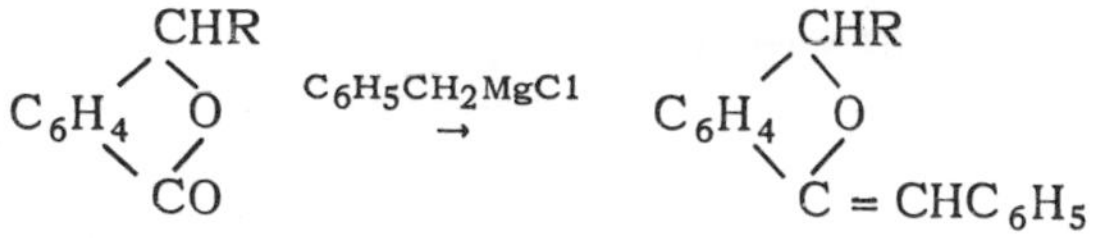

Monoaryl phthalides are capable also of "transanellar" cleavage of water to form furan derivatives:[157]

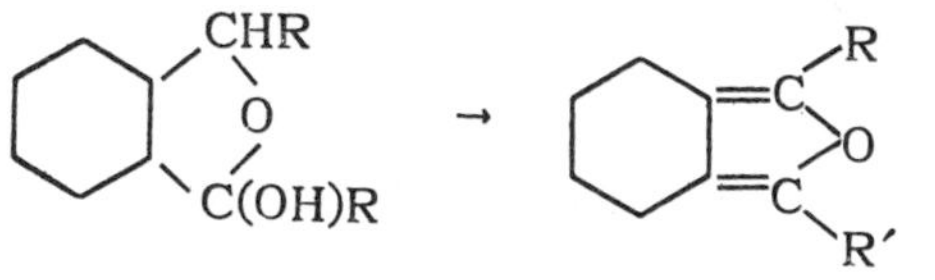

Glycols result from the reaction of phthalides with an excess of phenylmagnesium bromide:[158]

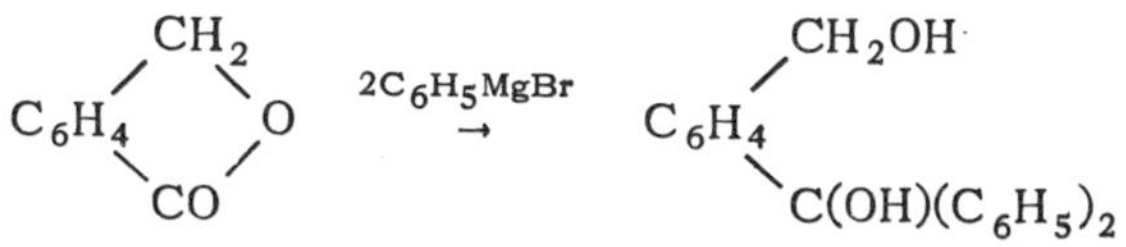

The reaction of *coumarin* with phenylmagnesium bromide results in the formation of a 2,2-diphenyl derivative if a substituent is present in 4 position.[159] If, on the other hand, substituents are present at positions 3 and 4, the compound reacts as a cyclic ketone. Ketone formation takes place to some extent also with unsubstituted and 3-substituted coumarins. Diphenylchromanol,

$$
\begin{array}{c}
C_6H_5 \\
| \\
CH \\
\diagup \quad \diagdown CH \\
C_6H_4 \qquad \parallel \\
\diagdown \quad \diagup CC_6H_5 \\
O
\end{array}
$$

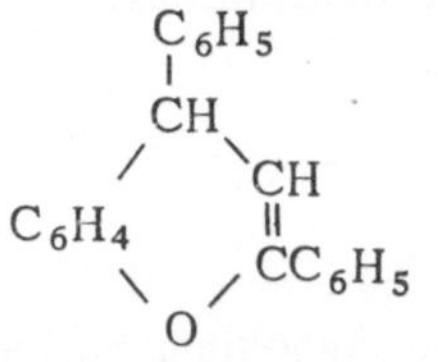

results through the reaction of coumarin with phenylmagnesium bromide.[160]

Reaction with Unsaturated Carboxylic Esters

Unsaturated esters generally react in a normal manner with organomagnesium halides, giving after hydrolysis, unsaturated alcohols as the final product. Addition at the double bonds may occur, however, when the multiple bonds are in the vicinity of the carboxyl group. Thus, 1,2- or 1,4-addition may take place with α,β-unsaturated esters, although normally these esters yield unsaturated alcohols:[161]

$$C_6H_5CH = CHCOOR \xrightarrow{CH_3MgI} C_6H_5CH = CHCOCH_3$$

$$\xrightarrow{CH_3MgI} C_6H_5CH = CHC(OH)(CH_3)_2$$

The type of substitution depends also upon the nature of the organomagnesium halide employed. Thus, the extent of the replacement of the alkoxy group in unsaturated carboxylic esters diminishes when arylmagnesium halides are used in the reaction, and the principal reaction becomes a 1,4-addition.

The direction of the reaction is influenced by substituents in the α-position. Thus, methacrylic ester reacts to yield 1,2- and 1,4-addition products:[162]

$$CH_2 = C(CH_3)COOC_2H_5 \xrightarrow{CH_3MgI} CH_2 = C(CH_3)COCH_3$$

$$\xrightarrow{CH_3MgI} \begin{array}{l} \nearrow CH_2 = C(CH_3)C(OH)(CH_3)_2 \\ \searrow CH_3CH_2CH(CH_3)COCH_3 \end{array}$$

Cinnamic ester gives a 5% yield of β,β-diphenylpropionic ester with phenylmagnesium bromide, while α-bromocinnamic ester gives a 70% yield of α-bromo-β,β-diphenylpropionic ester,[163] with some α-phenylcinnamic ester resulting by 1,4-addition.[164] A cyano group in the α-position in α,β-unsaturated esters hinders the replacement of the alkoxy group with the radical of the organomagnesium compound, and a direct addition at 1 and 4 positions takes place:[165]

$$C_6H_5CH = C(CN)COOC_2H_5 \xrightarrow{RMgX} C_6H_5CH(R)CH(CN)COOC_2H_5$$

A carboxyl group in the α-position has the same effect. For example, *benzalmalonic ester* gives exclusively the 1,4-addition product;

$$C_6H_5CH = C(COOC_2H_5)_2 \xrightarrow{CH_3MgI} C_6H_5CH(CH_3)CH(COOC_2H_5)_2$$

It is notable that the ester groups in the resulting product fail to react with an excess of the Grignard reagent. *Maleic ester* also yields a 1,4-addition product although, in this case, replacement of the alkoxy groups takes place when an excess of the Grignard reagent is used:

$$ROCOCH = CHCOOR \xrightarrow{C_6H_5MgBr} C_6H_5COCH(C_6H_5)CH_2COOR$$

$$\xrightarrow{C_6H_5MgBr} C_6H_5COCH(C_6H_5)CH_2COC_6H_5$$

Some desylacetophenone is also formed. Dimethylmaleic ester yields the saturated β-keto ester, $ROCOC(CH_3)(C_6H_5)CH(CH_3)COC_6H_5$, as the principal product with a little of the unsaturated ester.[166] *Atropic ester*, $CH_2{=}C(C_6H_5)COOR$, gives benzyldesoxybenzoin, $C_6H_5COCH(C_6H_5)CH_2C_6H_5$.[167] The ethoxy group in *ethoxymethylenemalonic ester* is replaced by the organic group in the magnesium compound:

$$C_2H_5OCH = C(COOR)_2 \xrightarrow{C_6H_5MgBr} (C_6H_5)_2CHCH(COOR)_2$$

α-Phenylcinnamalacetic methyl ester undergoes an exchange of the methoxy group,[168] while *vinylacrylic, sorbic, α-cyanocinnamalacetic* and *cinnamalmalonic esters* give 1,4-addition products.[169] Esters of the type

$$C_6H_5CH = CHCH(R)CH_2COOCH_3$$

form α,δ-addition products only.

Reaction with Acid Chlorides

The first stage in the reaction of acid halides with Grignard compounds involves the replacement of the chlorine atom by the organic group in the magnesium compound. This is followed by the normal reaction between ketones and organomagnesium halides:[170]

$$RCOCl \xrightarrow{R'MgX} RCOR' \xrightarrow{R'MgX} RC(R')_2OMgX$$

The ketone may be obtained by adding the required quantity of the magnesium compound to the acid chloride, thus avoiding the temporary presence of an excess of the magnesium compound. In some instances ketone formation takes place even in the presence of an excess of the magnesium compound. Thus, indylmagnesium halides react with carboxylic acid chlorides to form β-indyl ketones, although N-acyl derivatives are formed at low temperatures.[171] Diketones are obtained with dicarboxylic acid chlorides. Oxalyl chloride reacts in a somewhat complicated manner, giving β,β-biindoyl,

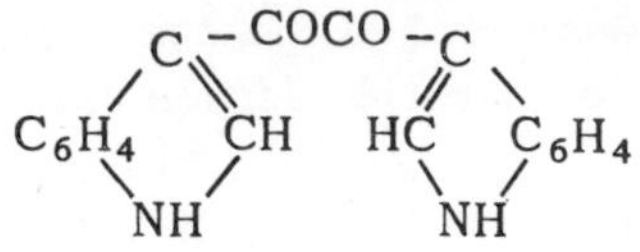

α,α-biindoyl, N,N'-biindoyl and α,β-biindoyl. Phosgene yields diindyl ketone.[172]

The reaction of *tert*-butylmagnesium chloride with propionylacetyl and isobutylacetyl chlorides proceeds in a complicated manner. In ethereal solution, the former yields a mixture of diethyl ketone, ethyl-*tert*-butyl ketone, propyl alcohol, propionic acid, diethyl carbinol propionate and ethyl-*tert*-butyl carbinol carbonate. Heated in xylene solution for eight hours with the magnesium compound, isobutyl acetyl chloride gives diisoamyl ketone and the isohexanol ester of isobutylacetic acid.

In the reaction of organomagnesium halides with acyl chlorides reduction of the chloride to an aldehyde and of the latter to an alcohol may take place.[173] The ketone, RCOR′, resulting from the exchange of the chlorine atom with the organic radical in the magnesium compound, can also undergo reduction to a carbinol.

Ethyl acetate had been reported as a byproduct in the reaction of many Grignard reagents with acetyl chloride, arising from the ether used as a solvent.[442] A 1,3-diketone formation has been observed in some instances due to enolization of the ketone resulting from the normal reaction, and its subsequent acylation. The monoketone may be prepared in good yield in such cases by adding the acid chloride slowly to an excess of the Grignard reagent.[443] A coupling reaction of the acyl chloride under the action of magnesium iodide has been noted, resulting in the formation of a 1,2-diketone.[444]

Acyl bromides react with Grignard reagents in the same way as acyl chlorides, but secondary reactions take place with acyl iodides.

The esterification of alcohols with acyl chlorides proceeds readily in the presence of metallic magnesium. Esters of tertiary alcohols, otherwise difficult to obtain, may be prepared readily and in good yield by this method.[174]

Reaction with Carboxylic Acid Anhydrides

Acid anhydrides react with organomagnesium halides in much the same manner as acyl chlorides. Reaction with a molecular equivalent of the reagent results, after hydrolysis of the magnesium complex, in the formation of a ketone:[175]

$$RCOOCOR + R'MgBr \rightarrow RR'C(OMgBr)OCOR \xrightarrow{H_2O} RCOR' + BrMgOCOR$$

Ketones may be prepared by this reaction from halomagnesium compounds of unsaturated hydrocarbons. A ketone is obtained through the reaction of acetylenemagnesium chloride with acetic anhydride at 25°; ketones are obtained also through the reaction of acetic anhydride with hexinyl-, phenylethinyl- and heptinylmagnesium halides.[176]

Dicarboxylic acid anhydrides, reacting with one molecular equivalent of Grignard reagents, are converted to keto acids. Thus, β-benzoylpropionic acid,

$C_6H_5COCH_2CH_2COOH$, is obtained from succinic anhydride and phenylmagnesium bromide. Phthalic anhydride gives *o*-benzoylbenzoic acid with phenylmagnesium bromide; diphenyl phthalide is obtained with an excess of the latter:[177]

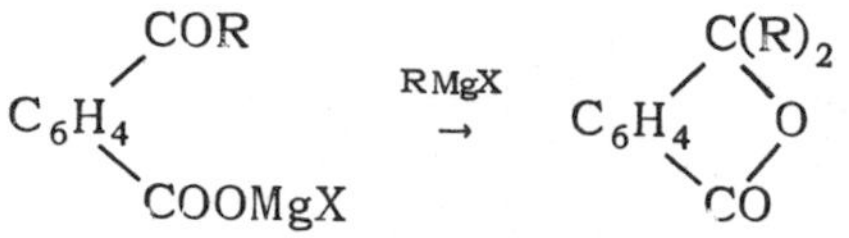

3-Methylphthalic anhydride, reacting with phenylmagnesium bromide, gives principally 6-methyl-2-benzoylbenzoic acid.[178] Phthalides are obtained also with tetrahydrophthalic anhydride and homophthalic anhydride.[179]

An α-substituent in the anhydride tends to inhibit the reaction at the adjacent carbonyl group.[445]

Pyrrolemagnesium halides give with phthalic anhydride pyrrolene phthalides. Indylmagnesium bromide gives two isomeric products

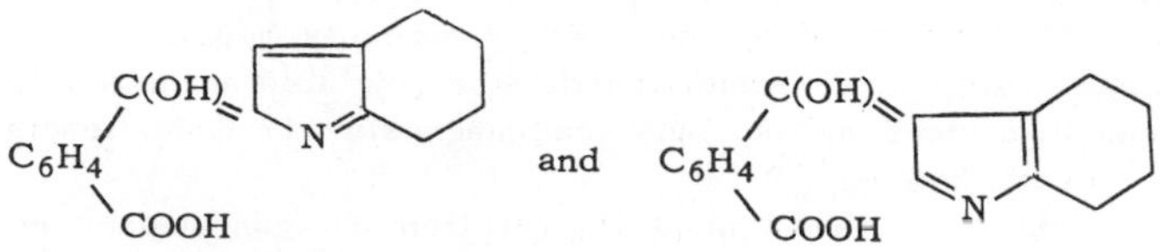

Magnesium alcoholates react with acid anhydrides to give the ester of the acid:

$$ROMgX + (CH_3CO)_2O \rightarrow CH_3COOR + CH_3COOMgX$$

Reaction with Carbon Dioxide

Carbon dioxide reacts with organomagnesium halides to form the halomagnesium compound of a carboxylic acid which on hydrolysis yields the free acid:[180]

$$RMgX + CO_2 \rightarrow RCOOMgX \rightarrow RCOOH$$

The reaction proceeds slowly because of the low solubility of carbon dioxide. It is best carried out at a low temperature, preferably at –20°.[181] A convenient procedure is to add solid carbon dioxide in small portions to the solution of the organomagnesium halide.[415] If gaseous carbon dioxide is used, the gas should be passed through the solution of the organomagnesium halide at a rapid rate.[182] An alternative procedure is to spray the solution of the organomagnesium halide into a flask filled with carbon dioxide.[183] The reaction can be accelerated by working under pressure.[184] The reaction rate and the yield vary, depending on the halide employed. Better results are obtained, with butylmagnesium chloride than with the corresponding bromide.[185]

Most *unsaturated* halomagnesium compounds appear to react abnormally, although many unsaturated carboxylic acids have been prepared successfully through the reaction of unsaturated halomagnesium compounds with carbon dioxide.[186] The reaction takes place more readily with magnesium compounds in which the metal is attached to the multiply-bound carbon. Thus, the halomagnesium compound obtained from ω-bromostyrene readily yields cinnamic acid,[187] and γ-phenylcrotonic acid results from the magnesium compound obtained from γ-bromoallylbenzene.[188] Acetylenemagnesium halides and similar organomagnesium compounds react normally with carbon dioxide forming carboxylic acid magnesium halides.

Alkyl dimagnesium halides reacting with carbon dioxide yield the dimagnesium salts of dicarboxylic acids.

If a mixture of the ethereal solution of a dihalide and metallic magnesium is used in the reaction, coupling reactions may take place. Thus, trimethylene bromide yields suberic acid:[189]

$$2BrCH_2CH_2CH_2Br \xrightarrow{Mg} BrMgCH_2(CH_2)_4CH_2MgBr$$

$$\xrightarrow{CO_2} BrMgOCOCH_2(CH_2)_4CH_2COOMgBr \xrightarrow{HCl} HOCOCH_2(CH_2)_4CH_2COOH$$

Sebacic acid and an acid with 14 carbon atoms are obtained from 1,4-dibromobutane in similar manner,[190] although the principal product is cyclopentanone. 1,5-Dibromopentane reacts similarly;[191] 1,7-dibromoheptane gives principally heptamethylenedicarboxylic acid; 1,10-diiododecane gives decamethylenedicarboxylic acid and higher homologs.

Pentyl dimagnesium bromide, like butylenedimagnesium bromide, reacts with carbon dioxide to form a cyclic ketone.[191]

Phenylmalonic acid is obtained through the reaction of organomagnesium halides with a halomagnesium phenylacetate followed by reaction with carbon dioxide:[192]

$$C_6H_5CH_2COOMgX \xrightarrow{C_2H_5MgX} C_6H_5CH(MgX)COOMgX$$

$$\xrightarrow{CO_2} C_6H_5CH(COOMgX)_2$$

Only aliphatic, aliphatic-aromatic and hydroaromatic Grignard reagents appear to be suitable for the reaction.

Dinaphthylmagnesium chloride reacts with carbon dioxide to form dinaphthylaceticmagnesium chloride. The free acid may be decarboxylated by heating to dinaphthylmethane.[193]

The reaction of iodomagnesium derivatives of phenolic compounds with carbon dioxide proceeds in the absence of a solvent and at a somewhat elevated temperatures. The reaction proceeds in solution in benzene or toluene with halomagnesium compounds derived from thymol, phloroglucinol and β-naphthol.[416]

Indylmagnesium iodide reacting with carbon dioxide yields the magnesium salt of N-indolecarboxylic acid,

$$C_6H_4 \begin{array}{c} CH \\ \diagup \diagdown \\ \diagdown \diagup \\ N-COOH \end{array} CH$$

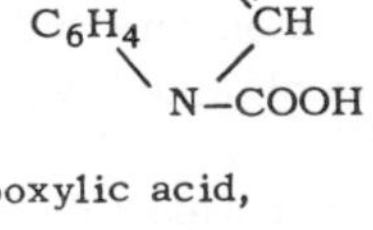

and a small amount of β-indolecarboxylic acid,

$$C_6H_4 \begin{array}{c} C-COOH \\ \diagup \diagdown \\ \diagdown \diagup \\ NH \end{array} CH$$

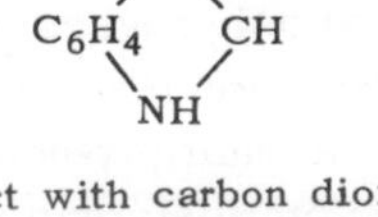

Halomagnesium alcoholates react with carbon dioxide to form the magnesium salt of half esters of carbonic acid:

$$ROMgX + CO_2 \rightarrow ROCOOMgX$$

These are unstable compounds that are decomposed by water to the original alcohol and carbon dioxide.

Halomagnesium compounds of *aryl amines* react to form salts of arylcarbamic acids:

$$ArN(R)MgI + CO_2 \rightarrow ArN(R)COOMgI$$

These undergo molecular rearrangement to form para and also some ortho aminobenzoic acids:

$$C_6H_5N(R)COOMgI \rightarrow IMgOCOC_6H_4NHR \rightarrow HOCOC_6H_4NHR$$

Tertiary amines of the type of dimethylaniline yield aromatic carboxylic acids directly by reaction with an alkylmagnesium iodide and carbon dioxide, although the method has not acquired preparative importance.[194]

The following acids, among others, have been prepared through the reaction of organomagnesium halides with carbon dioxide:

Fatty acids:[195] Acetic, propionic, butyric, valeric, isovaleric, isocaproic, heptylic, vinylacetic.

Fatty aromatic acids:[196] Phenylacetic, phenylbutyric, triphenylacetic.

Aromatic acids:[197] Benzoic, naphthoic, bromobenzoic, bromonaphthoic, terephthalic, thiophenecarboxylic.

Hydroaromatic acids:[198] Hexahydrobenzoic; hexahydro-*o*-, *m*- and *p*-toluic; hexahydro-*m*-xylylic; 1-methylcyclohexane-1-carboxylic; hexahydrophenylacetic; cyclopentane carboxylic; methylcyclopentane carboxylic; cycloheptanecarboxylic; camphorcarboxylic; hydropinenecarboxylic; bornylcarboxylic.

Phenolethercarboxylic acids:[199] Anisic; *p*-ethoxybenzoic; methoxy-, ethoxy- and propyloxy-2-naphthoic.

Dibasic Acids:[200] Pimelic, decamethylenedicarboxylic, terephthalic.

Ketones are the principal products of the reaction of carbon dioxide with warm solutions of *p*-chlorophenylmagnesium chloride and *p*-bromophenylmagnesium bromide.[417]

Reaction with Carbon Monoxide[446]

Primary aliphatic organomagnesium halides react with some difficulty with carbon monoxide, yielding unsaturated hydrocarbons:

$$RCH_2MgX + CO \rightarrow RCH_2C(=)OMgX$$

$$\xrightarrow{RCH_2MgX} RCH_2C(OMgX)(MgX)CH_2R \xrightarrow{H_2O} RCH = CHCH_2R$$

Secondary organomagnesium halides react partly in this manner, and partly to yield an addition compound with carbon monoxide, which dimerizes and eventually yields an acyloin:

$$2RMgX + 2CO \rightarrow 2[RCOMgX] \rightarrow RCOMgX = C(OMgX)R$$

$$\xrightarrow{H_2O} RCOCH(OH)R$$

This reaction takes place exclusively with *tert*-aliphatic and aromatic magnesium halides. The reaction is accelerated by alcohol and especially by magnesium ethoxide.

The reaction with phenylmagnesium bromide is carried out at 70-80° in an autoclave in the absence of a catalyst. The principal product of the reaction is benzoin.

p-Toluil and *α*-naphthil have been prepared by this method.

Reaction with Carbon Suboxide

Carbon suboxide, OC =C =CO, though a bifunctional carbonyl compound, reacts with only one molecule of methylmagnesium iodide in ethereal solution. Hydrolysis of the magnesium complex followed by self-condensation gives 2,4,6-triacetylphloroglucinol:[447]

$$3OC=C=CO + 3CH_3MgI \rightarrow 3CH_3C(OMgI)=C=CO$$

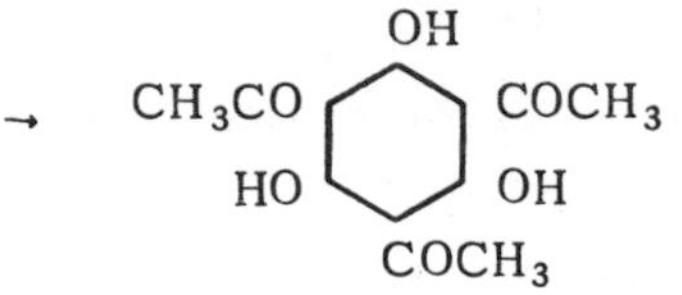

Reaction with Acid Amides

Acid amides normally react with two molecular equivalents of an organomagnesium halide to form magnesium compounds, which on hydrolysis yield ketones:[201]

$$RCONH_2 + 2R'MgX \rightarrow RR'C(OMgX)NHMgX + R'H$$

$$RR'C(OMgX)NHMgX + 2H_2O \rightarrow 2HOMgX + RR'C(OH)NH_2$$

$$\rightarrow RCOR' + NH_3$$

Another reaction can take place with N-substituted amides; the oxygen of the CO group may be replaced by two hydrocarbon residues of the organomagnesium halide to give a tertiary amine:[202]

$$R'CON(R'')_2 + 2RMgX \rightarrow R'C(R)_2N(R'')_2 + MgO + MgX_2$$

A self-condensation takes place occasionally, as in the case of N-diethylacetamide:

$$2CH_3CON(C_2H_5)_2 \xrightarrow{C_2H_5MgBr} CH_3COCH_2CON(C_2H_5)_2$$

A 65% yield of the condensation product results in this instance.

In common with most aromatic amides, aliphatic amides, with few exceptions, react with organomagnesium halides to form ketones. Formamide is among the exceptions. Yields are improved when the reaction is carried out at a higher temperature, using benzene or butyl ether as the solvent. The amides of higher fatty acids give better yields of ketone than those of lower fatty acids:[203]

Acetamide reacts poorly, while tribubstituted acetamides, $RR'R''CCONH_2$ often yield nitriles.[204] Methylethylphenyl-, diethylphenyl- and diphenylbenzylacetamide give the corresponding nitriles exclusively. Dimethylbenzylacetamide gives a mixture of the ketone and nitrile with phenylmagnesium bromide, but only the nitrile with ethylmagnesium bromide. Dimethylethyl- and trimethylacetamide give principally the ketone, with a little nitrile. The formation of an amino alcohol $(C_2H_5)_2NCH_2C(C_2H_5)_2OH$ has been observed in the reaction of N,N-diethylchloroacetamide, $ClCH_2CON(C_2H_5)_2$, with ethylmagnesium bromide.[448] As a general rule, *N-alkyl amides* give ketones. Halo magnesium compounds with branched chain hydrocarbon residues favor the formation of nitriles.[205] N-substituted secondary formamides generally yield aldehydes:[206]

$$HCONRR' + R''MgX \rightarrow HCR''(OMgX)NRR'$$

$$\xrightarrow{H_2O} R''CHO + HNRR' + HOMgX$$

Best results are obtained with methyl formanilide. *Diethylformamide* reacting with allylyne magnesium bromide gives 4-diethylamino-2,3,5,6-heptadiyne:[207]

$$HCON(C_2H_5)_2 + 2CH_3C \equiv CMgBr \rightarrow$$

$$(CH_3C \equiv C)_2CHN(C_2H_5)_2 + MgO + MgBr_2$$

With ethylmagnesium halides it gives exclusively 3-diethylamino-*n*-pentane,

$$(C_2H_5)_2CHN(C_2H_5)_2.$$

while with isobutylmagnesium bromide it gives a mixture of isovaleraldehyde and 2,6-dimethyl-4-diethylamino-*n*-heptane, $(C_4H_9)_2CHN(C_2H_5)_2$, in equal proportions. As a general rule, the smaller the hydrocarbon group present in the organomagnesium halide, the greater is the tendency toward the formation of a tertiary amine.[208]

Tetraethyloxamide, $(C_2H_5)_2NCOCON(C_2H_5)_2$, reacts with ethylmagnesium bromide to form propionylformic diethylamide, $C_2H_5COCON(C_2H_5)_2$ in 70% yield, diethylaminobutyric diethylamide, $(C_2H_5)_2NCH(C_2H_5)CON(C_2H_5)_2$ in 20% yield, and a little dipropyl. With phenylmagnesium bromide, it gives α-diethylaminodiphenylacetdiethylamide, $(C_2H_5)_2NC(C_6H_5)_2CON(C_2H_5)_2$.[209]

Good yields of ketones are obtained in the reaction of ethylmagnesium bromide with many monohydroxybenzoic diethylamides, although anisic diethylamide yields the ketone in only 30% yield. Protocatechuic, dimethylprotocatechuic, gallic and triacetogallic acid diethylamides fail to yield ketones.[210]

Amides of *α,β-unsaturated acids* react with Grignard reagents to give, in general, 1,2-addition compounds:[211]

$$RCH = CHCON(R')_2 \xrightarrow{R''MgX} RR''CHCH_2CON(R')_2$$

Methylmagnesium halides react in an exceptional manner, causing the replacement of the amino group with a methyl group:

$$RCH = CHCON(R')_2 + CH_3MgX \rightarrow RCH = CHCOCH_3 + XMgN(R')_2$$

A condensation reaction also takes place sometimes, however, giving rise to a dicarboxylic acid amide:[212]

$$CH_3CH = CHCON(C_6H_5)_2 + CH_3MgI \rightarrow (CH_3)_2CHCH = C(OMgI)N(C_6H_5)_2$$

$$\xrightarrow{CH_3CH:CHCON(C_6H_5)_2} (C_6H_5)_2NC(OMgI) = C[CH(CH_3)_2]CH(CH_3)CH_2CON(C_6H_5)_2$$

$$\xrightarrow{H_2O} (C_6H_5)_2NCOCH[CH(CH_3)_2]CH(CH_3)CH_2CON(C_6H_5)_2$$

The corresponding diketone is formed with an excess of the Grignard reagent. *Cinnamylanilides*, $C_6H_5CH = CHCON(R')C_6H_5$, give unsaturated ketones with methylmagnesium iodide, through the replacement of the anilido group with the methyl group, but 1,4-addition takes place with ethyl and phenylmagnesium bromides. N-substituted β-furylacrylamides also give 1,4-addition products.

Among *imides of dicarboxylic acids*, succinimide reacts with one molecular equivalent of an organomagnesium halide, giving an addition compound, hydrolysis of which leads to the formation of the inner amide of an unsaturated amino acids:

$$\overline{COCH_2CH_2CONR} + R'MgX \quad \rightarrow \quad XMgO\overline{C(R')CH_2CH_2CONR}$$

$$\overset{H_2O}{\rightarrow} \quad HO\overline{C(R')CH_2CH_2CONR} \quad \rightarrow \quad R'\overline{C = CHCH_2CONR}$$

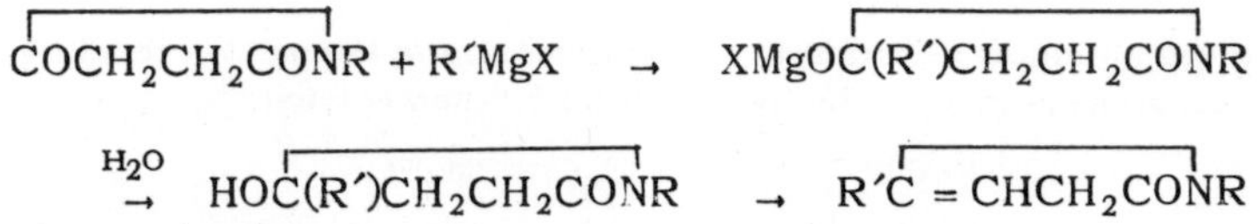

N-Methylsuccinimide reacts with one molecular equivalent of phenylmagnesium bromide to form 1-methyl-2-phenyl-2-hydroxy-5-oxotetrahydropyrrole,[213] while with two molecular equivalents of the compound it gives dibenzoylethane and methyl-2,5-diphenylpyrrole. N,N-Diethylphthalamic acid gives 3,3-substituted phthalides:[449]

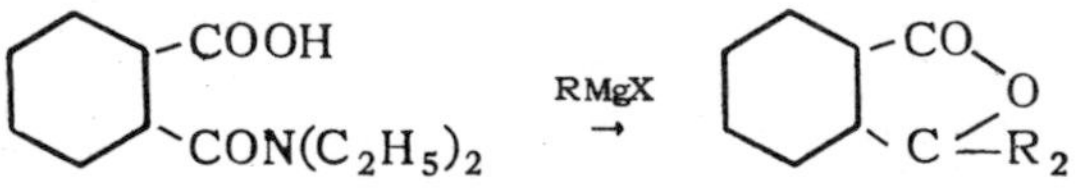

Phthalimide reacts with one carbonyl group giving an addition compound, which on hydrolysis gives the corresponding hydroxy compound or a keto amide:[214]

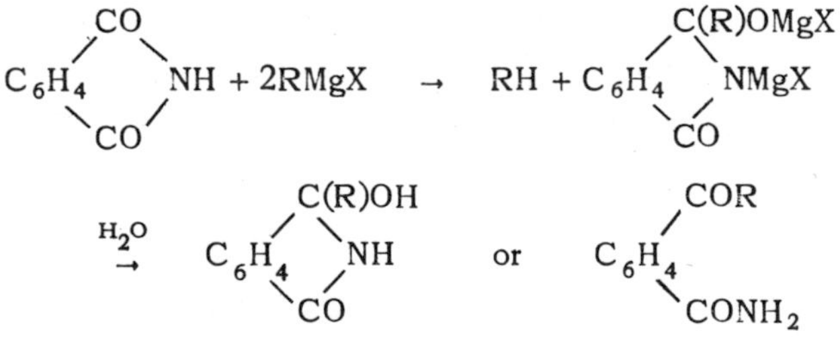

If R is an alkyl group, cleavage of the elements of water may occur resulting in the formation of an isoindolinone derivative:[215]

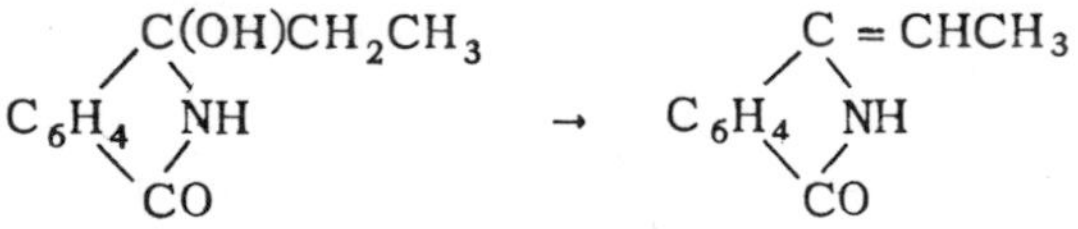

The reaction of *isatin* with organomagnesium halides results in the formation of

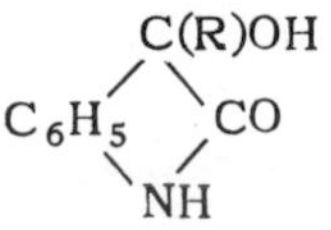

Reaction with Imino Ethers

The reaction of organomagnesium halides with imino ethers leads to the elimination of the alkoxy group:

$$C_6H_5C(OCH_3) = NC_6H_5 + RMgBr \rightarrow C_6H_5C(R) = NC_6H_5 + CH_3OMgBr$$

The reaction product of phenylmagnesium bromide and phenylimino methyl ether can be readily hydrolyzed to benzoin, while the condensation of benzylmagnesium bromide with the same imino ether gives a desoxybenzoin in low yield, and the condensation products of other magnesium halides yield resinous products.[217] The hydrolysis of the reaction product of phenylformimino ethyl ether, $C_2H_5OCH = NC_6H_5$, with Grignard reagents results in the formation of aldehydes, RCHO.[218]

Reaction with Acid Azides

The reaction of acid azides with organomagnesium halides generally results in the formation of 1,3-disubstituted triazines:[219]

$$RCON_3 + R'MgX \rightarrow RCON(MgX)N = NR'$$

$$\xrightarrow{H_2O} RCONHN = NR'$$

Carbamyl azide reacts with phenylmagnesium bromide forming the compounds

$$H_2NCONHN = NC_6H_5,\ N_3CONHNHCON_3$$

and $C_6H_5N = NNHCONHNHCONHN = NC_6H_5$. *Carbonyl azide*, N_3CON_3, is decomposed by phenylmagnesium bromide, while *azido formic ester* reacts in a complicated manner.

Ketones result under certain circumstances from the reaction of acid azides with Grignard reagents by the replacement of the azido group with the organic group in the Grignard reagent:

$$RCON_3 + R'MgX \rightarrow RCOR' + N_3MgX$$

Phenylcarbamyl azide, $C_6H_5NHCON_3$, and other substituted carbamic azides react in this manner with phenylmagnesium bromide.[220]

Reaction with Nitriles

Nitriles react normally with organomagnesium halides to form magnesium ketimines, hydrolysis of which results in the formation of ketones:[221]

$$RCN + R'MgX \rightarrow RC(=NMgX)R' \xrightarrow{H_2O} RC(:NH)R' \xrightarrow{HCl} RCOR'$$

A complex between the reagent and nitrile is formed rapidly and reversibly, which undergoes intramolecular rearrangement, with the radical attached to magnesium migrating with its pair of electrons to the nitrile carbon atom. This latter change is the rate determining step. Aliphatic nitriles with less electronegative radicals are, in general, more reactive toward Grignard reagents than are aromatic nitriles.

The procedure is to add the nitrile in ethereal solution to a solution of the Grignard reagent in ether, and to complete the reaction by warming the mixture on a water-bath.[222]

Aromatic ketimines may be obtained by decomposing the initial halomagnesium ketimine with an aqueous solution of ammonium chloride cooled to 0°. Decomposition may also be effected with liquid ammonia. Special care must be exercised in preparing mixed aromatic-aliphatic ketimines. Unstable ketimines may be isolated as their acyl derivatives, which are formed by treating the magnesium compound with the acyl chloride.[223]

Magnesium ketimines are readily converted to the corresponding ketone by treatment with dilute acids.

Mixed alkylaryl ketones may be prepared as follows: one-fourth molal proportion of the nitrile, dissolved in 100 cc of ether, is added gradually with stirring to a solution of one molecular proportion of the organomagnesium halide in ether, in the course of 15 minutes. The reaction mixture is allowed to stand overnight and is then poured into a mixture of 500 grams of ice and 300 cc of concentrated hydrochloric acid. The aqueous layer is separated and vigorously boiled under reflux for one hour. The liquid is finally cooled and extracted with ether, and the ketone is isolated by fractional distillation from the ether extract.

The yields of ketone show greater variations with phenylmagnesium bromide than with aliphatic organomagnesium halides. In the case of normal aliphatic organomagnesium compounds, the yield of ketone increases with increase in the number of carbon atoms in the radical.

Dimagnesium compounds generally give low yields of diketones. Thus, the dimagnesium compound derived from 1,5-dichloropentane gives with propionitrile, only a 20% yield of the diketone, $C_2H_5CO(CH_2)_5COC_2H_5$, with the monoketone $C_2H_5CO(CH_2)_4CH_3$ as the principal product.[5] Very good yields of the diketone are obtained when dicyanodiphenyl is made to react with phenylmagnesium bromide in benzene solution. Good yields of diketone are also obtained with this nitrile in the reaction with benzyl and ethylmagnesium bromides.[224]

Certain nitriles, among them acetonitrile, react as pseudoacids yielding a hydrocarbon:[225]

$$CH_2 = C = NH + C_2H_5MgBr \rightarrow CH_2 = C = NMgBr + C_2H_6$$

Chloroacetonitrile, phenylacetonitrile, propionitrile and γ-ethoxybutyronitrile show this *pseudo*acid character.[226] Nitriles which thus tend to act in the *pseudo*acid or imino form are partially polymerized under the action of organomagnesium halides.[226] Unsaturated nitriles are particularly subject to polymerization.[227] In the reaction of *n*-butylmagnesium bromide with valeronitrile carried out in methylal, the tertiary alcohol, $n(C_4H_9)_3COH$, is the major product obtained upon hydrolysis of the complex.[450] Cyclic condensation products may result from phenylacetonitrile by reaction with the ketimine.[451]

In α-substituted nitriles the cyano groups may be exchanged with the organic group in the organomagnesium halide.[228] Cyanhydrins react in the normal manner as a rule, although occasionally the cyano group in these compounds may be exchanged for the organic group in the Grignard reagent. Thus, cyclopentyl methyl ketone cyanhydrin, reacting with ethylmagnesium bromide, gives ethylmethylcyclopropylcarbinol.[229]

Exchange of the cyano group may take place with α-amino nitriles,

$$RCH(NR'R'')CN$$

If R is hydrogen then ketone formation predominates; if R is a lower alkyl or the cyclohexyl group, ketone formation is the principal reaction with alkylmagnesium halides. The exchange reaction predominates with phenyl and benzylmagnesium chlorides.[230]

Cyanoformic ester also undergoes exchange of the CN group:[231]

$$CNCOOC_2H_5 + C_2H_5MgBr \rightarrow C_2H_5COOC_2H_5 + CNMgBr$$

Further reaction of the resulting ester with the organomagnesium halide gives triethylcarbinol.

The cyano group in *γ-cyanoquinoline* can also be exchanged with an alkyl group. Reaction with benzylmagnesium chloride gives only γ-benzylquinoline, while ethylmagnesium bromide yields a mixture of γ-quinolyl ketone and γ-ethylquinoline.[232]

A few nitriles, among them *p*-dimethylaminobenzonitrile and *p*-methoxybenzonitrile, fail to react with ethyl and phenylmagnesium bromide.

Nitriles containing a *reactive methylene* group, such as malononitrile, benzyl cyanide, etc., react with organomagnesium halides giving the magnesium derivative of the nitrile:

$$CNCH_2CN + RMgX \rightarrow CNCH(MgX)CN + RH$$

The original nitrile is recovered unchanged when the resulting magnesium compound is hydrolyzed. In many instances the magnesio nitrile is capable of reacting with a further molecule of the Grignard reagent to form a magnesium ketimine. For example, the iodomagnesium derivative of ethyl cyanoacetate, reacting with ethylmagnesium iodide, gives a ketimine magnesium iodide:[233]

$$CNCH(MgI)COOC_2H_5 + C_2H_5MgI \rightarrow C_2H_5C(=NMgI)CH(MgI)COOC_2H_5$$

Ethyl diethylcyanoacetate gives with phenylmagnesium bromide the magnesium compound, $BrMgC(C_2H_5)_2COOC_2H_5$, which undergoes self-condensation, and the condensation product on hydrolysis yields ethyl-α-diethyl-γ-diethylacetylacetate.[234]

Phenylmalononitrile reacts with phenylmagnesium bromide to form the compound

$$C_6H_5C(=NMgBr)C(C_6H_5) = CC_6H_5MgBr$$

Dibenzylmalononitrile reacts with one equivalent of phenylmagnesium bromide; the resulting compound breaks down to dibenzylkeneneiminomagnesium bromide and benzonitrile, the former yielding dibenzylacetonitrile on hydrolysis.[235]

Phenylacetonitrile reacts with phenylmagnesium bromide to form the ketimine of phenyldesoxybenzoin. *Diphenylacetonitrile* forms a desoxybenzoinketimine with some tetraphenylsuccinonitrile.[236]

Dialkyl acetonitriles, $RR'CHCN$, react with *sec*-amine magnesium bromides to form the magnesium compounds $RR'C(MgBr)CN$.

Glutaronitrile, $CN(CH_2)_3CN$, reacts with phenylmagnesium bromide to give the halomagnesiumketimine derivative of 2-keto-6-phenyl-1,3,4-tetrahydropyridine, $C_6H_5\overline{C = CHCH_2CH_2CON}H$.[237]

Alkyloxy acetonitriles, $ROCH_2CN$, react with allylmagnesium bromide to form complexes which, on hydrolysis, yield diallyl(alkoxymethyl)carbinamines, $ROCH_2C(NH_2)(CH_2CH=CH_2)_2$.[238]

Benzoyl cyanide, C_6H_5COCN, gives with phenylmagnesium bromide the magnesium derivative of triphenylcarbinol, $(C_6H_5)_3COMgBr$.[239] Benzylmagnesium chloride reacts similarly, but with ethylmagnesium bromide the halomagnesium ketimine, $C_6H_5COC(C_2H_5)=NMgBr$, is formed. Other α-keto nitriles react in a similar manner. *Cyanoacetophenone*, $C_6H_5COCH_2CN$, reacts with one molecular equivalent of organomagnesium halides to form halomagnesium ketimines, $C_6H_5COCH_2C(R)=NMgX$.[240]

α-Amino nitriles may react with organomagnesium compounds in three possible ways:

$$RCH(NR'_2)CN \xrightarrow{R''MgX} \begin{cases} RCH(NR'_2)R'' \\ RCH(NR'_2)CR''{:}NMgX \\ RCH(NR'_2)CH(NR'_2)R \end{cases}$$

The first reaction predominates if R′ is a phenyl or benzyl group, and when R is a phenyl group; the second reaction predominates when R is hydrogen or a lower alkyl residue and R″ is an alkyl residue.[241]

α-Methyl-α-dimethylaminobutyronitrile and α-methyl-α-piperidobutyronitrile react according to the first scheme with ethyl- and phenylmagnesium bromides, and benzylmagnesium chloride. α-Dimethylaminobutenenitrile and α-piperidinobutenenitrile also react according to the first reaction with phenylmagnesium bromide.[242] Phenyl-α-piperidinoacetonitrile reacts according to the first scheme with phenyl- or benzylmagnesium bromide.[243]

Certain aliphatic α-amino nitriles form Schiff bases on reaction with Grignard compounds by elimination of hydrocyanic acid. This reaction takes place only with nitriles containing primary or secondary amino groups.

Monochloroacetonitrile, reacting with phenylmagnesium bromide, gives diphenylbenzoylcarbinol and chloroacetophenone;[244] indolylmagnesium halides give indolylacetonitriles.[452] γ-Chlorobutyronitrile reacts with Grignard reagents to form the magnesium chloroketimine, $ClCH_2CH_2CH_2C(=NMg)R$ and the magnesium cyclopropylketimine, $\overline{CH_2CH_2CH}C(=NMgX)R$. Pyrroline derivatives $\overline{RC=CHCH_2CH_2N}H$ may be obtained from the former.[245] Reacting with phenylmagnesium bromide, *δ-bromovaleronitrile* gives the magnesium derivative of α-phenyltetrahydropyridine.[246] ω-Bromo-*o*-cyanostyrene reacts with Grignard reagents to form a ketimine derivative which is converted to an isoquinoline on heating:[247]

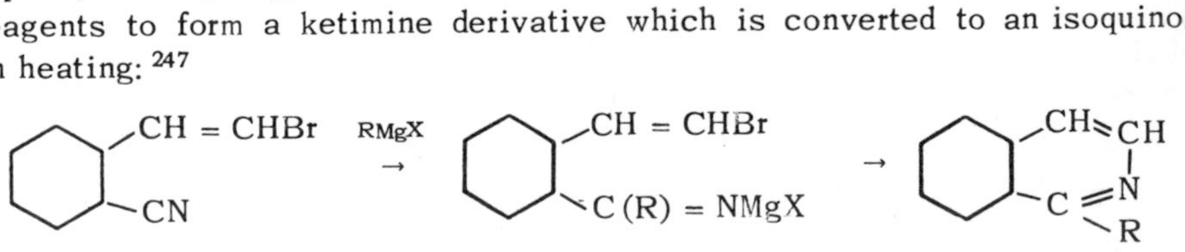

1,1-Dimethyl-3-durylpseudoindole has been obtained in 83% yield from *o*-cyanobenzoyldurene and methylmagnesium iodide:[418]

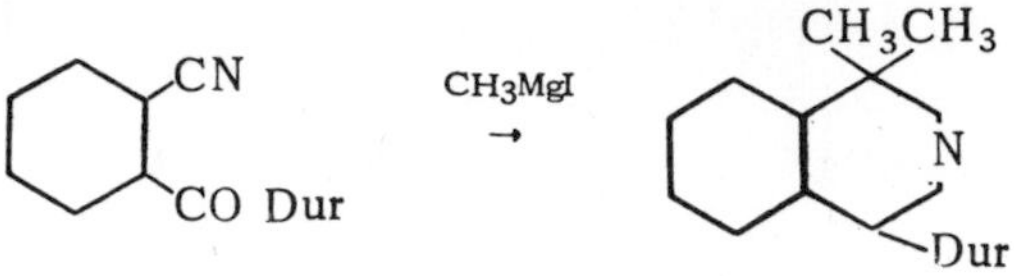

Arylsulfoacetonitriles, RSO_2CH_2CN, fail to react with organomagnesium halides.[248]

In *α, β-unsaturated* nitriles in which the ethylenic and nitrile multiple bonds form a conjugated system, an 1,4-addition may take place,

$$R'CH = CHC \vdots N + RMgX \rightarrow RR'CHCH = C = NMgX$$

Hydrolysis results in the formation of a saturated nitrile, $RR'CHCH_2CN$.[249] *α, β*-Unsaturated nitriles having a substituent in the *β*-position react normally, giving a magnesium ketimine. Cinnamonitrile and *β*-phenylcinnamonitrile yield a 1,4-addition product with ethylmagnesium bromide and the normal reaction product with phenylmagnesium bromide.

In the aromatic series, the reactivity of the nitriles toward phenylmagnesium bromide decreases in the order

$$p\text{-}ClC_6H_4CN > C_6H_5CN > m\text{-}CH_3C_6H_4CN > p\text{-}CH_3C_6H_4CN >$$
$$o\text{-}CH_3C_6H_4CN > p\text{-}(CH_3)_2NC_6H_4CN$$

i.e., the same as the electronegativity of the aromatic radicals in the Kharasch series.[453] The relative reactivities of Grignard reagents toward benzonitrile decrease in the order

$$2,4,6\text{-}(CH_3)_3C_6H_2MgX > p\text{-}CH_3C_6H_4MgX > C_6H_5MgX > C_2H_5MgX$$
$$n\text{-}C_3H_7MgX > i\text{-}C_3H_7MgX > n\text{-}C_4H_9MgX > s\text{-}C_4H_9MgX > t\text{-}C_4H_9MgX$$

This is the reverse of the order of activity toward benzophenone.[454]

Phthalonitrile, reacting with phenylmagnesium bromide, gives a cyclic imine of the probable formula

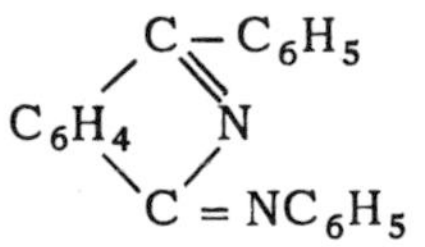

while with benzylmagnesium chloride a compound assumed to be 3,3-dibenzyl-1-aminoisoindole,

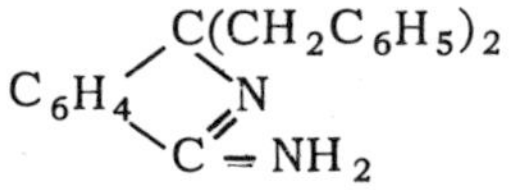

is obtained.[248] With methylmagnesium iodide a condensation product is obtained which on heating in a high boiling solvent is transformed to tetrabenzotriacaporphyrine.

2,3-Dimethoxybenzonitrile reacts with ethylmagnesium halides to form a complex which on hydrolysis yields a 2-alkyl-3-methoxybenzonitrile:[250]

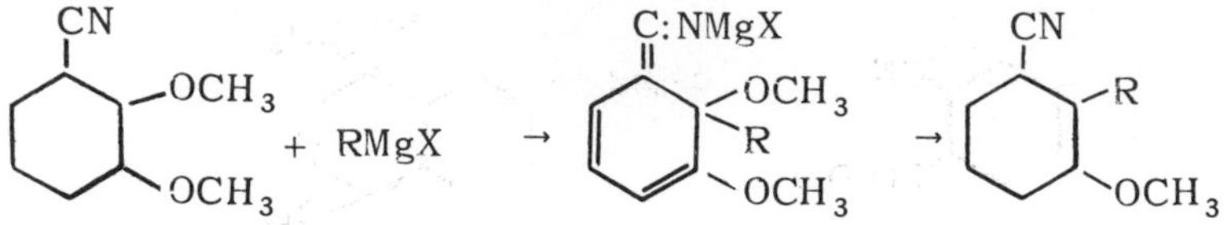

Phenylmagnesium bromide gives the 2-phenylnitrile and 2,3-dimethoxybenzophenone in equal amounts. The resulting nitriles are difficult to hydrolyze.

2-Cyanobenzaldehyde reacts with phenylmagnesium bromide to give the magnesium compound of 2-benzoylbenzhydrol, $C_6H_5C(=NH)C_6H_4CH(OH)C_6H_5$, which on hydrolysis yields 2,5-diphenyl-3,4-benzofuran,

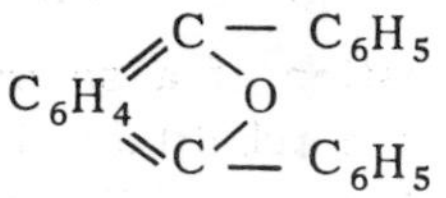

Isodurylaldehyde cyanhydrin gives with phenylmagnesium bromide a magnesium trimethyldesylamine:[251]

$$(CH_3)_3C_6H_2CH(OH)CN \xrightarrow{C_6H_5MgBr} (CH_3)_3C_6H_2CH(OH)C(=NMgBr)C_6H_5$$
$$\rightarrow (CH_3)_3C_6H_2COCH(C_6H_5)NH_2$$

Nicotionitrile gives with *n*-propylmagnesium halides the halomagnesium ketime of *n*-propyl 4-*n*-propyl-3-pyridyl ketone.[419]

4-Cyanoquinoline gives with organomagnesium halides RMgX, the magnesium compound,

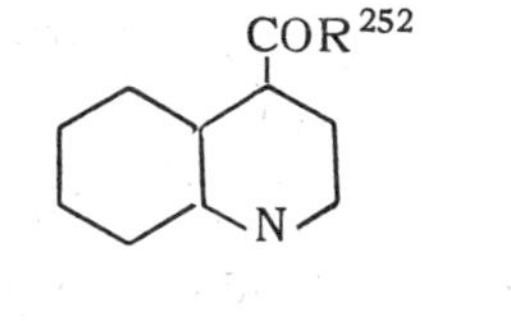

hydrolysis leads to the formation of the ketone

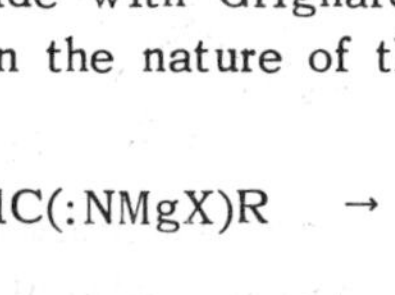

Reaction with Cyanogen Halides

The reaction of cyanogen chloride with Grignard reagents may proceed in one of two directions, depending on the nature of the organic group in the reagent:

$$ClCN + RMgX \nearrow ClC(:NMgX)R \rightarrow RCN + ClMgX$$
$$ClCN + RMgX \searrow XMgCN + RCl$$

The nitrile formed, reacting with a further molecule of organomagnesium halide, yields a halomagnesium ketimine.[253] With aliphatic and aromatic magnesium halides the nitrile is formed with few exceptions, while cycloaliphatic compounds yield the chloride as the main product.[254] Chlorinated compounds are obtained, in general, with compounds in which the magnesium is attached to a secondary carbon.[255] Organomagnesium halides of acetylene and other compounds in which the halomagnesium group replaces a mobile hydrogen, give nitriles with cyanogen chloride.[256] Cyanogen bromide and cyanogen iodide give halo compounds with all organomagnesium halides, although some nitrile is also obtained with cyanogen bromide.

The reaction of *cyanogen* with organomagnesium halides is similar to that with cyanogen chloride:[257]

$$CNCN + RMgX \begin{cases} \nearrow CNC(=NMgX)R \rightarrow RCN + XMgCN \\ \searrow RCN + XMgCN \end{cases}$$

The end product of the reaction is the same in either case. Acetylenedimagnesium bromide gives an addition product with cyanogen, which is decomposed on hydrolysis.

The nitrile group in *substituted cyanamides* reacts with Grignard reagents in a normal manner:[258]

$$RNHCN + 2\ R'MgX \rightarrow R'H + RN(MgX)C(=NMgX)R'$$

$$\xrightarrow{H_2O} RNHC(=NH)R'$$

Dimethylcyanamide reacts with phenylmagnesium bromide forming the magnesium derivative of dimethylbenzamidine, $(CH_3)_2NC(=NH)C_6H_5$.[259]

Reaction with Isonitriles, Isocyanates, etc.

Isonitriles react with organomagnesium halides to form addition compounds, which on treatment with mineral acids yield an amine and an aldehyde:[260]

$$RN = C + R'MgBr \rightarrow RN = C(R')MgBr$$

$$\rightarrow RN = CHR' \rightarrow RNH_2 + R'CHO$$

Isocyanates give with Grignard reagents magnesium derivatives of substituted amides:[261]

$$C_6H_5N = C{:}O + RMgI \rightarrow C_6H_5N = C(R)OMgI$$

$$\xrightarrow{H_2O} C_6H_5NHCOR$$

Thiocyanates, reacting with alkylmagnesium halides, give a sulfide and a cyanomagnesium halide:[262]

$$RSCN + R'MgBr \rightarrow RSR' + CNMgBr$$

With arylmagnesium halides, a nitrile and a mercaptomagnesium halide are obtained:

$$RSCN + R'MgBr \rightarrow RSMgBr + R'CN$$

Isothiocyanates generally yield halo magnesium thioamides:[263]

$$RN = C = S + R'MgBr \rightarrow RN(MgBr)CSR'$$

Phenylisothiocyanate reacts with an excess of phenylmagnesium bromide to form, after decomposition of the magnesium complex, *o*-phenylbenzhydrylaniline, $C_6H_5NHC_6H_4CH(C_6H_5)_2$.[264] Phenylisocyanate reacts similarly.

Isocyanuric esters react with Grignard reagents to form monohydroxydiketohexahydrotriazines:[265]

$$\overline{CH_3NCON(CH_3)CON(CH_3)CO} \xrightarrow{RMgX} \overline{CH_3NC(OH)(R)N(CH_3)CON(CH_3)CO}$$

Reaction with Ethers

Purely aliphatic ethers do not, in general, react with organomagnesium halides. Higher molecular ethers, and ethers of secondary alcohols react to some extent. Purely aromatic ethers and aromatic-aliphatic ethers react more or less readily with Grignard reagents;[266] the ether linkage is severed in the process, and a coupling of two organic groups occurs with the oxygen remaining attached to the more acidic residue:

$$ROR' + R''MgX \rightarrow ROMgX + R' - R''$$

With phenyl alkyl ethers, the alkyl residue is cleaved, and magnesium phenolate forms:[267]

$$C_6H_5OR + R'MgX \rightarrow C_6H_5OMgX + RR'$$

With benzyl alkyl ethers, the hydrocarbon residue of the Grignard compound attaches itself to the benzyl group:

$$C_6H_5CH_2OC_2H_5 + CH_3MgI \rightarrow C_6H_5CH_2CH_3 + C_2H_5OMgI$$

Phenol ethers with saturated alkyl groups react above 160°, while ethers with unsaturated groups may react at a considerably lower temperature. Thus, phenyl allyl ether reacts at about 50°, the alkyl residue of the Grignard compound combining with the allyl group. The reaction time varies from a few minutes after reaching the reaction temperature, to six hours.

Triphenylcarbinol ethers react with phenylmagnesium bromide giving tetraphenylmethane in low yield.[268]

Diphenyl ether reacts with ethylmagnesium bromide to form phenol and *o*-phenyl phenol.

The ring in methylenedioxy-4-ethylbenzene is ruptured on reaction with methylmagnesium iodide and 1,2-dihydroxy-4-ethylbenzene and 1,2-hydroxyethoxy-4-ethylbenzene are formed.[269]

Reaction with pyrylium salts results in substitution of the organic group of the Grignard reagent in the pyrylium ring at 4-position.[455]

Amino ethers of the type R_2NCH_2OR'(*) react with organomagnesium halides to form tertiary amines:[270]

$$(R)_2NCH_2OR' + R''MgX \rightarrow (R)_2NCH_2R'' + R'OMgX$$

N-Substituted morpholines may be prepared by this method through the reaction of 4-morpholinomethyl ether with organomagnesium compounds:

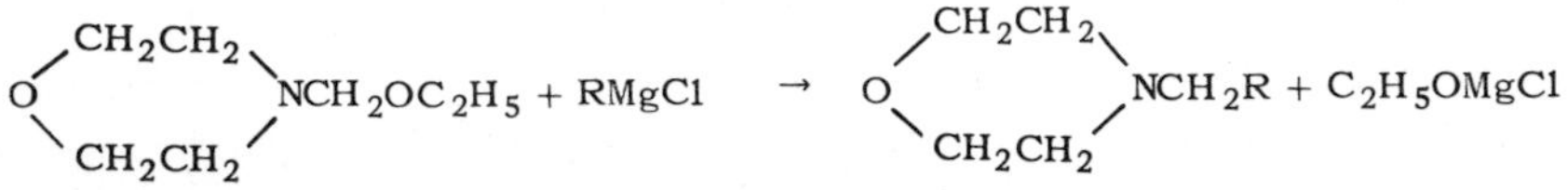

Yields with various Grignard reagents are as follows: ethylmagnesium bromide, 43.4%; amylmagnesium bromide, 59.4%; phenylmagnesium bromide, 64.4%; benzylmagnesium chloride, 66%; α-naphthylmagnesium bromide, 57.7%.[271]

1,2,3-Trimethoxy-5-cyanobenzene undergoes abnormal cleavage with alkylmagnesium halides:[456]

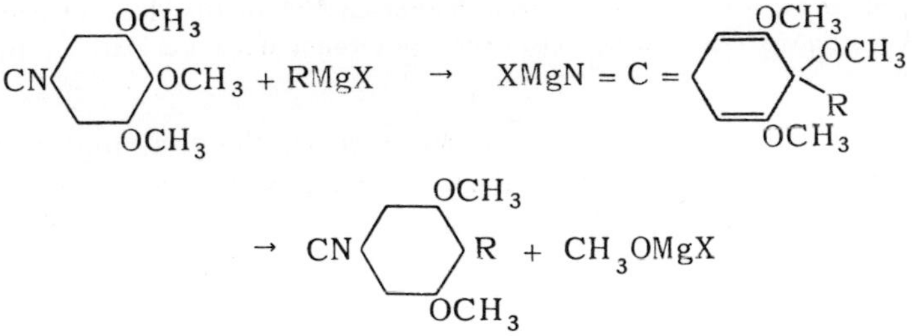

Other reactions of this type have also been observed.[457]

Reaction with Alkylene Oxides

The reaction of organomagnesium compounds with alkylene oxides leads to the formation of halomagnesium derivatives of alcohols:[273]

$$\overline{CH_2CH_2O} + RMgX \rightarrow RCH_2CH_2OMgX$$

A certain amount of the haloethoxy compound XCH_2CH_2OMgR is also formed. Hydrolysis of the magnesium compound yields the corresponding alcohol. Propylene 1,3-oxide reacts in a similar manner:

$$\overline{CH_2CH_2CH_2O} + RMgX \rightarrow RCH_2CH_2CH_2OMgX$$

On the other hand, oxides with a ring composed of more than three carbon atoms fail to react in this manner, a fact which seems to be related to the lack of strain in these rings.

(*) Amino ethers of this type are readily formed through the condensation of secondary amines with formaldehyde and the subsequent esterification of the resulting amino alcohol. Esterification proceeds most readily with higher alcohols.

Homologs of ethylene oxide yield secondary or tertiary alcohols:

$$\overline{RCH_2CH_2O} + RMgX \quad \rightarrow \quad RCH(OMgX)CH_2R' \quad \rightarrow \quad RCH(OH)CH_2R'$$

Styryl oxide gives a primary or secondary alcohol according to the conditions. When the oxide is added to the solution of the Grignard reagent, the primary alcohol magnesium halide is obtained, while if the solution of the organomagnesium halide is added to the oxide, the secondary alcohol derivative is obtained.[274]

Alkylene oxides undergo *isomerization* under the influence of the organomagnesium halides to aldehydes or ketones; these react with Grignard reagents to yield secondary or tertiary alcohols. The latter are, therefore, obtained as byproducts of the reaction of oxides with organomagnesium halides. Diethylmagnesium does not induce isomerization and thus gives only the secondary alcohol.[275]

The tendency in isomerization is toward the formation of aldehydes in preference to ketones. The relatively electron-deficient carbon atom of the oxirane ring should become the α-carbon atom as a result of the transformation.[453] In the case of unsymmetrical oxiranes the carbon atom bearing the more electronegative substituent becomes the α-carbon atom.

Ring contraction may occur in some measure in the reaction of organomagnesium halides with certain cyclic epoxy compounds as, for example, with cycloheptenyl oxide, magnesium bromide apparently playing the role of a catalyst:[276]

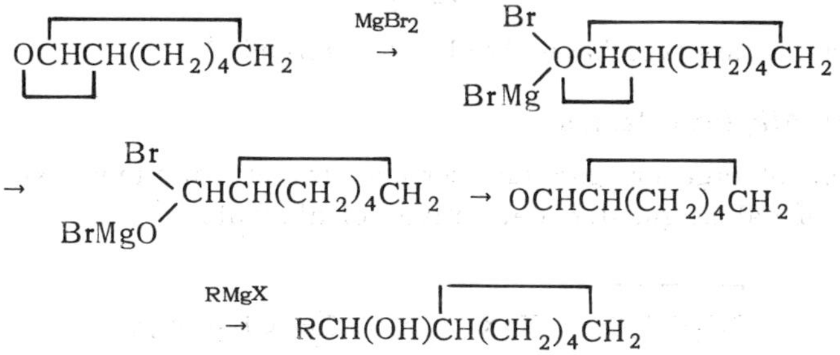

Ring contraction is observed also with cyclohexene oxide.[277] Ring contraction does not take place in the reaction of diethylmagnesium with cyclohexene oxide.[278]

An interesting cleavage takes place when α-oxidocarbonyl compounds are heated with phenylmagnesium bromide:[279]

$$C_6H_5CH\underset{O}{-\!\!-\!\!-}CHCOC_6H_5 + C_6H_5MgBr \quad \rightarrow \quad C_6H_5CH\underset{O}{-\!\!-\!\!-}CHC(C_6H_5)_2OMgBr$$

$$\rightarrow \quad C_6H_5CH = CHOMgBr + (C_6H_5)_2CO$$

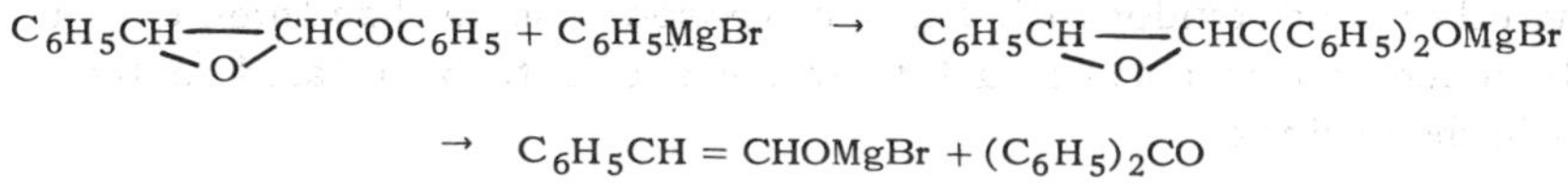

Reaction with Hydrocarbons

Organomagnesium halides react with aromatic hydrocarbons in the presence of traces of moisture and a minimum amount of ether. Benzylmagnesium chloride, reacting with benzene under these conditions, gives diphenylmethane.[420]

Wurtz Type Reaction

The reaction of organic halides with organomagnesium halides normally leads to the union of the organic residues in the reacting bodies:[280]

$$RX + R'MgX \rightarrow R.R' + MgX_2$$

Cobalt chloride acts as a catalyst in this reaction. The reaction is confined to reactive halides and is often accompanied by many side reactions. The yields are satisfactory only with methyl and tertiary alkyl groups, and with alkyl halides containing positive groups. Aromatic and mixed aromatic-aliphatic halides give good results.[281] Side reactions are minimized with the latter type of compounds when iodides are employed. The reaction proceeds at room temperature with compounds containing highly reactive halogens. With compounds in which the halogen is less reactive, the ether is distilled off and the reaction is carried out at a higher temperature.

The reaction of ethylmagnesium halides with ethyl halides results in the formation of equimolecular amounts of ethane and ethylene:

$$C_2H_5MgX + C_2H_5X \rightarrow C_2H_6 + C_2H_4 + MgX_2$$

Increase in the chain length of the hydrocarbon radical generally favors the coupling reaction.[282] Thus, iodides of hydrocarbons with 8 to 15 carbon atoms give coupling products in 25 to 28% yield, while chlorides of long chain hydrocarbons give Grignard compounds in good yield by an exchange of the halogen and the halomagnesium group.[5] Reduction products are formed exclusively in the reaction of *t*-butylmagnesium chloride with *n*-butyl, isobutyl, and lauryl chlorides.[422]

Coupling of the organic groups present in an organomagnesium compound may be effected by removal of the halomagnesium group by the action of freshly precipitated silver bromide dried below 80°. This offers the best method for the preparation of hexamethylethane.

Ethylene chlorohydrin, reacting with one molecular equivalent of an organomagnesium halide, yields chloroethoxymagnesium halide:

$$ClCH_2CH_2OH + RMgBr \rightarrow ClCH_2CH_2OMgBr + HR$$

Reaction with a second molecule of the magnesium compound leads to the formation of the compound RCH_2CH_2OMgBr.[283] The *toluenesulfonic* ester of ethylene chlorohydrin is cleaved at the sulfonic group on reaction with organomagnesium halides:[284]

$$CH_3C_6H_4SO_2OCH_2CH_2Cl + RMgX \rightarrow CH_3C_6H_4SO_2OMgX + RCH_2CH_2Cl$$

p-Toluenesulfonic-γ-propyl ester reacts similarly. *Halomethyl ethers* undergo the coupling reaction:[285]

$$ROCH_2X + R'MgX \rightarrow ROCH_2R' + MgX_2$$

Since such halo ethers are obtained through the reaction of hydrogen halides with a mixture of equivalent quantities of an alcohol and formaldehyde, the reaction offers an excellent method for the preparation of complex ethers.

Unsymmetrical dihalo ethers, such as $C_2H_5OCH(Cl)CH_2Cl$ also undergo the reaction, the organic group replacing the α-hydrogen:[286]

$$C_2H_5OCHClCH_2Cl + RMgX \rightarrow C_2H_5OCH(R)CH_2Cl + ClMgX$$

Pyrrolemagnesium bromide reacts with ethyl iodide forming β-ethylpyrrole:[287]

$$\overline{CH = CHCH = CHN}MgBr + IC_2H_5 \rightarrow \overline{CH = C(C_2H_5)CH = CHN}H + IMgBr$$

The reaction of *chlorinated ketones* with Grignard reagents at higher temperatures may result in the replacement of the halogen, with the carbonyl group remaining intact:[288]

$$CH_3COCH_2Cl + C_6H_5MgBr \rightarrow CH_3COCH_2C_6H_5 + ClMgBr$$

2,4-Dibromo-2,4-dimethyl-3-pentanone reacts in an abnormal manner with phenylmagnesium bromide, giving phenyltetramethyl acetone,

$$C_6H_5C(CH_3)_2COCH(CH_3)_2$$ [289]

Organomagnesium halides react with chlorocarbonic esters to form carboxylic esters:

$$R'MgX + ClCOOR \rightarrow R'COOR + ClMgX$$

An excess of the ester must be employed in order to prevent the formation of carbinols.[290]

In the reaction of organomagnesium halides with *acyl chlorides,* coupling of two acyl groups may take place resulting in the formation of diketones:[291]

$$RCOCl \xrightarrow{CH_3MgI} RCOCOR$$

Diphenylchloroacetyl chloride, $(C_6H_5)_2CClCOCl$, reacting with phenylmagnesium bromide gives diphenylketene. α-Pyrryl alkyl ketones may be obtained in 50 to 80% yield through the reaction of acid chlorides with pyrrylmagnesium halides.[292]

Among *unsaturated halides,* allyl halides react with organomagnesium compounds to form unsaturated hydrocarbons:

$$RMgX + XCH_2CH = CH_2 \rightarrow RCH_2CH = CH_2 + MgX_2$$

Allyl iodide and bromide react vigorously even in the cold. The method is of general applicability and yields are quite satisfactory.[293] The greater the number of phenyl groups joined to the alkyl group in the Grignard reagent, the more readily the reaction proceeds. 2,3-Dibromopropylene also undergoes this reaction:[294]

$$C_2H_5MgBr + BrCH_2CBr = CH_2 \rightarrow C_2H_5CH_2CBr = CH_2 + MgBr_2$$

1,3-Dibromopropylene reacts in this manner only with aromatic organomagnesium compounds.[295] The second halogen atom may also enter in reaction in the latter case:

$$RCH_2CH = CHBr + RMgX \rightarrow RCH_2CH = CHR + BrMgX$$

In addition coupling may occur in the direction of the reaction:

$$2\,RCH_2CH=CHBr + 2\,RMgX \rightarrow RCH_2CH=CHCH=CHCH_2R + R_2 + 2\,BrMgX$$

Allyl bromide reacts with acetylenemagnesium halides in the presence of cupric chloride or bromide:[296]

$$C_6H_5C\equiv CMgI + BrCH_2CH=CH_2 \rightarrow C_6H_5C\equiv CCH_2CH=CH_2 + BrMgI$$

The diacetylenic compound $C_6H_5C\equiv CCH_2C\equiv CC_6H_5$ has been obtained by the reaction of diiodomethane with a phenylmagnesium halide, $C_6H_5C\equiv CMgX$.[423]

Chloromethyl ether reacts readily with halomagnesium derivatives of acetylenic compounds forming acetylenic ethers:[424]

$$RC\equiv CMgX + ClCH_2OR' \rightarrow RC\equiv CCH_2OR' + XMgCl$$

Acetylenic nitriles have been obtained by the reaction of acetylenic Grignard compound with cyanogen chloride and hydrolysis of the resulting complex:[425]

$$RC\equiv CMgBr + ClCN \rightarrow RC\equiv CCCl(=NMgBr) \xrightarrow{H_2O} RC\equiv CCN + MgBrCl$$

Monoiodoacetylenes reacting with halomagnesium acetylides give disubstituted diacetylenes:[297]

$$RC\equiv CMgBr + IC\equiv CR \rightarrow RC\equiv CC\equiv CR + IMgBr$$

Monoiododiacetylene similarly yields a substituted triacetylene:[298]

$$C_6H_5C\equiv CMgBr + IC\equiv CC\equiv CH \rightarrow C_6H_5C\equiv CC\equiv CC\equiv CH + BrMgI$$

Substituted iodoacetylenes are obtained by adding the theoretically required quantity of iodine in ethereal solution to the solution of acetylenemagnesium halide:

$$RC\equiv CMgBr + I_2 \rightarrow RC\equiv CI + BrMgI$$

Disubstituted diacetylenes result in good yield when a half-molal equivalent of iodine is added to the solution of the acetylenemagnesium halide. Hydrocarbons with multiple acetylenic bonds may be prepared by adding iodine in various proportions to a solution of acetylenedimagnesium bromide.

Disubstituted acetylenes of great stability are obtained through the reaction of acetylenedimagnesium bromide with two molecular proportions of triphenyl methyl chloride, diphenylmethyl chloride and other similar compounds. Analogous compounds may be obtained also from monosubstituted acetylenemagnesium halides. Acetylenedimagnesium bromide does not react with triphenylchloroethane.

Polyhalo compounds generally react in a complicated manner. Phenylmagnesium bromide reacts with chloroform to give $(C_6H_5)_3CH$ and $(C_6H_5)_4C$, the latter as the principal product in the presence of iodoform or bromoform.[299] Carbon tetrachloride gives triphenylmethane by reaction with phenylmagnesium bromide:[300]

$$CCl_4 + 3C_6H_5MgBr \rightarrow (C_6H_5)_3CCl + 3ClMgBr$$

$$2(C_6H_5)_3CCl + C_6H_5MgBr \rightarrow (C_6H_5)_3C\cdots C(C_6H_5)_3 + C_6H_5Br + MgCl_2$$

Benzyl chloride and alkylmagnesium bromides react to form alkylbenzenes in good yield; diphenylmethyl and triphenylmethyl bromides also react in this manner. *Methoxybromophenylmethyl chloride* reacting with methylmagnesium iodide gives the coupling product, $CH_3OBrC_6H_3CH_2CH_2C_6H_3BrOCH_3$, in almost quantitative yield.[301] *Benzal chloride* reacts with phenylmagnesium bromide or methylmagnesium iodide to form principally stilbene dichloride, with small quantities of triphenyl and tetraphenylmethane;[302] with methylmagnesium chloride it gives cumol, 1,2-diphenyl-1-chloropropane and 2,3-diphenylbutane. *Benzotrichloride* gives dichloro and tetrachlorotolan.[303]

Triphenylmethane is obtained in good yield through the reaction of *diphenylmethyl bromide* with phenylmagnesium bromide.[304] The reaction of triphenylmethyl chloride with phenylmagnesium bromide leads to the formation of tetraphenylmethane.[305]

The reaction of *naphthylmethyl bromide* with naphthylmagnesium bromide results in the formation of α,α-dinaphthyl.[306] *Binaphthylmethyl chloride* reacts with phenylmagnesium chloride in the following manner:[307]

$$2\,(C_{10}H_7)_2CHCl + 2\,C_6H_5MgCl$$
$$\rightarrow\ (C_{10}H_7)_2CH.CH(C_{10}H_7)_2 + C_6H_5.C_6H_5 + 2\,MgCl_2$$

α-Naphthylmagnesium bromide also gives with binaphthylmethyl chloride only tetranaphthylethane and not the expected trinaphthylmethane.

1-Chloro-4-methyl-2-cyclohexanol gives 1,4-dimethyl-2-cyclohexanol with methylmagnesium iodide, while α-chlorocycloheptanol yields with the same reagent methylcyclohexyl carbinol:[308]

$$HOCH(CH_2)_5CHCl \xrightarrow{CH_3MgX} HOCH(CH_3)CH(CH_2)_4CH_2$$

o-Chlorocyclopentanone reacts with organomagnesium halides to form *ortho* substituted cyclopentanones:[309]

$$COCH_2CH_2CH_2CHCl + RMgX \rightarrow COCH_2CH_2CH_2CHR + ClMgX$$

Grignard compounds react with *monochloroamine* to form primary amines:[310]

$$RMgX + ClNH_2 \rightarrow RNH_2 + ClMgX$$

Best yields are obtained with organomagnesium chlorides. The reaction should be carried out under cooling. Yields vary greatly. *n*-Butylamine is obtained in 58.9% yield, benzylamine in 85%, and β-phenylethylamine in 74% yield. Methylmagnesium chloride reacts to form methyl chloride and the aminomagnesium halide, H_2NMgX. Alkyl halides form in other cases as a byproduct. Monobromoamine gives poor yields of substituted amines.

tert-Butylamine chloride and *tert*-butylmagnesium chloride react to form di-*tert*-butylamine:[311]

$$C_4H_9NHCl + C_4H_9MgCl \rightarrow (C_4H_9)_2NH + MgCl_2$$

Pyrrolemagnesium halides react with alkyl halides to give alkylated pyrroles.[312] Indylmagnesium bromide reacting with chlorocarbonic esters gives β-indolecarboxylic esters; with two molecular equivalents of chlorocarbonic ester, N-β-indole dicarboxylic ester results. Halogen atoms in cyanuric halides may be replaced with organic groups by reaction with organomagnesium halides.[313]

Thionyl chloride reacts with organomagnesium halides to give sulfoxides:[314]

$$SOCl_2 + 2RMgX \rightarrow SOR_2 + 2ClMgX$$

Sulfides and alcohols are formed as byproducts.

Organic sulfonyl chlorides may be obtained through the interaction of *sulfuryl chloride* with Grignard reagents:[315]

$$SO_2Cl_2 + RMgX \rightarrow RSO_2Cl + ClMgX$$

although it is necessary to carry out the reaction under very carefully controlled conditions.

Chlorothiocarbamic esters react with organomagnesium halides to give thiocarboxylic acid esters:[316]

$$RMgX + ClCSOR' \rightarrow RCSOR' + ClMgX$$

Alkylmagnesium chlorides react with *iodine* to form aliphatic iodides:[317]

$$RMgCl + I_2 \rightarrow RI + IMgCl$$

Coupling reactions take place between alkyl *sulfates* and organomagnesium halides:[459]

$$R_2SO_4 + R'MgX \rightarrow RR' + RSO_2MgX$$

An organic halide and an organomagnesium compound also form in the reaction:[460]

$$R_2SO_4 + R'MgX \rightarrow RX + RSO_4MgR'$$

$$2RSO_4MgR' \rightarrow R'_2Mg + (RSO_4)_2Mg$$

The reaction of diphenylmethanemagnesium chloride and methyl sulfate results in the formation of *sym*-tetraphenylethane in over 95% yield.[461]

Coupling reactions have also been observed with esters of arylsulfonic acids, though here again an alkyl halide is formed simultaneously:[462]

$$ArSO_2OR + R'MgX \rightarrow RR' + ArSO_2OMgX$$

$$ArSO_2OR + R'MgX \rightarrow RX + ArSO_2OMgR'$$

RX and RR′ may result by the further reaction of the arylsulfonylmagnesium compounds formed with the arylsulfonic esters. A sulfone may also form in the reaction:

$$ArSO_2OR + R'MgX \rightarrow ArSO_2R' + ROMgX$$

In the reaction of *sulfites* $(RO)_2SO_2$, *sulfinates* RSOOR′, and *sulfenates* RSOR′, with Grignard reagents, the alkoxyl group attached to sulfur is replaced by the organic group of the Grignard reagent.[463] *Thiolsulfates* RSOSR′ give with Grignard reagents R″MgX, sulfides, R″SR′, and sulfinic acids, RSO_2H.[464]

Coupling Induced by Oxidative Reactions

The halomagnesium group may be removed from Grignard reagents under the action of mildly oxidizing agents, thus bringing about the combination of the organic residues. The reaction may be carried out by use of active silver bromide:[318]

$$2(CH_3)_3CMgCl + 2AgBr \rightarrow (CH_3)_3CC(CH_3)_3 + MgCl_2 + MgBr_2 + 2Ag$$

The silver bromide used in the reaction should be prepared by precipitation from a warm solution of silver nitrate and dried at 80°. Silver chloride is inactive. Cupric chloride[319] and chromium chloride, $CrCl_3$,[320] may also be used in the reaction:

$$2C_6H_5MgBr + 2CuCl_2 \rightarrow C_6H_5.C_6H_5 + 2ClMgBr + Cu_2Cl_2$$

$$2C_6H_5CH_2MgBr + 2CrCl_3 \rightarrow C_6H_5CH_2CH_2C_6H_5 + 2CrCl_2 + 2ClMgBr$$

The reaction may also be brought about by use of the following: cyanides of silver, copper, mercury and nickel; silver cyanate, thiocyanates of copper and silver, silver carbonate, *tert*-silver phosphate, silver citrate, iron chloride, mercuric bromide and molybdenum pentachloride.[321] The reaction proceeds in a complicated manner with dialkyl sulfates,[322] two molecular proportions of the dialkyl sulfate reacting with one of alkylmagnesium halide:

$$2(CH_3)_2SO_4 + RMgX \rightarrow RCH_3 + CH_3X + (CH_3OSO_2O)_2Mg$$

When mixed alkyl sulfuric esters are employed, the group with fewer carbon atoms enters in reaction. Phenolic hydroxyl groups may be protected by etherification or esterification,[323] although the methoxy and ethoxy groups in anisol and phenetol react at the boiling temperature of these compounds.

o-Toluenesulfonic esters may be used in the reaction.[324] Good results are obtained with *p*-toluenesulfonic esters containing alkyl groups with at least four carbon atoms.

Reaction with Acids, Alcohols and Amines

Acids rapidly decompose organomagnesium halides, causing the removal of the halomagnesium group and its replacement with hydrogen:

$$RMgCl + HCl \rightarrow RH + MgCl_2$$

Because of the great reactivity of organomagnesium halides, this reaction takes place readily with compounds containing hydroxyl or amino groups:

$$RMgX + R'OH \rightarrow RH + R'OMgX$$

$$RMgX + R'NH_2 \rightarrow RH + R'NHMgX$$

Halomagnesium compounds of aniline are obtained as crystalline compounds through the reaction of aniline with an alkylmagnesium halide in ethereal solution:[325]

$$C_6H_5NH_2 + CH_3MgI \rightarrow C_6H_5NHMgI + CH_4$$

They absorb carbon dioxide to form carbamic esters, and react with acid esters to yield anilides.

Reducing Effect of Grignard Reagents

Grignard reagents occasionally cause the reduction of organic bodies. Primary and secondary alcohols may result from aldehydes, ketones or esters without the addition of a new group to the molecule of the compound. An olefinic compound may form in the process:

$$C_6H_5CHO + C_2H_5MgI \rightarrow C_2H_4 + C_6H_5CH_2OMgI \rightarrow C_6H_5CH_2OH$$

Occasionally coupling of the residues in the organomagnesium compound may take place. Isobutyl, isopropyl, and *n*-propylmagnesium halides are capable of bringing about reduction. The reducing properties increase in proportion to the length of the carbon chain and the extent of branching of the organic residue in the Grignard reagent. Strongly negative groups attached to the organic residue counteract the tendency to bring about reduction, while weakly negative groups enhance this tendency.[326] The addition reaction, which always proceeds simultaneously, takes place with greater speed in the latter case, counterbalancing the increase in the rate of reduction.

tert-Butylmagnesium bromide converts diisopropyl ketone to the corresponding secondary alcohol in 80% yield. The corresponding secondary alcohols are formed under the action of the same reagent from pentamethylacetone in 90% yield, from hexamethylacetone in 94% yield, from benzophenone in 38% yield. Phenylmethylcarbinol is obtained in 94% yield, from benzophenone under the action of cyclopentylmagnesium bromide.

Pinacones are the main product of the reaction of aromatic ketones with triphenylmagnesium bromide.[327] Thus, benzil yields stilbenediol. Certain aromatic ketones, among them phenyl-*o*-tolyl and *o*-tolyl-*p*-tolyl ketone, give pinacones on reaction with organomagnesium halides.

The reduction of carboxylic acids proceeds in a complicated manner.[328]

Oxidation of Grignard Reagents

Grignard compounds absorb oxygen readily. A peroxide is presumably formed first and, reacts with a molecule of unchanged magnesium compound to form the halomagnesium compound of an alcohol:

$$RMgX + O_2 \rightarrow [ROOMgX] \xrightarrow{RMgX} 2ROMgX$$

The reaction usually proceeds in a complicated manner, and does not constitute a satisfactory preparative method.[329]

The oxidation of methyl- and ethylmagnesium iodide leads to the formation of methyl or ethyl iodide:[330]

$$2C_2H_5MgI + O_2 \rightarrow 2C_2H_5I + 2MgO$$

Dimethyl-, methylethyl- and methylpropylcarbinols have been prepared from the corresponding organomagnesium halides by oxidation with *hydrogen peroxide*.[331]

Reaction with Nitrogen Compounds

Amines react with organomagnesium halides to form the halomagnesium derivative of the amine:

$$RNH_2 + R'MgX \rightarrow RNHMgX + R'H$$

Secondary cyclic amines such as piperidine, tetrahydroquinoline, etc., also react in this manner:

$$\overline{CH_2(CH_2)_3CH_2NH} + RMgX \rightarrow \overline{CH_2(CH_2)_3CH_2N}MgX + RH$$

Tertiary cyclic bases, such as pyridine and quinoline, react with Grignard reagents to form addition compounds:[332]

$$C_6H_5N + RMgX \rightarrow C_6H_5N(R)MgX$$

Quinoline gives a 4-benzyl and 2,4-dibenzyl derivative as well as a 2-benzyl derivative with benzylmagnesium chloride.[421] Addition compounds are also obtained from such compounds as indole, carbazole and pyrrole.

Quaternary bases derived from quinoline react with organomagnesium halides to form α-substituted dihydroquinolines:[333]

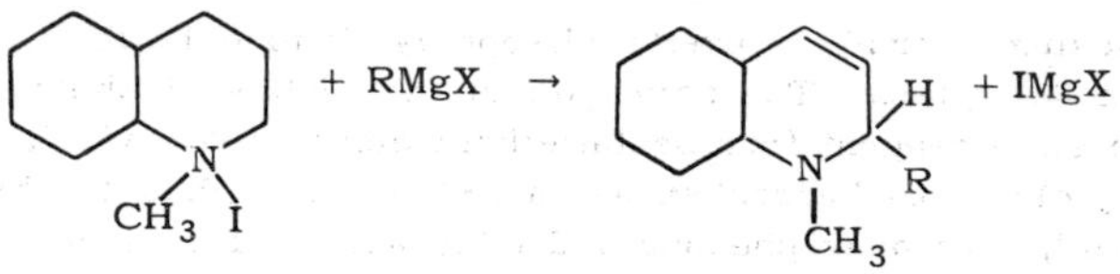

α-Substitution takes place even when a substituent is already present in that position. The substituent enters the 1-position in isoquinoline:[334]

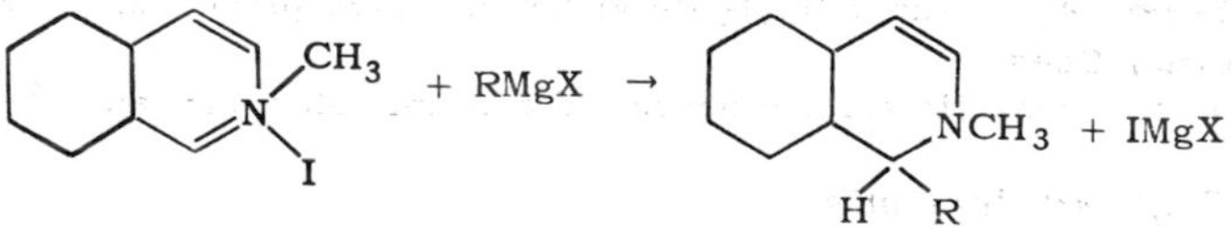

The organic group enters the α-position in azines:[466]

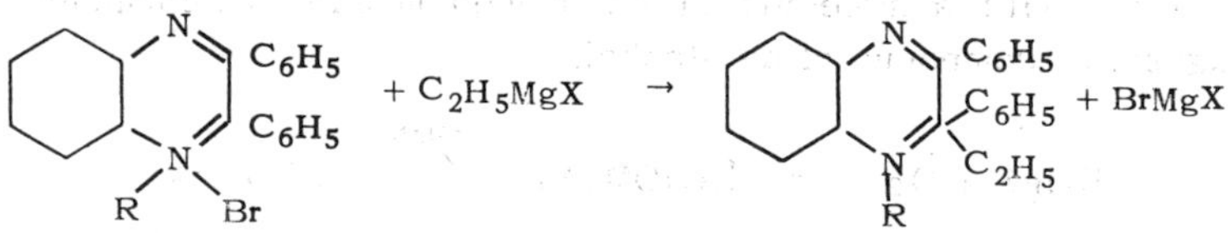

and at 10-position in phenazinium salts:[465]

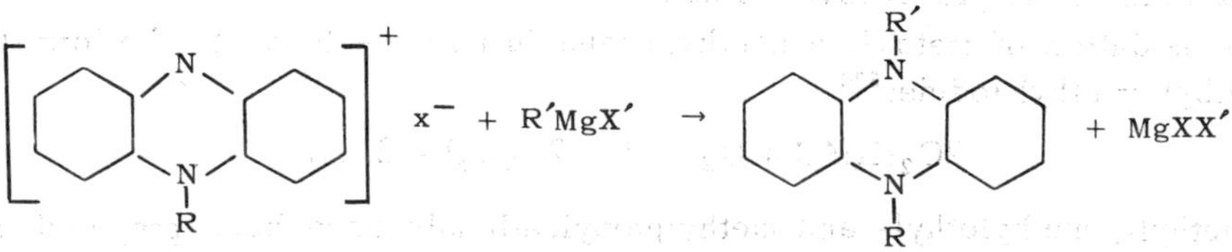

and the "transannellar" position in acridine:

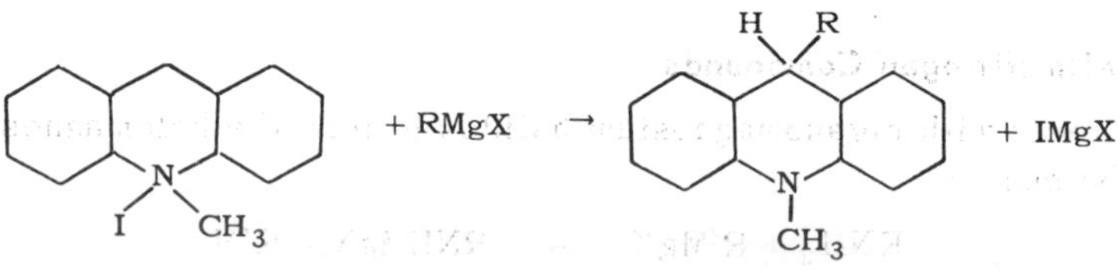

Grignard reagents react with the grouping –CH:N– in *Schiff bases* forming addition compounds, hydrolysis of which leads to the formation of secondary amines:[335]

$$C_6H_5N = CHC_6H_5 + RMgI \rightarrow C_6H_5N(MgI)CH(R)C_6H_5$$

$$\xrightarrow{H_2O} C_6H_5NHCH(R)C_6H_5$$

Aliphatic and alkylaromatic keto anils react both in the normal anil form and the tautomeric secondary amine form.[467] Compounds containing two –C:N– groupings form mono and disubstituted urethane diamines, depending on the proportion of the reagent employed.[336] *Hydramides*, $RCH(N = CHR)_2$, reacting with two molecular proportions of organomagnesium halides, yield, after hydrolysis, a primary amine and an aldehyde:

$$RCH(N = CHR)_2 + 2R'MgX \rightarrow RCH[N(MgX)CHRR']_2$$

$$\rightarrow 2RR'CHNH_2 + RCHO$$

In *diacetylaniline*, $C_6H_5N = C(CH_3)C(CH_3) = NC_6H_5$, only one double bond reacts with an organomagnesium halide.[337] The same holds true also of benzil dianil.

Carbodiamides, $RN = C = NR'$, also react with only one molecular equivalent of an organomagnesium halide:[338]

$$RN = C = NR + R'MgX \rightarrow RN(MgX)C(R') = NR \xrightarrow{H_2O} RNHC(R') = NR$$

Tetraalkylmethyleneimmonium salts give tertiary amines with Grignard reagents:[468]

$$[(CH_3)_2C = N(C_2H_5)_2]^+I^- + CH_3MgI \rightarrow t-C_4H_9N(C_2H_5)_2 + MgI_2$$

Thionylaniline gives sulfinic acid anilides:[339]

$$C_6H_5N = SO + RMgX \rightarrow C_6H_5N = S(R)OMgX \rightarrow C_6H_5NHSOR$$

Aldehyde hydrazones react with one molecular equivalent of Grignard reagents:

$$CH_2 = NN(CH_3)_2 + CH_3MgX \rightarrow CH_3CH_2N(MgX)N(CH_3)_2$$

$$\xrightarrow{H_2O} CH_3CH_2NHN(CH_3)_2$$

Condensation to *indoles* takes place with the reaction product of ketone phenylhydrazones and Grignard reagents. Thus, α-methylindole results from acetone phenylhydrazone, and α-phenylindole from acetophenone phenylhydrazone,[340] although trialkylacetophenone phenylhydrazones yield principally aniline and ketone:[341]

$$C_6H_5C(=NNHC_6H_5)C(R')_3 \xrightarrow{RMgX} RH + C_6H_5C[=NN(MgX)C_6H_5]C(R')_3$$

$$\xrightarrow{RMgX} R.R + C_6H_5C(=NMgX)C(R')_3 + C_6H_5N(MgX)_2$$

$$\rightarrow C_6H_5COC(R')_3 + C_6H_5NH_2$$

Only the carbonyl group reacts with Grignard reagents in monohydrazones of diketones.[98]

Normal addition of organomagnesium halides at the N = C double bond of phenylsemicorbazones of aldehydes in good yield has been reported.[471]

Benzaldehyde hydrazone is reduced to benzaldehyde benzhydrazone:

$$C_6H_5CH=NN=CHC_6H_5 \xrightarrow{2RMgBr} C_6H_5CH(MgBr)-N(MgBr)N=CHC_6H_5$$

$$\xrightarrow{H_2O} C_6H_5CH_2NH\cdot N=CHC_6H_5$$

The normal addition reaction also occurs simultaneously, giving benzaldehyde diphenylhydrazone, $(C_6H_5)_2CHNHN=CHC_6H_5$.

Azobenzene is reduced to hydrazobenzene by alkylmagnesium halides:[469]

$$C_6H_5N=NC_6H_5 + 2RMgX \rightarrow R.R + C_6H_5N(MgX)N(MgX)C_6H_5$$

$$\xrightarrow{H_2O} C_6H_5NHNHC_6H_5$$

Benzoylazobenzole, and *azodibenzoyl*, which contain conjugated double bonds, are partially reduced to hydrazo compounds, and the principal reaction is a 1,4-addition:[470]

$$C_6H_5N=NCOC_6H_5 + RMgX \rightarrow C_6H_5N(R)N=C(OMgX)C_6H_5$$

$$\xrightarrow{H_2O} C_6H_5N(R)N=N(OH)C_6H_5 \rightarrow C_6H_5N(R)NHCOC_6H_5$$

Azodibenzoyl, $C_6H_5CON=NCOC_6H_5$, yield a primary hydrazine, $R'NHNH_2$.

The reaction of Grignard reagents with *diazo compounds* generally results in the formation of alkylated hydrazones. For example, diazomethane reacting with a molecular equivalent of benzylmagnesium chloride gives formaldehyde benzylhydrazone:[342]

$$CH_2N_2 \xrightarrow{C_6H_5CH_2MgCl} CH_2=NNHCH_2C_6H_5$$

The hydrazone is reduced by the magnesium compound to the methylhydrazine derivative. A substituted hydrazine is obtained with an excess of the reagent:

$$H_2CN_2 + RMgX \rightarrow H_2C=NN(R)MgX \xrightarrow{RMgX} RCH_2N(MgX)N(R)MgX$$

$$\xrightarrow{H_2O} RCH_2NHNHR$$

When vapors of diazomethane diluted with nitrogen are passed through a cooled ethereal solution of phenylmagnesium bromide, dimagnesium phenylbenzylhydrazone is first formed; hydrolysis of this gives phenylbenzyl hydrazine which spontaneously changes to benzaldehyde phenylhydrazone:[343]

$$CH_2N_2 + C_6H_5MgBr \rightarrow CH_2 = NN(C_6H_5)MgBr$$

$$\xrightarrow{C_6H_5MgBr} C_6H_5CH_2N(MgBr)N(MgBr)C_6H_5 \xrightarrow{H_2O} C_6H_5CH_2NHNHC_6H_5$$

$$\xrightarrow{O_2} C_6H_5CH = NNHC_6H_5$$

Diphenyldiazomethane reacts with phenylmagnesium bromide to give, after hydrolysis of the original addition product, benzophenonephenylhydrazone:

$$(C_6H_5)_2CN_2 + C_6H_5MgBr \rightarrow (C_6H_5)_2C = NN(MgBr)C_6H_5$$

$$\xrightarrow{H_2O} (C_6H_5)_2C = NNHC_6H_5$$

Diazoacetic ester gives the methylhydrazone of glyoxylic ester in 30% yield:

$$C_2H_5OCOCHN_2 \xrightarrow{CH_3MgBr} C_2H_5OCOCH = NNHCH_3$$

With phenylmagnesium bromide, diazoacetic ester gives diphenylhydroxyacetaldehyde phenylhydrazone, $(C_6H_5)_2C(OH)CH = NNHC_6H_5$, together with other products.[344]

Aliphatic and aromatic *azides* react readily with organometallic compounds, giving a diazoamine as the final product of hydrolysis:[345]

$$\overline{RNN = N} + R'MgX \rightarrow RN(MgX)N = NR' \xrightarrow{H_2O} RNHN = NR'$$

or

$$RN = N \equiv N + R'MgX \rightarrow RN{:}NN(R')MgX \xrightarrow{H_2O} RN = NNHR'$$

The hydrogen of the hydroxyl group in *hydroxylamine* and one of the hydrogen atoms attached to nitrogen are replaced by the halomagnesium group by reaction with organomagnesium halides:

$$H_2NOH + 2RMgX \rightarrow XMgNHOMgX + 2RH$$

A small amount of an amine is also formed in accordance with the reaction:

$$H_2NOH + RMgX \rightarrow RNH_2 + HOMgX$$

Hydroxamic acids and *sulfohydroxamic* acids react in a similar manner.

O-Methylhydroxylamine gives a primary amine in good yield:[426]

$$CH_3ONH_2 + 2RMgX \rightarrow CH_3OMgX + RH + RNHMgX \rightarrow RNH_2$$

The reaction of *aromatic aldoximes* with organomagnesium halides generally proceeds in two directions and results, on the one hand, in the formation of amines, and on the other, of ketimines:[346]

$$RCH{=}NOH \begin{array}{l} \nearrow\ RNHCHO \xrightarrow{R'MgX} RNHCH(OH)R' \rightarrow RNH + R'CHO \\ \searrow\ RCN \xrightarrow{R'MgX} RR'C{=}NH \end{array}$$

Mixed aromatic-aliphatic ketoximes react in a different manner. Reaction with a large excess of the reagent in boiling diisoamyl ether results in the formation of the magnesium derivative of an α-hydroxy amine:

$$C_6H_5C({=}NOH)C_2H_5 \rightarrow C_6H_5COCH(NH_2)CH_3$$

$$\xrightarrow{RMgX} C_6H_5C(OMgX)(R)CH(NHMgX)CH_3$$

Another reaction takes place simultaneously, as follows:

$$C_6H_5C({=}NOH)C_2H_5 \xrightarrow{RMgX} C_6H_5\underset{\displaystyle C_2H_5}{\underset{|}{C}}(R)N(MgBr)OMgBr \rightarrow \begin{array}{l} C_6H_5C{-}R \\ \quad | \ \ NH \\ CH_3CH \end{array}$$

With some oximes the reaction with organomagnesium halides proceeds as follows:

$$RCH{=}NOH + 2R'MgX \rightarrow HOMgX + \underset{\displaystyle R'}{\underset{|}{RCH}}{-}\underset{\displaystyle MgX}{\underset{|}{NR'}}$$

$$\xrightarrow{H_2O} RCH(R')NHR' + HOMgX$$

Thus, benzaldoxime and phenylmagnesium bromide yield diphenylanilidomethane, $(C_6H_5)_2CHNHC_6H_5$

β-Phenylhydroxylamine, C_6H_5NHOH, reacting with phenylmagnesium bromide gives triphenyl hydrazine, $(C_6H_5)_2N.NHC_6H_5$. The phenylhydroxylamine is probably first converted to diphenylamine, which then condenses with a molecule of β-phenylhydroxylamine to form the trisubstituted hydrazine.

Nitric oxide reacts with phenylmagnesium bromide to form a complex which on hydrolysis gives nitrosophenylhydroxylamine in excellent yield: [347]

$$2NO + C_6H_5MgBr \rightarrow ONN(C_6H_5)OMgBr \xrightarrow{H_2O} ONN(C_6H_5)OH$$

Nitrogen peroxide, NO_2, reacts with aliphatic organomagnesium compounds to yield the halomagnesium derivative of β,β-dialkyl hydroxylamines, $(R)_2NOH$.[348]

Esters of nitrous and *nitric acids* give with alkylmagnesium halides, β,β-dialkylhydroxylamine derivatives: [472]

$$C_2H_5ONO + 2RMgX \rightarrow C_2H_5OMgX + (R)_2NOMgX \xrightarrow{H_2O} (R)_2NOH$$

Reduction to nitrous ester precedes the reaction with nitric esters.

Nitrosobenzene, reacting with phenylmagnesium bromide in ethereal solution at 15°, gives the halomagnesium derivative of diphenylhydroxylamine:[349]

$$C_6H_5NO + C_6H_5MgX \rightarrow (C_6H_5)_2NOMgX \xrightarrow{H_2O} (C_6H_5)_2NOH$$

A secondary amine also forms as a byproduct:

$$(C_6H_5)_2NOMgX + 2C_6H_5MgX \rightarrow (MgX)_2O + C_6H_5C_6H_5 + (C_6H_5)_2NMgX \xrightarrow{H_2O} (C_6H_5)_2NH$$

Reduction of the nitroso compound to an azo and a hydrazo compound is a competitive reaction which seems to be favored by low temperatures.

2-Chloro-2-nitrosopropane also yields hydroxylamine derivatives with ethylmagnesium bromide:[350]

$$(CH_3)_2C(Cl)NO + 2C_2H_5MgBr \rightarrow C_2H_6 + C_2H_4 + ClMgBr + (CH_3)_2C = NOMgBr \xrightarrow{H_2O} (CH_3)_2C = NOH$$

A certain amount of the unsaturated nitroso compound, $CH_3C(:CH_2)NO$, forms as a by-product. The reaction proceeds in a different manner with methylmagnesium chloride:

$$(CH_3)_2C(Cl)NO \xrightarrow{CH_3MgCl} CH_3CH_2CH(CH_3)N(CH_3)OH$$

Nitro compounds are often first reduced to nitroso compounds by Grignard reagents.[473] Aliphatic nitro compounds give hydroxylamine derivatives with organomagnesium halides. Thus, nitropropane and ethylmagnesium iodide give β-ethylpropylhydroxylamine, $CH_3CH_2CH_2N(OH)C_2H_5$, and a little β-ethyl-sec-amylhydroxylamine.[351]

The reaction of an α-nitro olefin with a Grignard reagent consists initially of a rapid 1,4-addition to the conjugated system C = C—N = O to form a complex which gives a nitroparaffin when decomposed with water. Further reaction of the initial complex with the Grignard reagent gives another complex which yields an oxime on hydrolysis.[474]

Aromatic nitro compounds give tetrasubstituted hydrazines with alkylmagnesium halides, but they yield secondary amines with arylmagnesium halides. The overall reaction in the latter case may be expressed as follows:[475]

$$RNO_2 + 4R'MgX \rightarrow RR'NMgX + R'OMgX + R'_2 + (XMg)_2O$$

α-Nitrostilbene, which contains a conjugated pair of double bonds, reacts with phenylmagnesium bromide to form isonitrotriphenylethane,[352] $(C_6H_5)_2CHC(C_6H_5) = NOOH$. *Nitrobenzene*, reacting with ethylmagnesium bromide, gives a small amount of the halomagnesium derivative of ethylphenylamine; with phenylmagnesium bromide it gives the halomagnesium compounds of diphenylamine and phenol, with some diphenyl. *α-Nitronaphthalene* gives phenyl-α-naphthylamine with phenylmagnesium bromide.

Nitro olefins react with alkyl or arylmagnesium halides to give nitroparaffins by a process of 1,4-addition.

Nitroso amines react with organomagnesium halides in the same manner as C-nitroso compounds, with this difference that the basic magnesium halide formed immediately separates out. Thus, diethylnitrosoamine, reacting with ethylmagnesium halides, gives the diethylhydrazone of acetaldehyde,

$$(C_2H_5)_2NN = CHCH_3.$$ [353]

Where the halide cannot form directly, reduction takes place. Thus, diethylnitrosoamine, reacting with phenylmagnesium bromide, gives diethylphenylhydrazine, $(C_2H_5)_2NNHC_6H_5$, and ethylphenylethylphenylhydrazine,

$$CH_3CH(C_6H_5)N(C_2H_5)NHC_6H_5.$$

The reaction occasionally results in the replacement of the nitroso group with the organic group in the Grignard compound. Thus, nitrosocarbazole yields diphenylcarbazole with phenylmagnesium bromide, and nitrosoacetanilide gives diphenylacetanilide with the same reagent.[354]

Azoxy compounds are generally reduced by alkylmagnesium halides:[355]

$$RNO = NR \xrightarrow{R'MgX} RN = NR$$

Benzonitril oxide, $C_6H_5C = N$ (with O bridging C and N), reacts with methylmagnesium iodide to form acetophenone oxime, $C_6H_5C(CH_3) = NOH$, some reduction also taking place.

Reaction with Compounds of Sulfur, Selenium, Phosphorus, Silicon and Other Elements

Organomagnesium halides react with sulfur dioxide to form sulfinic acids in 50 to 60% yield:[427]

$$C_6H_5MgBr + SO_2 \rightarrow C_6H_5SO_2MgBr \xrightarrow{H_2O} C_6H_5SO_2H$$

Diphenyl sulfoxide, $(C_6H_5)_2SO$, is formed as a byproduct.

Benzyl sulfoxide and benzyl sulfide have been obtained by the action of benzylmagnesium bromide on thionyl chloride.[428]

Carbon disulfide combines with organomagnesium halides in the same manner as carbon dioxide, giving thio acids:[356]

$$CS_2 + RMgX \rightarrow RCSSMgX \rightarrow RCSSH$$

Triphenylvinylmagnesium bromide gives triphenyldithioacrylic acid.[357]

The halomagnesium salts, RCSSMgX, reacting with alkyl sulfates give the crystalline methyl esters of the thio acid.[358]

Carbon sulfoxide, COS, reacts similarly with organomagnesium compounds, forming thiol acids. For example, *o*-tolylmagnesium bromide, reacting in ethereal solution with carbon sulfoxide, gives thiol-*o*-toluic acid,

$$CH_3C_6H_4COSH$$

in 73% yield.[359]

Aromatic thio ketones react with organomagnesium halides forming unstable tetraethylene sulfides from which sulfur separates more or less readily:[360]

$$2(R)_2CS + 2R'MgI \rightarrow R'-R' + R_2C(SMgI)C(SMgI)R_2$$

$$\rightarrow R_2\overset{S}{C-C}R_2 + MgI_2 + MgS$$

The reaction of phenylmagnesium bromide with sulfur chloride proceeds in a complex manner and results in the formation of chlorobenzene, bromobenzene, diphenyl, diphenyl sulfide, phenyl disulfide, etc.[428]

The reaction of organomagnesium halides with finely divided sulfur in an atmosphere of hydrogen gives the halomagnesium derivative of a thiol in 80% yield, providing sulfur is not present in excess.[361] The thiol derivative reacting with sulfur gives a disulfide:

$$2RSMgX + S \rightarrow RS{\cdot}SR + S(MgX)_2$$

The disulfide reacts with the organomagnesium halide to form a sulfide:

$$RSSR + RMgX \rightarrow RSR + RSMgX$$

Phenylmagnesium bromide reacts with *sulfur* to form the bromomagnesium compound of thiophenol.[361]

Thiocarboxylates yield mercaptans and tertiary alcohols with Grignard reagents:[476]

$$RCOSR' \xrightarrow{R''MgX} RR''_2COH + R'SH$$

Ethyl dithiobenzoate, $C_6H_5CSSC_2H_5$, is claimed to give triphenylmethyl mercaptan with phenylmagnesium halides.[477]

Sulfoxides, RSOR′, react additively with Grignard reagents.[478] Bromomagnesium selenophenol results in 81% yield from the reaction of phenylmagnesium bromide with *selenium*, providing the reaction is carried out in an atmosphere of hydrogen, and an excess of selenium is avoided.

Selenium monobromide reacts with ethylmagnesium bromide in the following manner:[479]

$$Se_2Br_2 + 2C_2H_5MgBr \rightarrow 2MgBr_2 + C_2H_5SeSeC_2H_5$$

$$\xrightarrow{C_2H_5Br} C_2H_5SeSe(C_2H_5)_2Br \xrightarrow{C_2H_5MgBr} HSeSe(C_2H_5)_3$$

Tellurium tetrachloride reacts with Grignard reagents with replacement of three chlorine atoms with the organic group of the Grignard reagent:[480]

$$TeCl_4 + 3RMgBr \rightarrow R_3TeCl + 3MgClBr$$

A portion of the tetrachloride is reduced to elemental tellurium; furthermore, an organo telluric compound is formed in the following manner:

$$R_3TeCl + RMgBr \rightarrow R_2Te + MgClBr + R_2$$

Phosphorus trichloride reacts vigorously with Grignard reagents forming mono-, di- and trisubstituted organic phosphorus compounds. The trisubstituted phosphine results exclusively with an excess of the Grignard reagent:[362]

$$PCl_3 + 3RMgX \rightarrow P(R)_3 + 3ClMgX$$

Tetrasubstituted phosphonium bromides are obtained as a byproduct:[363]

$$(C_6H_5)_3P \xrightarrow{C_6H_5MgBr\ +\ O_2} (C_6H_5)_4PBr$$

Cyclotetramethylenephenylphosphine has been obtained through the reaction of phenyldichlorophosphine with 1,4-dibromomagnesiumbutane:[364]

$$BrMgCH_2(CH_2)_2CH_2MgBr + Cl_2PC_6H_5$$

$$\rightarrow \overline{CH_2(CH_2)_2CH_2}PC_6H_5 + 2\ ClMgBr$$

The reaction of *phosphorus oxychloride*, $POCl_3$, with arylmagnesium halides results in the formation of compounds of the type $(R)_3PO$ and $(R)_2POCl$; the latter gives on hydrolysis $(R)_2POOH$.[365]

Triphenylphosphine dichloride, reacting with Grignard reagents, gives dihalomagnesium triphenylphosphine:

$$(C_6H_5)_3PCl_2 + 2RMgX \rightarrow (C_6H_5)_3P(MgX)_2 + 2RCl$$

The halomagnesium groups in this compound may be replaced with organic groups by reaction with alcohols:

$$(C_6H_5)_3P(MgX)_2 + 2ROH \rightarrow (C_6H_5)_3P(R)_2 + 2HOMgX$$

although the product is obtained in low yield. Triphenylphosphine dichloride is obtained through the reaction of triphenylphosphine oxide, $(C_6H_5)_3PO$, with phosphorus pentachloride.

Phosphorus thiochloride, $PSCl_3$, reacts with Grignard reagents in the same manner as phosphorus oxychloride.

Esters of oxyacids of phosphorus react with Grignard reagents exchanging the alkoxy group for the organic group in the reagent:[366]

$$P(OCH_3)_3 + 2C_6H_5MgBr \rightarrow 2CH_3OMgBr + (C_6H_5)_2POCH_3$$

$$\rightarrow CH_3(C_6H_5)_2PO$$

Triethyl phosphite, reacting with phenylmagnesium bromide, gives triphenylphosphine oxide, $(C_6H_5)_3PO$, in 10% yield; *triphenyl phosphite* gives triphenylphosphine in 60% yield. *Triethyl phosphate* reacts with phenylmagnesium bromide to from diethylphenylphosphonic ester, $C_6H_5PO(OC_2H_5)_2$ in 10% yield, and some diphenylphosphonic acid, $(C_6H_5)_2POOH$. *Triphenyl phosphate* gives with phenylmagnesium bromide, triphenylphosphine oxide in 17% yield.[367]

Phosphorus pentasulfide reacts with excess Grignard reagent to yield dithiophosphonic acid and trisubstituted phosphine sulfide:[458]

$$P_2S_5 + 6RMgX \rightarrow 2R_3PS + 3MgX_2 + 3MgS$$

$$P_2S_5 + 2RMgX \rightarrow [RPSSMgX]_2S$$

$$\xrightarrow[2HCl]{2H_2O} 2RPS(OH)SH + MgCl_2 + H_2S + MgX_2$$

Arsenic trichloride reacts with organomagnesium halides to give a mixture of mono-, di-, and trisubstituted arsines. The proportion of the trisubstituted product may be increased by using an excess of the halomagnesium compound, although the formation of the mono and disubstituted derivatives cannot be prevented entirely. The individual compounds formed are difficult to isolate. Diethylarsine chloride does not react with ethylmagnesium bromide.[368]

Pentahalides of arsenic treated with an excess of phenylmagnesium bromide yield only triphenyl arsine.

Dihalo arsines, reacting with dihalomagnesium compounds, give arsenic ring compounds.

$$RAsX_2 + (XMgCH_2CH_2)_2CH_2 \rightarrow \overline{RAsCH_2(CH_2)_3CH_2} + 2MgX_2$$

Pyrrolidine analogs are obtained from 1,4-dihalomagnesium butane.[369]

10-Chlorophenoxarsine, $C_6H_4\langle{}^{O}_{AsCl}\rangle C_6H_4$, and 10-chloro-9,10-dihydrophenarsazine, $C_6H_5\langle{}^{NH}_{AsCl}\rangle C_6H_4$, react with organomagnesium halides to give substituted arseno derivatives, $C_6H_4\langle{}^{O}_{AsR}\rangle C_6H_4$ and $C_6H_4\langle{}^{NH}_{AsR}\rangle C_6H_4$.[370]

Arsenious esters react with organomagnesium halides to form trisubstituted arsines:[371]

$$As(OR)_3 + 3R'MgX \rightarrow As(R')_3 + 3ROMgX$$

Arsenious oxide reacts with organomagnesium halides to form the halomagnesium derivatives of disubstituted arsine hydroxides:

$$As_2O_3 + 4RMgX \rightarrow 2(R)_2AsOMgX + MgX_2 + MgO$$

The reaction proceeds further with aliphatic and many aromatic organomagnesium compounds, resulting in the formation of trisubstituted arsines.[372]

Arylarsine oxides react with organomagnesium halides forming tetrasubstituted arsine oxides:[373]

$$2RAsO + 2R'MgX \rightarrow 2RR'AsOMgX \xrightarrow{H_2O} RR'AsOAsRR' + 2HOMgX$$

Esters of arsenic acid react in the same manner as those of arsenious acid.[374]

Monophenyl arsine reacts with Grignard reagents at boiling temperature to form phenylarsinedimagnesium halides, $C_6H_5As(MgX)_2$. The latter absorbs carbon dioxide from the air; it reacts with chlorocarbonic esters to form phenylarsine dicarboxylic esters, $C_6H_5As(COOR)_2$. Diphenylarsine similarly gives $(C_6H_5)_2AsMgX$ with organomagnesium halides.

Reacting with *o*-xylylene bromide, $C_6H_4(CH_2Br)_2$ diphenylarsinemagnesium halides give ω,ω'-bis-(diphenylarsine)-*o*-xylylene, $C_6H_4[CH_2As(C_6H_5)_2]_2$. With mercuric chloride, they give diphenylarsine chloride, $(C_6H_5)_2AsCl$.[375]

Arsenious sulfide reacts with Grignard reagents to form disubstituted arsine sulfides or trisubstituted arsines:

$$As_2S_3 + 4RMgBr \rightarrow (R_2As)_2S + 2MgS + 2MgBr_2$$

$$(R_2As)_2S + 2RMgBr \rightarrow 2R_3As + MgS + MgBr_2$$

Antimony trichloride reacts with organomagnesium halides in excess to form trisubstituted stibines:[376]

$$SbCl_3 + 3RMgX \rightarrow Sb(R)_3 + 3ClMgX$$

Phenylstibine dichloride reacts with tetramethyldimagnesium bromide to give cyclotetramethylenephenylstibine:[377]

$$C_6H_5SbCl_2 + BrMgCH_2CH_2CH_2CH_2MgBr$$

$$\rightarrow \overline{CH_2CH_2CH_2CH_2}SbC_6H_5 + 2ClMgBr$$

The reaction of xenyl-*o*-stilbine dichloride with methylmagnesium iodide leads to the formation of 2,2′-phenylenemethylstibine:[378]

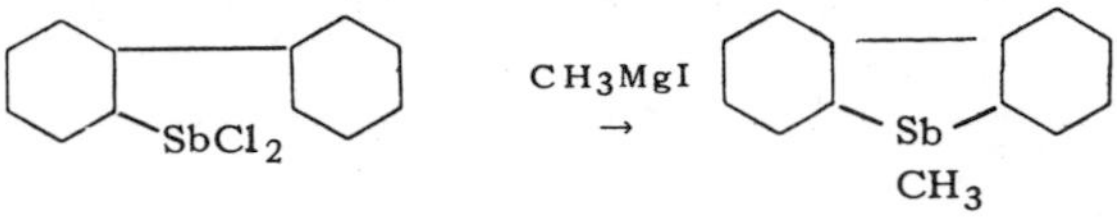

Reaction with Silicon Compounds

Silicon halides react vigorously with Grignard reagents, generally yielding a mixture of silicon alkyl compounds. This reaction offers the best method for the preparation of such compounds.[379]

The *procedure* is to add a solution of the organomagnesium halide to a solution of silicon tetrachloride in anhydrous ether with cooling and stirring. The magnesium halide separates as a precipitate, while the organosilicon compounds remain in solution. The latter may be isolated by distillation. The reaction generally proceeds slowly with arylmagnesium halides; it may be accelerated by distilling off the solvent and heating the residual mixture to 160–180° for several hours.[380] The organosilicon compounds are then isolated by crystallization after the decomposition of the organomagnesium compounds.

Silicon tetrachloride reacts vigorously to form a mixture of mono-, di-, tri- and tetra-alkyl silicones. It is possible to prepare the mono and tetra derivatives in good yield by use of the calculated quantity of the organomagnesium halide.[381]

Mixed alkyl and aryl silicanes are readily prepared through the reaction of silicon tetrachloride successively with two different organomagnesium halides.[382]

Complex compounds containing a silicon chain, such as

$$HOSiOSi(OH)(C_2H_5)Si(OH)_2Si(OH)_2C_2H_5,$$

are obtained when silicon tetrachloride in anhydrous ethereal solution is made to react with magnesium and ethyl bromide.

Hexachlorosilicoethane, Si_2Cl_6, reacts with methylmagnesium bromide to form hexamethylsilicoethane, $(CH_3)_3Si.Si(CH_3)_3$.[383]

Silicochloroform, $SiHCl_3$, yields triphenylsilane, $(C_6H_5)_3SiH$, by reaction with phenylmagnesium bromide.[384]

The reaction of silicon tetrachloride with pentane-1,5-dimagnesium bromide leads to the formation of cyclopentamethylenesilicane dichloride,

$$\overline{CH_2(CH_2)_3CH_2SiCl_2}.$$

The chlorine atoms in this compound may be replaced by alkyl groups.[385]

High molecular compounds are obtained from silicon tetrachloride by reaction with aryl dimagnesium halides of the type $p\text{-}BrMgC_6H_4MgBr$. Chlorosilicon compounds of the type $[-SiCl_2-C_6H_4-SiCl_2-C_6H_4-]_x$ are thus obtained. The chlorine in these may be replaced by alkyl groups by reaction with alkyl magnesium halides.

Organosilicon compounds which still contain chlorine bound to silicon are decomposed by water to hydroxy compounds or their polymers. In such polymers, silicon atoms are joined by oxygen atoms. *High molecular polymers* are formed directly during the reaction of silicon halides with the Grignard reagent, but in these polymers silicon atoms are joined directly.[386]

Silicon tetrafluoride reacts with alkylmagnesium bromides to give trialkyl silicofluorides:[387]

$$SiF_4 + 3RMgBr \quad \rightarrow \quad (R)_3SiF + 3FMgBr$$

Sodium fluosilicate reacting with benzylmagnesium chloride gives tetrabenzylmonosilane.[388]

Ethyl orthosilicate reacts with organomagnesium halides in much the same manner as orthocarbonic esters, only one ethoxy group becoming replaced with an organic group; hydrolysis of the resulting ester yields the corresponding acid:[389]

$$Si(OC_2H_5)_4 \quad \overset{RMgX}{\rightarrow} \quad RSi(OC_2H_5)_3 \quad \overset{H_2O}{\rightarrow} \quad RSiOOH$$

The reaction of ethyl orthosilicate with a large excess of butylmagnesium iodide leads to the formation of tetramethylsilane in 56% yield.[390]

Monosubstituted orthosilicic esters are also formed through the reaction of the triester of orthosilicic acid and its halides:[391]

$$HOSi(OC_2H_5)_3 + RX + Mg \quad \rightarrow \quad RSi(OC_2H_5)_3 + HOMgX$$

$$ClSi(OC_2H_5)_3 + RMgX \quad \rightarrow \quad RSi(OC_2H_5)_3 + ClMgX$$

Phenylethynyl silanes of the type $C_6H_5C\vdots CSi(OC_2H_5)_3$ polymerize during synthesis and subsequent distillation.[392] Benzyl ethyl silicone and ethylmagnesium bromide give benzyl diethyl silicol:[429]

$$\underset{C_2H_5}{\overset{C_6H_5}{>}}SiO + C_2H_5MgBr \quad \rightarrow \quad \underset{C_2H_5}{\overset{C_6H_5CH_2}{>}}Si\underset{OMgBr}{\overset{C_2H_5}{<}} \quad \rightarrow \quad \underset{C_2H_5}{\overset{C_6H_5CH_2}{>}}Si\underset{OH}{\overset{C_2H_5}{<}}$$

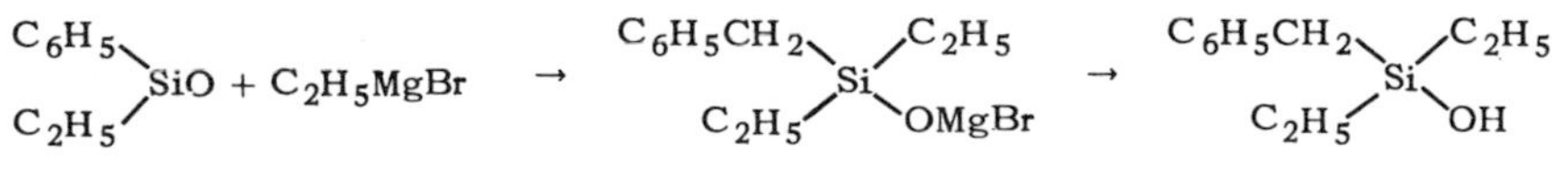

Reaction with Compounds of Boron, Scandium, and other Elements

Boron trichloride reacts with organomagnesium halides in the same manner as silicon halides. The reaction proceeds well with boron trifluoride, the number of hydrocarbon substituents increasing with increase in the amount of the Grignard reagent, and an excess of the reagent leading to the formation of the trisubstituted compounds.[393] The latter are liquids stable toward water that can be distilled without decomposition.

Boric esters react with organomagnesium halides in the manner of silicic esters:[394]

$$B(OR)_3 + R'MgX \rightarrow R'B(OR)_2 + ROMgX$$

Additional alkoxy groups can also be replaced by organic residues.[395]

Chlorides of scandium and *yttrium* react with organomagnesium halides in ethereal solution, forming the organoscandium or yttrium compound which retains the solvent in combination.[396]

Cyclohexyl derivatives of *lead, tin* and *bismuth* have been prepared through the reaction of the chlorides of these metals with cyclohexylmagnesium bromide.[397]

Cyclopentamethylenedimethylstanane results from the reaction of pentane-1,5-dimagnesium chloride and *dimethyltin diiodide:*[398]

$$ClMgCH_2(CH_2)_3CH_2MgCl + I_2Sn(CH_3)_2$$

$$\rightarrow \overline{CH_2(CH_2)_3CH_2}Sn(CH_3)_2 + 2IMgCl$$

The ethylbismuthane analog of the compound is similarly obtained from pentane-1,5-magnesium bromide and ethylbismuth dibromide.[399]

References

1. Barbier, *Compt. rend.*, **128**, 110 (1899).
2. Grignard, *ibid.*, **130**, 1322 (1900); *Ann. Univ. Lyon*, (2), I, **6**, 1 (1901); Runge, *Organometall Verbindungen* I, Stuttgart (1932). *Mechanism:* Barbier and Grignard, *Compt. rend.*, **128**, 111 (1899); **130**, 1323 (1900); Rheinboldt and Roleff, *Ber.*, **57**, 1921 (1924); Hess and Rheinboldt, *ibid.*, **54**, 2043 (1921); Meisenheimer, *Ann.*, **442**, 180 (1925).
3. Taboury, *Ann. chim.*, (8) **15**, 5 (1908); Baeyer, *Ber.*, **38**, 2759 (1905); Gilman, *et al.*, *J. Am. Chem. Soc.*, **51**, 1579 (1929); Wren, *Organometallic Compounds of Zinc and Magnesium* p. 2; Cusa and Kipping, *J. Soc. Chem. Ind.*, **53**, 213 (1934); Urion, *Compt. rend.*, **198**, 1244 (1934); Smith and Sprung, *J. Am. Chem. Soc.*, **65**, 1276 (1943); Tsarsus, *Compt. rend.*, **220**, 662 (1945); *Ann. chim.*, (12) **1**, 342 (1946).
4. Fuson, *J. Am. Chem. Soc.*, **48**, 2681 (1926); Krizewsky and Turner, *J. Chem. Soc.*, **115**, 559 (1919).
5. Oldham and Ubbelohde, *J. Chem. Soc.*, **1938**, 201.
6. Houben *et al.*, *Ber.*, **69**, 1766 (1936).
7. Grignard, *Compt. rend.*, **130**, 1322 (1900); *Ann. chim. phys.*, (7) **24**, 433 (1901), Baeyer and Villiger, *Ber.*, **35**, 1202 (1902); Grignard, *Bull. soc. chim.*, (3) **29**, 944 (1903); Tschelizeff, *Ber.*, **39**, 773, 1674, 1682, 1686, (1906); Thorp and Kann, *J. Am. Chem. Soc.*, **36**, 1022 (1914); Stadnikoff, *Ber.*, **47**, 2155 (1914); Hess and Rheinboldt, *ibid.*, **54**, 2043 (1921); Julibois, *Compt. rend.*, **155**, 353 (1912); **183**, 971 (1926); Terentieff, *Z. anorg. allgem. Chem.*, **156**, 73 (1926); Iwanow, *Compt. rend.*, **185**, 505 (1927); Kierzek, *Bull. soc. chim.*, (4) **41**, 1299 (1927).
8. Tschelinzew, *J. Russ. Phys.-Chem. Soc.*, **36**, 549 (1903); *Chem. Zentr.*, **1904 II**, 183; Bouveault, *Compt. rend.*, **138**, 1108 (1904).
9. Gilman and Vanderival, *Rec. trav. chim.*, **48**, 160 (1929).
10. Gilman and St. John., *Bull. soc. chim.*, (4) **45**, 1091 (1929); Rupe and Hirschmann, *Helv. Chim. Acta*, **11**, 1189 (1928); Meisenheimer and Schlichenmaier, *Ber.*, **61**, 2029 (1928).
11. Tschelinzeff, *Ber.*, **37**, 2081, 4538 (1904); **40**, 1487 (1907).
12. Pickard and Kenyon, *J. Chem. Soc.*, **89**, 262 (1906); Hepworth, *ibid.*, **119**, 1249 (1921); Job and Reich, *Compt. rend.*, **179**, 330 (1924); Gilman *et al.*, *Rec. trav. chim.*, **47**, 19 (1928).
13. Tschelinzeff, *Ber.*, **41**, 646 (1908).
14. Grignard, *Compt. rend.*, **198**, 625, 2217 (1934); Prévost, *Bull. soc. chim.*, (4) **49**, 1368 (1931); Urion, *Compt. rend.*, **198**, 1244 (1934); Clément, *ibid.*, **198**, 665 (1934). Mann and Watson, *J. Org. Chem.*, **13**, 502 (1948).
15. Gilman, *Bull. soc. chim.*, (4) **45**, 250 (1929).
16. Gilman and McCracken, *Rec. trav. chim.*, **46**, 463 (1927).
17. Marvel *et al.*, *J. Am. Chem. Soc.*, **50**, 2810 (1928); *French patents* 682,142 (1929); 744,545 (1932).

18. Gilman and Vanderwal, *Bull. soc. chim.*, (4) **45**, 641 (1929).
19. Meisenheimer and Caspor, *Ber.*, **54**, 1655 (1921); Hess and Rheinbold, *ibid.*, **54**, 2043 (1921); Meisenheimer and Schlichenmaier, *ibid.*, **61**, 720 (1928). *Cf.* Pfeiffer, *Organische Molekularverbindungen*, Vol. XI. Chemie in Einzeldarstellungen, Stuttgart, 1927.
20. Schlenk and Schlenk, *Ber.*, **62**, 920 (1929).
21. Tschelinzeff, *Ber.*, **37**, 4537 (1904); Tingle and Gorsline, *Am. Chem. J.*, **37**, 483 (1907); Spencer and Stokes, *J. Chem. Soc.*, **93**, 68 (1908); Spencer and Crewsdon, *ibid.*, **93**, 1821 (1908); Gilman and Brown, *J. Am. Chem. Soc.*, **52**, 3330 (1930); Gilman and St. John, *ibid.*, **52**, 5017 (1930); *Italian patent* 341,937 (1936); Schorigin *et al.*, *Ber.*, **66**, 1426 (1933).
22. Schoring *et al.*, *Ber.*, **64**, 2584 (1931); **66**, 1426 (1933).
23. Weissenborn, *U.S. patent* 2,058,373 (1935); *French patent* 807,632 (1936).
24. Krause, *Ber.*, **62**, 1877 (1929).
25. Späth, *Monatsh.*, **34**, 1965 (1913); Gilman and McCracken, *J. Am. Chem. Soc.*, **45**, 2462 (1913); Gilman and St. John, *Rec. trav. chim.*, **49**, 717 (1930); Rudd and Turner, *J. Chem. Soc.*, **1928**, 686; Gilman and Banderwol, Bull. *soc. chim.*, (4) **45**, 135 (1929); Krause, *Ber.* **62**, 1877 (1929).
26. Gilman *et al.*, *Rec. trav. chim.*, **54**, 584 (1935).
27. Grignárd, *Bull. soc. chim.*, (4) **13**, XI (1913).
28. *Cf.* Clément and Savard, *Compt. rend.*, **204**, 1742 (1937).
29. Meyer and Togel, *Ann.*, **347**, 55 (1906); Gilman *et al.*, *J. Am. Chem. Soc.*, **45**, 2462 (1923); **51**, 1579 (1929).
30. Gilman *et al.*, *Rec. trav. chim.*, **54**, 584 (1935); *J. Am. Chem. Soc.*, **57**, 1061 (1935); Kohler and Blanchard, *ibid.*, **57**, 367 (1935).
31. Beyer and Fritsch, *Ber.*, **74**, 494 (1941).
32. Malmgreen, *ibid.*, **35**, 3510 (1902).
33. Zelinsky and Moser, *ibid.*, **35**, 2684 (1902).
34. v. Braun, *Ber.*, **52**, 1725 (1919); Gilman and Heck, *ibid.*, **62**, 1379 (1929); Marxer, *Helv. Chim. Acta*, (Special number) **24-E**, 209 (1941).
35. Gibson and Johnson, *J. Chem. Soc.*, **1930**, 2525.
36. Swallen and Boord, *J. Am. Chem. Soc.*, **52**, 651 (1930).
37. Hammonet, *Compt. rend.*, **138**, 975 (1904).
38. Gilman and McGlumphy, *Bull. soc. chim.*, (4) **43**, 1322 (1928). *Cf.* Houben, *Ber.*, **36**, 2899 (1903); Cortese, *J. Am. Chem. Soc.*, **51**, 2266 (1929); Prévost and Richard, *Bull. soc. chim.*, (4) **49**, 1368, 1372 (1932); Henne *et al.*, *J. Am. Chem. Soc.*, **63**, 3474 (1941).
39. Krestinsky, *Ber.*, **55**, 2754, 2762, 2770 (1922); Davies and Kipping, *J. Chem. Soc.*, **99**, 296 (1911).
40. Krestinsky, *Ber.*, **55**, 2755 (1922).
41. Tiffeneau, *Compt. rend.*, **135**, 1346 (1902); Rupe and Proske, *Ber.*, **43**, 1231 (1910).
42. Rupe and Bürgin, *Ber.*, **43**, 172 (1910); Gilman and Harris, *J. Am. Chem. Soc.*, **49**, 1825 (1927).
43. Hurd and Webb, *J. Am. Chem. Soc.*, **49**, 546 (1927).
44. Luttringhaus *et al.*, *Ber.*, **71**, 1673 (1938).
45. Emschwiller, *Compt. rend.*, **183**, 665 (1926).
46. Zelinsky and Gutt, *Ber.*, **40**, 3049 (1907).
47. v. Braun and Sobecki, *ibid.*, **44**, 1918 (1911).
48. Gilman and Zoellner, *Bull. soc. chim.*, (4) **49**, 7 (1931).
49. Slotta and Heller, *Ber.*, **63**, 3030 (1930).
50. Angeli and Poggi, *Atti accad. Lincei*, (6) **7**, 966 (1928).
51. Salkind, *Ber.*, **64**, 289 (1931).
52. Mailhe and Murd, *Bull. soc. chim.*, (4) **11**, 328 (1912).
53. Salkind and Schmidt, *J. Russ. Phys-Chem. Soc.*, **46**, 681 (1914).
54. Harris, *Iowa State Coll. J. Sci.*, **6**, 425 (1932); Baeyer, *Ber.*, **38**, 2763 (1905). *Cf.* Gilman and Swiss, *J. Am. Chem. Soc.*, **62**, 1847 (1940).
55. Bodroux, *Compt. rend.*, **136**, 1138 (1903); Gomberg and Cone, *Ber.*, **39**, 3274 (1906).
56. Gibert, *Compt. rend.*, **205**, 443 (1937).
57. Overhoff and Proost, *Rec. trav. chim.*, **57**, 179 (1938) C. **1938 I**, 3338.
58. Jocitsch, *Bull. soc. chim.*, (3) **28**, 922 (1902); **30**, 208 (1903).
59. Gautier, *Ann. chim. phys.*, (8) **16**, 334 (1909); Dupont, *Compt. rend.*, **149**, 1381 (1909); **150**, 1121 (1910); Wohl and Mylo, *Ber.*, **45**, 339 (1912); Pieroni and Coli, *Gazz. chim. ital.*, **44** II, 349 (1914); Lespieau, *Compt. rend.*, **179**, 1606 (1924); Iotsitch, *J. Russ. Phys.-Chem. Soc.*, **34**, 100, 241 (1902); **35**, 554 (1903); **36**, 68 (1904); **38**, 252 (1906); *Bull. soc. chim.*, (3) **28**, 922 (1902); (3) **30**, 209 (1903); (3) **32**, 740 (1904); (3) **34**, 185 (1905); Dupont, *Compt. rend.*, **148**, 1522 (1909); Kleinfeller and Lohmann, *Ber.*, **71**, 2609 (1938).
60. Oddo, *Atti accad. Lincei*, (5) **13**, II, 187 (1904); *Gazz. chim. ital.*, **34 II**, 429 (1904); **38 I**, 625 (1908); Zalkind and Rosenfeld, *Ber.*, **57B**, 1690 (1924); Iotsitsch, *J. Russ. Phys.-*

Chem. Soc., **38**, 252 (1906); *Bull. soc. chim.*, (4) **4**, 981 (1908); Grignard *et al.*, *Compt. rend.*, **187**, 517 (1928); *Bull. soc. chim.*, (4) **43**, 931 (1928).
61. Thompson *et al.*, *J. Am. Chem. Soc.*, **63**, 752 (1941). Kroeger and Nieuwland, *J. Am. Chem. Soc.*, **58**, 1861 (1936); Meyer and Slreuli, *Helv. Chim. Acta*, **20**, 1179 (1937).
62. Hennion and Wolf, *Proc. Indian Acad. Sci.*, **48**, 98 (1939).
63. Grignard and Courtot, *Compt. rend.*, **152**, 272, 1493 (1911); **158**, 1763 (1914); Miller and Bachman, *J. Am. Chem. Soc.*, **57**, 766 (1935); Courtot, *Ann. chim.*, (9) **4**, 58 (1915).
64. Cf. Oddo, *Mem. reale accad. naz. Lincei Classe Sci., fis. mat. e nat.* (5) **14**, 510 (1923); Oddo, *Gazz. chim. ital.*, **39 I**, 649 (1909); Gilman and Pickens, *J. Am. Chem. Soc.*, **47**, 248 (1925); McCay and Schmidt, *ibid.*, **48**, 1933 (1926).
65. Challenger and Miller, *J. Chem. Soc.*, **1938**, 894.
66. *Cf.* Bert, *Bull. soc. chim.*, (4) **37**, 1577 (1925).
67. Swarts, *Bull. Acad. roy. Belg.* (5) **7**, 438 (1921); (5) **22**, 105 (1936).
68. Gilman and Heck, *J. Am. Chem. Soc.*, **53**, 377 (1931).
69. Grignard, *Ann. univ. Lyon*, (2) I, **6**, 12 (1901).
70. Gilman *et al.*, *J. Am. Chem. Soc.*, **47**, 2002 (1925); **62**, 1243 (1940); *Bull. soc. chim.*, (4) **41**, 1479 (1927); *Rec. trav. chim.*, **45**, 314 (1926); **48**, 155, 160, 193 (1929). *Chem. Zentr.* **1929 I**, 1818; Meisenheimer, *Ber.*, **61**, 2029 (1928).
71. Gilman *et al.*, *J. Am. Chem. Soc.*, **47**, 2002 (1925); **52**, 4949 (1930); **62**, 1243 (1940); *Bull. soc. chim.*, (4) **41**, 1479 (1927); *Rec. trav. chim.*, **48**, 155, 160, 193 (1929).
72. Gilman and Heck, *Rec. trav. chim.*, **49**, 218 (1930).
73. Gilman and Meyers, *Ind. Eng. Chem.*, **15**, 61 (1923); Gilman and St. John, *Bull. soc. chim.*, (4) **45**, 1091 (1929).
74. Ivanoff and Abdouloff, *Compt. rend.*, **196**, 491 (1933).
75. Zerewitinoff, *Ber.*, **41**, 2244 (1908); Sudborough and Hibbert, *J. Chem. Soc.*, **95**, 477 (1909); Davies and Kipping, *ibid.*, **99**, 296 (1911); Marvel *et al.*, *J. Am. Chem. Soc.*, **50**, 2810 (1928); Ivanoff and Abdouloff, *Compt. rend.*, **196**, 491 (1933); Carothers and Berchet, *J. Am. Chem. Soc.*, **55**, 2814 (1933); Paul, *Compt. rend.*, **192**, 964 (1931).
76. Kuhn and Suginomé, *Helv. Chim. Acta*, **12**, 919 (1929).
77. Schmalfuss and Wetzel, *J. prakt. Chem.*, (2) **109**, 158 (1925).
78. Gilman and St. John, *Rec. trav. chim.*, **49**, 222 (1930).
79. Entemann and Johnson, *J. Am. Chem. Soc.*, **55**, 2900 (1933).
80. v. Braun and Kirschbaum, *Ber.*, **52**, 1725 (1919); Gilman and Heck, *ibid.*, **62**, 1379 (1929).
81. Marshall, *J. Chem. Soc.*, **105**, 527 (1914); **107**, 509 (1915); **127**, 2184 (1925); Meisenheimer, *Ann.*, **442**, 180 (1925); **446**, 76 (1925); Terentjeff, *Z. anorg. Chem.*, **159**, 226 (1927); Meerwein and Schmidt, *Ann.*, **444**, 221 (1925); Schankland and Gomberg, *J. Am. Chem. Soc.*, **52**, 4973 (1930); Bogert and Powell, *ibid.*, **53**, 1604 (1931); Tolstopjatow and Swerdlowa, *J. Russ. Phys.-Chem. Soc.*, **2**, (64) 105 (1932).
82. Schlenk and Ochs, *Ber.*, **49**, 610 (1916); Grüttner and Krause, *ibid.*, **49**, 2674 (1916); Ziegler, *ibid.*, **54**, 737 (1921); **55**, 3406 (1922).
83. Grignard and Tissier, *Compt. rend.*, **134**, 107 (1902); Marvel *et al.*, *J. Am. Chem. Soc.*, **50**, 2810 (1928); Bourgom, *Bull. soc. chim. Belg.*, **33**, 101 (1924).
84. Viebel *et al.*, *Bull. soc. chim.*, (5) **6**, 990 (1939).
85. Späth, *Monatsh.*, **35**, 330, 471 (1914); Tschitschibabin and Jelgasin, *J. Russ. Phys.-Chem. Soc.*, **46**, 802 (1914).
86. Oddo and Cambieri, *Gazz. chim. ital.*, **70**, 559 (1940).
87. Tiffeneau and Delange, *Compt. rend.*, **137**, 573 (1903); Schmidlin and Garcia-Banus, *Ber.*, **45**, 3193 (1912); Gilman and Kirby, *J. Am. Chem. Soc.*, **54**, 345 (1932); Johnson, *ibid.*, **55**, 3029 (1933).
88. Carré, *Compt. rend.*, **148**, 1108 (1909); Austin and Johnson, *J. Am. Chem. Soc.*, **54**, 647 (1932); Carré, *Compt. rend.*, **151**, 149 (1910).
89. Gilman *et al.*, *J. Am. Chem. Soc.*, **49**, 1825 (1927); **51**, 3475 (1929).
90. Porter, *J. Am. Chem. Soc.*, **57**, 1436 (1935).
91. Tiffeneau *et al.*, *Bull. soc. chim.*, (5) **2**, 1848, 1855 (1935).
92. Campbell *et al.*, *J. Am. Chem. Soc.*, **60**, 2882 (1938).
93. Dupont, *Compt. rend.*, **149**, 1381 (1909); **150**, 1121 (1910).
94. Kleinfeller and Eckert, *Ber.*, **62**, 1598 (1929).
95. Salkind *et al.*, *J. Russ. Phys.-Chem. Soc.*, **8**, (70), 1382 (1938); **9**, 1525 (1939).
96. Darzens, *Compt. rend.*, **151**, 883 (1910); **203**, 1374 (1936); Darzens and Levy, *ibid.*, **204**, 272 (1937). *Cf.* Freylon, *Ann. chim.*, (8) **20**, 79 (1910).
97. Kohler and Erickson, *J. Am. Chem. Soc.*, **53**, 2301 (1931).
98. Busch and Rinck, *Ber.*, **38**, 1762 (1905); Diels and Johlin, *ibid.*, **44**, 403 (1911).
99. Auwers, *Ber.*, **48**, 1357, 1371 (1915).
100. Lemaire, *Bull. acad. Belg.*, **1909**, 83.
101. Crawford, *J. Am. Chem. Soc.*, **57**, 2000 (1935); **61**, 3310 (1939).
102. de Barry Barnett *et al.*, *J. Chem. Soc.*, **1927**, 1724.

103. Freund and Mayer, *Ber.*, **39**, 1117 (1906); Wohl and Meyer, *Bull. soc. chim.*, (4) **7**, 28 (1910); Lemonet, *Compt. rend.*, **157**, 724 (1913); Chamberlain and Dull, *J. Am. Chem. Soc.*, **50**, 3088 (1928).
104. Grignard, *Ann. univ. Lyon Sci.*, **6**, 1 (1901).
105. Béhal and Tiffeneau, *Bull. soc. chim.*, (4) **3**, 301 (1908).
106. Dilthey and Huchtemann, *J. prakt. Chem.*, (2) **154**, 238 (1940).
107. Meyer and Schuster, *Ber.*, **55**, 815 (1922); Vorlander and Siebert, *ibid.*, **39**, 1024 (1906); Ziegler and Sauermilch, *ibid.*, **63**, 1861 (1930).
108. de Barry Barnett *et al.*, *Ber.*, **64**, 49 (1931); *J. Chem. Soc.*, **1927**, 1724; **1928**, 1822.
109. de Barry Barnett and Wiltshire, *Ber.*, **62**, 3063 (1929); **63**, 1114 (1930); de Barry Barnett, *J. Chem. Soc.*, **1930**, 1348.
110. Späth, *Monatsh.*, **35**, 463 (1914).
111. Tchoubar and Sackur, *Compt. rend.*, **207**, 1105 (1938).
112. Zoeren, *U.S. patent*, 2,225,671 (1938); Földi and Demjén, *Ber.*, **74**, 930 (1941).
113 Clar and Engler, *Ber.*, **64**, 1597 (1931).
114. Kondo and Kokeguchi, *J. pharm. Soc. Japan*, **57**, 108 (1937).
115. Adams *et al.*, *J. Am. Chem. Soc.*, **48**, 1080, 1089 (1926).
116. Simonis *et al.*, *Ber.*, **38**, 3981 (1905); **39**, 897 (1906); **41**, 982 (1908).
117. Vène, *Compt. rend.*, **202**, 1681 (1936); *Ann. chim.*, (11) **10**, 194 (1938); *Bull. soc. chim.*, (5) **6**, 692 (1939).
118. Lemaire, *Bull. acad. roy. Belg.*, **1909**, 83.
119. *Cf.* however Kohler and Potter, *J. Am. Chem. Soc.*, **57**, 1316 (1935).
120. Stevens, *J. Am. Chem. Soc.*, **56**, 1425 (1934); **57**, 1112 (1935).
121, Colonge, *Bull. soc. chim.*, (5) **2**, 754 (1935); (5) **3**, 413 (1936); Meyer, *Helv. Chim. Acta*, **18**, 467 (1935).
122. Chaletzki, *J. Russ. Phys.-Chem. Soc.*, **6**, (68), 1 (1936).
123. Staudinger, *Die Ketene*, 1912, p. 93.
124. Whitmore and Pedlow, *J. Am. Chem. Soc.*, **63**, 758 (1941).
125. Auwers, *Ann.*, **352**, 219 (1907); *Ber.*, **55**, 2167 (1922).
126. Baeyer and Piccard, *Ann.*, **384**, 208 (1911).
127. Julian and Magnani, *J. Am. Chem. Soc.*, **56**, 2174 (1934).
128. Julian *et al.*, *ibid.*, **57**, 2508 (1935).
129. Grignard and Savard, *Compt. rend.*, **179**, 1573 (1924); *Bull. soc. chim. Belg.*, **36**, 97 (1927); *Chem. Zentr.*, **1927 I**, 2997.
130. Grignard and Blanchon, *Rocznicki Chem.*, **9**, 547 (1929).
131. Bredt-Savelsberg, *J. prakt. Chem.*, (2) **107**, 65 (1924).
132. Späth, *Monatsh.*, **35**, 319 (1914); *Ber.*, **47**, 766 (1914); Tschitschibabin and Jelgasin, *ibid.*, **47**, 48, 1843 (1914).
133. Kransfelder and Vogt, *J. Am. Chem. Soc.*, **60**, 1714 (1938); Grard, *Ann. chim.*, 336 (1930).
134. Späth, *Monatsh.*, **36**, 1 (1915); *Chem. Zentr.*, **1915 I**, 940.
135. Späth, *Monatsh.*, **35**, 330 (1914).
136. Stadnikoff, *J. Russ. Phys.-Chem. Soc.*, **47**, 2115 (1915).
137. Barbier and Loquin, *Compt. rend.*, **156**, 1443 (1913); Wieland *et al.*, *Z. physiol. Chem.*, **(6)**, 801 (1926); Dalmer *et al.*, *Ber.*, **68**, 1814 (1935); Reindel and Niederländer, *ibid.*, **68**, 1969 (1935); Morsman *et al.*, *Helv. Chim. Acta*, **20**, 3 (1937).
138. Vavon *et al.*, *Bull. soc. chim.*, (5) **1**, 806 (1934).
139. Tschitschibabin, *Ber.*, **38**, 561 (1905); Hepworth, *J. Chem. Soc.*, **115**, 1203 (1919); Ivanoff, *Compt. rend.*, **193**, 773 (1931).
140. Putochin, *Ber.*, **59**, 1991 (1926); Majima, *ibid.*, **55**, 3861 (1922).
141. Carothers, *Chem. Revs.*, **8**, 372 (1931).
142. Valeur, *Compt. rend.*, **132**, 833 (1901); **136**, 694 (1903); *Bull. soc. chim.*, (3) **29**, 683 (1903). *Cf.* Dilthey and Last, *Ber.*, **37**, 2639 (1904).
143. Guyot and Catel, *Compt. rend.*, **140**, 254, 1348 (1905); *Bull. soc. chim.*, (3) **35**, 1124 (1906). *Cf.* Howell, *J. Am. Chem. Soc.*, **42**, 2333 (1920).
144. Majima and Shigematsu, *Ber.*, **57**, 1449 (1924).
145. Stoermer, *ibid.*, **39**, 2288 (1906).
146. Tschitschibabin, *ibid.*, **37**, 186 (1904); Bodroux, *Compt. rend.*, **138**, 92, 700 (1904).
147. Tschitschibabin, *Ber.*, **37**, 186 (1904); **38**, 563 (1905); Bodroux, *Bull. soc. chim.*, (3) **31**, 585 (1904).
148. Tschitschibabin and Jalgasin, *Ber.*, **47**, 48 (1914).
149. Tschitschibabin, *ibid.*, **38**, 561 (1905).
150. Petrow, *Bull. acad. Sci. U.R.S.S.*, **1938**, 347; Bergmann and Weiss, *Ber.*, **64**, 1485 (1931); Clément, *Compt. rend.*, **202**, 425 (1936); de Jong, *Rec. trav. chim.*, **61**, 539 (1942).
151. Petrow *et al.*, *Bull. soc. chim.*, (5) **3**, 169 (1936); *J. Russ. Phys.-Chem. Soc.*, **7 (61)**, 565, 570, 2665 (1937); **8 (70)**, 199 (1938).
152. Henry, *Compt. rend.*, **144**, 308 (1907); *Bull. acad. roy. Belg.*, **1907**, 162.

153. Borden and Ramart, *Compt. rend.*, **183**, 214 (1926).
154. Paal and Weidenkaff, *Ber.*, **38**, 1686 (1905); **39**, 810 (1906); Kanao and Shinozuka, *J. pharm. Soc. Japan*, **50**, 148 (1930).
155. McKenzie and Duff, *Ber.*, **60**, 1335 (1927).
156. Weiss and Fastmann, *Monatsh.*, **47**, 727 (1926); Seidel, *Ber.*, **61 B**, 2267 (1928); Barnett *et al.*, *J. Chem. Soc.*, **1927**, 504. *Cf.* Seer and Dischendorfer, *Monatsh.*, **34**, 1493 (1914); Weiss and Sauermann, *Ber.*, **58 B**, 2736 (1925).
157. Guyot and Valette, *Ann. chim.*, (8) **23**, 363 (1911); *Chem. Zentr.*, **1911 II**, 457.
158. Guyot and Catel, *Compt. rend.*, **140**, 1460 (1905); Ludwig, *Ber.*, **40**, 3060 (1907).
159. Heilbron and Hill, *J. Chem. Soc.*, **1927**, 2005 (1927).
160. Lowenbein, *Ber.*, **57**, 1519 (1924); Majuna and Kotake, *ibid.*, **55**, 3871 (1922); Toffoli, *Gazz. chim. ital.*, **64**, 364 (1934); **65**, 487 (1935); Madelung and Hagar, *Ber.*, **49**, 2039 (1916).
161. Kohler and Heritage, *Am. Chem. J.*, **33**, 21, 153 (1905); Kohler, *ibid.*, **34**, 132 (1905); Marvel *et al.*, *J. Am. Chem. Soc.*, **70**, 1695 (1948); Hsing and Li, *ibid.*, **71**, 774 (1949); Alexander *et al.*, *ibid.*, **72**, 4791 (1950).
162. Blaise and Courtot, *Compt. rend.*, **140**, 370 (1905); Kohler, *Am. Chem. J.*, **36**, 529 (1907).
163. Kohler *et al.*, *Am. Chem. J.*, **33**, 21, 35 (1905); **34**, 568 (1906);
164. Kohler and Heritage, *Am. Chem. J.*, **33**, 153 (1905).
165. Kohler and Reimer, *ibid.*, **33**, 333 (1905).
166. Tarbel and Weaver, *J. Am. Chem. Soc.*, **62**, 2747 (1940); Purdie and Arup, *J. Chem. Soc.*, **97**, 1537 (1910).
167. McKenzie and Winton, *ibid.*, **1940**, 840.
168. Reimer and Reynolds, *Am. Chem. J.*, **40**, 428 (1908); Reynolds, *ibid.*, **46**, 198 (1911).
169. Kohler and Butler, *J. Am. Chem. Soc.*, **48**, 1036 (1926).
170. Grignard, *Compt. rend.*, **136**, 1200 (1903); Gilman *et al.*, *Rec. trav. chim.*, **48**, 748 (1929).
171. Oddo and Sessa, *Gazz. chim. ital.*, **41**, **I**, 234 (1911).
172. Cddo and Sanna, *ibid.*, **51**, II, 337 (1921); Sanna, *ibid.*, **52**, **II**, 165 (1923); Majima and Shigematsu, *Ber.*, **57**, 1449 (1924).
173. Whitmore *et al.*, *J. Am. Chem. Soc.*, **63**, 643 (1941).
174. Houben, *Ber.*, **39**, 1736 (1906); Yabroff and Porter, *J. Am. Chem. Soc.*, **54**, 2453 (1932); Spassow, *Ber.*, **70**, 1926 (1937).
175. Fournier, *Bull. soc. chim.*, (4) **7**, 836 (1910).
176. Kroeger and Nieuwland, *J. Am. Chem. Soc.*, **58**, 1861 (1936).
177. Komppa and Rohrmann, *Ann.*, **509**, 259 (1934); Weizmann *et al.*, *J. Chem. Soc.*, **1935**, 1367, 1370.
178. Newman, and McCleary, *J. Am. Chem. Soc.*, **63**, 1542 (1941); Newman *et al.*, *J. Am. Chem. Soc.*, **58**, 2376 (1936); **59**, 1003 (1937); **60**, 586, 1368 (1938); **61**, 244 (1939); **63**, 2109 (1941); **66**, 733 (1944); Nichol and Sandin; *ibid.*, **69**, 2256 (1947).
179. Price *et al.*, *ibid.*, **61**, 2760 (1939).
180. Grignard, *Ann. univ. Lyon*, (2) **II**, **6**, 26 (1901); Houben and Kesselkaul, *Ber.*, **35**, 2519 (1902); Bodroux, *Compt. rend.*, **137**, 710 (1903); Ivanow, *Bull. soc. chim.*, (4) **37**, 287 (1925); Kinney and Mayhne, *J. Am. Chem. Soc.*, **53**, 190 (1931); Gilman and Zoellner, *ibid.*, **53**, 1583 (1931).
181. Bodroux, *Compt. rend.*, **137**, 710 (1903); Iwanow, *Bull. soc. chim.*, (4) **37**, 287 (1925).
182. Gilman and St. John, *Rec. trav. chim.*, **49**, 1172 (1930); Iwanow, *Bull. soc. chim.*, (4) **37**, 287 (1925); Bodroux, *Compt. rend.*, **137**, 710 (1903); *Bull. soc. chim.*, (3) **31**, 24 (1904); Spencer and Stokes, *J. Chem. Soc.*, **93**, 70 (1908); Sobecki, *Ber.*, **43**, 1039 (1910).
183. Gilman *et al.*, *J. Am. Chem. Soc.*, **55**, 1258 (1933); *ibid.*, **46**, 2816 (1924); **50**, 1052 (1928).
184. Bogert and Tuttle, *J. Am. Chem. Soc.*, **38**, 1353 (1916).
185. Gilman and Zoellner, *ibid.*, **53**, 1583 (1931); *Organic Syntheses*, **I**, 310, 353 (1932).
186. Houben, *Ber.*, **36**, 2897 (1903); Tiffeneau, *Compt. rend.*, **138**, 985 (1904); v. Braun, *Ber.*, **44**, 1039 (1911); **52**, 1713 (1919).
187. Tiffeneau, *Compt. rend.*, **135**, 1346 (1902).
188. v. Braun and Kühn, *Ber.*, **58**, 2171 (1925).
189. Zelinsky and Gutt, *Ibid.*, **40**, 3049 (1907).
190. v. Braun and Sobecki, *ibid.*, **44**, 1925 (1911).
191. Grignard and Vignon, *Compt. rend.*, **144**, 1358 (1907).
192. Ivanow and Spassow, *Bull. soc. chim.*, (4) **49**, 19 (1931).
193. Schmidlin and Huber, *Ber.*, **43**, 2824 (1910).
194. Houben *et al.*, *ibid.*, **37**, 3978 (1904); **42**, 3729, 4488, 4815 (1909); **46**, 3833 (1913); Meunier, *Compt. rend.*, **136**, 758 (1905); Terentjew and Rubinstein, *Ber.*, **60**, 1879 (1927).
195. Houben and Kesselkaul, *Ber.*, **35**, 2519 (1902); Ivanoff, *Bull. soc. chim.*, (4) **37**, 287 (1925); Houben, *Ber.*, **35**, 2897 (1902).
196. Grignard, *Compt. rend.*, **138**, 1048 (1904); Zelinsky, *Ber.*, **35**, 2692 (1902); Houben and Kesselkaul, *ibid.*, **35**, 2519 (1902); Schmidlin, *ibid.*, **39**, 628 (1906); Ivanoff, *Bull. soc. chim.*, (4) **37**, 287 (1925); Mousseron and Du, *Bull. soc. chim.*, (5) **15**, 91 (1948); Moser and Sause, *J. Org. Chem.*, **15**, 631 (1950).

197. Houben and Kesselkaul, *Ber.*, **35**, 2519 (1902); Zelinsky, *ibid.*, **35**, 2692 (1902); Acree, *ibid.*, **37**, 625 (1904); Schroeter, *ibid.*, **36**, 3005 (1903); Houben, *ibid.*, **38**, 3796 (1905); Ivanoff, *Bull. soc. chim.*, (4) **37**, 287 (1925); Houben and Freund, *Ber.*, **42**, 4815 (1909); **46**, 3833 (1913); Schlenk and Ochs, *ibid.*, **48**, 679 (1915).
198. Zelinsky, *Ber.*, **35**, 2687, 4415 (1902); **36**, 208 (1903); **41**, 2627 (1908); Houben and Kesselkaul, *ibid.*, **35**, 3695 (1902); Brühl, *ibid.*, **36**, 668, 4273 (1903); Gutt, *ibid.*, **40**, 2061 (1907); Houben, *ibid.*, **38**, 3796 (1905).
199. Bodroux, *Compt. rend.*, **136**, 377, 617 (1903); *Bull. soc. chim.*, (3) **31**, 30 (1904).
200. Grignard and Vignon, *Compt. rend.*, **144**, 1358 (1907); Houben, *Ber.*, **38**, 3796 (1905); v. Braun, *ibid.*, **44**, 1918 (1911).
201. Béis, *Compt. rend.*, **137**, 575 (1903).
202. Maxim, *ibid.*, **182**, 1393 (1926). *Cf.* Kuffner and Polke, *Monatsh.*, **82**, 330 (1951).
203. Béis, *Compt. rend.* **137**, 575 (1903); Ryan and Nolan, *Proc. Roy. Irish Acad.*, **30**, B.1 (1912). *Cf.* McKenzie and Wren, *J. Chem. Soc.*, **93**, 310 (1908).
204. Ramart *et al.*, *Compt. rend.*, **185**, 282 (1927).
205. Whitmore *et al.*, *J. Am. Chem. Soc.*, **61**, 683 (1939).
206. Bouveault, *Compt. rend.*, **137**, 987 (1903).
207. Viguier, *ibid.*, **153**, 955 (1911).
208. Maxim and Mavrodineanu, *Bull. soc. chim.*, (5) **2**, 591 (1935); (5) **3**, 1084 (1936); *Cf.* Viguier, *Bull. soc. chim.*, (4) **41**, 809 (1927); Maxim *et al.*, *ibid.*, (4) **41**, 809 (1927); (5) **3**, 591 (1935); (5) **3**, 1084 (1936); Montague, *Compt. rend.*, **183**, 216 (1926); Busch and Fleischmann, *Ber.*, **43**, 2553 (1910); Couturier, *Compt. rend.*, **205**, 800 (1937); *Ann. chim.*, (11) **10**, 559 (1938).
209. Barré, *Compt. rend.*, **185**, 105 (1927).
210. Couturier, *ibid.*, **202**, 1994 (1936); **205**, 800 (1938); *Ann. Chim.*, (11) **10**, 559 (1938). *Cf.* Bruzan, *Compt. rend.*, **194**, 1662 (1932); Montagne and Rousseau, *ibid.*, **196**, 1165 (1933); Skraup and Moser, *Ber.*, **55 B**, 1080 (1922).
211. Kohler and Heritage, *Am. Chem. J.*, **33**, 21 (1905); Maxim and Ioanid, *Bull. Chim. Soc. Chim. România*, **10**, 116 (1928).
212. Nenitzescu, *Bull. Chim. Soc. Chim. România*, **12**, 48 (1930); **14**, 62 (1932).
213. Lukeš, *Bull. acad. Bohême*, **35**, 1925 (1928); Lukeš and Prelog, *Collection Czech Chem. Commun.*, **1**, 334 (1929).
214. Béis, *Compt. rend.*, **138**, 987 (1904); **139**, 61 (1904). *Cf.* Sachs and Ludwig, *Ber.*, **17**, 385 (1884); Goudet and Paillard, *Helv. Chim. Acta*, **7**, 638 (1924); Sachs and Ludwig, *Ber.*, **37**, 385 (1904); Lukeš *et al.*, *Chem. Listy*, **22**, 244 (1928); *Collection Czachoslav. Chem. Commun.*, **5**, 761 (1932); **7**, 482 (1935); **8**, 223 (1936); *C.A.*, **23**, 1408 (1929); **27**, 290 (1933); **30**, 1785, 5989 (1936).
215. Béis, *Compt. rend.*, **138**, 987 (1904); **139**, 61 (1904).
216. Kohn, *Monatsh.*, **31**, 747 (1910); Kohn and Ostersetzer, *ibid.*, **32**, 905 (1911); **37**, 25 (1915).
217. Marquis, *Compt. rend.*, **142**, 711 (1906).
218. Monier-Williams, *J. Chem. Soc.*, **89**, 273 (1906).
219. Bertho, *J. prakt. Chem.*, (2) **116**, 101 (1927).
220. Bertho, *l.c.;* Oliveri-Mandalà, *Gazz. chim. ital.*, **44 I**, 662 (1914).
221. Moureu and Mignonac, *Compt. rend.*, **156**, 1801 (1913); *Ann. chim.*, (4) **14**, 322 (1920); Bruylants, *Rec. trav. chim.*, **28**, 186 (1909); Pickard and Kenyon, *J. Chem. Soc.*, **101**, 629 (1912); Lipp and Quaedvlieg, *Ber.*, **62**, 2315 (1929); Shriner and Turner, *J. Am. Chem. Soc.*, **52**, 1267 (1930).
222. Ralston and Christensen, *Ind. Eng. Chem.*, **29**, 195 (1937).
223. Moureu and Mignonac, *Compt. rend.*, **170**, 1353 (1920); *Ann. Chim.*, (9) **14**, 322 (1920).
224. de Milt and Sartor, *J. Am. Chem. Soc.*, **62**, 1954 (1940).
225. Bruylants, *Bull. Acad. roy. Belg.*, **31**, 184 (1922).
226. Bruylants, *Bull. Acad. roy. Belg.*, (5) **8**, 7 (1922); Baerts, *Bull. soc. chim. Belg.*, **31**, 184, 421 (1922); Rondon, *ibid.*, **31**, 231 (1922); Breckport, *ibid.*, **32**, 386 (1924); **33**, 490 (1924); Ivanoff and Paounoff, *Compt. rend.*, **197**, 923 (1933).
227. Bruylants and Gevaert, *Bull. Acad. roy. Belg.*, (5) **9**, 27 (1923).
228. Béhal and Sommelet, *Bull. soc. chim.*, (4) **1**, 389 (1907); Wren, *J. Chem. Soc.*, **95**, 1592 (1909); Gauthier, *Ann. chim.*, (8) **16**, 289 (1909); *Compt. rend.*, **152**, 1100 (1911); Mathus, *Bull. soc. chim. Belg.*, **34**, 285 (1925); Bruylants, *Bull. Acad. roy. Belg.*, (5) **11**, 261 (1925); Geurden, *ibid.*, (5) **11**, 701 (1925); Paul, *Bull. soc. chim.*, (4) **45**, 152 (1929); Smith, *Ber.*, **64**, 427 (1931); Velghe, *Bull. Acad. roy. Belg.*, (5) **11**, 301 (1925); Chaletzki, *J. Russ. Phys.-Chem. Soc.*, **11**, 319 (1941).
229. Grignard, *Compt. rend.*, **152**, 388 (1911); Grignard *et al.*, *Ann. chim. phys.*, (9) **4**, 28 (1913); *Bull. soc. chim.*, (4) **39**, 1589 (1926); Nekrassoff, *J. Soc. Chim. Russe*, **59**, 915 (1927); Khaletskii, *J. Gen. Chem.*, (U.S.S.R.) **11**, 319 (1941).
230. Stevens *et al.*, *J. Chem. Soc.*, **1931**, 2568; Thompson and St. Stevens, *ibid.*, **1932**, 2607.
231. Bruylants, *Bull. Acad. roy. Belg.*, (5) **10**, 392 (1924); McKenzie and Duff, *Ber.*, **60**, 1341 (1927).

232. Rube and Pasternack, *Ber.*, **46**, 1026 (1913).
233. Blaise, *Compt. rend.*, **132**, 978 (1901).
234. Marrodin, *ibid.*, **191**, 1064 (1930); **192**, 363 (1931).
235. Erickson and Barnett, *J. Am. Chem. Soc.*, **57**, 560 (1935).
236. Ivanoff and Paounoff, *Compt. rend.*, **197**, 923 (1933); Smith, *Ber.*, **71**, 634 (1938).
237. Bruylants and Dewall, *Bull. Acad. roy. Belg.*, (5) **12**, 464 (1926); Compère, *Bull. soc. chim. Belg.*, **44**, 523 (1935).
238. Henze *et al.*, *J. Am. Chem. Soc.*, **61**, 1790 (1939); **63**, 2785 (1941).
239. de Coster, *Bull. soc. chim. Belg.*, **35**, 235 (1926).
240. Mavrodin, *Bull. Chim. Soc. Chim. România*, **15**, 99 (1933).
241. Bruylants, *Bull. Acad. roy. Belg.*, **10**, 166 (1924); **11**, 261 (1925); *Bull. soc. chim. Belg.*, **33**, 467 (1924); Stevens *et al.*, *J. Chem. Soc.*, **1931**, 2568; **1932**, 2607.
242. Bruylants, *Bull. soc. chim. Belg.*, **35**, 139 (1926).
243. Christiaen, *ibid.*, **33**, 483 (1924).
244. Mathus, *ibid.*, **34**, 285 (1925).
245. de Boaseré, *Bull. soc. chim. Belg.*, **32**, 26 (1923); Bruylants, *Bull. Acad. roy. Belg.*, **12**, 1082 (1928); Cloke, *J. Am. Chem. Soc.*, **51**, 1174 (1929); **62**, 117 (1940); Lipp and Seeles, *Ber.*, **62**, 2456 (1929); Starr *et al.*, *J. Am. Chem. Soc.*, **54**, 3971 (1932); Craig *et al.*, *ibid.*, **67**, 2155 (1945).
246. Cloke and Ayers, *J. Am. Chem. Soc.*, **56**, 2144 (1934).
247. Davis *et al.*, *J. Chem. Soc.*, **1939**, 360.
248. Tröger and Beck, *J. prakt. Chem.*, (2) **87**, 289 (1913); Weiss *et al.*, *Monatsh.*, **45**, 105 (1924); **48**, 451 (1927).
249. Bruylants, *Bull. soc. chim. Belg.*, **35**, 139 (1926); Kohler and Reimer, *Am. Chem. J.*, **33**, 333 (1905); Maxim and Aldea, *Bull. soc. chim.*, (5) **2**, 582 (1935); Fuson *et al.*, *J. Am. Chem. Soc.*, **60**, 1447 (1938); Birch and Robinson, *J. Chem. Soc.*, **1943**, 501; Hook and Robinson, *ibid.*, **1945**, 153.
250. Richtzenheim and Nippus, *Ber.*, **77 B**, 566 (1944); Fuson *et al.*, *J. Org. Chem.*, **13**, 489 (1948). *Cf.* Fuson *et al.*, *ibid.*, **13**, 496 (1948).
251. Weissberger and Glass, *J. Am. Chem. Soc.*, **64**, 1724 (1942).
252. Kaufmann *et al.*, *Ber.*, **46**, 2929 (1913).
253. Béhal, *Bull. soc. chim.*, (3) **31**, 461 (1904); Grignard *et al.*, *Ann. chim.*, (9) **12**, 364 (1919); Willemart, *Ann. chim.*, (10) **12**, 345 (1929).
254. Coleman and Leeper, *Proc. Iowa Acad. Sci.*, **47**, 201 (1940); Grignard *et al.*, *Bull. soc. chim.*, (4) **17**, 228 (1915); *Ann. chim. phys.*, (10) **5**, 5 (1926); Nekrassow, *Ber.*, **60**, 1755 (1927).
255. Grignard and Ono, *Bull. soc. chim.*, (4) **39**, 1589 (1926).
256. Grignard and Courtot, *ibid.*, (4) **17**, 228 (1915); Grignard and Perrichon, *Ann. chim.*, (10) **5**, 5 (1926).
257. Grignard *et al.*, *Compt. rend.*, **152**, 388 (1911); **155**, 44 (1912); **158**, 457 (1914); *Ann. chim. phys.*, (9) **4**, 28 (1915); **12**, 364 (1920); *Compt. rend.*, **154**, 281, 361 (1912); **158**, 1763 (1914); Miyagawa, *Ber.*, **57**, 1455 (1924).
258. Busch and Hobein, *Ber.*, **40**, 4296 (1907); Adams and Beebe, *J. Am. Chem. Soc.*, **38**, 2768 (1916); Vuylsteke, *Bull. sci. acad. roy. Belg.*, (5) **12**, 535 (1926); *C.A.*, **21**, 1108 (1927).
259. Vuylsteke, *Bull. acad. roy. Belg.*, (5) **12**, 535 (1926).
260. Sachs and Loevy, *Ber.*, **37**, 874 (1904).
261. Blaise, *Compt. rend.*, **132**, 38 (1901); Gilman *et al.*, *J. Am. Chem. Soc.*, **50**, 1214 (1928); **51**, 2252 (1929); Schwartz and Johnson, *J. Am. Chem. Soc.*, **53**, 1063 (1931); Young and Roberts, *ibid.*, **68**, 649 (1946).
262. Adams *et al.*, *J. Am. Chem. Soc.*, **42**, 2369 (1920).
263. Sachs and Loevy, *Ber.*, **36**, 585 (1903); **37**, 874 (1904). Gilman *et al.*, *J. Am. Chem. Soc.*, **51**, 2252 (1929).
264. Gilman *et al.*, *J. Am. Chem. Soc.*, **51**, 2252 (1929).
265. Sobotka and Bloch, *ibid.*, **59**, 2606 (1937).
266. Grignard, *Compt. rend.*, **138**, 1048 (1904); **151**, 322 (1910); Stadnikoff, *J. Russ. Phys.-Chem. Soc.*, **44**, 1219 (1912); Tschelinzeff and Pawloff, *ibid.*, **45**, 289 (1913); Simonis and Remmert, *Ber.*, **47**, 269 (1914).
267. Späth, *Monatsh.*, **35**, 319 (1914).
268. Gomberg and Kamm, *J. Am. Chem. Soc.*, **39**, 2009 (1917).
269. Späth, *Monatsh.*, **35**, 327 (1914); *Ber.*, **60**, 702, 1882 (1927); Kafuku *et al.*, *J. Pharm. Soc. Japan.*, **1925**, No. 521, p.1., **1926**, No. 533, pp. 56-58. *Chem-Zentr.* 1926 I, 69; II, 2791.
270. Robinson, *J. Chem. Soc.*, **123**, 532 (1923). *Cf.* Senkus, *J. Am. Chem. Soc.*, **67**, 1515 (1945).
271. Mason and Zef, *J. Am. Chem. Soc.*, **62**, 1450 (1940).
272. Bodroux, *Compt. rend.*, **138**, 1427 (1904); Kuhn and Morris, *Ber.*, **70**, 856 (1937).
273. Blaise, *Compt. rend.*, **134**, 551 (1902); Grignard, *ibid.*, **136**, 1260 (1903). *Cf.* Huston and Agett, *J. Org. Chem.*, **6**, 123 (1941). Yohe and Adams, *J. Am. Chem. Soc.*, **50**, 1505, (1928); Schorigin *et al.*, *Ber.*, **64B**, 2589 (1931); Cook and Hewett, *J. Chem. Soc.*, **1933**, 1107; Strating and Backer, *Rec. trav. chim.*, **55**, 910 (1936); Bergmann and Blum-Berg-

mann, *J. Am. Chem. Soc.*, **58**, 1679 (1936); Speer and Hill, *J. Org. Chem.*, **2**, 143 (1937); Bogert *et al.*, *J. Am. Chem. Soc.*, **60**, 319 (1938); Blicke and Zienty, *ibid.*, **61**, 95 (1939); Pilat and Turkiewitz, *Ber.*, **72B**, 1528 (1939); Kipping and Wild, *J. Chem. Soc.*, **1940**, 1241; Drezer, *Organic Syntheses*, Coll. vol. **I**, 306 (1941); Huston and Agett, *J. Org. Chem.*, **6**, 123 (1942); Newman, *ibid.*, **9**, 525 (1944); Cottle and Hollyday, *ibid.*, **12**, 510 (1947); Huston and Langham, *ibid.*, **12**, 90 (1947).

274. Kharasch and Crapp, *J. Org. Chem.*, **3**, 355 (1938).
275. Norton and Hass, *J. Am. Chem. Soc.*, **58**, 2147 (1936); Cottle and Powel, *ibid.*, **58**, 2267 (1936).
276. Bedos, *Compt. rend.*, **189**, 255 (1929).
277. Vavon and Mitchovitch, *ibid.*, **186**, 702 (1928).
278. Bartlett and Berry, *J. Am. Chem. Soc.*, **56**, 2683 (1934).
279. Kohler *et al.*, *ibid.*, **53**, 205 (1931); Bachmann and Wiselogle, *ibid.*, **56**, 1559 (1934).
280. Späth, *Monatsh.*, **34**, 1965 (1913); Kharasch and Klinman, *J. Am. Chem. Soc.*, **65**, 491 (1943); Wilds and McCormack, *J. Org. Chem.*, **14**, 45 (1949).
281. Bygden, *Ber.*, **45**, 3479 (1912); Spath, *Monatsh.*, **34**, 1965 (1913). *Cf.* Vavon *et al.*, *Compt. rend.*, **208**, 203 (1939).
282. Tissier and Grignard, *Compt. rend.*, **132**, 835 (1901).
283. Tiffeneau, *ibid.*, **137**, 989 (1908).
284. Umnowa, *J. Russ. Phys.-Chem. Soc.*, **45**, 882 (1913).
285. Hammonet, *Compt. rend.*, **138**, 813 (1904); *Bull. soc. chim.*, **254** (1908); Reychler, *ibid.*, (4) **1**, 1198 (1907); Hammonet, *ibid.*, (4) **3**, 254 (1908); Houben and Führer, *Ber.*, **40**, 4992 (1907).
286. Houben and Führer, *Ber.*, **40**, 4990 (1907).
287. Oddo and Mameli, *Gazz. chim. ital.*, **43 II**, 508 (1913); Hess *et al.*, *Ber.*, **48**, 1883 (1915).
288. Grignard, *Compt. rend.*, **141**, 44 (1905); *Ann. chim.*, (8) **10**, 23 (1907).
289. Gilman and Beaber, *J. Am. Chem. Soc.*, **45**, 839 (1923); Bert, *Compt. rend.*, **186**, 373 (1928); *French patent* 657,691 (1927); Rossander and Marvel, *J. Am. Chem. Soc.*, **50**, 1491 (1928).
290. Houben, *Ber.*, **36**, 3087 (1903); Grignard, *Compt. rend.*, **152**, 388 (1911); Grignard *et al.*, *Ann. chim.*, (9) **4**, 45 (1915); **12**, 564 (1919); *Bull. soc. chim.*, (4) **39**, 1589 (1926).
291. Fuson and Corse, *J. Am. Chem. Soc.*, **60**, 2063, 2269 (1938).
292. Oddo, *Gazz. chim. ital.*, **40 II**, 353 (1910); Oddo and Moschin, *ibid.*, **42 II**, 257 (1912); Sanna and Cheesa, *ibid.*, **58**, 121 (1928); Oddo and Dainotti, *ibid.*, **42 I**, 727 (1912).
293. Brooks and Humphreys, *J. Am. Chem. Soc.*, **40**, 833 (1918); Wilkinson, *J. Chem. Soc.*, **1931**, 3057.
294. Lespieau, *Compt. rend.*, **170**, 1584 (1920); **172**, 1236 (1921).
295. Bert, *Bull. soc. chim.*, (4) **37**, 879 (1925). *Cf.* Kirrmann, *Compt. rend.*, **182**, 1629 (1926).
296. Grignard *et al.*, *Bull. soc. chim.*, **43**, 141 (1928); Nieuwland *et al.*, *J. Am. Chem. Soc.*, **58**, 611 (1926); Danehy *et al.*, *J. Am. Chem. Soc.*, **58**, 611 (1936); Kharasch *et al.*, *J. Am. Chem. Soc.*, **65**, 491 (1943); *J. Org. Chem.*, **10**, 298 (1945).
297. Grignard and Perrichon, *Ann. chim.*, (10) **5**, 5 (1926).
298. Grignard and Tchéoufaki, *Compt. rend.*, **188**, 357 (1929). *Cf.* Walborsky *et al.*, *J. Am. Chem. Soc.*, **73**, 2590 (1951); Gensler and Thomas, *ibid.*, **73**, 460 (1951).
299. Oddo and Binaghi, *Gazz. chim. ital.*, **51**, II, 330 (1921); Binaghi, *ibid.*, **52 II**, 132 (1922).
300. Binaghi, *Gazz. chim. ital.*, **53**, 879 (1923).
301. Quelet, *Compt. rend.*, **198**, 2107 (1934).
302. Fuson *et al.*, *J. Am. Chem. Soc.*, **55**, 720, 2960 (1933).
303. Sanna, *R. Univ. Cagliar*, **5**, 76 (1935).
304. Bodroux, *Compt. rend.*, **161**, 131 (1915).
305. Gilman and Jones, *J. Am. Chem. Soc.*, **51**, 2840 (1929).
306. Schmidlin, *Ber.*, **42**, 2389 (1909).
307. Schmidlin, *ibid.*, **42**, 2377 (1909).
308. Godchot and Cauquil, *Compt. rend.*, **186**, 375, 995 (1928).
309. Mitchovitch, *ibid.*, **200**, 1601 (1935).
310. Coleman *et al.*, *J. Am. Chem. Soc.*, **50**, 1193 (1928); **55**, 2075, 3001 (1933).
311. Klages, *Ann.*, **547**, 25 (1941). *Cf.* Coleman *et al.*, *J. Am. Chem. Soc.*, **50**, 1193 (1928); **51**, 567 (1929); **55**, 2075, 3001, 3669 (1933); **58**, 27 (1936); **63**, 168 (1931). *Cf.* Coleman *et al.*, *Proc. Iowa Acad. Sci.*, **38**, 168 (1931); *C.A.*, **27**, 1862 (1933); Le Maistre *et al.*, *J. Am. Chem. Soc.*, **55**, 2075 (1933).
312. Oddo and Mameli, *Gazz. chim. ital.*, **43 II**, 504 (1913); **44 II**, 162 (1914); Hess *et al.*, *Ber.*, **46**, 3125 (1913); **47**, 1416 (1914); **48**, 1865 (1915); deJong, *Rec. trav. chim.*, **48**, 1029 (1929).
313. Ostrogovich, *Chem. Ztg.*, **36**, 738 (1912); Meyer and Näbe, *J. prakt. Chem.*, (2) **82**, 537 (1910).
314. Grignard and Zorn, *Compt. rend.*, **150**, 1177 (1910); Oddo, *Gazz. chim. ital.*, **41**, **I**, 11 (1911). Strecker, *Ber.*, **43**, 1131 (1910).
315, Cherbuliez and Schnauder, *Helv. Chim. Acta*, **6**, 249 (1923); Oddo, *Atti Accad. Lincei*, (5) **14 I**, 169 (1905); *Chem. Zentr.*, **1905 I**, 1145. *Cf.* Wedekind and Schenk, *Ber.*, **54 B**, 1604

(1921); Gilman and Fothergill, *J. Am. Chem. Soc.*, **51**, 3501 (1929); Burton and Davy, *J. Chem. Soc.*, **1948**, 528.
316. Delépine, *Compt. rend.*, **150**, 1607 (1910); **153**, 279 (1911).
317. Bodroux, *ibid.*, **135**, 1350 (1902).
318. Whitmore and Badertscher, *J. Am. Chem. Soc.*, **55**, 1561 (1933). *Cf.*, Flood and Calingaert, *ibid.*, **56**, 1211 (1934).
319. Kritschewsky and Turner, *J. Chem. Soc.*, **115**, 559 (1919); Sakellarious and Kyrimis, *Ber.*, **57**, 322 (1924).
320. Bennett and Turner, *J. Chem. Soc.*, **105**, 1057 (1914); *Cf.*, *however*, Job and Champetier, *Compt. rend.*, **189**, 1089 (1929); Champetier, *Bull. soc. chim.*, (4) **47**, 1131 (1930).
321. Michailenko and Protassow, *J. Russ. Phys.-Chem. Soc.*, **53**, 347 (1921); Gilman and Kirby, *Rec. trav. chim.*, **48**, 155 (1929); Gartner and Borgstrom, *J. Am. Chem. Soc.*, **51**, 3375 (1929); Gasopoulos, *Praktika Akad. Athenon*, **7**, 180 (1932).
322. Bert, *Compt. rend.*, **178**, 1182 (1924); Cope, *J. Am. Chem. Soc.*, **56**, 1578 (1934); Suter and Gerhart, *ibid.*, **55**, 3496 (1933); **57**, 107 (1935); Thorn *et al.*, *ibid.*, **58**, 796 (1936).
323. Simonis and Remmert, *Ber.*, **47**, 269 (1944); *German patents* 208,886; 208,962 (1909); *French patent* 847,743 (1937).
324. Gilman and Beaber, *J. Am. Chem. Soc.*, **45**, 839 (1923); **47**, 518 (1925); Gilman and Heck, *ibid.*, **50**, 2223 (1928); Ferns and Lapworth, *J. Chem. Soc.* **101**, 273 (1912).
325. Houben, *Ber.*, **37**, 3978 (1904); Meunier, *Compt. rend.*, **136**, 758 (1903). Bodroux, *Compt. rend.*, **138**, 1427 (1904); **142**, 401 (1906).
326. Kharasch and Weinhouse, *J. Org. Chem.*, **1**, 209 (1936).
327. Bachmann, *J. Am. Chem. Soc.*, **53**, 2758 (1931).
328. Mousseron and Granger, *Compt. rend.*, **204**, 986 (1937).
329. Wuyts, *ibid.*, **148**, 930 (1909); Bodroux, *ibid.*, **136**, 158 (1903); Iwanow, *Bull. soc. chim.*, (4) **39**, 47 (1926).
330. Meisenheimer and Schlichenmaier, *Ber.*, **61**, 2029 (1928).
331. Oddo and Binaghi, *Atti. accad. Lincei*, (5) **32 II**, 349 (1923).
332. Sachs and Sachs, *Ber.*, **37**, 3088 (1904); Oddo, *Atti accad. Lincei*, (5) **13**, II, 10 (1904); (5) **16 II**, 413, 538 (1907); Senier *et al.*, *J. Chem. Soc.*, **87**, 1469 (1905). Oddo, *Gazz. chim. ital.*, **37 I**, 568 (1907); Bergstrom and McAllister, *J. Am. Chem. Soc.*, **52**, 2845 (1930); Hoffman *et al.*, *J. Am. Chem. Soc.*, **55**, 2000 (1933); Lukeš, *Chem. Listy*, **27**, 97, 121 (1933); *C.A.*, **27**, 5323 (1933); Etienne, *Compt. rend.*, **219**, 622 (1944); Fuson *et al.*, *J. Org. Chem.*, **16**, 1529 (1951).
333. Freund *et al.*, *Ber.*, **37**, 4666 (1904); **42**, 1101 (1909); *J. prakt. Chem.*, (2) **98**, 233 (1918); Meisenheimer, *et al.*, *Ber.*, **58**, 2320 (1925); **56**, 1353 (1923). Craig, *J. Am. Chem. Soc.*, **60**, 1458 (1938).
334. Freund and Bode, *Ber.*, **42**, 1746 (1909). Bergmann and Rosenthal, *J. prakt. Chem.*, (2) **135**, 267 (1932).
335. Busch *et al.*, *J. prakt. Chem.*, (2) **77**, 20 (1907); *Ber.*, **37**, 2691 (1904); **38**, 1761 (1905); Anselmino, *ibid.*, **40**, 3465 (1905); Grammaticakis, *Compt. rend.*, **207**, 1224 (1938). Gilman *et al.*, *J. Am. Chem. Soc.*, **51**, 2252 (1929); Rehberg and Henze, *ibid.*, **63**, 2785 (1941).
336. van Alphen and Robert, *Rec. trav. chim.*, **54**, 360 (1935).
337. Montagne and Garry, *Compt. rend.*, **208**, 1735 (1939).
338. Busch and Hobein, *Ber.*, **40**, 4296 (1907).
339. Gilman and Morris, *J. Am. Chem. Soc.*, **48**, 2399 (1926); Sonn and Schmidt, *Ber.*, **57**, 1355 (1924).
340. Grammaticakis, *Compt. rend.*, **204**, 502 (1037). *Cf.* Grammaticakis, *Compt. rend.*, **202**, 1289 (1936); **204**, 1262 (1937); **208**, 287, 1910, 1998 (1939); **209**, 317 (1939); **210**, 569 (1940); **223**, 804 (1946); Wuyts and Lacourt, *Bull. soc. chim. Belg.*, **44**, 395 (1935); **45**, 445 (1936).
341. Grammaticakis, *Compt. rend.*, **206**, 1307 (1938).
342. Zerner, *Monatsh.*, **34**, 1608, 1631 (1913); Coleman *et al.*, *J. Org. Chem.*, **3**, 99 (1938). *Cf.* Hodgson and Marsden, *J. Chem. Soc.*, **1945**, 274.
343. Staudinger and Meyer, *Helv. Chim. Acta*, **2**, 619 (1920); Staudinger and Lüscher, *ibid.*, **5**, 75 (1922).
344. Zerner, *Monatsh.*, **34**, 1469, 1609 (1913).
345. Dimroth, *Ber.*, **38**, 683 (1905). *Cf.* Kleinfeller, *J. prakt. Chem.*, (2) **119**, 61 (1929); Kleinfeller and Bönig, *ibid.*, (2) **132**, 175 (1932).
346. Grammaticakis, *Compt. rend.*, **210**, 716 (1940). *Cf.* Hoch, *Compt. rend.*, **198**, 1865 (1934); **203**, 799 (1936); **204**, 358 (1937); Campbell *et al.*, *J. Org. Chem.*, **4**, 198 (1939); **8**, 99, 103 (1943); **9**, 184 (1944).
347. Sand and Singer, *Ber.*, **35**, 3186 (1902); *Ann.*, **329**, 190 (1903).
348. Wieland, *ibid.*, **36**, 2315 (1903).
349. Wieland *et al.*, *ibid.*, **45**, 494 (1912); **47**, 2113 (1914); **48**, 1117 (1915); **55**, 1802 (1922). *Cf.* Ingold, *J. Chem. Soc.*, **127**, 513 (1925).
350. Aston and Menard, *J. Am. Chem. Soc.*, **57**, 1920 (1935).

351. Bewald, *Ber.*, **40**, 3065 (1907).
352. Kohler and Stone, *J. Am. Chem. Soc.*, **52**, 761 (1930).
353. Wieland and Fressol, *Ber.*, **44**, 898 (1911).
354. Wieland and Roseau, *ibid.*, **48**, 1117 (1915).
355. Kurssanow *et al.*, *J. Russ. Phys.-Chem. Soc.*, **8**, (70), 1786 (1938). Gilman and Heck, *Rec. trav. chim.*, **50**, 522 (1931); Bachmann, *J. Am. Chem. Soc.*, **53**, 1524 (1931).
356. Houben *et al.*, *Ber.*, **35**, 3695 (1902); **40**, 1303, 1725 (1907); **39**, 3219, 5303 (1906).
357. Koelsch, *J. Am. Chem. Soc.*, **54**, 2045 (1932).
358. Houben and Schultze, *Ber.*, **43**, 2481 (1910).
359. Weigert, *ibid.*, **36**, 1007 (1903).
360. Schönberg, *ibid.*, **58**, 1796 (1925); **60**, 2351 (1927); *Ann.*, **454**, 37 (1927).
361. Taboury, *Ann. chim. phys.*, (8) **15**, 5 (1908); Wuyts and Cosyns, *Bull. soc. chim.*, (3) **29**, 689 (1903); Wuyts, *ibid.*, (4) **5**, 405 (1909).
362. Auger and Billy, *Compt. rend.*, **139**, 597 (1904). Dodonov and Medox, *Ber.*, **61 B**, 907 (1928); Williard *et al.*, *J. Am. Chem. Soc.*, **70**, 737 (1948). *Cf.* Gruttner *et al.*, *Ber.*, **48**, 1473 (1915); **49**, 437 (1916).
363. Grignard and Savard, *Compt. rend.* **192**, 592 (1931); Dodonow and Medox, *Ber.*, **61**, 907 (1928).
364. Grüttner and Krause, *Ber.*, **49**, 438, 2666 (1916); *German patent* 313,876 (1919).
365. Sauvage, *Compt. rend.*, **139**, 674 (1904); Pickard and Kenyon, *J. Chem. Soc.*, **89**, 262 (1906). *Cf.* Michael and Wegner, *Ber.*, **48**, 316 (1915); Kosolapoff, *J. Am. Chem. Soc.*, **64**, 2982 (1942); **71**, 369 (1949); **72**, 5508 (1950).
366. Gilman and Robinson, *Rec. trav. chim.*, **48**, 328 (1929).
367. Gilman and Robinson, *l.c.*, Gilman, *J. Am. Chem. Soc.*, **48**, 1063 (1926).
368. Auger and Billy, *Compt. rend.*, **139**, 597 (1904); Zappi, *Bull. soc. chim.*, (4) **23**, 322 (1918).
369. Grüttner and Krause, *Ber.*, **49**, 437 (1916); Zappi, *Bull. soc. Chim.*, *(4)* **19**, 290 (1916); Steinkopf *et al.*, *Ber.*, **55**, 2610 (1922); Grüttner and Wiernick,*ibid.*, **48**, 1473 (1915).
370. Lewis *et al.*, *J. Am. Chem. Soc.*, **43**, 891 (1921); Seide and Gorski, *Ber.*, **62**, 2186 (1929); Aeschlimann, *J. Chem. Soc.*, **1929**, 413.
371. *Cf.* Bertheim, *Handbuch d. organischen Arsenverbindungen* (1913), Chemie in Einzeldarstellung, Vol. IV.
372. Gryszkiewicz-Trochimovski, *Roczniki Chem.*, **6**, 794 (1926); **8**, 250 (1928); Blicke and Smith, *J. Chem. Soc.*, **51**, 1558 (1929); Sachs and Kantorowicz, *Ber.*, **41**, 2167 (1908).
373. Blicke and Smith, *J. Chem. Soc.*, **51**, 3479 (1929).
374. Gilman and Robinson, *Rec. trav. chim.*, **48**, 328 (1929).
375. Blicke and Oneto, *J. Am. Chem. Soc.*, **57**, 749 (1935).
376. Auger and Billy, *Compt. rend.*, **139**, 597 (1904); Hibbert, *Ber.*, **39**, 160 (1906); Morgan and Micklethwait, *J. Chem. Soc.*, **99**, 2286 (1911); Goddard, *ibid.*, **123**, 1161 (1923); Dyke *et al.*, *ibid.*, **1930**, 463; Seifter, *J. Am. Chem. Soc.*, **61**, 530 (1939).
377. Grüttner and Viernick, *Ber.*, **48**, 1759 (1915); Ingold *et al.*, *J. Chem. Soc.*, **1928**, 1280.
378. Morgan and Davies, *Proc. Roy. Soc.*, (London) Series A, **127**, 1 (1930).
379. Kipping, *Proc. Chem. Soc.*, **20**, 15 (1904); Dilthey, *Ber.*, **37**, 319 *Anm.*, 2 (1904).
380. Cusa and Kipping, *J. Chem. Soc.*, **1933**, 1040; Schumb and Saffer, *J. Am. Chem. Soc.*, **61**, 363 (1939).
381. Bygdén *Ber.*, **44**, 2640 (1911); Kipping *et al.*, *J. Chem. Soc.*, **1927**, 2734; **1930**, 1020; **101**, 2108 (1912); **123**, 2830 (1923); **93**, 439 (1908); **95**, 302 (1909); Gilliam *et al.*, *J. Am. Chem. Soc.*, **63**, 801 (1941); Melzer, *Ber.*, **41**, 3390 (1908); Dilthey and Eduardoff, *ibid.*, **37**, 1139 (1904); Dilthey, *ibid.*, **38**, 4132 (1905); Krause and Renwanz, *Ber.*, **62**, 1711 (1929); Schumb and Saffer, *J. Am. Chem. Soc.*, **61**, 363 (1939).
382. Kipping *et al.*, *J. Chem. Soc.*, **91**, 209 (1907); **93**, 198 (1908); **97**, 142 (1910); **99**, 138 (1911); **1929**, 357; Bygdén, *Ber.*, **44**, 2640 (1910); Martin, *ibid.*, **45**, 403 (1912); Giliam *et al.*, *J. Am. Chem. Soc.*, **63**, 801 (1941).
383. Bygdén, *Ber.*, **45**, 707 (1912); Kipping, *J. Chem. Soc.*, **123**, 2598 (1923); Martin, *Ber.*, **46**, 3289 (1913).
384. Reynolds *et al.*, *J. Am. Chem. Soc.*, **51**, 3067 (1929).
385. Grüttner and Wiernik, *Ber.*, **48**, 1474 (1915); Bygdén, *ibid.*, **48**, 1238, 1936 (1915); *Z. physiol. Chem.*, **90**, 246 (1915).
386. Martin, *Ber.*, **45**, 2097 (1912).
387. Gierut *et al.*, *J. Am. Chem. Soc.*, **58**, 897 (1936); Medokss, *J. Russ. Phys.-Chem. Soc.*, **8**, (70) 291 (1938); Medokss and Kolelkow, *ibid.*, **7**, (69) 2007 (1937); Manukin and Jakubowa, *ibid.*, **10**, (72), 1300 (1930); Schumb *et al.*, *J. Am. Chem. Soc.*, **60**, 2486 (1938).
388. Ssosstwenskaja, *J. Russ. Phys.-Chem. Soc.*, **8**, (70) 294 (1938).
389. Khotinsky and Seregenkoff, *Ber.*, **41**, 2946 (1908); Khotinsky, *ibid.*, **42**, 3088 (1909); Gilman, *J. Am. Chem. Soc.*, **48**, 1063 (1926); Post and Hofrichter, *J. Org. Chem.*, **4**, 363 (1939).
390. Post and Hofrichter, *J. Org. Chem.*, **4**, 363 (1939).
391. Andrianow and Gribanowa, *J. Russ. Phys.-Chem. Soc.*, **8**, (70), 552, 558 (1938); Kalinin, *Compt. rend. acad. Sci. (U.R.S.S.)* **26**, 365 (1940).
392. Volnov and Reutt, *J. Gen. Chem.*, *(U.S.S.R.)*, **10**, 1600 (1940).

393. Johnson *et al.*, *J. Am. Chem. Soc.*, **60**, 115 (1938); Krause *et al.*, *Ber.*, **54**, 2784 (1921); **55**, 1261 (1922); **59**, 777 (1926); **61**, 271 (1928); **63**, 934 (1930). *Cf.* Strecker, *ibid.*, **43**, 1131 (1910).
394. French and Fine, *J. Am. Chem. Soc.*, **60**, 352 (1938); Khotinsky and Melamed, *Ber.*, **42**, 3090 (1909); Johnson *et al.*, *J. Am. Chem. Soc.*, **60**, 105, 111 (1938); König and Scharrnbeck, *J. prakt. Chem.*, (2) **128**, 153 (1930); Milnikow and Rokitzkaja, *J. Russ. Phys.-Chem. Soc.*, **8**, (70), 1768 (1938); **7**, (69), 1472 (1937).
395. *Cf. also* Gilman *et al.*, *J. Am. Chem. Soc.*, **48**, 1063 (1926).
396. Pletz, *Compt. rend., Acad. Sci. U.R.S.S.*, **20**, 27 (1938).
397. Grüttner, *Ber.*, **47**, 3257 (1914).
398. Grüttner, Krause and Wiernik, *ibid.*, **50**, 1549 (1917). *Cf. German patent* 313,878 (1919).
399. Grüttner and Wiernik, *Ber.*, **48**, 1484 (1915). *German patent* 313,876 (1919).
400. Rowland *et al.*, *Abstracts of 117th meeting of ACS 1950*.
401. Oddo, *Gazz. chim. ital.*, **34**, (1), 429 (1904); **38**, (1), 625 (1908); Salkind and Rosenfeld, *Ber.*, **57**, 1690 (1924).
402. Fuson, *J. Org. Chem.*, **10**, 551 (1945).
403. Conant and Blatt, *J. Am. Chem. Soc.*, **51**, 1227 (1929); Whitmore and George, *ibid.*, **64**, 1240 (1942); Blicke and Powers, *ibid.*, **51**, 3378 (1929). *Cf.* Moersch and Whitmore, *ibid.*, **71**, 819 (1949); Nasarow, *Ber.*, **69 B**, 23 (1936); Kohler and Tishler, *J. Am. Chem. Soc.*, **54**, 1594 (1932); Fuson *et al.*, *ibid.*, **54**, 3665 (1932); Allen and Gates, *ibid.*, **64**, 2127 (1942).
404. Kayser, *Ann. chim.*, (11) **6**, 155, 188, 238 (1936); Ramart-Lucas and Salmon-Legagneur, *Bull. soc. chim.*, (4) **51**, 1078 (1932).
405. Fuson and Speck, *J. Am. Chem. Soc.*, **64**, 2446 (1942); Richtzenhain, *Ber.*, **77B**, 409 (1944); Fuson *et al.*, *J. Org. Chem.*, **13**, 489 (1948).
406. Kohler and Nygaard, *J. Am. Chem. Soc.*, **52**, 4128 (1930).
407. Allen and Gilman, *J. Am. Chem. Soc.*, **58**, 937 (1936); Dufraisse and Horlois, *Bull. soc. chim.*, (5) **3**, 1894 (1936).
408. Allen and Bell, *J. Am. Chem. Soc.*, **64**, 1253 (1942).
409. Koelsch and Rosenwald, *J. Org. Chem.*, **3**, 462 (1938). *Cf.* Koelsch and Anthes, *ibid.*, **6**, 558 (1941); Geissman and Morris, *J. Am. Chem. Soc.*, **66**, 716 (1944).
410. Fuson *et al.*, *J. Org. Chem.*, **6**, 845 (1941).
411. Lutz and Reveley, *J. Am. Chem. Soc.*, **63**, 3178 (1941).
412. Fuson *et al.*, *J. Org. Chem.*, **7**, 297 (1942); *J. Am. Chem. Soc.*, **64**, 1450, 2573 (1942).
413. Julian *et al.*, *J. Am. Chem. Soc.*, **57**, 1607 (1935); **56**, 2174 (1934). *Cf.* Fuson *et al.*, *ibid.*, **65**, 60 (1943); **71**, 2543 (1949); *J. Org. Chem.*, **13**, 496 (1948).
414. Clarke and Carleton, *J. Am. Chem. Soc.*, **33**, 1966 (1911).
415. *Cf.* Hussey, *ibid.*, **73**, 1364 (1951).
416. Oddo, *Gazz. chim. ital.*, **41**, 1, 255 (1911).
417. Bodroux, *Compt. rend.*, **137**, 710 (1903).
418. Fuson *et al.*, *J. Org. Chem.*, **16**, 648 (1951).
419. Frank and Weatherbee, *J. Am. Chem. Soc.*, **70**, 3482 (1948).
420. Kharasch *et al.*, *ibid.*, **60**, 2004 (1938). *Cf.* Hey and Water, *Chem. Revs.*, **21**, 169 (1937).
421. Bergmann and Rosenthal, *J. prakt. Chem.*, (2) **135**, 267 (1932).
422. Whitmore *et al.*, *J. Am Chem. Soc.*, **63**, 643 (1941).
423. Grignard *et al.*, *Bull. soc. chim.*, (4) **43**, 141 (1928).
424. Lespieau and Dupont, *ibid.*, (4) **1**, 4 (1907); *Ann. chim.*, (9) **2**, 280 (1914).
425. Grignard and Courtot, *Bull. soc. chim.*, (4) **17**, 228 (1915); Perrichon, *Thesis*, Lyon, 1925.
426. Sheverdina and Kocheshkov, *J. Gen. Chem. U.S.S.R.*, **8**, 1825 (1938). *Cf.* Jones, *J. Chem. Soc.*, **1946**, 781; Traube *et al.*, *Ber.*, **53**, 1477 (1920). Sheverdina and Kocheshkov, *Bull. acad. sci. U.R.S.S., Classe. sci. chim.*, **1941**, 75; *C.A.*, **37**, 3066 (1943).
427. Rosenheim and Singer, *Ber.*, **37**, 2152 (1904); Oddo, *Gazz. chim. ital.*, **41**, 1, 11 (1911); *C.A.*, **5**, 2635 (1911).
428. Strecker, *ibid.*, **43**, 1131 (1910).
429. Kipping and Hackford, *J. Chem. Soc.*, **99**, 140 (1911).
430. Schlenk and Schlenk, *Ber.*, **62 B**, 920 (1929). *Cf.* Cope, *J. Am. Chem. Soc.*, **57**, 2238 (1933).
431. Whitmore *et al.*, *J. Am. Chem. Soc.*, **54**, 3714 (1932); **55**, 1559 (1933); **60**, 2028 (1938); Gilman and Zoelbner, *ibid.*, **50**, 425 (1928); *Rec. trav. chim.*, **47**, 1058 (1928); Rheinboldt *et al.*, *J. prakt. Chem.*, (2) **134**, 257 (1933).
432. Andrianov and Gribanova, *J. Gen. Chem. (U.S.S.R.)* **8**, 552 (1938); *C.A.*, **32**, 7892 (1938).
433. Gaertner, *J. Am. Chem. Soc.*, **73**, 4400 (1951).
434. Pierce and Levene, *ibid.*, **75**, 1254 (1953); McBee *et al.*, *ibid.*, **75**, 2516 (1953); Haszeldine, *ibid.*, **75**, 3607 (1953).
435. Franke and Kuhn, *Monatsh.*, **25**, 865 (1904).
436. Henry, *Compt. rend.*, **145**, 21 (1907).
437. Kharasch and Tawney, *J. Am. Chem. Soc.*, **63**, 2308 (1941); Birch and Robinson, *J. Chem. Soc.*, **1943**, 501; Ruzicka *et al.*, *Helv. Chim. Acta*, **31**, 241 (1948); Stoll and Commarmont, *ibid.*, **31**, 554 (1948).

438. Lipp and Quaedvlieg, *Ber.*, **62 B**, 2311 (1929); Fuson *et al.*, *J. Org. Chem.*, **6**, 845 (1941); **7**, 297 (1942); **13**, 496 (1948); *J. Am. Chem. Soc.*, **67**, 597 (1945); Gaertner, *Chem. Revs.*, **45**, 493 (1949).
439. Fuson *et al.*, *J. Am. Chem. Soc.*, **65**, 60 (1943); **71**, 2542 (1949); *J. Org. Chem.*, **13**, 496 (1948).
440. Conant and Blatt, *J. Am. Chem. Soc.*, **51**, 1227 (1929); Ivanoff and Spasoff, *Bull. soc. chim.*, (4) **49**, 375 (1931); Shivers *et al.*, *J. Am. Chem. Soc.*, **65**, 2051 (1943); Zook *et al.*, *ibid.*, **68**, 2404 (1946); Spielman and Schmidt, *ibid.*, **70**, 606 (1948).
441. Petrov *et al.*, *Bull. soc. chim.*, (5) **3**, 169 (1936); *J. Gen. Chem.*, *(U.S.S.R.)*, **8**, 199 (1938); *C.A.*, **32**, 5376 (1938); *Sci. Records. Gorky State Univ.*, No. 7, 3, 14 (1939); *C.A.*, **35**, 435 (1941); **37**, 1379 (1943).
442. Whitmore and Wheeler, *J. Am. Chem. Soc.*, **60**, 2899 (1938).
443. Fuson *et al.*, *ibid.*, **59**, 1508 (1937); **60**, 2269 (1938); Whitmore, and Lewis, *ibid.*, **64**, 1618 (1942).
444. Fuson and Corse, *ibid.*, **60**, 2063 (1938).
445. Kitchin and Sandin, *ibid.*, **67**, 1645 (1945). *Cf.* Weizmann *et al.*, *J. Chem. Soc.*, **1935**, 1370.
446. Jegrowa, *J. Russ. Phys.-Chem. Soc.*, **46**, 1319 (1914); *Chem. Zentr.*, **1915 I**, 1055; Eidus *et al.*, *Bull. acad. sci. U.R.S.S. Classe sci. chim.*, **1945**, 672; *C.A.*, **42**, 5838 (1948); Fries and Schimmelschmidt, *Ber.*, **58 B**, 2835 (1925); Fieser *et al.*, *J. Am. Chem. Soc.*, **58**, 1055 (1936); Arnold *et al.*, *ibid.*, **63**, 3444 (1941); Dauben *et al.*, *Anal. Chem.*, **19**, 8281 (1947); *J. Am. Chem. Soc.*, **69**, 1389 (1947); *J. Org. Chem.*, **13**, 313 (1948); Hussey, *J. Am. Chem. Soc.*, **73**, 1364 (1951).
447. Billman and Smith, *ibid.*, **61**, 457 (1939); **74**, 3174 (1952).
448. Sou Phou Ti, *Compt. rend.*, **192**, 1462 (1931).
449. Maxim and Andreeseu, *Bull. soc. chim.*, (5) **5**, 54 (1938).
450. Bourgom, *Bull. soc. chim. Belg.*, **33**, 101 (1924).
451. Rondou, *ibid.*, **31**, 397 (1922); Bruylants, *Bull. acad. roy. Belg. Classe Sci.*, (5) **8**, 7 (1922); *Chem. Zentr.*, **1923 I**, 85.
452. Majima and Hoshino, *Ber.*, **58 B**, 2042 (1925); Akbori and Saitu, *ibid.*, **63 B**, 2245 (1930).
453. Kharasch *et al.*, *J. Chem. Education*, **5**, 404 (1928); **8**, 1703 (1931); **11**, 82 (1934); **13**, 7 (1936).
454. Kharasch and Weinhouse, *J. Org. Chem.*, **1**, 209 (1936).
455. Lowenbein and Rosenbaum, *Ann.*, **448**, 223 (1926).
456. Häller and Schaffer, *J. Am. Chem. Soc.*, **61**, 2175 (1939).
457. Richtzenhein, *Ber.*, **77 B**, 1 (1944); Richtzenhein and Nippus, *ibid.*, **77 B**, 566 (1944); Fuson *et al.*, *J. Org. Chem.*, **13**, 484, 489, 496 (1948); **16**, 631, 643 (1951); *J. Am. Chem. Soc.*, **64**, 2446 (1942); **71**, 2543 (1949).
458. Malateska, *Gazz. chim. ital.*, **76**, 167 (1946); **77**, 509 (1947); *C.A.*, **41**, 2012 (1947); **42**, 541 (1948).
459. Werner and Zilkens, *Ber.*, **36**, 2116 (1903); Houben, *ibid.*, **36**, 3083 (1903).
460. Suter and Gerhart, *J. Am. Chem. Soc.*, **57**, 107 (1935); Cope, *ibid.*, **56**, 1578 (1934).
461. Gilman and Kirby, *ibid.*, **48**, 1733 (1926).
462. Suter and Gerhart, *J. Am. Chem. Soc.*, **57**, 107 (1935); Kenyon *et al.*, *J. Chem. Soc.*, **127**, 399 (1925); **1935**, 1072; Gilman and Heck, *J. Am. Chem. Soc.*, **50**, 2223 (1928); Rossander and Marvel, *ibid.*, **50**, 1491 (1928).
463. Strecker, *Ber.*, **43**, 1131 (1910); Bert, *Compt. rend.*, **178**, 1826 (1924); Gilman *et al.*, *J. Am. Chem. Soc.*, **48**, 2715 (1926); **45**, 839 (1923); *Bull. soc. chim.*, (4) **45**, 636 (1929).
464. Gilman *et al.*, *J. Am. Chem. Soc.*, **47**, 851 (1925).
465. Hilleman, *Ber.*, **71 B**, 42 (1938); McElvain, *J. Chem. Soc.*, **1937**, 1704.
466. Aston *et al.*, *J. Am. Chem. Soc.*, **56**, 1163 (1934).
467. Short and Watt, *J. Chem. Soc.*, **1930**, 2293; Montagne, *Compt. rend.*, **199**, 671 (1934). *Cf.* Plancher and Ravenna, *Atti. accad. Lincei*, (5) **15**, 11, 555 (1906); *Chem. Zentr.*, **1907 I**, 111.
468. Reiber and Stewart, *J. Am. Chem. Soc.*, **62**, 3026 (1940).
469. *Cf.* Gilman *et al.*, *ibid.*, **47**, 2406 (1925); *Rec. trav. chim.*, **49**, 212, (1930); *J. Org. Chem.*, **2**, 84 (1937).
470. Stollé and Reichert, *J. prakt. Chem.*, (2) **122**, 344 (1929).
471. Grammaticakis, *Compt. rend.*, **228**, 323 (1949). *Cf.* Biquard, *Bull. soc. chim.*, (5) **3**, 656, 666 (1936); (5) **5**, 207 (1938).
472. Hepworth, *J. Chem. Soc.*, **119**, 251 (1921).
473. Hepworth, *ibid.*, **117**, 1004 (1920); Oddo, *Gazz. chim. ital.*, **41 I**, 273 (1911); Gilman and Heck, *Rec. trav. chim.*, **50**, 522 (1931).
474. Buckley, *J. Chem. Soc.*, **1947**, 1494; Buckley and Ellery, *ibid.*, **1947**, 1497.
475. Sursanov and Solodkov, *J. Gen. Chem.*, *(U.S.S.R.)*, **5**, 1487 (1935); *C.A.*, **30**, 2181 (1936). *Cf.* Gilman and McCracken, *J. Am. Chem. Soc.*, **49**, 1052 (1927).
476. Hepworth and Clapham, *J. Chem. Soc.*, **119**, 1188 (1921); Gilman *et al.*, *J. Am. Chem. Soc.*, **48**, 2715 (1926).

477. *Cf.* Wuyts *et al.*, *Bull. soc. chim. Belg.*, **38**, 194 (1929); **39**, 58 (1930); **40**, 665 (1931); **41**, 196 (1932).
478. Grignard and Zorn, *Compt. rend.*, **150**, 1177 (1910); Hepworth and Clapham, *J. Chem. Soc.*, **119**, 1185 (1921); Wildi *et al.*, *J. Am. Chem. Soc.*, **73**, 1965 (1951); *Cf.* Kohler and Potter, *ibid.*, **57**, 1316 (1935).
479. Peroni and Coli, *Gazz. chim. ital.*, **44 II**, 349 (1914); *Chem. Zentr.*, **1915 I**, 730.
480. Lederer, *Compt. rend.*, **151**, 611 (1911); *Ber.*, **49**, 1071, 1076, 1385, 1615, 2002, 2529, 2533, 2663 (1916); **50**, 238 (1917); **52**, 1989 (1919); **53**, 1430, 1674, 2342 (1920).

CHAPTER 13

FRIEDEL–CRAFTS REACTION

Discovered through an accidental observation that amyl chloride reacted with benzene in the presence of metallic aluminum to form a substituted benzene, Friedel-Crafts reaction has become one of the most important synthetic methods in organic chemistry. It consists essentially in the combination of an organic residue with the group R of a halo compound RX under the influence of aluminum chloride:

$$C_6H_6 + RX \xrightarrow{AlCl_3} C_6H_5R + HX$$

The basic condition for the condensation is the formation of a tertiary compound with the halide, which is in the nature of a solvate of the pseudo-salt of the aluminum chloride with the organic halide, that adds to the organic body. The reaction completes itself within the complex; the complex decomposes into the organic halide and aluminum chloride, and recombination of the latter takes place with more of the halide.[1] The reaction is applicable in general to aromatic hydrocarbons and their derivatives, and to alkyl and acyl halides.

REACTIONS INVOLVING ALIPHATIC HALO COMPOUNDS

The condensation of alkyl chlorides with benzene or its homologs in the presence of aluminum chloride results in the formation of an alkylated derivative of the hydrocarbon. The reaction proceeds with varying degrees of ease, depending on the character of the halide, compounds with a mobile halogen reacting most readily. The reaction is retarded or inhibited by negative substituents, such as halogens or nitro groups in the aromatic compound, the effect being the more pronounced the greater the number of such substituents. Alkyl groups, on the other hand, cause an increase in the reactivity of the aromatic compound. The activating power of various groups or elements, arranged in descending order, is as follows:

HO, CH_3O, $(CH_3)_2N$, CH_3, H, Cl, Br, I, OCH, CH_3CO, ROCO, NO_2, CN

The introduction of activating groups, CH_3O for example, may render an inactive compound, such as a nitrated aromatic hydrocarbon, capable of reaction. Alkylation proceeds most readily with tertiary halides, and least readily with primary halides. Benzyl halides are of the same order of reactivity as tertiary halides.

The reactivity of various halogens in alkylation reactions decreases in the order[2] fluorine, chlorine, bromine and iodine,(*) which is the reverse of the normal order of reactivity of these elements.

As a consequence of the activating influence of alkyl groups, reaction with alkyl halides may result in the formation of a mixture of mono-, di-, and poly-substituted products. It is often quite difficult to separate the individual compounds from such mixtures.

The reactivity of various cyclic compounds, arranged in descending order, is as follows: pyrrole, furan, thiophene, anthracene, naphthalene, tetralin, pyridine.[1] Amino furans are less reactive than aromatic amines.

All six of the hydrogen atoms in benzene are replaceable with methyl, ethyl and *n*-propyl groups, but a maximum of four isopropyl groups or three *tert*-butyl groups can enter the nucleus.

All aromatic hydrocarbons and most heterocyclic compounds, especially thiophene, furan and pyrrole, react well. Pyridine is resistant. Phenols, phenol ethers, substituted amines also react readily. An ester group in the nucleus hinders the reaction, though α-naphthoic acid ester may be alkylated. Many polynuclear hydrocarbons and heterocyclic compounds do not give satisfactory results in alkylation reactions because of too high a degree of reactivity. Deactivating groups, rendering such compounds less reactive, may make possible a smooth reaction, giving satisfactory yields of alkylated products. This is the case, for example, with carboxylated furans.

One or more halogen atoms in di- or polyhalo aliphatic hydrocarbons may be replaced by aromatic groups, depending on the conditions. Ring formation may also occur with these compounds. Of particular interest is the reaction of di- and trihalomethanes with aromatic compounds in the presence of aluminum chloride. Dichloromethane yields diarylmethanes and anthracene derivatives with aromatic compounds:[3]

$$H_2CCl_2 + 2\ C_6H_6 \rightarrow CH_2(C_6H_5)_2 + 2HCl$$

$$H_2CCl_2 + CH_2(C_6H_5)_2 \rightarrow C_6H_4\begin{matrix} CH_2 \\ \\ CH_2 \end{matrix}C_6H_4 + 2HCl$$

Anthracene is formed through the reduction of the dihydroanthracene in the course of the reaction. Tri- and tetraphenylmethanes result through the reaction of chloroform and carbon tetrachloride with benzene;[4] tetraphenylethylene is also obtained with the former.[5] Carbon tetrachloride reacts with benzene to form, first, dichlorodiphenylmethane and on further reaction, triphenylchloromethane.[6] Analogous products are obtained from homologs of benzene. The dichloro product obtained with toluene decomposes violently when the compound is subjected to distillation. Reaction with xylene results in partial resinification.

(*) The order of reactivity in acylation reactions is the reverse of this.

The dealkylating effect of aluminum chloride may be effectively utilized in the preparation of monoalkylated aromatic compounds by diluting the mixture of mono-, di- and polyalkylated products resulting from the normal Friedel-Crafts reaction with benzene, and heating under reflux after the addition of aluminum chloride.

Rearrangement is also induced by aluminum chloride in aromatic halo compounds.[7] Thus, bromobenzene is partially converted to benzene and dibromobenzene; diiodobenzene and benzene similarly result from iodobenzene, while chlorobenzene remains unaffected.

The reaction of *aralkyl halides* with aromatic compounds in the presence of aluminum chloride generally proceeds in a satisfactory manner, benzyl chloride yielding with benzene diphenylmethane and a little anthracene.[8] p-Chloromethyldiphenylmethane is obtained when this reaction is carried out in nitrobenzene.[9] Benzyl chloride polymerizes in contact with aluminum chloride. It would appear that the aromatic group in aralkyl halides reacts with aluminum chloride to form a complex, thus inducing a greater activity in the chlorine of the side chain.

The condensation of *m*-bis(bromomethyl)benzene with benzene takes an unexpected course, giving principally diphenylmethane.[10] The probable course of the reaction appears to be as follows:

$$2C_6H_6 + BrCH_2C_6H_4CH_2Br \rightarrow HBr + (C_6H_5)_2CH_2 + C_6H_5CH_2Br$$

$$\xrightarrow{C_6H_6} 2(C_6H_5)_2CH_2$$

Both chlorine atoms in *benzal chloride* and its homologs are replaceable with aromatic residues. *Benzotrichloride,* $C_6H_5CCl_3$, reacts with benzene in the presence of aluminum chloride to form triphenylmethane.[11]

A halogen atom directly attached to the aromatic nucleus cannot, in general, be replaced with aromatic groups through Friedel-Crafts reaction. Condensation takes place, however, when the halogen is sufficiently labile. The reactivity of the halogen increases with increase in the "aromaticity" of the hydrocarbon. *Fluorine* in the ring is more reactive than bromine or chlorine.

When the method is applied to bromo phenols, and in particular to tribromophenol, in reaction with aromatic hydrocarbons, transfer of a bromine atom from the phenol to the aromatic hydrocarbon may occur, the reaction proceeding with vigor. Bromobenzene and bromotoluene result in good yield with benzene and toluene.[12] Perylene may be chlorinated by this method, but cannot be brominated.[13] The reaction proceeds best with a catalyst containing appreciable quantities of ferric chloride.

Preparation of Aluminum Chloride

The aluminum chloride may be prepared directly from metallic aluminum and gaseous hydrogen chloride; or the commercial product may be employed after it is purified by sublimation. Sublimation is carried out by passing the vapors of aluminum chloride through a tube 40 cm long and 2 cm diameter filled with clean, fat-free pieces of aluminum.[14] A satisfactory product should be granular and have the appearance of amber. White, or nearly white pieces are partially decomposed by atmospheric moisture and should not, in general, be used.

A highly reactive catalyst may be prepared by proceeding in the following manner: Five grams of aluminum powder, 1 gram of mercuric chloride and 0.5 gram of iodine are placed in benzene, and the liquid is heated to boiling, under reflux, while a current of dry hydrogen chloride is conducted through it until the color of iodine disappears and no more hydrogen is evolved.[15]

Procedure

The general procedure in carrying out the Friedel-Crafts reaction is as follows: The aluminum chloride is rapidly added to a small amount of the inert solvent to be used in a reaction flask protected from atmospheric moisture with a calcium chloride tube. The mass is agitated and a mixture of the halide, hydrocarbon and the solvent is added from a dropping funnel in small portions, at such a rate that no large excess of the unreacted halide is present at any time. After the addition of the halide-hydrocarbon mixture, the flask is heated on a water bath until the evolution of hydrogen chloride ceases. Heating for a longer period than is required for the completion of the reaction should be avoided. The usual time of heating is 12 to 15 hours. After completion of the reaction, the mixture is cooled and water is added carefully, with constant agitation, until decomposition is complete. Some hydrochloric acid is then added in order to bring all the aluminum compounds into solution, the organic layer is separated, washed with dilute sodium hydroxide solution and water, dried and fractionally distilled.

The use of a solvent may be dispensed with in many cases. For example, in alkylating benzene or its homologs, a satisfactory procedure is to add the halide or the solution of the halide in the hydrocarbon, gradually, over a period of one hour or longer, to a mixture of the hydrocarbon and aluminum chloride placed in the reaction vessel. Vigorous agitation is essential for satisfactory results.[16] A large excess of the hydrocarbon is used to avoid the formation of polysubstitution products. The use of a five-fold excess generally gives satisfactory results. It is important, of course, that the reagents be *dry*.

In special cases the use of an excess of the aromatic compound is not required. Thus, in preparing *tert*-butylphenol approximately equimolecular quantities of *tert*-butyl chloride and phenol are allowed to react at 5°C in the presence of a quantity of aluminum chloride amounting to about 1% of the weight of the phenol used. The mass is then gradually heated to 100° and is maintained at this temperature until the reaction is complete. It is then cooled somewhat and is washed with 4% of its weight of 50% aqueous sodium carbonate suspension, filtered and distilled, whereupon 4-*tert*-butylphenol is obtained in about 70% of theoretical yield. Only about 1% of the 2-isomer and 7% of the 2,4-disubstituted phenol is formed in the reaction.

An interesting modification of the procedure is exemplified by the preparation of *tert*-butylphenol directly from *isobutylene*. This gas is passed through a solution of the phenol in CCl_4 containing aluminum chloride and a small quantity of *tert*-butyl chloride.

The latter serves to initiate the reaction, and the hydrogen chloride formed reacts with the olefin added to form more *tert*-butyl chloride.[17]

The reaction of aromatic compounds with organic halides in the presence of aluminum chloride is reversible, the hydrogen chloride formed in the reaction tending to decompose the condensation product:

$$RR' + HCl \rightleftarrows RCl + R'H$$

For this reason, the acid formed must be removed as rapidly as possible.

The quantity of catalyst required for alkylation reactions is generally quite small, the use of about one-tenth molal fraction often giving satisfactory results. The amount of catalyst necessary for successful reaction in any given case is best determined by preliminary experiments. In the alkylation of *furans* a molecular equivalent of the catalyst must be used.

Polysubstituted derivatives are obtained by using the required excess of alkyl chloride and a larger amount of catalyst. Proper regulation of temperature becomes of importance then, because of the tendency of the aluminum chloride catalyst to cause *meta* substitution under forced conditions, while normally under mild conditions the second alkyl group enters the *para* position. *Meta* substitution is favored when a large excess of the catalyst is used and the reaction time is extended. Thus, 1,3,5-triethylbenzene may be obtained in 85% yield from benzene and ethyl bromide by using 3.3 molal proportions of ethyl bromide with 2 molal equivalents of aluminum chloride, and allowing the reaction mixture to stand at 0 to 25° for 24 hours.(*)

The results obtained in the Friedel-Crafts reaction may depend to a large extent on the quality of the catalyst employed.[18] While pure, anhydrous aluminum chloride usually gives the best results, the commercial grade of the compound has often been known to give better results. It has also been the experience of many investigators that aluminum chloride which has been kept for a time gives better results than the wholly anhydrous product. The reaction of stilbene bromide with benzene takes place best in the presence of aluminum chloride which has been previously exposed to atmospheric humidity for one or two hours. The introduction of a little moisture seems to exert a favorable effect in many other instances. It is desirable to carry out preliminary tests to determine whether the entirely anhydrous product, or aluminum chloride exposed to atmospheric moisture gives the best results in any particular case. In some instances, the addition of some aluminum hydroxide dried at 130° is beneficial. The catalyst may also be partially deactivated by nitrobenzene, benzophenone or acetone for the purpose of improving its effect.[19]

Occasionally the results obtained with anhydrous aluminum chloride may differ from those obtained by use of the hydrated product. Thus, benzene and trichloracetyl chloride give the compound $(C_6H_5)_2C = C(OH)C_6H_5$ or its isomer, $(C_6H_5)_2CHCOC_6H_5$ when anhydrous aluminum chloride is used, but when moist,

(*) When the *para*-substituted derivative is desired gaseous boron trifluoride is employed as a catalyst, and the reaction is carried out at 60°.

somewhat sticky chloride is used, ω-trichloroacetophenone results in moderate yield.

The presence of ferric chloride in the aluminum chloride is of advantage in alkylation reactions. Thus, the reaction of benzyl chloride and toluene proceeds more readily with aluminum chloride containing ferric chloride, the reactivity increasing with increase in ferric chloride up to a point where a half molal excess of this compound is present.[20] The reaction of chloroform with benzene is also favored by the presence of ferric chloride in the aluminum chloride.[21]

The *solvents* generally used in carrying out the reaction include carbon disulfide, nitrobenzene, and petroleum ether. Diethyl ether and other ethers cannot be used since these compounds take part in the reaction. Nitrobenzene and other nitrated aromatic hydrocarbons present the advantage that they dissolve the aluminum chloride complexes formed in the course of the reaction.

Use of Catalysts other than Aluminum Chloride

Many halides have been tested as catalysts for the Friedel-Crafts type reactions. The use of aluminum bromide involves the disadvantage of greater ease of decomposition. Ferric chloride may be used to advantage in certain cases,[22] although oxidation and chlorination reactions also often take place when this compound is used as a catalyst. Stannic chloride, a milder catalyst, is suitable for certain reactions. Sodium aluminofluoride and zirconium chloride[23] seem to be active catalysts.

Beryllium dichloride, boron trifluoride, tetrachlorides of titanium, zirconium, hafnium and thallium, and pentachlorides of neobium and tantalum are effective catalysts. Tantalum pentachloride is as active as aluminum chloride. Beryllium dichloride is effective only at comparatively high temperatures. The use of other metal halides has also been investigated.[24]

Position of Entrance of Alkyl Groups

Substituents already present in the aromatic nucleus usually exert their normal orienting influence in the Friedel-Crafts reaction. Thus, hydroxy, alkoxy, aryloxy, methyl, amino, chloromethyl, diphenyl and benzyl groups and halogens generally exert an *ortho-para*-directing influence. On the other hand, formyl, carboxyl, nitro, dichloromethyl and keto groups exert a *meta*-directing influence. *Para*-substituted compounds are the normal products when two alkyl groups enter the benzene nucleus, but *meta*-substituted compounds are often obtained under forced conditions. Alkylation of *meta*-xylene results in the formation of the 1,3,5-compound.[25] Hydroquinone dimethyl ether gives with ethyl chloracetate, the dimethyl ether of homogentisic acid, $(CH_3O)_2C_6H_3CH_2COOH$, saponification of the ester taking place in the course of the reaction.[26]

The formation of *alkylnaphthalenes* does not proceed smoothly. Ethyl halides and their immediate homologs yield a mixture of alkylnaphthalene, with the β-compound predominating. The product always contains β,β-dinaphthyl and a compound of unknown structure resulting from the action of aluminum chloride on naphthalene. β-Methylnaphthalene is substituted principally in the 6-position. Friedel-Crafts reaction with tetralin results exclusively in the formation of a β-substituted product.[27]

In the alkylation of *furan* derivatives, the entering alkyl group generally goes in the α-position if this position is available. In a disubstituted furan in which one substituent is an *ortho-para*-directing group while the other is *meta*-directing, the alkyl group generally enters the β-position contiguous to the *ortho-para*-directing group.[28] *Furoic esters* are readily alkylated by Friedel-Crafts method, the alkyl group entering the α-position.[29] In the reaction of *furfural* with isopropyl chloride, the alkyl group enters the 4-position,[30] while with butyl and amyl chlorides the reaction leads to substitution at the 5-position, normal-, iso- and *tert*-butyl chlorides all yielding 5-*tert*-butyl-2-furfural.

The entering positions of various halides into the nucleus of a number of cyclic compounds are indicated in the following table:

Alkyl Halide	Aromatic Compound	Position of Attachment of Entering Alkyl Group
$(CH_3)_2CHCl$	toluene	1, 3
CH_3Cl	*m*-xylene	5
"	*p*-xylene	2
"	*o*-xylene	4
"	1,2,4-trimethylbenzene	5
CH_3I	1,3,5-trimethylbenzene	2
n-C_4H_5Cl	toluene	3, 4
$\overline{CH_2(CH_2)_4CH}Cl$	chlorobenzene	4
$C_6H_5CH_2Cl$	resorcinol	4
"	2-chlorophenol	4, 6
"	4-chlorophenol	6
o-$ClC_6H_4CH_2Cl$	phenol	2, 4
"	2,6-dichlorophenol	4
m-$ClC_6H_4CH_2Cl$	phenol	4
"	2,6-dichlorophenol	4
p-$ClC_6H_4CH_2Cl$	phenol	4
"	2,6-dichlorophenol	4
$C_6H_5CH_2Cl$	1-benzylnaphthalene	8

Methyl chloride yields a mixture of isomeric mono-, di- and poly-substituted products; ethyl and isopropyl chlorides also give such a mixture of isomeric mono- and poly-substituted compounds.

Isomerization Induced During Friedel-Crafts Reaction

Alkyl halides may undergo rearrangement during Friedel-Crafts reaction, and generally become converted to the most highly branched isomer.[31] *n*-Propyl chloride, for example, undergoes isomerization, and is converted to isopropyl chloride under the influence of aluminum chloride. Similarly, *n*-butyl bromide is isomerized to *sec*-butyl chloride, and the latter to *tert*-butyl chloride. This fact may be explained by assuming that cleavage of hydrogen chloride takes place with the formation of an olefin, which reacts with the hydrogen chloride in accordance with Markownikow's rule to form the isomeric halide. Temperature is an important factor in this transformation.[32] Thus, while it is possible to obtain a 40% yield of *n*-propylbenzene from *n*-propyl chloride and benzene, if the reaction is carried out at −6°; at higher temperatures a large proportion of the isopropyl derivative is obtained.

Under vigorous conditions break-down of the carbon chain of the alkyl group may also take place. This occurs, for example, with *n*-octyl bromide, which when condensed with ethyl-5-bromo-2-furoate gives 4-*tert*-butyl-5-bromo-2-furoate in 46% yield. Similarly, the reaction of *n*-amyl bromide with ethyl-5-bromo-2-furoate results in the formation of ethyl-5-*tert*-butyl-2-furoate and 4-*tert*-butyl-5-bromo-2-furoate. In the alkylation of ethyl-4-bromofuroate with *n*-amyl chloride, the bromine is removed, and ethyl-5-*tert*-butyl-2-furoate results.

Alkyl groups of alkylated benzenes may also undergo rearrangement during Friedel-Crafts reaction.[33] Thus, 2,2-dimethyl-4-*n*-butylbenzene changes to 1,3-dimethyl-5-*sec*-butylbenzene, and 1,3-dimethyl-5-*sec*-butyl benzene is converted to 1,3-dimethyl-5-*tert*-butylbenzene under the action of aluminum chloride. Naphthalene undergoes condensation and decomposition under the influence of the catalyst; for this reason the alkylation of naphthalene may be successfully carried out only under very mild conditions.

Condensations of Benzene and its Derivatives with Various Types of Halo Compounds

The rules that hold in the condensation of alkyl halides with benzene and its derivatives have already been discussed. Reactions involving representative compounds from various classes of these compounds will now be considered.

5-*tert*-Butylxylene results through the interaction of isobutyl chloride with *m*-xylene. The compound serves as a starting point in the preparation of xylene musk, and is obtained in excellent yield by passing a stream of gaseous isobutylene through a mixture of *m*-xylene, anhydrous aluminum chloride and a little isobutyl chloride.[34] Phenol may be alkylated with butyl, isobutyl, or isoamyl chloride in the presence of an equimolecular amount of aluminum chloride. When carrying out condensations with phenols, the hydroxyl groups are protected by alkylation or carbomethoxylation.[394] The best yields, ranging up to 60%, are obtained in the absence of a solvent on heating at 110° for four to six hours. Some alkyl phenyl ethers are also formed in the reaction.[35] Careful control of temperature is necessary in order to obtain the desired isomer.[36] Thus, thymol is the main reaction product obtained from isopropyl chloride and *m*-cresol when the reaction is carried out at −10°, but isothymol results in almost quantitative yield when the reaction is conducted at 30 to 60°. Alkylated derivatives of *diphenyl ether* may be obtained by reaction with *sec*-butyl chloride at 100° for 2½ hours. The mono substituted product is formed in 71% yield, and the di- and tri-substituted derivatives in 24% and 5% yield respectively. *Dichlorophenyl ether* and *sec*-butyl chloride, reacting at 90-95° for less than one hour, give the mono-*tert*-butyl derivative in 52% yield, and the disubstituted derivative in 16% yield.[37] 3-Propylanisole is readily alkylated with *tert*-butyl chloride.[38] The alkylation of aromatic N-acylamides takes place readily, acetanilide giving *p*-*tert*-butylacetanilide in 94% yield with *tert*-butyl chloride.[39]

Ethylidene chloride, CH_3CHCl_2, reacting with benzene in the presence of aluminum chloride gives a *sym*-diphenylethane and 9,10-dihydro-9,10-dimethylanthracene.[40] The reaction of 2,2-dichloropropane with xylene results in the formation of 2,2-di-*m*-xylylpropane.[41] 1,1-Dichloroheptane gives *a,a*-diphenylheptane with benzene.[42] Di-*tert*-1,4-dichlorides condense with aromatic hydrocarbons to form ring systems, 2,5-dichloro-2,5-dimethylhexane giving with benzene 1,1,4,4-tetramethyl-1,2,3,4-tetrahydronaphthalene.[43] Phenols react similarly. Fluorene results through the reaction of *dichloromethane* with diphenyl;[44] on the other hand, dibromomethane reacting with mesitylene gives dimesitylmethane.[45] Reaction with pseudocumene proceeds with much greater difficulty.[46] Dichlorobenzenes condense normally with *chloroform* giving triarylmethanes.[47] *Carbon tetrachloride* gives with chlorobenzene 4,4′-dichlorobenzophenone chloride, $Cl_2C(C_6H_4Cl)_2$, together with some 2,4′-dichlorobenzophenone; the reaction proceeds well and in the same manner with bromobenzene,[48] but only a trace of dimethoxybenzophenone is obtained with anisole.[49] The reaction of carbon tetrachloride proceeds in the same manner also with *ortho, meta* and *para* dichlorobenzenes and *para*-dibromobenzene,[50] *para*-dichlorobenzene giving 2,5,2′,5′-tetrachlorobenzophenone chloride at room temperature, but a phenyl fluorene derivative at 55°. Bibenzyl is the principal product of the reaction of *methylchloroform* with benzene.[51] 1,2,3-Trichloropropane reacts with benzene to form diphenylpropane, together with some dibenzylmethane.[52] The corresponding bromo compound reacts in a similar manner. Anthracene results through the reaction of benzene with *sym-tetrabromoethane;* toluene and xylenes give methylated anthracenes in much smaller yield. Negative results have been obtained in attempts to apply the Friedel-Crafts reaction to halonitro compounds such as *nitrosyl chloride* or *chloropicrin.*

Vinyl chloride reacting with benzene in the presence of a catalyst consisting of aluminum chloride and mercuric chloride gives principally *asym*-diphenylethane and a small amount of 9,10-dimethyldihydroanthracene.[53] With vinyl bromide and aluminum chloride, diphenylethane[54] or bromoethylbenzene,[55]

$$C_6H_5CH_2CH_2Br,$$

are obtained as the principal products, depending on the conditions. Appreciable quantities of ethyl benzene with small amounts of styrene and dimethyl anthracene are the secondary products of the reaction in the first case, and bromoethylbenzene in the second. *Allyl chloride* and benzene give 1,2-diphenylpropane;[56] *dibromoethylene* gives diphenylethylene,[57] $CH_2 = CH(C_6H_5)_2$, while *vinylidene chloride* and benzene yield resinous products.[58] Anthracene results from *tetrachloroethylene* and benzene.[59]

The reaction of *benzyl chloride* with benzene, which results in the formation of diphenylmethane, may be carried out by conducting a dry current of hydrogen chloride through a mixture of benzyl chloride and benzene containing aluminum turnings.[60] The reaction is applicable to homologs of benzene and benzyl chloride.[61]

When aluminum chloride is added slowly to a mixture of benzyl chloride and toluene, benzyltoluene is formed; when, however, benzyl chloride is added to a mixture of toluene and aluminum chloride, a solid product is obtained, consisting of 1,6- and 2,7-dimethylanthracenes.[62]

Benzyltoluene results in small yield only through the reaction of *m-methylbenzyl chloride* and benzene.[63] Phenol and bromobenzyl chloride yield a benzylphenol together with some phenyl bromobenzyl ethers, although no ether is obtained with bromophenol. Benzyl chloride condenses with *anisole* at the boiling point of the mixture of the two compounds, and in the absence of a catalyst; the condensation takes place at 0° in the presence of aluminum chloride.[64] In the reaction of *p*-benzoylaminophenylpropyl chloride, $C_6H_5CONHC_6H_4(CH_2)_3Cl$, with benzene, the principal product is *p*-benzoylaminodiphenylpropane, a small amount of a hydrindine derivative,

$$C_6H_5CONHC_6H_3\begin{matrix} \diagup CH_2 \diagdown \\ \diagdown CH_2 \diagup \end{matrix}CH_2$$

also forming.

Benzal chloride, $C_6H_5CHCl_2$, and benzene yield triphenylmethane and dihydrodiphenylanthracene,[65] while with xylene there is formed 9,10-diphenyl-2,3,6,7-tetramethyanthracene, together with much tar.[66] Benzal chloride and veratrol give principally phenyldiveratrylmethane, with some 9,10-diphenyl-2,3,6,7-tetramethoxy-9,10-dihydroanthracene.[67]

Triphenylchloromethane reacts with diphenylamine in the absence of a catalyst to form 4-anilinotetraphenylmethane, $(C_6H_5)_3CC_6H_4NHC_6H_5$; in the presence of aluminum chloride, a compound believed to be *p*-diphenylmethyl- *p'*-phenylaminophenyl is formed. *1-Chloro-2-phenylethane* gives dibenzyl with benzene.[68] *1-Chloro-4-phenylbutane* and *1-chloro-5-phenylpentane* undergo internal condensation giving tetralin and phenylcyclopentane respectively.[69] 1-Chloro-3-phenylpropane gives largely a viscous oil of comparatively high molecular weight and a little hydrindone,

$$C_6H_4\begin{matrix} \diagup CH_2 \diagdown \\ \diagdown CH_2 \diagup \end{matrix}CH_2$$

while *1-chloro-3-phenylbutene* is not affected by aluminum chloride.[70] *Styrene dibromide,* $C_6H_5CHBrCH_2Br$, reacting with benzene gives dibenzyl,[71] while *β-bromostyrene dibromide,* $C_6H_5CH\,BrCH\,Br_2$, gives tetraphenylethane. The last-named compound results also through the reaction of tolan dibromide, $C_6H_5CBr = CBrC_6H_5$, and benzene.[72]

Friedel-Crafts condensation of *cyclohexyl chloride* with benzene results in the formation of phenylcyclohexane in 76% yield.[73] Substituted cyclohexane chlorides react similarly. Isomeric tolylcyclohexanes obtained by condensation of the halide with toluene cannot be separated by fractional distillation.[74]

Cyclohexyl bromide and *m*-xylene give a dicyclohexyl-*m*-xylene and 5-cyclohexyl-*m*-xylene. *Bornyl chloride* and toluene yield a mixture of *m*- and *p*-bornyltoluene in good yield.[75] In the reaction of *2-chloro-1-acetylcyclohexane* and benzene, migration of the halogen occurs and 4-phenyl-1-acetylcyclohexane results.[76] Migration of the halogen occurs also in the condensation of 1,2-dibromo- or 1,2-dichlorocyclohexane with benzene, the halogen entering the *p*- or *m*-position.[77]

Friedel-Crafts reaction does not, in general, proceed readily with *halo ethers*. Benzyl ethers and their homologs have been obtained in approximately 30% yield from chloromethyl ether and mixed chloromethyl ethyl and isopropyl ethers by reaction with benzene or its homologs in carbon disulfide solution at 0°.[78] 8-Chloropropyl- and ϵ-chloroamyl phenyl ether react poorly.[79] Diphenylmethane has been obtained in almost theoretical yield from chloromethyl ethyl ether and benzene.[80] The condensation of α,β-dichloroethyl ether with benzene proceeds in a complex manner.[81]

In the reaction of *halo aldehydes* with aromatic compounds the normal Friedel-Crafts condensation may be accompanied with a Baeyer condensation and occasionally also an aldol condensation. The reaction often proceeds in a complicated manner. Thus, *chloral* gives with benzene tetraphenylethane, diphenyldichloroethylene, triphenylvinyl alcohol and other products.

An aldol type condensation with subsequent cleavage of hydrogen halide has been reported to take place in the reaction of polymeric bromoisobutyraldehyde with benzene in carbon disulfide solution in the presence of aluminum chloride:[82]

$$(CH_3)_2CBrCHO + C_6H_6 \rightarrow (CH_3)_2CBrCH(OH)C_6H_5$$

$$\rightarrow (CH_3)_2C = C(OH)C_6H_5 + HBr$$

Trimethylphenyl carbinol, $C_6H_5CH(OH)CCl_3$, has been obtained in 80% yield from chloral and benzene.[83]

The reaction of *halo ketones* with aromatic compounds may proceed in a normal manner, chloracetone giving methyldesoxybenzoin with toluene,[84] and phenylacetone in 32% yield with benzene.[85] Desyl chloride,

$$C_6H_5COCH(Cl)C_6H_5$$

gives diphenylacetophenone with benzene, and 4,4′-dichloromethylbenzophenone $CO(C_6H_4CH_2Cl)_2$ gives 4,4′-dibenzylbenzophenone with the same hydrocarbon.[86]

The reaction of chloromethylene dibenzoate, $(C_6H_5COO)_2CHCl$, gives benzoylbenzhydrol, $C_6H_5COOCH(C_6H_5)_2$, with benzene.[87]

The Friedel-Crafts reaction proceeds normally, as a rule, with *halo acids*, although dehydrogenation often takes place with the formation of polynuclear compounds. Thus, trichloroacetic acid and benzene give fluorene-9-carboxylic acid.[88] α,β-Diphenylbutyric acid results, together with some 9,10-dihydro-9-methylphenanthrene-10-carboxylic acid, from α,β-dibromobutyric acid and benzene.[89] Normal products of condensation result from γ-chlorobutyric acid and benzene or toluene,[90] and from γ,δ-dibromovaleric acid and benzene.[91] δ-Chloro-

γ-valerolactone gives with benzene at $60 - 80°$ principally γ,δ-diphenylvaleric acid, together with some δ-phenylvaleric acid, anthracene-9,10-dibutyric acid, and a little anthraquinone.[91] Ethyl chloroformate, $ClCOOC_2H_5$, reacts with the same hydrocarbon to give ethylbenzene.[92] Other esters of chloroformic acid react in a similar manner.

Haloalkyl benzamides readily undergo the Friedel-Crafts reaction. Thus, ϵ-chloroamylbenzamide gives with benzene, benzoyl- ϵ-phenylamylamine in 90% yield:[79]

$$C_6H_5CONH(CH_2)_4CH_2Cl + C_6H_6 \xrightarrow{AlCl_3} C_6H_5CONH(CH_2)_4CH_2C_6H_5 + HCl$$

Chloroalkylimides of dicarboxylic acids, such as chloromethylsuccinimide, behave similarly.[93]

In the reaction of N-chloroacetanilide with benzene the halogen apparently first migrates into the aromatic nucleus, subsequent reaction with benzene giving diphenylacetamide:[94]

$$C_6H_5N(Cl)COCH_3 \xrightarrow{AlCl_3} \underset{H}{\overset{Cl}{>}}C_6H_4 = NCl(AlCl_2)COCH_3 \cdot$$

$$\xrightarrow{C_6H_6} C_6H_5C_6H_4NHCOCH_3$$

While N-ω-bromoethyl-N-ethylaniline undergoes internal condensation under the influence of aluminum chloride to form N-methyldihydrindole,

$$C_6H_4 \overset{\overset{\displaystyle CH_2}{\diagup\;\diagdown}}{\underset{\underset{\displaystyle CH_3}{N}}{\diagdown\;\diagup}} CH_2$$

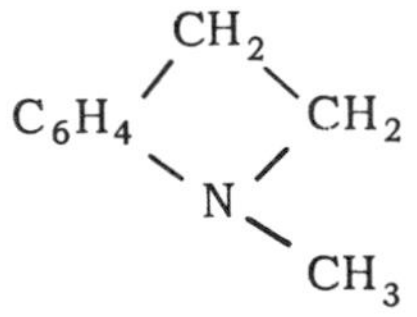

in 35% yield, internal condensation is not the rule with ω-halo-N-alkylarylamines.[95]

The Friedel-Crafts reaction does not proceed with halo nitro compounds with replacement of the nuclear halogen. In the aralkyl series nitrobenzyl chlorides undergo the reaction smoothly, but higher nitrophenylalkyl halides fail to condense.

The reaction of *diazonium halides* with aromatic hydrocarbons in the presence of aluminum chloride may proceed in two directions:[96]

$$C_6H_5N_2Cl + C_6H_6 \begin{array}{c} \nearrow C_6H_5N_2C_6H_5 + HCl \\ \searrow C_6H_5C_6H_5 + N_2 + HCl \end{array}$$

A certain amount of decomposition to the aromatic chloride and nitrogen also takes place. The reaction is applicable also to heterocyclic compounds, β-phenylthiophene, α- and γ-phenylpyridines and 1-phenylquinoline.

The reaction of β-chloroethyltoluene-*p*-sulfonate with benzene in the presence of aluminum chloride results in the formation of dibenzyl:[96]

$$CH_3C_6H_4SO_3CH_2CH_2Cl + 2C_6H_6 \rightarrow$$
$$C_6H_5CH_2CH_2C_6H_5 + CH_3C_6H_4SO_3H + HCl$$

In the reaction of β,β-bis(*p*-chlorophenyl) propiophenone with benzene in the presence of aluminum chloride, the phenyl group replaces the entire halophenyl radical:[97]

$$(p\text{-}ClC_6H_4)_2CHCH_2COC_6H_5 + 2C_6H_6 \xrightarrow{AlCl_3}$$
$$(C_6H_5)_2CHCH_2COC_6H_5 + 2C_6H_5Cl$$

The reaction is reversible. This exchange may also be effected with *p*-chlorobenzalacetone.[98]

In the attempted condensation of benzene with *p*-chlorobenzalquinaldine, α-benzhydrylquinaldine results, apparently in accordance with the following scheme:[99]

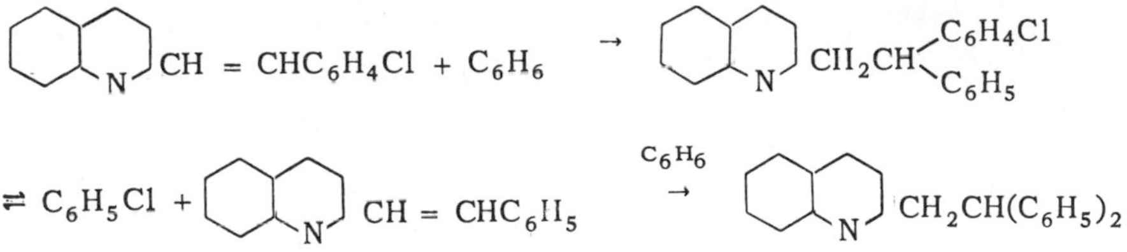

para- and *meta*-bromobenzalquinaldine react similarly. *p*-Chlorobenzallepidine yields α-benzhydryllepidine in an analogous manner.[100]

The reaction of α-chloronaphthalene with benzene proceeds smoothly to give α-phenylnaphthalene in 40% yield, together with a small amount of the β-isomer.

Chlorophenylanthrone,

$$C_6H_4\langle{}^{C(Cl)C_6H_5}_{CO}\rangle C_6H_4$$

reacts with dimethylaniline in carbon disulfide solution in the presence of aluminum chloride to form dimethylaminodiphenylanthrone,[101]

$$C_6H_4\langle{}^{C(C_6H_5)C_6H_4N(CH_3)_2}_{CO}\rangle C_6H_4$$

The chloride of anthraquinone reacts similarly to form tetramethyldiaminodiphenylanthrone.[102] Dimethylaniline condenses with 3-chloro-1,2-Benzisothiazole-1-dioxide to,[103]

$$C_6H_4 \underset{SO_2}{\overset{C \cdot C_6H_4N(CH_3)_2}{\diamond}} N$$

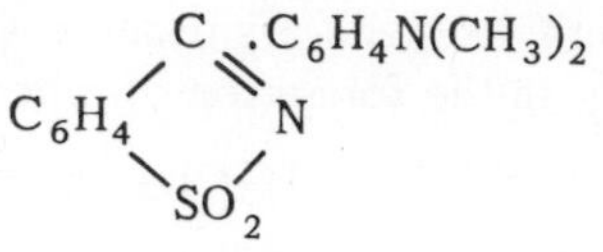

9-Chloroacridine gives with dialkylanilines 9-(dialkylaminophenyl)acridine.[104] Halo anthrones condense with aromatic hydrocarbons to give arylated anthrones:[101]

$$C_6H_4 \underset{CO}{\overset{CHCl}{\diamond}} C_6H_4 + C_6H_6 \xrightarrow{AlCl_3} C_6H_4 \underset{CO}{\overset{CHC_6H_5}{\diamond}} C_6H_4 + HCl$$

$$C_6H_4 \underset{CO}{\overset{C(Cl)C_6H_5}{\diamond}} C_6H_4 + C_6H_6 \rightarrow C_6H_4 \underset{CO}{\overset{C(C_6H_5)_2}{\diamond}} C_6H_4 + HCl$$

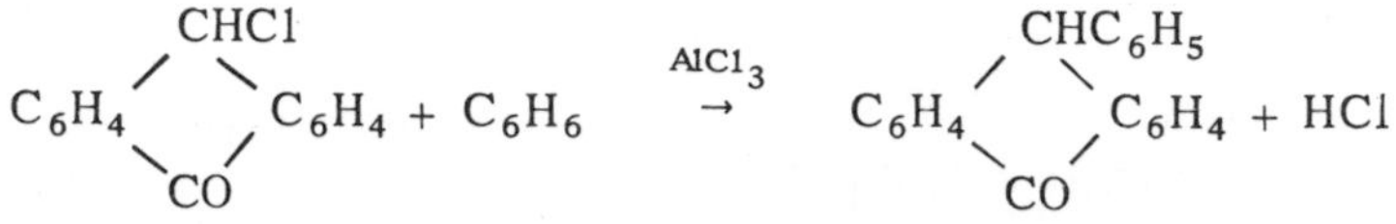

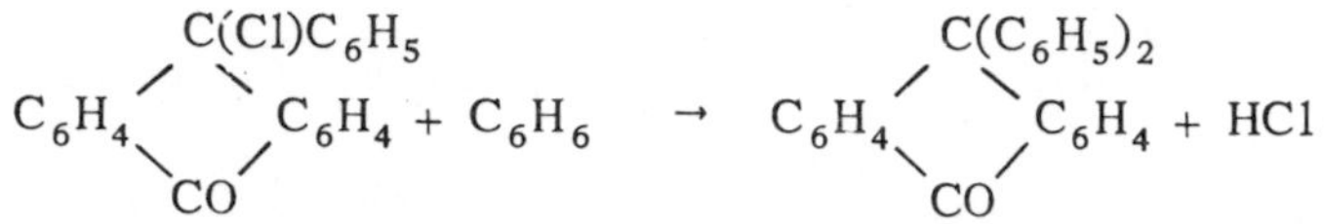

N-Methyl-3,3-dichlorooxindole also reacts smoothly with aromatic compounds to give the 3,3-diaryl derivative:[105]

$$C_6H_4 \overset{NCH_3}{\underset{CCl_2}{\diamond}} CO + 2C_6H_6 \rightarrow C_6H_4 \overset{NCH_3}{\underset{C(C_6H_5)_2}{\diamond}} CO + 2HCl$$

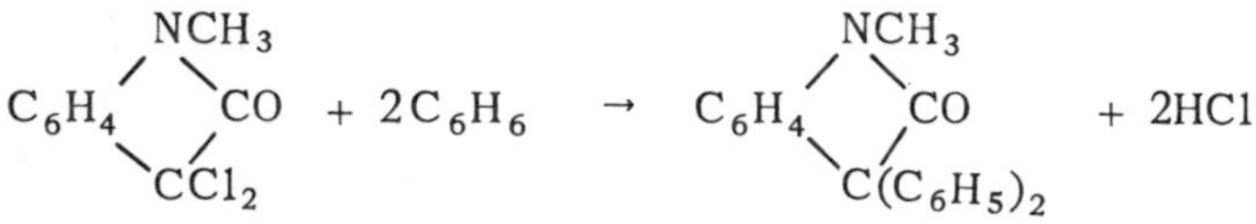

The N-ethyl derivative reacts similarly. Halo quinazolines also undergo the Friedel-Crafts condensation, giving 2-phenylquinazolines with benzene:

$$C_6H_4 \overset{HC=N}{\underset{N=C\ Cl}{|}} + C_6H_6 \rightarrow C_6H_4 \overset{HC=N}{\underset{N=CC_6H_5}{|}} + HCl$$

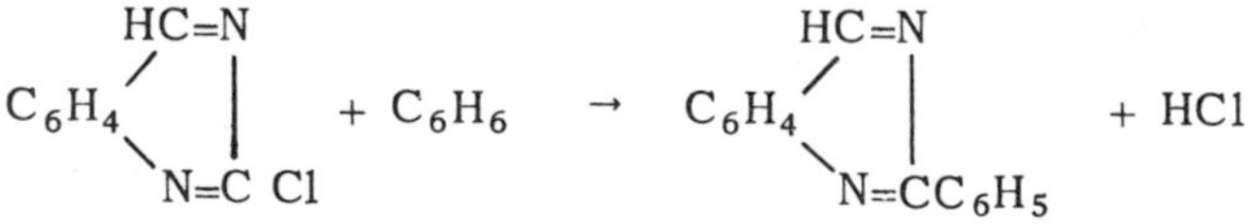

Both chlorine atoms in 2,4-dichloroquinazoline are replaceable with aromatic groups. A hydroxy group does not inhibit the reaction, and a nitro group is also without inhibitive action if a hydroxy group is present in the molecule. The chlorine atoms in *cyanuric chloride* Cl $\overline{\text{CN:C(Cl)=NC(Cl)=N}}$, are replaceable with aromatic groups by Friedel-Crafts reaction.

Cyanogen halides are capable of undergoing the Friedel-Crafts reaction.[106] Nitriles are obtained in good yield if freshly prepared cyanogen bromide is employed in the reaction.[107] More satisfactory results are obtained, in general, with phenol ethers than with hydrocarbons.[108] Thus 2,4-dimethoxybenzonitrile is obtained in good yield from the dimethyl ether of resorcinol. 1-Cyano-2,5- and 3,4-dimethoxybenzene, 1-cyano-2,3,4-trimethoxybenzene, 1-cyano-4-ethoxy- and 2-methoxynaphthalene are also obtained in satisfactory yield from the corresponding methyl ethers. The reaction often proceeds poorly, however, and results in the formation of considerable proportions of symmetrical triazole derivatives.

Reactions with Napthalene

Aluminum chloride brings about the decomposition of naphthalene and causes various types of condensations; for this reason the alkylation of this hydrocarbon may be effected successfully only under mild conditions. *Methyl chloride* reacts with naphthalene with difficulty and gives methylnaphthalene in very low yield. The reaction of *ethyl chloride* with naphthalene results in the formation of β-methylnaphthalene and small amounts of α-methyl-, α- and β-ethyl-, and dimethylnaphthalene and β,β-binaphthyl; simultaneously a considerable quantity of methane is evolved.[109] β-Ethylnaphthalene has been prepared through the reaction of ethyl bromide with naphthalene in the presence of aluminum chloride with cautious heating.[110] Isopropylnaphthalene results through the condensation of *n*-propyl chloride with naphthalene;[111] isobutyl bromide and naphthalene give *tert*-butylnaphthalene,[112] and amyl chloride and naphthalene yield β-amylnaphthalene. Bromobenzene condenses with naphthalene to form α-phenylnaphthalene in 20% yield.[113] *Tert*-Butyl chloride may be condensed with α- and β-naphthol.[114] Diphenyldichloromethane, $(C_6H_5)_2CCl_2$, reacting with naphthalene gives diphenyl α-naphthylmethyl chloride,[115] $C_6H_5C(Cl)C_{10}H$-. The reaction may proceed further, however, to form a fluorene derivative,[116]

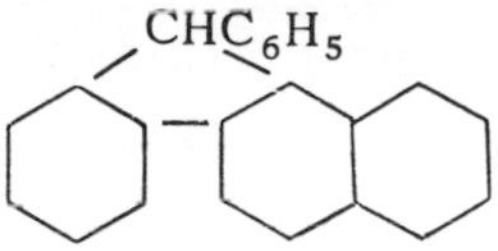

The reaction with α-naphthol proceeds in a similar manner. Tetralin cannot be methylated or butylated by Friedel-Crafts reaction.[117]

The alkylation of polynuclear hydrocarbons has been achieved by carrying out the reaction under pressure.[118]

Reactions with Heterocyclic Compounds

Furan itself is apparently incapable of undergoing the Friedel-Crafts reaction, although condensation proceeds successfully with furan derivatives containing negative substituents.[119] In the alkylation of furan derivatives, it is necessary to use a molecular equivalent of aluminum chloride. Ferric and stannic chlorides are less effective catalysts than aluminum chloride for the alkylation of furan derivatives.

Thiophene may be alkylated by Friedel-Crafts reaction, but the yields are very low, considerable resinification taking place during the reaction. With benzal chloride, a phenyl di-α-thienylmethane, $C_6H_5CH(C_4H_3S)_2$, results in small yield.[120] The same product is also obtained with benzotrichloride.[121] *2-Furyl phenyl ketone* condenses with *tert*-butyl chloride to 5-*tert*-butyl-2-furyl phenyl ketone. The product is obtained in 30% yield.[122] Furan esters may be alkylated readily, although methyl and ethyl halides do not react with these compounds.

The condensation of *thiophene* with benzyl chloride may be brought about without much resinification by the use of tin tetrachloride as a catalyst, diphenylthienylmethane and benzhydrylthiophene being the products formed. The last named is obtained in 50% yield.[122]

REACTIONS INVOLVING ACYL HALIDES

The reaction of acid halides with aromatic compounds in the presence of aluminum chloride proceeds more readily than that of alkyl chlorides. In contrast to the reaction with the latter, however, a somewhat more than the molecular equivalent of the catalyst is required, one molecular equivalent apparently combining with the acid halide, while the small excess acts as a catalyst for the reaction:

$$RCOCl + C_6H_6 \rightarrow RCOC_6H_5 + HCl$$

The reaction is quite general and a large variety of acyl halides may be condensed with aromatic compounds, including the halides of fatty and aromatic acids, carbonyl chloride, thiophosgene and sulfonyl chloride.

It is generally agreed that a complex is formed between the acyl halide and aluminum chloride, $RCOCl.AlCl_3$,[123] possibly one of the type

$$[RCO]^+ [AlCl_4]$$ [124]

The aromatic compound may be assumed to react in the orthoquinoid form:

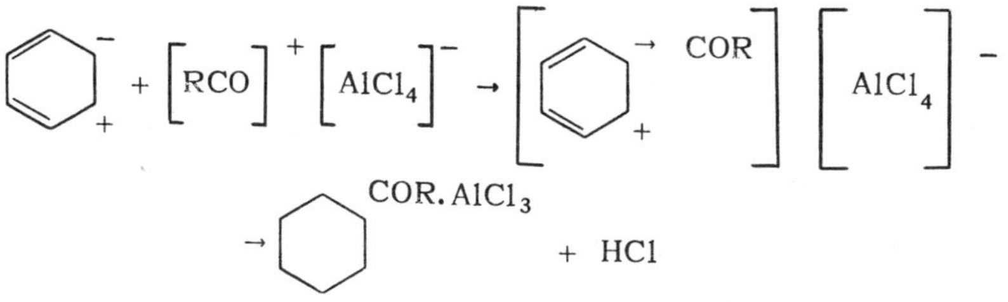

A complex is, thus, also formed between the resulting ketone and aluminum chloride, possibly of the type

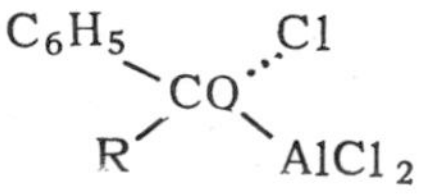

This is decomposed upon the addition of water. It may be presumed also that the aromatic hydrocarbons are activated by aluminum chloride, due to the formation of a coordination compound with the catalyst. With homologs of benzene, a migration of the alkyl group may take place in the course of Friedel-Crafts reaction, *o*- and *p*-bromotoluene giving, for example, 1-methyl-3-bromo-4-benzophenone at 0°.

Friedel-Crafts acylation proceeds successfully not only with aromatic hydrocarbons, but also with many of their halo, alkoxy or even amino derivatives.

Nitro and phenolic compounds do not, in general, undergo the reaction. As a general rule, electronegative groups, if present in the hydrocarbon component, have an inhibiting effect on the reaction. The effect is most marked with benzene and monoalkylbenzenes, so that acylation of nitrobenzene, benzoic acid or benzophenone, for example, is impossible. Nitro derivatives of phenol ethers are capable of undergoing the reaction.[125] The extent of the reaction of monohalotoluenes with acyl chlorides depends upon the position of the halogen in the ring, *p*-chlorotoluene failing to react with *o*-bromoethylbenzoyl bromide. *Dihalo* aromatic compounds react slowly with acyl chlorides,[126] though the condensation of chloracetyl chloride with *m*-dichlorobenzene proceeds readily. Aromatic *nitriles* in which the cyano group is joined to a nuclear carbon atom fail to undergo the Friedel-Crafts reaction. Such nitriles are partially converted to triazines under the influence of aluminum chloride and aliphatic acid chlorides.[127] Alkyl aromatic nitriles in which the cyano group is attached to an alkyl group are capable of undergoing the Friedel-Crafts reaction.[128]

Unsatisfactory results are obtained also with aromatic N-dialkylamines, these compounds yielding complex condensation products. Somewhat better results are obtained in the reaction of these compounds with aliphatic acyl chlorides than with aroayl halides. Zinc chloride has proved to be a more satisfactory catalyst with this class of compounds. Benzanilideimide chloride,

$$ClC(:NC_6H_5)C_6H_5$$

forms an exception and condenses readily with N-dialkylanilines.[129] N-Arylacetamides undergo the normal Friedel-Crafts condensation with acyl halides.[130] The reaction proceeds with special ease with haloacyl halides.

The effect of a negative group becomes less marked in polyalkylated derivatives. The inhibitive effect of negative substituents is also less marked in polynuclear hydrocarbons and certain heterocycles such as thiophene and furan.

Cleavage of the *alkyl group* in alkoxy aromatic compounds may take place during a Friedel-Crafts acylation reaction. Cleavage takes place, for example, in the reaction of toluylchlorides with *p*-chloroanisole,[131] and in the acylation of *m*-dialkoxy benzenes. Demethylation is often observed in the reaction of trimethoxy benzenes. As is usually the case, the methoxy group in *ortho* position is affected in this reaction. 1,2-Dimethoxybenzene reacting with chloroacetyl chloride in nitrobenzene solution at 40° gives ω-chloro-3,4-dimethoxyacetophenone with a considerable proportion of ω-chloro-3,4-dihydroxyacetophenone. This represents an unusual case of cleavage involving *meta* and *para* methoxy groups.[132] Dealkylation of both alkoxy groups takes place very readily in the acylation of hydroquinone dialkyl ethers by Friedel-Crafts reaction.[133] Pyrogallol trimethyl ether reacting with acetyl chloride gives 2-hydroxy-3,4-dimethoxyacetophenone;[134] pyrogallol dimethyl ether and benzoyl chloride give 3,4-dihydroxy-5-methoxybenzophenone.[135] Cleavage of an alkyl group from an alkoxyl group in the *o*-position with respect to the entering acyl group does not always take place. Thus, 2,4,6-trimethoxyacetophenone may be obtained in quantitative yield from phlorglucinol trimethyl ether.[136] A methoxy group in the *p*-position with respect to the entering acyl group strongly resists demethylation. A partial cleavage of the alkyl group is observed in the acylation of alkyl ethers of α- and β-naphthol;[137] cleavage of both methyl groups takes place in the reaction of 2,6-dimethoxynaphthalene with benzoyl chloride, and a 1,5-dibenzoyl derivative is formed.[138] Substituents in aroyl halides do not exert as marked an effect as those in the hydrocarbon component.[139] Alkoxy aryl acyl chlorides condense normally with aromatic compounds, although cleavage of the alkyl group may take place with the formation of the corresponding hydroxy ketone. Cleavage of the methyl group takes place for example in the reaction of salicylyl chloride methyl ether with benzene, but not with *para*- and *meta*-methoxybenzoyl chloride.[140]

Cleavage or migration of acyl groups attached to an aromatic nucleus under the influence of aluminum chloride has been observed occasionally. 9-Acyl anthracenes, for example, are converted to 1- and 2-acyl isomerides; 1-acetylacenaphthene changes to 5,6- and 3,8-diacetylacenaphthenes.

The order of reactivity of acyl halides in acylation reactions is, in descending order: acyl iodides > acyl bromides > acyl chlorides > acyl fluorides;[141] this is the opposite of the order of reactivity in alkylation reactions.

In the acylation of aromatic hydrocarbons, it is generally impossible to introduce more than one acyl group into the nucleus, because of the hindering action of first acyl group that enters the nucleus. This does not hold true of *polyalkylated* benzenes, which can yield diacyl derivatives,[142] although *para*-xylene fails to give a diacylated derivative. The activating influence of longer chain alkyl groups is considerably less than that of short chain groups. In a compound containing an acetyl group in *ortho* position with respect to two methyl groups, a second acetyl group may enter the nucleus. In keeping with this rule, *sym*-triethyl benzene and ethyl mesitylene are capable of giving diacetyl derivatives, and diacetyl derivatives are obtained, in nearly theoretical yield, from mesitylene, durene and isodurene, while pseudocumene gives only a monoacyl derivative. Acylation of alkyl benzenes by the Friedel-Crafts method does not result in the migration of the alkyl groups present in the nucleus.

The presence of one or two keto groups in a polynuclear hydrocarbon does not prevent the entrance of an additional acyl group into the molecule. Where the possibility of the formation of polyacylated derivatives exists, the time allowed for the reaction largely determines the number of acyl groups that enter the nucleus.

Aluminum chloride may cause the reduction of nitro compounds giving a β-phenylhydroxylamine which rearranges to a *p*-aminophenol derivative.[113]

Friedel-Crafts condensation with *unsaturated* aliphatic *acyl chlorides* may take an abnormal course, acrylyl chloride, for example, giving a large proportion of *p*-xylylethyl *p*-xylyl ketone, $(CH_3)_2C_6H_3CO\ CH_2CH_2C_6H_3(CH_3)_2$, with some *p*-xylyl vinyl ketone.[143] Hydrindone derivatives may also result instead of the unsaturated ketones.[144]

Arylated propionyl chlorides generally give hydrindones by internal condensation, whereas arylbutyryl chlorides yield tetrahydronaphthalene derivatives.

Arylvaleryl chlorides also generally give tetrahydronaphthalene deri
A compound with a seven-membered ring has been obtained from phenylvaleryl
chloride.[145] As a general rule, aryl derivatives of branched chain acyl halides
give better yields of cyclic products than those of straight chain acid halides.
Alkyl groups present in the aromatic nucleus also favor ring formation.[146]

Aralkyl derivatives of benzoyl chloride may also undergo ring closure; thus,
o-9-phenanthrylbenzoyl chloride gives a benzanthrone derivative.[147]

Ring closure of aralkyl acid halides with an ether linkage in a 3- or 4-carbon
chain leads to the formation of an oxygen ring compound:[148]

$$C_6H_5OCH_2CH_2COCl \quad \rightarrow \quad C_6H_4 \begin{matrix} O-CH_2 \\ | \\ CO-CH_2 \end{matrix} + HCl$$

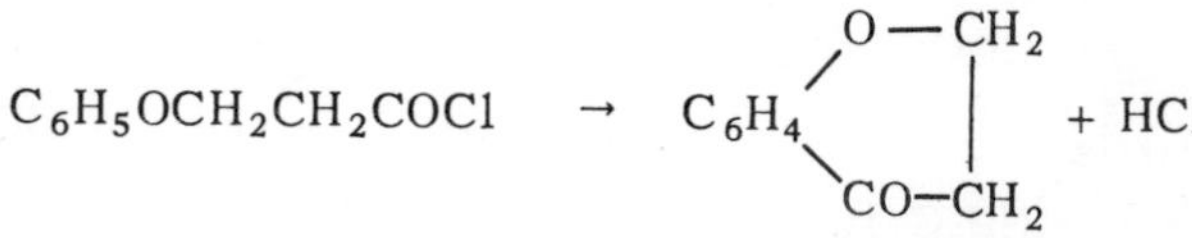

Flavones are obtained in theoretical yield from β-aryloxycinnamoyl chlorides:[149]

$$C_6H_5OC(C_6H_5) = CHCOCl \quad \rightarrow \quad C_6H_4 \begin{matrix} O-CC_6H_5 \\ \| \\ CO-CH \end{matrix} + HCl$$

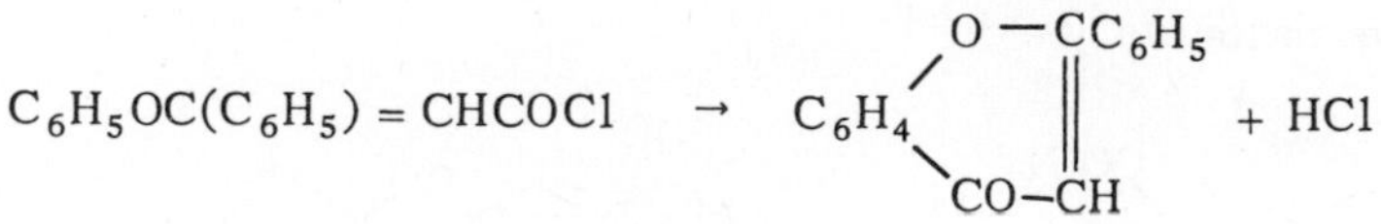

Condensation products with propiolyl chloride have been cyclized to flavones
under the influence of dilute caustic.

Various nitrogen heterocycles may be formed through the cyclization of aromatic amino acyl chlorides. Thus, oxindoles result in 80% yield through the
action of aluminum chloride on N-chloroacetylarylamines:[150]

$$C_6H_5NHCOCH_2Cl \quad \rightarrow \quad C_6H_4 \begin{matrix} CH_2 \\ \diagup \quad \diagdown \\ CO \\ \diagdown \quad \diagup \\ NH \end{matrix} + HCl$$

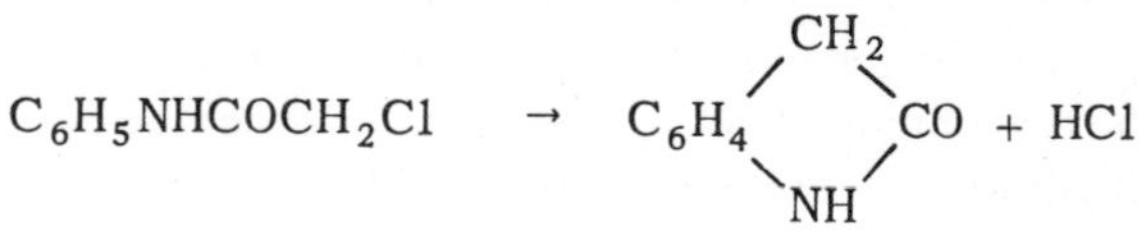

The method is not applicable to aryl derivatives of glycyl chloride and to most
aralkyl derivatives of this chloride.[151] The cyclization of these compounds may
be effected, however, by first sulfonating the amino group:

$$C_6H_5(CH_2)_2NHCH_2COOH + C_6H_5SO_2Cl$$
$$\rightarrow \quad HCl + C_6H_5(CH_2)_2N(SO_2C_6H_5)CH_2COOH$$

$$\xrightarrow{PCl_5, \ AlCl_3} \quad C_6H_4 \begin{matrix} CH_2-CH_2 \\ \diagup \quad \diagdown \\ NSO_2C_6H_5 \\ \diagdown \quad \diagup \\ CO-CH_2 \end{matrix}$$

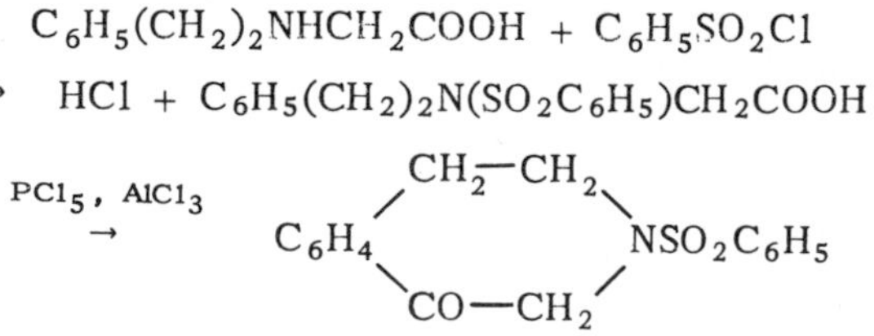

The benzene sulfonyl group may be removed readily by hydrolysis.

Isatins result through the cyclization of the reaction product of arylamines
and oxalyl chloride:

$$C_6H_5NHCH_3 + ClCOCOCl \rightarrow C_6H_5N(CH_3)COCOCl$$

$$\rightarrow \quad C_6H_4 \underset{N-CH_3}{\overset{CO}{\diagup \diagdown}} CO + HCl$$

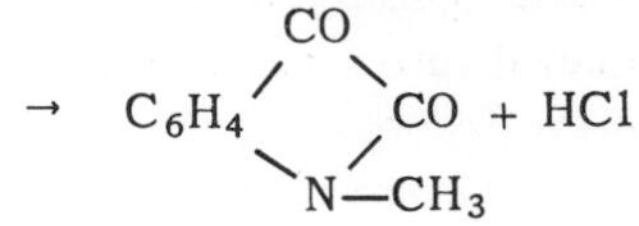

This method is of fairly general applicability. The reaction product of diphenyl-amine and oxalyl chloride gives acridine carboxylic acid.[152]

Acridones result through the internal condensation of diphenylamine car-boxylic acid chloride and other similar compounds:[153]

$$NO_2C_6H_3 \underset{NH\,C_6H_5}{\overset{COCl}{\diagup \diagdown}} \rightarrow NO_2C_6H_3 \underset{NH}{\overset{CO}{\diagup \diagdown}} C_6H_4 + HCl$$

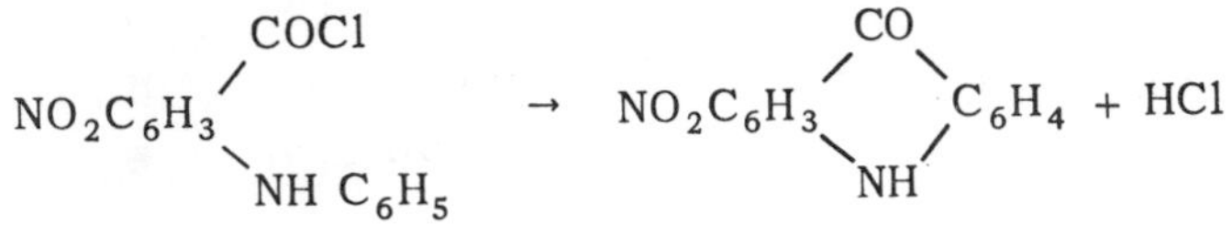

The reaction is also applicable to compounds of the quinoline series. Thus, 2-phenylquinoline-3-carboxylic acid chloride gives 2,3-benzo-1-aza-9-oxo-fluorene in quantitative yield:[154]

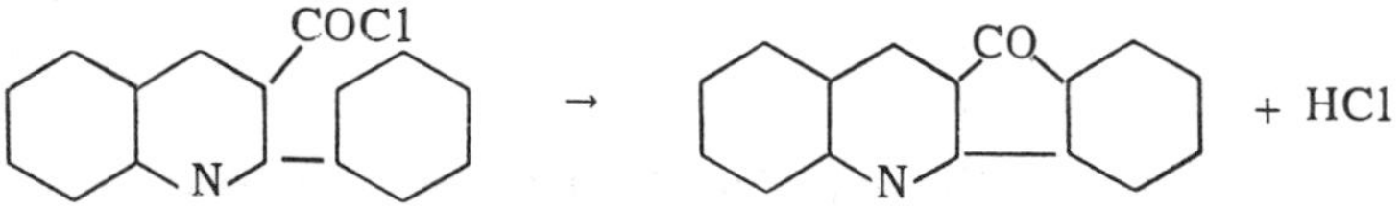

Some acylated derivatives of lutidine carboxylic acid chloride and pyridinedi-carboxylic acid chloride have also been cyclized.[155]

S-(o-Carboxyphenyl)thioglycolyl chloride gives 3-hydroxythianaphthene-7-carboxylic acid chloride on treatment with aluminum chloride. Ring closure takes place with increasing ease with increase in the molecular weight of the aryl group, 6-ethoxynaphthalene-2-thioglycolic acid chloride giving the cor-responding ketodihydrothionaphthene in 80% yield:[156]

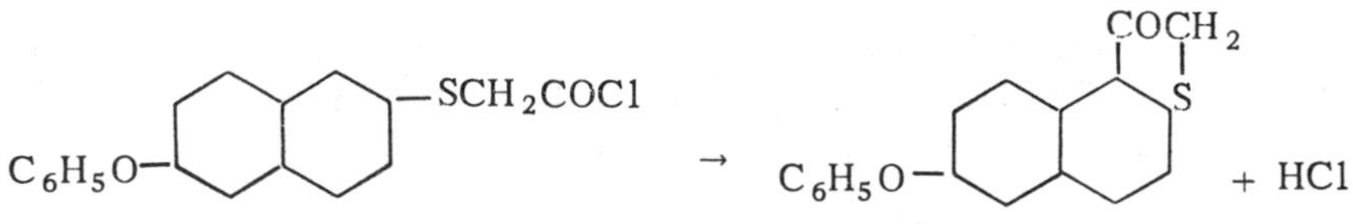

Ring closure of α-alkyl-5-arylthioglycolic acid chlorides with aluminum chloride does not proceed readily. Thus, α-p-thiocresylisopropionyl chloride yields only a small amount of a condensation product which is probably 2,5-dimethyl-3-hydroxythianaphthene.

Procedure

In the preparation of simple acyl benzenes, aluminum chloride, somewhat in excess of a molecular equivalent, is gradually added to a mixture of the hydro-carbon and acyl chloride, and the whole is warmed on a water bath until the evolution of hydrogen chloride ceases.[157] The reaction often proceeds exothermally in the beginning, and may be completed in many cases by brief refluxing. A diluent may be used in carrying out the reaction.

As an example, 290 gm of aluminum chloride are added to a mixture of 240 gm benzene, an equal weight of benzoyl chloride and 400 cc carbon disulfide, the mixture is allowed to stand overnight and is then heated for two to three hours on a water bath. The reaction is complete when a drop of the mixture, treated with water, does not give off an odor of benzoyl chloride. After the completion of the reaction, dilute hydrochloric acid is added to the reaction mixture, the carbon disulfide layer is separated, the solvent is evaporated off and a little alcohol is added to the hot residue. On cooling, benzophenone separates out as a crystalline mass.

Good results have been obtained in the acylation of toluene, xylene and cymene, by carrying out the reaction at 0° in vacuum, and adding the acid chloride drop by drop to the cooled mixture of aluminum chloride and the hydrocarbon.[158] In order to prevent the formation of tarry or resinous matter, it is best to stop the reaction short of completion.[159]

Perrier preferred to prepare the acyl chloride-aluminum chloride complex in carbon disulfide solution, and to add the hydrocarbon to this complex.[160] Yields may be improved in some instances by use of a fairly large excess of aluminum chloride.

In acylating highly reactive compounds, a diluent is used to moderate the reaction, the diluent apparently diminishing the vigor of the catalytic effect by combining with a portion of the catalyst. Nitrobenzene and *sym*-tetrachloroethane are satisfactory solvents for the condensation of phenols, polynuclear hydrocarbons and heterocyclic compounds. In some cases, and especially with solid hydrocarbons, an excess of the acyl chloride may be used to keep the reaction mass in a liquid condition, thus avoiding the use of an inert solvent. Carbon disulfide may also be employed as a diluent in the latter case.

The condensation of phenols with acid chlorides may be carried out successfully at a low temperature by using nitrobenzene as a solvent.[161] The method is especially suitable for the preparation of ketones with a long side-chain, though less favorable results are obtained with polyhydric phenols and with *para*-substituted phenols. The method works poorly with phlorglucinol because of the low solubility of this compound in nitrobenzene. An improved method makes use of the one-to-one molecular complex of phenol and aluminum chloride; the complex reacts with the acyl chloride at 120 to 140° in the absence of solvents to give the keto phenol in 80 to 90% yield.[162] Phorglucinol may be effectively acylated by dissolving the phenol and aluminum chloride in nitrobenzene, heating on the water bath until the evolution of hydrogen chloride ceases, then adding the acyl chloride.

In the preparation of acylated naphthalenes best results seem to be obtained when two molal proportions of aluminum chloride and naphthalene are used to one of acid chloride.[163] The formation of resinous products is prevented when the aluminum chloride is added gradually to a mixture of the acid chloride and naphthalene in an appropriate solvent.

In carrying out the acylation of thiophene, strict observance of detail of the proper experimental conditions is essential. A good yield of phenyl thienyl ketone is obtained on adding a solution of benzoyl chloride and thiophene in carbon disulfide, to a suspension of aluminum chloride in the same solvent. Much tar is formed if the solution of the acyl chloride is added to a suspension of aluminum chloride in thiophene.[164]

Acylation with pyridine dicarboxylic acid chlorides is best effected by first preparing the aluminum chloride complex of the acyl chloride by gently heating the mixture of components, and then adding the hydrocarbon.[165]

The reaction of carbonyl chloride with hydrocarbons is apparently accelerated by the carbonyl chloride-aluminum chloride complex, consisting of 37.5% of the former and 62.5% of the latter. This fact is taken advantage of, for example, in the preparation of 4,4′-diphenyldicarboxylic amide, which is effected by heating at 60 to 140° a mixture of diphenyl and the carbamyl chloride-aluminum chloride complex diluted with dichlorobenzene, until the evolution of hydrogen chloride ceases.

Urea dichloride is mixed with a solution of the hydrocarbon in about three times its weight of carbon disulfide, the aluminum chloride is added gradually with good agitation, and the whole is warmed for a short period. The carbon disulfide layer is decanted off and the product is carefully treated with water. The amide is isolated by crystallization. Good results are obtained by this procedure with toluene and other homologs of benzene, naphthalene, acenaphthene and thiophene. Cymene fails to react. The method is applicable to ethers of phenol and naphthol.

Monohalobenzophenones are best prepared through the reaction of halo aromatic acid chlorides with benzene hydrocarbons rather than of halo hydrocarbons with benzoyl chloride or its homologs.[166] Polyhalobenzoyl chlorides react very slowly, however, and somewhat better yields are obtained through the reaction of a polyhalo aromatic hydrocarbon with the non-halogenated acyl chloride,[167] although the yields are very low in either case.

The solvent employed in the Friedel-Crafts condensation influences the rate and yield of the acylation reaction, as well as the position of the entering acyl group in the aromatic compound. In general, reaction proceeds with maximum speed in benzene, because the aluminum chloride complexes are soluble in this hydrocarbon. The reaction velocity in ligroin is nearly as rapid at the beginning, but there is an appreciable drop after the initial vigorous reaction, because the complex formed is insoluble in ligroin. Reaction is fairly rapid at the start in chlorobenzene and bromobenzene. The reaction is less rapid in carbon disulfide, though more regular. The reaction is also rapid initially in nitrobenzene but the rate declines as the catalyst dissolves.

Best results are obtained with pure aluminum chloride. The presence of ferric chloride in the catalyst is especially undesirable. The reaction is accelerated by actinic rays, the effect being particularly marked with halogenated derivatives of benzene.

Ferric chloride may be used as a catalyst for some acylation reactions. It can be used, for example, in the acylation of phenols. One equivalent of ferric chloride is used for each phenolic hydroxyl group in the aromatic compound, the chloride being added in small portions. It is often necessary to heat the reaction mixture on the water bath to complete the reaction. Iron chloride causes the introduction of acyl groups into the molecule of di- and polyhydric phenols.

Ferric chloride causes the condensation of aliphatic acid chlorides to keto acid chlorides:[168]

$$2C_2H_5COCl \xrightarrow{FCl_3} C_2H_5COCH(CH_3)COCl + HCl$$

These compounds are decomposed to a ketone, carbon dioxide and hydrochloric acid, by the action of water, but yield keto esters with alcohols:

$$C_2H_5COCH(CH_3)COCl + C_2H_5OH \rightarrow$$
$$C_2H_5COCH(CH_3)COOC_2H_5 + HCl$$

In some reactions the use of a mild catalyst is required, as for example, in the acylation of thiophene, which polymerizes considerably under the influence of aluminum chloride. Stannic chloride is a suitable catalyst in such cases giving, with thiophene and an equivalent of acetyl chloride, a 79 to 83% yield of acetylthiophene.

Position of Attachment of Acyl Groups

In the Friedel-Crafts acylation of monosubstituted benzene derivatives, the acyl group enters the *para* position with respect to the substituent.[167] In the reaction of acyl chlorides with *para*-alkyl ethers, the acyl group enters the *ortho* position with respect to the alkyl or aryloxy group. With *ortho*-alkylated ethers the acyl group enters the *para* position with respect to the alkyl or aryloxy group, while with *meta*-alkylated ethers, the acyl group enters the *ortho* position. The orienting influence of a *meta*-methyl group surpasses that of the alkyl or aryloxy group. The position of attachment of an acyl group cannot be safely predicted for polyalkyl phenol ethers. In the reaction of acetyl chloride with diphenylmethane, a mixture of acetophenone and 4-acetyldiphenylmethane and 4,4′-diacetyldiphenylmethane are obtained.[169]

The acylation of *naphthalene* with aliphatic acid chlorides results in the formation of a mixture of α- and β-acylnaphthalenes. The solvents employed exert an important influence on the course of the reaction. The proportions of α- and β-isomers formed are in ratio of 3:1 when carbon disulfide is used as a solvent; at lower temperatures the proportion of the α-isomer increases. In petroleum ether, the α- and β-isomers are formed in nearly equal quantities. Nitrobenzene favors the formation of the β-isomer, while in bromobenzene the α-isomer is obtained as the main product.[170] Acylation with aromatic acid chlorides results principally in the formation of the α-isomer, and the course of the reaction is little influenced by the solvent or the temperature. With substituted naphthalenes, several isomers are formed simultaneously. *Tetralin* is acylated exclusively at the unhindered β-position.

Acenaphthene is acylated at the 3-position, a little of the 1-acetyl isomer also forming.[171] *Perinaphthalene* gives a 9-benzoyl derivative with benzoyl chloride.[172] *Anthracene* gives a mixture of 1- and 2-acyl derivatives with aliphatic acid chlorides, although under mild conditions the 9-acyl derivative is obtained.[173] *Dihydroanthracene* gives 9-benzoyl-9,10-dihydroanthracene with benzoyl chloride.[174] *Phenanthrene* gives 2- and 3-acetyl derivatives;[175] with benzoyl chloride in nitrobenzene solution, the 3-benzoyl derivative is obtained together with small quantities of 1- and 2-benzoyl derivatives,[176] while in carbon disulfide solution 1-benzoylphenanthrene is obtained. *Fluorene* gives a 2-acetyl derivative.[177] *Hydrindene* gives the β-acetyl derivative with acetyl chloride. *Pyrene* gives a 3-acetyl derivative, disubstitution resulting in the formation of 3,8- and 3,10-acetyl derivatives;[178] with aromatic acid chlorides a 3-acyl derivative is obtained in benzene solution at temperatures below 20°.[179]

The position occupied by the entering acyl group in various compounds is given in the following table:

Acyl Halide	Cyclic Compound	Position of Attachment of Acyl Group
Acetyl chloride	*o*-xylene	4
	m-xylene	4
	1,2,4-trimethylbenzene (pseudocumene)	5
	1-methyl-3-ethylbenzene	6
	1,4-dimethyl-2-ethylbenzene	5
	1,3-dimethyl-4-ethylbenzene	6
	1-methyl-2-propylbenzene	4
	1-methyl-3-propylbenzene	4
	1-methyl-4-isopropylbenzene	6
	1-3-dimethyl-5-*tert*-butyl benzene	4
	o-chlorotoluene	5
	1,2,4-triethylbe nzene	5
bezoyl chloride	1,4-dimethyl-2-chlorobenzene	5
valeryl chloride	1-methyl-2-methoxybenzene	5
acetyl chloride	anisole	4
benzoyl chloride	2,4-xylenol methyl ether	5
acetyl chloride	1-methyl-3,4-dimethoxybenzene	6
	1-methyl-3,5-dimethoxybenzene	4; 6
acyl halides	*o*-dimethoxybenzene	4
	1,2,5-trimethoxybenzene	4
	1,2,3-trimethoxybenzene	4
	1,2,4-trimethoxybenzene	5
aroyl chlorides	2-chloroanisole	4
	4-chloroanisole	6
acyl chlorides	2,4-dimethoxybenzoic acid	5
phenylacetyl chloride	phenol	4
	1-methyl-2-hydroxybenzene	5
	1-methyl-3-hydroxybenzene	6
acetyl chloride	resorcinol	4
	4-ethylresorcinol	6
	2-methoxydiphenyl ether	5; 4′
	2,2′-dimethoxydiphenyl ether	4′,5; 5,5′

Acyl Halide	Cyclic Compound	Position of Attachment of Acyl Group
chloroacetyl chloride	4-acetamino-1,2-dimethylbenzene	5
acetyl chloride	biphenyl	4; 4,4′
	1-methylnaphthalene	4
	2-methylnaphthalene	8; 6, 8
	2,6-dimethylnaphthalene	1
	1-benzylnaphthalene	4
	2-benzylnaphthalene	6
benzoyl chloride	1-methoxynaphthalene	4
acetyl chloride	2-methoxynaphthalene	1
benzoyl chloride	1,5-dimethoxynaphthalene	4, 8
	2,6-dimethoxynaphthalene(*)	1, 5
acetyl chloride	1-bromonaphthalene	4
	2-bromonaphthalene	1
benzoyl chloride	1,5-dichloronaphthalene	8
p-chlorobenzoyl chloride	1,4-dichloronaphthalene	8
acetyl chloride	tetralin	1
acyl chlorides	thiophene	2
	2-methylthiophene	5
	3-methylthiophene	2
carbamyl chloride	3,4-dimethylthiophene	2
acetyl chloride	2-methyl-3-carbethoxypyrrole	5

(*)Cleavage of both methyl groups occurs during the reaction.

Reactions of Benzene and its Derivatives with Various Types of Acyl Halides

Acetyl chloride gives *p*-chloroacetophenone in good yield with chlorobenzene;[180] with *diphenyl ether*, *p*-phenoxyacetophenone or 4,4′-diacetyldiphenyl is obtained.[181] *Ethyleneglycoldiphenyl ether* gives with acetyl chloride ethyleneglycol bis-(4-chloracetylphenyl) ether.[182] The 4-acetyl derivative of resorcinol diethyl ether or 4,6-diacetyl resorcinol monoethyl ether results from the reaction of acetyl chloride and *resorcinol diethyl ether*, depending on the proportions of the acid chloride and of aluminum chloride.[183] With *5-methylresorcinol* and acetyl chloride, 4,7-dimethyl-5-hydroxy coumarin and orsacetophenone result. Stearoyl biphenyls have been obtained from stearoyl chloride and *biphenyl* or *substituted biphenyls*.[184] The condensation of stearoyl chloride and *salicylic acid* results in the formation of 5-stearoyl-2-hydroxybenzoic acid.[185]

Reactions with Haloacyl Halides

As a rule, only the halogen attached to the carbonyl group in haloacyl halides is replaced with an aromatic radical in the Friedel-Crafts reaction,[186] although internal condensation may take place involving a reactive group in the aromatic residue and the halogen of the haloacyl radical.

Chloroacetyl chloride reacting with *p*-tolylmethyl sulfide gives a keto dihydrothionaphthene,

$$CH_3C_6H_3 \underset{\displaystyle S}{\overset{\displaystyle CO}{\diagdown \diagup}} CH_2$$

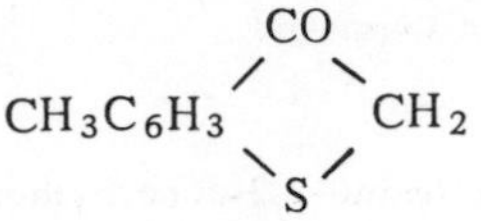

in 50% yield; with *phenoxyacetic acid*, p-(chloracetyl)-phenoxyacetic acid, $ClCH_2COC_6H_4OCH_2COOH$, results, while with diphenyl ether, bis-(ω-chloracetylphenyl) ether is obtained.[187] An excess of chloracetyl chloride reacting with biphenyl gives p,p'-bis-(chloracetyl)-biphenyl in 35% yield.[188] Bromacetyl bromide gives monoacylated derivatives with toluene, xylene and ethyl benzene, but a diacylated product with mesitylene,[189] a behavior which is also shown by α-bromopropionyl and α-bromobutyryl chlorides. Bromacetyl bromide reacting with resorcinol dimethyl ether gives α-bromo-2-hydroxy-4-methoxyacetophenone, together with a little of the α-chloracetyl derivative.[190] Coumarins may be formed if an alkyl group is present in the *meta* position with respect to an alkoxy group.[191] *Dichloracetyl chloride* gives with phenetole, dichloracetyl-phenetole. The reaction of *trichloracetyl chloride* with *benzene* takes an unusual course, resulting in the formation of triphenyl vinyl alcohol,

$$(C_6H_5)_2C = C(C_6H_5)OH$$

although the normal condensation product, trichloracetophenone is obtained when moist aluminum chloride is used in the reaction.[192]

β-*Chloropropionyl chloride* reacting with phenol gives phenyl β-chloropropionic ester in 45 to 50% yield. On treatment with water, the ester is transformed to o-hydroxyphenyl β-chloroethyl ketone in 40% yield, and this is transformed to chromanone,[193]

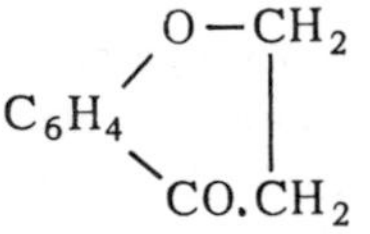

$$C_6H_4 \underset{\displaystyle CO.CH_2}{\overset{\displaystyle O-CH_2}{\diagup \diagdown \quad |}}$$

The reaction of α-bromisopropyl bromide with benzene proceeds in an abnormal manner, giving 2-methylhydrindone.[194] β-*Chlorobutyryl chloride* gives with p-cresol methyl ether, o-β-(chlorobutyryl)-p-cresol, which on treatment with alkali yields 2,6-dimethylchromanone,

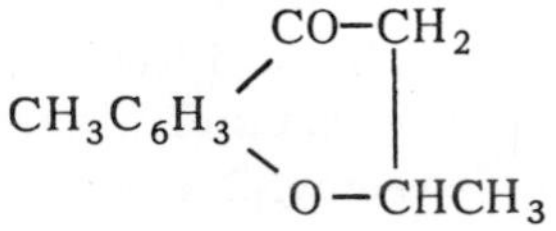

$$CH_3C_6H_3 \underset{\displaystyle O-CHCH_3}{\overset{\displaystyle CO-CH_2}{\diagup \quad\quad |}}$$

With α-*bromoisobutyryl bromide* and sym-m-xylenol methyl ether, 1,1,3,5-tetramethylcoumarone,

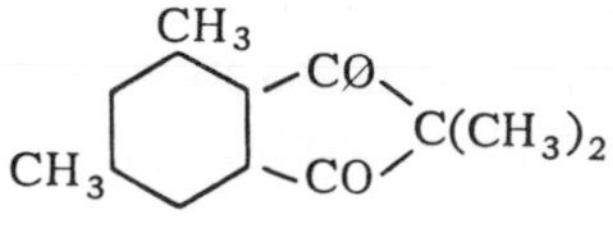

is obtained. Resorcinol gives with α-*bromovaleryl chloride*, 1-propyl-5-hydroxy-coumarone,

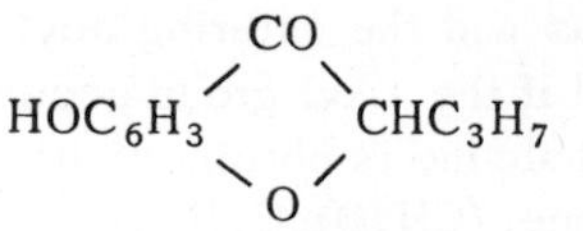

α-Bromo-β-phenylpropionyl chloride and hydroquinone dimethyl ether reacting in carbon disulfide solution give 2-hydroxy-5-methoxyphenyl α-bromo-β-phenylethyl ketone.[195] β-Phenyl-α,β-dibromopropionyl chloride, $C_6H_5CHBrCHBrCOCl$, reacts with benzene to form the compound

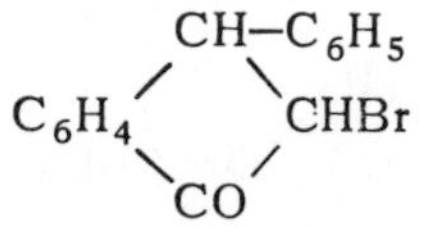

Esters of *α-halo acids* may undergo ring closure, a β-halo ester being probably formed as an intermediate:[196]

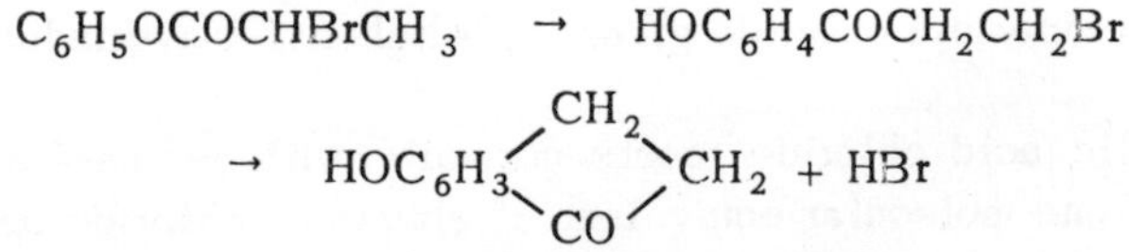

$$C_6H_5OCOCHBrCH_3 \rightarrow HOC_6H_4COCH_2CH_2Br$$

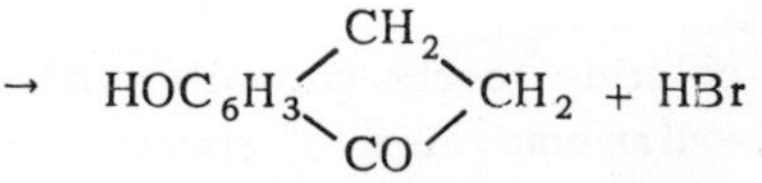

A ketonic group present in the aromatic nucleus favors ring closure.

Reactions with Unsaturated Acid Halides

Crotoyl chloride, $CH_3CH{=}CHCOCl$, reacts with *p*-xylene to form a hydrindone. Hydrindone formation does not take place, however, with benzene, toluene and *o*- and *m*-xylenes.[197] Hydrindone formation takes place also with *p*-cresol methyl ether.[198] With *sym-m*-xylenol methyl ether, 2,5,7-trimethylchromanone results:[199]

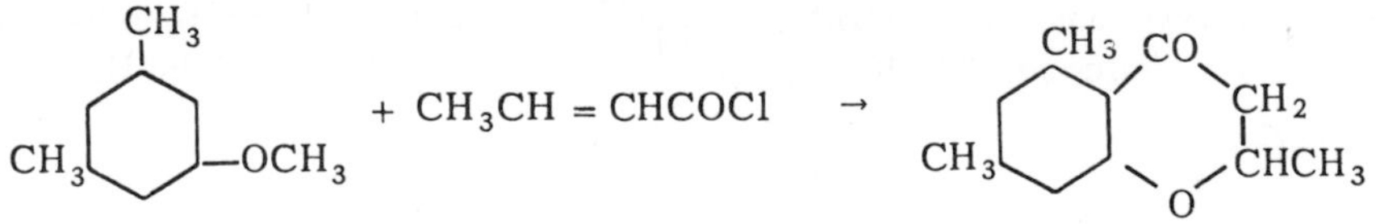

β,β-Dimethylacrylyl chloride, $(CH_3)_2C = CHCOCl$, gives with benzene, isobutenyl phenyl ketone in 40% yield;[200] with pseudocumene, isopropylidene-2,4,5-trimethylacetophenone is obtained.[201] With *p*-cresol methyl ether, *o*-isobutenyl-*p*-cresyl ketone is formed, which may be converted by heating to 2,2,6-trimethylchromanone,

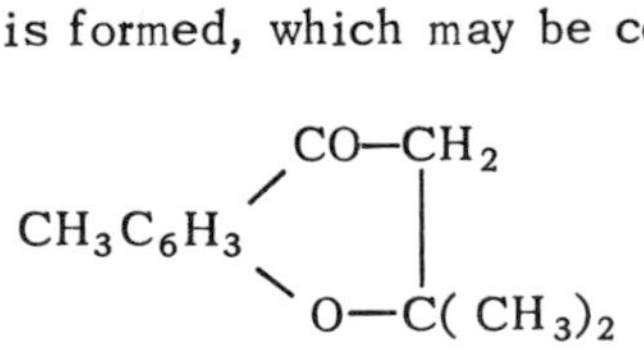

Cinnamoyl chloride gives a hydrindone and β,β-diphenylpropiophenone with benzene;[202] some of the normal reaction product is also obtained with bromobenzene and mesitylene. The normal chalcone formation is observed with toluene, *o*-xylene and, in some measure, with *m*-xylene. The direction in which the reaction proceeds is determined largely by the relative position of the allyl groups in the aromatic nucleus and the entering acyl group; ring closure is retarded or completely prevented if the alkyl group occupies the meta position with respect to the acyl group. A chalcone is obtained with biphenyl. Cinnamoyl chloride gives 2,4-dimethoxychalcone, $(CH_3O)_2C_6H_3COCH=CHC_6H_5$, with resorcinol dimethyl ether,[203] and 2′, 4′-dihydroxychalcone with resorcinol; with o-cresol, 3-methyl-4-hydroxy-chalcone is obtained,[204] while with phorglucinol, 5,7-dihydroxyflavone,

$$
(HO)_2C_6H_2 \diagdown \hspace{-1.2em} \diagup \begin{array}{l} CO-CH_2 \\ | \\ O-CHC_6H_5 \end{array}
$$

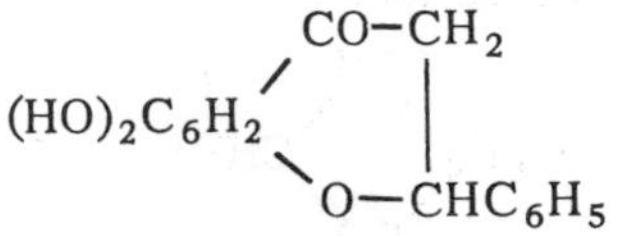

results. *α-Chloro-trans-cinnamoyl* chloride gives 2-chloro-3-phenyl-1-hydrindone with benzene, and 2-chloro-3-phenyl-5,7-dimethyl-1-hydrindone with m-xylene. *β-Chloro-trans*-cinnamoyl chloride gives 3,3-diphenyl-1-hydrindone with benzene.[205]

Phenylpropiolic acid chloride reacts normally with p-cresol methyl ether in the presence of one molecular equivalent of aluminum chloride and under strong cooling. When two molecular equivalents of aluminum chloride are used, and the reaction is carried out at room temperature, 5-methyl-2-hydroxy-β-chlorochalcone, $CH_3C_6H_3(OH)COCH = C(Cl)C_6H_5$, is obtained in 60% yield.[206]

Reaction with certain Aryl-substituted and Miscellaneous other Aliphatic Acyl Chlorides

β-Phenylpropionyl chloride gives the normal condensation product with aromatic hydrocarbons in low yield, because of ring closure in the chloride.[207] Carbomethoxyoxycoumaroyl chloride, $CH_3OCOOC_6H_4CH_2CH_2COCl$, gives with phlorglucinol a chalcone, $CH_3OCOC_6H_4CH=CHCOC_6H_2(OH)_3$ and the flavanone

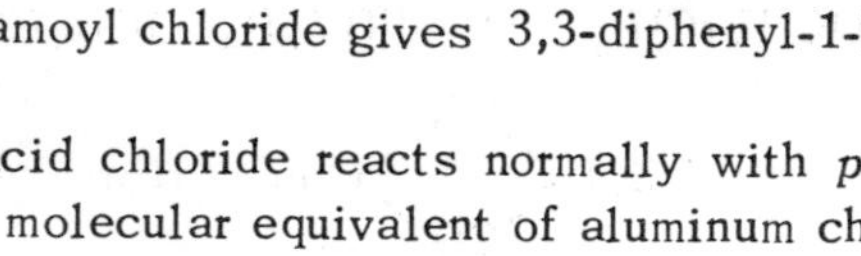

$$
(HO)_2C_6H_3 \diagdown \hspace{-1.2em} \diagup \begin{array}{l} CO-CH_2 \\ | \\ O-CHC_6H_4OCOOCH_3 \end{array} \quad [208]
$$

γ-Phenylbutyryl chloride and its derivatives containing alkyl groups in the side chain undergo internal condensation yielding ketotetrahydronaphthalene and its alkyl substituted derivatives.[393] Triphenylvinyl alcohol, $(C_6H_5)_2C=C(OH)C_6H_5$, results through the Friedel-Crafts reaction of *acetylmandelyl chloride*,

$$
C_6H_5CH(OCOCH_3)COCl
$$

with benzene.[209]

Diphenylacetyl chloride, $(C_6H_5)_2CHCOCl$, gives chiefly triphenylmethane and some triphenylvinyl alcohol, with benzene.[210] *Phenyl p-tolylacetyl chloride* and benzene give diphenylmethane and triphenyl carbinol. Attempted acylation of benzene with phenyl-α-naphthylacetyl chloride results in the formation of a ring compound,

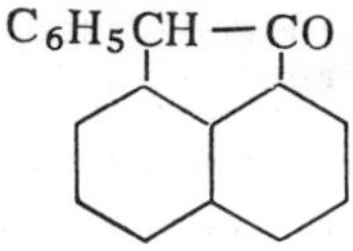

Phenoxyacetyl chloride, $C_6H_5OCH_2COCl$, gives with resorcinol dimethyl ether, 2,4-dimethoxyphenyl phenoxymethyl ketone.[211]

Carbamyl chloride, H_2NCOCl, reacting with benzene and other aromatic hydrocarbons in carbon disulfide solution gives benzamide.[212] N-Alkylcarbamyl chlorides react in a similar manner. Carbamyl chloride condenses readily also with mono- and polyphenol ethers and with ethers of polynuclear phenols and thio ethers.[213] Mono-substitution takes place with diphenyl and disubstitution takes place with ethyleneglycol diphenyl ether.

Carbamyl chloride may be prepared by heating cyanuric chloride in a stream of dry hydrogen chloride. The gas is passed directly into a slurry of a solution of the aromatic hydrocarbon in carbon disulfide and aluminum chloride.[212] Carbamyl chloride, while unstable in the free state, forms a stable complex with aluminum chloride, which is obtained readily by adding aluminum chloride, in small quantities, to a solution of carbamyl chloride in carbon disulfide, and distilling the solvent by gently heating the mass.

Benzamidoacetyl chloride (hippuryl chloride), $C_6H_5CONHCH_2COCl$, reacts with veratrole to form 4-benzamidoacetylveratrole,

$$(CH_3O)_2C_6H_3COCH_2NHCOC_6H_5$$

Other 1,2-dialkoxybenzenes react similarly.

Phthalylglycyl chloride reacts with benzene to form a ketone,

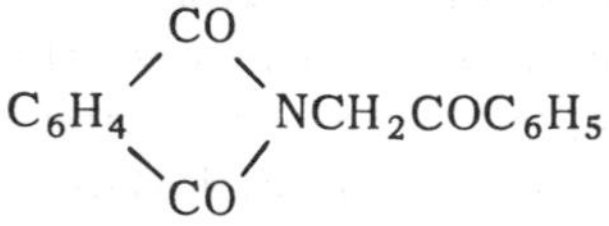

with veratrole, α-phthalimido-3,4-dimethoxyacetophenone is obtained. Homologs of this acyl chloride react similarly.[214] ζ-Phthalimidooenantophenone has been obtained in good yield by this method.[215] Amino ketones may be obtained by hydrolysis of the reaction product, and the reaction offers a satisfactory method for the preparation of α-amino aralkyl ketones.[216] Phthalimidohydrocinnamoyl chloride gives β-phthalimidohydrindone,

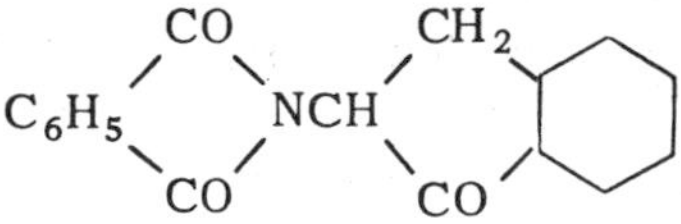

Reactions with Aromatic Acid Chlorides

Benzoyl chloride reacting with *o-* and *m-dichlorobenzenes* gives 3,4- and 2,4-dichlorobenzophenone respectively.[217] Tarry products are obtained with *p*-dichloro and *p*-dibromobenzenes.[218] The Friedel-Crafts reaction of *thiophenol*

ethers with benzoyl chloride proceeds readily with the formation of phenoxyphenyl alkyl sulfides in 80 to 85% yield.[219] The reaction proceeds with even greater ease with alkylated thiophenol ethers. The reaction of benzoyl chloride with *triphenylmethane* results in the formation of a monobenzoylated derivative;[220] with diphenyl, 4-benzoyldiphenyl is obtained,[221] halobenzoyl chlorides reacting in a similar manner.[222] With *asym-m*-xylenol methyl ether, *ortho* substitution occurs with simultaneous saponification of the ether group and with the formation of some *meta*-acylated product.[398] Benzoyl chloride and *hydroquinone* yield 2,5-dibenzoylhydroquinone.[223] Both bromines are replaced with the chlorophenyl group in the reaction of *ω-brom-o-toluyl bromide* with chlorobenzene.[218] *Iodobenzoyl chloride* reacting with iodobenzene gives diiodobenzophenone in about 4.5% yield.[224] *Anthraquinonecarboxylic acid chloride* gives benzoylanthraquinone with benzene, and 1-*p*-chlorobenzoylanthraquinone with chlorobenzene.[225]

Pyridinecarboxylic acid chloride gives pyridyl phenyl ketones with aromatic hydrocarbons, although the presence of a small amount of thionyl chloride appears to be essential for the success of the reaction.

4-Dimethyamino-1-naphthoyl chloride gives with dimethylaniline, 4-dimethylaminophenyl-4′-dimethylamino-1-naphthoyl ketone,[226] although only tarry products are obtained in the reaction of the chloride with 1-(dimethylamino) naphthalene.

The chlorides of *p*- and *m*-nitrobenzoic acid are capable of undergoing the Friedel-Crafts reaction, while *o*-nitrobenzoyl chloride reacts only in exceptional cases, as for example, with anisole with which it gives 2-nitro-4-methoxybenzophenone.[227] *o*-Nitrobenzoyl chloride may be made to react with benzene, however, by using ferric chloride as a catalyst instead of aluminum chloride.[228] 4-Bromo-3-nitrobenzoyl chloride reacts normally with bromobenzene giving 4,4′-dibromo-3-nitrobenzophenone.[229] Dinitrosubstitution does not influence the course of the reaction, 4-chloro-3,5-dinitrobenzoyl chloride yielding 4-chloro-3,5-dinitrobenzophenone with benzene.[230] Dinitrosalicylyl chloride gives with benzene 2,4-dinitroxanthone.[231]

Reactions with Dibasic Acid Halides

Reactions with Phosgene

Phosgene is capable of reacting with many aromatic compounds in the absence of catalysts[232] but the reaction generally proceeds more readily in the presence of aluminum chloride. The complex, $C_6H_5COCl.AlCl_3$, results through the reaction with benzene in the presence of aluminum chloride; it reacts rapidly with an additional molecule of benzene to form benzophenone. The complex is insoluble in carbon disulfide and may be obtained in good yield when the reaction with benzene is carried out in this solvent. Benzoic acid results through the hydrolysis of the complex. Hexamethylbenzophenone results from the reaction of phosgene and pseudocumene,[233] but only the carboxylic acid chloride is obtained with durene and pentamethylbenzene when the reaction is carried out at 0 to −10°. 4,4-Diphenylbenzophenone is obtained with diphenyl and phosgene. [234]

Reactions with Oxalyl Chloride

Oxalyl chloride is decomposed by aluminum chloride to phosgene and carbon monoxide, [235] and the products of Friedel-Crafts reaction with this chloride are often identical with those of phosgene. The products obtained with some compounds depends on the conditions.

Thus, benzophenone is obtained in good yield upon the gradual addition of 26 gm of aluminum chloride to a solution of 12.7 gm of oxalyl chloride in a mixture of 25 gm benzene and 50 cc carbon disulfide, while benzoyl chloride results in almost quantitative yield when oxalyl chloride is added slowly to a strongly cooled mixture of benzene, carbon disulfide and aluminum chloride. [236] With oxalyl bromide a small amount of benzil is obtained.

The course of the reaction depends also on the reactivity of the aromatic compound. Carboxylic acid chlorides are obtained if the rate of reaction of the aromatic component is much lower than the rate of decomposition of the chloride, while on the other hand, arylglyoxylic acid chlorides are formed with the more reactive aromatic compounds. Open-chain diketones are obtained with very reactive hydrocarbons and with ethers, and with certain types of cyclic compounds ring closure may take place giving cyclic diketones.

The reaction of oxalyl chloride with biphenyl results in the formation of p-biphenylcarboxylic acid chloride, [237] while p,p'-ditolyl-(p,p'-dimethylbiphenyl) gives principally a dicarboxylic acid chloride and a considerable proportion of p,p'-dimethylphenanthraquinone. o,o-Bitolyl and its m,m'-isomer give exclusively the corresponding dicarboxylic acid chloride. With diphenylmethane, diphenylmethane-4-monocarboxylic and -4,4'-dicarboxylic acid chlorides are obtained. [238] Triphenylmethane reacts similarly giving mono-, di- and tricarboxylic acids.

The reaction of oxalyl chloride with phenols results first in the formation of ester chlorides of oxalic acid, and these rapidly undergo transformation, giving salicylic acid chloride or a derivative thereof: [239]

$$C_6H_5OH + ClCOCOCl \rightarrow HCl + C_6H_5OCOCOCl$$

$$\rightarrow C_6H_4{\overset{\displaystyle COCl}{\underset{\displaystyle OH}{\Big\langle}}} \xrightarrow{H_2O} C_6H_4{\overset{\displaystyle COOH}{\underset{\displaystyle OH}{\Big\langle}}}$$

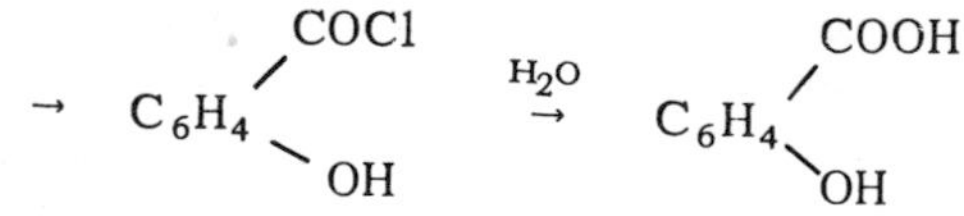

Ring formation takes place with m-cresol, and the reaction product is a methyl-coumarandione,

$$CH_3C_6H_3{\overset{\displaystyle CO}{\underset{\displaystyle O}{\big\langle}}}{\overset{\displaystyle}{\underset{\displaystyle}{\big\rangle}}}CO$$

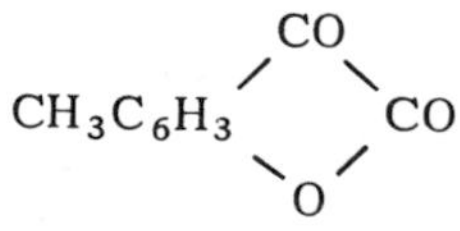

Other phenols having a methyl group in the *meta* position with respect to the hydroxyl group also yield coumarandiones.

Anisole and oxalyl chloride give anisil, $CH_3OC_6H_4COCOC_6H_4OCH_3$ in 90% yield.[173]   A diketone is obtained also in the reaction of oxalyl chloride with *o-cresol methyl ether*, while with *m-* and *p-*cresol methyl ethers the corresponding hydroxy acids are obtained.[241] Protocatechuic acid results from *veratrole*,[242] and *phenetole* gives 4,4'-diethoxybenzil.[243]   With *resorcinol dimethyl ether*, 2,4,2',4'-tetramethoxybenzophenone results,[244] while *hydroquinone dimethyl ether* yields 2,5,2',5'-tetramethoxybenzophenone.[245]

The Friedel-Crafts reaction with oxalyl chloride and *diphenyl sulfide* results in the formation of 4,4'-diphenylthiolbenzil,[246] $C_6H_5SC_6H_4COCOC_6H_4SC_6H_5$.

Oxalyl chloride and *ethyl aniline* give N-ethylisatin,[247]

$$C_6H_4 \overset{\displaystyle CO}{\underset{\displaystyle N-C_2H_5}{\diagup \diagdown}} CO$$

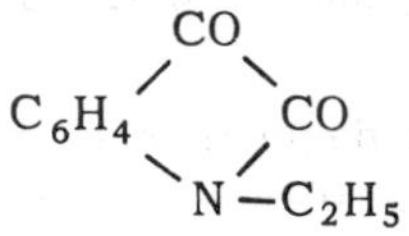

The reaction appears to be a general one for aromatic alkylamines.

Acridinecarboxylic acid results from the reaction of oxalyl chloride with *diphenylamine.* *o-*Anilinobenzoylformyl chloride is the probable intermediate.[152]

Methyl chloroglyoxylate, $CH_3OCOCOCl$, condenses with *mesitylene* to give methyl mesitylglyoxylate; ethyl chloroglyoxylate and *cymene* yield ethyl cymyl-glyoxylate,[248] $(CH_3)_2CHC_6H_3(CH_3)COCOOC_2H_5$. Glyoxylic esters,

$$ROC_6H_4COCOOC_2H_5$$

are also obtained with alkylphenol ethers and ethyl chloroglyoxylate.

Reactions with Malonyl Chloride

The Friedel-Crafts condensation of malonyl chloride with aromatic hydrocarbons results in the formation of diketones of the type $RCOCH_2COR$, a ketone $RCOCH_3$, and a hydrocarbon.[249]   An indandione results from diethylmalonyl chloride, $(C_2H_5)_2C(COCl)_2$ and benzene, while with dimethylmalonyl chloride and an equivalent of benzene, isopropyl phenyl ketone, dimethyldibenzoyl-methane and a lactone, $(C_6H_5)_2\overline{CC(CH_3)_2COO}$ are obtained.[250] Dimethylmalonyl chloride gives an indandione when an excess of benzene is used. Toluene gives a diketone while cymene forms an indandione with this halide.

Diethylmalonyl chloride reacting with *veratrole* in carbon disulfide solution in the presence of aluminum chloride gives 5,6-dimethoxy-, 5-methoxy-6-hydroxy-, 5,6-dihydroxy-, and 4,5-dihydroxy-2,2-diethylindan-1,3-diones.[251] With resorcinol dimethyl ether and malonyl chloride, 7-hydroxy-5-methoxyindan-1,3-dione,

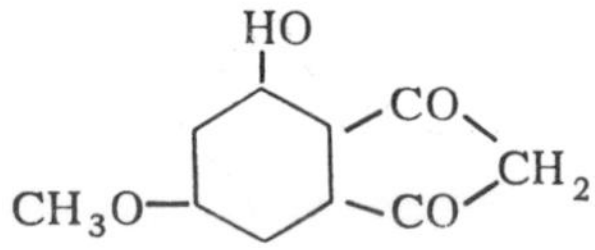

is obtained,[251] while with diethylmalonyl chloride and *hydroquinone dimethyl ether*, 4-hydroxy-7-methoxy-2,2-diethylindandione and 3-diethyl-6-methoxybenzotetronic acid are formed.[250]

Reactions with Succinyl Chloride and Miscellaneous Other Dicarboxylic Acid Chlorides

Succinyl chloride is capable of reacting with one or two molecular proportions of *benzene* to form β-benzoylpropionyl chloride or α-β-dibenzoylethane.[252] The chloride may also react as a lactone, giving with benzene γ,γ-diphenylbutyrolactone.[253] In the reaction with *toluene*, the diketone as well as the ditolylbutyrolactone, $(CH_3C_6H_4)_2\overline{CCH_2CH_2COO}$ are obtained.[253] *Halosuccinyl chlorides* react normally to form the corresponding dibenzoyl derivatives, without appreciable change to optical isomers.[254]

Adipyl chloride, $ClCO(CH_2)_4COCl$, forms 1,4-dibenzoylbutane with benzene. Ethyl δ-benzoylvalerate has been obtained in 80% yield from ethyl adipyl chloride.[255]

Fumaryl chloride, $ClCOCH{=}CHCOCl$, gives with *benzene trans*-dibenzoylethylene in 74% yield. The corresponding derivatives are obtained with toluene, mesitylene and with chlorobenzene.[256] Reacting with benzene at room temperature, fumaryl chloride gives bis-(*p*-phenylbenzoyl) ethylene;[257] with anisole, dianisoylethylene is obtained in small yield.[256] Reacting in carbon disulfide solution with *dibromofumaryl chloride,* mesitylene gives *trans*-bis-(2,4,6-trimethylbenzoyl)dibromoethylene; reaction proceeds more readily with the *trans* than with the *cis* isomer.

The chlorocarbonyl group farthest removed from the methyl group in *mesaconyl chloride* enters the Friedel-Crafts reaction:

$$\begin{array}{c} CH_3CCOCl \\ \| \\ Cl\,COCH \end{array} + C_6H_5Br \xrightarrow{AlCl_3} \begin{array}{c} CH_3CCOCl \\ \| \\ BrC_6H_4COCH \end{array} + HCl$$

while the reverse holds true of *citraconyl chloride:*

$$\begin{array}{c} CH_3CCOCl \\ \| \\ HCCOCl \end{array} + C_6H_5Br \xrightarrow{AlCl_3} \begin{array}{c} CH_3CCOC_6H_4Br \\ \| \\ HCCOCl \end{array} + HCl$$

The bromobenzoyl derivative is obtained in very small yield in the latter case.

Cis-pseudo-β-benzoyldibromoacrylyl chloride, $C_6H_5\overline{CClCBr = CBrCOO}$, gives with benzene 1,1-diphenyl-2-bromo-3-carboxyindene,

$$\begin{array}{ccc} & C{=}(C_6H_5)_2 & \\ C_6H_4 & & CBr \\ & CCOOH & \end{array}$$

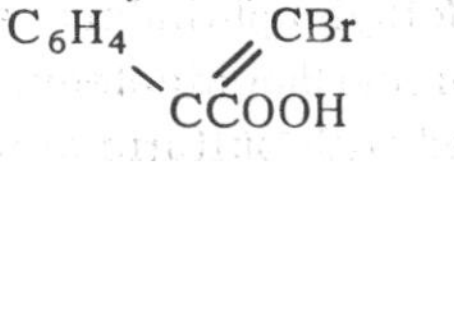

Phthaloyl chloride reacting with benzene in the presence of aluminum chloride at a low temperature and for a prolonged period gives 2-benzoylbenzoic acid, while rapid reaction at a higher temperature leads to the formation of diphenylphthalide.[258] Diphenylphthalide is obtained from the reaction of phthaloyl chloride with phenetole,[259] and bis-(trimethoxyphenyl)-phthalide with pyrogallol.[260] Reaction with *p*-tolyl methyl sulfide gives 2′,7′-dimethyl-1-thiofluoran in 50% yield.[261] Acid chlorides of monoalkyl esters of aromatic dicarboxylic acids, $ROCOC_6H_4COCl$, reacting with benzene give the keto esters,

$$ROCOC_6H_4COC_6H_5.$$ [262]

o-Benzoylbenzoyl chloride, $C_6H_5COC_6H_4COCl$, gives with benzene phthalophenone,[263]

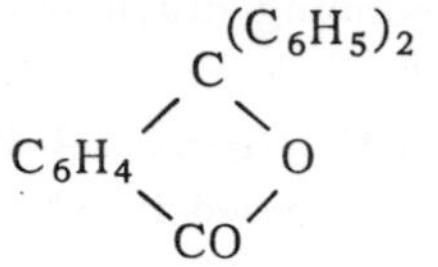

Dicarboxylic acid chlorides of polynuclear hydrocarbons condense with benzene forming dibenzoyl derivatives.[264]

Isophthalyl chloride reacts normally with benzene to form isophthalophenone, *m*-$C_6H_5COC_6H_4COC_6H_5$.[265]

o-Phthalyl tetrachloride, $Cl_3CC_6H_4COCl$, gives with benzene diphenylanthrone,[266]

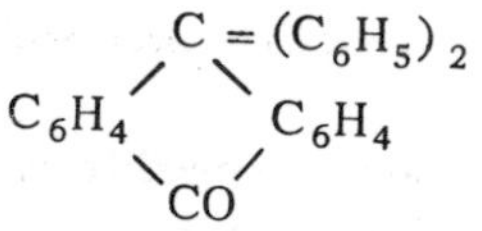

Reactions with Polynuclear Compounds

Acetylation of *naphthalene* results in the formation of α- and β-naphthyl methyl ketones in a total yield of 75%, the α-isomer forming 50 to 70% of the ketones.[267] With β-methylnaphthalene, 6- and 8-acetyl and 6,8-diacetyl derivatives are obtained,[268] while α-methylnaphthalene gives the 4-acetyl derivative.[269] Benzoyl chloride gives with naphthalene 1- and 2-benzoylnaphthalenes.[270] The 1-benzoyl derivative is obtained by adding freshly sublimed aluminum chloride in small portions to a carbon disulfide solution of the hydrocarbon and benzoyl chloride cooled to 0°.[271] Diacylated derivatives are readily obtained from 2,6- and 2,7-dimethylnaphthalene.[272] Dichloracetyl-α-naphthyl ether is obtained through the reaction of dichloracetyl chloride and α-naphthyl methyl ether, while β-naphthyl methyl ether fails to react with the chloride.[182] Acylation of the β-compound with some acid chlorides proceeds well, the acyl group entering largely the 1-position in carbon disulfide solution, and the 6-position in nitrobenzene. α-Methylnaphthalene and β-chloropropionyl chloride give 1-methyl-4-(β-chloropropionyl)naphthalene; the latter condenses to an indanone derivative when heated with sulfuric acid:[273]

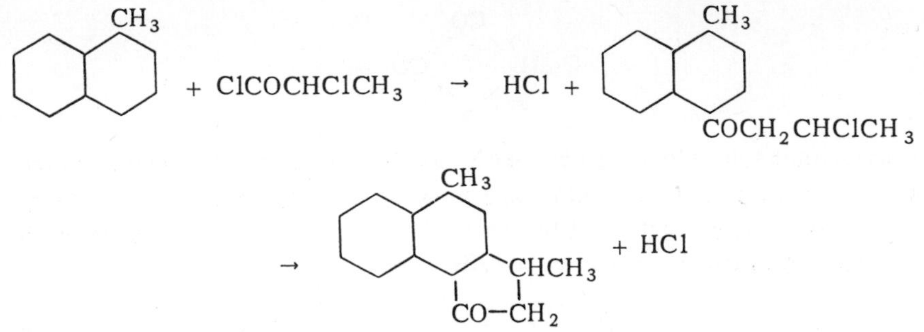

Indanones are similarly obtained from α-chloro-, α-bromo-, and 1,6-dimethylnaphthalene. β-chlorobutyryl chloride reacts in the same manner as β-chloropropionyl chloride. It may be noted that ring closure of this type occurs in the benzene series only when more than two alkyl groups are attached to the aromatic nucleus.

Acyl halides give with tetralin, β-acyltetralin.[274]

Friedel-Crafts acylation reaction has been applied to *acenaphthene*,[275] and to a very limited extent also to *anthracene*.[276] It may be pointed out that *ms*-acetylanthracene isomerizes under the influence of aluminum chloride to α- and β-acetylanthracenes.

Phenanthrene is best acylated in solution in nitrobenzene at 0 to 15°, the product consisting largely of the 3-acyl derivative with a small amount of the 2-acyl derivative. 9,10-Dihydrophenanthrene is acylated exclusively at the 2-position.

Carbamyl chloride condenses readily with polynuclear hydrocarbons to form monocarboxylic amides; with naphthalene α-naphthoic amide is formed, while with 1-ethylnaphthalene, 1-ethyl-4-carboxynaphthalene amide results.[277] Aralkylcarbamyl halides reacting with pyrene give the 3-carbamyl derivative, disubstitution taking place when two molecular proportions of the halide are employed.[278]

The Friedel-Crafts reaction of *oxalyl chloride* with naphthene gives a mixture of α- and β-naphthoic acids;[279] with α-naphthyl methyl ether in carbon disulfide solution, 1,1′-dimethoxy-4,4′-binaphthoyl, $CH_3OC_{10}H_6COCOC_{10}H_6OCH_3$, is obtained in 60% yield,[280] while β-naphthyl methyl ether gives benzocoumarandione,

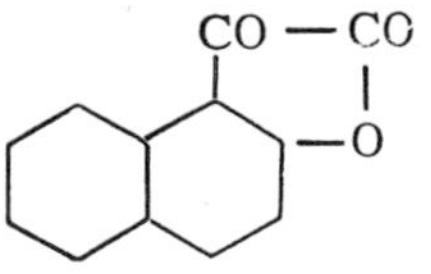

and a little methoxyacenaphthenequinone. β-Naphthyl benzyl ether gives a yellow acid of unknown structure. Oxalyl chloride reacting with β-thionaphthol in the absence of aluminum chloride forms β-thionaphthyloxalyl chloride; this is transformed under the action of aluminum chloride to β-thionaphthisatin,

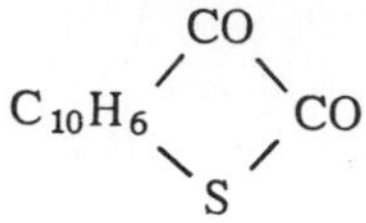

β-N-Ethylaminonaphthalene gives with oxalyl chloride β-ethylnaphthindole-1,2-dione. *N-Monoarylaminoanthraquinones* and oxalyl chloride give N-anthraquinonylisatins. The reaction of the chloride with *tetrahydroacenaphthene* leads to the formation of two isomeric carboxylic acids,[281]

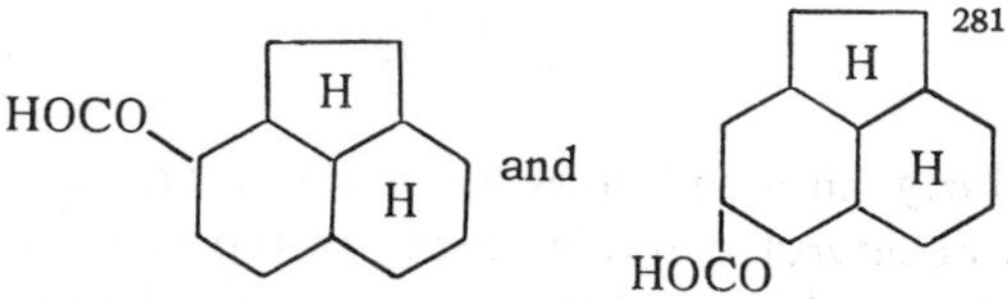

In the reaction of *anthracene* with oxalyl chloride, carboxylation takes place, but the normal acylation reaction also proceeds simultaneously, giving aceanthraquinone:

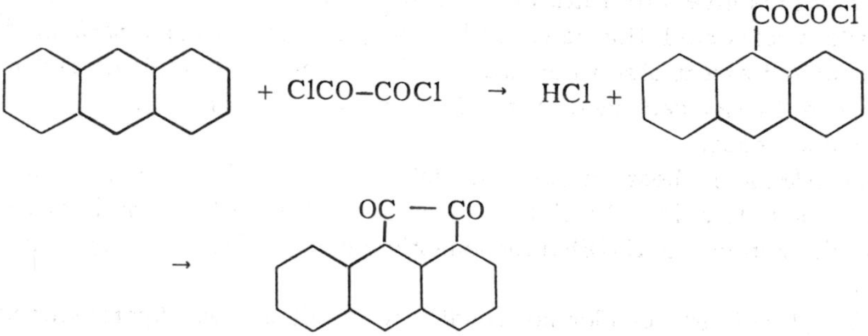

Carboxylation and quinone formation is also observed with β-methylanthracene, methylanthraquinone being the principal product of the reaction.[282]

Attempts have been made to use oxalylimido chloride instead of the acid chloride in order to avoid the difficulty involved in the use of the latter. Acenaphthoquinones have been obtained by this method from methyl and ethyl ethers of β-naphthol in 75% and 44% yield respectively.[283]

The Friedel-Crafts reaction of *malonyl chloride* with naphthalene results in the formation of *peri*-naphthindandione,[284]

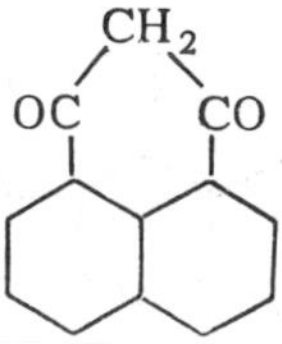

Three isomeric products are obtained with dimethylmalonyl chloride, 1,8-, 1,2- and 2,3-naphthodimethylindandione.[285] An indandione results also from the reaction of malonyl chloride and β-naphthol.[251] Uncrystallizable products are obtained from ethers of naphthols and of resorcinol. *Anthracene* gives anthracene-1,9-indandione.[286] Diethylmalonyl chlorides give diethylphenanthrone with anthracene, and 5,6-acenaphthenedimethylindandione and isoacenaphthenedimethylindandione with *acenaphthene.*[285]

The reaction of *succinyl chloride* with naphthalene results in the formation of α- and β-succinyl derivatives.

Reactions with Heterocyclic Compounds

Furan derivatives are capable of undergoing acylation by the Friedel-Crafts reaction, although stannic or ferric chlorides are preferable as catalysts for the condensation. *Coumarone* undergoes polymerization under the action of aluminum chloride and cannot, therefore, be acylated by use of this reagent; its dihydro derivatives, on the other hand, readily undergo the reaction. Thus *coumaran* gives 5-benzoylcoumaran,

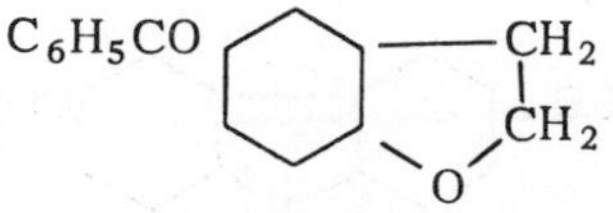

with benzoyl chloride.[287] Similarly, *chroman,* condensing with benzoyl chloride gives 6-benzoylchroman,

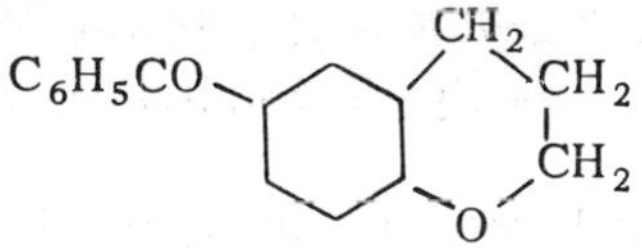

Dibenzofuran undergoes normal acylation with acetyl chloride to yield 3-acetylbenzofuran,[288]

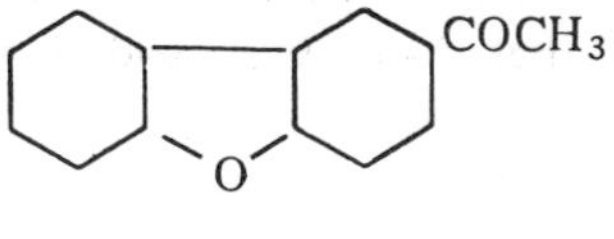

Diphenylene dioxide,

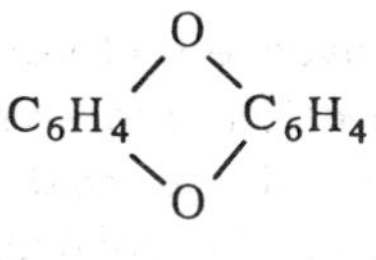

gives a 2,6-diacyl derivative,[289] while *xanthene,*

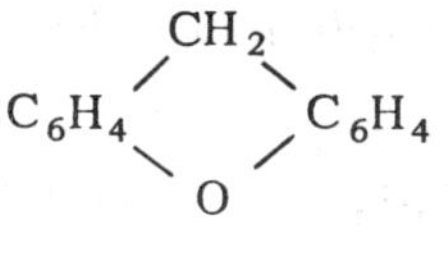

gives a 2-acyl derivative.[290]

Heterocyclic nitrogen compounds generally resist acylation by the Friedel-Crafts reaction, although many compounds of this class have been acylated. *Pyridine* fails to undergo the reaction, but an energetic evolution of hydrogen chloride may take place occasionally, resulting in the formation of tarry matter.[291] Acylated pyridines may be obtained, however, through the condensation of a pyridine carboxylic acid chloride with aromatic compounds. *Pyrrole* is acetylated to 2-acetylpyrrole in the absence of aluminum chloride,[292] while carbethoxyalkylpyrroles may be converted to acylated alkylpyrroles in almost quantitative yield, in the presence of aluminum chloride.[293]

Quinoline and most of its derivatives fail to undergo the Friedel-Crafts acylation. Some exceptions are known; thus, 8-hydroxyquinoline gives 5-acyl-8-hydroxyquinolines; 8-methoxyquinoline reacting with chloracetyl chloride in petroleum ether gives 8-methoxychloracetylquinoline in 80% yield.[294] 1-Acetyl-1,2,3,4-tetrahydroquinoline gives with chloracetyl chloride the 6-chloracetyl derivative.[295]

The acylation of *carbazole* by the Friedel-Crafts reaction leads to the formation of 3,6-diacylcarbazoles,[296]

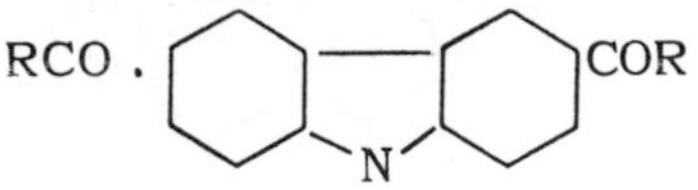

N-alkylated carbazoles also yielding 3,6-diacyl derivatives. N-acylcarbazoles, on the other hand, yield a 2-acyl-N-acyl pyrazole.[297] The Friedel-Crafts acylation of carbazoles is not easily accomplished; 5-chloro-1-phenyl-3-pyrazole, $C_6H_5NN = C(CH_3)CH = CCl$ readily undergoes the reaction however, giving the 4-aroyl derivatives. Aliphatic acyl chlorides and aroyl chlorides with strongly negative substituents in the *meta* or *para* position fail to undergo the reaction.[298] 1-Tolyl-3-methyl-4-chloropyrazole gives the 4-phenylketone with acyl halides in 90% yield, but 1-methyl- and 1-ethyl-chloropyrazole fail to undergo the reaction.

REACTIONS INVOLVING ACID ANHYDRIDES

Acid anhydrides may be employed effectively in the Friedel-Crafts reaction in place of acid halides. The reaction proceeds well with aliphatic or aromatic dicarboxylic anhydrides, and some of the most important practical applications of Friedel-Crafts synthesis involve the condensation of such anhydrides with aromatic compounds. *Ortho*-Benzoylbenzoic acid is obtained, for example, through the reaction of phthalic anhydride with benzene:[299]

$$C_6H_4\begin{matrix} / \text{CO} \backslash \\ \\ \backslash \text{CO} / \end{matrix}O + C_6H_6 \rightarrow HOCOC_6H_4COC_6H_5$$

When anhydrides are used in Friedel-Crafts reaction, sufficient aluminum chloride must be employed to allow for oxonium salt formation with both carbonyl groups such as

$$\underset{CH_3CO-O-COCH_3}{\overset{\overset{\cdot\cdot}{Cl}\ \ AlCl_2\ \ \overset{\cdot\cdot}{Cl}\ \ AlCl_2}{}}$$

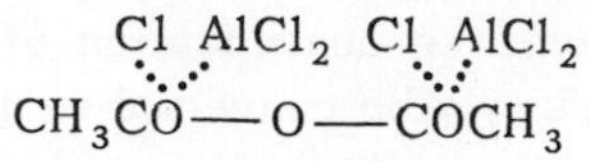

Substituents in the aromatic component have the same influence in the reaction with acid anhydrides as with acid halides. Alkylbenzenes and polynuclear hydrocarbons react more readily than benzene.[*] Halogens attached to carbon atoms in the aromatic ring exert a retarding influence, though exceptionally, fluorobenzene condenses readily with phthalic anhydride to form 4-fluoro-2-benzoylbenzoic acid. The intensity of the effect increases with the number of halogen atoms present in the nucleus, though it is possible to obtain 3′,4′-dichloro-2-benzoylbenzoic acid in 70% yield by the reaction of o-dichlorobenzene with phthalic anhydride at 100°.[300] Monochloronaphthalenes undergo normal condensation,[301] while 1,4-dichloronaphthalene gives a mixture of keto acids.[302] Esters of benzoic acid do not condense with phthalic anhydride, but the presence of a hydroxy group in the nucleus of the ester may bring about the reaction.

Where the possibility of formation of isomers exists, the isomeric compounds generally form simultaneously. Thus, 2-methylphthalic anhydride gives with benzene both 2-benzoyl-3- and -6-methylbenzoic acids, and naphthalene-1,2-dicarboxylic anhydride gives both α-benzoyl-β-naphthoic and β-benzoyl-α-naphthoic acids. Only one of the possible isomers is obtained with 3- and 4-nitro- and 3,5-dinitrophthalic anhydrides. Condensation takes place successfully with the former only with moist aluminum chloride, while anhydrous aluminum chloride causes resinification. The condensation of the three bromotoluenes with phthalic anhydride gives the same bromotolylbenzoic acid.[303]

Disubstitution is not common in the reaction of dicarboxylic acids with aromatic compounds, because of the inhibitive influence of the acyl group that first enters the nucleus. Disubstitution may also be hindered in the reaction with phthalic anhydride because of the formation of phthalides, which form in preference when an excess of the anhydride is employed, and also through ring closure which takes place under the extreme conditions necessary to bring about polysubstitution.

The Friedel-Crafts condensation generally proceeds well with substituted phthalic anhydrides. Tetrachlorophthalic anhydride shows enhanced reactivity, giving good yields of tetrachlorobenzoic acids. The great reactivity of this compound is indicated by its ability to react with p-dichlorobenzene and even with trichloro and nitrobenzenes.

The use of a deficiency of aluminum chloride in condensations with acid anhydrides favors the formation of phthalides;[304] phthalide formation is also favored by rapid initial heating, a fact which appears to be explained by the appearance of a viscous aluminum chloride complex capable of converting the still unreacted anhydride into the phthalide.

---

[*]Resinous products are obtained from the reaction of certain alkylbenzenes with phthalic anhydride.

The keto acids resulting from the condensation of dicarboxylic acid anhydrides with aromatic compounds may be converted to quinones. Quinone formation may be brought about directly in the course of Friedel-Crafts synthesis by carrying out the reaction in an aluminum chloride-sodium chloride melt at a temperature of 200° or over, the normal keto acids forming at lower temperatures. It may be noted, in this connection that benzoylbenzoic acid gives the lactone

$$C_6H_4 \underset{\diagdown CO \diagup}{\overset{\diagup C(Cl)C_6H_5 \diagdown}{{}}} O$$

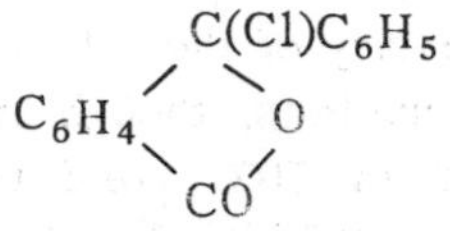

on treatment with phosphorus pentachloride.[305]

The Friedel-Crafts reaction may also be carried out by use of *esters* or *free acids* instead of the anhydrides. Yields with the acids are as high as with the anhydrides, although the reaction product is less pure. A two and one-half molal proportion of aluminum chloride is used, and a small amount of thionyl chloride or phosphorus trichloride is added. These halides should not be used in the reactions with anhydrides.

Procedure

The general procedure followed in carrying out the reaction with acid anhydrides is to heat a mixture of the anhydride with an excess of the hydrocarbon and aluminum chloride until the evolution of hydrogen chloride ceases. Alternatively, one-half mole of the hydrocarbon, 200 cc of carbon disulfide, 1.1 mole of aluminum chloride are mixed, one-half mole of the acid anhydride is added with stirring and the mass is heated on the water bath for half an hour with continued agitation. The reaction mixture is then cooled and poured on ice. the solvent is evaporated off, and the product is taken up with ether. The ethereal extract is washed with water, and with a limited quantity of dilute sodium carbonate solution, dried, the ether is evaporated off and the product is purified by distillation. Excellent yields of the keto compound are obtained by this procedure.[306]

In carrying out the reaction with monobasic acid anhydrides, it is necessary to use three molal proportions of aluminum chloride in order to utilize at least a portion of the acid formed in the first stage of the reaction.[307] One mole of aluminum chloride causes the decomposition of the anhydride to the halide of the acid and to an aluminum dichloride salt:

$$(RCO)_2O + AlCl_3 \quad \rightarrow \quad RCOCl + RCOOAlCl_2$$

the second mole is utilized in the formation of a molecular complex with the acyl chloride, while the third mole reacts with the dichloroaluminum salt, converting this to the reactive complex $RC(Cl)O \equiv AlCl_3$.

The usual procedure in carrying out the reaction of *phthalic anhydride* with aromatic hydrocarbons is to suspend one equivalent of aluminum chloride in a solution of the hydrocarbon in $1\frac{1}{2}$ to 2 parts of a solvent such as carbon disulfide, and to add a second equivalent of aluminum chloride and of phthalic anhydride with good agitation. Agitation is continued after the addition of all the chloride. Reaction generally proceeds automatically, although gentle warming may be necessary to initiate it. When the initial vigorous reaction subsides the mixture is heated under reflux with good agitation until the evolution of hydrogen chloride ceases. Heating for 2 to 20 hours may be necessary depending on the nature of the aromatic component. Better results are obtained in some instances when the aluminum chloride is added gradually and with good stirring to a cold solution of the phthalic anhydride and the aromatic compound in an appropriate solvent. After completion of the reaction the product is cautiously decomposed by the addition of the required quantity of dilute hydrochloric acid; the organic layer is washed with water, the solvent is removed by steam distillation, and the residue is extracted repeatedly with boiling dilute sodium carbonate solution. The free keto acid may be isolated from the aqueous solution of its sodium salt thus obtained by acidifying with dilute hydrochloric or sulfuric acid after cooling.

Petroleum ether, nitrobenzene and chlorobenzene may also be used as solvents; or the reaction may be simply carried out in excess of the hydrocarbon. In condensations with naphthalene and many homologs of benzene, chlorobenzene may be employed with satisfactory results. Excellent yields of naphthoylbenzoic acid are obtained by the reaction of naphthalene with phthalic anhydride in benzene, toluene or xylene solution. A purer product is obtained, however, when the reaction is carried out in *o*-dichlorobenzene solution. Yields are lower when carbon disulfide is used as a solvent. Satisfactory results are obtained in the reactions with phthalic anhydride when tetrachloroethane is used as a solvent.[308] Nitrobenzene, though inert toward acid chlorides and most anhydrides, undergoes the Friedel-Crafts reaction with tetrachlorophthalic anhydride.[309]

Good yield and products of greater purity are obtained with phthalic anhydride when the reaction is carried out at temperature lower than 45°, preferably at 25°.

The reaction may be best carried out in a jacketed ball-mill mounted on a horizontal axis, partially filled with iron balls or blocks of various sizes, and equipped with charging and discharging vents, and an exit opening for the hydrogen chloride evolved in the reaction. The complex is generally obtained as a free-flowing powder which is readily discharged and converted to the ketoacid.

The use of more than two molecular equivalents of aluminum chloride in reactions with phthalic anhydride favors the formation of phthalide. Phthalide formation is also favored by prolonged heating, a too rapid rate of heating, excessive reaction temperatures and inadequate mixing. The use of only one molal equivalent of aluminum chloride results in a considerable reduction in the yield of keto acid, and the formation of a little phthalide.

Keto acids resulting from the condensation of tetrahalophthalic anhydride with aromatic compounds yield phthalides upon treatment with acetic anhydride.[310] Keto acids obtained from tetraiodophthalic anhydride give rather low yields of phthalides by this treatment. Attempts to bring about ring closure in tetraiodobenzoyl compounds by treatment with aluminum chloride or sulfuric acid has resulted in decomposition.[311] Ring closure of *o*-hydroxybenzoyltetrachlorobenzoic acid through the removal of the chlorine atom in *ortho* position is brought about by simple heating with alkali:

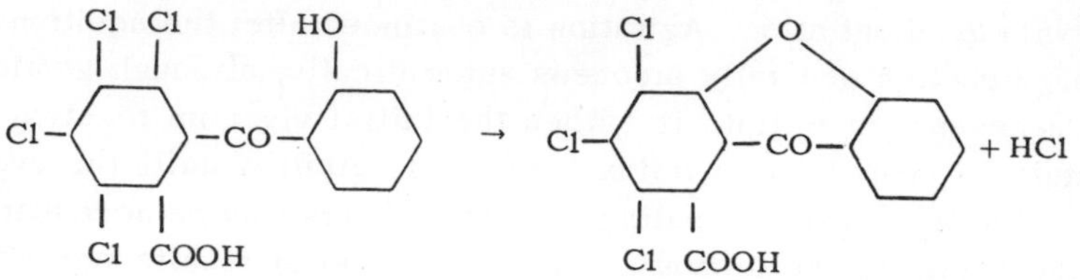

A satisfactory procedure for the preparation of β-benzoylacrylic acid is to shake 30 gm maleic anhydride suspended in benzene with 40 to 50 gm aluminum chloride and to heat the mixture after the lapse of 24 hours to 40 to 50° for ten to fifteen hours. The product is treated, as usual, with cold, dilute hydrochloric acid and the unreacted benzene is distilled off. The reaction with phenetole proceeds much more readily and β-(4-ethoxybenzoyl)acrylic acid may be prepared in good yield by gradually adding 24 gm aluminum chloride to a solution of 18 gm of phenetole and 10 gm of maleic anhydride in 80 cc carbon disulfide cooled in ice, and subsequently heating the mixture at 40 to 50° for three hours.

The condensation of phthalic anhydride in slight excess with phenols in the presence of a molecular equivalent of aluminum chloride and in the absence of a solvent generally results in the formation of phenolphthalein.

Position of Attachment of Acyl Groups

The carbonyl group generally enters the *ortho* position in the reaction of phthalic anhydride with phenols, naphthols and hydroxy anthracenes in solvents such as carbon disulfide or *sym*-tetrachlorethane. β-Naphthol gives a compound of the probable formula

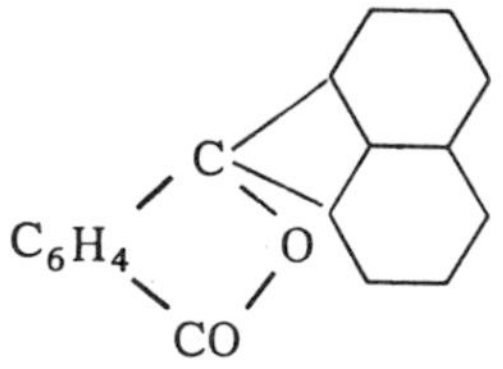

The position of entrance of the acyl group in the molecule of various organic compounds is given in the table below.

Acid Anhydride	Aromatic Compound	Position of Attachment of Acyl Group
succinic	1-methylnaphthalene	4
	2-methylnaphthalene	6
	2-isopropylnaphthalene	6
	2, 3-dimethylnaphthalene	7
	2,7-dimethylnaphthalene	1
maleic	1, 3-dimethylbenzene	4
	1, 2, 4-trimethylbenzene	5
	1-methyl-2-methoxybenzene	5
	1-methyl-4-methoxybenzene	6
	1-methyl-3-methoxybenzene	6
	1,4-dimethoxybenzene	6

Acid Anhydride	Aromatic Compound	Position of Attachment of Acyl Group
phthalic	1,3-dichlorobenzene	4
	2-chlorodiphenyl	4′
	4-chlorodiphenyl	4′
	2,5-dimethylthiophene	3
3,6-dichlorophthalic	toluene	4
	o-xylene	3
	m-xylene	?
	p-xylene	5
	naphthalene	1
	chlorobenzene	4
	p-dichlorobenzene	5
	1-hydroxy-4-methylbenzene	2

Reactions with Succinic and other Saturated Dicarboxylic Anhydrides

The Friedel-Crafts reaction of *succinic anhydride* with *benzene* results in the formation of β-benzoylpropionic acid. The reaction proceeds readily with *alkylated benzenes*, the yield ranging 80 to 90% of the theoretical.[312] Condensation proceeds readily also with *phenol ethers*. The reaction with *phenols* may be successfully carried out at 120 to 125° in *sym*-tetrachloroethane solution.[313] Monoethyl ethers of dihydroxyphenols do not undergo the reaction as readily as the dimethyl ethers.[314] Chlorobenzene is also capable of undergoing the reaction with succinic anhydride.[315] With *diphenyl*, β-(4-phenylbenzoyl)propionic acid is obtained in 70% yield.[316]

Succinic anhydride and *naphthalene* and *alkylated naphthalenes* readily undergo Friedel-Crafts condensation.[317] With *tetralin*, β-6-(1,2,3,4-tetrahydronaphthoyl)-propionic acid results in 90% yield.[318] The reaction of the anhydride with acenaphthene results in the formation of β-(1-acenaphthoyl) and β-(3-acenaphthoyl)propionic acids. When the condensation is carried out in a molten mixture of aluminum chloride and sodium chloride at 150°, perisuccinoyl-acenaphthene,

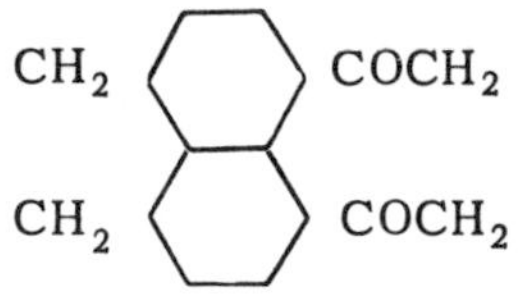

is obtained.[319] *Anthracene* gives β-(2-anthroyl)propionic acid in 10% yield. *Phenanthrene* and *phenanthrone* derivatives undergo the condensation, 9,10-dihydrophenanthrene giving β-2-(9,10-dihydrophenanthroyl)propionic acid;[320] *retene* gives 6-retoylpropionic acid.[321] while *chrysene* yields β-(2-chrysenoyl)propionic acid.[322] *Thiophene* reacts normally with succinic anhydride forming β-(α-thenoyl)-propionic acid, while *dibenzothiophene* gives β-2-dibenzothienoylpropionic acid.[323] *Carbazole* reacts with two molecular equivalents of the anhydride to form carbazole-2,6-bis-ketobutyric acid.

Pyrotartaric anhydride, CH_3CHCH_2COOCO, gives with benzene, β-benzoyl-α-methylpropionic acid in 60% yield;[324] with 2-methylnaphthalene, this anhydride yields β-(6-methyl-2-naphthoyl)-α-methylpropionic acid.[325] *α,α-Dimethylsuccinic* anhydride undergoes the Friedel-Crafts reaction with benzene forming α,α-dimethyl-β-benzoylpropionic acid.[326] Diethylsuccinic anhydride reacts similarly.[327] *Phenylsuccinic anhydride* and benzene give β-benzoyl-β-phenyl- and β-benzoyl-α-phenylpropionic acids;[328] with veratrole, β-veratroyl-α-phenylpropionic acid is obtained in 84% yield.[329]

Glutaric anhydride, $COCH_2CH_2CH_2COO$, gives with benzene, γ-benzoylbutyric acid in 80 to 85% yield, while β-methyl-β-ethylglutaric anhydride yields γ-benzoyl-β-methyl-β-ethyl-*n*-butyric acid. β-Phenylglutaric anhydride fails to undergo the Friedel-Crafts reaction with benzene, but yields ketohydrindene-3-acetic acid by internal condensation under the conditions of the reaction.

Polymeric anhydrides of *adipic* and *sebacic acids*, reacting with benzene under the conditions of Friedel-Crafts reaction give mixtures of a diketone, the corresponding alkane ω-benzoyl fatty acid and a dibasic acid:[330]

$$(CO(CH_2)_nCOO)_x + xC_6H_6 \rightarrow \frac{x}{4}C_6H_5CO(CH_2)_nCOC_6H_5$$
$$+ \frac{x}{2}C_6H_5CO(CH_2)_nCOOH + \frac{x}{4}HOCO(CH_2)_nCOOH$$

Dibasic lactonic acid anhydrides of the type $OCOCH(R)CHCHCOOCO$ condense with aromatic hydrocarbons and phenol ethers forming keto lactonic acids:[331]

$$OCOCH(CH_3)CHCHCOOCO + p\,CH_3C_6H_4CH_3$$
$$\rightarrow OCOCH(CH_3)CH(COOH)CHCOC_6H_3(CH_3)_2$$

Reactions with Maleic and other Unsaturated Dicarboxylic anhydrides

The reaction of *maleic anhydride* with benzene leads to the formation of benzoylacrylic acid.[332] Disubstitution takes place when the reaction is carried out in the presence of a large excess of aluminum chloride and of the hydrocarbon, α-phenyl-β-benzoylpropionic acid, $C_6H_5COCH_2CH(C_6H_5)COOH$, being then the product.

Benzoylacrylic acid is converted to a fluorescent compound, probably dibenzoylquinone, when it is heated above its melting point, or is treated with dehydrating agents, such as acetic anhydride, acetyl chloride or phosphoryl chloride.

The condensation of maleic anhydride with phenol ethers results in the formation of keto acids, and succinic acid derivatives. With resorcinol dimethyl ether, (dimethoxyphenyl)-succinic anhydride is obtained.[333] Dihydroxynaphthoquinone,

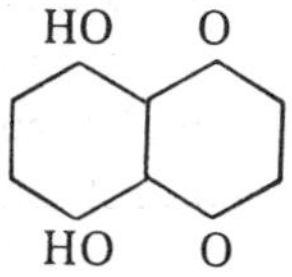

results through the condensation of *resorcinol* and maleic anhydride in an aluminum chloride – sodium chloride melt at 200°.[334] Maleic anhydride and 3-isohexylhydroquinone give 1,1-dimethyl-1,2,3,4-tetrahydroquinazarin,

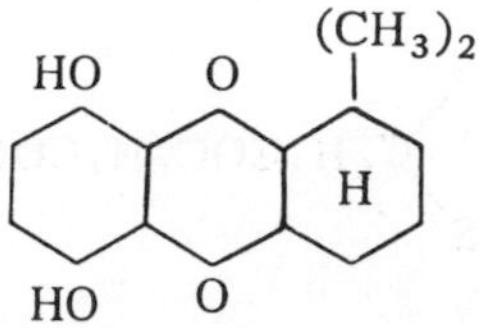

Naphthalene and maleic anhydride reacting in anhydrous benzene in the presence of aluminum chloride, give β-(1-naphthoyl) and β-(2-naphthoyl)acrylic acids, in a total yield of 70 to 80%.[335]

Dibromomaleic anhydride reacts normally with aromatic hydrocarbons giving with benzene, benzoyldibromoacrylic acid.[336]

Citraconic anhydride gives with benzene, α-methyl-β-benzoylacrylic acid in 20% yield.[335] Methylpropylmaleic anhydride also undergoes the reaction with difficulty, while diphenylmaleic anhydride fails to react.[337]

Reactions with Phthalic Anhydride and other Cyclic Dicarboxylic Anhydrides

The reaction of *phthalic anhydride* with *dichlorobenzenes* proceeds with greater ease than with monochlorobenzenes, the yield of the product being almost quantitative with *m*-dichlorobenzene, 70% with the *ortho*-isomer and 28% with the *para* compound. 4-Acetamino-1,2-dimethylbenzene gives with phthalic anhydride, 2′-acetamino-4′,5′-dimethyl-2-benzoylbenzoic acid.[338]

The reaction of an excess of phthalic anhydride with phenols in the presence of aluminum chloride results in the formation of hydroxyanthraquinones. In the absence of a solvent, phthaleins are obtained as the principal product, while in tetrachloroethane solution, hydroxybenzoylbenzoic acids are obtained.[401]

The best procedure for the production of anthraquinone is to start with the hydroxybenzoylbenzoic acid, using concentrated sulfuric acid or sulfuric acid monohydrate as the condensing agent. The use of oleum causes sulfonation as well as ring closure and decomposition of the phenol ethers. Dealkylation may be avoided by using phosphorus pentoxide as the condensing agent.

Phthalic anhydride gives a monosubstitution product with *dibenzofuran*,

$$C_6H_4 \overset{\diagup O \diagdown}{\rule{1.2cm}{0.4pt}} C_6H_4 \quad {}^{339}$$

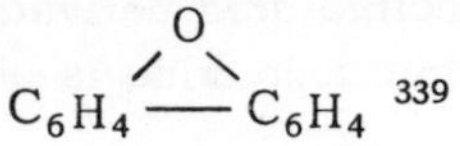

with phenanthrindone two isomeric carboxybenzoylphenanthrindones are obtained. *Thiophene* yields 2-(2-thenoyl)-benzoic acid;[340] similarly *thianaphthene* gives 2-(2-thianaphthenoyl)-benzoic acid,[341] and *dibenzothiophene* yields 2-(2-dibenzothenoyl)-benzoic acid.[323] Thianthrene,

$$C_6H_4 \overset{\diagup S \diagdown}{\underset{\diagdown S \diagup}{}} C_6H_4$$

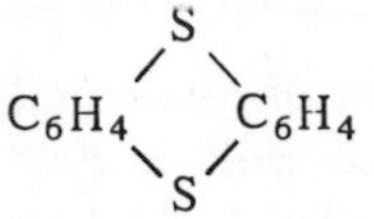

gives a mixture of mono- and disubstituted products,[342]

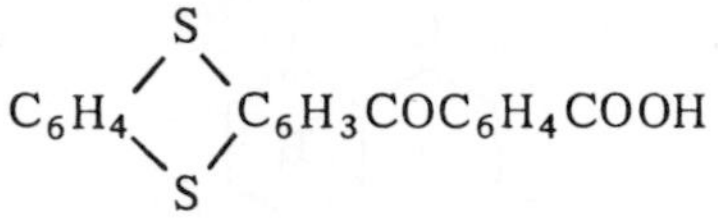

$$C_6H_4 \overset{\diagup S \diagdown}{\underset{\diagdown S \diagup}{}} C_6H_3COC_6H_4COOH \text{ and}$$

$$HOCO\ C_6H_4CO\ C_6H_3 \overset{\diagup S \diagdown}{\underset{\diagdown S \diagup}{}} C_6H_3COC_6H_4COOH$$

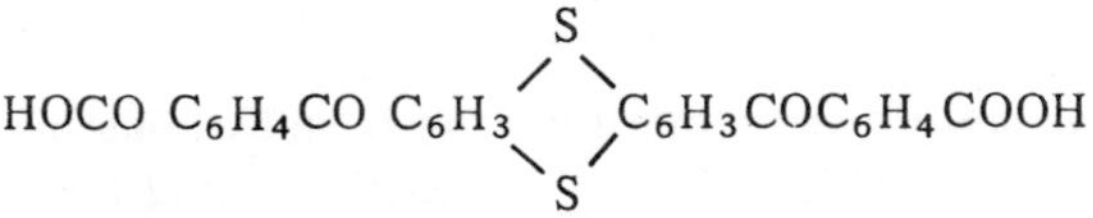

while *phenothiazine* gives a dibasic acid in poor yield.[342] *Carbazole* gives a disubstitution product, 3,6-bis-(2-carboxybenzoyl)-carbazole,[343] replacement of the N-hydrogen also occurring with the formation of 9-(2-carboxybenzoyl)-carbazole.

Methoxyphthalic anhydrides readily undergo the Friedel-Crafts reaction with aromatic hydrocarbons and with polyhydroxyquinones. 3,4-Dimethoxyphthalic anhydride and anisole yield 3,4-dimethoxy-2-anisoyl benzoic acid;[344] *o-*, *m-* and *p*-cresols give 2-hydroxymethylbenzoyl derivatives.[345] Cresol methyl ethers give the compounds

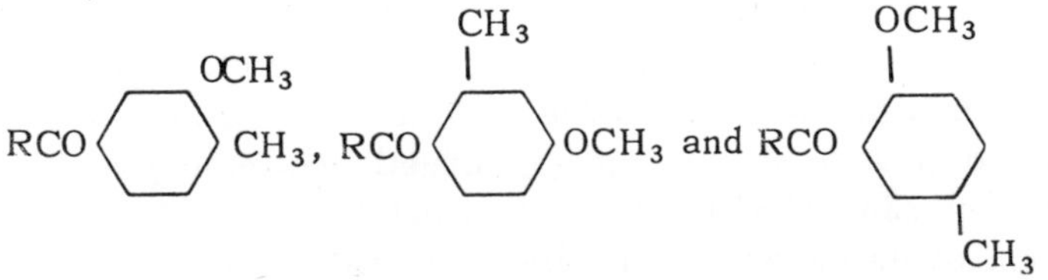

R representing the group $(CH_3O)_2C_6H_2COOH$-.[346] 3,5-Dimethoxyphthalic anhydride reacting with *o*-nitro-*m*-cresol gives 3,5-dimethoxy-2-(4-hydroxy-2-methyl-5-nitrobenzoyl)-benzoic acid.[345]

Hemimellitic anhydride,

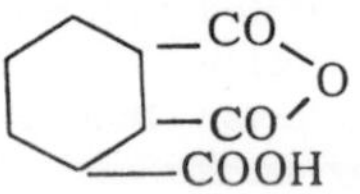

gives with benzene, benzoylphthalic acid;[347] on prolonged heating, this is converted to 2,3-dibenzoylbenzoic acid. The potassium salt of hemimellitic anhydride gives benzoylisophthalic acid,

$$
\begin{array}{c}
\text{—COOH} \\
\text{—COC}_6\text{H}_5 \\
\text{COOH}
\end{array}
$$

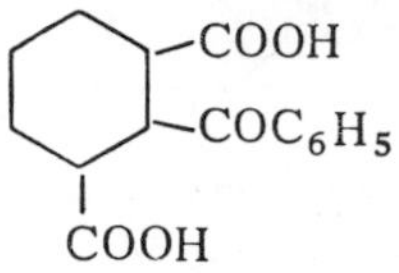

Amino keto acids may be prepared through the reaction of acetylaminophthalic anhydride with aromatic hydrocarbons or phenols, and hydrolyzing the resulting aroyl-o-acetylaminobenzoic acid.[348]

The introduction of halogen in the molecule of phthalic anhydride increases the ease with which the anhydride undergoes the Friedel-Crafts reaction. 3-*Bromophthalic anhydride* and benzene give 2-bromo-6-benzoic acid, while the 4-bromoisomer gives a mixture of 3-bromo-6-benzoyl and 6-bromo-2-benzoylbenzoic acids in about equal proportion.[349] 4-Bromophthalic anhydride is capable of reacting also with bromo and chlorobenzene and with chloronaphthalenes.[350] The products of the reaction may be converted to indanthrones.[351] 3,6-Dichlorophthalic anhydride reacts with difficulty with p-dichlorobenzene giving 3,6-dichloro-2-(2,5-dichlorobenzoyl)benzoic acid.[309] Dihalophthalic anhydrides react also with dialkylanilines, 3,6-dibromophthalic anhydride giving with dimethylaniline, 3,6-dibromo-2-(4-dimethylaminobenzoyl)-benzoic acid in 70% yield.[352]

The Friedel-Crafts reaction with nitrophthalic anhydrides often yields isomeric keto acids in low yield.[353] 3,5-Dinitrophthalic anhydride gives with toluene, 3,5-dinitro-2-(4-methylbenzoyl)benzoic acid;[354] 4-nitrophthalic anhydride, on the other hand, gives two isomeric products with m-cresol, 2-nitro-2-(2-hydroxy-4-methylbenzoyl)-benzoic acid and the 5-nitro isomer.[355] 3-Nitro-2-(2-hydroxy-4-methylbenzoyl)-benzoic acid is obtained from 3-nitrophthalic anhydride and m-cresol.[356] Nitrophthalic anhydride cannot be condensed with phenols.[395]

The Friedel-Crafts reaction between 4-sulfophthalic anhydride and benzene proceeds readily; the condensation proceeds also with p-dichlorobenzene. The products of reaction may be converted to anthraquinone sulfonic acids.

Sulfobenzoic acid anhydride,

$$
\text{C}_6\text{H}_4
\begin{array}{c}
\diagup \text{CO} \diagdown \\
\diagdown \text{SO}_2 \diagup
\end{array}
\text{O}
$$

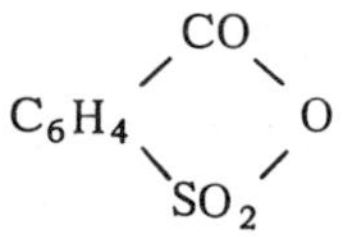

undergoes the Friedel-Crafts reaction with aromatic hydrocarbons giving with benzene benzophenone sulfonic acid.

Homophthalic anhydride,

$$
\text{C}_6\text{H}_4
\begin{array}{c}
\diagup \text{CO} - \text{O} \\
\diagdown \text{CH}_2 - \text{CO}
\end{array}
$$

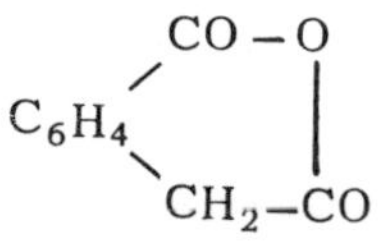

gives with benzene β-desoxybenzoincarboxylic acid and a small amount of iso-benzalphthalide,

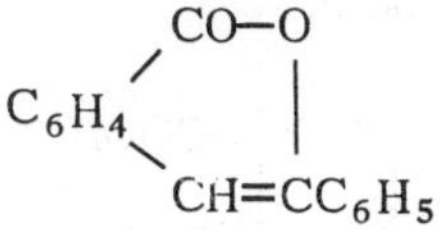

$$C_6H_4 \diagup \begin{matrix} CO-O \\ | \\ CH=CC_6H_5 \end{matrix} \quad 357$$

Thianaphthene-2,3-dicarboxylic anhydride and benzene give a 92% yield of 3-benzoylthianaphthene-2-carboxylic acid,

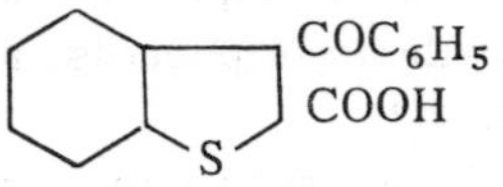

Quinolinic acid anhydride reacting with benzene under the conditions of the Friedel-Crafts reaction gives β-benzoylpyridine-α-carboxylic acid: [358]

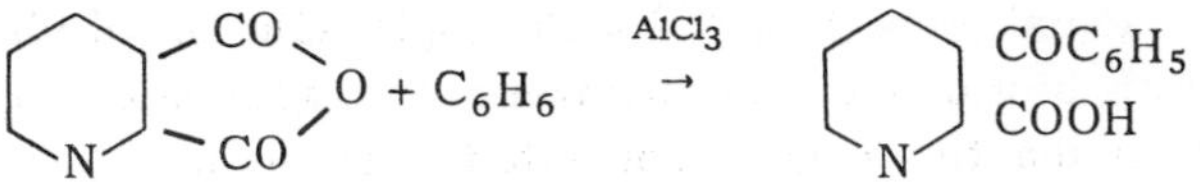

Cinchomeronic acid anhydride yields with benzene 4-benzoylnicotinic acid and a little 3-benzoyl-isonicotinic acid. [359]

Camphoric anhydride and benzene give principally phenylcamphoric acid: [360]

$$\begin{matrix} CH_2C(CH_3)-CO \\ | \quad\quad\quad \diagdown \\ C(CH_3)_2 \quad O + C_6H_6 \\ | \quad\quad\quad \diagup \\ CH_2CH\text{------}CO \end{matrix} \quad \rightarrow \quad \begin{matrix} CH_2\text{---}C(CH_3)COC_6H_5 \\ | \\ C(CH_3)_2 \\ | \\ CH_2\text{---}CHCOOH \end{matrix}$$

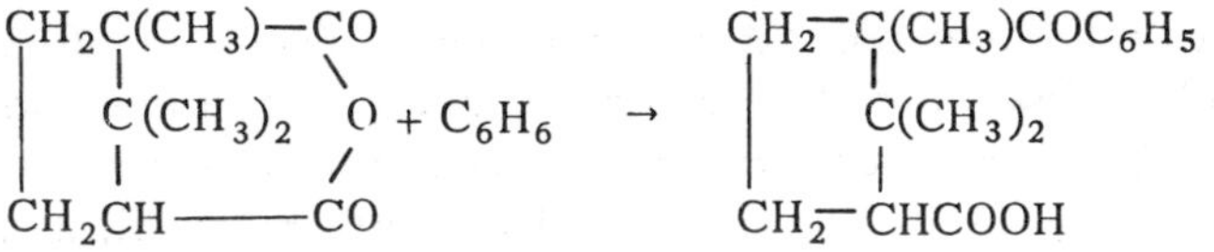

Toluene yields the ketoacids

$$\begin{matrix} CH_2C(CH_3)\ CO\ C_6H_4CH_3 \\ | \\ C(CH_3)_2 \\ | \\ CH_2CHCOOH \end{matrix} \quad\quad \begin{matrix} CH_2\text{---}C(CH_3)COOH \\ | \\ C(CH_3)_2 \\ | \\ and\ \ CH_2\text{---}CHCOC_6H_4CH_3 \end{matrix}$$

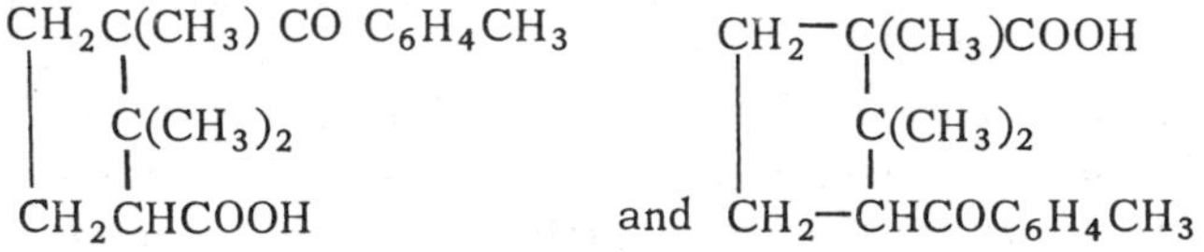

Anisole gives similar compounds. [361]

REACTIONS WITH HALO COMPOUNDS OF SULFUR, SELENIUM, PHOSPHORUS AND ARSENIC

Sulfur monochloride, S_2Cl_2, and benzene reacting in the presence of aluminum chloride give diphenyl disulfide. [362] Toluene gives 4,4′-dimethyldiphenyl sulfide. *Sulfur dichloride*, SCl_2, gives with benzene, diphenyl sulfide as the sole product if the reaction is carried out at 0°; chlorobenzene and thianthrene are also formed at 60°. [363]

Thianthrene is obtained in good yield when sulfur dichloride dissolved in benzene is slowly added to a cooled suspension of aluminum chloride in benzene, and the mixture is gradually heated to 40 - 45°:[364]

$$2SCl_2 + 2C_6H_6 \quad \rightarrow \quad C_6H_4 \underset{S}{\overset{S}{\diagdown\diagup}} C_6H_4 + 4HCl$$

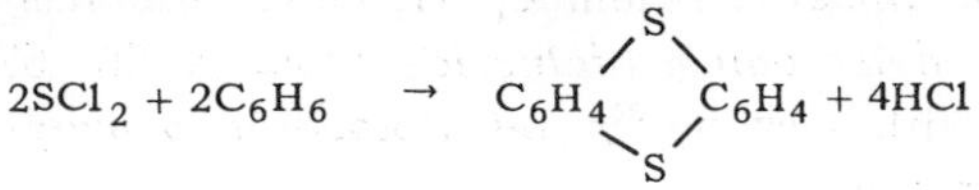

Malonic ester reacts with sulfur monochloride in the presence of aluminum chloride to form a sulfide and disulfide, $(ROCO)_2CHSCH(COOR)_2$ and $(ROCO)_2CHSSCH(COOR)_2$. Sulfur dichloride gives only the sulfide.

Aromatic *sulfo chlorides* undergo the Friedel-Crafts reaction. Thus, 1-anthraquinoylsulfur chloride gives with benzene 1-anthraquinoyl phenyl sulfide.[365] The reaction with the 2-anthraquinoyl compound proceeds similarly. *Trichloromethyl sulfochloride*, Cl_3CSCl, gives thiobenzophenone with benzene.

Thionyl chloride gives sulfoxides by reaction with aromatic compounds:[366]

$$SOCl_2 + 2C_6H_6 \quad \rightarrow \quad C_6H_5SOC_6H_5 + 2HCl$$

The sulfoxides obtained from phenol ethers are converted to thio ethers on warming with an excess of thionyl chloride.[367] Reaction of the sulfoxide with a second molecule of phenol ether gives phenol ether sulfonium bases:

$$(C_2H_5OC_6H_4)_2SO + HCl \quad \rightarrow \quad (C_2H_5OC_6H_4)_2S(Cl)OH$$

$$(C_2H_5OC_6H_4)_2S(Cl)OH + C_2H_5OC_6H_5 + SOCl_2$$

$$\rightarrow \quad (C_2H_5OC_6H_4)_3SCl + SO_2 + 2HCl$$

The sulfoxide may be obtained in 40% yield when the use of an excess of the condensing agent is avoided and one molecular proportion of thionyl chloride and two of phenetole are employed.

The course of Friedel-Crafts reaction with *sulfonyl chloride*, $SOCl_2$, and aromatic hydrocarbons varies according to the temperature at which the reaction is carried out;[368] this holds true also of *pyrosulfuryl chloride*.[369] *Benzenesulfonyl chloride* reacts normally to form sulfones:[370]

$$C_6H_5SO_2Cl + HR \quad \rightarrow \quad C_6H_5SOR + HCl$$

Alkoxy and halo benzenesulfonyl chlorides also readily undergo the reaction. Benzenesulfonyl fluoride reacts similarly.[371]

The reaction of bis-(p-bromophenyl)sulfonium chloride with benzene results in the formation of phenylbis-(p-bromophenyl)sulfonium chloride:

$$(BrC_6H_4)_2SCl_2 + C_6H_6 \quad \rightarrow \quad (BrC_6H_4)_2S(Cl)C_6H_5 + HCl$$

The reaction of 5,5-dichlorothianthrene proceeds in a similar manner:

$$C_6H_4 \underset{S}{\overset{SCl_2}{\diagup\diagdown}} C_6H_4 + C_6H_6 \quad \rightarrow \quad C_6H_4 \underset{S}{\overset{S(Cl)C_6H_5}{\diagup\diagdown}} C_6H_4 + HCl$$

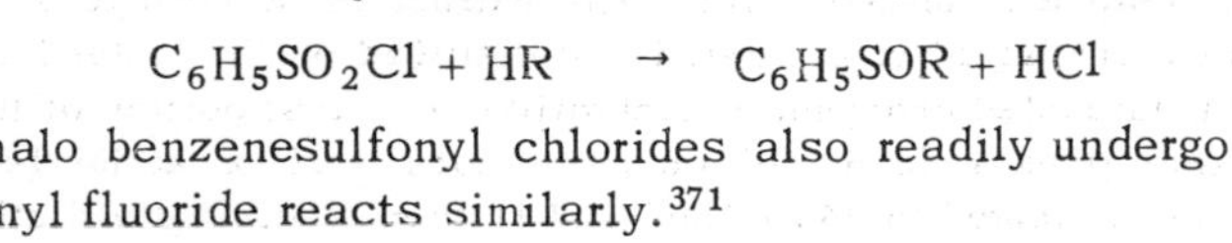

Thiophosgene reacting with benzene under the conditions of Friedel-Crafts reaction gives thiobenzophenone;[372] with phenol ethers, the corresponding thio arylketones are obtained.[373]

Applied to *selenium tetrachloride* and benzene, Friedel-Crafts reaction leads to the formation of diphenyl selenide, triphenyl selenium chloride and chlorobenzene.[374] *Diphenylselenium dichloride* gives a 66 - 67% yield of triphenylselenium chloride with benzene.[375] *o-Chloroselenobenzoyl chloride* gives with benzene, selenoxanthone,

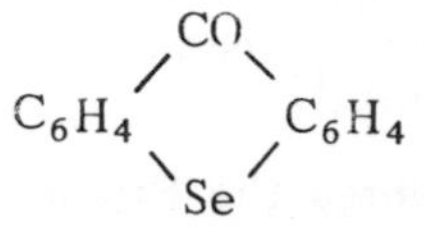

$$
\begin{array}{c}
\quad\; CO \\
\diagup \quad \diagdown \\
C_6H_4 \quad\quad C_6H_4 \quad\text{376} \\
\diagdown \quad \diagup \\
\quad\; Se
\end{array}
$$

Phosphorus trichloride undergoes the Friedel-Crafts reaction with many aromatic compounds giving chlorophosphines of the aromatic series:[377]

$$PCl_3 + C_6H_6 \quad \rightarrow \quad C_6H_5PCl_2 + HCl$$

The reaction proceeds very slowly with benzene; alkylated benzenes generally react more readily, and yields of phosphines ranging 25 to 30% have been obtained with toluene, xylenes and ethylbenzene. Reaction proceeds poorly also with cumene, cymene, dibenzyl, diphenyl, diphenylmethane and mesitylene, the last named giving the chlorophosphine in only 3 to 5% yield. Satisfactory results have been obtained with *tert*-aromatic amines, anisole, phenetole, and chloro- and bromobenzene. The reaction has also been applied to diphenyl ether,[378] and tetrahydro- and decahydronaphthalenes.[379] In preparing anisyl and phenetyl derivatives, aluminum chloride containing some oxychloride should be used, since pure aluminum chloride causes the cleavage of the alkoxy groups. Iodobenzene, benzonitrile, benzophenone and ethyl benzoate do not undergo the reaction, while chloro- and bromotoluenes react poorly.

The preparation of dichlorophenylphosphine may be cited as representative of the procedure generally followed:

A mixture of 150 gm of the hydrocarbon, with 200 gm of phosphorus trichloride and 30 gm aluminum chloride is heated for 30 hours, first gently, then vigorously. The liquid, which separates into two layers, is extracted repeatedly with dry petroleum ether until the residue is almost solid. The extract is allowed to stand 12 hours and the supernatant clear liquid is separated and distilled on the water bath to remove the solvent and any unreacted phosphorus trichloride. If a test portion of the residue added to petroleum ether gives a cloudy solution, the process of extraction is repeated, otherwise, the residue is heated to 140 - 150° and is then fractionally distilled in a stream of carbon dioxide.

Phosphorus oxychloride reacts with aromatic and heterocyclic compounds giving the corresponding phosphates.[380]

Arsenic trichloride undergoes the Friedel-Crafts reaction with benzene giving principally triphenylarsine, and some diphenylarsine chloride and phenylarsine dichloride. The reaction is carried out by adding aluminum chloride to a boiling solution of arsenic trichloride in the hydrocarbon.[381] It should be borne in mind, that aluminum chloride causes the decomposition of many aromatic arsenic derivatives. Styrene gives with arsenic trichloride polymeric compounds. Phenyl α-naphthyl ether condenses with arsenic trichloride forming 7-chloro-α,β-naphthaphenoxarsine,[382]

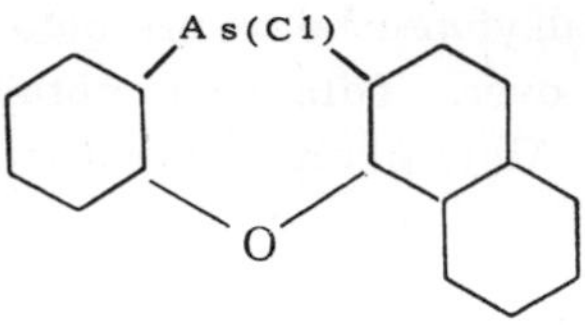

diphenyl ether gives 6-chlorophenoxarsine,[383]

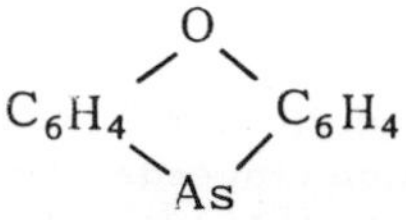

Phenylmethylchloroarsine undergoes the Friedel-Crafts reaction with benzene, toluene, mesitylene and bromobenzene to form trisubstituted arsines.[382] γ-Phenyl-*n*-propyl)-methylchloroarsine is converted to As-methyltetrahydroarsinoline,

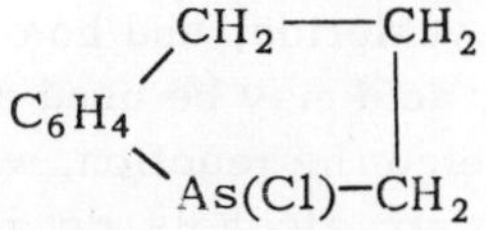

Phenyldichloroarsine reacts with acetyl chloride to form acetophenone in 52% yield.[384] Dichloroarsinobenzoyl chloride reacting with benzene gives arsinoaryl ketones:[385]

$$Cl_2AsC_6H_4COCl + C_6H_6 \rightarrow HCl + Cl_2AsC_6H_4COC_6H_5$$
$$\xrightarrow{H_2O} OAsC_6H_4COC_6H_5 + 2HCl$$

The condensation of dichloro-*p*-arsinobenzoyl chloride with phenyl ethers proceeds quite smoothly, although the products obtained are difficult to isolate and purify. They may be isolated in the form of arsonic acids after conversion to such acids by oxidation.

Phenyl-β-chlorovinylchloroarsine and diphenyl-β-chlorovinylarsine result through the condensation of *chlorovinyldichloroarsine*, $ClCH = CHAsCl_2$, with benzene.[386] Treatment of phenyl β-chlorovinylchloroarsine with aluminum chloride results in ring closure with the formation of chloroarsindole

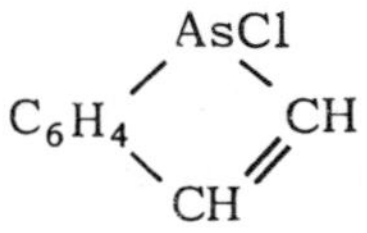

VARIANTS OF FRIEDEL-CRAFTS REACTION

Use of Alkyl Sulfates and other Alkyl Esters

Alkyl sulfates and certain other alkyl esters such as carbonates and orthosilicates are capable of undergoing the Friedel-Crafts reaction, these esters assuming the function of the halides or anhydrides in the usual Friedel-Crafts condensation. The yield of alkylated benzenes obtained by use of these esters may range from 43 to 71% or over. Toluene is obtained in 60% yield from benzene and methyl sulfate.[387] Alkyl phenol ethers may also be employed in the reaction.

Alkylation by Use of Alcohols

Aromatic compounds may be alkylated by use of alcohols in the presence of 70 to 80% sulfuric acid.

The reaction is best carried out at 70 to 80°, completion of the reaction requiring from three to five hours. Condensation proceeds in some instances at 40°. If the aromatic compound is insoluble in the alcohol, it is added gradually. The alcohol should not be added too rapidly in order to avoid self-condensation.

The use of concentrated sulfuric acid brings about resinification. Stannic chloride, aluminum chloride, phosphorus pentachloride phosphoric acid,[396] perchloric acid, phosphorus oxychloride, and boron trifluride[397] have also been employed as catalysts. Acetic acid may be used as a diluent.

Methyl alcohol does not undergo the reaction, while ethyl alcohol reacts only at 170° under pressure. Primary alcohols do not give the normal alkylated product but one in which the carbon atom adjacent to that bearing the hydroxyl group in the alcohol is united with the nuclear carbon atom. For example, *n*-propyl alcohol yields the isopropyl derivative, and *n*-butyl alcohol gives a *sec*-butyl derivative, while isobutyl alcohol gives the *tert*-butyl compound. It appears possible that an unsaturated hydrocarbon is first formed, that the sulfuric acid combines with this, and the resulting sulfate then reacts with the aromatic compound. This view receives support in the exceptional behavior of benzyl alcohol. This compound gives the normal substitution product, forming diphenylmethane, for example, with benzene.[388] Benzhydrol heated with toluene in the presence of phosphorus pentoxide gives diphenyltolylmethane in almost theoretical yield.

The substituent generally enters the *para* position with respect to groups already present in the aromatic radical, but a small amount of the *ortho*-substituted product also results. Negative groups tend to inhibit the reaction, although alkyl groups, if present in the nucleus, counteract the effect of such groups.

In the *naphthalene* series sulfonation takes place invariably and the entering sulfo group influences the direction of substitution. An α-sulfo compound gives the β-isopropyl derivative and a β-sulfo compound yields the α-isopropyl derivative.

As an example, 45 gm of isopropyl alcohol are added dropwise to a mixture of 60 gm naphthalene and 500 cc of 80% sulfuric acid heated to 80° in the course of two and a half hours with good agitation. Stirring is continued half an hour longer while the temperature is maintained at 80°. A mixture of sulfonated mono, di and poly isopropylnaphthalenes is thus obtained.

The sulfonic group may be removed by dilution of the final reaction mixture to an acid content of 60% and subjecting it to distillation with superheated steam. The oil that distills over contains some unconverted naphthalene; this is eliminated by steam-distillation at atmospheric pressure. The residual oil is finally fractionated repeatedly with care. Monoisopropylnaphthalenes distill over between 144 and 149°, diisopropylnaphthalenes between 166 and 180° and the triisopropyl products between 188 and 201°. The solid residue contains some tetraisopropylnaphthalene.[389]

Certain α-hydroxy acids or their derivatives are capable of undergoing the reaction with phenols.[390] Thus, mandelic acid, reacting with phenol in the presence of 73% sulfuric acid gives phenylhydroxyphenylacetic acid, the hydroxy group in the phenyl occupying the *para* or *ortho* positions. Diphenyleneglycolic acid, heated to melting with a mixture of phenol and stannic chloride, gives diphenylhydroxyphenylacetic acid:

$$(C_6H_5)_2C(OH)COOH + C_6H_5OH \rightarrow (C_6H_5)_2C(C_6H_4OH)COOH + H_2O$$

Secondary alcohols react with aluminum chloride to form complexes $AlCl_2OR$ which are capable of reacting with hydrocarbons to give alkylated derivatives:

$$AlCl_2OR + C_6H_6 \rightarrow RC_6H_5 + AlCl_2OH$$

The reaction is carried out at 30°, using a half molal equivalent of aluminum chloride to every two or three moles of the aromatic compound. Alkylated aromatic compounds may be obtained by this reaction in yields ranging up to 70%. Cumol, *p*-cymene, diisopropylbenzene, *sec*-butylbenzene and *sec*-butyltoluene have been prepared by this method.[391] The reaction proceeds with greater ease with tertiary alcohols.

Ethyl ether may be employed in the Friedel-Crafts reaction for the purpose of introducing ethyl groups in the aromatic nucleus. Breakdown of ether apparently precedes its reaction with the aromatic body. Hexaethylbenzene is the final product of the reaction with benzene.

The reaction of phenol with *formic acid* in the presence of aluminum chloride or zinc chloride results in the formation of leukaurin, which is oxidized to aurin by atmospheric oxygen:

$$HCOOH + 3C_6H_5OH \rightarrow 2H_2O + HOC_6H_4CH(C_6H_4OH)_2$$

$$\xrightarrow{O_2} OC_6H_4 = C(C_6H_4OH)_2$$

Reaction with Unsaturated Compounds

Alkylation of aromatic compounds may be effected by reaction with unsaturated bodies in the presence of aluminum chloride. The subject is considered in Chapter 17 dealing with unsaturated compounds. Alkylation reactions with alcohols and ethers may be assumed to be preceded by the formation of unsaturated compounds. The reaction of quinone with aromatic substances, which results in the formation of 2,5-aromatic derivatives, represents a case of reaction of an unsaturated body with an aromatic compound.

Phenyl isocyanate reacting with aromatic hydrocarbons in the presence of aluminum chloride gives anilides.[399]

Anisol reacts with carbon disulfide in the presence of aluminum chloride forming *p*-dithiocarbomethoxyphenol, $HOC_6H_4CS_2CH_3$.[400]

Zincke's Method

Benzyl halides and their derivatives heated with aromatic hydrocarbons and zinc dust react to form benzylated aromatic derivatives:[392]

$$C_6H_5CH_2Cl + C_6H_6 \rightarrow C_6H_5CH_2C_6H_5 + HCl$$

The zinc dust only serves to initiate the reaction, which proceeds automatically once it begins. It may be necessary, however, to introduce additional small amounts of zinc dust, if the reaction slows down to any great extent. Nascent hydrochloric acid appears to be the true catalyst in this reaction. Metallic iron, and in a few exceptional cases, copper, silver, and titanium have been used in place of zinc, although these metals are far less effective than zinc. Aluminum amalgam is a very effective catalyst.[240] It should be noted that when zinc dust is added to benzyl chloride, a vigorous reaction ensues resulting in the formation of a resinous mass.

Homologs of diphenylmethane may be prepared successfully by this method, the benzyl group entering the *para* or *ortho* positions with respect to an alkyl group already present in the nucleus. α-Bromoethylbenzene gives with benzene 7-methyldiphenylmethane, $C_6H_5CH(CH_3)C_6H_5$, while phenylbromoacetic ester gives with toluene, 4-methyl- and 2-methyldiphenylmethane-7-carboxylic acids, $CH_3C_6H_4CH(C_6H_5)COOH$.

The method is of limited applicability, and furthermore presents the disadvantage that the zinc dust employed in the reaction causes the removal of halogens from certain aromatic halides.

References

1. Friedel and Crafts, *Comp. rend.*, **84**, 1392 (1877); Elbs, *Kohlenstoffverbindungen II*, 128 (1891) Biltz, *Ber.*, 26, 1960 (1893); Gustavson, *J. prakt. Chem.*, (2) **68**, 209 (1903); (2) **72**, 57 (1905) *Compt. rend.*, **136**, 1065 (1903); 140 940 (1905); Steele, *J. Chem., Soc.*, **83**, 470 (1903); Larsen, *Z. physik. Chem.*, **48**, 424 (1904); Gleditsch, *Bull. soc. chim.*, (3) **35**, 1095 (1906); Wieland and Bettay, *Ber.*, **55**, 2246 (1922); Staudinger *et al. Helv.Chim. Acta*, **4**, 342 (1921); Oliver, *Rec. trav. chim.*, **33**, 91 (1914); Schroeter *et al.*, *Ber* **57**, 1990 (1924); Schaarschmidt, *Z. anorg. Chem.*, **37**, 286 (1924); Schleicher, *J. prakt. Chem.*, (2) **105**, 355 (1923); Nenitzescu, *Ann*, **491**, 218 (1931); Wertyporoch *et al.*, *Ber.* **64**, 1359 (1931); *Z. physiol. Chem.*, **162**, 398 (1932); *Ann.*, **500**, 28 (1933); Nenitzescu, and Contuniari, *Ber.*, **65**, 1449 (1932); Biltz, *J. prakt. Chem.*, (2) **142**, 196 (1935); Reichstein, *Helv. Chim. Acta*, **13**, 349 (1930); Fairbrother, *J. Chem., Soc.*, **1937**, 503.
2. Calloway, *J. Am. Chem. Soc.*, **59**, 1474 (1937).
3. Lavaux and Lombard, *Bull. Soc. Chim*, (4) **7**, 913 (1910).
4. Friedel and Crafts, *Bull. soc. chim.*, (2) **28**, 50 (1877).
5. Schwarz, *Ber.*, **14**, 1516 (1881).
6. Friedel and Crafts, *Compt. rend.* **84**, 1450 (1877), Fischer and Fischer, *Ann.* **194**, 242 (1878); Gomberg *et al*, *Ber.* **33**, 3144 (1900); *J. Am. Chem. Soc.*, **22**, 752 (1900); **23**, 177 (1901); Böeseken, *Rec. trav. chim.*, **24**, 1 (1905).
7. Dumreicher, *Ber.*, **15**, 33, 1866 (1882), Roux, *Ann. chim.*, (6) **12**, 343 (1887); Kohn and Müller, *Monatsh.*, **30**, 407 (1909); Noller and Adams, *J. Am. Chem. Soc.*, **46**, 1889 (1924); Rohfert, *Ber.*, **63**, 1939 (1930); Salkind and Stetzuro, *ibid.*, **64**, 953 (1930); Mashek, *Monatsh.*, **56**, 116 (1930); Groggins, *Ind. Eng. Chem.*, **23**, 893 (1931); Kimura, *Ber.*, **67**, 394 (1934), Nenitzescu *et al.*, *ibid.*, **70**, 346, 1883 (1937).

8. Friedel and Balsohn, *Bull. soc. chim.*, (2) **33**, 337 (1880), Friedel and Crafts, *Ann. chim. phys.*, (6) **1**, 480 (1884); Schramm, *Ber*, **26**, 1706 (1893); Lavaux and Lombard, *Bull. soc. chim.*, (4) **7**, 539 (1910).
9. Wertyporoch and Farnik, *Ann.*, **491**, 265 (1931)
10. Reindel and Siegel, *Ber.*, **56**, 1550 (1923)
11. Doebner and Magatti, *ibid.*, **12**, 1462 (1879)
12. Kohn and Müller, *Monatsh.*, **30**, 407 (1909); Kohn, *ibid.*, **33**, 923 (1912)
13. Zincke *et al.*, *Ber.*, **60**, 577 (1927)
14. Wurster, *Angew. Chem.*, **43**, 877 (1930). *Cf* Prins, *Rec. trav. chim.*, **54**, 577 (1935).
15. Radziewanowksi, *Ber.*, **28**, 1137 (1895); Estreicher, *ibid.*, **33**, 439 (1900); Korczýnski, *ibid.*, **35**, 868 (1902); Kozak, *Anz. Akad. Krakau*, 1906, 407; Ray, *J. Chem., Soc.*, **117**, 1337 (1920)
16. Jacobson, *Ber.* **14**, 2624 (1881); Galle, *ibid.*, **16**, 1745 (1883); Baur, *ibid.*, **24**, 2833 (1891); Boedtker, *Bull. soc. chim.*, (2) **81**, 558 (1910); v. Auwers and Kolligs, *Ber.*, **55**, 3872 (1922); Smith, *Organic Syntheses*, **10**, 32 (1930).
17. Böeseken, *Rec. trav. chim.*, **24**, 6 (1905); Linner, *French patent* 697,711
18. Biltz, *Ber.*, **26**, 1960 (1893); Gleditsch, *Bull. soc. chim.*, (3) **35**, 1095 (1906); Staudinger *et al.*, *Helv. Chim. Acta*, **4**, 342 (1921); Biltz, *J. prakt. Chem.*, (2) **142**, 196 (1935).
19. Nenitzescu and Cantuniari, *Ber.*, **65**, 1449 (1932).
20. Martin *et al.*, *J. Am. Chem. Soc.*, **57**, 2584 (1935).
21. Boswell and Laughlin, *Can. J. Research*, **1**, 400 (1929).
22. Bialobrzeski, *Ber.*, **30**, 1773 (1897); Battagay and Kappeler, *Bull. soc. chim.*, (4) **35**, 992 (1924); *German patent* 554,879 (1932).
23. Krishnamurti, *J. Madras Univ.*, **1928**, 4; *Chem. Zentr.*, **1929, I**, 2156; Wertyporoch, *Ber.*, **66**, 1232 (1933).
24. Kaschtanow, *J. Gen. Chem. (U.S.S.R.)*; **3** (65), 229 (1933); *Chem. Zentr.*, **1933 II**, 2512; Tronow *et al.*, *J. Gen. Chem. (U.S.S.R.)*, **1**, 1910 (1932).
25. Bradley and Kenner, *J. Chem. Soc.*, **1935**, 383.
26. Osborne, *Proc. Physiol. Soc.*, **1903**, XIII - XIV.
27. Borbot, *Bull. soc. chim.*, (4) **47**, 1314 (1930).
28. Gilman, *et al.*, *J. Am. Chem. Soc.*, **56**, 220 (1934).
29. Reichstein *et al.*, *Helv. Chim. Acta*, **18**, 721 (1935).
30. Gilman *et al.*, *J. Am. Chem. Soc.*, **56**, 745 (1934); **57**, 909 (1935).
31. Knowaloff and Egoroff, *J. Russ. Phys.-Chrm. Soc.*, **30**, 1031 (1898). Gossin, *Bull. soc. chim.*, (2) **41**, 446 (1884); Silva, *ibid.*, (2) **43**, 317 (1885); Anschütz and Immendorff, *Ber.*, **17**, 2816 (1884); **18**, 657 (1885); Jacobson, *ibid.*, **18**, 338 (1885); Anschütz, *Ann.*, **235**, 177 (1886); Schramm, *Monatsh.*, **9**, 624 (1888); Senkowski, *Ber.*, **23**, 2412 (1890); Genvresse, *Bull. soc. chim.*, (3) **9**, 508 (1893); Tissier, *Ann. chim.*, (6) **29**, 360 (1843); Baur, *Ber.*, **27**, 1610 (1894); Nölting, *Chem. Ztg.* **17**, 170 (1893).
32. Ipatieff *et al.*, *J. Org. Chem.*, **5**, 253 (1940).
33. Nightingale and Smith, *J. Am. Chem. Soc.*, **61**, 101 (1939); Nightingale and Carton, *ibid.*, **62**, 280 (1940).
34. Gerhardt, *Riechstoff. Ind. u. Kosmetik.*, **5**, 67 (1930); *C. A.*, **24**, 4897 (1930); *German patent* 184,230.
35. Tsukervanik and Tambovtseva, *Bull. Univ. Asie Centrale* **22**, 221 (1938).
36. Carpenter, *U. S. patent* 2,064,885 (1936).
37. Coleman and Perkins, *U. S. patent* 2,170,809 (1939).
38. Cousin and Lions, *J. Proc. Roy. Soc. N. S. Wales*, **70**, 413 (1937).
39. Herstein, *U. S. patent* 2,092,970; 2,092,972; 2,092,973 (1937).
40. Angelbis and Anschütz, *Ber.*, **17**, 165 (1884); Anschütz and Romig, *ibid.*, **18**, 662 (1885); Anschütz, *Ann.*, **235**, 302 (1886).
41. Goudet and Schenker, *Helv. Chim. Acta*, **10**, 132 (1927).
42. Auger, *Bull. soc. chim.*, (2) **47**, 49 (1887). *Cf.* Kraft, *Ber.*, **19**, 2982 (1886).
43. Bruson and Kroeger, *J. Am. Chem. Soc.*, **62**, 36 (1940).
44. Adam, *Compt. rend.*, **103**, 207 (1886).
45. Wenzel and Kugel, *Monatsh.*, **35**, 953 (1914).
46. Wenzel and Drada, *ibid.*, **35**, 973 (1914).
47. Wilson and Huang, *J. Chinese Chem. Soc.*, **4**, 1428 (1936). Cf. Wilson and Cheng, *J. Org. Chem.*, **5**, 223 (1940).
48. Norris and Green, *Am. Chem. J.*, **26**, 492 (1901); Norris and Twieg, *ibid.*, **30**, 392 (1903).
49. Böeseken, *Rec. trav. chim.*, **24**, 1 (1905).
50. Böeseken, *ibid.*, **27**, 5 (1908); Wilson and Cheng, *J. Org. Chem.*, **5**, 223 (1940).
51. Kuntze and Fechner, *Ber.*, **36**, 472 (1903).
52. Claus and Mercklin, *ibid.*, **18**, 2932 (1885).
53. Böeseken and Bactet, *Rec. trav. chim.*, **32**, 184 (1913).
54. Anschütz, *Ann.*, **235**, 331 (1886).
55. Hanriet and Guilbert, *Compt rend.*, **98**, 525 (1884); *Ber.*, **17**, 208 (1884).

56. Wispek and Zuber, *Ann.*, **218**, 374 (1883).
57. Demole, *Ber.*, **12**, 2245 (1879). *Cf.* Anschutz, *Ann.*, **235**, 158 (1886).
58. Coleman *et al.*, *U. S. patent* 2,135,122 (1938).
59. Bouneyrat, *Bull. soc. chim.*, (3) **19**, 557 (1898).
60. Radziewanowski, *Ber.*, **28**, 1136 (1895).
61. Perkin and Hodgkinson, *J. Chem. Soc.*, **37**, 726 (1880); Senff, *Ann.*, **220**, 228, 247 (1883); Friedel and Crafts, *Ann. chim.*, (6) **1**, 481, 482 (1884); Louise, *ibid.*, (6) **6**, 174 (1885); Geigy and Kőnigs, *Ber.*, **18**, 2402 (1885); Beaurepaire, *Bull. soc. chim.*, (2) **50**, 678 (1888); Fournier, *ibid.*, (3) **7**, 654 (1892); Cassirer, *Ber.*, **25**, 3021, 3025 (1892); Schramm *ibid.*, **26**, 1709 (1893); Moses, *ibid.*, **33**, 2627 (1900).
62. Friedel and Crafts, *Compt. rend.*, **84**, 1450 (1877); Friedel, *Bull. soc. chim.*, (2) **37**, 530 (1882); Lavaux and Lombard, *ibid.*, (4) **7**, 539 (1910).
63. Senff, *Ann.*, 220, 225 (1883).
64. Nenitzescu *et al.*, *ibid.*, **491**, 210 (1931); Goldschmidt and Larsen, *Z. physik.-Chem.*, **48**, 424 (1904).
65. Linebarger, *Am. Chem. J.*, **13**, 556 (1891).
66. Barnett, *J. Chem. Soc.*, **1939**, 348.
67. Graves *et al.*, *J. Proc. Roy. Soc. N. S. Wales*, **71**, 318 (1938).
68. Anschütz, *Ann.*, **235**, 329 (1886).
69. v. Braun and Deutsch, *Ber.*, **45**, 1267 (1912).
70. v. Braun *et al.*, *ibid.*, **46**, 1266 (1913).
71. Anschütz, *Ann.*, **235**, 338 (1886). *Cf.* Schramm, *Ber.*, **26**, 1706 (1893).
72. Anschütz, *Ann.*, **235**, 204 (1886).
73. Mayes and Turner, *J. Chem. Soc.*, 1929, 500.
74. Kursanoff, *Ann.*, **318**, 309 (1901).
75. Kamieński and Lewiowna, *Roczniki Chem.*, **14**, 1348 (1934).
76. Nenitzescu and Gavat, *Ann.*, **519**, 260 (1935).
77. Nenitzescu and Curcaneanu, *Ber.*, **70**, 346 (1937).
78. Sommelet, *Compt. rend.*, **157**, 1443 (1913).
79. v. Braun, *Ber.*, **43**, 2837 (1910).
80. Verley, *Bull. soc. chim.*, (3) **17**, 906 (1897); Huston and Friedmann, *J. Am. Chem. Soc.*, **38**, 2527 (1916).
81. Gardeur, *Bull. Acad. roy. Belg.* (3) **34**, 920 (1898).
82. Franke and Klein, *Monatsh.*, **33**, 1233 (1912).
83. Dinesmann, *Compt. rend.*, **141**, 201 (1905).
84. Collet, *Bull. soc. chim.*, (3) **17**, 506 (1897).
85. Mason and Terry, *J. Am. Chem. Soc.*, **62**, 1622 (1940).
86. Connerade, *Bull. soc. chim. Belg.*, **44**, 411 (1935).
87. Wenzel and Bellak, *Monatsh.*, **35**, 965 (1914).
88. Delacre, *Bull. soc. chim.*, (3) **27**, 875 (1902).
89. Earl and Wilson, *J. Proc. Roy. Soc. N. S. Wales*, **65**, 178 (1932).
90. Eikman, *Chem. Weekblad*, **4**, 727 (1907).
91. Beyer, *Ber.*, **70**, 1101 (1937).
92. Rennie, *J. Chem. Soc.*, **41**, 33 (1882); Friedel and Crafts, *Ann. chim. phys.*, (6) **1**, 527 (1884); *Cf.* Kunckell and Ulex, *J. prakt. Chem.*, (2) **86**, 518 (1912); **87**, 227 (1913).
93. Cherbuliez and Sulzer, *Helv. Chim. Acta*, **8**, 567 (1925).
94. Kranzlein *et al.*, *U. S. patent*, 2,012,569 (1935).
95. v. Braun *et al.*, *Ber.*, **50**, 1637 (1917).
96. Möhlau and Berger, *ibid.*, **26**, 1994 (1893); Knowles, *J. Am. Chem. Soc.*, **43**, 896 (1921); Clemo and Walton, *J. Chem. Soc.*, **1928**, 723.
97. Eaton *et al.*, *J. Am. Chem. Soc.*, **56**, 687 (1934).
98. Fuson *et al.*, *ibid.*, **56**, 2103 (1934).
99. Fuson *et al.*, *ibid.*, **55**, 2001 (1933).
100. Fuson *et al.*, *ibid.*, **58**, 1979 (1936).
101. Tetry, *Compt. rend.*, **128**, 1406 (1899).
102. Haller and Guyot, *ibid.*, **136**, 535 (1903).
103. Fritsch, *Ber.*, **29**, 2290 (1896).
104. Druzdov, *Russian patent* 51,908 (1937).
105. Myers and Lindwall, *J. Am. Chem. Soc.*, **60**, 2153 (1938). *Cf.* Inagaki, *J. Parm. Soc. Japan*, **53**, 686 (1933).
106. Friedel and Crafts, *Ann. chim. pays.*, (6) **1**, 528 (1884); Steinkopf, *Ann.*, **430**, 89 (1923); Merz and Weith, *Ber.*, **10**, 756 (1877); Scholl and Nörr, *ibid.*, **33**, 1052 (1900).
107. Karrer and Zeller, *Helv. Chim. Acta*, **2**, 482 (1919).
108. Karrer *et al.*, *ibid.*, **3**, 261 (1920).
109. Bodroux, *Bull. soc. chim.*, (3) **25**, 491 (1901). *Cf.* Homer, *J. Chem. Soc.*, **97**, 1141 (1910).
110. Brunel, *Ber.*, **17**, 1179 (1884).
111. Roux, *Ann. chim. phys.*, (6) **12**, 307 (1887); *Bull. soc. chim.*, (2) **41**, 379 (1884).

112. Baur, *Ber.*, **27**, 1623 (1894). *Cf.* Wegscheider, *Monatsh.*, **5**, 237 (1884); Gump, *J. Am. Chem. Soc.*, **53**, 380 (1931).
113. Chattaway, *J. Chem. Soc.*, **63**, 1185 (1893).
114. Koenigsberger, *U. S. patent* 1,788,529 (1931).
115. Gomberg, *Ber.*, **37**, 1637 (1904).
116. Clar, *ibid.*, **63**, 512 (1930).
117. *Cf.* Boedker and Rambach, *Bull. soc. chim.*, (4) **35**, 633 (1924).
118. *French patent* 818,185 (1936). *Cf. British patent* 473,653 (1936).
119. Gilman and Calloway, *J. Am. Chem. Soc.*, **55**, 4197 (1933).
120. Tohl and Nahke, *Ber.*, **29**, 2205 (1896).
121. Nahke, *ibid.*, **30**, 2041 (1897).
122. Stadnikov and Goldfarb, *ibid.*, **61**, 2341 (1928); Gilman and Calloway, *J. Am. Chem. Soc.*, **55**, 4197 (1933).
123. Gustavson, *Bull. soc. chim.*, (2) **42**, 325 (1884); *J. prakt. Chem.*, (2) **37**, 108 (1888); Böeseken, *Rec. trav. chim.*, **19**, 19 (1900); Perrier, *Ber.*, **33**, 815 (1900); Menshutkin, *J. Russ. Phys.-Chem. Soc.*, **42**, 1310 (1910); Olivier, *Rec. trav. chim.*, **54**, 943 (1935).
124. Eitel and Berbalk, *Monatsh.*, **79**, 153 (1948).
125. Stockhausen and Gattermann, *Ber.*, **25**, 3521 (1892).
126. Böeseken, *Rec. trav. chim.*, **27**, 10 (1908).
127. Krafft and von Hansen, *Ber.*, **22**, 803 (1889); Krafft and Koenig, *ibid.*, **23**, 2382 (1890).
128. Kunckell, *Ber.*, **39**, 3145 (1906).
129. Shah an lchapora, *J. Chem. Soc.*, **1935**, 894.
130. Kunckell, *Ber.*, **33**, 2641 (1900); Kunckell and Schneider, *J. prakt. Chem.*, **86**, 429 (1912).
131. Hayashi, *J. prakt. Chem.*, (2) **123**, 289 (1929).
132. Stephen and Weizmann, *J. Chem. Soc.*, **105**, 1049 (1914).
133. *Cf.* Simonis and Lear, *Ber.*, **59**, *2908* (1926).
134. Perkin and Weizmann, *J. Chem. Soc.*, **89**, 1654 (1906).
135. Mauthner, *J. prakt. Chem.*, (2) **133**, 126 (1932).
136. Gulati and Venkataraman, *J. Chem. Soc.*, **1936**, 267.
137. Witt and Braun, *Ber.*, **47**, 3216 (1914).
138. Fierz-David and Jaccard, *Helv. Chim. Acta*, **11**, 1042 (1928).
139. Olivier, *Rec. trav. chim.*, **33**, 244 (1914).
140. Graebe and Ullmann, *Ber.*, **29**, 824 (1896); Staudinger and Kon, *Ann.*, **384**, 99 (1911); Orekhov and Brouty, *Bull. soc. chim.*, (4) **47**, 621 (1930).
141. Calloway, *J. Am. Chem. Soc.*, **59**, 1474 (1937).
142. Baum and Meyer, *Ber.*, **28**, 3212 (1895); Kliegel and Huber, *ibid.*, **53**, 1646 (1920). *Cf.* Königs and Nef. *ibid.*, **19**, 2431 (1886); Freund, *Monatsh.*, **17**, 399 (1896).
143. Moureau, *Bull. soc. chim.*, (3) **9**, 568 (1893).
144. Kohler, *Am. Chem. J.*, **42**, 375 (1909).
145. Kipping and Hunter, *J. Chem. Soc.*, **79**, 602 (1901).
146. Meyer and Stamm, *Ber.*, **56**, 1424 (1923).
147. Bergmann and Berlin, *J. Chem. Soc.*, **1939**, 493.
148. Arndt and Källner, *Ber.*, **57**, 202 (1924).
149. Ruhemann, *ibid.*, **46**, 2188 (1913).
150. Stollé *et al.*, *J. prakt. Chem.*, (2) **128**, 1 (1930).
151. *Cf.* Braun and Wirz, *Ber.*, **60**, 102 (1927).
152. Stollé, *J. prakt. Chem.*, (2) **105**, 137 (1922).
153. Ullmann and Wagner, *Ann.*, **355**, 359 (1907).
154. Borsche and Sinn, *ibid.*, **532**, 146 (1937).
155. Borsche and Hahn, *ibid.*, **537**, 219 (1939).
156. Runne *et al*, *U. S. patent* 1,765,703 (1930).
157. Elbs, *J. prakt. Chem.*, (2) **33**, 180 (1886); Friedel and Crafts, *Ann. chim.*, (6) **1**, 507 (1884).
158. Bourcet, *Bull. soc. chim.*, (3) **15**, 945 (1896); Verley, *ibid.*, (3) **19**, 137 (1898).
159. Claus and Wollner, *Ber.*, **18**, 1856 (1882).
160. Perrier, *ibid.*, **33**, 815 (1900); Böeseken, *Rec. trav. chim.*, **20**, 102 (1901). *Cf.* Sorge, *Ber.*, **35**, 1065 (1902).
161. Rosenmund and Schulz, *Arch. Pharm.*, **265**, 308 (1927).
162. Rosenmund and Lohfert, *Ber.*, **61**, 2601 (1928); Sandulesco and Girard, *Bull. soc. chim.*, (4) **47**, 1300 (1936).
163. Stobbe and Lenzher, *Ann.*, **380**, 93 (1911).
164. Minnis, *Organic Syntheses* **12**, 62 (1932).
165. Wolffenstein and Hartwich, *Ber.*, **48**, 2043 (1915).
166. Hofmann, *Ann.*, **264**, 160 (1891); Demuth and Dittrich, *Ber.*, **23**, 3609 (1890).
167. Dittrich, *Ann.*, **264**, 174 (1891).
168. Hamonet, *Bull. soc. chim.*, (3) **2**, 334 (1889).
169. Duval, *Compt. rend.*, **146**, 341 (1908); *Bull. soc. chim.*, (4) **7**, 796 (1910).
170. Caille, *Compt. rend.*, **153**, 393 (1911); Weitzenböck and Lieb., *Monatsh.*, **33**, 562 (1912);

Chopin, *Bull. soc. chim.*, (4) **35**, 613 (1924); St. Pfau and Ofner, *Helv. Chim. Acta*, **9**, 669 (1926); Rivkin, *J. Gen. Chem. (U.S.S.R.)*, **5**, 277 (1935); Brunner and Grof, *Monatsh.*, **66**, 433 (1935).
171. Fieser and Hershberg, *J. Am. Chem.,Soc.*, **61**, 1272 (1939).
172. Fieser and Hershberg, *ibid.*, **60**, 1658 (1938).
173. Liebermann and Zsuffa, *Ber.*, **44**, 202 (1911); Liebermann *et al.*, *ibid.*, **45**, 1186 (1912).
174. v. Braun *et al.*, *Ber.*, **53**, 1155 (1920); Nenitzescu *et al.*, *ibid.*, **72**, 819 (1939).
175. Mosettig and Kamp, *J. Am. Chem. Soc.*, **52**, 3704 (1930). *Cf.* Bachmann and Edgerton, *ibid.*, **62**, 2219 (1940).
176. Bachmann, *J. Am. Chem. Soc.*, **57**, 555 (1935).
177. Rieveschl and Ray, *Chem. Revs.* **23**, 365 (1938).
178. Vollmann *et al.*, *Ann.*, **531**, 1 (1937).
179. Scholt *et al.*, *Ber.*, **70**, 2180 (1937).
180. Collet, *Bull. soc. chim.*, (3) **21**, 68 (1899); Gautier, *Ann. chim. phys.*, (6) **14**, 373 (1888). Straus and Ackermann, *Ber.*, **42**, 1812 (1909); Judefind and Reid, *J. Am. Chem. Soc.*, **42**, 1044 (1920); Meyer *et al.*, *Ber.*, **65**, 1333 (1932).
181. Kipper, *Ber.*, **38**, 2490 (1905); Dilthey *et al.*, *J. prakt. Chem.*, (2) **117**, 337 (1927). *Cf.* Tomita, *J. Pharm. Soc. Japan*, **57**, 689 (1937).
182. Kunckell and Johannssen, *Ber.*, **31**, 169 (1898).
183. Mauthner, *J. prakt. Chem.*, (2) **119**, 311 (1928).
184. Ralston and Christensen, *U. S. patent* 2,033,541 (1936); Ford, *Iowa State Coll. J. Sci.*, **12**, 121 (1937).
185. Seidel and Engelfried, *Ber.*, **69**, 2567 (1936).
186. Collet, *Bull. soc. chim.*, (3) **17**, 66, 506 (1897); *Compt. rend.*, **125**, 717 (1897); **126**, 1577 (1898); Kunckell, *Ber.*, **38**, 2609 (1905); Halle and Britton, *J. Am. Chem. Soc.*, **41**, 841 (1919).
187. Kunckell, *Ber. deut. pharm. Ges.*, **23**, 188 (1890); Tomita, *J. Pharm. Soc. Japan*, **56**, 906 (1936).
188. Silver and Lowy, *J. Am. Chem. Soc.*, **56**, 2429 (1934).
189. Collet, *Compt. rend.*, **125**, 305 (1897); *Bull. soc. chim.*, (3) **17**, 506 (1897); Kunckell, *Ber. deut. pharm. Ges.*, **22**, 180 (1912). *Cf.* Heidelberger, *J. Biol. Chem.*, **21**, 458 (1915); McKeever, *J. Am. Chem. Soc.*, **62**, 2088 (1940).
190. v. Auwers and Pohl, *Ann.*, **405**, 264 (1914); v. Auwers and Müller, *Ber.*, **50**, 1172 (1917).
191. v. Auwers, *Ber.*, **49**, 809 (1916); *Ann.*, **421**, 59, 108 (1920).
192. Biltz *et al.*, *J. prakt. Chem.*, (2) **142**, 193 (1935).
193. Mayer and Zütphen, *Ber.*, **57**, 200 (1924).
194. Kishner, *J. Russ. Phys.-Chem. Soc.*, **46**, 1411 (1914).
195. Shriner and Damschroder, *J. Am. Chem. Soc.*, **60**, 894 (1938).
196. v. Auwers and Hilliger, *Ber.*, **49**, 2410 (1916); v. Auwers, *Ann.*, **439**, 132 (1924); Mayer and Zutphen, *Ber.*, **57**, 200 (1924); Krollpfeiffer and Schultze, *ibid.*, **57**, 600 (1924).
197. v. Auwers and Risse, *Ann.*, **502**, 282 (1933).
198. v. Auwers, *ibid.*, **421**, 1 (1920).
199. v. Auwers and Doll, *ibid.*, **421**, 86 (1920).
200. Darzens, *Compt. rend.*, **189**, 766 (1929).
201. Smith and Prichard, *J. Am. Chem. Soc.*, **62**, 770 (1940).
202. Kohler *et al.*, *Am. Chem. J.*, **44**, 60 (1910); v. Auwers and Risse, *Ann.*, **502**, 282 (1933).
203. v. Auwers and Risse, *Ber.*, **64**, 2216 (1931).
204. Neurath, *Monatsh.*, **27**, 1145 (1906).
205. v. Auwers and Hugel, *J. prakt Chem.*, (2) **143**, 157 (1935).
206. Simonis and Lear, *Ber.*, **59**, 2908 (1926)
207. v. Braun and Deutsch, *ibid.*, **45**, 2171 (1912).
208. Rosenmund and Rosenmund, *ibid.*, **61**, 2608 (1928).
209. Anschütz and Förster, *Ann.*, **368**, 89 (1909).
210. Klingemann, *ibid.*, **275**, 83 (1893); Biltz, *Ber.*, **32**, 650 (1899).
211. Gattermann, *Ann.*, **244**, 61, 71 (1888); v. Auwers and Berger, *Ber.*, **27**, 1733 (1894); Stoermer and Atenstädt, *ibid.*, **35**, 3560 (1902).
212. Gattermann *et al.*, *Ann.*, **244**, 29 (1888); *Ber.*, **32**, 1117 (1899).
213. Gattermann, *Ann.*, **244**, 61, 71 (1888).
214. Gabriel, *Ber.*, **41**, 244 (1908); **42**, 4056 (1909); Gabriel and Coleman, *ibid.*, **41**, 2016 (1908).
215. Gabriel, *Ber.*, **42**, 4050 (1909).
216. Hildesheimer, *ibid.*, **43**, 2796 (1910).
217. Böeseken, *Rec. trav. chim.*, **27**, 10 (1908); Diesbach and Dobbelmann, *Helv. Chim. Acta*, **14**, 369 (1931).
218. *Cf.* Mayer and Fischbach, *Ber.*, **58 B**, 1251 (1925).
219. v. Auwers and Beyer, *ibid.*, **37**, 1733 (1894).
220. Tschitschibabin, *ibid.*, **40**, 3969 (1908); *J. Russ. Phys.-Chem. Soc.*, **39**, 1160 (1907); **40**, 3969 (1908).

221. Hey and Jackson, *J. Chem. Soc.*, **1936**, 802; Staudinger and Kon, *Ann.*, **384**, 97 (1911); Norris *et al.*, *Ber.*, **43** 2956 (1910).
222. Gomberg and Bailar, *J. Am. Chem. Soc.*, **51**, 2233 (1929).
223. Doebner and Wolf, *Ber.*, **12**, 661 (1879).
224. Hoffmann, *Ann.*, **264**, 165 (1891). *Cf.* Montagne, *Ber.*, **51**, 1486 (1918).
225. Schaarschmidt, *Ber.*, **48**, 831 (1915).
226. Gokhle and Mason, *J. Chem. Soc.*, **1931**, 118.
227. v. Auwers, *Ber.*, **36**, 3890 (1903).
228. Boëtius and Römisch, *ibid.*, **68**, 1924 (1935).
229. Schöpff, *ibid.*, **24**, 3771 (1891).
230. Ullmann, *Ann.*, **366**, 79 (1909).
231. Ullmann, *ibid.*, **366**, 87 (1909).
232. Pace, *Gazz. chim. ital.*, **59**, 578 (1929).
233. Wenzel and Wobisch, *Monatsh.*, **35**, 987 (1914).
234. Adam, *Ann. chim. phys.*, (6) **15**, 258 (1886).
235. Staudinger, *Ber.*, **41**, 3561 (1908).
236. Staudinger, *ibid.*, **41**, 3558 (1908).
237. Liebermann and Zsuffa, *ibid.*, **44**, 852 (1911).
238. Liebermann *et al.*, *ibid.*, 1186 (1912).
239. Stolle, *ibid.*, **47**, 1130 (1914); Stolle and Knabel, *ibid.*, **54**, 1213 (1921).
240. Sharma and Dutt, *J. Indian Chem. Soc.*, **12**, 774 (1935); Schroeter, *Ann.*, **418**, 198 (1919); Chakrabarty and Dutt, *J. Indian Chem. Soc.*, **5**, 513 (1928); Hirst and Cohen, *J. Chem. Soc.*, **67**, 827 (1895).
241. Mitter and Mukherjee, *J. Indian Chem. Soc.*, **16**, 393 (1939).
242. Mitter and Mukherjee, *l.c.*; *Cf. however*, Staudinger *et al.*, *Helv. Chim. Acta*, **4**, 334 (1921).
243. Schönberg and Kraemer, *Ber.*, **55**, 1174 (1922).
244. Staudinger *et al.*, *Helv. Chim. Acta*, **4**, 334 (1921).
245. Dilthey *et al.*, *J. prakt. Chem.*, **141**, 331 (1934).
246. Stollé, *Ber.*, **46**, 3915 (1913); *German patent* 281,046 (1913).
247. Chuit and Bolle, *Bull. soc. chim.*, (4) **35**, 200 (1924).
248. Behal and Auger, *ibid.*, (3) **9**, 696 (1893).
249. Freund and Fleischer, *Ann.*, **373**, 291 (1910).
250. Freund and Fleischer, *ibid.*, **409**, 268 (1915).
251. Black *et al.*, *J. Chem. Soc.*, **1931**, 272.
252. Etaix, *Ann. chim. phys.*, (7) **9**, 372 (1896).
253. Auger, *ibid.*, (6) **22**, 310 (1891); *Bull. soc. chim.*, (2) **49**, 345 (1888); Lutz, *J. Am. Chem. Soc.*, **49**, 1106 (1927). Limpricht, *Ann.*, **312**, 110 (1900).
254. Limpricht *l.c.*
255. Lutz, *l.c.*
256. Conant and Lutz, *J. Am. Chem. Soc.*, **45**, 1303 (1923).
257. Oddy, *ibid.*, **45**, 2156 (1923).
258. Baeyer, *Ann.*, **202**, 50 (1880); Scheiber, *ibid.*, **390**, 121 (1912).
259. Haller and Guyot, *Compt. rend.*, **120**, 296 (1895).
260. Perkin and Weizmann, *J. Chem. Soc.* **89**, 1657 (1906).
261. Weiss and Knapp, *Monatsh.*, **50**, 392 (1928).
262. Smith, *J. Am. Chem. Soc.*, **43**, 1920 (1921).
263. Meyer, *Monatsh.*, **25**, 1177 (1904).
264. Vollmann *et al.*, *Ann.*, **531**, 1 (1937).
265. Ador, *Bull. soc. chim.*, (2) **33**, 56 (1880).
266. Haller and Guyot, *Compt. rend.*, **121**, 102 (1895).
267. Samuelsson, *Svenck Kem. Tid.*, **34**, 7 (1922).
268. Dziewonski and Brand, *Roczniki Chem.*, **12**, 693 (1933).
269. Dziewonski and Marusinska, *Bull. acad. polonaise*, **1938 A**, 316. *Cf. French patent* 642,907 (1927); *British patent* 279,506 (1927).
270. Roux, *Ann. chim.*, (6) **12**, 341 (1887); Rospendowski, *Compt. rend.*, **102**, 872 (1886); Elbs, *J. prakt. Chem.*, (2) **35**, 503 (1887); Montagne, *Rec. trav. chim.*, **26**, 273 (1907).
271. Caille, *Compt. rend.*, **153**, 393 (1911).
272. Clar *et al.*, *Ber.*, **62**, 950 (1929); Cook, *J. Chem. Soc.*, **1931**, 489.
273. Meyer and Müller, *Ber.*, **60**, 2278 (1927).
274. Scharwin, *ibid.*, **35**, 2511 (1902).
275. Graebe, *Ann.*, **327**, 91 (1903); Fleischer and Wolff, *Ber.*, **53**, 925 (1920); Mayer and Kaufmann, *ibid.*, **53**, 289 (1920).
276. Lipmann *et al.*, *Ber.*, **32**, 2249 (1899); **33**, 3086 (1900); Perrier, *ibid.*, **33**, 816 (1900); Nenitzescu *et al.*, *Ann.*, **491**, 210 (1931).
277. Gattermann, *Ann.*, **244**, 29 (1888).
278. Sheldrick and Wyer, *British patents* 486,668 (1938); 510,901.
279. Liebermann and Zsuffa, *Ber.*, **44**, 202 (1911).

280. Staudinger *et al.*, *Helv. Chim. Acta*, **4**, 334 (1921). *Cf.* Gina, *Gazz. chim. ital.*, **47 I**, 51 (1917).
281. v. Braun *et al.*, *Ber.*, **53**, 1155 (1920).
282. Dansi and Sempronj, *Gazz. chim. ital.*, **66**, 182 (1936); Liebermann *et al.*, *Ber.*, **45**, 1186 (1912).
283. Staudinger *et al.*, *Helv. Chim. Acta*, **4**, 342 (1921).
284. Fleischer and Retze, *Ber.*, **55**, 3280 (1922); *German patent* 283,365 (1915).
285. Freund and Fleischer, *Ann.*, **399**, 182 (1913).
286. Kardos, *Ber.*, **46**, 2090 (1913).
287. Kostanecki *et al.*, *ibid.*, **40**, 3660 (1907).
288. Galewsky, *Ann.*, **264**, 187 (1891).
289. Tomita, *J. Pharm. Soc. Japan*, **54**, 891 (1934); **56**, 906 (1936); **58**, 498 (1938).
290. Heller and Kostanecki, *Ber.*, **41**, 1324 (1908).
291. Engler and Rosumoff, *ibid.*, **24**, 2527 (1891); Wolffenstein and Hartwich, *ibid.*, **48**, 2043 (1915).
292. Hess, *Ber.*, **48**, 1969 (1915); Fischer, *Z. Physiol. Chem.*, **155**, 99 (1926); Ann. **462**, 210 (1928); **481**, 193 (1930); **489**, 62 (1931).
293. Fischer and Schubert, *Z. physiol. Chem.*, **155**, 99 (1926).
294. Fränkel and Grauer, *Ber.*, **46**, 2551 (1913); Wolffenstein and Hartwich, *ibid.*, **48**, 2043 (1915).
295. Kunckell and Vollhase, *Ber.*, **42**, 3196 (1909).
296. Plant *et al.*, *J. Chem. Soc.*, **1935**, 741.
297. Plant and Williams, *ibid.*, **1934**, 1142.
298. Michaelis and Rojahn, *Ber.*, **50**, 737 (1917).
299. Friedel and Crafts, *Compt. rend.*, **36**, 1363 (1878); **92**, 833 (1881).
300. Phillips, *J. Am. Chem. Soc.*, **49**, 473 (1927).
301. Heller, *Ber.*, **45**, 665 (1912).
302. Waldmann, *J. prakt. Chem.*, (2) **131**, 71 (1931).
303. Heller, *Ber.*, **45**, 793 (1912); Heller and Bardroff, *ibid.*, **58**, 497 (1925).
304. Bubidge and Qua, *J. Am. Chem. Soc.*, **36**, 732 (1914); Lawrance, *ibid.*, **42**, 1871 (1920); Stephens, *ibid.*, **43**, 1950 (1921); McMullen, *ibid.*, **43**, 1965 (1921).
305. Haller and Guyot, *Compt. rend.*, **119**, 139 (1894).
306. Ray and Dutt, *J. Indian Chem. Soc.*, **5**, 103 (1928); Noller and Adams, *J. Am. Chem. Soc.*, **46**, 1892 (1942).
307. Groggins and Nagel, *Ind. Eng. Chem.*, **26**, 1313 (1934).
308. Ullmann *et al.*, *Ber.*, **52**, 2098 (1919); **55**, 306 (1922); Fieser and Dietz, *J. Am. Chem. Soc.*, **51**, 3141 (1929).
309. Hoffmann, *Monatsh.*, **36**, 805 (1915).
310. Lawrance and Oddy, *J. Am. Chem. Soc.*, **44**, 339 (1922).
311. Ullmann and Schmidt, *Ber.*, **52**, 2098 (1919); Eckert and Klinger, *J. prakt. Chem.*, (2) **121**, 281 (1929).
312. duBarry Barnett and Sanders, *J. Chem. Soc.*, **1933**, 434.
313. Ravel *et al.*, *J. Univ. Bombay*, **7**, ft. 3, 184 (1938).
314. Dalal and Nargund, *J. Indian Chem. Soc.*, **14**, 406 (1937).
315. Skraup and Schwamberger, *Ann.*, **462**, 135 (1928); Allen *et al.*, *Can. J. Research*, **11**, 382 (1934).
316. Hey and Wilkinson, *J. Chem. Soc.*, **1940**, 1030.
317. Borsche and Sauernheimer, *Ber.*, **47**, 1645 (1914); Giua, *ibid.*, **47**, 7115 (1914); Haworth, *J. Chem. Soc.*, **1932**, 1125; Fieser and Peters, *J. Am. Chem. Soc.*, **54**, 4347 (1932); Fieser and Seligman, *ibid.*, **59**, 883 (1937).
318. Hewett, *J. Chem. Soc.*, **1940**, 293.
319. Fieser and Peters, *J. Am. Chem. Soc.*, **54**, 4347 (1932).
320. Burger and Mosettig, *ibid.*, **59**, 1302 (1937); Fieser and Cason, *ibid.*, **62**, 1293 (1940); Bachmann and Edgerton, *ibid.*, **62**, 2550 (1940).
321. Adelson and Bogert, *J. Am. Chem. Soc.*, **59**, 1776 (1937).
322. Beyer, *Ber.*, **71**, 915 (1938).
323. Gilman and Jacoby, *J. Org. Chem.*, **3**, 108 (1938).
324. Klobb, *Bull. soc. chim.*, (3) **23**, 511 (1900).
325. Howorth and Bolam, *J. Chem. Soc.*, **1932**, 2248.
326. Desai and Wali, *Proc. Indian Acad. Sci.*, **A6**, 135 (1937).
327. Sen Gupta, *J. prakt. Chem.*, (2) **151**, 82 (1938).
328. Anschütz *et al.*, *Ann.*, **354**, 150 (1907); Ali *et al.*, *J. Chem. Soc.*, **1937**, 1013.
329. Robinson and Young, *ibid.*, **1935**, 1414.
330. Hill, *J. Am. Chem. Soc.*, **54**, 4105 (1932); Plant and Tomlinson, *J. Chem. Soc.*, **1935**, 1092.
331. Tschitschibabin and Schtschukina, *Ber.*, **63**, 2793 (1930).
332. Pechmann, *ibid.*, **51**, 881 (1882); Gabriel and Colman, *ibid.*, **32**, 395 (1899).
333. Rice, *J. Am. Chem. Soc.*, **53**, 3153 (1931).
334. Zahn and Ochwat, *Ann.*, **462**, 72 (1928).
335. Bogert and Ritter, *J. Am. Chem. Soc.*, **47**, 526 (1925).
336. Lutz, *ibid.*, **52**, 3405 (1930).
337. Kozniewski and Marchlewski, *Anz. Akad. Wiss. Krakau*, **1906**, 81; *Chem. Zentr.*, **1906 II**, 1191.
338. Kranzlein, *Ber.*, **70**, 1952 (1937).
339. Stümmer, *Monatsh.*, **28**, 411 (1907).

340. Steinkopf, *Ann.*, **407**, 94 (1914); Ernst, *Ber.*, **19**, 3278 (1886).
341. Mayer, *Ann.*, **488**, 276 (1931).
342. Scholl and Seer, *Ber.*, **44**, 1233 (1911).
343. Scholl and Neovius, *ibid.*, **44**, 1249 (1911).
344. Bistrzycki *et al.*, *ibid.*, **31**, 2790 (1898).
345. Graves and Adams, *J. Am. Chem. Soc.*, **45**, 2439 (1923).
346. Gardner and Adams, *ibid.*, **45**, 2455 (1933).
347. Graebe and Leonhardt, *Ann.*, **290**, 217 (1896).
348. Lawrance, *J. Am. Chem. Soc.*, **42**, 1871 (1920).
349. Stephens, *ibid.*, **43**, 1950 (1921).
350. Waldmann *et al.*, *J. prakt. Chem.*,(2) **126**, 65, 59 (1930); (2) **127**, 201 (1930).
351. *British patent* 358,078 (1930).
352. Severin, *Compt. rend.*, **142**, 1274 (1906).
353. Lawrance, *J. Am. Chem. Soc.*, **43**, 2577 (1921).
354. Mitter and Goswann, *J. Indian Chem. Soc.*, **8**, 685 (1931).
355. Mitter and Chatterji, *ibid.*, **8**, 783 (1931).
356. Eder and Widmer, *Helv. Chim. Acta*, **5**, 3 (1922).
357. Graebe and Trümpy, *Ber.*, **31**, 375 (1898). *Cf.* Buu-Hoi, *Compt. rend.*, **209**, 562 (1939).
358. Jephcott, *J. Am. Chem. Soc.*, **50**, 1189 (1928).
359. Philips, *Ber.*, **27**, 1923 (1894); Freund, *Monatsh.*, **18**, 447 (1897); Fulda, *ibid.*, **20**, 762 (1899); Kirpel, *ibid.*, **30**, 355 (1909).
360. Burker, *Bull. soc. chim.*, (3) **4**, 112 (1890); Burker and Sabil, *Compt. rend.*, **119**, 426 (1894).
361. Eykman, *Chem. Weekblad* **4**, 727 (1907).
362. Böeseken and Koning, *Rec. trav. chim.*, **30**, 116 (1911).
363. Böeseken, *ibid.*, **24**, 209 (1905). *Cf.* Friedel and Crafts, *Ann. chim. phys.*, (6) **1**, 530 (1884).
364. Kraft and Lyons, *Ber.*, **29**, 435 (1896). *Cf.* Fries and Vogt, *Ann.*, **381**, 312 (1911); Genvresse, *Bull. soc. chim.*, (3) **15**, 409 (1896).
365. Fries, *Ber.*, **45**, 2965 (1912); Fries and Schurmann, *ibid.*, **52**, 2170 (1919).
366. Schonberg, *Ber.*, **56**, 2275 (1923).
367. Smiles and Le Rossignol, *J. Chem. Soc.*, **89**, 696 (1906).
368. Ruff, *Ber.*, **35**, 4453 (1902).
369. Steinkopf and Buchheim, *ibid.*, **54**, 2963 (1921).
370. Beckurts and Otto, *ibid.*, **11**, 2066 (1878); Böeseken, *Rec. trav. chim.*, **19**, 24 (1900); Haehl, *Compt. rend.*, **177**, 194 (1923); Olivier and Böeseken, *Rec. trav. chim.*, **33**, 91 (1913); **33**, 244 (1914); **35**, 109, 166 (1915); Heppenstall and Smiles, *J. chem. Soc.*, **1938**, 899.
371. Heppenstall and Smiles, *l. c.*
372. Fries and Schurmann, *Ber.*, **52**, 2170 (1919).
373. Gattermann, *ibid.*, **28**, 2869 (1895).
374. Bradt *et al.*, *Proc. Indian Acad. Sci.*, **41**, 227 (1931); **41**, 215 (1931); *J. Org. Chem.*, **1**, 540 (1937). *Cf.* Chabrie, *Bull. soc. chim.*, (2) **50**, 133 (1888); (3) **2**, 796 (1889); (3) **11**, 1080 (1894); *Compt. rend.*, **109**, 182 (1889); *J. Chem. Soc.*, **56**, 41 (1889); Kraft *et al.*, *Ber.*, **26**, 2813 (1893); **27**, 1761 (1894); **29**, 429 (1896).
375. Leicester and Bergstrom, *J. Am. Chem. Soc.*, **51**, 3587 (1929); Leicester, *Organic Syntheses* **18**, 30 (1928). *Cf.* Leicester and Bergstrom, *J. Am. Chem. Soc.*, **54**, 4428 (1931).
376. Lesser and Weiss., *Ber.*, **57**, 1077 (1924).
377. Michaelis, *Ann.*, **293**, 193 (1896); **294**, 1 (1896); **315**, 43 (1901); *Ber.*, **12**, 1009 (1879); Michaelis and Panek, *ibid.*, **13**, 653 (1880); *Ann.*, **212**, 203 (1882).
378. Davies and Morris, *J. Chem. Soc.*, **1932**, 2880.
379. Lindner, *Ber.*, **55**, 2025 (1922); *Z. anal. Chem.*, **66**, 301 (1925); **86**, 141 (1931); *Monatsh.*, **53**, 263, 274 (1929); **70**, 1 (1937). *Cf.* Woodstock, *U. S. patent* 2,137,792 (1938).
380. Tschunkur and Kinepen, *German patent* 367,954; Britton and Bass, *U. S. patent* 2,117,290 (1938); *British patent* 455,014 (1936); Bass, *U. S. patent* 2,033,918 (1936).
381. Wieland and Kulenkampff, *Ann.*, **431**, 30 (1923); La Coste and Michaelis, *ibid.*, **201**, 184 (1880).
382. Burrows and Turner, *J. Chem. Soc.*, **119**, 426 (1921); Hunt and Turner, *ibid.*, **127**, 2667 (1925); Aeschlimann, *ibid.*, **127**, 811 (1925).
383. Lewis *et al.*, *J. Am. Chem. Soc.*, **43**, 891 (1921).
384. Malinowski, *J. Gen. Chem. (U.S.S.R.)*, **5**, 1355 (1935).
385. Lewis and Cheetham, *J. Am. Chem. Soc.*, **43**, 2117 (1921). *Cf.* Lewis and Cheetham, *ibid.*, **45**, 510 (1923).
386. Das-Gupta, *J. Indian Chem. Soc.*, **14**, 231 (1937).
387. Kane and Lowy, *J. Am. Chem. Soc.*, **58**, 2605 (1936).
388. Meyer and Wurster, *Ber.*, **6**, 964 (1873); Houston and Friedmann, *J. Am. Chem. Soc.*, **38**, 2527 (1916).
389. Meyer and Bernhauer, *Monatsh.*, 53/54, 743 (1929).
390. Bistrzycki and Flattau, *Ber.*, **28**, 989 (1895); **30**, 124 (1897); Bistrzycki and Simonis, *ibid.*, **31**, 2812 (1898); Cramer, *ibid.*, **31**, 2813 (1898); Simonis, *ibid.*, **31**, 2821 (1898).
391. Zukerwanig and Nasarowa, *J. Russ.-Phys. Chem. Soc.*, **5**, 767 (1935).

392. Zincke, *Ann.*, **159**, 374 (1871); **161**, 93 (1872); *Ber.*, **5**, 799 (1872); **6**, 137 (1873); **9**, 1761 (1876); Walker, *ibid.*, **5**, 686 (1872); Mazzara, *Jahresb.*, **1878**, 402; Weber, *ibid.*, **1878**, 402; Plascuda and Zincke, *Ber.*, **6**, 906 (1873); Senff, *Ann.*, **220**, 225 (1883); Paternò, *J. prakt. Chem.*, (2) **4**, 458 (1871); Paternò and Fileti, *Gazz. chim. ital.*, **3**, 121, 251 (1873); Paternò and Mazzara, *Ber.*, **11**, 2030 (1878); Mazzara, *Gazz. chim. ital.*, **11**, 347 (1881); Boscogrande, *Atti. accad. Lincei*, (5) **6, II**, 306 (1897).
393. Wilkinson *et al.*, *J. Chem. Soc.*, **1930**, 423, 2537; **1931**, 1333.
394. Fischer, *Ber.*, **42**, 1018 (1909); Fischer and Rapaport, *ibid.*, **46**, 2393 (1913).
395. Mitter and Duff, *J. Indian Chem. Soc.*, **13**, 228 (1936).
396. Tzukervanik, *J. Gen. Chem. U.S.S.R.*, **15**, 699 (1945); Sears, *J. Org. Chem.*, **13**, 120 (1948).
397. Hennion and Pieroneck, *J. Am. Chem. Soc.*, **64**, 2751 (1942); Vermillion and Hill, *ibid.*, **67**, 2209 (1945).
398. Hanssen, *Dissertation, Tubingen* (1926); Meisenheimer *et al.*, *J. prakt. Chem.*, (2) **119**, 315 (1928).
399. Leuckart, *Ber.*, **18**, 873 (1885); *J. prakt. Chem.*, (2) **41**, 301 (1890).
400. Jorg, *Ber.*, **60**, 1466 (1927); Gilman and Calloway, *J. Am. Chem. Soc.*, **55**, 4197 (1933).
401. Ullmann *et al.*, *Ber.*, **52**, 2098 (1919); **53**, 830 (1920).

CHAPTER 14

ALIPHATIC NITRO AND NITROSO COMPOUNDS, SULFONIC AND SULFINIC ACIDS, AND RELATED COMPOUNDS

NITRO COMPOUNDS

Preparations

Aliphatic nitro compounds may be obtained through the direct nitration of aliphatic hydrocarbons, or other aliphatic compounds; through the replacement of halogens in organic halo compounds by the nitro group; and through the addition of nitrogen peroxide to unsaturated hydrocarbons. They are also formed by the oxidation of oximes and by miscellaneous other methods.

Direct Nitration of Aliphatic Compounds [1]

Nitric acid is practically without action on normal paraffin hydrocarbons in the cold and at moderately elevated temperatures. Nitration may take place, however, on heating hydrocarbons with nitric acid at temperatures in excess of 140°. Normal hydrocarbons from hexane to decane may be nitrated by refluxing with a mixture of nitric and sulfuric acids, primary nitro paraffins alone resulting from the reaction.[2] Hexane heated in a sealed tube at 140° with nitric acid of density 1.075 gives nitrohexane in 60% yield.[3] As a general rule, primarily bound hydrogens are replaced least readily, and tertiarily bound hydrogens most readily.[4] Nitration proceeds quite readily in some cases. Thus, 1,4-dinitrodiisobutyl, $(CH_3)_2C(NO_2)CH_2CH_2C(NO_2)(CH_3)_2$, forms readily when diisobutyl is heated with dilute nitric acid. Nitric acid of density 1.42 attacks *n*-hexane, *n*-heptane and *n*-octane, the last named the most rapidly, giving nitrooctane and dinitrooctane in 60 to 70% yield.[230]

Halo paraffins are nitrated more readily than the corresponding hydrocarbons, and many halo nitro paraffins may be obtained in excellent yield by direct nitration. Thus, 1-chloro-2-nitroisobutane results in very good yield through the nitration of 1-chloroisobutane:[5]

$$(CH_3)_2CHCH_2Cl + HNO_3 \rightarrow (CH_3)_2C(NO_2)CH_2Cl + H_2O$$

Primary and secondary halo compounds give nitro compounds or oxidation products in this reaction, depending on their structure, while tertiary halo compounds liberate hydrogen chloride on treatment with nitric acid.[5]

Direct nitration of nitroform results in the formation of tetranitromethane.[7]

The nitro group may be introduced in the side chain of the lower homologs of benzene by heating with dilute acid (density 1.12–1.01) in a sealed tube at 100° for several hours.[8] Phenylnitromethane may be obtained by this method in 50% yield. Ethylbenzene gives α-nitroethylbenzene.

Direct nitration of organic substances is accompanied by oxidative reactions, fission of carbon to carbon bonds, and the formation of considerable amounts of polynitro compounds. Occasionally polynitro compounds may form in such quantities as to make it possible to utilize the reaction for the preparation of these compounds.[9] Dinitroparaffins are formed in large amounts, together with the mononitro product, through the nitration of saturated hydrocarbons containing two isopropyl groups:[10]

$$(CH_3)_2CH(CH_2)_nCH(CH_3)_2 + 2HNO_3 \rightarrow (CH_3)_2C(NO_2)(CH_2)_nC(NO_2)(CH_3)_2 + 2H_2O$$

The use of a mixture of nitric and sulfuric acids is not desirable for the nitration of aliphatic compounds,[11] since primary nitro paraffins are readily hydrolyzed by hot sulfuric acid, and secondary and tertiary isomers are converted to tars.

The use of ethyl nitrate and sodium ethoxide promotes nitration by increasing the solubility of the hydrocarbon and the nitrating agent.[12]

Aluminum nitrate has been recommended as a catalyst for the reaction, although its real function is probably that of raising the boiling point of the mixture, an effect which may also be brought about by use of sodium nitrate.

Aliphatic ketones are much more reactive toward nitric acid than aromatic hydrocarbons. Many among them give with nitric acid of 1.38 density dinitroketones and dinitroparaffins, along with other compounds.[13] The formation of dinitroparaffins may be assumed to take place as follows:

$$RCOCH_2R' \xrightarrow{HONO} RCOC(:NOH)R' \xrightarrow{HONO} RCOC(NO_2)_2R'$$

$$\xrightarrow{H_2O} RCOOH + R'CH(NO_2)_2$$

Entirely pure nitric acid fails to react in the cold, but reaction proceeds vigorously upon the addition of nitrous acid.

Keto acids,[14] secondary alcohols,[15] aldehydes,[16] and nitrolic acids[17] give on nitration, among other products, dinitro compounds, although the reactions proceed in a complicated manner in every case.

The nitration of glycerine is carried out with a mixture containing 35% nitric acid, 63% sulfuric acid and 0.1% nitrous acid.

Carboxylic acids, subjected to the action of nitric acid or its hydrates, react to form well crystallized compounds which are derivatives of orthonitric acid.[231]

$$2RCOOH + HNO_3 \rightarrow (RCOO)_2N(OH)_3$$

The acetyl derivative $(CH_3COO)_2N(OH)_3$ is obtained by adding one molal proportion of acetic anhydride to an equivalent of nitric acid of density 1.42 which consists largely of the hydrate H_3NO_4. The compound is isolated by fractional distillation (b. p. 128°).

When nitric acid of density 1.48 is mixed with acetic anhydride, considerable heat is generated, and reaction may proceed with violence even when external cooling is applied, especially if the nitric acid contains some nitrous acid.[232] The danger of violent reaction may be avoided by adding acetic acid to the mixture. The possibility of a violent reaction is increased when "mixed acids" are used. Danger of a violent reaction may be avoided in that case by using nitric acid free from nitrous acid, adding the acetic anhydride slowly, and cooling the reaction mixture effectively.

Direct nitration of *isovaleric acid* results in the formation of β-nitroisovaleric acid,[18] $(CH_3)_2C(NO_2)CH_2COOH$; similarly α-nitro-β, β-dimethylacrylic ester, $(CH_3)_2C = C(NO_2)COOC_2H_5$, results through the nitration of β, β-dimethylacrylic ester.[19] More vigorous nitration of isovaleric acid and other aliphatic acids containing tertiary carbon atoms results in the formation of dinitro paraffins:[233]

$$(CH_3)_2CHCH_2COOH + 2HNO_3 \rightarrow$$
$$(CH_3)_2C(NO_2)_2 + HOCH_2COOH + H_2O$$

$$(CH_3)_2CHCOOH + 2HNO_3 \rightarrow (CH_3)_2C(NO_2)_2 + CO_2 + 2H_2O$$

Acetic anhydride subjected to the action of cold concentrated nitric acid for several days reacts to form tetranitromethane in 80% yield.[20] The reaction proceeds more readily with anhydrous nitric acid.

Acetyl nitrate is formed on dissolving pure nitric anhydride in acetic anhydride.[234] This compound is dangerous, as it readily changes to the unstable nitroacetic acid.

Nitroisosuccinic acid, $CH_3C(NO_2)(COOC_2H_5)_2$, is obtained by adding isosuccinic acid dropwise to a mixture of fuming nitric acid and acetic anhydride maintained at 40 to 50°.[235]

Isonitrosoacetoacetic ester has been obtained by adding the required quantity of sodium nitrite fairly rapidly to a solution of acetoacetic ester in nitric acid. Interaction of the isonitroso ester and nitric acid of 1.15 density containing a little nitrous acid for a short period results in the formation of nitrooxamino acetic ester, which may be recovered by extraction with ether after the reaction mixture has been diluted with water:[236]

$$CH_3COC(:NOH)COOC_2H_5 + HONO_2 \rightarrow HON{:}C(NO_2)COOC_2H_5 + CH_3COOH$$

On treating the crystals of the compound with hydrogen chloride, chloroximinoacetic acid is obtained in quantitative yield:

$$HON = C(NO_2)COOC_2H_5 + HCl \rightarrow HON = CClCOOC_2H_5 + HNO_2$$

Nitroacetic ester is obtained by adding a cold mixture of nitric acid and acetic anhydride dropwise to a well agitated mixture of acetoacetic ester and acetic anhydride maintained at 32 to 34°. Nitroacetoacetic ester has been used for the synthesis of many aliphatic nitro compounds.

Cupric nitrate in admixture with acetic anhydride, reacting with acetic ester, gives the metallic derivative of nitroacetic ester. Malonic and isosuccinic esters may also be nitrated by this method.

Reactive methylene groups may be nitrated with alkyl nitrates in the presence of alkali alcoholates.[237] The reaction results in the formation of the sodio derivative of the *aci* form of the nitro compound:

$$XCH_2Y + C_2H_5ONO_2 + NaOC_2H_5 \rightarrow XC(=NOONa)Y + 2C_2H_5OH$$

The methylene group in acetoacetic ester, malononitrile, benzyl- and *p*-nitrobenzyl cyanide, di- and trinitrotoluene, etc., has been nitrated by this method.

A very convenient method of preparation of *phenylnitromethane* consists in hydrolyzing and decarboxylating the nitro compound resulting from the reaction of benzyl cyanide with methyl nitrate in the presence of sodium methylate:[238]

$$C_6H_5C(:NOONa)CN \rightarrow C_6H_5C(:NOONa)COONa$$
$$\rightarrow C_6H_5CH=NOOH$$

Treatment of the sodium salt of the acid with hydrochloric acid at -5° results in the formation of the *aci* form of the nitromethane. The *aci* compound in ethereal solution kept 3 to 4 days changes to phenylnitromethane. Other arylated nitromethanes have been prepared by this method.[239]

Nitromalonic ester and nitromalonamide may be obtained through the direct nitration of malonic ester.[21] Nitration of methylmalonic acid results in the formation of 1,1,1-trinitroethane.

The reaction of nitrogen trioxide or tetroxide with malonic ester results in the formation of oxomalonic ester.[240] A nearly quantitative yield may be obtained by adding a little sodium to the reaction mixture.

Vapor Phase Nitration[22]

Paraffin hydrocarbons may be nitrated in the vapor phase by nitric acid at temperatures in excess of 250°. The reaction results in the formation of all possible isomers of the nitrated hydrocarbon. Cleavage of the hydrocarbon chain also takes place, so that nitrated hydrocarbons resulting from all radicals derivable by the fission of the various carbon to carbon bonds are found in the reaction mixture. Thus, carrying out the reaction at 420° with a 1 to 1 molecular proportions of nitric acid and hydrocarbon, ethane yields 73% nitroethane and 27% nitromethane,[23] while *n*-butane gives 50% 2-nitrobutane, 27% 1-nitrobutane, 5% 1-nitropropane, 12% nitroethane and 6% nitromethane.[24]

The reaction proceeds very rapidly at the higher temperature range; thus at 420° reaction is complete in less than one second with a mixture of the hydrocarbon with two molecular equivalents of nitric acid.[25]

The ease of nitration decreases in the order $(R)_3CH$, $(R)_2CH_2$, RCH_3. The reaction velocity increases with rise in temperature, a greater proportion of the primary nitration product being obtained at higher temperatures, with a smaller proportion of product resulting from the fission of the carbon chain. There is, however, an optimum point[24] beyond which a rise in temperature causes a substantial increase in products of pyrolysis. For this reason, strict control of the temperature within ±0.5° is observed in commercial practice. Di and polynitro compounds are not formed during vapor phase nitration,[26] even when nitroparaffins are employed in the reaction.[27]

In the vapor phase nitration of hydrocarbons, varying quantities of alcohols, acids, aldehydes, ketones, carbon monoxide, carbon dioxide and water are formed. Conversions to the desired product in a single passage may reach a maximum of 40%, based on the nitric acid used. In properly conducted commercial practice, utilization of nitric acid is in the neighborhood of 90%, since the nitrogen oxides formed in the reaction are recovered, reconverted to acid and returned to the process.

The proportion of different nitrated products formed in the nitration of various hydrocarbons is given in the following table:[28]

Hydrocarbon	Nitration Product	%
ethane	nitromethane	10-20
	nitroethane	80-90
propane	nitromethane	9
	nitroethane	26(?)
	1-nitropropane	36
	2-nitropropane	33
n-butane	nitrobutane	6
	nitroethane	12
	1-nitropropane	5
	1-nitrobutane	27
	2-nitrobutane	50
isobutane	nitromethane	3
	2-nitropropane	20
	1-nitroisobutane	65
	2-nitroisobutane	7
n-pentane	nitromethane	1
	nitroethane	7
	1-nitropropane	14
	1-nitrobutane	12.5
	1-nitropentane	22
	2-nitropentane	21
	3-nitropentane	23
isopentane	nitromethane	6
	nitroethane	6
	2-nitropropane	6
	2-nitrobutane } 1-nitroisobutane }	12
	1-nitro-3-methylbutane	13
	2-nitro-3-methylbutane	27
	2-nitro-2-methylbutane	19
	1-nitro-2-methylbutane	11

Nitration was carried out at 420° with the first four hydrocarbons, at 400° with the fifth and at 380° with the last.

Normal aliphatic hydrocarbons may be nitrated in the vapor phase at 100° with nitrogen peroxide in the presence of arsenic or antimony:[29]

$$CH_3CH_2CH_3 \xrightarrow{N_2O_4} CH_3CH_2CH_2NO_2$$

2-Methyl-2-nitropropane has been obtained from isobutane in 90% yield at 200° by this method.[30]

Paraffins have been nitrated by mixing their vapors with dry gaseous nitrogen tetroxide, N_2O_4, and passing the mixture through a tube filled with glass rings and heated in an electric oven.[241] Nitration of methane begins below 200°, that of propane below 100°. Both mono- and dinitrated products are formed. The ratio of mono and dinitro compounds obtained is usually 60:40. Methane gives a low yield of nitrated products.

Replacement of Halogens with Nitro Groups

Meyer's Reaction

Nitro paraffins result by the reaction of alkyl iodides with silver nitrite, the reaction often proceeding quite vigorously.[31]

The procedure is to add the alkyl iodide gradually to somewhat more than the equivalent quantity of dry, finely pulverized silver nitrite, preferably diluted with an equal volume of dry sand. The reaction is usually completed by heating the mixture on a water bath.

Silver nitrite is best prepared by mixing lukewarm concentrated solutions of silver nitrate and potassium nitrite and allowing the mixture to cool to crystallization. A 20% excess of potassium nitrite over the theoretically required quantity is employed for best results.[242]

The reaction proceeds well with methyl, ethyl and primary *n*-propyl iodides, but less satisfactory results are obtained with secondary alkyl iodides, while tertiary iodides give only small yields of nitroparaffins.[32] Straight chain iodides give higher yields of the nitro compound than branched chain compounds.

In the reaction of silver nitrite with alkyl iodides nitro compounds, as well as nitrous esters are often obtained. Methyl iodide gives the nitro compound exclusively, but other alkyl iodides yield the nitro compound and nitrous ester in varying proportions.[33] Alkyl bromides give higher yields of the nitro compound than are obtained from alkyl iodides.[34]

Silver nitrite may be replaced in this reaction with mercuric nitrite,[35] but sodium and potassium nitrites give unsatisfactory results.

Nitro paraffins are obtained also through the reaction of certain alkyl sulfates with silver nitrite.[36]

Meyer's reaction is applicable to the preparation of nitro alcohols,[37] nitro ethers, nitro ketones[243] and many other types of aliphatic nitro compounds.[244] It cannot be employed for the preparation of α-nitro acids from α-halo acids, but reaction proceeds in a satisfactory manner when the halogen is at a greater distance from the carbonyl group. Thus, β-nitropropionic acid may be obtained readily from β-iodopropionic acid:[38]

$$ICH_2CH_2COOH + AgNO_2 \rightarrow NO_2CH_2CH_2COOH + AgI$$

The reaction is also adapted for the preparation of unsaturated nitro compounds,[39] and of polynitro paraffins:[38]

$$RR'C(X)NO_2 + AgNO_2 \rightarrow RR'C(NO_2)_2 + AgX$$

The silver salt of nitroform reacts with alkyl halides forming a trinitrated hydrocarbon, ethyl iodide giving, for example, trinitropropane,

$$CH_3CH_2C(NO_2)_3$$ [245]

Kolbe's Reaction

Salts of α-halocarboxylic acids react with sodium nitrite to form salts of α-nitrocarboxylic acids which decompose readily on slow distillation in aqueous solution, yielding *nitroparaffins* and a metallic bicarbonate:[40]

$$ClCH_2COONa + NaNO_2 \rightarrow NO_2CH_2COONa + NaCl$$

$$NO_2CH_2COONa + H_2O \rightarrow CH_3NO_2 + NaHCO_3$$

Sodium glycollate, $HOCH_2COONa$, is a byproduct resulting from the reaction of the chloroacetate with the sodium bicarbonate formed. Some nitriles are also formed, together with nitro compounds.[41] A portion of the nitromethane is lost in the form of the sodio derivative of metazonic acid by reaction with sodium bicarbonate:[246]

$$2CH_3NO_2 + NaHCO_3 \rightarrow HON = CHCHNOONa + CO_2 + 2H_2O$$

A little hydrocyanic acid is also formed, making necessary some precautions to prevent poisoning with its highly toxic vapors.

The following is a satisfactory procedure for the preparation of *nitromethane:*

Five hundred grams of chloroacetic acid are dissolved in 1000 cc water and neutralized by the gradual addition of 200 to 300 gm of calcined sodium carbonate with stirring. The resulting liquid is mixed with a solution of 300 gm of sodium nitrite in 500 cc of water. One-fourth of the mixture is placed in the reaction flask and is brought to a boil; the remainder is then added gradually while the contents of the flask is kept boiling. Heating is continued after the addition of all the solution until no more nitromethane distills over. The vapors distilling over are condensed and collected; the nitromethane is separated from the small amount of water, and is dried and distilled over a little mercuric oxide.

Homologs of nitromethane may be prepared by this method from α-halo carboxylic acids.

gem-Dinitrocompounds are obtained through the interaction of potassium nitrite and α-bromonitroparaffins:

$$CH_3CH(NO_2)Br + KNO_2 \rightarrow CH_3CH(NO_2)_2 + KBr$$

Polynitroparaffins are obtained through the interaction of the sodium salt of nitroparaffins with halo nitro paraffins:[42]

$$R_2C = NOONa + XC(NO_2)R'_2 \rightarrow R_2C(NO_2)C(NO_2)R'_2 + NaX$$

The yields are generally highest with chlorides and lowest with iodides; they are higher with secondary nitroalkanes than with the primary compounds.

Dimethyl sulfate and the less reactive diethyl sulfate may be used for the preparation of nitromethane and nitroethane by reaction with potassium nitrate.[247]

The reaction of ethyl sulfate with alkaline or alkalineearth nitrites leads to the formation of ethyl nitrite.[248]

Nitro Derivatives from Unsaturated Compounds

Nitric acid, reacting with ethylene and its homologs, gives saturated nitro alcohols which are further oxidized to nitro acids, the latter decomposing to a nitrated hydrocarbon:[43]

$$CH_2 = CH_2 + HONO_2 \rightarrow NO_2CH_2CH_2OH$$

$$\xrightarrow{HNO_3} NO_2CH_2COOH \rightarrow CH_3NO_2$$

The nitrated hydrocarbons formed may, in turn, be acted upon by nitric acid to form polynitro derivatives:

$$CH_3NO_2 \xrightarrow{HNO_3} CH(NO_2)_3$$

Ethylene yields β-nitroethyl nitrate, $NO_2CH_2CH_2ONO_2$, when treated with a mixture of nitric and sulfuric acids.

α,α-Diphenylene reacts very readily with the mixed acid to form α,α-diphenyl-β-nitroethyl alcohol:[249]

$$(C_6H_5)_2C = CH_2 \xrightarrow{HNO_3 + H_2SO_4} (C_6H_5)_2C(OH)CH_2NO_2$$

Stilbene also adds nitric acid readily, as does *phenanthrene*.[250] The nitro alcohol resulting from stilbene loses water to form the corresponding nitrated ether.

The nitro alcohol formed from certain unsaturated compounds lose the elements of water and yield unsaturated nitro compounds. Isoamylene, for example, gives nitroisoamylene:[251]

$$(CH_3)_2C = CHCH_3 + HNO_3 \rightarrow (CH_3)_2C(OH)CH(NO_2)CH_3$$

$$\rightarrow (CH_3)_2C = C(NO_2)CH_3 + H_2O$$

Halogenated ethylenes are susceptible to nitration with nitric acid.[252]

Acetylene reacts vigorously when led into a hot mixture of nitric and sulfuric acids, giving nitroform.[44] The reaction may also be carried out by conducting acetylene into cold nitric acid and heating the resulting product with sulfuric acid. The yield is improved when the reaction is carried out in the presence of a trace of mercuric nitrate.

While nitrogen trioxide, N_2O_3, adds rather readily to triple bonds, the addition of this compound to tolan and phenylpropiolic acid has never been carried out successfully.

Phenylacetylene gives with nitrogen trioxide phenylfuroxan, $C_6H_5\overline{C = N\cdot O}N\cdot \underline{CH\cdot O}$.

The dinitronitroso compound $C_6H_5C(NO_2)(NO)CH(NO_2)NO$ and phenyldinitrosoethylene are probably the intermediates formed in this reaction.[253]

Nitrous gases generated by heating arsenic with concentrated nitric acid react with tolan in ethereal solution to form dinitrostilbene, $C_6H_5C(NO_2) = C(NO_2)C_6H_5$.[254]

Haloolefins, refluxed with a mixture of concentrated and fuming nitric acids, give halo nitro derivatives. Thus, dichlorodinitromethane results from symmetrical dichloroethylene.[45]

Nitrotriiodoethylene, $I_2C = CINO_2$, and dinitrodiiodoethylene, $NO_2Cl = CINO_2$, result through the action of fuming nitric acid or nitrogen trioxide, N_2O_3, on tetraiodoethylene.[46]

Dinitro paraffins are obtained through the reaction of olefin hydrocarbons with nitrogen peroxide:[47]

$$(CH_3)_2C = C(CH_3)_2 + N_2O_4 \rightarrow (CH_3)_2C(NO_2)C(NO_2)(CH_3)_2$$

The reaction is usually carried out in an inert solvent, such as benzene. 1,2-Dinitro-, 1,2-trimethyl- , 1,1-dinitro-1,1,2-triphenylethane, and 1,2-dinitro-1,2-diphenylethane have been prepared by this method. α,α-Diphenylethylene, $(C_6H_5)_2C = CH_2$, gives the nitro alcohol if all moisture is not carefully eliminated. Halogenated olefins give halo dinitro olefins by this reaction.[48]

1,4-Diphenylbutadiene-1,3 gives with nitrogen peroxide 1,4-dinitrobutene.[255] Alkalies convert the compound to α,δ-diphenylene-α-nitrobutadiene. Dibenzalacetone,

$$(C_6H_5C = CH)_2CO,$$

adds nitrogen peroxide only at one double bond.[256] Anthracene adds two nitro groups at the meso position on reaction with nitrogen peroxide.[257] Phenylacetylene, tolan and phenylpropiolic acid add one molecular equivalent of nitrogen peroxide to form dinitro compounds.[258]

Dinitro compounds resulting from the reaction of ethylenic compounds with nitrogen peroxide lose nitrous acid readily to give mononitrated ethylenes:

$$-CHNO_2CHNO_2- \quad \rightarrow \quad -C(NO_2) = CH- + HNO_2$$

The reaction of nitrogen trioxide with olefinic compounds generally results in the formation of pseudonitrosites:[259]

$$2C_6H_5CH = CH_2 + 2N_2O_3 \quad \rightarrow \quad [C_6H_5CHCH_2NO_2]_2N_2O_2$$

The compound derived from styrene is highly unstable and is converted to α-nitroacetophenoxime, $C_6H_5C(=NOH)CH_2NO_2$, when boiled with absolute alcohol for one-half hour.[260] The pseudonitrosite derived from cyclohexene is converted to the potassium salt of *aci* nitrohexanol,

$$\overline{CH_2CH_2CH_2CH_2CH(OH)C} = NOOH$$

on boiling with alcoholic potassium hydroxide.[261]

Benzalacetone reacting with nitrogen trioxide under a variety of conditions gives benzalacetone nitroxime, $C_6H_5C(:NOH)CH(NO_2)COCH_3$, which changes to an inner anhydride, phenylmethylnitroisoxazole, $C_6H_5\overline{C = NOC(CH_3) = C}NO_2$. The pseudonitrosite is obtained under certain conditions when the reaction is carried out in ethereal solution. The pseudonitrosite is obtained from anethole, $CH_3OC_6H_4CH{=}CHCH_3$, when the reaction is carried out in alcoholic solution with good cooling. The pseudonitrosite is changed to anisylnitroethyl ketoxime, $CH_3OC_6H_4C(=NOH)CH(NO_2)CH_3$, when boiled with alcohol, and to β-nitroanethole, $CH_3OC_6H_4CH = C(NO_2)CH_3$, when treated with 10% alcoholic caustic with cooling. Hot caustic converts the pseudonitrosite to anisaldehyde.[262]

Dinitroparaffins also result through the condensation of nitroolefins with nitrated hydrocarbons having a reactive methylene group:[49]

$$C_6H_5CH = CHNO_2 + NO_2CH_2C_6H_5 \quad \rightarrow \quad C_6H_5CH(CH_2NO_2)CH(NO_2)C_6H_5$$

The reaction of nitryl chloride with halogenated olefins results in the formation of halo nitro compounds:[50]

$$H_2C = CHBr + ClNO_2 \quad \rightarrow \quad NO_2CH_2CHClBr$$

$$ClCH = CHCl + ClNO_2 \quad \rightarrow \quad NO_2CH(Cl)CHCl_2$$

Miscellaneous Methods

Nitro compounds are formed from oximes by reaction with certain oxidizing agents. Thus, hypohalites reacting with oximes give halo nitro compounds:

$$RR'C = NOH + HOX \rightarrow H_2O + RR'C(NO)X \xrightarrow{HOX} RR'C(NO_2)X$$

Similar results are obtained through the reaction of oximes with nitrosyl chloride.[51]

Pseudonitroles resulting from the reaction of nitrogen peroxide with oximes are readily oxidized by chromic acid or other oxidizing agents to the corresponding dinitroderivatives:

$$R_2C = NOH + N_2O_4 \rightarrow HONO + R_2C(NO_2)NO \rightarrow R_2C(NO_2)_2$$

Tetranitro derivatives have been prepared by this method from dioximes.[52] 1,6-Diphenyl-1,1,6,6-tetranitrohexane and 1,10-diphenyl-1,1,10,10-tetranitrodecane have been obtained in 60 and 90% yield respectively from the corresponding dioximes by carrying out the reaction in dry ether at 0°.

Tertiary nitro paraffins are obtained through the oxidation of tertiary hydroxylamines with sulfomonoperacid:[53]

$$R_1R_2R_3CNHOH \rightarrow R_1R_2R_3CNO \rightarrow R_1R_2R_3CNO_2$$

Tertiary amines also undergo this reaction, but secondary amines are only partially converted to nitro compounds by this method.

Homologs of nitroethanol have been prepared through the condensation of aliphatic nitro compounds with aldehydes in the presence of alkali carbonates.[54] Nitro paraffins may, thus, be condensed with aromatic aldehydes by use of alcoholic potassium hydroxide,[55] and in some cases by use of organic bases.[56]

Halo nitro paraffins are obtained by the halogenation of nitro paraffins.[57] A few halo nitro paraffins have been prepared by the treatment of nitro alcohols with phosphorus pentachloride:[58]

$$CH_3CH(OH)CH_2NO_2 + PCl_5 \rightarrow CH_3CHClCH_2NO_2 + POCl_3 + HCl$$

Polyhalo nitro paraffins are obtained by this reaction from nitro aldehydes.

Unsaturated nitro compounds may be obtained by refluxing an ethereal solution of the acetate of α,β-nitro alcohols:[59]

$$2RCH(NO_2)C(OAc)R_2 + Na_2CO_3 \rightarrow$$
$$2RC(NO_2){:}CR_2 + 2AcONa + CO_2 + H_2O$$

Benzene may be used as a solvent instead of ether, and sodium carbonate may be replaced by sodium bisulfate.

Nitroethylene, $CH_2 = CHNO_2$, has been obtained by distilling nitroethyl alcohol with sodium bisulfate.[60] This compound polymerizes readily.

Nitro alcohols, $RCH(OH)CH_2NO_2$, treated with zinc chloride give nitro olefins, $RCH = CHNO_2$.

Pseudonitroles or meso nitronitroso paraffins are obtained by the reaction of nitrous acid with secondary nitro paraffins or of silver nitrite with mesohalo nitroso paraffins.[61] They are best prepared through the reaction of nitrogen peroxide and ketoximes:[62]

$$4(CH_3)_2C{:}NOH + 3N_2O_4 \rightarrow 4(CH_3)_2C(NO)NO_2 + 2H_2O + 2NO$$

With dioximes peroxides may result:

$$C_6H_5C({:}NOH)C({:}NOH)Cl \xrightarrow{N_2O_4} \begin{array}{c} NO{.}ON \\ \| \quad \| \\ C_6H_5C - CCl \end{array}$$

When compounds of the type $C_6H_5CR{:}NOH$ are allowed to react with nitrogen tetroxide, the major product is the corresponding dinitromethane if R is H, CH_2OH or CH_3CO, but not when R is COOH, CH_3 or C_6H_5.[263] The reaction of some 1,2-diketomonoximes with nitrogen tetroxides proceeds as follows:[264]

$$RCOC({:}NOH)R' \xrightarrow{N_2O_4} RCOC(NO_2)_2R'$$

$$\xrightarrow{H_2O} R'CH(NO_2)_2 + RCOOH$$

Nitrolic acids result from the reaction of nacsent nitrous acid with primary nitro compounds.[297] They are obtained more readily through the reaction of α-isonitroso carboxylic acids with nitrogen peroxide in ethereal solution:[63]

$$HON = CHCOOH + N_2O_4 \rightarrow HON = CHNO_2 + CO_2 + HNO_2$$

The reaction of hydroxylamine with dibromonitro paraffins gives rise to nitrolic acids:[64]

$$CH_3CBr_2NO_2 + H_2NOH \rightarrow CH_3C({:}NOH)NO_2 + 2HBr$$

Nitrolic acids are formed also through the reaction of silver nitrite with hydroxamic acid chlorides.[65]

Nitrolic acids and pseudonitroles are white in color in the solid state, but they assume an intense blue color in solution, or when melted. They are considered to be polymerized in the solid condition. These compounds have a strong characteristic odor and a sweet taste. They are soluble in water and redden litmus, although they have a low electric conductivity and are weak acids.[66] The alkali metal salts of these acids crystallize well, but are unstable and decompose on heating, and change to a colorless isomer when standing in sunlight. The colorless isomer formed under irradiation cannot be reconverted either to the red form, or to the original nitrolic acid. Heat transforms nitrolic acids to carboxylic acids:

$$2CH_3C({:}NOH)NO_2 \rightarrow 2CH_3COOH + NO_2 + 3N$$

This decomposition takes place also on long storage in the cold.

Nitramines

Primary nitramines are obtained readily by the action of the calculated amount of a mixture of nitric and sulfuric acids on the amine.[265] Amines have been converted to nitramines by the action of ethyl nitrate. The reaction proceeds smoothly when the amine and nitrate are simply mixed.

Urea nitrate may be converted to *nitrourea* by the action of sulfuric acid.[266] *Nitro-*

urethane may be prepared in a similar manner. Nitroguanidine is prepared by the action of concentrated sulfuric acid on guanidine nitrate:[267]

$$H_2NC(:NH)NH_2HNO_3 \xrightarrow{-H_2O} H_2NC(:NH)NHNO_2$$

Cyclic ammonium nitrates may also be converted to nitramines by treatment with sulfuric acid.[268]

Properties of Nitro Paraffins

Nitromethane and its homologs are colorless liquids insoluble in water, possessing a characteristic odor. They may be distilled without decomposition. The lower homologs are heavier than water, but density decreases with increase in molecular weight, nitrobutane being lighter than water.

Dinitroparaffins are usually colorless, waxy solids, although many have been obtained in the crystalline form. They are insoluble in water, slightly soluble in hydrocarbons, but dissolve readily in most organic solvents.

Nitroethane has explosive properties and can be detonated with a cap. The higher homologs are more stable, but may explode when heated under pressure. *gem*-Dinitro paraffins are stable compounds that may be distilled without decomposition. Dinitromethane forms an exception and decomposes very readily.

Reactions of Nitro Compounds

Reactions with Alkali Hydroxides

Primary and secondary nitro compounds are capable of existing in two isomeric forms, the *nitro* and the *aci* forms:

$$RCH_2NO_2 \rightleftharpoons RCH = NOOH$$

As a consequence of the presence of the *aci* isomer in nitro paraffins, these compounds exhibit some degree of electric conductivity. Reaction with alkalies leads to the formation of the alkali metal derivative of the *aci* form:[67]

$$RCH_2NO_2 + NaOH \rightarrow RCH = NOONa + H_2O$$

Reaction with concentrated alkalies may result in the formation of a carboxylic acid salt.[68]

Dinitro compounds of the type $RCH(NO_2)CH(NO_2)R'$, may be partially denitrated under the action of sodium hydroxide to form unsaturated mononitro compounds:[69]

$$RCH(NO_2)CH(NO_2)R \xrightarrow{NaOH} RCH = C(NO_2)R$$

$$C_6H_5CH(NO_2)CH(NO_2)COOH \xrightarrow{NaOH} C_6H_5CH = CHNO_2$$

The nitro group in tertiary nitro compounds, such as nitroisobutylglycerine $NO_2C(CH_2OH)_3$ and its halo and benzoic esters, may be removed by reaction with potassium hydroxide.[6]

When nitroethane is made to react with an equivalent of sodium hydroxide in aqueous solution at 0°, there is a gradual decrease of the molecular conductivity of the solution over a period of 50 minutes, as a result of the gradual disappearance of the sodium hydroxide through its reaction with the nitro compound,[70] the time of reaction is determined by the rate of transformation of the *nitro* to the *aci* form. The reverse transformation of the *aci* form to the *nitro* form takes place slowly, and is complete only at the end of several hours at 0°. For this reason, addition of an excess of acid to the solution of the alkali metal salt of the nitro compound results in the formation of a considerable proportion of an aldehyde:[71]

$$2RCH = NOONa + 2HCl \rightarrow 2RCHO + N_2O + H_2O + 2NaCl$$

An aldehyde or a ketone results when an aqueous solution of the sodium salt of a nitroparaffin is added dropwise to a 25% aqueous solution of sulfuric acid.

While the *aci* forms of nitro paraffins are, in general, unstable, *aci*-nitrotoluene, $C_6H_5CH = NOOH$, has been isolated in the pure form.[72]

aci-Nitroethane, which is obtained by acidifying an aqueous solution of sodium nitroethane at a low temperature, gives bromonitroethane when treated with bromine. Ethyl nitrolic acid is obtained through the reaction of the *aci* compound with nitrous acid. *aci-Nitroform* has been obtained as an oil which eventually sets to a crystalline mass. On attempted recrystallization it changes to the *nitro* form.

In certain reactions, *aci* nitro paraffins change to hydroxamic acids. Thus, the sodio derivative of nitroethane treated with benzoyl chloride gives benzoylacethydroxamic acid:[73]

$$CH_3CH = NOOH \rightleftharpoons CH_3C(OH) = NOH$$

$$\xrightarrow{C_6H_5COCl} CH_3CH(OH) = NOCOC_6H_5$$

A number of nitro compounds are converted to hydroxamic acids when treated in ethereal solution with gaseous hydrochloric acid.[74]

The alkali metal salts of nitro paraffins are readily soluble in water. The ease of formation of the salt decreases with increasing molecular weight and compounds such as nitrobutane and nitropentane dissolve only on long shaking with aqueous alkali. The salts may be precipitated in the crystalline form by the addition of alcohol.

In its behavior toward alkalies, *nitromethane* stands aside from other nitroparaffins. Like other nitroparaffins, the compound at first yields a sodio derivative when treated with aqueous sodium hydroxide, but this condenses with an equivalent of nitromethane to form the sodium salt of metazonic acid:[75]

$$H_2C = NOONa + HCH_2NO_2 \rightarrow NaON(OH)CH_2CH_2NO_2$$

$$\rightarrow NaONO = CHCH = NOH$$

Metazonic acid in turn yields the sodio compound of sodium nitroacetate when treated with sodium hydroxide:

$$HON = CHCH = NOONa \rightarrow CNCH = NOONa$$

$$\xrightarrow{NaOH + H_2O} NaOCOCH = NOONa$$

The sodio nitroacetate is obtained in crystalline form when nitroethane is added dropwise into a 50% aqueous solution of sodium hydroxide heated to 50°, the mixture is boiled for 10 minutes after all the nitroethane has been added, and finally cooled.[76] Transformation to nitroacetonitrile may be accomplished by treating metazonic acid with sulfuryl chloride.

Nitroform, $HC(NO_2)_3$, is strongly acidic in aqueous solution, and readily forms metallic salts. The metallic salts are colorless and soluble in ether.

Nitro paraffins may yield isoxazoles when treated with a trace of alkali:[77]

$$2RCH_2NO_2 \rightleftharpoons 2RCH=NOOH \xrightarrow{RCH_2NO_2}$$

$$HONOCH(R)C(R)NO_2CH(R)NOOH$$

$$\rightarrow NOCH(R)C(R)(NO_2)CH(R)NO \rightleftharpoons HON=C(R)C(R)NO_2C(R)=NOH$$

$$\rightarrow HON=C(R)CH(R)C(R)=NOH \rightarrow HON=C(R)CH(R)COR$$

$$\rightarrow \overline{RC=C(R)C(R)=NO}$$

Dibromodinitromethane, treated with sodium hydroxide, gives the sodium salt of monobromodinitromethane,[78] a reaction which is analogous to the formation of nitroform from tetranitromethane.

Alcoholic potassium hydroxide causes deep seated decomposition in nitro compounds.

Reactions Involving Alkali Metal Derivatives of Nitro Paraffins

Halo nitro paraffins result through the interaction of halogens with the sodium salt of nitro paraffins. Thus, chloronitromethane is obtained by adding the dry sodium salt of nitromethane to a saturated aqueous solution of chlorine.[79] Monochloro derivatives of nitroethane, and 1- and 2-nitropropane have been obtained by bubbling chlorine through an aqueous solution of the sodium salt of the nitro paraffins.[80] Dichlorodinitromethane, iodonitromethane and chloro derivatives of nitroethane and nitropropane have been prepared by this method. The calcium salts may also be used for the purpose.[81] Bromine, reacting with an alkaline solution of a nitro compound gives the bromo-substituted nitro compound. Both α-hydrogen atoms in primary nitro compounds are replaceable with bromine by this treatment. Treatment of sodio nitro paraffins with a deficiency of halogen results in the formation of dinitro paraffins:[82]

$$(R)_2C=NOONa \rightarrow (R)_2CXNO_2 \xrightarrow{NaONO=C(R)_2} (R)_2C(NO_2)C(NO_2)(R)_2$$

Nitronic esters are obtained through the reaction of alkyl halides and nitro paraffins in the presence of sodium ethoxide:[83]

$$RR'CHNO_2 \rightarrow RR'C=NOOH \xrightarrow{XCH_2R''} RR'C=NOOCH_2R''$$

These esters are unstable and decompose on heating to an oxime and an aldehyde:

$$RR'C=NOOCH_2R'' \rightarrow RR'C=NOH + R''CHO$$

It may be pointed out that methyl esters of nitrolic acids are obtained by the action of diazomethane on nitro paraffins.

The reaction of alkali metal salts of nitro paraffins with acyl chlorides gives acyl nitro alkanes:[73]

$$RR'C = NOONa + ClCOR'' \rightarrow RR'C = NOOCOR'' + NaCl$$

When the sodium derivative of nitromethane is treated with mercuric chloride, a white precipitate is formed which is probably the mercuric salt or *aci* nitromethane. The compound loses water rapidly, thereby becoming converted to mercuric fulminate.[85]

Alkali metal salts of primary nitro paraffins reacting with diazobenzoic salts give nitro hydrazones, the so-called nitroazo paraffins. Thus, nitroacetaldehyde hydrazone, $CH_3C(NO_2) = NNHC_6H_5$, results from potassium nitroethane and diazobenzene nitrate.[86]

Primary and secondary nitro paraffins, reacting with carbon disulfide in the presence of alkalies, give salts of nitro thio acids. For example, with nitromethane the alkali metal salt of nitrothioacetic acid is obtained:[87]

$$CH_3NO_2 + CS_2 + 2NaOH \rightarrow NaONO = CHCSSNa + 2H_2O$$

When sulfuric acid is added to an aqueous solution of sodium nitrite and the sodio derivative of a primary nitro compound, a nitrolic acid, $RC(:NOH)NO_2$, is obtained. When a secondary nitro compound is similarly treated a pseudonitrole, $RR'C(NO)NO_2$, is obtained. These reactions proceed readily with nitro compounds with up to five carbon atoms.[88] Nitrous acid does not react with tertiary nitro compounds.

Nitro paraffins yield α-bromo derivatives when subjected to the action of bromine in the absence of a base, but in the presence of phosphorus pentoxide and under intense illumination. Treatment with chlorine under the same conditions results in the formation of chlorinated derivatives other than the α-chloro compound. Nitroethane gives exclusively 2-chloro-1-nitroethane; 1-nitropropane yields 2- and 3-chloro-1-nitropropanes; 2-nitropropane gives 1-chloro-2-nitropropane, while 1-nitrobutane yields 2-, 3- and 4-monochloro-1-nitrobutanes. 2-Chloronitro- and 3-chloronitro derivatives are obtained from 1-nitro-2-methylpropane.

Halo nitro paraffins treated with zinc alkyls exchange their halogen with the alkyl group of the zinc alkyl.[89]

Reaction with Acids

Many Nitro paraffins break down to a fatty acid and hydroxylamine when heated with concentrated hydrochloric acid:[90]

$$CH_3CH_2NO_2 + H_2O + HCl \rightarrow CH_3COOH + H_2NOH.HCl$$

This reaction takes place also on refluxing the nitro paraffin with aqueous sulfuric acid. Secondary nitro paraffins are completely resinified when treated with hydrochloric acid.

Heated to 60° with concentrated sulfuric acid, primary nitro paraffins are converted to hydroaxamic acids:[91]

$$RCH_2NO_2 \rightleftharpoons RCH = NOOH \rightarrow RCH(OH)NO \rightarrow RC(= NOH)OH$$

Nitro olefins are converted to an aldehyde and an acid on heating with dilute sulfuric acid:

$$RCH = C(NO_2)R' \xrightarrow{H_2O} RCH(OH)CH(NO_2)R' \rightarrow RCHO + R'CH_2NO_2$$

$$R'CH_2NO_2 + H_2O + H_2SO_4 \rightarrow R'COOH + H_2NOH.H_2SO_4$$

Reaction with Aldehydes and Ketones

Primary nitro paraffins combine with aldehydes and ketones in the presence of a trace of alkali to form nitro alcohols:[92]

$$RCH_2NO_2 + R'CHO \rightarrow RCH(NO_2)CH(OH)R'$$

The reaction is a type of aldol condensation. Methoxides, hydroxides and carbonates of potassium and sodium are effective catalysts, as are also many organic bases.

The nitro alcohol resulting from this reaction may, in turn, condense with an additional molecule of the aldehyde to form a nitro diol:

$$RCH(NO_2)CH(OH)R' + R'CHO \rightarrow R'CH(OH)C(R)(NO_2)CH(OH)R'$$

This reaction occurs readily with formaldehyde. Nitromethane yields trimethylolnitromethane, $(HOCH_2)_3CNO_2$, with formaldehyde.[93]

A molecular equivalent of nitro paraffin may also condense with the nitro alcohol with elimination of water and the formation of a dinitro derivative:

$$RCH_2NO_2 + RCH(NO_2)CH(OH)R' \rightarrow [RCH(NO_2)]_2CHR' + H_2O$$

The reaction proceeds only to the nitro alcohol stage when a tertiary amine is used as a catalyst.

An aldol condensation of the aldehyde, and the formation of an isoxazole by the self-condensation of the nitro paraffin take place as competing reactions. Aldol condensation is held to a minimum by using just sufficient catalyst to insure a reasonably rapid reaction, and adding the aldehyde gradually to the nitro paraffin.

Both aldehydes and nitro paraffins vary in their ability to undergo the reaction. Formaldehyde and nitromethane are highly reactive, but reactivity decreases with increase in molecular weight. Chloral is exceptionally reactive. Condensation of more than one molecule of aldehyde with one of a nitro paraffin other than nitromethane takes place with difficulty, except with formaldehyde. The reaction proceeds only to the first stage with nitromethane and aldehydes with more than five carbon atoms.

Secondary nitro paraffins undergo condensation with aldehydes, although much more slowly than the primary compounds, while tertiary nitro paraffins fail to react.

Ketones also react with primary nitro paraffins in the same manner as aldehydes, pyridine or other slightly basic substances acting as effective catalysts for the reaction:[93]

$$(CH_3)_2CO + 2CH_3NO_2 \rightarrow (CH_3)_2C(CH_2NO_2)_2 + H_2O$$

Unsaturated nitro compounds are also formed through the condensation of aldehydes with primary nitro paraffins when the reaction is carried out in the presence of an alkylamine or other appropriate condensing agent: [94]

$$RCHO + H_2C(NO_2)R' \rightarrow RCH = C(NO_2)R + H_2O$$

Alkyl amino alcohols and aldehyde ammonias are also capable of condensing with nitro alcohols. [95]

Reaction with Organomagnesium Halides

Primary nitroparaffins generally give complexes with alkylmagnesium halides which on hydrolysis yield alkyl hydroxylamines: [269]

$$RCH = NOOH \xrightarrow{\text{AlkMgI}} RCH(Alk)N(OMgI)_2 \rightarrow RCH(Alk)N\begin{smallmatrix} Alk \\ \\ OH \end{smallmatrix}$$

$$\text{or } RCH(MgI)N(OMgI)_2(Alk)_2 \rightarrow RCH_2\begin{smallmatrix} Alk \\ \\ OH \end{smallmatrix}$$

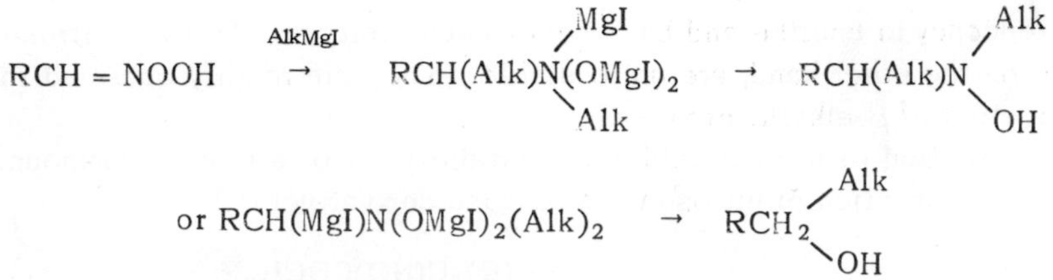

Many nitro alkyls, including nitromethane, -ethane and -propane, reacting with methylmagnesium iodide simply liberate methane. [270]

The reaction of aryl magnesium halides with aromatic nitro compounds is considered to proceed in the following manner: [271]

$$RNO_2 + R'MgX \rightarrow \begin{smallmatrix} R \\ \\ R \end{smallmatrix}N\begin{smallmatrix} OMgX \\ \\ O \end{smallmatrix} \xrightarrow{R'MgX} R'OMgX + \begin{smallmatrix} R \\ \\ R' \end{smallmatrix}NOMgX$$

$$\xrightarrow{2R'MgX} R' - R' + \begin{smallmatrix} R \\ \\ R \end{smallmatrix}NMgX + (MgX)_2O$$

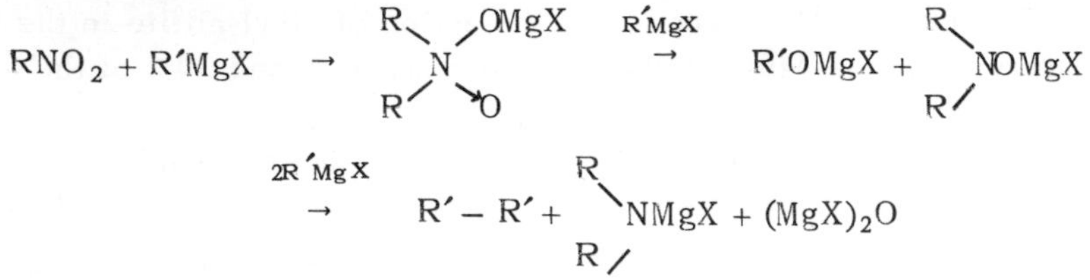

Reduction of Nitro Compounds

Nitro paraffins give primary amines when reduced with metallic iron and acetic acid. Reduction with stannous chloride and hydrochloric acid results in the formation of β-alkyl hydroxylamines, RNHOH, together with amines and ammonia. [96] If reduction is carried out in the presence of strong hydrochloric acid, oximes are obtained from primary and secondary nitro paraffins, which are further decomposed to the corresponding aldehyde or ketone. [97] Zinc dust and water reduce nitro compounds to hydroxylamines. [98] Oximes are obtained on refluxing nitro paraffins with zinc dust and glacial acetic acid: [99]

$$RR'CHNO_2 \xrightarrow{H_2} RR'C = NOH + H_2O$$

Oximes and primary amines and not diamines are the products obtained on reducing gem-dinitro compounds: [99]

$$RR'C(NO_2)_2 \rightarrow RR'C(NOH)_2 \rightarrow RR'C = NOH \rightarrow RR'CHNH_2$$

Carbonyl compounds are also formed in the reaction. Carboxylic acids may also result through the reduction of primary dinitro paraffins. [100]

Oximes of aliphatic aldehydes result when nitro olefins are reduced.[101]

Zinc ethyl reacting with nitroethane gives β-ethyl-β-*sec*-butyl hydroxylamine.[102]

The electrolytic reduction of nitro compounds in 10 to 15% alcoholic sulfuric acid at 15-20° results in the formation of hydroxylamines. Amines are obtained when the reduction is carried out at 70 to 75°.

NITROSO COMPOUNDS

Primary and secondary nitroso compounds, RCH_2NO and $RR'CHNO$, show a strong tendency to enolize and have never been isolated. Tertiary nitroso compounds, on the other hand, are quite stable. They are readily obtained through the oxidation of β-alkylhydroxylamines.

Direct reaction of nitrous acid with certain types of aliphatic compounds results in the formation of nitroso or isonitroso derivatives:[103]

$$R_2CHCOCH_2R + HONO \rightleftarrows \begin{matrix} (R)_2C(NO)COCH_2R \\ (R)_2CHCOC(=NOH)R \end{matrix} + H_2O$$

The two types of derivatives are obtained in varying proportions, depending on the nature of the organic compound with which the nitrous acid is made to react. Nitrosation also takes place under the action of ethyl nitrite in the presence of acetyl chloride, 49% of the nitroso compound and 34% of the oxime being obtained with ethyl isopropyl ketone.[104]

vic-Nitroso nitro compounds, also termed *pseudonitrosites,* are obtained through the reaction of nitrogen trioxide with certain olefinic compounds:

$$\overset{|}{\underset{|}{C}} = \overset{|}{\underset{|}{C}} + N_2O_3 \rightarrow NO.\overset{|}{\underset{|}{C}}.\overset{|}{\underset{|}{C}}.NO_2$$

This type of addition takes place with many aromatic compounds.[105] Unsaturated compounds of the aliphatic series generally yield nitroso nitrites, the true *nitrosites,* $NO.\overset{|}{\underset{|}{C}}-\overset{|}{\underset{|}{C}}.ONO$, on reaction with nitrogen trioxide. Pseudonitrosites may also form, however, from aliphatic unsaturated compounds. Thus, when nitrogen trioxide in ethereal solution is added to a well-cooled ethereal solution of isobutylene, $(CH_3)_2C = CH_2$, in a quantity slightly less than that required by theory, a crystalline product is obtained which is probably the dimer of 2-nitroso-1-nitroisobutane, $(CH_3)_2C(NO)CH_2NO_2$. An oily product which remains in solution is also formed and would appear to be the monomeric nitro-nitroso compound.[106] Nitrogen trioxide reacting with dimethylbutadiene gives 1-nitro-4-nitroso-2,3-dimethylbutylene,

$$NOCH_2C(CH_3) = C(CH_3)CH_2NO_2$$

The reaction of nitrogen trioxide with dihydrobenzene follows a similar course, giving nitro nitroso cyclohexene

$$\overline{CH_2CH_2CH(NO)CH = CHCHNO_2}$$

Aliphatic nitroso alcohols are known only in the form of their acetates, nitrates or nitrites. A few such compounds have been obtained through the oxidation of the corresponding hydroxylamine derivatives with a mixture of potassium bichromate and sulfuric acid.[107]

The reaction of oximes, RR′C = NOH, with nitrosyl halides, XNO, leads to the formation of *gem*-halo nitroso derivatives, RR′C(NO)Cl.[108 51]

Oximes treated with bromine water or with bromine in solution in pyridine give bromonitroso compounds:[109]

$$(CH_3)_2C = NOH + Br_2 \rightarrow (CH_3)_2C(NO)Br + HBr$$

Chloronitroso compounds are obtained when the bromine is replaced by chlorine in these reactions. The reaction fails to take place with oximes of the type RR′C = NOH in which R and R′ are a carboxy, cyano, phenyl or substituted phenyl groups. Pseudonitroles result when halonitroso compounds are made to react with silver nitrite:

$$(CH_3)_2C(NO)Br + AgNO_2 \rightarrow (CH_3)_2C(NO)NO_2 + AgBr$$

The reaction of nitrosyl halides with olefinic hydrocarbons results in the formation of *vic*-halonitroso compounds:

$$RR'C = CRR' + ClNO \rightarrow RR'C(Cl)C(NO)RR'$$

The reaction is carried out at 0° in solution in carbon tetrachloride or in a mixture consisting of 20% carbon tetrachloride and 80% acetic acid.[110]

Nitroso paraffins are crystalline solids with an odor reminiscent of camphor. In the solid state they are generally dimeric, but dissociate when melted, or when brought into solution. The monomers are usually blue in color. Aliphatic nitroso compounds are converted to nitro paraffins when treated with hot nitric acid.

OXIMES

Preparation

The method of preparation of oximes from carbonyl compounds and from hydroxylamine has been discussed in connection with carbonyl compounds. Oximes are obtained also through the oxidation of primary or secondary amines with sulfomonoper acid, the reaction apparently proceeding the two stages:

$$RR'CHNH_2 \rightarrow RR'CHNHOH \rightarrow RR'C = NOH$$

Aldoximes are further oxidized in this reaction to oxamic acids, RC(:NOH)OH.

Oximes result, further, by the reduction of the potassium derivative of primary or secondary nitro compounds with stannous chloride. The reaction is carried out by adding the solution of the alkali metal salt to a solution of stannous chloride in hydrochloric acid:[272]

$$RR'C{:}NOOH \rightarrow RR'C{:}NOH$$

Reduction may be effected also with sodium amalgam in the cold,[273] zinc dust, and sodium hydroxide, or sodium and alcohol.[274]

The reaction of dithio acids with hydroxylamine hydrochloride results in the formation of oximes:[111]

$$RCSSH \xrightarrow{HONH_2,\,HCl} RCH = NOH$$

The condensation of nitrous acid with compounds containing a reactive methylene also results in the formation of oximes:[112]

$$RCOCH_2R' + ONOH \rightarrow RCOC({:}NOH)R' + H_2O$$

The readiness with which the reaction proceeds is dependent on the reactivity of the methylene group. β-Diketones are especially reactive. Amyl nitrite may be used to advantage with compounds which react with difficulty, sodium ethoxide or hydrogen chloride being used as catalysts for the reaction. The oxime resulting from acetoacetic ester decomposes to the keto oxime,

$$CH_3COCH{:}NOH,$$

and carbon dioxide when converted to the free acid. The reaction of nascent nitrous acid with α-alkylacetoacetic acid results in the formation of a diketo monoxime:[113]

$$CH_3COCH(CH_3)COOH + HNO_2 \rightarrow CH_3COC({:}NOH)CH_3 + CO_2 + H_2O$$

The use of an excess of nitrous acid results in the formation of diketones by reaction with the oximino ketone:[114]

$$RCOC({:}NOH)R' + HONO \rightarrow RCOCOR' + N_2O + H_2O$$

Hydroxylamine causes the rupture of the molecule of dihydropyridine, giving a dioxime:[115]

$$CH = CHCH_2CH = CHNH + 2N_2NOH \rightarrow NH_3 + CH_2(CH = CHNHOH)_2$$
$$\rightarrow HON = CHCH_2CH_2CH_2CH = NOH$$

Oxamic acids are obtained on reacting esters with a hot methanolic solution of hydroxylamine:[116]

$$C_2H_5OCOCOOC_2H_5 + 2H_2NOH \rightarrow HOC({:}NOH)C({:}NOH)OH + 2C_2H_5OH$$

Yields of hydroxamic acid do not exceed 40%.

Properties of Oximes

With the exception of some members of the aliphatic series, which are liquids at ordinary temperature, oximes are generally crystalline solids. They are weakly acidic in their reaction, their dissociation constants ranging between 10^{-10} and 10^{-12}. The acidity of aliphatic oximes decreases with increasing molecular weight. Acidity is enhanced by the presence of a carbonyl group adjacent to the oxime group. [117] In the aromatic series the degree of acidity is influenced by substituents in the aromatic ring.

Oximes often exhibit *hydrogen bonding*.[118] The presence of hydrogen bonding is in-

dicated, for example, in salicylaldehyde oxime, C_6H_4 $\overset{\displaystyle C}{\underset{\displaystyle OH}{\diagdown}}$ NOH, which differs in its

physical and chemical properties from the oximes of *meta*- and *para*-hydroxybenzaldehydes.[119]

Interesting facts have come to light in the study of the stereoisomerism of oximes. The possibility of stereoisomerism in oximes is due to the existence of a doubly bound nitrogen in these compounds. With oximes of the type, RR'C:NOH, in which R and R' are unlike radicals or atoms, the existence of two isomeric modifications is possible depending on the position occupied by the hydroxyl group with respect to R and R',

$$\begin{matrix} RCR' \\ \| \\ NOH \end{matrix} \qquad \text{and} \qquad \begin{matrix} RCR' \\ \| \\ HON \end{matrix}$$

It has not been possible, however, in every case, to relate the structure of the isomers to one or other of the accepted configurations. In many cases, also, it has not been possible to obtain the predicted modifications. Isomerism is not observed, for example, in aliphatic aromatic ketoximes of the type, $C_6H_5C(:NOH)CH_3$. In contrast, purely aromatic unsymmetrical ketoximes show stereoisomerism unfailingly. Saturated unsymmetrical ketoximes also have not been resolved into isomers, although when such oximes are subjected to the Beckmann transformation, they yield both of the isomeric amides to be expected from the isomeric oximes.[120] Aliphatic aldoximes also exist in one form, and yield a nitrile when treated with acetic anhydride.[121]

Reactions of Oximes

Oximes may be acylated by treatment with acid chlorides:

$$RR'C = NOH + ClCOR'' \rightarrow RR'C = NOCOR'' + HCl$$

If the reaction is carried out in the presence of an adequate quantity of alkali, the original configuration of the oxime is not changed.[122] Acylated ketoximes are hydrolyzed to the oxime and acid very readily in acid or basic solution. Acylation of aldoximes takes place successfully only under very mild conditions. The *anti* form of aldoximes treated with dehydrating agents generally loses water to yield a nitrile:

$$\begin{matrix} RCH \\ \| \\ HON \end{matrix} \rightarrow RC \equiv N + H_2O$$

Basic hydrolysis of acylated *anti* forms also yield the nitrile, while acylated *syn* forms give the oxime.

Acylated oximes are of neutral reaction and do not possess the amphoteric nature of the parent oxime.

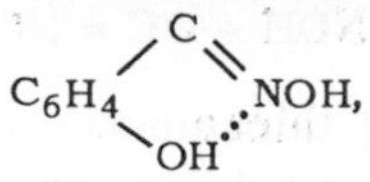

Hydrocyanic acid adds to oximes, RR′C=NOH, to give α-hydroxyaminonitriles, RR′C(NHOH)CN.

The reaction of oximes with isocyanates leads to the formation of carbamic acid derivatives:

$$C_6H_5CH = NOH + OC = NC_6H_5 \rightarrow C_6H_5CH = NOCONHC_6H_5$$

The corresponding thiocarbamic derivatives obtained from isothiocyanates are usually unstable, and decompose spontaneously, or undergo autoxidation in air forming a variety of products.[123]

Alkylation of oximes may be brought about by treatment with alkyl sulfates in the presence of caustic, giving N– and O–alkylated derivatives:

$$RR'C = NOH + (CH_3)_2SO_4 + NaOH \rightarrow \begin{cases} RR'C{:}N(CH_3){:}O \\ RR'C{:}NOCH_3 \end{cases} + NaCH_3SO_4$$

The N-methylated product is obtained exclusively on treating acetoxime with methyl iodide. If, however, alkylation with alkyl iodides is carried out in the presence of sodium ethoxide, the N- and O-alkylated products are formed simultaneously.[124] The best method available for the preparation of N-alkylated oximes is the direct synthesis by use of alkyl hydroxylamine and the appropriate aldehyde or ketone.[125]

The possibility of the existence of two isomeric forms, the oxime and the nitrone forms, in equilibrium has been postulated in explanation of the formation of N- and O-alkyl derivatives in the alkylation of oximes:

$$RR'C = NOH \rightleftarrows RR'C = NOH$$

Evidence has been secured of the existence of two isomeric forms of indanone and tetralone oximes through spretrographic examination. An increase in the chain length of straight-chain aliphatic ketones would appear to favor the true oxime structure, whereas, branching at the 2-carbon atom apparently favors the isoxime structure.[126] The N-alkyl aldoximes are believed to have the nitrone structure, $RCH = N(CH_3){:}O$[127], while acetyl oximes are O-substituted derivatives.[128]

N-Alkylated oximes are weakly basic, while O-alkylated derivatives do not show basic properties. The former are more resistant to hydrolysis and have a higher melting point than the latter.

Treated with chlorine, oximes give *gem*-chloronitroso compounds:

$$2CH_3CH = NOH + Cl_2 \rightarrow 2CH_3CHClNO + HCl$$

Reaction with *nitrosyl chloride* in ethereal solution at 0° leads to the formation of chloro oximes:[129]

$$C_6H_5CH = NOH + 2NOCl \rightarrow C_6H_5CCl = NOH + HCl + 2NO$$

Yields may reach 60%, although acetaldoxime gives the chloro oxime in only 7.4% yield.

Ketoximes are converted to nitro paraffins on oxidation with sulfomonoperacids, while aldoximes give both nitro paraffins and hydroxamic acids by the same treatment:

$$RCH{:}NOH \rightleftarrows \begin{matrix} RCH{:}NOOH \rightarrow RCH_2NO_2 \\ RC(OH){:}NOH \end{matrix}$$

Oximes are compounds of amphoteric nature, yielding salts with both acids and bases:

$$RR'C{:}NOH + HCl \rightarrow RR'C{:}NOH.HCl$$

$$RR'C{:}NOH + NaOH \rightarrow RR'C{:}NONa + H_2O$$

They give complex salts with nickel, the dimethyl glyoxime complex being the best known representative of this type of compounds.

Detection of Oximes

Oximes may be detected qualitatively by oxidation with iodine and testing for liberated nitrous acid by the Griess reagent, which consists of a mixture of α-naphthylamine, acetic acid and sulfanilic acid.

Chloronitroso derivatives obtained from aldoximes by the action of chlorine give a dark red coloration with ferric chloride, while those derived from ketoximes give a blue to green color.

SULFONIC ACIDS

Preparation

Aliphatic sulfonic acids are obtained in a few instances through direct sulfonation; reaction with chlorosulfonic acid has also been successfully carried out in some instances. Oxidation of thiols is one of the most generally applicable methods for the preparation of sulfonic acids. The reaction of alkali metal sulfites with organic halogen compounds is also applicable in many cases. Another reaction leading to the formation of sulfones is the addition of sulfuric acid at olefinic double bonds. Sulfonyl chlorides result through the simultaneous reaction of sulfur trioxide and chlorine with hydrocarbons. These reactions will be considered in the order named.

Direct Methods of Sulfonation

Certain aliphatic hydrocarbons are sulfonated readily under the action of fuming sulfuric acid, the ease of reaction often differing little from that of aromatic hydrocarbons with the same reagent. Thus, *n*-hexane, *n*-heptane and *n*-octane are readily sulfonated by this method at water bath temperature.[130] The reaction of hot sulfuric acid with paraffin results in the formation of oxidation products. Methane is not acted upon by fuming sulfuric acid of 15% SO_3 content.

Many carbonyl compounds are sulfonated by fuming sulfuric acid. Formyl methionic acid, $OCHCH(SO_3H)_2$, results, for example, through the action of fuming sulfuric acid on acetaldehyde,[131] the product also resulting through the action of fuming sulfuric acid on acetylene.

Formylmethionic acid gives formylchloromethionic acid, $OCHCCl(SO_3H)_2$, with chlorine; decomposition of this compound with aqueous sodium hydroxide results in the formation of sodium chloromethionate, $ClCH(SO_3Na)_2$. This offers the best method for the preparation of the last named compound.[132]

Methylmethionic acid, $CH_3C(SO_3H)_2CHO$, results from the reaction of propionaldehyde with 50% fuming sulfuric acid. Treatment of acetone with the same reagent results in the formation of a trisulfonic acid,

$$HSO_3CH_2COCH(SO_3H)_2$$ [133]

Methyl benzyl ketone heated with concentrated sulfuric acid gives toluene-ω-sulfonic acid:[134]

$$C_6H_5CH_2COCH_3 + H_2SO_4 \rightarrow C_6H_5CH_2SO_3H + CH_3COOH$$

Camphor yields camphor sulfonic acid when treated with sulfuric acid in solution in acetic anhydride.[135]

When propionic acid is treated with *sulfur trioxide* the mixed anhydride of propionic and sulfuric acids is obtained; this compound undergoes rearrangement on heating, giving α-sulfopropionic acid. A mixture of propionic anhydride and sulfuric acid yields the same product. The α-sulfonic acid results in 75% yield through the reaction of oleum with propionic acid. Similar reactions are observed with *n*-butyric, isobutyric, *n*-valeric, methylethylacetic and methyl-*n*-propylacetic and succinic acids.[136] The direct sulfonation method is not applicable, however, to the preparation of alkyl-sulfonated arylaliphatic acids, since the aromatic nucleus is preferentially sulfonated.[137]

Sulfonation of acetanilide or of acetamide with 35% fuming sulfuric acid results in the formation of methane trisulfonic acid, obtained as the tripotassium salt in 57% yield.[138]

Aliphatic carboxylic acids may be converted to their α-sulfonic derivatives by direct sulfonation. α-Sulfonic acids are best prepared by sulfonation of the appropriate alkyl malonic acid and subsequent partial decarboxylation.[275] The reaction of propionic anhydride with pyrosulfuric acid results in the formation of α-sulfopropionic acid in 75% yield.[276] Several simple α-sulfoolefinic acids have been prepared through the sulfonation of α,β-unsaturated acids and β-halo acids.[277]

Acetic acid reacts with chlorosulfonic acid to form sulfoacetic acid, and this is converted to *methionic acid* on treatment with fuming sulfuric acid:[278]

$$CH_3COOH + ClSO_3H \rightarrow HCl + HOSO_2CH_2COOH$$

$$\xrightarrow{SO_3} HOSO_2CH_2SO_2OH$$

Methionic acid is best prepared, however, through the reaction of fuming sulfuric acid with acetylene.[279] The gas is readily absorbed with great evolution of heat when it is led into the acid. The course of the reaction is as follows:

$$HC \equiv CH + 2H_2SO_4 \rightarrow (HO)_2CHCH(SO_3H)_2$$

$$\xrightarrow{SO_3} HSO_3CH_2SO_3H + CO_2 + SO_2 + H_2O$$

Acetyl chloride reacts with chlorosulfonic acid at a temperature somewhat in excess of 45° forming sulfoacetyl chloride:[139]

$$CH_3COCl + ClSO_3H \rightarrow HCl + CH_3COOSO_2Cl \rightarrow HSO_3CH_2COCl$$

Further sulfonation takes place if the reaction is carried out above 60°, and results in the formation of methanedisulfonic monochloride:

$$HSO_3CH_2COCl + ClSO_3H \rightarrow HSO_3CH_2SO_2Cl + CO_2 + HCl$$

Propionyl chloride yields a small amount of sulfopropionic acid, with a considerable quantity of a condensation product,[140] while butyryl chloride fails to give a sulfonic derivative.[141]

Chlorosulfonacetic acid is obtained through the reaction of chloracetic acid with chlorosulfonic acid at 140-150°.[142] Chloromethane disulfonic acid forms as a by product of the reaction. *α*-Chloro and *α*-bromopropionic acids give the sulfonic acids in 25 and 30% yield.

Cyanacetanilide and other similarly substituted amides are readily sulfonated by chlorosulfonic acid in chloroform solution:[143]

$$CNCH_2CONHC_6H_5 + 2ClSO_3H$$
$$\rightarrow CNC(SO_3H)_2CONHC_6H_5 + 2HCl$$

The reaction of sulfur trioxide with succinic anhydride results in the formation of *sym-dl*-disulfosuccinic acid. Sulfonation of maleic or fumaric acid with excess sulfur trioxide takes place readily at 60-70° without attack at the double bond.[144]

Isobutylene, acted upon by dioxane sulfotrioxide gives principally 2-methylpropane-3-sulfonic acid:[145]

$$CH_2 = C(CH_3)_2 + O(CH_2CH_2)_2OSO_3$$
$$\rightarrow CH_2 = C(CH_3)CH_2SO_3H + O(CH_2CH_2)_2O$$

Styrene and sulfamic acid react at 150° to form an ammonium sulfonate:[146]

$$C_6H_5CH = CH_2 + H_2NSO_3H \rightarrow C_6H_5CH = CHSO_3NH_4$$

Similar reactions take place with anethole, apiole and isosafrole.

Oxidation of Thiols to Sulfonic Acids

Thiols, or mercaptans, are rapidly oxidized by concentrated nitric acid, with sulfonic acids as the final products. The reaction in general proceeds quite vigorously.[147] Many sulfones have been prepared by this method, among them ethane-, propane-, propane-2-, butane-1-, butane-2-, 2-methylpropane-1-, and pentane-1-sulfonic acids.

Better yields of sulfonic acids are obtained when lead salts of the thiols rather than the free thiols are used in the reaction.[148] In the normal paraffin series, yields in excess of 60% of the theoretical have been obtained with compounds containing 9 to 14 carbon atoms. The lead sulfonates obtained can be converted to the free acids by treatment with isopropyl alcoholic hydrochloric acid. The higher alkyl sulfonic acids may be prepared in good yields by oxidation of the corresponding thiols, or disulfides in acetone or acetic acid solution with potassium permanganate or potassium dichromate. Ethane-1,1-disulfonic acid is obtained through the oxidation of thialdine,

$$CH_3\overline{CHSCH(CH_3)NHCH(CH_3)S}$$

with permanganates of potassium or zinc.[149]

Oxidation of many alkyl thiocyanates with nitric acid results in the formation of sulfonic acids in good yield.[150] The reaction becomes violent when concentrated nitric acid is used, and an appreciable quantity of sulfuric acid forms.

Sulfonyl chlorides are obtained with many of the alkylation products of thiourea when these are subjected to the action of chlorine.[151] The yields are good with primary alkyl derivatives, low with secondary alkyl compounds, while the tertiary butyl compound fails to give a sulfonyl chloride. *Dangerous explosions* have occurred on occasions during the course of these reactions, due probably to the formation of nitrogen trichloride.

Replacement of Halogens with the Sulfonic Group

Sulfonic acids result through the reaction of many alkyl halides with alkali metal sulfites or ammonium sulfite:[152]

$$RX + NaHSO_3 \rightarrow RSO_3H + NaX$$

The reaction generally proceeds well with compounds having a reactive halogen. Sulfonates have been obtained in yields ranging from 50 to 90% from chloro or bromo compounds. Sulfonates are obtained in yields ranging from 60 to 70% on heating *n*-octyl, *n*-decyl, myristyl, cetyl and octadecyl bromides, or lauryl chloride with an excess of sodium sulfite in an autoclave at 200° for several hours.[153] Sec-amyl-, *n*-hexyl-, and *sec*-hexyl bromide do not give sulfonates by this reaction.

Ethylene chlorohydrin reacting with sodium sulfite gives sodium isethionate,

$$HOCH_2CH_2SO_3Na.$$[154]

Chloracetone reacts with potassium sulfite in aqueous solution to form potassium acetone sulfonate.[155] *Phenacyl bromide,* $C_6H_5COCH_2Br$, similarly reacts with sodium sulfite in aqueous alcoholic solution forming sodium benzoyl methane sulfonate in 90% yield.[156] Chloropicrin, Cl_3CNO_2, gives potassium nitroformenedisulfonate,

$$NO_2CH(SO_3K)_2,$$

with potassium bisulfite.[286]

The reaction of *allyl iodide* with potassium sulfite results in the formation of a complex of potassium allyl sulfonate and potassium iodide:

$$4CH_2 = CHCH_2I + 4K_2SO_3 \rightarrow (CH_2 = CHCH_2SO_3K)_4.KI + 3KI$$

With methallyl chloride and sodium sulfite, sodium 2-methylpropane-3-sulfonate,

$$CH_2 = C(CH_3)CH_2SO_3Na,$$

results.

Benzyl chloride reacts readily with sodium sulfite in alcoholic solution to form toluene ω-sulfonic acid, $C_6H_5CH_2SO_3Na$.[157] This compound may be obtained also by heating benzyl chloride with a solution of sodium hydrosulfite in the presence of zinc dust.[158] The 2- and 4-chloro- and all monomitrobenzylsulfonic acids have been prepared similarly.

The reaction of diphenylchloromethane with aqueous sodium sulfi^e results in the formation of *sym*-tetraphenylmethyl ether, $(C_6H)_2CHOCH(C_6H_5)_2$. Sodium *p*-anisyldiphenylmethane sulfonate results from the reaction of sodium sulfite with *p*-anisyldiphenylmethane chloride.[159]

α-Halo acids are capable of reacting with sodium sulfite, forming α-sulfocarboxylic acids.[160] Esters of halo acids react more readily than the salts.[161] It is of advantage to employ 40% aqueous ethanol as a solvent in carrying out the reaction with esters. Ammonium α-bromophenylacetate and ammonium sulfite react at room temperature giving the sulfo acid salt in 70% yield; at higher temperatures the hydrolysis reaction becomes predominant, and yields of the sulfo acid are low. The corresponding α-chloro acid gives the sulfo acid in only 35% yield, while ethyl α-bromophenylacetate gives a theoretical yield of the sulfo compound. Bromomalonic acid is reduced by sodium bisulfite, while ethylbromomalonic acid is reduced and hydrolyzed simultaneously. Bromosuccinic acid is converted by reaction with sodium bisulfite to maleic and fumaric acids, the formation of sulfosuccinic acid occurring simultaneously. *α,α′-Dibromosuccinic acid* reacting with potassium bisulfite is first converted into fumaric acid, which then adds a mole of bisulfite to form the sulfo compound.[162]

The reaction of methylene chloride with potassium sulfite yields methane disulfonic acid *(methionic acid)* in 85% yield.[163] The compound is also obtained through the decomposition of formylmethionic acid, $OCHCH(SO_3H)_2$, with aqueous alkali.[164] Sodium chloromethanesulfonate, $ClCH_2SO_3Na$, is readily obtained on refluxing *chlorobromomethane* with aqueous sodium sulfite solution.[165]

Sodium ethane-1,2-disulfonate is obtained in 95% yield through the reaction of ethylene bromide with a saturated aqueous solution of alkali sulfite.[166] Propane-1,2-disulfonic acid is obtained similarly, in the form of its ammonium salt, from *propylene bromide* and ammonium sulfite solution.[167] *Butylene bromide* has been reported to give only the olefin; but *isobutylene bromide* gives 2-methylpropane-1,2-disulfonic acid. Trimethylene bromide and polymethylene bromides also give disulfonates by reaction with sodium sulfite.[168]

An unsaturated disulfonic acid has been obtained through the reaction of 2,3-dimethyl-1,2,3,4-tetrabromobutane in good yield:[169]

$$BrCH_2C(CH_3)BrC(CH_3)BrCH_2Br + 3(NH_4)_2SO_3 + H_2O$$

$$\rightarrow NH_4SO_3CH_2C(CH_3){:}C(CH_3)CH_2SO_3NH_4 + 4NH_4Br + H_2SO_4$$

The corresponding trisulfonic acid results from the reaction of 1,2,3-tribromopropane with the sulfite, while 2,3-dibromopropane gives a mixture of isomeric hydroxysulfonic acids. Unsaturated products are obtained from compounds containing a tertiary halogen.

Chloral hydrate reacts with potassium sulfite to form the potassium salt of formylmethionic acid, $OCHCH(SO_3H)_3$.[170] Potassium trichloroacetate, boiled with aqueous potassium sulfite, reacts to form potassium sulfochloroacetate:

$$Cl_3CCOOK + 2K_2SO_3 + H_2O$$

$$\rightarrow\ KSO_3CH(Cl)COOK + 2KCl + KHSO_4$$

Bromine converts the sulfochloro acid to sulfochlorobrommethane:

$$HSO_3CHClCOOH + Br_2\ \rightarrow\ HSO_3CHClBr + CO_2 + HBr$$

Chlorpicrin gives with potassium sulfite nitromethionic acid, which, reacting with more potassium sulfite, gives potassium methanetrisulfonate in 67% yield. [171]

The reaction of 2-bromo-1-propylamine with sodium sulfite leads to the formation of 2-aminopropane-1-sulfonic acid. [172]

Gabriel's method may be employed for the preparation of amino sulfonic acids. Thus, 3-aminopropane-1-sulfonic acid has been obtained in the form of its sodium salt from 3-bromopropylphthalimide and sodium sulfite, and subsequent decomposition of the reaction product with sodium hydroxide: [172]

$$C_6H_4 \begin{array}{c} CO \\ \diagdown \\ CO \end{array} NCH_2CH_2CH_2Br + Na_2SO_3$$

$$\rightarrow\ NaBr + C_6H_4 \begin{array}{c} CO \\ \diagdown \\ CO \end{array} NCH_2CH_2CH_2SO_3Na$$

$$\xrightarrow{\text{NaOH}}\ C_6H_4(COONa)_2 + H_2NCH_2CH_2CH_2SO_3Na$$

4-Aminobutane-1-sulfonic acid has been obtained in a similar manner from bromobutylphthalimide.

A related method makes use of chloroalkyl arylamides. 5-Aminopentane-1-sulfonic acid has been obtained, for example, from chloropentane benzamide: [172]

$$C_6H_5CONH(CH_2)_5Cl\ \xrightarrow{Na_2SO_3}\ C_6H_5CONH(CH_2)_5SO_3Na$$

$$\xrightarrow{\text{NaOH}}\ H_2N(CH_2)_5SO_3Na$$

A sulfonic acid is obtained by the reaction of sodium bisulfite with fuchsone:

$$(C_6H_5)_2C = \langle\bigcirc\rangle = O + NaHSO_3\ \rightarrow\ (C_6H_5)_2C(SO_3Na)C_6H_4OH$$

A similar reaction takes place between sulfurous acid and dyestuffs of the molachite green and pararosaniline type: [173]

$$(H_2NC_6H_4)_2C = C_6H_4 = NH + H_2SO_3\ \rightarrow\ (H_2NC_6H_4)_2C(SO_3H)C_6H_4NH_2$$

These sulfonic acids are unstable and decompose on boiling with acids or alkalies.

Sulfurous acid replaces the hydroxyl group in certain alcohols with the sulfonic group. Tetramethyldiaminobenzhydrol gives bis(tetramethylaminophenyl)-methanesulfonic acid: [281]

$$HOCH[C_6H_4N(CH_3)_2]_2 + H_2SO_3 \rightarrow H_2O + HSO_3CH[C_6H_4N(CH_3)_2]_2$$

The reaction proceeds well also with sodium acid sulfite.[282]

Triphenyl methyl carbinol and the corresponding *p*-tolyl compound react very slowly with acidified solutions of sodium bisulfite to give the corresponding sulfonate. Tri-*p*-anisyl methyl carbinol reacts very rapidly to form the sulfonate:[174]

$$(CH_3OC_6H_4)_3COH + NaHSO_3 \rightarrow (CH_3OC_6H_4)_3CSO_3Na + H_2O$$

Sulfonic Acids from Olefins

The formation of sulfonic acids through the reaction of bisulfites with unsaturated compounds is considered in the section dealing with unsaturated compounds (Chapter 17). The salient facts may be pointed out here.

Bisulfites of alkali metals are capable of adding at the multiple bond of many unsaturated compounds to form sulfonic acids:

$$\underset{|}{\overset{|}{C}} = \underset{|}{\overset{|}{C}} + NaHSO_3 \rightarrow H\underset{|}{\overset{|}{C}}.\underset{|}{\overset{|}{C}}.SO_3Na$$

The reaction is influenced by the pH of the solution in which it takes place. Thus, ethylene fails to react with ammonium bisulfite at pH 4.8, while reaction proceeds at an appreciable rate at pH 5.9. With propylene, the reaction proceeds at a maximum rate in the pH range 5.1 to 6.1. The yields of sulfonate obtained with olefin hydrocarbons are not, in general, high. Addition apparently does not take place according to Markownikoff's rule.

Sulfo aldehydes have been obtained through the reaction of bisulfites with unsaturated aldehydes.[284] The C-C double bond is attacked with bisulfites in practically all unsaturated ketones.

Unsaturated fatty acids add sodium bisulfite readily to form the corresponding sulfonates.[285] When the double bond is in the α-position, β-sulfonic acids always result. Maleic acid adds bisulfite readily forming sulfosuccinic acid; the reaction takes place less readily with fumaric acid. Acetylene carboxylic acids also add bisulfites to form sulfonated olefinic acids, and in some instances also, saturated disulfonic acids.

Reed's Reaction

The reaction of certain aliphatic hydrocarbons with a gaseous mixture of sulfur dioxide and chlorine under the action of actinic rays leads to the formation of sulfochlorides:[175]

$$RH + SO_2 + Cl_2 \rightarrow RSO_2Cl + HCl$$

Atomic chlorine is probably formed through the action of the rays and reacts with the hydrocarbon to form a free radical, which then in turn combines with sulfur dioxide to form a sulfonic radical and this finally reacts with molecular chlorine forming the sulfochloride and regenerating the atomic chlorine:

$$RH + Cl^{\cdot} \rightarrow HCl + R^{\cdot} \xrightarrow{SO_2} RSO_2^{\cdot}$$

$$RSO_2^{\cdot} + Cl_2 \rightarrow RSO_2Cl + Cl^{\cdot}$$

In working with liquid hydrocarbons, the *procedure* is to pass a mixture of chlorine and sulfu. dioxide through the hydrocarbon subjected to radiation from a tungsten lamp, while the mass is cooled and agitated. Passage of the gaseous mixture is continued until the theoretically calculated gain in weight is attained. Radiation of wave length in the range 3300-5000 Å may be employed when the reaction is carried out in a pyrex flask, while if a quartz vessel is used, radiation of wave length 1800-2000 Å may be employed.

The reaction is carried out in a solvent, usually carbon tetrachloride, if the hydrocarbon is gaseous.[176] The hydrocarbon, sulfur dioxide and chlorine are mixed and the mixture is led into the solvent. It is important that an excess of sulfur dioxide over the chlorine, ranging from 50 to 300%, be present at all times, since otherwise an explosive reaction between the free chlorine and the hydrocarbon may take place under the influence of actinic rays. After the completion of the reaction, the solvent is removed by distillation, and the mono sulfonyl chlorides are separated by distillation under vacuum. The residue generally consists of solid disulfochlorides which may be isolated by crystallization.

It is important to use purified hydrocarbons. Petroleum hydrocarbons should be subjected to a preliminary purification by washing with sulfuric acid.

The reaction takes place readily with saturated aliphatic hydrocarbons, and with alicyclic hydrocarbons such as cyclohexane. Many derivatives of long chain hydrocarbons, as for example, alcohols, acids, halides, nitriles, also undergo the reaction. The reaction is applicable, under certain conditions, to long chain alkyl benzenes and olefins.[177] Olefins generally yield products which on hydrolysis give hydroxy sulfonic acids.[178]

Sulfonyl chlorides resulting from short chain hydrocarbons may be isolated by fractionation. A mixture of propane-1- and propane-2-sulfonyl chlorides have been obtained from propane. Butane gives butane-1- and butane-2-sulfonyl chlorides in the proportion of 33% and 67% respectively, while isobutane gives only the primary sulfonyl chloride. Disulfonyl chlorides are formed when the reaction time is extended, butane giving the 1,4- and 1,3- isomers in the proportion of 20% of the former and 80% of the latter, and isobutylene giving only the 1,3-disulfonyl chloride.

The separation of the isomeric compounds resulting from the reaction of high molecular hydrocarbons is very difficult, if not impossible. The matter is complicated by the fact that polysubstitution proceeds progressively during the reaction. Thus, when 10 to 20% of the hydrocarbons has been converted to the sulfonyl chloride, 90% of the product is present as the monosulfonyl chloride and 10% as the disulfonyl chloride; at 50% conversion, the proportion of the mono compound is only 70% of the total chlorosulfonated products, while at 70% conversion, equal amounts of the mono and disulfonyl chlorides are obtained.

Aliphatic sulfonyl chlorides are also formed through the reaction of sulfuryl chloride, SO_2Cl_2, with paraffin hydrocarbons in the presence of a nitrogenous base, such as pyridine, under the action of actinic rays.[179] Thus, cyclohexylsulfonyl chloride results in 55% yield when sulfuryl chloride is added dropwise to a solution of cyclohexane in benzene containing a little pyridine subjected to the action of actinic rays.

Sulfonic Acids by Miscellaneous Reactions

Alkyl sulfonic acids are formed through the reaction of alkyl sulfates with alkali sulfites:[283]

$$ROSO_3Na + Na_2SO_3 \rightarrow RSO_3Na + Na_2SO_4$$

Methyl sulfate heated with aqueous potassium sulfite at 80 to 90° gives sodium methylsulfonate,[180] and sodium ethyl sulfate heated with a concentrated aqueous solution of sodium sulfite at 110 to 120° yields sodium ethylsulfonate.[181] Salts of alkyl sulfites are converted to alkyl sulfonates when treated with alkali metal halides or thiocyanates. Salts of alkyl sulfonates are formed by saturating alcoholic solutions of alkali metal alcoholates with dry sulfur dioxide.[286]

The reaction of sulfur trioxide with ethyl alcohol gives ethionic acid:

$$C_2H_5OH + SO_3 \rightarrow C_2H_5OSO_3H \xrightarrow{SO_3} HSO_3CH_2CH_2OSO_2H$$

This compound is converted to isethionic acid, $HOCH_2CH_2SO_3H$, on hydrolysis.[182]

Ether, reacting with sulfur trioxide at 0°, gives ethyl sulfate; this, on further reaction with sulfur trioxide, gives isethionic acid sulfate and the compound $\overline{CH_2CH_2SO_2OSO_2O}$.[183]

Diphenyldiazomethane reacts with sulfur dioxide in solution in methyl alcohol to form the methyl ester of diphenylmethane sulfonic acid:[184]

$$(C_6H_5)_2CN_2 + CH_3OH + SO_2 \rightarrow (C_6H_5)_2CHSO_3CH_3 + N_2$$

The free acid may be obtained by saponification of the ester.

Isethionic acid results through the reaction of ethylene oxide with sodium bisulfite:[185]

$$\overline{CH_2CH_2O} + NaHSO_3 \rightarrow HOCH_2CH_2SO_3Na$$

Epichlorhydrin reacts similarly with sodium bisulfite at 100°. The reaction appears to be a general one, and other hydroxy sulfonic acids have been prepared by its use.

Aminomethionic acid results in the form of its potassium salt through the reaction of potassium cyanide and potassium bisulfite:[186]

$$KCN + 2KHSO_3 + H_2O \rightarrow H_2NCH(SO_3K)_2 + KOH$$

Disulfocarboxylic acids are obtained through the condensation of malonic acid with the bisulfite addition products of unsaturated aldehydes:[187]

$$KSO_3CH_2CH(OH)SO_3K + H_2C(COOH)_2$$
$$\rightarrow KSO_3CH_2C(OH)(SO_3K)CH_2COOH + CO_2 + H_2O$$

Aliphatic mercaptans, disulfides and thiocyanates, treated with aqueous solution of chlorine, give the corresponding sulfonyl chlorides.[188] Pseudothiourea complexes, which result through the reaction of aliphatic chlorides and thiourea, also yield sulfonyl chlorides by the same treatment.

Reactions of Sulfonic Acids

Aliphatic sulfonic acids are not affected by boiling alkalies. Heating with 5% sodium hydroxide above 300° in a sealed tube results in slow decomposition.[189] They are decomposed to alcohol and an alkali sulfonate by fusing with alkalies.

Boiling triarylmethanesulfonic acids, such as $(C_6H_5)_2C(SO_3H)C_6H_4OH$, with acids results in the formation of triaryl carbonol with liberation of sulfur dioxide.

Phosphorus pentachloride converts sulfonic acids to sulfonic chlorides:

$$RSO_2OH + PCl_5 \rightarrow RSO_2Cl + POCl_3 + HCl$$

Ethane-1,1-disulfonic acid gives ethane-1,1-disulfonyl chloride, but potassium methionate heated with phosphorus pentachloride gives chloromethanesulfonyl chloride, $ClCH_2SO_2Cl$. Potassium ethane-1,1-disulfonate similarly treated gives 2-chloroethanesulfonyl chloride:

$$CH_3CH(SO_3K)_2 + 3\ PCl_5 \rightarrow$$

$$ClCH_2CH_2SO_2Cl + SO_2Cl_2 + 2KCl + 2POCl_3 + PCl_3$$

Ethane-1,2-disulfonyl chloride is obtained through the reaction of sodium ethane-1,2-disulfonate or the free acid with phosphorus pentachloride.[190] It is also obtained in quantitative yield through the reaction of phosgene with the free acid in toluene solution.

Ethane-1,2-disulfonyl chloride loses sulfur dioxide on boiling with water and gives ethylenesulfonic acid, $CH_2 = CHSO_3H$. The amide of this acid is formed when the chloride is treated with ammonia. The anilide is similarly obtained through the reaction of aniline with the chloride. Propane-1,2-disulfonic acid chloride reacts similarly.

Phosphorus pentabromide gives with sulfonic acids the corresponding sulfonyl bromides, although if the reaction is carried out in the presence of phosphorus tribromide, the sulfonic acid becomes reduced and a disulfide results, unless the sulfonyl group is in combination with a carbon atom joined to a benzene ring. In the latter case, the sulfonic group is replaced with bromine, benzyl bromide resulting, for example, from toluene-ω-sulfonic acid:[191]

$$C_6H_5CH_2SO_3H \rightarrow C_6H_5CH_2SO_2Br$$

$$C_6H_5CH_2SO_2Br + PBr_5 \rightarrow C_6H_5CH_2Br + SOBr_2 + POBr_3$$

Oxidation of toluene-ω-sulfonic acid with hydrogen peroxide causes the removal of the sulfonic group and the formation of benzaldehyde:[192]

$$C_6H_5CH_2SO_3H \xrightarrow{H_2O_2} C_6H_5CHO + H_2SO_4$$

Sodium 2-bromoethanesulfonate reacts with ammonia to form the sodium salt of taurine,

$H_2NCH_2CH_2SO_3Na$.[193] Taurine may also be obtained through the reaction of ammonia with ethionic acid.[194]

The reaction of 2-bromoethanesulfonic acid with potassium ethoxide leads to the formation of the double salt of potassium ethylenesulfonate and potassium bromide,

$$(CH_2 = CHSO_3K)_2\ KBr$$

although sodium ethylene sulfonate, and not a double compound, is obtained with sodium 2-chloromethanesulfonate and sodium hydroxide.

Nitrous acid reacts with aminoethionic acid to form diazomethionic acid.[195] Potassium bisulfite reacts with the potassium salt of this acid to give the addition compound $KSO_3NNHC(SO_3K)_2$, which rapidly changes to potassium methanetrisulfonate, $HC(SO_3K)_3$.

Sodium hydroxymethanesulfonate condenses with phenols to form sodium *p*-cresol-ω-sulfonate:[198]

$$C_6H_5OH + HOCH_2SO_3Na \rightarrow HOC_6H_4CH_2SO_3NA + H_2O$$

The reaction proceeds in a similar manner with other phenolic compounds.

Aliphatic disulfonamides do not form N-chloro compounds.

A notable difference between α- and β-sulfonic acids is the resistance shown by the optically active forms of the latter to factors that generally bring about racemization.

SULFINIC ACIDS

Aliphatic sulfinic acids, RSO_2H, are obtained in the form of their salts through the oxidation of dry mercaptides in air. They are also obtained as their zinc salt through the reaction of zinc alkyls with sulfur dioxide, or of alkylmagnesium halides with sulfur dioxide[287] or sulfuryl chloride:[288]

$$(C_2H_5)_2Zn + 2SO_2 \rightarrow (C_2H_5SO_2)_2Zn$$

$$2C_2H_5MgBr + 2SO_2 \rightarrow (C_2H_5SO_2)_2Mg + MgBr_2$$

$$2C_2H_5MgI + SO_2Cl_2 \rightarrow C_2H_5SO_2MgI + C_2H_5Cl + MgICl$$

The reaction of metallic zinc with sulfonyl chlorides also gives the zinc salt of sulfinic acids:

$$2C_2H_5SO_2Cl + 2Zn \rightarrow 2(C_2H_5SO_2)_2Zn + ZnCl_2$$

Alkali metal sulfonates are reduced to sulfinic acids with zinc dust and acetic acid. α-Hydroxysulfinic acids have been prepared by this method. Sodium hydroxymethylsulfinate is prepared commercially by this procedure:[289]

$$HOCH_2SO_3Na \xrightarrow{H_2} HOCH_2SO_2Na$$

The compound may be obtained through the reaction of formaldehyde with sodium hydrosulfite in the presence of sodium hydroxide:[290]

$$H_2CO + NaOH + Na_2S_2O_4 \rightarrow HOCH_2SO_2Na + Na_2SO_3$$

It is sold under the trade name "Rongalite."

Sulfinic esters are obtained by esterifying the free acids with the appropriate alcohol in the presence of hydrogen chloride, or by the reaction of alkali metal sulfonates with chlorocarbonic esters:[197]

$$RSO_2Na + ClCO_2R' \rightarrow RSOOR' + CO_2 + NaCl$$

True sulfinic esters are decomposed by water or by alkalies into the alcohol and sulfinic acid or alkali sulfinates, while the isomeric sulfones are unaffected by water or alkalies. Potassium permanganate in acetic acid solution converts sulfinic esters to sulfonic esters.[198] The free acids are converted to sulfonic acids by the same treatment. Acid permanganate is without action on sulfones.

Trichloromethylsulfo chloride results through the reaction of chlorine with moist carbon disulfide:[291]

$$CS_2 + 5Cl_2 + 2H_2O \rightarrow Cl_3CSOCl + 4HCl + SCl_2$$

The chloride is remarkably stable and may be crystallized from boiling water. It fails to react with ammonia and amines.

Chlorosulfinic esters, ClSOOR, are obtained by the reaction of the appropriate alcohol with thionyl chloride. The ester may be isolated and purified by distillation under vacuum.[292] Benzyl alcohol and phenol fail to undergo the reaction.

A few chlorides of the hypothetical aliphatic *sulfenic acid* RSOH are known. *Perchloromethylmercaptan*, Cl_3CSCl is formed by the action of chlorine on carbon disulfide.[293] Malonamide and -toluidide react with sulfur dichloride, SCl_2, forming compounds of the type $(RNHCO)_2C(SCl)_2$; methylmalonanilide and -toluidide give compounds of the type $(RNHCO)_2C(CH_3)SCl$. Only one hydrogen atom in malon-*n*-propylamide and -naphthylamide is replaced with the SCl group.[294]

Amides of Oxyacids of Sulfur

Amides of oxyacids of sulfur are formed through the reaction of amines with chlorides of these acids. The reaction of sulfuryl chloride, SO_2Cl_2 with the hydrochlorides of secondary amines results in the formation of sulfamic acid chlorides, R_2NSO_2Cl. Reaction with the free secondary amines gives tetraalkylsulfonamides $SO_2(NR_2)_2$. Ethylenedisulfo chloride reacts with aniline to form vinylsulfonanilide:

$$ClSO_2CH_2CH_2SO_2Cl + 3C_6H_5NH_2 \rightarrow$$
$$CH_2 = CHSO_2NHC_6H_5 + 2C_6H_5NH_2HCl + SO_2$$

Reaction proceeds in this manner even in cold dilute benzene solution. The course of the reaction is the same with homologs of aniline.[295]

Aliphatic thionylamines are formed through the reaction of aliphatic amines with thionyl chloride:

$$C_2H_5NH_2 + SOCl_2 \rightarrow C_2H_5N = SO + 2HCl$$

They are formed also by the reaction of aliphatic amines with thionylaniline.

Aliphatic amides do not yield chloroamides with sodium hypochlorite.

SULFONES

Sulfones, RSO_2R', may be prepared by reactions similar to those employed in the preparation of sulfonic acids. They may be obtained by the oxidation of organic sulfides; through the reaction of halogenated organic compounds with sulfinates and finally through the addition of sulfur dioxide to certain unsaturated compounds.

Sulfones by Oxidation of Sulfides

Organic sulfides are readily converted to sulfones under the action of a variety of oxidizing agents, such as concentrated or fuming nitric acid, potassium permanganate, hypochlorous acid or sodium hypochlorite, chromic acid and hydrogen peroxide.[296] Oxidation often proceeds only to the sulfoxide stage when nitric acid is employed as the oxidizing agent. The use of hydrogen peroxide dissolved in acetic acid is to be preferred, since the yields of sulfones obtained by means of this reagent are high and the final products are easy to isolate and purify. Furthermore, groups other than sulfide or sulfoxide are rarely attacked by this reagent. Chromic acid and potassium permanganate are generally used in aqueous acid solution.

Alkyl sulfonyl carboxylic amides may be obtained in good yield from the corresponding sulfides by this method.[199]

Amino sulfones may be prepared by oxidizing aliphatic amino sulfides with potassium permanganate in acid solution.[200] Methyl γ-aminopropyl-, methyl δ-aminobutyl sulfonates, and α-amino-β-methylsulfonylpropane have been prepared by this method.[201] Gabriel's method can also be employed successfully for the preparation of amino sulfones:[202]

$$\left[C_6H_4 \begin{array}{c} CO \\ \diagdown \\ CO \end{array} NCH_2CH_2 \right]_2 S \xrightarrow{CrO_3} \left[C_6H_4 \begin{array}{c} CO \\ \diagdown \\ CO \end{array} NCH_2CH_2 \right]_2 SO_2$$

$$\xrightarrow{KOH} \left[C_6H_4 \begin{array}{c} COOK \\ \diagdown \\ CONHCH_2CH_2 \end{array} \right]_2 SO_2 \xrightarrow{HCl} (H_2NCH_2CH_2)_2SO_2$$

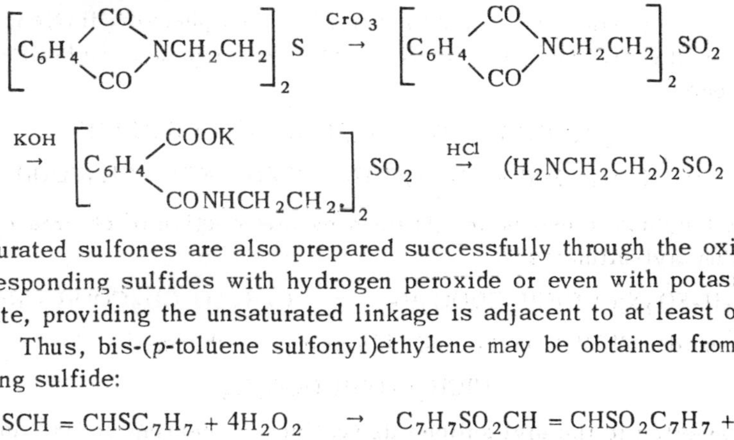

Unsaturated sulfones are also prepared successfully through the oxidation of the corresponding sulfides with hydrogen peroxide or even with potassium permanganate, providing the unsaturated linkage is adjacent to at least one sulfur atom.[203] Thus, bis-(p-toluene sulfonyl)ethylene may be obtained from the corresponding sulfide:

$$C_7H_7SCH = CHSC_7H_7 + 4H_2O_2 \rightarrow C_7H_7SO_2CH = CHSO_2C_7H_7 + 4H_2O$$

and m-phenylene divinyl sulfone has been prepared similarly from m-phenylene divinyl sulfide:

$$CH_2 = CHSC_6H_4SCH = CH_2 \rightarrow CH_2 = CHSO_2C_6H_4SO_2CH = CH_2$$

Ethane disulfo compounds may be prepared by condensing mercaptans with pyruvic acid, and oxidizing the resulting disulfide with potassium permanganate:

$$CH_3COCOOH + RSH + R'SH \rightarrow H_2O + CH_3C(SR)(SR')COOH$$

$$\rightarrow CH_3CH(SO_2R)SO_2R'$$

Ethyl trithioorthoformate loses one of the sulfide groups on oxidation, giving a disulfone, although ethyl trithioorthoacetate is readily converted to the corresponding trisulfone. Oxidation of benzyl trithioorthoformate with potassium permanganate results in the formation of bis-benzylsulfonylmethane, together with the sulfide disulfone,

$$(C_6H_5CH_2SO_2)_2CHSCH_2C_6H_5$$

The trisulfone is obtained readily from 1,2,2-tris(ethylthiol)-propane by oxidation.[204]

Sulfones from Halo Compounds

Sulfones result through the interaction of organic halo compounds with sodium sulfinates. With alkyl halides the reaction proceeds best by use of the silver salt:

$$RI + AgSO_2R' \rightarrow RSO_2R' + AgI$$

Halogenated hydrocarbons in which two halogen atoms are attached to the same carbon atom give halomonosulfones. Chloroform fails to react, while benzotrichloride gives a monosulfone. Disulfones are obtained from trichloroethanes.

Chloracetone reacts readily in alcoholic solution with sodium aryl sulfinates to form aryl sulfonyl acetones.[205] Reaction proceeds readily also with ω-chloracetophenone.

α, γ-Dichloracetone and γ, γ-dibromacetone give the corresponding disulfones with sodium benzenesulfinate;[206] $\alpha,\alpha,\gamma,\gamma$-tetrachloracteone also gives a disulfone, the remaining halogens being replaced with hydrogen.[207]

β,β'-Dibromopropiophenone reacting with sodium phenylsulfinate in alcoholic solution in the presence of potassium acetate forms α-phenylsulfonyl-β-benzoylethylene:

$$C_6H_5COCH_2CHBr_2 + C_6H_5SO_2Na + CH_3COOK$$
$$\rightarrow C_6H_5COCH = CHSO_2C_6H_5 + NaBr + KBr + CH_3COOH$$

Aryl sulfonylacetic esters are obtained by the reaction of chloroacetic esters with sodium arylsulfinates:[208]

$$C_6H_5SO_2Na + ClCH_2COOC_2H_5 \rightarrow C_6H_5SO_2CH_2COOH + NaCl$$

Chloracetamide, $ClCH_2CONH_2$, and chloracetyl urethane,

$$ClCH_2CONHCOOC_2H_5$$

can be converted to the aryl sulfone derivatives by heating at 100° in a sealed tube with sodium aryl sulfinate in alcoholic solution.[209] The sulfonyl acetonitriles have been similarly prepared from chloracetonitrile.[210] The reaction of α-chloropropionitrile with sodium sulfinates proceeds at 130-140°.

The reaction of ethyl α-chloracetoacetate with sodium p-toluenesulfinate in alcoholic solution results in the formation of ethyl p-toluenesulfonyl acetate:

$$C_7H_7SO_2Na + CH_3COCHClCOOC_2H_5 + C_2H_5OH$$
$$\rightarrow C_7H_7SO_2CH_2COOC_2H_5 + CH_3COOC_2H_5 + NaCl$$

Sodium dichloracetate reacts with aqueous sodium benzenesulfinate to form chloromethyl phenyl sulfone:[211]

$$C_6H_5SO_2Na + Cl_2CHCOONa + H_2O$$
$$\rightarrow C_6H_5SO_2CH_2Cl + NaCl + NaHCO_3$$

The reaction of *α,α*-dichloropropionic acid with sodium phenylsulfinate takes in part a different course, yielding bis-phenylsulfonyl ethane:

$$CH_3CCl_2COONa + 2C_6H_5SO_2Na + H_2O$$
$$\rightarrow C_6H_5SO_2CH_2CH_2SO_2C_6H_5 + 2NaCl + NaHCO_3$$

β-Chloroisocrotonic acid gives *β*-phenylsulfonylcrotonic acid with sodium phenylsulfinate:[212]

$$CH_3CCl{=}CHCOONa + C_6H_5SO_2Na \rightarrow CH_3C(SO_2C_6H_5) = CHCOONa + NaCl$$

The isomeric *β*-chloroisocrotonic acid reacts similarly.

Acyl chlorides reacting with potassium *p*-toluenesulfinate in ethereal solution at 110° under pressure yield *α*-keto sulfones.[213]

Sulfones from Sulfinic Acids and Aldehydes

p-Toluenesulfinic acid forms unstable addition compounds with aliphatic and aromatic aldehydes:[214]

$$CH_3C_6H_4SO_2H + H_2CO \rightarrow CH_3C_6H_4SO_2CH_2OH$$

Compounds derived from aromatic aldehydes are more stable than those obtained from aliphatic aldehydes. Addition first takes place at the double bond with cinnamic aldehyde and further reaction yields a disulfone,

$$C_6H_5CH(SO_2C_6H_4CH_3)CH_2CH(OH)SO_2C_6H_4CH_3,$$

a compound which has not, however, been obtained in the pure form because of its instability.

Sulfones from Olefins and Sulfur Dioxide

Butadiene and many of its homologs react with sulfur dioxide forming cyclic olefinic sulfones, together with amorphous polymeric compounds:[215]

$$CH_2 = CHCH = CH_2 + SO_2 \rightarrow CH_2CH = CHCH_2SO_2$$

The reaction with butadiene has been carried out under various conditions; it has been effected by use of a saturated aqueous solution of ammonium sulfite at 120°; further with water saturated with sulfur dioxide at room temperature; with an ethereal solution of sulfur dioxide at 100°, and with liquid sulfur dioxide. 2,4-Hexadiene, *trans,trans*-1,4-diphenyl-1,3-butadiene and *cis,cis*-1,4-dicarboxy-1,3-butadiene fail to react.

The reaction of olefins with a single double bond with sulfur dioxide leading to the formation of polymeric compounds is discussed under unsaturated aliphatic compounds (Chapter 17).

Reactions of Sulfones

Sulfones are in general unaffected by boiling dilute alkalies, although, *p*-nitrobenzyl alkyl sulfones are decomposed by hot 20% sodium hydroxide.

Lower alkyl sulfones are converted to an olefin and potassium sulfinate when heated at 200-235° with fused 90% potassium hydroxide. Butyl sulfone decomposes slowly by this treatment, though butyl methyl, butyl ethyl and butyl propyl sulfones decompose fairly readily. η-Octyl sulfone fails to react. Phenyl β-phenyl ethyl sulfone gives benzene and styrene, while phenyl sulfone is converted to phenol, benzene and diphenyl.

Phenylsulfonylacetone is decomposed to phenyl methyl sulfone and potassium acetate on heating with alcoholic potassium hydroxide:

$$C_6H_5SO_2CH_2COCH_3 + KOH \rightarrow C_6H_5SO_2CH_3 + CH_3COOK$$

Ethyl β,β-diphenylsulfonylbutyrate treated with a cold concentrated solution of potassium hydroxide gives an unsaturated sulfone:

$$CH_3C(SO_2C_6H_5)_2CH_2COOC_2H_5 + 2KOH$$
$$\rightarrow CH_3C(SO_2C_6H_5) = CHCOOK + H_2O + C_2H_5OH + C_6H_5SO_2K$$

Sodium hydroxide decomposes propane-1,2-bis-sulfonylacetic acid to an unsaturated sulfone:[216]

$$CH_3CH(SO_2CH_2COONa)CH_2SO_2CH_2COONa + NaOH$$
$$\rightarrow CH_3CH = CHSO_2CH_2COONa + NaSO_2CH_2COONa + H_2O$$

Treated with aqueous bromine, this compound undergoes an unusual degradation, giving bis-(tribromomethyl) sulfone:

$$CH_3CH = CHSO_2CH_2COOH + 6Br_2 + H_2O$$
$$\rightarrow (Br_3C)_2SO_2 + CO_2 + CH_3CHO + 6HBr$$

bis-(*p*-tolylsulfonyl)-acetatamide is hydrolyzed to bis-(*p*-tolylsulfonyl)methane:[217]

$$(C_7H_7SO_2)_2CHCONH_2 + H_2O \rightarrow (C_7H_7SO_2)_2CH_2 + NH_3 + CO_2$$

1,2-Disulfones differ from other disulfones in that they break down on heating with alkalies into a sulfone alcohol and a sulfinate (*Stuffer's rule*):[218]

$$C_6H_5SO_2CH_2CH_2SO_2C_6H_5 + NaOH \rightarrow C_6H_5SO_2CH_2CH_2OH + C_6H_5SO_2Na$$

The reaction proceeds extremely slowly with bis(phenylsulfonyl)ethane, requiring eight days for completion at 100°. Cyclic disulfones of this type, in which the sulfur atom forms part of the ring, also undergo this reaction:[219]

$$\overline{CH_2SO_2CH_2CH_2SO} + NaOH \rightarrow NaSO_2CH_2SO_2CH_2CH_2OH$$

The free acid loses sulfur dioxide readily giving $CH_3SO_2CH_2CH_2OH$.

Sulfones are decomposed on heating at 200-235° with sodium ethoxide containing a trace of alcohol, even higher alkyl sulfones undergoing this reaction.[220]

Heating the benzyl derivative of ethyl benzenesulfonylacetate with sodium ethoxide at 100° results in the formation of sodium cinnamate:

$$C_6H_5CH_2CH(SO_2C_6H_5)COOC_2H_5 + 2C_2H_5ONa$$
$$\rightarrow (C_2H_5)_2O + C_6H_5SO_2Na + C_6H_5CH = CHCOONa + C_2H_5OH$$

Treatment of cyclic sulfones of the type $CH_3C = CHCH_2SO_2CH_2$ in anhydrous ether with metallic potassium causes rupture of the ring, and the formation of the potassium salt of an unstable sulfinic acid, which dimerizes rapidly:

$$2CH_3C = CHCH_2SO_2CH_2 + 2K$$
$$\rightarrow KSO_2CH_2CH = C(CH_3)CH = CHC(CH_3) = CHCH_2SO_2K$$

The monomeric sulfone $(CH_3)_2C = CHCH_2SO_2K$, is obtained when the reaction is carried out in moist ether.

Ozonization of cyclic sulfones of this type causes the formation of diketo sulfones, or cyclic ethers derived from them:

$$CH_3C = C(CH_3)CH_2SO_2CH_2 \xrightarrow{O_3, H_2O} (CH_3COCH_2)_2SO_2$$
$$\rightarrow CH_3C = CHSO_2CH = C(CH_3)O$$

β-Hydroxyethyl phenyl sulfone is oxidized to phenylsulfonylacetic acid:[221]

$$C_6H_5SO_2CH_2CH_2OH \rightarrow C_6H_5SO_2CH_2COOH$$

Reaction with ammonia converts hydroxy sulfones of this type to amino ethyl sulfones:[222]

$$CH_3SO_2CH_2CH_2OH + NH_3 \rightarrow CH_3SO_2CH_2CH_2NH_2 + H_2O$$
$$2CH_3SO_2CH_2CH_2OH + NH_3 \rightarrow (CH_3SO_2CH_2CH_2)_2NH + 2H_2O$$

The sulfonic group brings about the activation of the methyl group to which it is attached. Thus, sulfonyl acetonitriles readily condense with aromatic aldehydes in the presence of basic catalysts:[223]

$$C_6H_5CHO + CH_2(CN)SO_2C_6H_5 \rightarrow C_6H_5CH = C(CN)SO_2C_6H_5 + H_2O$$

The methylene hydrogen in 1,1-disulfones is readily replaced with halogens. The dihalo compounds are obtained by the action of aqueous chlorine or bromine, or by iodine in potassium iodide solution.[224]

Bis-(*n*-butylsulfonyl)dibromomethane reacting with potassium iodide in aqueous solution liberates iodine:[225]

$$(C_4H_9SO_2)_2CBr_2 + 4KI + 2H_2O$$
$$\rightarrow (C_4H_9SO_2)_2CH_2 + 2I_2 + 2KBr + 2KOH$$

Bis-(ethylsulfonyl)diiodomethane reacts with ethyl sodiomalonate forming the ethyl ester of bis-ethylsulfonylmethane and ethyl ethylenetetracarboxylate:[226]

$$(C_2H_5SO_2)_2CI_2 + 2NaCH(COOC_2H_5)_2$$

$$\rightarrow (C_2H_5SO_2)_2CH_2 + (C_2H_5OCO)_2C = C(COOC_2H_5)_2 + 2NaI$$

Phenylsulfonylacetone reacting with thiosulfonic acids gives an alkyl thiol derivative, the thiol group replacing one of the methylene hydrogens:[227]

$$C_6H_5SO_2CH_2COCH_3 + CH_3C_6H_4SO_2SCH_3$$

$$\rightarrow C_6H_5SO_2CH(SCH_3)COCH_3 + CH_3C_6H_4SO_2H$$

Attempts to oxidize the methylene group in phenylsulfonylacetonitrile were unsuccessful.[228] Ethyl nitrate does not react with phenylsulfonylacetonitrile. The reaction of Grignard reagents with phenylsulfonylacetonitrile does not yield the ketone.[229]

The trisulfones of the general formula $(RSO_2)_3CH$ are strongly acidic in character; they liberate carbon dioxide from carbonates in the cold but are precipitated from aqueous solutions of their salt by acetic acid.

Phenylsulfonylacetamide, treated with bromine and potassium hydroxide, does not undergo the Hofmann reaction but is converted to $C_6H_5SO_2CHBr_2$ and $C_6H_5SO_2CBr_3$.[84]

Aromatic aliphatic sulfones with a hydroxy group in the aliphatic group, heated with caustic, undergo rearrangement very rapidly:

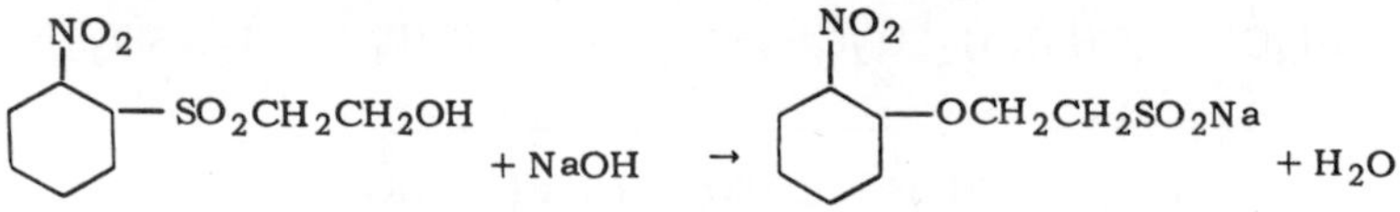

A similar rearrangement may also take place with a hydroxyl group in a second molecule.

THIOSULFURIC AND THIOSULFONIC ACIDS

Alkyl thiosulfuric acids, $RSSO_3H$, are formed as their alkali metal salts, through the reaction of alkyl iodides or bromides with the alkali metal salts of of thiosulfuric acid:

$$C_2H_5I + NaSSO_3Na \rightarrow C_2H_5S.SO_3Na + NaI$$

They are also obtained by the action of iodine on a mixture of sodium mercaptide and sodium sulfite:

$$C_2H_5SNa + NaSO_3Na + I_2 \rightarrow C_2H_5SSO_3Na + 2NaI$$

The free acids are not stable, and decompose to a mercaptan and monosodium sulfate. The salts decompose on heating to alkyl disulfides, a metallic sulfate and sulfur dioxide.

Alkyl thiosulfonic acids, RSO_2SH, are obtained in the form of their potassium salt through the interaction of sulfonic chlorides and potassium sulfide:

$$C_2H_5SO_2Cl + K_2S \rightarrow C_2H_5SO_2SK + KCl$$

The esters of these acids are obtained by the oxidation of mercaptans or disulfides with dilute sulfuric acid:

$$2C_2H_5SH \rightarrow C_2H_5SSC_2H_5 \rightarrow C_2H_5SO_2.SC_2H_5$$

These esters result also through the interaction of alkyl bromides with the potassium salt of the thiosulfonic acid:

$$C_2H_5SO_2SK + BrC_2H_5 \rightarrow C_2H_5SO_2SC_2H_5 + KBr$$

References

1. Konowalow, *Compt. rend.*, **114**, 26 (1892); *Ber.*, **25**, 1244 (1892); **26**, Ref. 880 (1893); **27**, R468 (1894); **28**, 1852 (1895); **29**, 2199 (1896); *J. Rus. Phys.-Chem. Soc.*, **31**, 57 (1898); Henry, *Rec. trav. chim.*, **17**, 1 (1898); Zaloziecki and Frasch, *Ber.*, **35**, 386 (1902). Konowalow, *J. Russ. Phys.-Chem.*, **38**, 109 (1906). Worstall, *Am. Chem. I.*, **20**, 202 (1892); **21**, 210, 218 (1899); Francis and Young, *J. Chem. Soc.*, **73**, 928 (1898); Markownikow, *Ber.*, **32**, 1443 (1899); **33**, 1905 (1900); Defize, *Chem. Weekblad*, **38**, 63 (1941); Gilbert, *J. Chem. Education*, **18**, 435 (1941); Haas and Riley, *Chem. Revs.*, (3) **32**, 373, 415 (1943); Michael and Carlson, *J. Am. Chem. Soc.*, **57**, 1268 (1935); Nelles, *Angew. Chem.*, **54**, 77 (1941); Whitmore, *J. Am. Chem. Soc.*, **55**, 4164 (1935). *Cf.* Ellis, *The Chemistry of Petroleum Derivatives* II, 1087 (1937); McCleary and Degering, *Ind. Eng. Chem.*, **30**, 64 (1938); Hass *et al.*, *ibid.*, **30**, 67 (1938); **39**, 817 (1947).
2. Worstall, *Am. Chem. J.*, **20**, 202 (1898); **21**, 210 (1899). *Cf.* Henry, *Rec. trav. chim.*, **24**, 352 (1905).
3. Konowalow, *J. Russ. Phys. Chem. Soc.*, **25**, 472 (1894); *J. Chem. Soc.*, **66**, 265 (1894).
4. Konowalow, *J. Chem. Soc.*, **66**, 265 (1894).
5. Konowalow, *J. Russ. Phys.-Chem. Soc.*, **36**, 220, 537 (1904); **38**, 607 (1906).
6. Kleinfeller, *Ber.*, **62**, 1582, 1590 (1929); Kleinfeller and Stahmer, *ibid.*, **66**, 1127 (1933).
7. Hantzsch, *Ber.*, **39**, 2479 (1906).
8. Konowalow, *ibid.*, **28**, 1860 (1895).
9. Worstall, *Am. Chem. J.*, **20**, 202 (1898); **21**, 210, 218 (1899). Francis and Young, *J. Chem. Soc.*, **73**, 928 (1899); Gärtner, *U. S. patent*, 1,632,959 (1927); Haines and Adkins, *J. Am. Chem. Soc.*, **47**, 1419 (1925); Poni and Costachescu, *Ann. Sci. Univ. Jassy*, **2**, 52 (1902); **3**, 119 (1903); *J. Chem. Soc.*, (1) **84**, 596 (1903).
10. Konowalow, *Ber.*, **29**, 2200 (1896); *J. Russ. Phys.-Chem. Soc.*, **38**, 109, 124 (1906).
11. Markovnikov, *Ber.*, **32**, 1444 (1899); **33**, 1906 (1900).
12. Wislecenus *et al.*, *ibid.*, **35**, 1757 (1902); **38**, 670 (1905).
13. Chancel, *Compt. rend.*, **86**, 1405 (1878); **94**, 399 (1882); **96**, 1466 (1883); **99**, 1053 (1884); **100**, 601 (1885); *Bull. soc. chim.*, (2) **31**, 504 (1879). Kurtz, *Ann.*, **161**, 208 (1872); Fileti and Ponzio, *J. prakt. Chem.*, (2) **50**, 370 (1894); **51**, 498 (1895); **55**, 186 (1897); **58**, 362 (1898); *Gazz. chim. ital.*, **24 II**, 290 (1894); **27 I**, 255 (1897); **28 II**, 262 (1898).
14. Chancel, *Compt. rend.*, **96**, 1466 (1883).
15. Ponzio, *Gazz. chim. ital.*, **31 I**, 401 (1901).
16. Ponzio, *J. prakt. Chem.*, (2) **53**, 431 (1896).
17. Behrend and Tryller, *Ann.*, **283**, 243 (1894).
18. Bredt, *Ber.*, **15**, 2318 (1882).
19. Bouveault, *Bull. soc. chim.*, (3) **25**, 800, 808, 910 (1901).
20. Chattaway, *J. Chem. Soc.*, **97**, 2099 (1910); *Chem. News*, **102**, 307 (1910).
21. Franchimont and Klobbie, *Rec. trav. chim.*, **8**. 283 (1889); Wahl, *Bull. soc. chim.*, (3) **25**, 926 (1901); Ulpiani *et al.*, *Gazz. chim. ital.*, **32 II**, 235 (1902); **33 I**, 379 (1903); Ratz, *Monatsh.*, **25**, 701 (1904); Hantzsch, *Ber.*, **40**, 1528 (1907); Battaglia, *Gazz. chim. ital.*, **38 I**, 356 (1908).
22. Haas, *Proc. Indiana Acad. Sci.*, **48**, 104 (1939); *U. S. patents* 2,071,122 (1937); 1,967,667 (1934); 2,174,242 (1940); 2,236,905 (1941); 2,153,065 (1939); 2,260,258 (1942); *French patent* 797,329 (1936).
23. Haas *et al.*, *Ind. Eng. Chem.*, **32**, 427 (1940).
24. Haas and Patterson, *ibid.*, **30**, 67 (1938).
25. Haas *et al.*, *ibid.*, **28**, 339 (1936).
26. Darsky, *ibid.*, **33**, 1138 (1941).
27. McCleary and Degering, *ibid.*, **30**, 64 (1938).
28. Haas *et al.*, *ibid.*, **28**, 339 (1936); **30**, 67 (1938); **31**, 648 (1939).
29. Urbanski and Slon, *Compt. rend.*, **203**, 620 (1936).
30. Levy, *Brit. patent* 527,031 (1940).
31. Meyer *et al.*, *Ann.*, **171**, 1 (1874); **175**, 88 (1875); **180**, 111 (1876); *Ber.*, **5**, 203 (1872); **25**, 1701 (1892); Kissel, *ibid.*, **15**, 1574 (1882).
32. Kaufler and Pomeranz, *Monatsh.*, **22**, 492 (1901).
33. Bewald, *Ber.*, **25**. Ref. 571 (1892); Kissel *ibid.*, **15**, 1574 (1882); Michael, *J. prakt. Chem.*, (2) **60**, 322 (1899); Tscherniak, *Ann.*, **180**, 157 (1876); Meyer and Forster; *Ber.*, **9**, 529 (1876). Neogi and Chowdhuri, *J. Chem. Soc.*, **109**, 701 (1915).

34. Reynolds and Adkins, *J. Am. Chem. Soc.*, **51**, 279 (1929); Shriner and Young, *ibid.*, **52**, 3332 (1930); Kuhn and Albrecht, *Ber.*, **60 B**, 1297 (1927).
35. Ray, *Ann.*, **316**, 252 (1901); Kaufler and Pomeranz, *Monatsh.*, **22**, 495 (1901). *Cf.* Lucas, *Ber.*, **32**, 3179 (1899).
36. Walden, *Ber.*, **40**, 3214 (1907).
37. Demuth and Meyer, *ibid.*, **21**, 3529 (1888); *Ann.*, **256**, 28 (1889). *Cf.* Wieland and Sakellarios, *Ber.*, **52**, 898 (1919).
38. Brackebusch, *Ber.*, **6**, 1290 (1873); Ter Meer, *Ann.*, **181**, 1 (1876); Henry, *Bull. acad. roy. Belg.*, (3) **36**, 149 (1898).
39. Brackebusch, *Ber.*, **7**, 225 (1874); Henry, *Bull. acad. roy. Belg.*, (3) **34**, 547 (1898); Meyer and Askenasy, *Ber.*, **25**, 1701 (1892).
40. Kolbe, *J. prakt. Chem.*,(2) **5**, 427 (1872); Hirano, *J. Pharm. Soc. Japan*, **50**, 869 (1930).
41. Hess and Riley, *Chem. Revs.*, (3) **32**, 415 (1943).
42. Nenitzescu and Isăcescu, *Ber.*, **63**, 2491 (1930); Seigle and Hass, *J. Org. Chem.*, **5**, 100 (1940); *U. S. patent* 2,181,531 (1939).
43. McKie, *J. Chem. Soc.*, **1927**, 962; Wieland *et al.*, *Ber.*, **53**, 203 (1920); **54**, 1770 (1921); Kohler and Drake, *J. Am. Chem. Soc.*, **45**, 1281 (1923); Friedländer and Schüler, *Ber.*, **16**, 848, 1032 (1883); *Ann.*, **229**, 203 (1885).
44. Chattaway, *J. Chem. Soc.*, **97**, 2099 (1910); Testoni and Mascavelli, *Rend. accad. Lincei*, (5) **10**, 442 *Chem. Zentr.* **1901 II**, 177.
45. Burrows and Hunter, *J. Chem. Soc.*, **1932**, 1357.
46. Biltz and Kedesdy, *Ber.*, **33**, 2190 (1900).
47. Schmidt, *Ber.*, **35**, 2336 (1902); **36**, 1775 (1903); Demyanow, *J. Russ. Phys.-Chem. Soc.*, **36**, 151 (1904); *Ber.*, **40**, 245 (1907); Scidorenko, *Chem. Zentr.*, **1907 I**, 399. Argo *et al.*, *J. Phys. Chem.*, **23**, 578 (1919); Biltz, *Ber.*, **35**, 1528 (1902); Franklin and Wilkins, *Brit. patent* 532,686 (1941); Haas and Riley, *Chem. Revs.*, **32**, 376 (1943); Michael and Carlson, *J. Org. Chem.*, **4**, 169 (1939); **5**, 1 (1940); *J. Am. Chem. Soc.*, **59**, 843 (1937); Wieland *et al.*, *Ann.*, **424**, 71 (1921) *Ber.*, **54**, 1776 (1921) *Cf.* Haitinger *Monatsh.*, **2**, 287 (1881).
48. Campbell, *Ind. Eng. Chem.*, **33**, 809 (1941); Biltz, *Ber.*, **35**, 1521 (1902).
49. Hein, *Ber.*, **44**, 2016 (1911).
50. Steinkopf and Kühnel, *ibid.*, **75 B**, 1323 (1942).
51. Birckenbach and Sennewald, *Ann.*, **489**, 7 (1931); Panzio, *Gazz. chim. ital.*, **36 II**, 100, 338 (1906); Rheinboldt *et al.*, *Ann.*, **451**, 161 (1927); **455**, 300 (1927).
52. Ponzio and Bigliotti, *Gazz. chim. ital.*, **64**, 861 (1934).
53. Bamberger and Seligman, *Ber.*, **36**, 685 (1903).
54. Henry, *Compt. rend.*, **120**, 1265 (1895); **121**, 210 (1895); *Rec. trav. chim.*, **16**, 250 (1897); **18**, 261 (1899); *Ber.*, **30**, 2206 (1897); **33**, 3169 (1900); Piloty and Ruff, *ibid.*, **31**, 221 (1898); Demjanow, *J. Russ. Phys.-Chem. Soc.*, **35**, 23 (1903).
55. Thiele, *Ber.*, **32**, 1293 (1899).
56. Knoevenagel and Walter, *ibid.*, **37**, 4502 (1904).
57. Meyer, *Ann.*, **171**, 49 (1874); *Ber.*, **7**, 1313 (1874); Tscherniak, *ibid.*, **8**, 609 (1873); *Ann.*, **180**, 123 (1876); Meyer and Tscherniak, *ibid.*, **180**, 112 (1876); Züblin, *Ber.*, **10**, 2085 (1877); Bewald, *ibid.*, **24**, 974 (1891).
58. Henry, *Bull. acad. roy. Belg.*, (3) **34**, 547 (1898); Pauwels, *Rec. trav. chim.*, **17**, 27 (1898); Shaw, *Bull. acad. roy. Belg.*, (3)**34**, 1019 (1898); *Rec. trav. chim.*, **17**, 50 (1898).
59. Loevenich and Gerber, *Ber.*, **63 B**, 1707 (1930); Schmidt *et al.*, *ibid.*, **58 B**, 2430 (1925); Schwarz and Nelles, *U.S. Patent* 2,257,980 (1941); Shilov, *J. Russ. Phys.-Chem. Soc.*, **62**, 95 (1930); Wallach, Ann., **332**, 305 (1904); Weiland and Sakellarios, *Ber.*, **52**, 898 (1919).
60. Wieland and Sakellarios, *Ber.*, **52**, 898 (1919).
61. Meyer, *Ann.*, **175**, 120 (1875); Meyer and Locher, *ibid.*, **180**, 1361 (1876); Piloty and Stock, *Ber.*, **35**, 3093 (1902).
62. Schöfer, *ibid.*, **34**, 1911 (1901), Bamberger, *ibid.*, **33**, 1783 (1900).
63. Ponzio, *Gazz. chim. ital.*, **33 I**, 508 (1903).
64. Meyer, *Ann.*, **175**, 127 (1875).
65. Piloty and Steinbeck, *Ber.*, **35**, 3104 (1902).
66. Graul and Hantzsch, *ibid.*, **31**, 2864 (1898); Hantzsch and Barth, *ibid.*, **35**, 216 (1902).
67. Nef, *Ann.*, **270**, 331 (1892); **280**, 263, 920 (1894); *Ber.*, **29**, 1218 (1896); Ponzio, *J. prakt. Chem.*, (2) **65**, 197 (1902); Holleman, *Rec. trav. chim.*, **14**, 129 (1895); **15**, 362 (1896); **16**, 162 (1897); *Ber.*, **33**, 2913 (1900); Hantzsch *et al.*, *Ber.* **29**, 699, 2251 (1896); **32**, 575, 607, 628, 3137 (1899); de Bruyn, *Rec. trav. chim.*, **14**, 89, 151 (1895); Meyer, *Ber.*, **27**, 3154 (1894); Jackson, *Am. Chem. J.*, **20**, 444 (1898); Michael, *J. prakt. Chem.*, (2) **37**, 507 (1888); *Ber.* **29**, 1796 (1896); Thurston and Shriner, *J. Org. Chem.*, **2**, 183 (1937).
68. Ponzio, *ibid.*, (2) **67**, 137 (1902).
69. Shilov, *J. Russ. Phys.-Chem. Soc.*, **62**, 95 (1930).
70. Thurston and Shriner, *J. Org. Chem.*, **2**, 183 (1937).
71. Nef, *Ann.*, **280**, 266 (1894); *Ber.*, **29**, 1223 (1896); Hantzsch and Veit, *ibid.*, **32**, 613 (1899).

72. Nef, *Ber.*, **29**, 1223 (1896); Hantzach and Schultze, *ibid.*, **29**, 2251 (1896). Holleman, *Rec. trav. chim.*, **15**, 356, 365 (1896).
73. Jones, *Am. Chem. J.*, **20**, 1 (1898).
74. Steinkopf and Jürgens, *J. prakt. Chem.*, (2) **84**, 686 (1911).
75. Friese, *Ber.*, **9**, 394 (1876). *Cf.* Lecco, *ibid.*, **9**, 705 (1876); Kimich, *ibid.*, **10**, 140 (1877); Dunstan and Goulding, *Trans. Chem., Soc.*, **1900**, 1262; Scholl, *Ber.*, **34**, 862 (1901); Meister, *ibid;*, **40**, 3435 (1907); Steinkopf and Bohrman, *ibid.*, **41**, 1048 (1908); Steinkopf and Kirchhoff, *ibid.*, **42**, 2031 (1909).
76. Steinkopf, *ibid.*, **42**, 3925 (1909); Steinkopf and Kirchhoff, *ibid.*, **42**, 3438 (1909).
77. Lippincott, *J. Am. Chem. Soc.*, **62**, 2604 (1940); *U. S. patent* 2,260,256 (1941).
78. Willstätter and Hottenroth, *Ber.*, **37**, 1778 (1904).
79. Tscherniak, *ibid.*, **8**, 609 (1875).
80. Henry, *Compt. rend.*, **120**, 1265 (1895); *Bull. acad. roy. Belg.*, (3) **34**, 547 (1898).
81. Losanich, *Ber.*, **17**, 848 (1884); Henry, *Bull. acad. roy. Belg.*, (3) **34**, 547 (1898); Shaw, *ibid.*, (3) **34**, 1019 (1898); *Rec. trav. chim.*, **17**, 50 (1898).
82. Seigle and Haas, *J. Org. Chem.*, **5**, 100 (1940). Cf. Nenitzescu and Isacescu, *Ber.*, **63**, 2491 (1930).
83. Gotting, *Ber.*, **21**, 58 (1888).
84. Tröger and Hille, *J. prakt. Chem.*, (2) **71**, 201 (1905).
85. Meyer and Rilliet, *Ber.*, **5**, 1030 (1872); Nef, *Ann.*, **280**, 263 (1894).
86. Bamberger, *Ber.*, **31**, 2626 (1898).
87. Freund, *ibid.*, **52**, 542 (1919).
88. Meyer *et al.*, *Ann.*, **175**, 120 (1875); **180**, 136 (1876); **214**, 328 (1882); Tscherniac, *ibid.*, **180**, 166 (1876).
89. Bevad, *Ber.*, **26**, 129 (1893). *Cf.* Melinkov, *J. Gen. Chem. (U.S.S.R.)*, **7**, 456 (1937).
90. Preibisch, *J. prakt. Chem.*, (2) **7**, 480 (1873); **8**, 316 (1874); Meyer and Locher, *Ann.*, **180**, 163 (1876).
91. Lippincott and Haas, *Ind. Eng. Chem.*, **32**, 1093 (1940).
92. Henry, *Compt. rend.*, **120**, 1265 (1895); **121**, 210 (1895); *Bull. acad. roy. Belg.*, (3) **34**, 547 (1898); Thiele *Ber.*, **32**, 1293 (1899); Mousset, *Bull. acad. roy. Belg.*, **1901**, 622; Bouveault and Wahl, *Compt. rend.*, **134**, 1226 (1902); **135**, 41 (1902); Knoevenagel and Walter, *Ber.*, **37**, 4502 (1904); Chattaway *et al.*, *J. Chem. Soc.*, **1936**, 1294; Weiss, *ibid.*, **1942**, 245; Cox, *U. S. patent* 2,301,259 (1943).
93. Henry, *Bull. soc. chim.*, (3) **13**, 999 (1895); Fraser and Kon, *J. Chem. Soc.*, **1934**, 604.
94. Fraser and Kon, *J. Chem. Soc.*, **1934**, 604; Hass and Riley, *Chem. Revs.*, (3) **32**, 415 (1943); Worrall, *J. Am. Chem. Soc.*, **56**, 1556 (1934); **62**, 3253 (1940).
95. Henry, *Ber.*, **38**, 2027 (1905); Dunden *et al.*, *ibid*, **38**, 2036 (1905).
96. Hoffmann and Meyer, *Ber.*, **24**, 3530 (1891); Kirpal, *ibid.*, **25**, 1714 (1892).
97. Konowaloff, *J. Russ. Phys.-Chem. Soc.*, **30**, 960 (1898).
98. Bamberger, *Ber.*, **37**, 1350 (1894).
99. Johnson and Degering, *J. Am. Chem. Soc.*, **61**, 3194 (1939).
100. Ponzio, *J. prakt. Chem.*, (2) **65**, 197 (1902); **66**, 478 (1902); Scholl, *ibid.*, (2) **66**, 206 (1902).
101. Bouveault and Wahl, *Bull. soc. chim.*, (3) **29**, 643 (1903).
102. Mamlock and Wolffenstein, *Ber.*, **34**, 2500 (1901).
103. Aston and Mayberry, *J. Am. Chem. Soc.*, **57**, 1888 (1935).
104. *Cf.* Hodgson and Davies, *J. Chem. Soc.*, **1939**, 1013.
105. Wieland, *Ann.*, **328**, 154 (1903); **329**, 225 (1903); Wallach, *ibid.*, **332**, 306 (1904).
106. Ssidorenko, *J. Russ. Phys.-Chem. Soc.*, **38**, 955 (1906).
107. Piloty and Ruff, *Ber.*, **31**, 221 (1898); Piloty, *ibid.*, **31**, 218 (1898).
108. Rheinboldt and Dewald, *Ann.*, **455**, 300 (1927).
109. Piloty, *Ber.*, **31**, 452 (1898); Piloty and Stock, *ibid.*, **35**, 3093 (1902); Ponzio, *Chem. Zentr.*, **1906 I**, 1692, *Atti Accad. Sci. Torino*, **41**, (1906). *Cf.* Möhlau and Hoffman, *Ber.*, **20**, 1504 (1887).
110. Kaufman and Röver, *Fette u. Seifen*, **37**, 103 (1940); Mitchell and Carson, *J. Chem. Soc.*, **1936**, 1005; Rheinboldt and Dewald, *Ann.*, **455**, 300 (1927); **460**, 305 (1928).
111. Wuyts and Koeck, *Bull. soc. chim., Belg.* **41**, 196 (1932).
112. Claisen *et al.*, *Ber.*, **22**, 526 (1889); **20**, 656, 2194 (1887); *Ann.*, **274**, 95 (1893); Ponzio and Gaspari, *J. prakt. Chem.*, (2) **58**, 392 (1898); *Gazz. chim. ital.*, **29 I**, 471 (1899); Semper and Lichtenstadt; *Ber.*, **51**, 928 (1918).
113. Meyer and Züblin, *Ber.*, **11**, 322 (1878). *Cf.* Ceresole, *ibid.*, **15**, 1874 (1882); Ponzio and Prandi, *J. prakt. Chem.*, (2) **58**, 401 (1898).
114. Manasse, *Ber.*, **21**, 2176 (1888).
115. Shaw, *J. Chem. Soc.*, **1937**, 300.
116. Ponzio *et al.*, *Gazz. chim. ital.*, **56**, 705, 709 (1926); **57**, 633 (1927); **60**, 886 (1930); **63**, 159 (1933).
117. Gandini and Costanza, *Gazz. chim. ital.*, **67**, 104 (1937).

118. Alexander, *Proc. Roy. Soc. (London).* (A) **179**, 470 (1942).
119. Brady, *J. Chem. Soc.*, **1931**, 105; *Science Progress*, **29**, 484 (1935).
120. Hantzach, *Ber.*, **24**, 4018 (1891).
121. Dollfus, *ibid.*, **25**, 1910, 1913 (1892). *Cf.* Dunstan and Dymond, *J. Chem. Soc.*, **65**, 213, 218, 225, 227 (1894).
122. Vermillion *et al.*, *J. Org. Chem.*, **5**, 68, 75 (1940); **6**, 507 (1941).
123. Georghin *et al.*, *Bull. soc. chim.*, (4) **41**, 50 (1927); (4) **49**, 120 (1931); *Ann. sci. univ. Jassy*, **16**, 389 (1931); (I) **26**, 575 (1940); *J. prakt. Chem.*, (2) **128**, 239 (1930); (2) **130**, 71 (1931).
124. Janny, *Ber.*, **16**, 170 (1883); Goldschmidt and Zanoli, *ibid.*, **25**, 2594 (1892); Dunstan and Goulding, *J. Chem. Soc.*, **71**, 573 (1897); **79**, 628 (1901).
125. Brady *et al.*, *J. Chem. Soc.*, **1926**, 2386.
126. Ramart-Lucas *et al.*, *Compt. rend.*, **185**, 561, 718 (1927); **195**, 959 (1932); **198**, 97, 267 (1934); **201**, 1387 (1935); *Bull. soc. chim.*, (5) **1**, 119 (1934); (5) **5**, 987 (1938).
127. Lindemann and Tschang, *Ber.*, **60 B**, 1725 (1927).
128. Brady and Grayson, *J. Chem. Soc.*, **1933**, 1037.
129. Rheinboldt *et al.*, *Ann.*, **451**, 161, 273 (1927).
130. Worstall, *Am. Chem. J.*, **20**, 664 (1898).
131. Delépine, *Compt. rend.*, **133**, 876 (1901); *Bull. soc. chim.*, (3) **27**, 7 (1902); Rathke, *Ann.*, **161**, 152 (1872).
132. Backer, *Rec. trav. chim.*, **49**, 1054 (1930).
133. Delépine, *Compt. rend.*, **133**, 877 (1901); *Bull. soc. chim.*, (3) **27**, 10 (1902); Schroeber, *Ann.*, **418**, 161 (1919); Klaver, *Rec. trav. chim.*, **54**, 208 (1935).
134. Krekeler, *Ber.*, **19**, 2625 (1886).
135. Armstrong and Lowry, *J. Chem. Soc.*, **81**, 1444 (1902); Bredt *et al.*, *Ber.*, **35**, 1290 (1902); Wedekind, *Chem. Ztg.*, **36**, 658 (1913); Wedekind *et al.*, *Ber.*, **56**, 640 (1923); Grahm, *J. Chem. Soc.*, **101**, 746 (1912); Lipp and Lausberg, *Ann.*, **436**, 274 (1924); Burgess and Lowry, *J. Chem. Soc.*, **127**, 279 (1925); Loudon, *ibid.*, **1933** 823; Lipp and Knapp, *Ber.*, **73 B**, 915 (1940).
136. Franchimont, *Compt. rend.*, **92**, 1055 (1881); *Rec. trav. chim.*, **7**, 26 (1888); Hemilian, *Ann.*, **176**, 2 (1875); Buckton and Hofmann, *ibid.*, **100**, 152 (1857); Backer and DeBoer, *Rec. trav. chim.*, **43**, 297 (1924); Peski, *ibid.*, **40**, 736 (1921); Backer and Toxopeus, *ibid.*, **45**, 890 (1926); DeVarda, *Gazz. chim. ital.*, **18**, 91 (1888); Haymann, *Monatsh.*, **9**, 1064 (1888); Ludwig, *ibid.*, **9**, 666 (1888).
137. Dupont and Labaune, *C. A.*, **7**, 2188 (1913).
138. Buckton and Hofmann, *Ann.*, **100**, 133 (1856); Kipping, *J. Chem. Soc.*, **1931**, 222, Bucker and Klaassens, *Rec. trav. chim.*, **49**, 1107 (1930); Bagnall, *J. Chem. Soc.*, **75**, 278 (1899).
139. Krajčinović, *Ber.*, **59 B**, 2117 (1926).
140. Krajčinović, *ibid.*, **62 B**, 579 (1929).
141. Krajčinović, *ibid.*, **63 B**, 2276 (1930).
142. Andreasch, *Monatsh.*, **7**, 159, 171 (1886).
143. Naik and Amin, *J. Indian Chem. Soc.*, **5**, 579 (1928).
144. Backer and van der Zanden, *Rec. trav. chim.*, **49**, 735 (1930).
145. Luter *et al.*, *J. Am. Chem. Soc.*, **63**, 978 1954 (1941).
146. Quilico *et al.*, *Atti. accad. Lincei.*, (6) **7**, 141, 1050 (1928); *C.A.* **23**, 1628 (1929).
147. Lowig and Weidmann, *Ann.*, **47**, 153 (1839); **49**, 329 (1840); Kopp, *ibid.*, **35**, 346 (1840); Dugnet, *Rec. trav. chim.*, **21**, 77 (1902); Claus, *Ber.*, **5**, 660 (1872); **8**, 532 (1875); Grabowski, *Ann.*, **175**, 344 (1875); Vivian and Reid, *J. Am. Chem. Soc.*, **57**, 2559 (1935); Levene and Mikeska, *J. Biol. Chem.*, **63**, 85 (1925); **65**, 515 (1925); **59**, 473 (1924); Mylius, *Ber.*, **5**, 978 (1872); Pauly, *ibid.*, **10**, 942 (1877); Wagner and Reid, *J. Am. Chem. Soc.*, **53**, 3411 (1931); Erdmann and Gerathewahl, *J. prakt. Chem.*, (1) **34**, 447 (1845); Hofmann, *Ann.*, **69**, 227 (1849); Medlock, *ibid.*, **69**, 224 (1849); Pelouze and Cahours, *ibid.*, **127**, 192 (1863).
148. Noller and Gordon, *J. Am. Chem. Soc.*, **55**, 1090 (1933); McBain and Williams, *ibid.*, **55**, 2250 (1933).
149. Guareschi, *Ber.*, **12**, 682 (1879); *Ann.*, **222**, 302 (1884).
150. Muspratt, *Ann.*, **65**, 251 (1848); Medlock, *ibid.*, **69**, 224 (1849); Bogert, *J. Am. Chem. Soc.*, **25**, 289 (1903); Hunter and Sorenson, *ibid.*, **54**, 3365 (1932).
151. Johnson and Sprague, *J. Am. Chem. Soc.*, **58**, 1348 (1936); **59**, 1837, 2439 (1937).
152. Graebe, *Ann.*, **146**, 37 (1868); Strecker, *ibid.*, **148**, 90 (1868); Bender, *ibid.*, **148**, 96 (1868); Collman, *ibid.*, **148**, 101 (1868); Hemilian, *Ann.*, **168**, 146 (1873); Stuffer, *Ber.*, **23**, 3228 (1890); Duguet, *Bull. acad. roy. Belg.*, **1906**, 87; Zuffanti, *J. Amer. Chem. Soc.*, **62**, 1044 (1940); Latimer and Bost, *J. Org. Chem.*, **5**, 24 (1940); Wagner and Reid, *J. Am. Chem. Soc.*, **53**, 3411 (1931).
153. Reed and Tartar, *J. Am. Chem. Soc.*, **57**, 570 (1935); Pilat and Turkiewicz, *Ber.*, **72 B**, 1527 (1939).
154. Collmann, *Ann.*, **148**, 107 (1868).

155. Bender, *Zeit. Chem.*, **1870**, 162; Kriwaxin, *ibid.*, **1871**, 267; Luter *et al.*, *J. Am. Chem. Soc.*, **60**, 538 (1938).
156. Parkes and Tinsley, *J. Chem. Soc.*, **1934**, 1861.
157. Kostsova, *J. Gem. Chem.*, *(U.S.S.R.)*, **11**, 63 (1941); Bõhler, *Ann.*, **154**, 50 (1869); Mohr, *ibid.*, **221**, 216 (1883); Fromm and De Seixas Palma, *Ber.*, **39**, 3312 (1906); Johnson and Ambler, *J. Am. Chem. Soc.*, **36**, 381 (1914).
158. Fromm and De Seixas Palma, *l.c.*
159. Baeyer and Villiger, *Ber.*, **36**, 2793 (1903).
160. Strecker, *Ann.*, **148**, 90 (1868); Stillich, *J. prakt. Chem.*, (2) **73**, 538 (1906); Hemilian, *Ann.*, **176**, 9 (1875); Bitto, *Ber.*, **30**, 1642 (1897); Rosenthal, *Ann.*, **233**, 15 (1886); Backer and van Mels, *Rec. trav. chim.*, **49**, 177 (1930).
161. Backer and van Mels, *Rec. trav. chim.*, **49**, 363 (1930).
162. Bougault and Mouchel-La-Fosse, *Compt. rend.*, **156**, 396 (1913); Credner, *Zeit Chem.*, **1870**, 77; Hagglund and Ringbom, *Z. anorg. allgem. Chem.*, **150**, 231 (1926).
163. Backer, *Rec. trav. chim.*, **48**, 949 (1929).
164. Schroeter, *Ber.*, **31**, 2189 (1898); *Ann.*, **303**, 114 (1898); **418**, 183 (1919); Muthmann, *Ber.*, **31**, 1880 (1898).
165. Demars, *Bull. sci. pharmacol.*, **29**, 425 (1922).
166. Bender, *Ann.*, **148**, 96 (1868); Kohler, *Am. Chem. J.*, **19**, 731 (1897); James, *J. Chem. Soc.*, **43**, 44 (1883); Autenrieth and Rudolph, *Ber.*, **34**, 3473 (1901).
167. Monari, *Ber.*, **18**, 1349 (1885); Clutterbuck and Cohen, *J. Chem. Soc.*, **121**, 120 (1922).
168. Monari, *l.c.*, Clutterbuck and Cohen, *l.c.;* Stone, *J. Am. Chem. Soc.*, **58**, 488 (1936); **62**, 571, 572 (1940).
169. Pope and Kipping, *J. Chem. Soc.*, **1930**, 2591.
170. Backer, *Rec. trav. chim.*, **48**, 571 (1929).
171. Rathke, *Ann.*, **167**, 219 (1873); Backer and Klaassens, *Rec. trav. chim.*, **49**, 1107 (1930).
172. Rumpf, *Bull. soc. chim.*, (5) **5**, 871 (1938).
173. Schiff, *Compt. rend.*, **64**, 182 (1866); Hantzsch and Osswald, *Ber.*, **33**, 308 (1900); Durrschnabel and Weil, *ibid.*, **38**, 3495 (1906).
174. Baeyer and Villiger, *Ber.*, **35**, 3016 (1902); Mothurf, *ibid.*, **37**, 3158 (1904).
175. Hass *et al.*, *Ind. Eng. Chem.*, **29**, 1335 (1937); Kharasch and Read, *J. Am. Chem. Soc.*, **61**, 3089 (1939); Schumacher and Stauff, *Die Chemie*, **55**, No. **45/46**, 341 (1942); Stauff, *Z. Elektrochem.*, **48**, 550 (1942); Tinker and Fox, *U.S. patent* 2,174,507 (1939);Reed, *U.S. patent* 2,263,312 (1941); Richmond, *U.S. patent* 2,174,505 (1939); Fox, *U.S. patent* 2,174,509 (1939).
176. Herold *et al.*, *U.S. patent* 2,352,097 (1944); Reed, *U.S. patent* 2,174,492 (1939).
177. Ross, *U.S. patent* 2,420,383 (1947); Fox, *U.S. patent* 2,321,022 (1943).
178. McQueen, *U.S. patent* 2,212,995. *C.A.* **35**, 465 (1941).
179. Kharasch *et al.*, *J. Am. Chem. Soc.*, **62**, 2393 (1940); **61**, 3089 (1939); *U.S. patent* 2,383,319 (1945).
180. Marvel *et al.*, *J. Am. Chem., Soc.*, **51**, 1272 (1929).
181. Rosenheim and Sarow, *Ber.*, **38**, 1302 (1905).
182. Magnus, *Ann.*, **27**, 367 (1833); Müller, *Ber.*, **6**, 1031 (1873).
183. Hübner, *Ann.*, **223**, 198 (1884).
184. Staudinger and Pfenninger, *Ber.*, **49**, 1950 (1916).
185. Darmstädter, *Ann.*, **148**, 126 (1868).
186. Étard, *Compt. rend.*, **88**, 649 (1879); v. Pechmann and Manck, *Ber.*, **28**, 2374 (1895); Backer and Mulder, *Rec. trav. chim.*, **51**, 769 (1932); Délepine and Demars, *Bull Sci. Pharmacol.*, **29**, 14 (1922).
187. Nottbohm, *Ann.*, **412**, 49 (1916).
188. Battagay and Krebs, *Compt. rend.*, **206**, 1262 (1938); Bruson and Eastes, *U.S. patent* 2,142,934 (1939); Douglas and Johnson, *J. Am. Chem. Soc.*, **60**, 1486 (1938); **61**, 2548 (1939); Johnson and Sprague, *ibid.*, **58**, 1348 (1936); **59**, 1837, 2439 (1937); *Science*, **83**, 528 (1936); Johnson, *U.S. patents* 2,146,744; 2,147,346; 2,174,856 (1939).
189. Wagner and Reid, *J. Am. Chem. Soc.*, **53**, 3411 (1931).
190. Königs, *Ber.*, **7**, 1163 (1874); Kohler, *Am. Chem. J.*, **19**, 731 (1891).
191. Hunter and Sorensen, *J. Am. Chem. Soc.*, **54**, 3364 (1932).
192. Mandel and Neuberg, *Biochem. Z.*, **71**, 180 (1915).
193. Rumpf, *Bull. soc. chim.*, (5) **5**, 871 (1938); Kohler, *Am. Chem. J.*, **20**, 692 (1898); Marvel *et al.*, *J. Am. Chem. Soc.*, **49**, 1833 (1927); *Organic Syntheses* **10**, 98 (1930).
194. Hausmann, *Germ. Patent* 589,948 (1934).
195. v. Pechmann and Manck, *Ber.*, **28**, 2374 (1895); Pechmann, *ibid.*, **29**, 2161 (1896).
196. Raschig, *Schwefel und Stickstoff-Studien.* p. 242 (1924); *Germ. patent* 165,807; Shearing and Smiles, *J. Chem. Soc.*, **1937**, 1348.
197. Otto and Rössing, *Ber.*, **18**, 2493 (1885).
198. Otto and Rössing, *ibid.*, **19**, 1225 (1886).

199. D'Ouville and Connor, *J. Am. Chem. Soc.*, **60**, 34 (1938); Jensen and Lundquist, *Dansk. Tids. Farm.*, **14**, 129 (1940); Pomerantz and Connor, *J. Am. Chem. Soc.*, **61**, 3386 (1939).
200. Schneider, *Ann.*, **386**, 344 (1912).
201. Schneider, *ibid.*, **375**, 225 (1910); Schneider and Kauffmann, *ibid.*, **392**, 7 (1912); Mylius, *Ber.*, **49**, 1100 (1916).
202. Gabriel and Colmann, *Ber.*, **44**, 3628 (1911).
203. Fromm and Seibert, *ibid.*, **55 B**, 1014 (1922); Ufer, *Germ. Patent* 635,396; *C. A.*, **31**, 112 (1937).
204. Stuffer, *Ber.*, **23**, 1414 (1890).
205. Tröger *et al.*, *J. prakt. Chem.*, (2) **55**, 398 (1897); (2) **87**, 289 (1913); (2) **111**, 176,193 (1925); (2) **112**, 243 (1926); Otto and Otto, *ibid.*, (2) **36**, 401 (1887).
206. Otto and Tröger, *Ber.*, **25**, 2423 (1892); Otto and Otto, *J. prakt. Chem.*, (2) **36**, 417 (1887).
207. Otto, *ibid.*, **22**, 1967 (1889).
208. Michael and Comey, *Am. Chem. J.*, **5**, 116 (1883); Ashley and Shriner, *J. Am. Chem. Soc.*, **54**, 4410 (1932); *Germ. patent* 646,630; *Brit. patent* 415,877.
209. Frerichs, *Arch. Pharm.*, **237**, 289 (1899); Tröger *et al*, *J. prakt. Chem.*, (2) **71**, 201 (1905); *Arch. Pharm.*, **253**, 214 (1915); D'Ouville and Connor, *J. Am. Chem. Soc.*, **60**, 34 (1938).
210. Tröger *et al.*, *J. prakt. Chem.*, (2) **71**, 201,236 (1905).
211. Otto, *Ber.*, **19**, 1835 (1886).
212. Autenrieth, *Ann.*, **259**, 336 (1890).
213. Kohler and MacDonald, *Am. Chem. J.*, **22**, 219 (1899).
214. Meyer, *J. prakt. Chem.*, (2) **63**, 167 (1901); Kohler and Reimer, *Am. Chem. J.*, **31**, 163 (1904).
215. Bruin, *Verslag Akad.* Wetenschappen, **23**, 445 (1914); *C.A.* **9**, 623 (1915); Eigenberger, *J. prakt. chem.*, (2) **127**, 307 (1930); (2) **129**, 312 (1931); (2) **131**, 289 (1931); Backer and Bottema, *Rec. trav. chim.*, **51**, 294 (1932); Backer and Strating, *ibid.*, **53**, 525 (1934); Böeseken and van Zuydewijn, *Proc. Acad. Sci. Amsterdam*, **37**, 760 (1934); *C.A.*, **29**, 2145 (1935); van Zuydewijn and Böeseken, *Rec. trav. chim.*, **53**, 673 (1934); Backer and Strating, *ibid.*, **54**, 170 (1935); Sorokin and Puzitzkii, *Sintet. Kauchuk*, No. 6, 12 (1933); *C.A.* **28**, 3339 (1934); Staudinger, *French patent* 698,857; *C.A.* **25**, 3360 (1931); van Zuydewijn, *Rec. trav. chim.*, **56**, 1047 (1937); **57**, 445 (1938); Backer *et al*, *ibid.*, **54**, 538 (1935); **56**, 1069 (1937); **58**, 778 (1939).
216. Reuterskiöld, *J. prakt. Chem.*, (2) **129**, 121 (1931).
217. D'Ouville and Connor, *J. Am. Chem. Soc.*, **60**, 34 (1938); Jensen and Lundquist, *Dansk. Tids. Farm.*, **14**, 129 (1940).
218. Stuffer, *Ber.*, **23**, 3232 (1890); Otto and Damkohler, *J. prakt. Chem.*, (2) **30**, 171, 321 (1884).
219. Baumann and Walter, *Ber.*, **26**, 1124 (1893).
220. Fenton and Ingold, *J. Chem. Soc.*, **1930**, 705.
221. Tröger and Buddle, *J. prakt. Chem.*, (2) **66**, 130 (1902).
222. Walter, *Ber.*, **27**, 3046 (1894).
223. Tröger *et al.*, *J. prakt. Chem.*, (2) **104**, 335 (1922); (2) **114**, 349 (1926); (2) **112**, 243 (1926).
224. Fromm, *Ann.*, **253**, 141 (1889); Baumann, *Ber.*, **19**, 2811 (1886); Stuffer, *ibid.*, **23**, 3226 (1890).
225. Stutz and Shriner, *J. Am. Chem. Soc.*, **55**, 1242 (1933); Shriner *et al.*, *ibid.*, **52**, 2068 (1930).
226. Bischoff, *Ber.*, **30**, 487 (1897).
227. Gibson, *J. Chem. Soc.*, **1931**, 2637; *ibid.*, **1932**, 1819; **1933**, 306; Kipping, *ibid.*, **1935**, 18; Gibson, *J. Am. Chem. Soc.*, **55**, 2611 (1933).
228. Tröger and Kroseberg, *J. prakt. Chem.*, (2) **87**, 67 (1913).
229. Tröger *et al.*, *ibid.*, (2) **87**, 289 (1913); (2) **111**, 176 (1925).
230. Worstall, *Am. Chem. J.*, **20**, 202 (1898); Hopkins, *U.S. patent* 1,588,027 (1926).
231. Pictet and Genequand, *Ber.*, **36**, 2215 (1903).
232. Berl and Smith, *ibid.*, **41**, 1840 (1908).
233. Bredt, *ibid.*, **14**, 1780 (1881); **15**, 2318 (1882).
234. Pictet and Khotinsky, *ibid.*, **40**, 1163 (1907).
235. Steinkopf and Supan, *ibid.*, **43**, 3245 (1910).
236. Houben and Hauffmann, *ibid.*, **46**, 2834 (1913).
237. Wislicenus and Endres, *ibid.*, **35**, 1755 (1902).
238. Black and Babers, *Organic Syntheses*, **19**, 73 (1931).
239. Wislicenus and Wren, *Ber.*, **38**, 502 (1905).
240. Conrad *et al.*, *Ann.*, **209**, 211 (1881); Curtiss, *Am. Chem. J.* **33**, 603 (1905); **35**, 477 (1906); Curtiss and Kosatlek, *J. Am. Chem. Soc.*, **33**, 962 (1911); Gilman, *Organic Syntheses*, Coll. vol. I, 261 (1932); Gilman and Johnson, *J. Am. Chem. Soc.*, **50**, 3341 (1928); Schmidt and Widman, *Ber.*, **42**, 1886 (1909).
241. Urbanski and Slon, *Compt. rend.*, **203**, 620 (1936); **204**, 870 (1937).
242. *Cf.* Meyer, *Ber.*, **24**, 4244 (1891); Russanow, *ibid.*, **25**, 2635 (1892).
243. Lucas, *Ber.*, **32**, 601, 3179 (1899).
244. *Cf.* Gabriel, *ibid.*, **38**, 1692 (1905).
245. Hantzsch and Kissel, *ibid.*, **32**, 3137 (1899).
246. Pritzel and Adkins, *J. Am. Chem. Soc.*, **53**, 234 (1931).

247. Kaufler and Pomeranz, *Ak. Math. Nat. KI*, **110** II, (1901); Walden, *Ber.*, **40**, 3216, 4301 (1907).
248. Ray and Neogi, *Proced. Chem. Soc.*, **29**, 259 (1906); *Chem. Zentr.*, **1907** I, 235.
249. Kohler and Drake, *J. Am. Chem. Soc.*, **45**, 1281 (1923).
250. Wieland and Rahn, *Ber.*, **54**, 1774 (1921).
251. Wieland and Rahn, *l.c.*, Wieland and Reindal, *ibid.*, **54**, 1775 (1921).
252. Biltz, *Ber.*, **35**, 1529 (1902); Burrows and Hunter, *J. Chem. Soc.*, **1932**, 1357.
253. Wieland and Blumich, *Ann.*, **424**, 71 (1921); *Chem. Zentr.*, **1921** III, 1245.
254. Schmidt, *Ber.*, **34**, 619 (1901).
255. Wieland and Stenzel, *ibid.*, **40**, 4828 (1907); *Ann.*, **360**, 299 (1908); Michael and Carlson, *J. Am. Chem. Soc.*, **57**, 1268 (1935); **61**, 1955 (1939); *J. Org. Chem.*, **4**, 169 (1939).
256. Gabriel, *Ber.*, **18**, 2438 (1885).
257. Meisenheimer, *Ann.*, **330**, 147 (1904).
258. Wieland *et al.*, *Chem Zentr.*, **1921** III, 1245; *Ann.*, **424**, 71 (1921); Schmidt, *Ber.*, **34**, 619 (1901).
259. Wieland and Blumich, *Ann.*, **424**, 71 (1921); Wieland *et al.*, **340**, 63 (1905).
260. Wieland, *Ber.*, **36**, 2558 (1903); *Ann.*, **328**, 154 (1903); Angeli, *Gazz. chim. ital.*, **23 II**, 124 (1893); **25 II**, 188 (1895); Schmidt, *Ber.*, **35**, 2323 (1902); Schmidt and Austin, *ibid.*, **35**, 3721 (1902); Sommer, *ibid.*, **28**, 1328 (1895); **29**, 356 (1896).
261. Wieland and Blumich, *Ann.*, **429**, 71 (1921), *Chem. Zentr.*, **1921**, III, 1244.
262. Wieland, *Ann.*, **328**, 154 (1903); **329**, 225 (1903); *Ber.*, **36**, 3020 (1903).
263. Ponzio, *Gazz. chim. ital.*, **22** I, 171 (1897); **39** I, 324 (1909); *J. prakt. Chem.*, (2) **62**, 543 (1900).
264. Ponzio, *Gazz. chim. ital.*, **22** I, 171 (1897); **39** I, 324 (1909); **31** I, 133, 262 (1901); Ponzio and de Gaspari, *ibid.*, **28** II, 269 (1898).
265. Thiele and Lachmann, *Ann.*, **288**, 1 (1895).
266. Lachmann and Thiele, *Ber.*, **27**, 1519 (1894).
267. Desvergnes, *Rev. chim. ind.*, **38**, 265 (1929); *Chem. Zentr.* **1930** I, 820.
268. Decker, *Ber.*, **38**, 1275 (1905).
269. Moureu, *Compt. rend.*, **132**, 837 (1901); Oddo, *Atti accad. Lincei*, (5) **13** II, 220 (1904); Bewad, *Ber.*, **21**, R481 (1888); **22**, R250 (1889); **40**, 3065 (1907); Pickard and Kenyon, *Proc. Chem. Soc.*, **23**, 153 (1907); *Chem. Zentr.*, **1907** II, 1063; *Cf.* Wieland, *Ber.*, **36**, 2315 (1903); Hepworth, *J. Chem. Soc.*, **117**, 1004 (1920).
270. Preibisch, *J. prakt. Chem.*, (2) **8**, 310 (1874); Steinkopf, *Ber.*, **41**, 4457 (1908); Steinkopf and Kirchhoff, *ibid.*, **42**, 3438 (1909); Wahl, *Bull. soc. chim.*, (4) **5**, 180 (1909); Zerewitinoff, *Ber.*, **43**, 3590 (1911); Gilman and McCracken, *Bi. Z* **202**, 439 (1928); *Chem. Zentr.*, **1929** I, 2407.
271. Kurssanow and Ssoloikow, *Shurn.* Ser. A. **5**, (67), 1487 (1935); *Chem. Zentr.*, **1936** II, 2351.
272. v. Braum and Sobecki, *Ber.*, **44**, 2533 (1911); v. Braum and Kruber, *ibid.*, **45**, 394 (1912).
273. Bamberger and Weiler, *J. prakt. Chem.*, (2) **58**, 333 (1898).
274. Hantzsch and Schultze, *Ber.*, **29**, 2252 (1896).
275. Backer and Toxopeus, *Rec. trav. chim.*, **45**, 890 (1926).
276. Backer and Dubsky, *ibid.*, **39**, 694 (1920).
277. Backer and Mulder, *ibid.*, **62**, 4653 (1943).
278. Baumstark, *Ann.*, **140**, 82 (1866).
279. Schroeter, *ibid.*, **418**, 161 (1919).
280. Rathka, *ibid.*, **161**, 149 (1872).
281. *German patent* 69,948.
282. *German patent* 67,434.
283. *German patent* 55,007.
284. Ludwig, *Ber.*, **9**, 592 (1882); Harries; *Ann.* **330**, 188 (1904); Knoevenagel, *Ber.*, **37**, 4038 (1904).
285. Messel, *Ann.*, **157**, 15 (1871).
286. Rosenheim and Liebknecht, *Ber.*, **31**, 408 (1898); Rosenheim and Sarow, *ibid.*, **38**, 1301 (1905); Fox, *Z. physiol. Chem.*, **41**, 458 (1902); Szarvasy, *Ber.*, **30**, 1836 (1897).
287. Grignard, *Ann. chim.*, (7) **24**, 457 (1901); Rosenheim and Singer, *Ber.*, **37**, 2152 (1904); Borsche and Lange, *ibid.*, **38**, 2766 (1905); Houben and Doescher, *ibid.*, **39**, 3503 (1906).
288. Oddo, *Atti accad. Lincei*, (5) **14**, I 169 (1905).
289. Raschig, *Ber.*, **59**, 859 (1926); Bazlen, *ibid.*, **60**, 1470 (1927); Schumann *et al.*, *U.S. patent* 1,714,686; 1,714,687 (1929); *C.A.*, **23**, 3479 (1929).
290. Wood, *Chem. Age.*, **38**, 85 (1938).
291. Hantzsch, *Ann.*, **196**, 86 (1897);
292. Stahler and Schirm, *Ber.*, **44**, 319(1911). *Cf.* Gerhard and Chancel, *ibid.*, **20**, 3337 (1888).
293. Rathke, *Ann.* **167**, 195 (1873); Klason, *Ber.*, **20**, 2376 (1887); *German patent* 83, 124; *Ber.*, **28**, R 942 (1895).
294. Naik and Jadhav, *Quart. J. Indian Chem. Soc.*, **3**, 260 (1926).
295. Autenrieth and Koburger, *Ber.*, **36**, 3626 (1903).
296. Shriner *et al.*, *J. Am. Chem. Soc.*, **52**, 2060 (1930); Böhme, *Ber.*, **69**, 1610 (1936); Tarbell and Weaver, *J. Am. Chem. Soc.*, **63**, 2941 (1941); Rheinboldt and Giesbrecht, *ibid.*, **68**,

973 (1946); Buckley *et al.*, *J. Chem. Soc.*, **1947**, 1515, Klenk *et al.*, *J. Am. Chem. Soc.*, **70**, 3848 (1948); Cope *et al.*, *ibid.*, **72**, 59 (1950); Overberger *et al.*, *ibid.*, **72**, 2858 (1950).

297. Meyer and Askenasy, *Ber.*, **25**, 1701 (1892); Meyer, *Ann*, **175**, 93 (1875); Lemole, *ibid.*, **175**, 146 (1875); Tscherniac, *ibid.*, **180**, 166 (1876); Meyer and Constam, *ibid.*, **214**, 329 (1882); Wieland and Sempler, *Ber.*, **29**, 2522 (1906); Meister. *ibid.*, **40**, 3446 (1907).

CHAPTER 15

ORGANO METALLIC COMPOUNDS

ORGANIC DERIVATIVES OF ALKALI METALS

The direct reaction of alkali metals with hydrocarbons is comparatively rare and is generally observed with highly phenylated compounds. Thus, potassium reacts with triphenylmethane at an elevated temperature forming potassium triphenylmethane, $(C_6H_5)_3CK$.[1] The reaction takes place readily in liquid ammonia, in which the alkalihydrocarbon compounds behave as salts and are not ammonolyzed.[2] Sodium tri-(trinitrophenyl)methane, $NaC[C_6H_2(NO_2)_3]_3$, may be prepared from the hydrocarbon and alcoholic sodium hydroxide.[3] The reaction of potassium with symmetrical tetraphenylethane results in the formation of potassium diphenylmethane.[4] The reaction can best be brought about by use of a potassium-sodium alloy, and is applicable to other polyarylethanes.

Diphenylbenzene reacts with sodium to form a disodio compound,

naphthalene and anthracene give

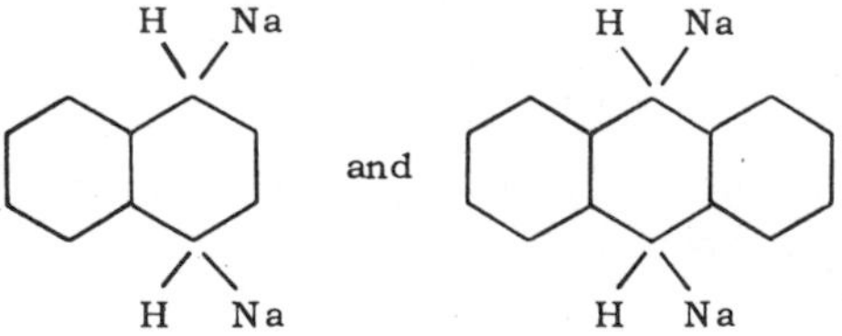

respectively.[5] The reaction of naphthalene with sodium in liquid ammonia results in the formation of 1,2,3,4-tetrasodio-1,2,3,4-tetrahydronaphthalene which is slowly ammonolyzed.[6]

Sodium can replace a hydrogen atom of *methylene groups* activated by two aromatic groups, or two unsaturated residues. Methylene groups activated by two carboxyl, cyano or carbonyl groups, or by a combination of any two of these groups, also react with sodium or sodium amide.

Acetylene combines with sodium at the melting point of the latter forming monosodium acetylide; above 210° both hydrogens in the molecule of acetylene are replaced with sodium.[7] The reaction proceeds smoothly only if the metal surface is kept free of the acetylide formed.

In the *polymerization of unsaturated* compounds to rubber-like substances with sodium, an organometallic compound is formed as an intermediate and reacts with an olefin molecule, the reaction proceeding step by step with the formation of progressively complex units.[8]

$$CH_2 = CHCH = CH_2 + KR \rightarrow RCH_2CHKCH = CH_2$$

$$\xrightarrow{CH_2 = CHCH = CH_2} CH_2 = CHCHKCH_2CH(CH_2R)CH = CH_2$$

$$\xrightarrow{CH_2 = CHCH = CH_2} CH_2 = CHCHKCH_2CH(CH = CH_2)CH_2CH(CH_2R)CH = CH_2, \text{ etc.}$$

Alkali metal derivatives of hydrocarbons may form also by the reaction of the free metal with *organic halides*. Thus, phenyl sodium results in 87% yield through the reaction of chlorbenzene with sodium suspended in toluene.[9] The phenyl sodium reacts with the toluene, however, when the reaction mixture is heated, forming benzyl sodium in 80% yield. *p*-Toluyl sodium also reacts with toluene in this manner, but *p*-toluyl lithium remains intact.[10]

A migration of the metal and a phenyl group occurs in the reaction of sodium in liquid ammonia with β-chloro-α,α,α-triphenylethane:[11]

$$(C_6H_5)_3CCH_2Cl + 2Na \rightarrow NaCl + (C_6H_5)_3CCH_2Na$$

$$\rightarrow (C_6H_5)_2CNaCH_2C_6H_5$$

A similar rearrangement is observed also in the reaction of 1,1,3-triphenylindene with sodium in ethereal suspension:[12]

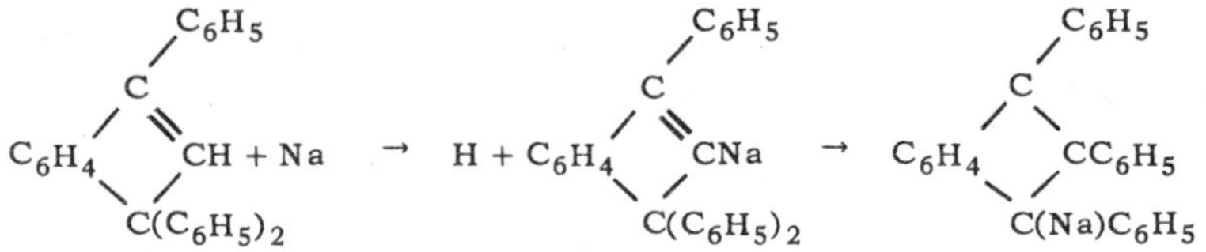

Certain *aromatic ethers* are cleaved under the action of metallic sodium yielding an organosodium compound:[13]

$$C_6H_5OC_6H_5 + 2Na \rightarrow C_6H_5Na + C_6H_5ONa$$

Sodium-potassium alloys are particularly effective in bringing about this reaction.[13] α-Naphthol ethyl ether, phenetol, as well as diphenyl ether are cleaved in this manner. Phenylisopropylpotassium has been obtained by the reaction of potassium with methyl phenylisopropyl ether:

$$C_6H_5C(CH_3)_2OCH_3 + 2K \rightarrow C_6H_5CK(CH_3)_2 + CH_3OK$$

Alkali metal derivatives of diphenylmethane have been prepared in the same manner from benzhydrol methyl ether.

Purely aliphatic ethers, including ethers derived from tertiary carbinols, are not attacked under mild conditions.[14] Reaction takes place if the C-atom attached to oxygen bears at least one phenyl group. Methyl ethers of diphenylmethylcarbinol, $(C_6H_5)_2CHCH_2OCH_3$, and diphenylethylcarbinol,

$$(C_6H_5)_2CHCH_2CH_2OCH_3$$

also undergo the reaction. Certain thio ethers are also cleaved under the influence of alkali metals:[15]

$$(C_6H_5)_3CSC_6H_5 + K_2 \rightarrow (C_6H_5)_3CK + KSC_6H_5$$

Organo sodium compounds result through the reaction of metallic sodium with organic derivatives of other metals, such as those of zinc, cadmium, mercury and lead.[16] Best results are obtained with organo mercury compounds.[244]

The metal becomes covered with a yellow incrustation in the course of the reaction. The reaction mixture is cooled to the freezing point of the sodium amalgam, and the latter is loosened by shaking and separated by filtration under a nitrogen atmosphere.

The reaction must be carried out under strictly anhydrous conditions. The nitrogen should be purified by first passing it over heated copper, then successively through aqueous sodium hydroxide, anhydrous calcium chloride, phosphorus pentoxide, and an ethereal solution of triphenylmethyl. The last named indicates the complete absence of moisture and oxygen in the gas if it retains its intensely red color.

Methyl, ethyl, *n*-propyl, *n*-octyl and phenyl compounds have been prepared successfully by this method. Methyl sodium explodes when exposed to air. Ethyl sodium is spontaneously inflammable in air, and is instantly decomposed by water and ammonia; it is a highly reactive body and enters in reaction with all classes of organic compounds except paraffins.

Organo alkali metal compounds may be readily estimated by causing them to react with an excess of butyl bromide, and determining the alkali metal bromide formed by the Volhard method.[245] The solution of the alkali metal compound is shaken with butyl bromide, the mixture is extracted with water, the aqueous layer is separated, neutralized and the alkali metal bromide in solution is then determined.

Properties and Reactions of Organosodium Compounds

Sodium alkyls and aryls are generally colorless compounds insoluble in common organic solvents. Their solution in zinc alkyls conducts the electric current.[17] Potassium compounds are similar to the sodium derivatives.

Compounds in which the carbon atom combined with sodium is attached to an aromatic group, or to an equivalent conjugated group, are colored and behave as electrolytes in many organic solvents.

Organo sodium compounds and other organo alkali metal compounds combine rapidly with atmospheric oxygen and ignite spontaneously or burn quietly. They are rapidly decomposed by water into a hydrocarbon and an alkali metal hydroxide. They combine with carbon dioxide forming the alkali metal salts of a carboxylic acid:

$$RMe + CO_2 \rightarrow RCOOMe$$

Alkali metal compounds of the type of sodio triarylmethanes react with carbonyl and carboxyl compounds. Thus, sodiotriphenylmethane reacting with formaldehyde yields the sodio derivative of triphenylmethyl carbinol; with benzaldehyde and with furfural phenyltriphenylmethyl carbinol and furfuryl triphenylmethyl carbinol derivatives result, and with methyl benzoate, phenyl triphenylmethyl ketone, $C_6H_5COC(C_6H_5)_3$ is obtained. Benzylsodium, $C_6H_5CH_2Na$, reacts with formaldehyde to form the sodio derivative of o-tolylmethyl alcohol.[246] Compounds capable of reacting in the enolic form exchange one hydrogen atom for sodium. Alkyl halides also react with this type of sodio derivatives, methyl iodide giving with sodio triphenylmethane, triphenylethane, and brombenzene giving tetraphenylmethane.[18]

Alkyl iodides and bromides reacting with sodium carbide generally yield symmetrically substituted acetylenes:

$$NaC \vdots CNa + 2RI \rightarrow RC \vdots CR + 2NaI$$

Isobutyl iodide gives only acetylene and isobutylene, while bromobenzene fails to react even at 180°. Alkyl sulfates may be employed instead of the halides, and the reaction may be carried out in liquid ammonia. Dialkyl acetylenes result in ammonia solution when medium molecular weight alkyl halides and halides soluble in liquid ammonia are employed in the reaction, other halides yielding largely mono alkyl acetylenes.[19]

Mono alkyl acetylenes are obtained from the reaction of normal alkyl halides with monosodium acetylene, the reaction proceeding in a satisfactory manner when highly purified materials are used. The reaction has been carried out successfully with alkyl iodides up to $C_{16}H_{33}I$. Dialkyl acetylenes may form as a by-product in the process. The reaction cannot be successfully carried out with unsaturated halides and with aromatic halides.[20]. The reaction of branched chain halides with sodium acetylide generally results in the formation of olefins:

$$HC \equiv CNa + RR'CHCH_2X \rightarrow CH \equiv CH + NaX + RR'C = CH_2$$

Acetylenic ketones are obtained through the reaction of acid halides with sodio phenylacetylene, the reaction proceeding best with acid bromides:

$$C_6H_5C \equiv CNa + BrCOR \rightarrow C_6H_5C \equiv CCOR + NaBr$$

Sodium alkylacetylides, $RC \equiv CNa$, react with trioxymethylene to form acetylenic alcohols of the type $RC \equiv CCH_2OH$. Other aldehydes react to form secondary acetylenic alcohols, $RC \equiv CCH(OH)R'$. Reaction with formic esters results in the formation of acetylenic aldehydes, $RC \equiv CCHO$. The reaction of ketones such as benzophenone and acetophenone with sodio phenylacetylene gives tertiary acetylenic alcohols of the type $C_6H_5C \vdots CC(OH)RR'$. The carbinols formed in these reactions are, of course, obtained in the form of their sodio derivatives and may be converted to the free carbinols by hydrolysis or by decomposition with acid.

Sodio phenylacetylene reacts with *p*-totyl isocyanate forming phenylpropiolic thio-*p* toluidide, $C_6H_5C \equiv CCSNHC_6H_4CH_3$. The reaction is similar with *m*-tolyl isocyanate, although the yield of the toluidide is smaller in this case.[21]

Organo Lithium Compounds

Organo lithium compounds may be obtained simply through the interaction of organic halides with metallic lithium:

$$RX + 2Li \rightarrow RLi + LiX$$

Many halides which fail to form Grignard compounds, or yield such compounds with difficulty, react with lithium to form organo lithium compounds.[22] The reaction proceeds in a more satisfactory manner than with other alkali metals because the resulting organo lithium compound reacts slowly with the organic halide. The reaction should be carried out under an atmosphere of hydrogen or other inert gas.[23] The method gives good yields, especially with the higher alkyl halides and aromatic halides.[24]

The *procedure*, with the less reactive halides, is to add 2 to 2.2 atom equivalents of lithium to a mole equivalent of the halide and to agitate the mixture for 24 hours. A few glass beads are added to the mixture to keep the surface of the metal clean. Initial cooling is not required when alkyl chlorides are used in the reaction.

In dealing with highly reactive halides, the metal is added to ether and some of the halide introduced to initiate the reaction, after which the halide is added gradually and at such a rate that the reaction mixture boils vigorously. After the addition of all the halide, the mixture is heated to boiling under reflux for ½ to 1 hour. The yields generally range between 70 and 95% of the theoretically expected quantity.

The halides must be carefully purified. It is not generally necessary to free the hydrogen of the last traces of oxygen, but it is important to avoid contact of the reaction mixture with air, moisture or carbon dioxide.

Alkyl chlorides react in a satisfactory manner, bromides giving somewhat lower yields. The yields decrease with increase in the chain length of the alkyl halide. The reaction proceeds more rapidly in ether than in benzene, although the resulting lithium alkyl reacts with ether to form lithium ethoxide:[25]

$$(C_2H_5)_2O + LiR \rightarrow C_2H_5OLi + RH + C_2H_4$$

Ethereal solutions of the lithium compound are often sufficiently stable, however, for practical purposes. Cyclohexane may also be used as a solvent, though the reaction proceeds at even slower rate in this medium than in benzene. Methyl iodide alone among alkyl iodides yields a lithium compound by this method.[22] Secondary and tertiary alkyl halides are unreactive and do not give an alkyl lithium.

All aryl halides react in a more or less satisfactory manner, the bromides giving the best results. Both benzene and ether may be used as a solvent, since lithium aryls do not react with the latter. Benzyllithium cannot be obtained by this method from benzyl halides and lithium; the compound is readily obtained by the reaction of benzyl magnesium halides with lithium.[26]

Organo lithium compounds may also be prepared by an exchange reaction from certain organo lithium compounds and organic halides:[27]

$$RX + R'Li \rightarrow RLi + R'X$$

The iodo compounds react most readily.[28] The reaction is applicable to many organic halides which fail to react directly with metallic lithium. Thus, *m*-bromobenzotrifluoride which does not react with lithium, gives the lithium derivative in excellent yield with *n*-butyllithium. 4-Bromoresorcinol and *o*-iodoanisole react readily with phenyllithium,[29] while *o*-bromoanisole reacts gradually.[30] Bromine in *meta*- and *para*-bromodimethylaniline and other similar *meta* and *para*-Brominated aromatic bases is readily replaced by lithium, as is also the halogen in halo pyridines and halo quinolines. Chlorine and fluorine are not generally replaced since they cause the activation of a hydrogen atom in the molecule and its preferential replacement with lithium; in the absence of a susceptible hydrogen atom in the molecule, chlorine or fluorine may be replaced by the metal. The halogen bound to aliphatic groups may also be replaced with lithium by means of this reaction.

In many of these reactions the organo lithium compound first formed rapidly reacts with the unconverted halide, with the formation of lithium halide and the coupling of the two organic groups. This process takes place very readily in the case of benzyl bromide and results in the formation of dibenzyl, $C_6H_5CH_2CH_2C_6H_5$. Two aromatic groups are joined with some difficulty, although the reaction proceeds well with aromatic halides in the presence of catalytic amounts of metal halides.[31]

Many organic lithium compounds may be prepared by an *exchange reaction* between butyllithium and a hydrocarbon or a hydrocarbon derivative:

$$RH + C_4H_9Li \rightarrow RLi + C_4H_{10}$$

The reaction rate depends both upon the nature of the organic compound entering in reaction with butyllithium and the solvent in which the reaction is carried out. The effect of the solvent is strikingly brought to evidence in the reaction of fluorene with butyllithium, which proceeds instantly in ether, but requires several hours' heating when carried out in benzene. The metal passes from the lighter to the heavier group in this reaction,[32] and with arylated compounds tends to combine with the carbon atom bearing the greatest number of aryl groups. Good yields of the lithium derivative are obtained with many types of compounds, 60% from phenyl ether, 57% from triphenylcarbinol, 90% from benzothiophene, 60% from 2-methoxydibenzofuran, 53-61% from phenoxathiin, 50% from phenyl-*p*-tolylmethane, and 80% from phenyl-*α*-naphthylmethane.

The ease of replacement of an aromatic hydrogen with lithium is increased by the presence in the nucleus of electronegative substituents such as a methoxy group or fluorine. Two *meta* standing substituents favor the reaction. The metal enters the *ortho* position with respect to an amino or carbinol group, while the triphenylamine group directs the metal to the *meta* position.

The reaction proceeds with difficulty with *triphenylmethane*, which has to be heated at 50-60° for several hours with the alkyl lithium; on the other hand, *bis-diphenylvinylmethane*, $[(C_6H_5)_2C{:}CH]_2CH_2$, is readily converted to the lithium derivative

$$[(C_6H_5)_2C{:}CH]_2CHLi$$

by reaction with phenyllithium. Anisole gives the ortho substituted product o-$CH_3OC_6H_4Li$, in 70% yield when heated at 100° for several hours with phenyllithium; resorcinol dimethyl ether similarly gives 2,6-dimethoxyphenyllithium in 70% yield. This latter compound is obtained with difficulty by other methods.

Heterocyclic compounds with oxygen, sulfur or nitrogen in the ring are capable of forming lithium compounds by reaction with lithium alkyls or aryls.[33] The hydrogen atom attached to a carbon atom nearest the hetero atom is replaced by the metal. Thus, *α*-furyl and 4-dibenzofuryllithium are easily obtained from furan and dibenzofuran respectively by reaction with phenyllithium.

Pyridine reacting with an alkyl lithium gives an addition compound which on heating at 70 to 100° is converted to a 2-alkylpyridine:[34]

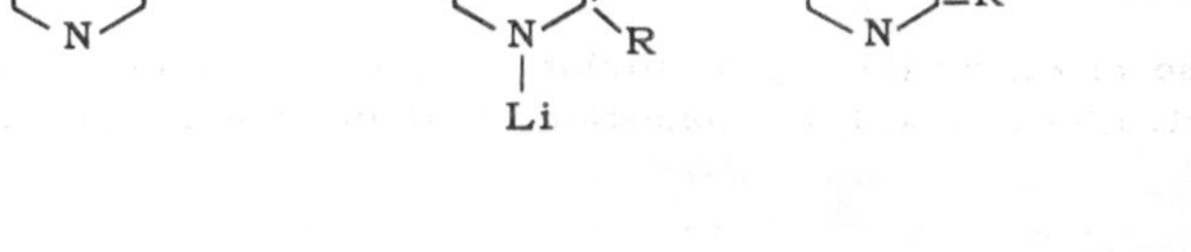

Quinoline, isoquinoline and *acridine* also give similar addition compounds with lithium alkyls; some of these compounds are partially converted to alkyl derivatives of the base on heating, while others, including the acridine derivatives, remain unchanged. Hydrolysis of the lithium addition compound results in the formation of the alkylated dihydro compound which can be dehydrogenated by boiling with nitrobenzene or silver oxide in alcohol.

An exchange reaction takes place between quinaldine and phenyl lithium:

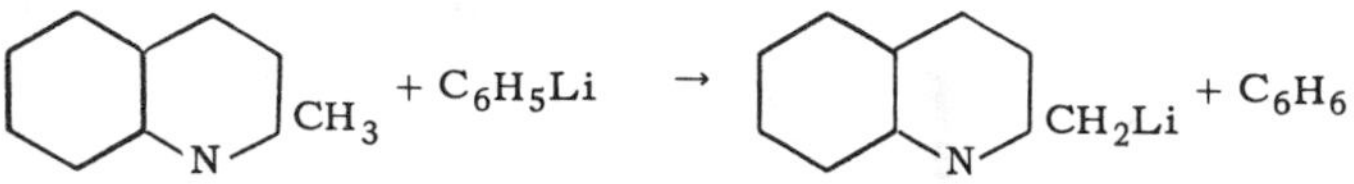

α-Picoline reacts similarly, while *lutadine* yields a dilithium derivative.[34]

The reaction of *nitriles* with phenyllithium may proceed in two directions:

$$(C_2H_5)_2CHCN + C_6H_5Li \rightleftarrows \begin{cases} (C_2H_5)_2CLiCN \\ (C_2H_5)_2CHC(:NLi)C_6H_5 \end{cases}$$

The substitution reaction is favored and the addition reaction suppressed by adding a little diethylamine or dicyclohexylamine.[35]

Lithium dialkylamines react with nitriles in ethereal solution forming the lithium derivative of the nitrile, the metal replacing an α-hydrogen atom:[36]

$$R_2CHCN + LiNR'_2 \rightarrow R_2CLiCN + HNR'_2$$

The resulting lithium nitrile may be converted to a tertiary nitrile by reaction with an alkyl halide, an allyl derivative being obtained, for example, with allyl chloride.

An atom of lithium may be introduced into the molecule of an organic compound by an exchange reaction between a metallic derivative of the organic compound and phenyllithium or a suitable alkyl lithium.[26] Thus, benzyllithium, a compound otherwise difficultly accessible, may be obtained through the interaction of benzylmagnesium chloride and phenyllithium:

$$C_6H_5CH_2MgCl + 2C_6H_5Li \rightarrow C_6H_5CH_2Li + (C_6H_5)_2Mg + LiCl$$

and *p*-tolyllithium results through the reaction of tritolylbismuth with butyllithium:[37]

$$(CH_3C_6H_4)_3Bi + 3C_4H_9Li \rightarrow 3CH_3C_6H_4Li + (C_4H_9)_3Li$$

Exchange of the halomagnesium group in organomagnesium compounds,[38] or of mercury in mercury dialkyls,[39] may also be effected by direct reaction with metallic lithium:

$$RMgX + 2Li \rightarrow RLi + LiX + Mg$$

$$(C_2H_5)_2Hg + 2Li \rightarrow 2C_2H_5Li + Hg$$

Phenyllithium may be prepared readily by this method, although the reaction has been shown to be reversible.

Alkylated lithium amines may be prepared readily through the interaction of lithium alkyls with amines:[35]

$$LiR + HN(C_2H_5)_2 \rightarrow LiN(C_2H_5)_2 + HR$$

The reaction proceeds also with other alkali metal alkyls. It should be noted that alkali metals can replace directly only one hydrogen atom in ammonia or in aromatic amines.

Many aromatic compounds give addition products with lithium, diphenyl giving, for example,

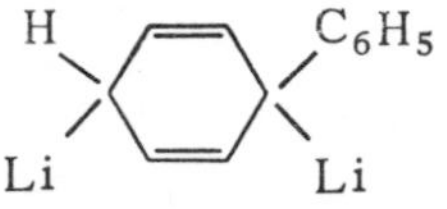

and naphthalene and anthracene giving

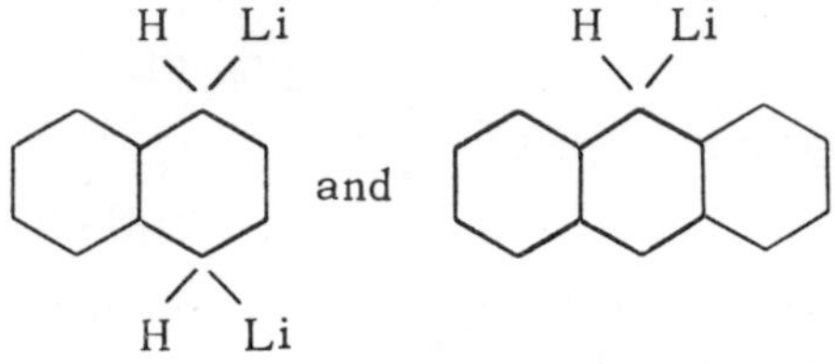

respectively.

Properties and Reactions of Organo Lithium Compounds

Alkyl and aryl lithiums are colorless liquids or low melting solids, soluble in organic solvents. In contrast with organo sodium or potassium compounds, they are quite stable and may be distilled or sublimed unchanged. They are covalent substances that show little or no electric conductivity in solution in zinc alkyls. Ethyllithium burns explosively when exposed to air.

Organo lithium compounds are the least reactive in the series of organo alkali compounds; the reactivity of compounds of other alkali metals increases in the order:[40 50]

$$RNa < RK < RRb < RCs$$

Organo lithium compounds exhibit certain of the reactions of Grignard reagents, but possess a greater reactivity than the latter. The majority of the reactions take place instantaneously and almost quantitatively in the cold. They differ from Grignard reagents in that they are capable of adding to unsaturated aliphatic hydrocarbons which contain two conjugated double bonds. Thus, 1,1-diphenylethylene adds butyllithium according to the equation:[41]

$$(C_6H_5)_2C=CH_2 + C_4H_9Li \rightarrow (C_6H_5)_2C(Li)CH_2C_4H_9$$

Fulvenes such as

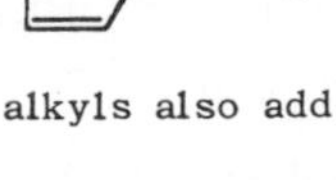

readily undergo the reaction. Lithium alkyls also add to certain hydrocarbons such as anthracene.

Organo lithium compounds react with compounds containing carbonyl groups in the manner of organo magnesium halides to form the lithium derivatives of glycols in excellent yield. Thus, reaction between dimethyl phthalate and phenyllithium[42] proceeds smoothly; the product of the reaction, after hydrolysis, is the glycol

$$C_6H_4[C(C_6H_5)_2OH]_2 .$$

The reaction with the keto alcohol $(C_6H_5)_2C(OH)CH_2COC_6H_5$ and phenyllithium proceeds at -80° and results in the formation, after hydrolysis, of

$$(C_6H_5)_2C(OH)CH_2C(OH)(C_6H_5)_2$$

in 70% yield.

Organo lithium compounds react in the normal manner of Grignard reagents with certain carbonyl compounds with which organo magnesium halides fail to react normally.[43] Thus, while methyl phthalate does not react in the normal manner with phenylmagnesium bromide, a ditertiary alcohol results, as mentioned above, through the reaction of the ester with phenyllithium. Sterically hindered carbonyl compounds, which are not acted upon by Grignard reagents, readily undergo reaction with organo lithium derivatives. In effect, it would appear that phenyllithium, for example, never fails to react with a carbonyl group.[44] Phenyllithium reacts smoothly with the carbonyl group in α,β-unsaturated ketones:[45]

$$C_6H_5CH = CHCOC_6H_5 + C_6H_5Li \rightarrow C_6H_5CH = CHC(OLi)(C_6H_5)_2$$

This is in contrast with the abnormal behavior of organo magnesium halides. Benzyl lithium, like benzyl sodium, reacts anomalously with formaldehyde, giving the lithium derivative of *o*-tolylmethyl alcohol.[246]

A difference in behavior is also observed in the reaction of phenyllithium and phenylmagnesium with benzophenoneanil, $(C_6H_5)_2C = NC_6H_5$, the former giving

$$(C_6H_5)_3CNHC_6H_5$$

while the latter

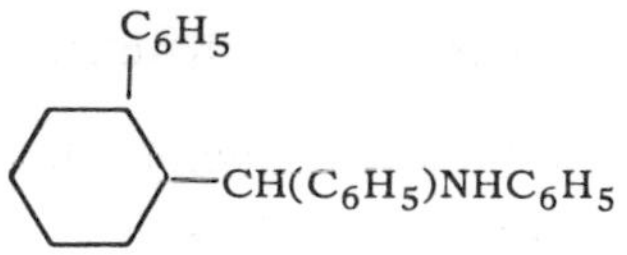

as the end product of the reaction.[46]

Under ordinary conditions of procedure, such as when the gas is bubbled through the solution of the lithium compound, the reaction of *carbon dioxide* with organo lithium compounds results in the formation of a ketone, R_2CO as the principal product, with small amounts of a tertiary alcohol, R_3COH and a carboxylic acid RCOOH. If, however, the reaction is so carried out that a high concentration of carbon dioxide prevails in the reaction mixture, the principal product is a carboxylic acid.[47] This condition holds for example, when the solution of the reagent is dropped on carbon dioxide snow. 2,4-Dimethoxy- and 2,3,6-trimethoxybenzoic acids have been obtained from the corresponding lithium compounds.[48]

All three chlorine atoms in thallium chloride may be replaced with alkyl or aryl groups by reaction with lithium alkyls or aryls.[49]

2,6-Dimethoxybenzaldehyde has been obtained in 55% yield through the reaction of 2,6-dimethoxyphenyllithium and N-methylformanilide.

Estimation of Organolithium Compounds

The amount of organolithium compound in a solution may be estimated by the method developed by Ziegler.[51] The lithium compound is decomposed by water, and the resulting alkali is titrated with standard acid.

A correction may be made for the free lithium hydroxide in the mixture by adding benzyl chloride to couple with and eliminate the alkyl lithium and titrating the residual hydroxide with standard acid.[52] An alternative procedure is to add benzylamine or *p*-toluidine to the solution of the lithium compound, and to titrate with a standard solution of alcohol in ether until the deep color of the amine complex is discharged.

ORGANIC COMPOUNDS OF SILVER, GOLD, AND PLATINUM

Phenyl silver, C_6H_5Ag, has been obtained by the reaction of silver chloride with phenylmagnesium halides under carefully regulated conditions.[53] The compound decomposes gradually even at -18°. Decomposition is complete at this temperature within a few hours even in the absence of light. Decomposition proceeds rapidly at room temperature with the evolution of thick clouds of diphenyl, and occasionally a violent explosion may take place.

Diethylgold bromide, $(C_2H_5)_2AuBr$, has been obtained through the reaction of ethylmagnesium bromide with an ethereal solution of partially dehydrated hydrobromoauric acid, $HAuBr_4{\cdot}3H_2O$, or of gold chloride,[54] the yield under the most favorable conditions being only 10 to 15% on the basis of the gold compound employed. The propyl, butyl, amyl, benzyl, phenethyl, and cyclohexyl compounds have also been prepared by this method.[55] Instead of hydrobromoauric acid, the addition compound of auric bromide or chloride with pyridine may be used.[56]

Monoalkyl gold halobromides, RAuXBr, are obtained through the reaction of bromine with dialkyl aurohalides in chloroform solution at room temperature:

$$R_2AuX + Br_2 \rightarrow RAuXBr + RBr$$

The *direct auration* of the aromatic nucleus by auric chloride is possible. The first product of the reaction is an aryl gold dichloride:[57]

$$RH + AuCl_3 \rightarrow RAuCl_2 + HCl$$

If steps are not taken to stop the reaction at this stage, the very unstable diaryl gold halides, R_2AuCl, are formed, which decompose very rapidly giving aurous chloride:

$$R_2AuCl + HCl \rightarrow RCl + RH + AuCl$$

"Pyrrole black",

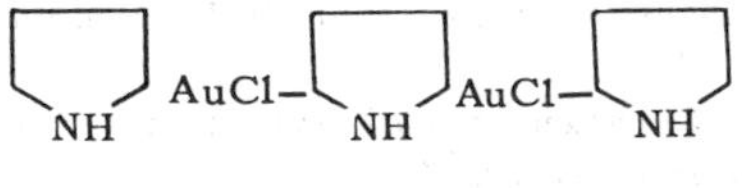

results as a precipitate on adding pyrrole to a 10% solution of gold chloride.[58]

Dialkyl gold halides are generally colorless, crystalline compounds or liquids, with a characteristic pine wood-like odor. They are fairly unstable and are decomposed by by light. They decompose on standing a few days. They are rapidly destroyed when heated above 60 to 120°.

Monoalkyl gold dihalides are even less stable than dialkyl gold halides.[59] The compounds known to date are ruby-red crystalline solids, soluble in benzene, chloroform, and carbon tetrachloride, giving red solutions. Oxygenated solvents such as ether, alcohol, and acetone, decompose these compounds rapidly giving metallic gold, aurous halide and a dialkyl gold halide.

While monoaryl gold dihalides are fairly stable, diaryl compounds are very unstable and for this reason have not been obtained in the pure form.

Trimethylplatinum iodide, $(CH_3)_3PI$, has been prepared by the action of methylmagnesium iodide on platinic chloride:[247]

$$PtCl_4 + 3CH_3MgI \rightarrow (CH_3)_3PtI + 2MgCl_2 + MgI_2$$

Methylmagnesium iodide is prepared in the smallest possible amount of ether, and the solution is diluted with five volumes of anhydrous benzene. To this is added the mixture of platinum chloride and ether with good cooling and constant agitation. Stirring is continued for an hour, then the mass is poured into ice-water. The trimethylplatinum iodide is recovered from the benzene layer by evaporation under vacuum. It is purified by crystallization from boiling benzene. An additional amount of the compound may be recovered from the aqueous layer by extraction with benzene. One hundred percent excess of the methylmagnesium iodide must be employed. Platinic chloride dissolves only partially in ether; sufficient amount of the latter should be used to convert the undissolved chloride into a syrup.

The iodide may be readily transformed to the hydroxide $(CH_3)_3PtOH$ by boiling with a suspension of freshly precipitated silver hydroxide in moist acetone. The salts of the hydroxide may be prepared by reaction with acids.

Tetramethylplatinum, $(CH_3)_4Pt$, has been prepared in 46% yield from trimethylplatinum iodide and methylsodium. Hydrogen chloride converts the compound to trimethylplatinum chloride.[248]

Hexamethyldiplatinum, $(CH_3)_3PtPt(CH_3)_3$, has been made in 60% yield by heating trimethylplatinum iodide with powdered potassium in dry benzene.[248] Iodine in ethereal solution converts the compound to trimethylplatinum iodide.

A complex of trimethylplatinum with acetyl acetone,

$$CH \overset{\displaystyle C(CH_3)O}{\underset{\displaystyle C(CH_3):O}{<}} > Pt(CH_3)_3$$

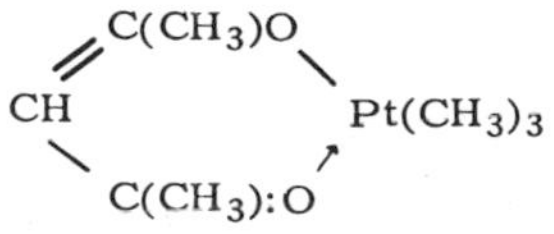

has been obtained through the reaction of trimethylplatinum iodide with thallous acetylacetone in benzene solution.[249]

MAGNESIUM DIALKYLS

The methods of preparation and the reactions of organo magnesium halides have been dealt with in Chapter 12. In this section the preparation and properties of magnesium dialkyls alone need be considered.

Magnesium dialkyls result through the reaction of metallic magnesium with an alkyl sodium in the presence of metallic mercury:[60]

$$Mg + 2NaC_2H_5 + Hg \rightarrow Mg(C_2H_5)_2 + Na_2Hg$$

The reaction would appear to be preceeded by the formation of a mercury dialkyl through the reversible process:

$$2NaC_2H_5 + Hg \rightleftharpoons Hg(C_2H_5)_2 + 2Na$$

the mercury alkyl then reacting with magnesium to form the magnesium dialkyl.

Magnesium dialkyls burn spontaneously in air, and are even capable of abstracting oxygen from carbon dioxide. They may be stored unchanged in an atmosphere of hydrogen or nitrogen.

Magnesium dialkyls form etherates that are somewhat soluble in ether, the dimethyl compound to the extent of 0.08 gm mole per 100 cc, the diethyl and di-*n*-butyl derivatives to a much greater extent.[61]

Magnesium diphenyl is a highly reactive compound.[62]

ORGANOZINC COMPOUNDS

Alkyl zinc iodides may be prepared through the reaction of an alkyl iodide with metallic zinc in the absence of a solvent.[63] The reaction proceeds best when a coppered zinc powder, the so-called *zinc copper couple,* is employed. The use of a solvent and an accelerator is also often desirable.

One *procedure* commonly employed is to add a molal equivalent of the alkyl iodide to 130 gm of the zinc-copper couple suspended in 250 cc of absolute ether containing a few centigrams of iodine, and to boil the mixture under a reflux condenser. The operation should be carried out under an atmosphere of nitrogen or carbon dioxide.[64]

An alternative and more satisfactory procedure is based on the fact that the reaction proceeds at water bath temperature in the absence of iodine when ethyl acetate is used as a solvent. The reaction, in fact, proceeds so vigorously that it is necessary to add the iodide-acetate mixture to the zinc-copper couple in small portions, and to discontinue heating the mixture once the reaction is under way. The reaction may be moderated by diluting the iodide-acetate mixture with benzene, toluene, xylene or tetralin. In working with the low molecular alkyl iodides, a half-molal equivalent of ethyl acetate is used, diluted with twice its weight of the aromatic diluent, and two atomic equivalents of the coppered zinc are employed. The flask may be heated in a calcium chloride bath under reflux to about 100°. The reaction is generally complete within a short time. The addition of a little iodine accelerates the reaction which, once it sets in proceeds smoothly providing the mixture is occasionally stirred. After the initial vigorous reaction has subsided, the temperature gradually rises to 110°, and within one-half to three quarter-hour the reaction is complete, and refluxing ceases. The mixture is then diluted with a volume of the aromatic solvent equal to that originally used, it is shaken well and allowed to cool. The supernatent liquid is then poured off, the residual zinc is washed with a little of the aromatic solvent, the washings are combined with the main body of the liquid and the solvent is removed by evaporation. The product is a viscous, colorless liquid that fumes in air. It is oxidized on exposure to air with separation of iodine. The yield is, in general, about 80% of the theoretical with primary alkyl iodides, and 60% with secondary iodides. Tertiary iodides fail to give satisfactory results.

The reaction takes place less readily with methyl iodide than with other alkyl iodides. When the method is employed for the preparation of zinc methyl iodide, it is essential to add some iodine to the reaction mixture, and to extend the reaction time to one to one and a half hours.

It is advisable not to work with quantities of alkyl iodide in excess of 80 to 100 gm at any one time.

Only alkyl iodides of the highest purity should be used in the reaction, and the aromatic solvent and acetic ester must be completely anhydrous. The hydrocarbon may be conveniently dried by distillation; the acetic ester should be washed four times with saturated salt solution, kept 24 hours over anhydrous calcium chloride, and distilled over this dehydrating agent, rejecting the first and last fractions. *Petroleum hydrocarbons* boiling in the range 85 to 90° should be used as a diluent in the preparation of *secondary* zinc alkyl halides, since benzene hydrocarbons react with secondary alkyl iodides. The hydrocarbon is shaken with fuming sulfuric acid in order to free it from aromatic constituents and unsaturated hydrocarbons, and is subsequently dried and carefully rectified, collecting the fraction that distills between 85 and 90°.

Alkyl bromides may be employed in the reaction, providing Furstenhoff's complex, $AlBr_3 \cdot Al(C_2H_4Br)_3$, is added as a catalyst.[65]

The zinc-copper couple is prepared in the following manner: Zinc turnings broken into pieces 2-3 mm long are heated with 1/10 their weight of copper powder in a stoppered flask on a free flame just to the melting point of zinc for a short time with constant stirring. The mixture is shaken for a time and is allowed to cool.[65] The material may also be prepared by heating zinc with copper oxide. Etching the zinc with sulfuric acid also activates the metal.

Alkyl zinc halides may also be prepared through the reaction of zinc chloride with alkyl magnesium halides:[66]

$$ZnCl_2 + RMgX \rightarrow RZnCl + MgXCl$$

Fused zinc chloride is used in solution in two molal equivalents of ether. The alkyl zinc halide is isolated by distillation under vacuum. This reaction is well suited for the preparation of high molecular zinc halides.

Zinc dialkyls and mixed zinc dialkyls may be obtained through the further reaction of alkyl zinc halides with alkyl magnesium halides:[67]

$$RZnI + R'MgX \rightarrow RZnR' + MgXI$$

Zinc dialkyls may also be prepared through the reaction of mercury dialkyls with metallic zinc. The method is applicable to the preparation of zinc diaryls:[68]

$$Zn + HgAr_2 \rightarrow ZnAr_2 + Hg$$

The reaction is suitably carried out in boiling xylene under an atmosphere of nitrogen, hydrogen or carbon dioxide. Zinc di-β-naphthyl has been obtained by this method, but di-α-naphthylmercury failed to react at 140° in the course of forty hours. Dibenzylmercury also fails to undergo the reaction.

Estimation of Zinc Alkyl Halides

Alkyl zinc halides react with iodine in the following manner:

$$RZnX + I_2 \rightarrow RI + ZnXI$$

This reaction has been utilized for the estimation of the zinc alkyl halide content of solutions of these compounds.[65] To this end, a known amount of the solution is added to an excess of standard ethereal solution of iodine, and the mixture is shaken vigorously. The resulting solution is acidified with dilute acetic acid, and the excess iodine is titrated with standard sodium thiosulfate solution in the usual manner.

Properties and Reactions of Zinc Alkyls

Zinc dialkyls are colorless liquids that may be stored undecomposed in the absence of light and air. They may be heated to 200° without decomposition. They are monomolecular in the vaporized condition or in solution. Zinc diaryls are white crystalline compounds.

Zinc dialkyls are highly reactive toward oxygen, and may react also with many oxygenated compounds and with other negative elements or groups. The lower members ignite immediately when exposed to air; the pyrogenic character decreases with increasing molecular weight. They may cause burns when brought into contact with the skin, but they apparently are not, otherwise, toxic. Zinc alkyls are stable toward carbon dioxide, but react vigorously with water, forming zinc hydroxide and a hydrocarbon. Reaction with alcohols leads to the formation of zinc alcoholates, and reaction with ammonia gives zinc amide, $Zn(NH_2)_2$, and a hydrocarbon. Zinc diaryls also react vigorously with water.

Dry distillation of alkyl zinc halides yields a dialkyl zinc:

$$2RZnI \rightarrow ZnR_2 + ZnI_2$$

In contrast with alkyl magnesium halides, alkyl zinc halides give the normal Wurtz type reaction with tertiary alkyl halides.[69]

ORGANOBERYLLIUM COMPOUNDS

Beryllium dialkyls may be prepared through the reaction of metallic beryllium with mercury alkyls at 130°.[70] The best method of preparation of beryllium dialkyls is through the reaction of anhydrous beryllium chloride or bromide with alkyl magnesium halides in ethereal solution.[71]

Alkyl beryllium halides have been prepared by the reaction of alkyl halides with metallic beryllium activated with mercuric chloride.[72]

Beryllium dialkyls are highly reactive; dimethyl and diethylberyllium ignite automatically in moist air, while butylberyllium combines vigorously with atmospheric oxygen without igniting. Beryllium dialkyls react readily with water forming beryllium hydroxide and a hydrocarbon. Beryllium dimethyl ignites in carbon dioxide; reacting with carbon dioxide in ethereal solution it forms acetic acid, while the ethyl compound gives triethyl carbinol.[73]

Beryllium alkyl halides are, in general, less reactive than beryllium dialkyls or Grignard compounds.[250] Alkyl beryllium halides are soluble in ether. These compounds are changed on slight heating to a dialkyl beryllium and beryllium halides.

ORGANOCADMIUM COMPOUNDS

Cadmium alkyls are obtained very readily by the reaction of cadmium bromide with alkyl magnesium halides. The pure alkyl cadmium may be isolated from the reaction mixture by distillation under vacuum. The receiver should, however, be cooled with liquid air in order to avoid loss of the vapors of cadmium alkyl.[74] Cadmium diphenyl has been obtained through the reaction of cadmium bromide with phenyllithium.[75]

Cadmium alkyls are unstable liquids, only methylcadmium remaining unchanged for any length of time on storage. They deposit metallic cadmium when heated at 150°, decomposition becoming vigorous at 180°. They are oxidized vigorously when exposed to air, and ignite when dropped on a filter paper.

ORGANIC DERIVATIVES OF MERCURY

Direct Reaction of Mercury with Alkyl Halides

Metallic mercury reacts with certain alkyl iodides to form alkyl mercury iodides:[76]

$$RI + Hg \rightarrow RHgI$$

The reaction proceeds with methyl, benzyl, and methylene iodides,[77] and very readily with allyl iodide, $CH_2 = CHCH_2I$.[78]

Organic iodides and bromides react readily with mercury amalgamated with sodium to form mercury dialkyls:[251]

$$2RI + Hg + 2Na \rightarrow R_2Hg + 2NaI$$

The reaction is accelerated by esters such as ethyl acetate. It takes place very readily with the aliphatic halides, best yields being obtained at a low temperature with an amalgam containing about 0.1% sodium. A more concentrated amalgam and a higher temperature are required with aromatic halides.

Secondary alkyl iodides react vigorously with sodium amalgam without, however, forming organomercury compounds. Cyclohexyl iodide reacts to form cyclohexylmercury iodide instead of the expected dicyclohexylmercury. Ethylene dibromide and trimethylene dibromide react but do not form organo mercury compounds, whereas tetramethylene diiodide and pentamethylene diiodide or dibromide react to form mercury ring compounds.[79]

β-Iodopropionic esters yield β-mercury-bis-propionic esters, while α-halo esters fail to give mercury derivatives by this reaction. As a general rule, an unusually reactive halide does not give a mercury compound. Examples of such halides are, aside from the α-halo esters mentioned, benzyl halides and phenacyl halides, $C_6H_5COCH_2X$. The method also fails with bromo compounds containing amino, hydroxy, nitro, and carboxyl groups, since these groups react with metallic sodium. The reaction fails to take place with chloro compounds.

In the aromatic series mercury derivatives have been obtained by this method from brominated dimethylaniline, diethylaniline, dimethyl-*p*-toluidine, anisoles and phenetoles.

Alkyl Mercury Halides

Alkyl mercury halides may be conveniently prepared through the reaction of concentrated halo acids with mercury dialkyls:

$$HgR_2 + HX \rightarrow RHgX + RH$$

Of two unlike radicals in an unsymmetrical dialkyl mercury, RR′Hg, the halo acid removes the more electronegative. This fact has been made the basis of comparison of the degree of electronegativity of hydrocarbon groups.[80]

Alkyl mercury halides may also be made by the reaction of halogens with mercury dialkyls:

$$HgR_2 + X_2 \rightarrow RHgX + RX$$

The reaction proceeds quite vigorously, and it is necessary to dilute the halogen to prevent the spontaneous ignition of the reaction mixture.

One of the most satisfactory methods of preparation of alkyl mercury halides is to heat mercury dialkyls with a mercuric halide:

$$HgR_2 + HgX_2 \rightarrow 2RHgX$$

This reaction takes place quite readily as a rule, in the cold in some instances, although in most cases it is necessary to heat the components in alcoholic or acetone solution.[81] Benzylmercury chloride and cyclohexylmercury chloride may be prepared readily by this method. The reaction is applicable to cyclic mercury compounds, cyclomercurypentamethylene, $\overline{CH_2(CH_2)_3CH_2Hg}$, giving pentanedimercury chloride, $ClHgCH_2(CH_2)_3CH_2HgCl$, with mercuric chloride. The reaction is applicable also to mercury diaryls, phenylmercury chloride and α-naphthylmercury chloride being obtained without difficulty from the corresponding diaryl compounds.[82]

Chloromethylmercury chloride is obtained through the reaction of mercuric chloride with diazomethane:[83]

$$CH_2N_2 + HgCl_2 \rightarrow ClCH_2HgCl + N_2$$

Alkyl mercury halides can also be made through the interaction of an alkyl magnesium halide with a mercury halide:

$$RMgI + HgI_2 \rightarrow RHgI + MgI_2$$

An alkyl mercury halide or a dialkyl mercury may be obtained by this method depending on the proportions of the reagents, and in most cases a mixture of the alkyl mercury halide and dialkyl mercury is obtained. α-Naphthylmercury halides are best prepared by this method.[84] The simple mercury dialkyls, including the secondary and tertiary derivatives, are obtained by use of an excess of the appropriate alkyl magnesium halide.[85]

A series of mixed mercury dialkyls have also been prepared through the reaction of the appropriate Grignard reagents with an alkyl mercury halide.[86]

Mercury dibenzyl may be prepared through the reaction of a benzylmagnesium halide with mercuric chloride.[87] This compound may also be obtained in good yield through the reaction of benzylmercury iodide with an alkaline sodium stannite solution:[88]

$$2C_6H_5CH_2HgI + Na_2SnO_2 + 2NaOH$$
$$\rightarrow Hg(CH_2C_6H_5)_2 + Hg + 2NaI + Na_2SnO_3 + H_2O$$

Mixed mercury dialkyls have been obtained by the decarboxylation method of Kharasch.[89] These compounds are very unstable and change on standing into symmetrical mercury dialkyls.

Alkyl mercury halides may be converted to mercury dialkyls by treatment with metallic copper:[90]

$$2RHgX + 2Cu \rightarrow HgR_2 + Hg + 2CuX$$

This method appears to be quite general. Mercury dialkyls may also be obtained from alkyl mercury halides by treatment with sodium amalgam, generally in the presence of ethyl acetate:[91]

$$2RHgX + 2Na \rightarrow HgR_2 + Hg + 2NaX$$

Amalgam of low sodium content should be used.

The conversion of alkyl mercury halides to mercury dialkyls may be brought about, in general, by reduction in neutral or alkaline medium. *Sodium stannite* is the usual reducing agent employed, the reaction proceeding in the following manner:

$$2RHgX + Na_2SnO_2 + H_2O \rightarrow HgR_2 + Hg + 2NaX + NaHSnO_3$$

Reduction of *diethyl ether dimercury chloride* with sodium stannite results in the formation of a white precipitate, probably $\overline{OCH_2CH_2HgHgCH_2CH_2}$, which sinters when heated at 80° and decomposes at 140-150°, forming mercuric diethylene oxide,

$$\overline{OCH_2CH_2HgCH_2CH_2}$$

Reduction of alkyl mercury halides proceeds well also with aqueous sodium thiosulfate solution:

$$2RHgX + 2Na_2S_2O_3 \rightarrow 2NaX + 2RHgS_2O_3Na$$

$$\rightarrow HgR_2 + Na_2Hg(S_2O_3)_2$$

Alkyl mercury halides which dissolve readily in a concentrated solution of sodium thiosulfate react particularly well with this compound, the mercury dialkyl separating from the aqueous solution.[92]

In a few instances compounds of the type RHgX are converted to mercury dialkyls simply by heating.

Mercuration by Means of Mercuric Oxide

Certain types of organic compounds may be mercurated by reaction with mercuric oxide. Mercury derivatives of alcohols, ketones, aldehydes and certain compounds containing a reactive methylene group have been prepared by this method.

Treatment of alcohol with mercuric oxide and alkali results in the formation of a mixture of poorly defined compounds and, as the end product of the reaction, mercarbide, $\overline{HgOHgC}(HgOH)\cdot\overline{C(HgOH)HgOHg}$. Treated with hydrochloric acid, this yields the compound $(ClHg)_3CC(HgCl)_3$. When heated to 230° the compound explodes violently, although it is stable to shock. Reacting with potassium cyanide it forms a dicyano compound, CNHgC(Hg)C(Hg)HgCN, which, when treated with hot hydrochloric acid, is converted to $ClHgCH_2CH_2HgCl$.[93] Mercarbides, i. e., compounds in which all carbon valencies other than those at play between atoms of the carbon skeleton are satisfied with mercury, are also obtained from acetaldehyde, acetone, propyl alcohol, amyl alcohol, cellulose, starch, sugar, acetylene and acetic acid.[94] Methyl alcohol and formaldehyde do not give mercarbides.

Hydroxymercurymercuryacetic acid, HOHgC(Hg)COOH, results in polymeric form when sodium acetate is heated on a steam bath with mercuric oxide and concentrated sodium hydroxide until all the oxide disappears.[95] The compound is also obtained on treatment of ethanolmercury iodide, $HOCH_2CH_2HgI$, with mercuric oxide and aqueous potassium hydroxide. The compound may be converted to the nitrate, $NO_3HgC(Hg)COOH$, which decomposes on heating. Di(chloromercury)acetic acid, $(ClHg)_2CHCOOH$ is formed on treating the compound with dilute hydrochloric acid.

Acetoacetic ester and malonic ester react with mercuric oxide yielding compounds in which mercury replaces the hydrogen of the reactive methylene group. Methyl malonate gives mercury bismalonic methyl ester, $Hg[CH(COOCH_3)_2]_2$, contrary to the general rule that in direct mercuration of organic compounds, mercury becomes attached only to one carbon atom.[96] Hydroxymercuryacetic acid, $HOHgCH_2COOH$, results when this compound is hydrolyzed and subsequently decarboxylated. Hydroxymercurymethylmalonic methyl ester, $HOHgC(CH_3)(COOCH_3)_2$, results on shaking methylmalonic methyl ester with mercuric oxide at $37°$ for a few days. On saponification and subsequent decarboxylation, this compound yields the inner anhydride of α-hydroxymercurypropionic acid, $CH_3\overline{CHCOOH}g$.[97]

All ketones react with mercuric iodide in the presence of caustic, acetone giving, for example, $CH_3\overline{COCHH}gHgHgI_2$.[98]

Reaction of Mercury Salts with Unsaturated Compounds

Mercuric salts react in aqueous solution with olefins forming addition compounds, the groups HgX and OH entering the molecule at the point of unsaturation.[99] Thus, ethylene reacts with mercury salts to yield compounds of the type $HOCH_2CH_2HgX$, together with a dimercurated ether,

$$XHgCH_2CH_2OCH_2CH_2HgX,$$

a polymeric compound, $(CH_2 = CHHgX)_n$, also forming under certain conditions.

The reaction of olefins with mercury salts proceeds more vigorously in *alcoholic solution*, the alcohol taking part in the reaction:[100]

$$\overset{|}{\underset{|}{C}} = \overset{|}{\underset{|}{C}} + HOR + Hg(OCOCH_3)_2$$

$$\rightarrow \quad RO\overset{|}{\underset{|}{C}} - \overset{|}{\underset{|}{C}}\cdot HgOCOCH_3^{(*)} + HOCOCH_3$$

The mercury atom always attaches itself to the carbon atom bearing the greatest number of hydrogen atoms, a fact which is in agreement with Markownikoff's rule. The reaction of ethylene with alcoholic mercuric acetate may be accelerated by working under pressure; thus, under a pressure of 10 to 20 atm, the reaction is complete within a few minutes. The reaction is quite general and proceeds with all alcohols.

Fumaric and common cinnamic acids do not give addition products with mercury salts, while their *cis* isomers, namely, maleic and allocinnamic acids readily add HgX and OH or OR groups. Propenylphenyl derivatives, such as isosafrol also fail to give an addition product, the mercuric salt simply acting as an oxidizing agent to give a glycol:

$$CH_2\overset{O}{\underset{O}{\diagup\diagdown}}C_6H_3CH = CHCH_3 \quad \rightarrow \quad CH_2\overset{O}{\underset{O}{\diagup\diagdown}}C_6H_3CH(OH)CH(OH)CH_3$$

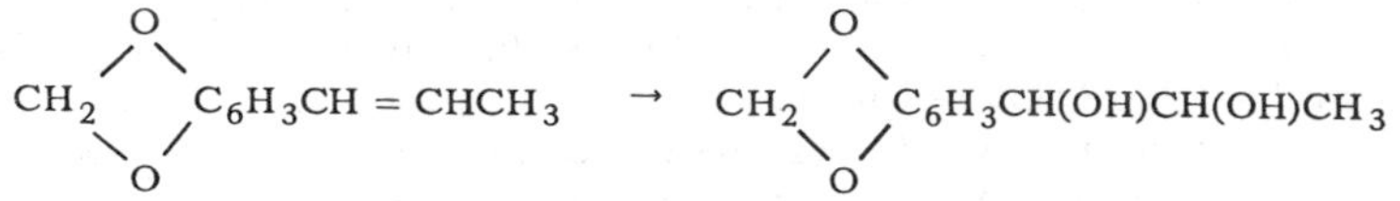

(*) The structure of these compounds is still a matter of dispute, some authors maintaining that they are co-ordination compounds,

$$\underset{\cdot\cdot\ \ \cdot\cdot}{C = C} \quad [101]$$
$$XHgOR$$

This is in contrast with the behavior of the corresponding allyl compounds, such as safrol, which add the groups HgX and OH or OR in the usual manner. Two isomeric compounds are obtained in this reaction.

The addition of mercury salts to double bonds in organic compounds of complicated structure proceeds in much the same manner as with ethylene and the simpler olefins. The former, like the latter, react in aqueous solution to form a mercurated alcohol and a dimercurated ether. The reaction proceeds with ease in alcoholic solution.

The mercurated compounds resulting through the reaction of mercury salts in alcoholic solution yield the original unsaturated compounds when treated with acids. The mercury atom in these compounds is readily removable if a halogen atom or a negative group is attached to the neighboring carbon atom. Addition compounds of unsaturated acids, treated with sodium iodide, give the original acid; thus, $HOCH_2\overline{CHCOOHg}$ gives sodium acrylate, $CH_2 = CHCOONa$, when treated with this reagent. Treated with ammonia and hydrogen sulfide, the mercurated products of esters of allocinnamic acid yield alkoxy hydrocinnamic esters of the type $C_6H_5CH(OR)CH_2COOR'$.

Acetylene and other hydrocarbons with a triple bond react readily with mercury salts in solution forming insoluble amorphous mercurated compounds, the nature of which has not been established, although there is some evidence that they contain a mercarbide group, i.e., a completely mercurated methyl group. Treated with a mineral acid, the product derived from acetylene yields acetaldehyde.

Carbon monoxide behaves as an unsaturated compound toward mercury salts. Reacting with mercuric acetate in methyl alcoholic solution, it gives acetoxymercury formic methyl ester, $CH_3COOHgCOOH$.

Mercury Acetylides

A voluminous precipitate of mercury acetylide, HgC_2, forms on conducting acetylene into an alkaline solution of mercuric cyanide. The compound is extremely explosive in the dry condition. Mercury-bis-monochloracetylene, $Hg(C{:}CCl)_2$, is formed on shaking monochloracetylene with an alkaline solution of mercuric cyanide in a hydrogen atmosphere;[102] heated above its melting point, the compound explodes, though less violently than mercury acetylide.

Dialkyl mercury acetylides, $RHgC{:}CHgR$, are obtained readily through the reaction of alkylmercury halides with acetylene in alcoholic caustic solution.[103]

Properties and Reactions of Mercury Alkyls

Alkyl mercury halides generally show an appreciable vapor pressure at room temperature, and are volatile with steam. They possess a metallic odor and are highly toxic. They generally melt without decomposition in the temperature range 100-200°. They are very slightly soluble in water, fairly soluble in alcohol and readily soluble in ether and benzene. They are not associated in solution.

Mercury dialkyls are, in general, colorless liquids with a characteristic odor. The lower members can be distilled under atmospheric pressure, while the higher members may be distilled only under vacuum. They decompose, as a rule, in the temperature range 160-200°, some with explosive violence. Only dimethylmercury is stable on storage; all other mercury dialkyls decompose gradually, with the separation of metallic mercury.[104] All are extremely toxic, and the danger of poisoning is greatly enhanced in the case of the lower members because of their volatility.[105]

Alkyl mercury halides are generally unaffected by solutions of strong bases, and organo mercury iodides can be crystallized unchanged from hot alkali. This is a characteristic, in general, also of aryl mercury halides. Mercurated phenols form an exception, however; the mercury-carbon bond in these compounds is severed by treatment with alkalies and by boiling with potassium iodide, although nitrophenols remain unaffected by the latter reagent. Only very few compounds of the type RHgX react with aqueous solutions of bases to form hydroxides, RHgOH.

The stability of the mercury-carbon bond varies over a wide range. In some compounds the bond is so weak that the compound reacts with soluble sulfides or with hydrogen sulfide almost instantly to give mercuric sulfide, while in other compounds, as for example in mercarbides, the bond strength is so great that the compound remains unchanged on long boiling with concentrated hydrochloric acid. In many cases in which mercuric sulfide is not formed immediately, an organo mercury sulfide is obtained which, when heated at 100°, breaks down into mercuric sulfide and a dialkyl mercury:

$$2RHgX + H_2S \rightarrow 2HX + (RHg)_2S \rightarrow HgR_2 + HgS$$

This change also takes place gradually on long standing. Compounds in which a mercury atom is attached to an α-carbon atom with respect to a keto group may lose mercury on treatment with cold 0.25*N* hydrochloric acid.

Alkyl mercury hydroxides, RHgOH, may be prepared from the corresponding halides, preferably the iodides, by treatment with moist silver oxide or a 40% methanolic solution of caustic. The hydroxides are weakly basic and are soluble in water and alcohol. They react with an alcoholic solution of carbon disulfide in the presence of caustic to form xanthates,[106] while in the absence of caustic they yield a hydrosulfide and carbon sulfoxide:

$$RHgOH + CS_2 \rightarrow R'HgSH + COS$$

They combine with phenols to form phenolates.[107]

Organo mercury compounds reacting with an excess of halogen give an organic halide and a mercury halide. This reaction is useful in the determination of the structure of these compounds.

It should be noted that mercury is always *bivalent* in its organic derivatives. In contrast to the behavior of the organic derivatives of other metals of the second group of the Periodic System, organo mercury compounds are stable toward atmospheric oxygen.

Mercuration of Aromatic Compounds with Mercuric Acetate

The method of preparation of organo mercury derivatives depending on the interaction of organic halides and amalgamated sodium,[108] while applicable to a limited number of aryl halides, presents many disadvantages and is seldom employed for the preparation of aromatic mercury compounds. *o*-Mercury dianisyl, $Hg(C_6H_4OCH_3)_2$, results from the reaction of *o*-bromoanisol with 1½% sodium amalgam, and *p*-mercury-bis-dimethylaniline[109] may be similarly obtained from *p*-bromodimethylaniline.

Aromatic compounds are capable of direct mercuration by reaction with mercuric acetate:[110]

$$C_6H_6 + Hg(OCOCH_3)_2 \rightarrow C_6H_5HgOCOCH_3 + CH_3COOH$$

Mercurated benzene may be obtained by this method in 80% yield providing the acetic acid formed in the reaction is neutralized with mercuric oxide or alcohol. The reaction is of general applicability but presents the disadvantage that the product consists of a difficultly separable mixture of isomers, where isomer formation is possible; and furthermore, the formation of polymercurated compounds can not be avoided in many instances. It is a fact worth noting that mercury salts which do not hydrolyze also fail to react with aromatic compounds. Since mercury salts of all oxyacids are hydrolyzed to a considerable extent, they are capable of reacting with aromatic compounds, although the best results are obtained with the acetate.

Groups which facilitate bromination also have a favorable effect on the course of the mercuration reaction, although as a rule, fewer mercury atoms than bromine atoms enter the nucleus. The reverse holds true also, and nitrobenzene,[111] for example, which is difficult to brominate is mercurated with difficulty. Mercury is never observed to enter the meta position with respect to an orienting group.

Phenols may be readily mercurated with mercuric acetate,[112] reaction being complete in less than half an hour, and a mixture of *o*- and *p*-isomers resulting which are difficult to purify. A mercury phenolate is apparently formed first, but rapidly undergoes molecular rearrangement giving the nuclearly mercurated derivative. 2,4-Diacetoxymercury phenol results when phenol is heated with two molecular proportions of an aqueous solution of mercuric acetate. *p-Cresol* reacts with mercuric acetate in alcoholic solution more readily than phenol.[113] *Phenol ethers* react much less readily than the free phenols, and yield only monomercurated derivatives.[114] The reaction is best carried out by use of solid mercuric acetate.

Acetophenone in excess reacts at 150° with mercuric acetate in an abnormal manner to form phenacylmercuric acetate, $C_6H_5COCH_2HgOCOCH_3$.[115]

Benzoic acid is mercurated by fusing it with a molecular equivalent of mercuric acetate and holding the mass at the melting temperature until the reaction is complete. Acetoxymercurybenzoic methyl ester results from *methyl benzoate* and mercuric acetate.[81] *Anthranilic methyl ester* gives N-isodiacetoxymercury anthranilic methyl ester, $CH_3COOHgC_6H_3(COOCH_3)NHHgOCOCH_3 \cdot H_2O$.[116] Phthalic acid heated with mercuric acetate gives *o*-hydroxymercury benzoic anhydride,

```
      Hg
     /  \
C6H4     O
     \  /
      CO
```

a compound which is also obtained from benzoic acid and mercuric acetate.[117] Mercurated derivatives have been prepared from many organic acids.[118]

It is possible that mercuration of *aromatic amines* is always preceded by the combination of the mercury with the amino nitrogen to form an ammonium compound which then undergoes molecular rearrangement to form the nuclearly mercurated compound, the mercury entering the *para* and the *ortho* positions.[254] Treatment of freshly distilled *aniline* with an aqueous solution of mercuric acetate results in the formation of *p*-aminophenylmercury acetate in good yield. The reaction is complete within approximately three hours. A little of the *ortho* compound also forms in the process and is found in the mother liquors. Continued mercuration leads to the formation of 2,4-diacetoxymercury aniline.[119] Strong alkalies convert the *para* acetoxymercury compound into the ether-insoluble anhydride, $\overline{HNC_6H_4Hg}$. Mercuration of *monomethylaniline* with mercuric acetate results in the formation of *p*-methylaminophenylmercury acetate.[120] Similarly *p*-dimethylaminophenylmercury acetate results through the mercuration of dimethylaniline in 50% alcoholic solution. *Para*-bromodimethylaniline gives an *o*-acetoxymercury*p*-bromodimethylaniline,[121] and *o*-acetoxymercury-*p*-nitromonomethylaniline has been obtained from *p*-nitromonomethylaniline.[122] Of the three isomeric nitrodimethylanilines only the *para* isomer cannot be mercurated with mercuric acetate. Similar mercurated products may also be obtained from ethylaniline, diethylaniline, acetanilide, diphenylamine, nitranilines, toluidines, benzylaniline, naphthylamine and related compounds. *p*-Acetaminophenylmercury acetate has been obtained by the reaction of *acetanilide* with a molecular equivalent of mercuric acetate in boiling aqueous solution.[123] The reaction of *o-toluidine* with one molecular equivalent of mercuric acetate in dilute alcoholic solution results in the formation of 15% of mono and 85% of the dimercurated compounds.[124] No monomercurated product has been obtained from *m-toluidine*. An excess of mercuric acetate favors the formation of the trimercurated product. *p*-Toluidine yields a monomercury product.[125] 2,4-Diacetoxymercury-α-naphthylamine is formed through the reaction of *α-naphthylamine* with mercuric acetate in alcoholic solution.[126] No monomercurated compound has been obtained from 1,5-naphthylamine sulfonic acid, the product of the reaction being a diacetoxymercury compound. Only a monomercurated compound has been obtained, on the other hand, from 2,6-naphthylamine sulfonic acid.

In the monomercuration of nitrobenzene, the ortho, meta and para isomers are formed in the ratio 5:4:1.[252] This anomalous behavior is observed also with the three nitrotoluenes.[253] When a hydroxyl group is present in the nitrated aromatic body, it facilitates mercuration, and also exert the predominant orienting influence. Mercuration then takes place in ortho and para positions, but there is a strong tendency toward the formation of dimercury derivatives by substitution in both positions at once.

Aromatic arsenical compounds may be normally mercurated, and it is therefore possible to obtain mixed aromatic arsenic and mercury compounds by this method.[127]

Three or four mercury atoms enter the molecule when *phenyl-S-pyrazolones* are treated with mercuric acetate, some attaching themselves to carbon atoms, in the benzene ring, some to those in the pyrazolone ring.[128] For example, 3-methyl-1-phenyl-5-pyrazolone, mercurated in methyl alcoholic solution, gives 1-acetoxymercuryphenyl-3-methyl-3,4-diacetoxymercury-4-methoxy-3,4-dihydro-5-pyrazolone:

$$\overbrace{CH_3\cdot C = CH\cdot CON(C_6H_5)NH} \rightarrow CH_3\overbrace{C(HgOAc)C(OCH_3)(HgOAc)CON(C_6H_4HgOAc)NH}$$

If a phenyl group is present at position 3 and a hydrogen atom at position 4, then it is possible to mercurate the phenyl group. If no hydrogen atom is present at position 4, mercuration becomes impossible except at elevated temperatures.

Thiophene reacts with mercuric acetate more readily than benzene, giving 2-acetoxymercury-5-hydroxymercury thiophene.[129]. An α,α'-dimercurated derivative results when thiophene is heated with a benzene solution of mercuric acetate at refluxing temperature. Substituted thiophenes are mercurated without difficulty if at least one α-position is available for substitution; if both α-positions are occupied, mercuration in a β-position is still possible, although only under vigorous conditions.

Mercuration with other Mercury Compounds

Mercuration of aromatic compounds may be effected by mercuric chloride under certain conditions. Mercuric chloride reacts extremely slowly with phenol; thus, only a 2% conversion may be obtained after four days' heating of a mixture of the two compounds. Reaction takes place more readily, however, in the presence of sodium acetate, a 40% conversion being achieved in the same period.

The reaction proceeds well when mercuric chloride is employed in conjunction with glycerine and sodium bicarbonate, a procedure which is applicable to many other types of aromatic compounds.[130] α-Furylmercury chloride,

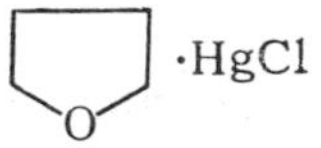

results through the reaction of furan with mercuric chloride in the presence of mercuric acetate, a little 2,5-dichloromercuryfuran also forming.

Nitrophenols with no substituents in *ortho* or *para* position react readily with mercuric oxide or with mercuric salts in the presence or in the absence of a solvent. The primary product is usually the inner anhydride involving the hydroxymercury group and the *aci* form of the nitro group. On treating the anhydride with sodium hydroxide, a colored sodium salt is obtained, while, on treating with hydrochloric acid, a colorless chloromercury compound is obtained; sulfuric acid gives a colorless hydroxymercury compound.

Replacement of Acid Groups with Mercury

The sulfinic acid group in aromatic sulfinic compounds may be replaced with the chloromercury group by heating with mercuric chloride:[131]

$$C_6H_5SO_2H + HgCl_2 \rightarrow C_6H_5HgCl + SO_2 + HCl$$

o-Nitrophenylmercury chloride results in 75% yield when an alcoholic solution of *o*-nitrophenylsulfinic acid is heated to boiling with mercuric chloride for 45 minutes.[132] The compound is obtained as a precipitate and is purified by extraction with acetone. *m*-Nitrophenylmercury chloride may be similarly prepared from *m*-nitrophenylsulfinic acid and mercuric chloride, a 42% yield being realized on heating the reaction mixture for 20 hours.

Boric acid and arsenious oxide[133] groups in aromatic borates and arsenoxides may be replaced similarly:

$$C_6H_5B(OH)_2 + HgCl_2 + H_2O \rightarrow C_6H_5HgCl + HCl + H_3BO_3$$

$$2RAsO + 8NaOH + HgCl_2 \rightarrow HgR_2 + 2NaCl + 2Na_3AsO_3 + 4H_2O$$

4,4′-Mercury-bis-3-nitro-4-phenol is obtained, for example, by heating a solution of *m*-nitro-*p*-hydroxyphenylarsenious oxide with mercuric chloride.

Mercury salts of aryl carboxylic acids lose carbon dioxide on heating to yield C-mercurated derivatives:

$$(RCOO)_2Hg \rightarrow HgR_2 + 2CO_2$$

The method works satisfactorily only with compounds containing strongly negative substituents:[134]

$$[(NO_2)_3C_6H_2CO_2]_2Hg \rightarrow Hg[C_6H_2(NO_2)_3]_2 + 2CO_2$$

Decomposition proceeds further with fatty aromatic acids, and results in the union of two organic groups through carbon bonds:

$$[(NO_2)_2C_6H_3CH_2COO]_2Hg \quad \rightarrow \quad 2CO_2 + Hg[CH_2C_6H_3(NO_2)_2]_2$$

$$\rightarrow \quad (NO_2)_2C_6H_3CH_2CH_2C_6H_3(NO_2)_2 + Hg$$

Nesmejanow's Synthesis

Aromatic diazonium compounds combine with mercuric chloride to form complexes; these may be decomposed by heating in the presence of copper powder to yield nuclearly mercurated derivatives: [135]

$$C_6H_5N_2Cl \cdot HgCl_2 + 2Cu \quad \rightarrow \quad C_6H_5HgCl + 2CuCl + N_2$$

The copper powder used in the reaction is prepared by treating zinc powder with a copper sulfate solution, washing the product successively with water, alcohol and ether, and drying in air.

Side reactions are avoided by carrying out the reaction at -10 to $-20°$, and adding the mercury complex slowly to the suspension of the copper powder in a solvent, preferably acetone.[136] The reaction may be carried out in the temperature range $0°$ to $5°$ by using a mixture of the diazo compound and finely divided mercury kept in suspension in an inert solvent by vigorous agitation:[137]

$$RN_2Cl + Hg \quad \rightarrow \quad RHgCl + N_2$$

Nesmejanow's reaction offers a versatile method applicable to a great many diazo compounds and has made possible the preparation of a great variety of of aryl mercury derivatives not otherwise accessible.

Mercuration by Means of Grignard Reagents

Many aryl magnesium halides reacting with arylmercury halides give mercury diaryls. The method is of limited applicability however.[138] A few mixed alkyl mercury aryl compounds have been prepared successfully through the reaction of Grignard reagents with an organo mercury halide by carefully avoiding any undue rise in temperature during the reaction. Benzyl phenyl, ethyl phenyl, benzyl ethyl and benzyl-*o*-tolyl derivatives have been prepared by this method.[139]

Mercury Heterocycles

Cyclomercury tetramethylene, $\overline{CH_2(CH_2)_2CH_2Hg}$, results in the polymeric form when a 2% sodium amalgam is made to react with 1,4-diiodobutane.[140] Cyclomercury pentamethylenes have also been obtained in the polymeric form.

The reaction of *o*-dibromobenzene with sodium amalgam results in the formation of a tricyclic mercury compound:[141]

$$2C_6H_4Br_2 + 2HgNa_2 \quad \rightarrow \quad C_6H_4 \underset{Hg}{\overset{Hg}{\diagup\diagdown}} C_6H_4 + 4NaBr$$

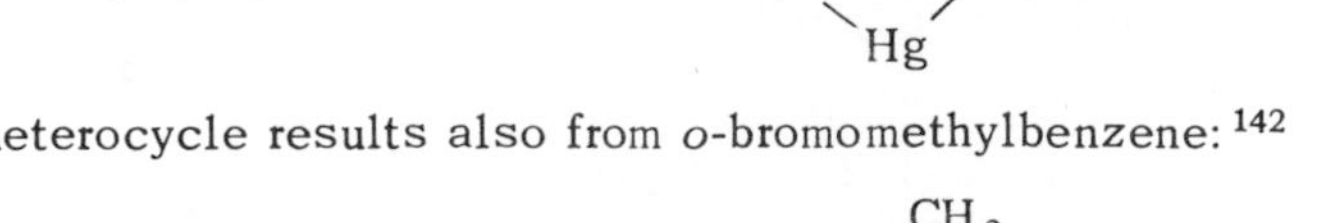

A mercury heterocycle results also from *o*-bromomethylbenzene:[142]

$$C_6H_4(CH_2Br)_2 + HgNa_2 \quad \rightarrow \quad C_6H_4 \underset{CH_2}{\overset{CH_2}{\diagup\diagdown}} Hg + 2NaBr$$

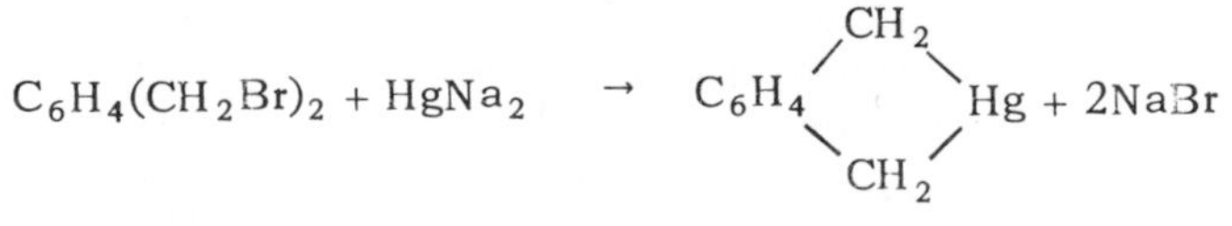

Reactions of Arylmercury Compounds

Treatment of aryl mercury acetates or other aryl mercury salts with sodium stannite results in the formation of mercury diaryls. Mercury diphenyl is obtained in 95% yield, for example, from phenylmercury acetate:

$$2C_6H_5HgOCOCH_3 + Na_2SnO_2 + 2NaOH$$
$$\rightarrow Hg(C_6H_5)_2 + Hg + 2NaOCOCH_3 + Na_2SnO_3 + H_2O$$

The formation of mercury diaryls from aryl mercury salts may be brought about also by use of other reducing agents. *p*-Mercury-bis-dimethylaniline,

$$Hg[C_6H_4N(CH_3)_2]_2$$

results, for example, on treating *p*-dimethylaminophenylmercury hydroxide with sodium sulfide.[143] Mercury di-α-thienyl may be obtained by treating α-thienylmercury chloride with an excess of sodium iodide in acetone solution. The conversion may be brought about in some instances by heating with a xylene suspension of molten sodium; β-mercury dithienyls may be prepared only by this method.[144]

o-Mercury-bis-benzoic methyl ester is obtained on heating the sulfide

$$(CH_3OCOC_6H_4Hg)_2S$$

at 120°.[145]

Mercury diaryls may be employed for the production of arylated boron or antimony halides:

$$BBr_3 + 2Hg(C_6H_5)_2 \rightarrow (C_6H_5)_2BBr + 2C_6H_5HgBr$$
$$SbCl_3 + 2Hg(C_6H_5)_2 \rightarrow (C_6H_5)_2SbCl + 2C_6H_5HgCl$$

Arylated phosphorus, silicon and tin halides may be prepared similarly from the halides of these elements.

Diphenylmercury reacts with dry hydrogen chloride with evolution of heat giving benzene and mercuric chloride. Treated with concentrated hydrochloric acid at a moderate temperature, it is converted to phenylmercury chloride. Nitric acid reacts violently with diphenylmercury even at −15°, forming mercuric nitrate and nitrobenzene.[145]

The mercury atom in 4-mercurypyrazolones is replaced by hydrogen on treatment with ammonium sulfide. Mercury in other than the 4-position is not readily removed by this treatment.[146]

Aryl mercury compounds can generally undergo the normal diazo coupling reaction. Amino aryl mercury compounds may be diazotized. For example, *o*-mercury-bis-*p*-aminobenzoic acid can be converted to the corresponding hydroxy compound by diazotization followed by boiling with water; *p*-acetoxymercury aniline can be diazotized and coupled with a variety of aromatic compounds.[147]

Mercury derivatives of many type of organic compounds such as camphor, coumarin and its derivatives, cystein, etc. have been made by the methods discussed in connection with aromatic compounds.[148]

ORGANIC COMPOUNDS OF ALUMINUM

Organic derivatives of aluminum, as well as of other metals of the third group of the periodic table, namely, gallium, indium and thallium, may be prepared through the reaction of Grignard reagents with the halides of these metals. They may be obtained also in many cases through the reaction of the metal halides with an organo mercury or organo zinc compound.

Aluminum alkyls result when metallic aluminum is made to react with mercury alkyls: [149]

$$3HgR_2 + 2Al \rightarrow 2AlR_3 + 3Hg$$

The reaction of aluminum chloride with organo magnesium halides in ethereal solution results in the formation of etherates of aluminum alkyls:

$$AlCl_3 + 3C_2H_5MgBr + (C_2H_5)_2O$$
$$\rightarrow Al(C_2H_5)_3{\cdot}(C_2H_5)_2O + 3MgClBr$$

These are obtained more simply through the reaction of alkyl halides in ethereal solution with "electron metal" which is an alloy of aluminum and magnesium. Alkyl magnesium and alkyl aluminum compounds are probably formed simultaneously in the beginning in this reaction. The ethereates are stable compounds that can be distilled without decomposition. [150] Their boiling points usually range 100 to 200° above that of ether. The etherates behave toward water and oxygen in the same manner as the ether-free compounds.

Metallic aluminum reacts with ethyl iodide to form diethylaluminum iodide and ethylaluminum diiodide:

$$3C_2H_5I + 2Al \rightarrow (C_2H_5)_2AlI + C_2H_5AlI_2$$

Triphenylaluminum has been obtained through the reaction of metallic aluminum with diphenylmercury at 140°, the reaction requiring 10 to 15 hours for its completion. This compound also forms an etherate, but the etherate may be decomposed by heating at 150°. The ether-free compound melts at 230°, but cannot be distilled without decomposition. The etherate of *tri-p-tolylaluminum* can only be decomposed at a temperature at which resinification takes place. The compound may be prepared from di-*p*-tolylmercury and metallic aluminum in benzene solution and may be readily obtained in the solvent-free condition from this solution.

Properties and Reactions of Organoaluminum Compounds

Aluminum alkyls ignite on exposure to air, and react with water with the formation of aluminum hydroxide and a hydrocarbon. Aluminum alkyls are dimolecular in solution and in the gaseous condition. When these compounds are heated above their boiling point, they dissociate into simple molecules, the degree of dissociation increasing with rise in temperature. [151]

Triphenylaluminum is soluble in benzene and its homologs but is insoluble in petroleum ether. Water reacts with the compound so vigorously that contact with water may cause its ignition.

Aluminum trialkyls form addition compounds with ammonia, $AlR_3{\cdot}NH_3$, which are attacked by atmospheric oxygen. [152] Triphenylaluminum combines with metallic sodium. [153]

ORGANIC COMPOUNDS OF THALLIUM

Dialkyl thallium chlorides, R_2TlCl, are readily obtained through the reaction of thallium chloride with zinc alkyls in ethereal solution.[154] They may be obtained also through the reaction of thallium chloride with organo magnesium halides:[155]

$$TlCl_3 + 2RMgX \rightarrow R_2TlCl + MgX_2 + MgCl_2$$

An excess of the alkyl magnesium halide should not be employed, since otherwise the thallium halide would be reduced. The yields obtained are low with the *sec*-propyl compound, about 30%, because of the greater instability of the halide. Diisopropylthallium halides decompose when heated to 150°, larger amounts with explosion.

Dicyclohexylthallium chloride, $(C_6H_{11})_2TlCl$, has been obtained in 33% yield by the interaction of a cyclohexylmagnesium halide with thallium chloride.[156]

The monoalkyl compounds may be obtained through the reaction of thallium chloride with the dialkyl thallium halide:[157]

$$R_2TlX + TlX_3 \rightarrow 2RTlX_2$$

This reaction can be used also for the preparation of monoaryl thallium halides.

Triethylthallium has been prepared by the reaction of diethylthallium chloride with ethyllithium at a low temperature.[158] The compound decomposes on long heating to its melting point. It can be distilled under vacuum without decomposition, providing the temperature is not allowed to exceed 100°. It is stable in dry air.

Triphenylthallium, $Tl(C_6H_5)_3$, results in good yield from the reaction of diphenylthallium bromide with phenyllithium.[159]

Diethyltriphenylmethanethallium, $(C_2H_5)_2TlC(C_6H_5)_3$, is obtained by the reaction of diethylthallium chloride with triphenylmethane sodium.

Diaryl thallium halides are most conveniently prepared through the reaction of thallium chloride with aryl compounds of mercury, bismuth or lead:[160]

$$TlCl_3 + 2Hg(C_6H_5)_2 \rightarrow (C_6H_5)_2TlCl + 2C_6H_5HgCl$$

$$TlCl_3 + 2Bi(C_{10}H_7)_3 \rightarrow (C_{10}H_7)_2TlCl + 2(C_{10}H_7)_2BiCl$$

Di-α-thienylthallium bromide, $(C_4H_3S)_2TlBr$, may also be prepared by this method.[161]

Monoaryl thallium compounds of the type $RTlX_2$ have been prepared from monoaryl bismuth hydroxides and thallium chloride:[162]

$$C_6H_5Bi(OH)_2 + TlCl_3 + H_2O \rightarrow C_6H_5TlCl_2 + Bi(OH)_3 + HCl$$

Diaryl thallium halides are more stable than the dialkyl compounds, and are insoluble in most solvents; they are soluble, however, in hot pyridine. Compounds containing the secondary alkyl groups are appreciably more unstable than those with the normal groups.

Dialkyl thallium halides may be converted to the corresponding hydroxides by reaction with silver oxide. The hydroxides withdraw carbon dioxide from the air, and precipitate hydroxides of metals from solutions of their salts.

Dialkyl thallium derivatives of enolic forms of certain diketones have been prepared, which are apparently chelate coordinated compounds.[255] An example is the dimethyl-thallium derivative of acetylacetone

$$CH \underset{C(CH_3):O}{\overset{C(CH_3)O}{}} Tl(CH_3)_2$$

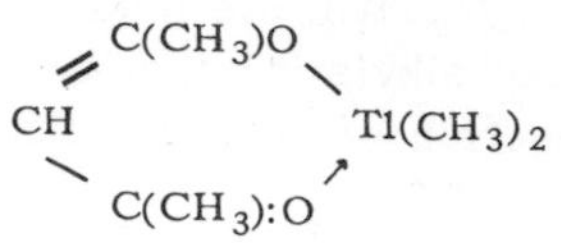

They may be sublimed under diminished pressure and dissolve in benzene and hexane, forming non-ionized solutions. In aqueous solution these compounds exist in an ionized condition with an alkaline reaction, and the thallium dialkyl can be titrated quantitatively.

Monoalkyl thallium halides decompose on heating to thallous halide and an alkyl halide:

$$RTlX_2 \quad \rightarrow \quad TlX + RX$$

while diaryl compounds decompose to thallous halide and a diaryl:

$$R_2TlX \quad \rightarrow \quad TlX + R_2$$

Monoaryl thallium halides, on the other hand, undergo rearrangement forming a diaryl thallium halide and thallium trihalide:

$$2RTlX_2 \quad \rightarrow \quad R_2TlX + TlX_3$$

Di-*p*-tolylthallium fluoride in aqueous solution gives a precipitate of the nitrite even with very dilute nitric acid. This reaction may serve for the detection of nitric acid in minute quantities, even in concentrations as low as 1:125,000.

ORGANIC COMPOUNDS OF GALLIUM

Trimethyl gallium has been prepared from gallium trichloride and dimethyl zinc.[163] Triethyl gallium results when metallic gallium is heated with diethylmercury at 160° for a long period. The compound has been isolated in the ether-free form and as the etherate.[164] The etherates of gallium trialkyls result when gallium halides are made to react with ethereal solutions of alkyl magnesium halides.

Trimethyl gallium reacts vigorously with oxygen, and ignites on exposure to air even at -76°.[163] Organogallium compounds are, as a rule, less vigorously attacked by oxygen than are organoaluminum or organolithium compounds. Reacting with water at room temperature, they are converted to the monohydroxy compounds, R_2GaOH. When it is heated at 100° with water, the methyl compound is converted to $CH_3Ga(OH)_2$.

Trimethylgallium reacts with ammonia to form the compound $(CH_3)_3Ca \cdot NH_3$; treated with an ethereal solution of hydrogen chloride this gives the compounds $(CH_3)_2GaCl \cdot NH_3$, $(CH_3)_2GaCl \cdot 2NH_3$ and CH_3GaCl_2.[165]

ORGANIC COMPOUNDS OF INDIUM

Trimethylindium has been prepared through the reaction of metallic indium with dimethylmercury at 100° in the presence of a trace of mercuric chloride, the reaction requiring eight days for its completion.[166] Water reacts with the compound at ordinary

temperatures to form methylindium hydroxide, $CH_3In(OH)_2$. Alcohol reacts similarly.
Diphenylindium chloride, $(C_6H_5)_2InCl$, has been obtained through the reaction of indium chloride with diphenylmercury.

ORGANIC COMPOUNDS OF LEAD

Lead trialkyls, or more properly, hexaalkyldileads, result when alkyl halides are made to react under appropriate conditions with a lead-sodium alloy.[167] The compounds may be prepared in purer form through the interaction of lead dichloride and alkyl magnesium halides:[301]

$$3PbCl_2 + 6C_2H_5MgBr \rightarrow 3MgCl_2 + 3MgBr_2 + 3Pb(C_2H_5)_2$$
$$\rightarrow Pb + Pb_2(C_2H_5)_6$$

The reaction proceeds satisfactorily if the mixture is effectively cooled. The method is applicable to the preparation of triaryl leads.

Hexaalkyl dileads have been prepared by the reaction of trialkyl lead bromides with sodium in anhydrous ammoniacal solution.[301]

The reaction of lead chloride with Grignard reagents results in the formation of tetraalkyl leads when it is carried out at a higher temperature:[302]

$$2PbCl_2 + 4RMgX \rightarrow PbR_4 + 4MgClX + Pb$$

The Grignard solution is added to lead dichloride suspended in diethyl ether, and the mixture is refluxed for several hours in order to decompose the R_6Pb_2 formed Toluene or xylene may be added to the reaction mixture in order to raise the refluxing temperature. At the conclusion of the reaction the liquid is treated with water, the organic layer is separated and the lead compound is recovered by distilling off the solvent. The crude product usually contains some R_6Pb_2, from which it may be freed by repeated distillation, until no further separation of metallic lead is observed.

The method is applicable to the preparation of tetraaryl lead. In the preparation of the latter the mixture is treated with water, and the insoluble residue, which consists of the tetraaryllead in admixture with some metallic lead and R_6Pb_2, is filtered and the compound is isolated by extraction with an appropriate solvent.

Tricyclohexyllead results in good yield by this reaction without the formation of the tetracyclohexyl compound.[169]

Unsaturated lead alkyls are also formed in this reaction, especially from higher molecular alkyl magnesium halides. The formation of unsaturated compounds may be avoided by using an excess of the Grignard reagent. Tetra isobutyl lead cannot be prepared by this method.[168] The reaction is applicable to the preparation of lead triaryls and tetraaryls.[170] Tetraphenyl lead can be prepared by this reaction without difficulty, although *p*-tolylmagnesium bromide gives appreciable quantities of unsaturated compounds, and *p*-xylylmagnesium bromide gives the triaryl compound exclusively.[171] Lead tetrabenzyl may be prepared by this method, though the compound has not been obtained in the pure form because it is very readily oxidized when exposed to air.[172]

The reaction of alkyl lead halides with organomagnesium compounds yields alkyl leads and may be employed for the preparation of mixed lead alkyls. Ethyl-trimethyllead has been obtained through the reaction of trimethyllead bromide with ethylmagnesium bromide:

$$(CH_3)_3PBr + C_2H_5MgBr \rightarrow (CH_3)_3PbC_2H_5 + MgBr_2$$

In the preparation of tetraalkyl leads from lead halides and alkyl magnesium bromides the formation of unsaturated compounds raises difficulties in the purification of the alkyl lead. These difficulties may usually be overcome by converting the crude tetraalkyl lead to trialkyl lead bromide and then reacting this with a molecule of the alkyl magnesium bromide.

Lead tetraalkyls may be prepared through the reaction of alkyl halides with a lead-sodium alloy.[167] The reaction is carried out by simply pouring the organic halide onto the finely divided lead-sodium alloy placed in a flask provided with a reflux condenser:

$$PbNa_4 + 4C_2H_5I \rightarrow Pb(C_2H_5)_4 + 4NaI$$

No reaction takes place, at least at room temperature, unless a small amount of water or ethyl acetate is present in the alkyl halide.[256]

In the commercial process for the preparation of tetraethyllead, 0.4 molecular equivalent of pyridine is dissolved in four molecular equivalents of ethyl bromide, the solution is added to one molecular equivalent of finely ground lead sodium alloy. Water is then added very slowly and with continual stirring, and the mixture is cooled in order to avoid a violent reaction. When further addition of water no longer causes a reaction, sufficient water is introduced to make the mass fluid and the tetraethyllead is distilled with steam. The product is washed free from pyridine, it is allowed to stand until clear, and is then separated from the water layer by decantation.

Tetramethyllead has been obtained in very good yield from methyl iodide and an alloy consisting of 20% sodium and 80% lead.

A trialkyl lead is first formed in this reaction and is converted to the tetraalkyl compound by further reaction. Conversion of triethyllead to tetraethyllead takes place less readily than that of trimethyllead to tetramethyllead, and the yield of the ethyl compound is consequently lower. Only the methyl and ethyl derivatives can be conveniently prepared by this method. The higher molecular compounds are best prepared by chlorinating the lead trialkyl first formed in the reaction, and treating the resulting dialkyl lead dichloride with an alkyl magnesium halide:[173]

$$2R_3Pb + 3Cl_2 \rightarrow 2R_2PbCl_2 + 2RCl$$

$$R_2PbCl_2 + 2RMgX \rightarrow PbR_4 + 2MgXCl$$

The reaction is of general applicability and would appear to offer the preferred method for the preparation of lead tetraalkyls.

Mixed tetraaryl or arylalkyl derivatives may be prepared by this method. Lead trialkyl aryls are obtained with greater difficulty than lead mono- and dialkylaryls, because of the difficulty of separating the individual compounds from the complex mixtures resulting from the reaction.[174] Lithium aryls may be substituted for aryl magnesium halides in this reaction.

A highly satisfactory method for the preparation of tetraalkyl or tetraaryl leads depends upon the reaction of lead chloride with an organolithium compound and an organic iodide:

$$3RLi + PbCl_2 + RI \rightarrow R_4Pb + 2LiCl + LiI$$

The reaction is carried out by adding the solution of the organolithium compound to the mixture of the other reagents without the application of external cooling. The reaction proceeds essentially at refluxing temperature because of its exothernic nature. Tetramethyllead has been obtained by this method in 92% yield, and tetraphenyllead in 80% yield.[303]

Alkyl Grignard reagents have been substituted for alkyl lithium in this reaction with fairly satisfactory results.[304] Unsatisfactory results have been obtained with phenylmagnesium halides.

Tetraethyllead has been prepared by the reaction of lead chloride with diethylzinc:[257]

$$2Zn(C_2H_5)_2 + 2PbCl_2 \rightarrow Pb(C_2H_5)_4 + Pb + 2ZnCl_2$$

Diaryl leads may be obtained through the reaction of lead chloride with aryl magnesium halides at a low temperature.

Diphenyllead may be prepared by adding one mole of lead chloride slowly and with good stirring to an ethereal solution of 0.2 mole of phenylmagnesium bromide maintained below 2°. The reaction is carried out in an atmosphere of nitrogen. The product is treated with water the diphenyllead is extracted with benzene, and is isolated by precipitation with alcohol. All these operations should also be carried out in an atmosphere of nitrogen. The compound is obtained in 15% yield.

Di-*o*-tolyllead is the only other representative of this class of compounds isolated. The ready dissociation of compounds of this type has apparently prevented their isolation.

Triaryl leads may be prepared through the reaction of lead chloride with the appropriate amount of aromatic Grignard compounds.

A quarter molal proportion of lead chloride is added in small portions to three-fourths molal proportions of the Grignard compound in 400 cc of dry ether. The mixture is heated for two hours on a water bath; the product is then washed with water and alcohol, and the triaryl lead is extracted with hot benzene, and is purified by crystallization from the same solvent. The yield is over 50%.

The fact that tetraaryl leads may be obtained through the reaction of aromatic Grignard reagents with lead chloride has been pointed out. The compounds may be prepared also through the reaction of aryl halides with lead-sodium alloy.

Trialkyl lead monohalides may be obtained by heating a mixture of tetraalkyl lead and a dialkyl lead dihalide:[175]

$$PbR_4 + R_2PbX_2 \rightleftarrows 2R_3PbX$$

An equilibrium is often reached, and all three compounds are present in the final reaction mixture.

Trimethyllead chloride may be obtained through the chlorination of tetramethyllead in dilute solution under strong cooling.

Triethyllead monochloride is prepared in the following manner:[258] Carbon dioxide snow is added to a 20% solution of lead tetraethyl in ethyl acetate, and a slow current of chlorine is passed through the solution until the gas ceases to be absorbed. The temperature must be kept below -60° during the reaction by the continued addition of carbon dioxide snow. After the completion of the reaction, the temperature is allowed to rise, and the mixture is heated on a water bath to 50°. Finally the solution is filtered and concentrated in vacuum to obtain the compound in a crystalline form. The yield is practically quantitative.

Triphenyl-*o*-hydroxyphenyllead has been prepared in 70% yield through the reaction of triphenyllead chloride and lithium *o*- lithiophenoxide.[259]

Triaryl lead halides may be obtained through the reaction of diaryl lead chlorides with a diaryl mercury:

$$(C_6H_5)_2PbCl_2 + Hg(C_6H_5)_2 \rightarrow (C_6H_5)_3PbCl + C_6H_5HgCl$$

The preparation of triaryl lead monohalides by halogenation of lead tetraaryls, while possible, involves difficulties, since the reaction leads principally to the formation of the diaryl lead dihalides even under strong cooling. Bromination in ethereal solution, even at -75°, gives principally the dibromide. Triphenyllead bromide has been obtained in good yield, however, by brominating tetraphenyllead in pyridine.[176]

Triphenyllead iodide results when triphenyllead is shaken with a mixture of 1 part of iodine in alcoholic solution and 2 parts of water; the compound is also obtained when a benzene solution of triphenyllead is added dropwise to a pyridine solution of iodine.

Triaryl leads react with bromine to form triaryl lead bromides. They give diaryl lead dibromides with an excess of the halogens.[260]

Dialkyl lead dihalides may be obtained by the halogenation of lead tetraalkyls.

The *procedure* may be illustrated by the method employed for the preparation of dimethyl lead dichloride. Tetramethyl lead is chlorinated to the monochloride; solid carbon dioxide is added as soon as the chlorine color becomes visible, and the passage of chlorine is continued with stirring, whereupon the dichloride gradually precipitates out as a white, crystalline solid. When the temperature rises to -10°, passage of chlorine is stopped, the vessel is cooled in a freezing mixture and allowed to stand for half an hour. The supernatant liquid is then poured off, the precipitate is washed by decantation, filtered, washed with ether and dried. The compound is obtained in a very pure form in quantative yield.[177]

While bromine reacts with lead tetraalkyls at -75° replacing only one alkyl group, reaction with tetra-*sec*-propyl lead leads to the formation of the dialkyl lead dibromide.

Dialkyl lead dihalides are, as a rule, less stable than trialkyl lead monohalides; dichloro compounds are more stable than the dibromo compounds.

Diphenyllead dinitrate is obtained when tetraphenyllead is heated to boiling with concentrated nitric acid.

Monoalkyl lead trihalides result when alkyl plumbic acids RPbO·OH, are dissolved in dilute halo acids.

Alkyl plumbic acids are obtained through the reaction of sodium plumbite with alkyl iodides:

$$RI + NaHPbO_2 \rightarrow RPbOOH + NaI$$

These compounds are of amphoteric character and dissolve both in halogen acids and in aqueous caustic.

Trialkyl lead hydroxides are obtained from the halo compounds by reaction with potassium hydroxide or with silver oxide. Trimethyllead hydroxide,

$$(CH_3)_3PbOH$$

results, for example, by shaking an ethereal solution of trimethyllead bromide with aqueous potassium hydroxide solution or with silver oxide for 24 hours in a shaking machine and concentrating the resulting solution in a platinum dish over calcium oxide.[178]

Compounds of the type R_3PbNa, in which R is an alkyl or aryl radical, have been obtained through the reaction of a trialkyl or triaryl lead halide, R_3PbX, with sodium in liquid ammonia.[305] Compounds of this type may also be obtained through the action of sodium on hexaalkyl or hexaaryl dilead.[306] Lithium, potassium, rubidium, calcium, strontium and barium react in the same manner as sodium.

Lithium derivatives of the type of triphenyllead lithium, can be obtained from the reaction of an aryl lithium with lead dichloride in ether at a low temperature:[307]

$$2C_6H_5Li + PbCl_2 \rightarrow (C_6H_5)_2Pb + 2LiCl$$

$$(C_6H_5)_2Pb + C_6H_5Li \rightarrow (C_6H_5)_3PbLi$$

The second step is reversible, and for that reason the reactions of $(C_6H_5)_3PbLi$ are those either of diphenyllead or of phenyllithium, depending on the conditions.

Lead derivatives of *heterocyclic compounds*, such as tetrafuryl- and tetrathienyllead, may be obtained by the usual methods. One of the most commonly used methods is based on the reaction of heterocyclic magnesium halides with lead halides.[179]

Lead heterocycles have been obtained through the interaction of dialkyl lead dihalides with dimagnesium halides of the appropriate chain length. Thus, diethylcyclopentamethylenelead, $\overline{CH_2(CH_2)_3CH_2Pb}(C_2H_5)_2$ has been obtained from diethyllead dichloride and the halomagnesium compound derived from 1,5-dibromopentane.[180]

The ring in this compound may be ruptured by reaction with a halogen under carefully controlled conditions, to form compounds of the type $(C_2H_5)_2Pb(X)CH_2(CH_2)_3CH_2X$. The halogen attached to lead in this latter may be replaced with an organic group by reaction with an organo magnesium halide, while the halogen attached to carbon undergoes the normal reactions of organic halides, giving, for example, a halomagnesium derivative.

Properties and Reactions of Organolead Compounds

Lead tetraalkyls with primary hydrocarbon groups are mobile, colorless, strongly refractive liquids, stable in air and in contact with water and in diffuse daylight. The methyl compound remains unchanged on storage. The compounds may be distilled undecomposed at atmospheric pressure, providing their boiling point does not exceed 140°. Tetramethyllead may explode when it comes in contact with a hot glass surface. Lead tetraalkyls with secondary hydrocarbon groups are much less stable. They become turbid within a short time when exposed to air, and gradually decompose. They undergo gradual decomposition even when stored in sealed tubes in the absence of light. Lead tetraalkyls with tertiary groups are not known. Mixed lead tetraalkyls, with the exception of those containing secondary alkyl groups, are also stable and show no tendency toward molecular rearrangement to simple lead tetraalkyls even on several days' storage.

Tetraalkyl leads are soluble in common organic solvents, such as ether, benzene, chloroform, or anhydrous alcohol. They are generally insoluble in water. *Sym*-tetraaryl leads are soluble in acetone, chloroform and aromatic hydrocarbons, but they are almost insoluble in alcohols and ethers.

Lead tetraalkyls are highly toxic and act upon the nervous system. Poisoning may follow inhalation of very small amounts of the vapors over a long period.

Organic derivatives of tetravalent lead are more stable than those derived from trivalent lead. Organic derivatives of divalent lead are very unstable and only a few compounds of this type are known; the diphenyl and ditolyl derivatives have been prepared in the pure form.[181] They decompose on heating to form a trivalent lead compound. The stability of lead trialkyls varies according to their molecular weight. Trimethyllead readily changes to tetramethyllead at room temperature; the conversion of triethyllead to the tetraethyl derivative takes place slowly in boiling ether, and the higher lead trialkyls undergo the transformation only on boiling. Triethyllead readily combines with atmospheric oxygen. Lead triaryls are more stable; thus, triphenyllead is completely stable in air in the solid condition, although it gradually oxidizes when in solution. In the conversion of lead triaryls to lead tetraaryls by heat, substituents have a marked influence. For example, triphenyllead is readily converted to the tetrasubstituted derivative by heating at 155°, but the conversion of tri-*p*-tolyllead takes place with much greater difficulty.

The ease of cleavage of alkyl groups in mixed di- and trialkyl lead halides under the action of halogens increases with increasing molecular weight.[182] This fact makes possible the preparation of many mixed di or tiralkyl lead halides and lead tetraalkyls with three or four different radicals. The cyclohexyl group is held more firmly than aliphatic groups.

In arylalkyl lead compounds the aryl group is replaced by a halogen atom in preference to an alkyl group.[183]

The bond strength of aryl groups in aryl lead halides decreases with increase in the molecular weight of the group. The bond strength increases in the following order:

$$\alpha\text{-naphthyl} < p\text{-xylyl} < p\text{-tolyl} < \text{phenyl} < \text{methyl}$$

Determined on the basis of the ease of their cleavage in the reaction

$$R_1R_2R_3R_4Pb + HCl \rightarrow R_1R_2R_3PbCl + HR_4$$

organic groups may be arranged in an ascending order of electronegativity. On this basis the α-furyl group exceeds the α-thienyl group, and the latter in turn exceeds the phenyl group in degree of electronegativity. For this reason the former two groups are considered to be superaromatic in character.

The thermal decomposition of lead tetraalkyls, especially tetramethyl and tetraethyllead, leads to the formation of free alkyl radicals.[184]

ORGANIC COMPOUNDS OF TIN

The interaction of tin tetrachloride with zinc dialkyls or with alkyl magnesium halides leads to the formation of *tin tetraalkyls:*[185]

$$SnCl_4 + 2Zn(C_2H_5)_2 \rightarrow Sn(C_2H_5)_4 + 2ZnCl_2$$

$$SnCl_4 + 4C_2H_5MgBr \rightarrow Sn(C_2H_5)_4 + 2MgCl_2 + 2MgBr_2$$

Organo lithium compounds can be used in this reaction to advantage:[185]

$$SnCl_4 + 4(CH_3)_2NC_6H_4Li \rightarrow Sn[C_6H_4N(CH_3)_2]_4 + 4LiCl$$

It is necessary to make use of an excess of the alkylating agent in order to avoid the formation of any appreciable quantity of trialkyl tin halides. Small quantities of the latter are eliminated by dissolving the crude reaction product in ether and passing a current of dry ammonia through the solution, whereupon the trialkyl tin haloammoniate, $R_3SnX \cdot 2NH_3$, precipitates out.[187] Larger quantities of the trialkyl tin halides are best removed by shaking the crude reaction product with an alcoholic solution of neutral potassium fluoride, which converts the trialkyl tin compound to the difficultly soluble fluoride.[188]

In the preparation of larger quantities of tin tetraalkyls, a suspension of the etherate of tin tetrachloride is prepared by adding this compound dropwise to twice its volume of ether cooled in ice, and the suspension of the etherate is then added to the ethereal solution of the alkyl magnesium halide.[188] In preparing the higher boiling compounds, the reaction can be moderated by the use of dry benzene as a diluent.

Mixed alkyl tin halides are obtained from alkyl tin halides by reaction with organomagnesium halides.[189] Treated with iodine, these mixed tin alkyls release the lighter alkyl groups:[190]

$$(CH_3)_3SnC_2H_5 + I_2 \rightarrow (CH_3)_2SnIC_2H_5 + CH_3I$$

1,4-di-Trimethylstannobenzene,

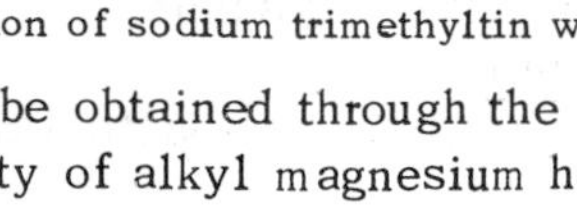

results through the interaction of sodium trimethyltin, $(CH_3)_3SnNa$, with *p*-chlorobenzene in liquid ammonia solution.[191] Similarly, di-trimethylstannomethane,

$$(CH_3)_3SnCH_2Sn(CH_3)_3$$

is obtained through the reaction of sodium trimethyltin with dichloroethane.[192]

Trialkyltin halides may be obtained through the reaction of tin tetrachloride with the calculated quantity of alkyl magnesium halides.[193] They are formed also by the reaction of hexaethyldistannanes with halogens or alkyl halides:[194]

$$(C_2H_5)_3Sn \cdot Sn(C_2H_5)_3 + I_2 \rightarrow 2(C_2H_5)_3SnI$$

$$(C_2H_5)_3Sn . Sn(C_2H_5)_3 + C_2H_5I \rightarrow Sn(C_2H_5)_4 + (C_2H_5)_3SnI$$

Trialkyl and triaryl tin halides are further formed by heating tetraalkyl or tetraaryl tins with tin tetrahalides:[195]

$$3SnR_4 + SnX_4 \rightarrow 4R_3SnX$$

These compounds may also be obtained by the reaction of tin tetraalkyls with mono or dialkyl tin halides. Monoaryl tin trihalides result in 80% yield when one molal proportion of tetraaryl tin is heated with three molal equivalents of tin tetrahalide at 200-225° for 1½ to 2 hours.[196]

Triaryl tin iodides alone among triaryl tin halides can be prepared through the direct reaction of tin tetraaryls with iodine. The monobromo compounds may be obtained by bromination in the presence of pyridine.[197] Tetracyclohexyltin can be converted to tricyclohexyltin monobromide through the direct action of bromine.[198]

Trialkyl tin fluorides are obtained in quantitative yield by treating trialkyl hydroxides in aqueous solution with hydrogen fluoride.[199] Alkyl tin fluorides react with alkyl magnesium halides in the same manner as the other alkyl tin halides and may serve for the preparation of mixed tin alkyls.

Trialkyl tin hydroxides are obtained from trialkyl tin halides by reaction with potassium hydroxide or ammonia.[200]

Alkyl halides react with metallic tin, when heated under pressure, to form *dialkyl tin dihalides;* thus, methyl iodide heated with tin filings gives dimethyltin diiodide, $(CH_3)_2SnI_2$, and diethyl bromide similarly yields diethyltin dibromide. The reaction proceeds far more readily when a tin-sodium alloy is employed instead of tin.[201] While dialkyl tin dihalides are the first product of the reaction, other reactions also take place through the action of metallic sodium; these are exemplified by the following:

$$(C_2H_5)_2SnBr_2 + 2Na \rightarrow Sn(C_2H_5)_2 + 2NaBr$$

$$(C_2H_5)_2SnBr_2 + C_2H_5Br + 2Na \rightarrow (C_2H_5)_3SnBr + 2NaBr$$

$$(C_2H_5)_2SnBr_2 + 2C_2H_5Br + 4Na \rightarrow Sn(C_2H_5)_4 + 4NaBr$$

$$2(C_2H_5)_3SnBr + 2Na \rightarrow (C_2H_5)_3Sn{\cdot}Sn(C_2H_5)_3 + 2NaBr$$

Hexaalkyl distannanes may also form through the decomposition of dialkyl tins:

$$3Sn(C_2H_5)_2 \rightarrow (C_2H_5)_3Sn{\cdot}Sn(C_2H_5)_3 + Sn$$

The reaction of aluminum carbide with tin tetrachloride results in the formation of dimethyltin dichloride.[202] This reaction may be utilized for the detection of tin in low concentrations, because of the intense odor of the resulting alkyltin halide.

Dialkyl tin dihalides may also be prepared by heating a mixture of a tetraalkyl lead and lead tetrachloride.

Diaryl tin dihalides result through the reaction of mercury diaryls with stannous halides:[203]

$$HgAr_2 + SnX_2 \rightarrow Ar_2SnX_2 + Hg$$

These compounds may be obtained also, though in rather low yield, from diazonium chloride–tin tetrachloride complexes by decomposition with copper powder:

$$2ArN_2Cl{\cdot}SnCl_4 + 2Cu \rightarrow Ar_2SnCl_2 + 2CuCl_2 + 2N_2$$

Diphenyltin dichloride is obtained from tetraphenyltin by heating with an equivalent of tin chloride or by chlorination.[204]

Dicyclohexyltin dibromide results on long boiling of tetracyclohexyltin with the calculated quantity of bromine in carbon tetrachloride or chloroform.

Hexaalkyl distannanes, $R_3Sn{\cdot}SnR_3$, result, together with other compounds, on heating trialkyl tin iodides with a 20% sodium-tin alloy. They are prepared in the pure form by reducing trialkyl tin halides with sodium, preferably in liquid ammonia. The compounds are obtained in yields ranging from 85 to 95% of those theoretically expected. Final purification is effected by vacuum distillation.[205]

Hexaphenyldistannane results in nearly quantitative yield when triphenyltin halides are reduced with sodium in xylene. This method is adaptable to the preparation of other hexaaryl distannanes.[206] Hexaphenyldistannane is formed also from diphenyltin under the action of phenylmagnesium bromide, and this offers an excellent method of preparation of the compound. In the preparation of hexaphenyldistannane by the latter method, a small amount of dodecaphenylpentastannane is also formed. This compound probably has the structure $Sn[Sn(C_6H_5)_3]_4$.

Diphenyltin dihydride, $(C_6H_5)_2SnH_2$, results through the reaction of ammonium bromide with disodiumtin diphenyl, $(C_6H_5)_2SnNa_2$, in liquid ammonia. The compound rapidly decomposes to diphenyltin and hydrogen.

Monoalkyl tin triiodides result from the addition of alkyl iodides to tin diiodide:[193]

$$SnI_2 + RI \rightarrow RSnI_3$$

Tin dialkyls are comparatively unstable and have been little investigated. They tend to form derivatives of tetravalent tin through intermolecular rearrangement, and are readily oxidized. They are generally colored.

A polymeric form of dimethyltin, $[(CH_3)_2Sn]_x$, is believed to result from the reaction of dimethyltin dibromide with metallic sodium in liquid ammonia.[207] The compound reacts very vigorously with oxygen, at times with explosive violence. It reacts with sodium in liquid ammonia to form first $NaSn(CH_3)_2Sn(CH_3)_2Na$, and on further reaction, $(CH_3)_2SnNa_2$. This last reacts with the free group $[Sn(CH_3)_2]_x$, giving, again,

$$NaSn(CH_3)_2Sn(CH_3)_2Na.$$

The reaction of disodium tin dimethyl with dimethyltin dibromide results in the formation of disodium hexamethylstannopropane:[207]

$$(CH_3)_2SnBr_2 + 2Na_2Sn(CH_3)_2 \rightarrow NaSn(CH_3)_2Sn(CH_3)_2Sn(CH_3)_2Na + 2NaBr$$

This compound is highly reactive and yields diethylhexamethylstannopropane,

$$C_2H_5Sn(CH_3)_2Sn(CH_3)_2Sn(CH_3)_2C_2H_5$$

with ethyl bromide; reacting with trimethyltin bromide, it gives dodecamethylstannopentane, $(CH_3)_3Sn[Sn(CH_3)_2]_3Sn(CH_3)_3$. Dimethylstannomethylene, $(CH_3)_2Sn = CH_2$, results through the reaction of disodium tin dimethyl with methylene chloride; the compound apparently polymerizes on standing.

Diethyltin, $Sn(C_2H_5)_2$, results through the reaction of ethyl iodide with an alloy consisting of one part of sodium and six parts of tin.[208] The compound has also been obtained by the reduction of diethyltin dichloride with zinc, and through the reaction of stannous chloride with zinc ethyl.

Dialkyl tin oxides are formed through the oxidation of tin dialkyls in air.[209] They are also obtained from dialkyl tin dihalides and aqueous ammonia,[210] or through the reaction of alkyl iodides with an alkaline solution of tin chloride.[211]

Tin diaryls may be obtained through the reaction of water-free stannous chloride with aryl magnesium bromides. Di-*p*-tolyl, di-*p*-xylyl, di-*α*-naphthyltin, and many other tin diaryls have been prepared by this method. Tin diaryls may also be prepared through the reaction of diaryl tin dihalides with sodium in liquid ammonia, although they are then obtained in the polymeric form.[212]

Alkyl stannonic acids are obtained in the form of their sodium salts through the reaction of alkyl halides with an alcoholic solution of sodium- or potassium stannite.[213] Thus, sodium methylstannite is obtained with methyl iodide:

$$CH_3I + NaSnOONa \rightarrow CH_3SnOONa + NaI$$

$$\text{or} \quad CH_3I + Sn(ONa)_2 \rightarrow \begin{matrix} CH_2 \\ \quad \diagdown \\ \quad\quad Sn(ONa)_3 \\ \quad \diagup \\ I \end{matrix} \rightarrow CH_3SnOONa + NaI$$

The reaction with methyl iodide requires about 24 hours for its completion. The methyl compound is isolated by saturating the liquid with carbon dioxide, evaporating it down to a third of its original volume, filtering the crude acid and heating it with hydriodic acid to convert it to methyltin triiodide; the latter is finally hydrolyzed with warm aqua ammonia.[193] Concentrated hydrochloric acid reacts with methylstannonic acid, converting it to the complex acid $H_2(SnCH_3Cl_5)$, which is the analog of hexachlorostannic acid, H_2SnCl_6.

Allyl and dichloromethylstannonic acids have been prepared successfully by this method by carrying out the reaction at a low temperature.[214] The method has been applied also to aliphatic halohydrins.[215]

Aryl stannonic acids result most simply by the hydrolysis of monoaryl tin trihalides $RSnCl_3$,[216] with boiling water. They are formed also through the interaction of stannous halides with aryl halides in the presence of potassium hydroxide.[214]

Tin Heterocycles

Diethylcyclopentamethylenetin, $\overline{CH_2(CH_2)_3CH_2Sn}(C_2H_5)_2$, has been obtained through the interaction of diethyltin dibromide and pentane-1,5-dimagnesium chloride.[217] The dimethyl analog may be obtained similarly. When cautiously treated with bromine, the diethyl compound is converted to

$$(C_2H_5)_2Sn(Br)CH_2(CH_2)_3CH_2Br$$

The bromine attached to the metal in this compound may be replaced with an alkyl group by reaction with an alkyl magnesium bromide, and the resulting bromo compound may be converted to the corresponding organomagnesium bromide, which undergoes the normal reactions of this type of compound.

Properties and Reactions of Organotin Compounds

Tin tetraalkyls are colorless liquids of generally low freezing points, insoluble in water and aqueous alcohol, but miscible with absolute alcohol and other organic solvents. They are stable in contact with water, and may be distilled under atmospheric pressure without decomposition. They are also stable in contact with steam at 105°. These compounds are co-ordinatively saturated and show no tendency to polymerize or to form etherates or ammoniates.

Heated with concentrated hydrochloric acid, tin tetraalkyls react to form trialkyl tin halides:

$$SnR_4 + HCl \rightarrow R_3SnCl + RH$$

Treatment with iodine also brings about fission of an alkyl group:

$$SnR_4 + I_2 \rightarrow R_3SnI + RI$$

Tetraphenyltin is a crystalline compound, soluble in chloroform and warm benzene, slightly soluble in cold benzene and in ether, insoluble in water and almost insoluble in alcohol. Other tin tetraaryls resemble tetraphenyltin in regard to their solubility.

Mixed alkyl aryl tins react with silver nitrate in alcoholic solution with fission of an aromatic group and the formation of an organo tin nitrate:

$$2(C_6H_5)_3SnCH_3 + 3AgNO_3 \rightarrow 2(C_6H_5)_2Sn(CH_3)NO_3 + (C_6H_5Ag)_2 \cdot AgNO_3$$

Mercuric chloride reacts in a similar manner. Tetraphenyltin does not, however, react with silver nitrate.

Organic groups attached to the metal in tin tetraalkyls and -aryls may be cleaved by reaction with halogens. The ease of cleavage decreases in the order C_6H_5, $C_6H_5CH_2$, CH_3, C_2H_5, $n.C_3H_7$.[218] This order does not hold for cleavage under the influence of halogen acids.[219]

Trialkyl tin halides possess a very unpleasant and very persistent odor. Dialkyl tin dihalides are odorless in the pure form. They are soluble in organic solvents, including petroleum ether. Monoalkyl tin trihalides are soluble in water and are rapidly hydrolyzed in aqueous solution. They are also soluble in organic solvents.

Trialkyl tin hydroxides do not show any similarity to alcohols. The mixed trialkyl tin alkoxides, R_3SnOR', are rapidly decomposed by water. Dialkyl tin dihydroxides, $R_2Sn(OH)_2$, with lower alkyl groups are apparently unstable and lose water to form the corresponding oxide; on the other hand stable dihydroxides containing tertiary alkyl groups such as *tert*-butyl and *tert*-amyl are known.[220]

Hexaalkyl distannanes are generally colorless liquids; only the isobutyl compound is solid at room temperature. They are oxidized in air, rather slowly when in the pure form, giving trialkyl tin oxides. Halogens react with these compounds in the cold to form trialkyl tin halides, while sulfur gives sulfides. In dilute boiling benzene solution hexamethyldistannane dissociates to $(CH_3)_3Sn$. Hexaphenyldistannane shows the phenomenon of *ultradissociation* in dilute solution, or at higher temperatures, the molecular weight appearing to be lower than that of triphenyltin.[221] Solid hexaphenyldistannane appears to be at least dimolecular. Hexacyclohexyldistannane is completely stable in air and when exposed to light, and may be kept unchanged without special precautions.

Tin diaryls are yellowish amorphous solids, soluble in benzene, chloroform and ethylene bromide. The solutions are a deep red color, but assume a yellow color when greatly diluted. In freshly prepared solutions in benzene, these compounds are originally monomolecular, but gradually polymerize, finally yielding pentadiaryl tins, the transformation being complete within a few days. They are gradually oxidized in air to colorless diaryl tin oxides. Oxidation proceeds more rapidly with the lower molecular tin diaryls. Treated with bromine in chloroform solution, tin diaryls react to form diaryl tin dibromides. When diphenyltin is heated at 205°, it decomposes giving a variety of products. Heated at 100° in the presence of phenylmagnesium bromide, the compound yields hexaphenyldistannane in 50% yield. This reaction does not take place with the higher molecular compounds.

Aryl stannous acids are amorphous solids, soluble in alkalies as well as in mineral acids. They are very weakly acidic. Alkyl stannic acids are amphoteric in nature. Their salts with metals are decomposed by carbon dioxide.

The *anhydrides of aryl thiostannonic acids*, $(RSnS)_2S$, are obtained when hydrogen sulfide is conducted through a solution of aryl stannonic acid in hydrochloric acid.

ORGANIC COMPOUNDS OF GERMANIUM

Germanium tetraalkyls are prepared through the reaction of germanium tetrachloride with zinc alkyls.[300] Tetraethylgermanium and the higher homologs may be prepared more conveniently by the reaction of germanium tetrachloride with alkyl magnesium halides.[261] Mixed tetraalkyl germaniums can also be prepared by this method.

Tetraphenylgermanium results by the reaction of germanium tetrachloride and bromobenzene with metallic sodium, the reaction proceeding fairly vigorously.[222] Tetra-*p*-tolylgermane, as well as a number of tetraalkyl germanes have been prepared by this method. The reaction of phenylmagnesium bromide with germanium tetrabromide proceeds less satisfactorily;[223] a phenylgermanium halide is first formed, which can only be converted to tetraphenylgermanium by use of a very large excess of the Grignard reagent.

Organolithium compounds have also been used for the preparation of organogermanium compounds.[262]

Mixed germanium aryl alkyl compounds containing two or three aromatic groups may be obtained from the sodio derivatives of germanium di- or triaryls by reaction with alkyl halides in liquid ammonia:[224]

$$(C_6H_5)_3GeNa + CH_3I \rightarrow (C_6H_5)_3GeCH_3 + NaI$$

Haloalkyl germanes result through the alkylation of germanium tetrahalides or through the reaction of halogens with tetraalkyl germanes.

Trimethylgermanium bromide, $(CH_3)_3GeBr$, has been obtained by the reaction of tetramethylgermanium with hydrogen bromide in the presence of aluminum bromide.[225] Water hydrolyzes the compound, probably to $[(CH_3)_3Ge]_2O$. Tetraphenylgermane is likewise converted to the monobromide by this method.

Diphenylgermanium dibromide is obtained in good yield, through the bromination of tetraphenylgermanium in boiling carbon tetrachloride.[226] The use of ethylene dibromide as a solvent greatly facilitates the reaction and gives a much greater yield of the dibromo compound. Ammonolysis of the dichloride in liquid ammonia gives the imide $(C_6H_5)_2Ge{:}NH$.

Dihalogermanes R_2GeX_2 have been synthesized through the reaction of germanium halides with organomagnesium halides. They have been prepared also by the interaction of metallic germanium with organic halides.[263]

Dichlorodimethylgermane has been obtained, together with trichloromethylgermane, by heating methyl chloride under pressure at 320 with metallic germanium mixed with an equal weight of copper.[264]

A ring compound with five carbon atoms has been obtained by treating germanium tetrachloride with the dihalomagnesium compound from 1,5-dibromopentane.[265]

Monoalkyl germanium iodides result in almost quantitative yield when alkyl iodides are heated with an equivalent of germanium iodide. The reaction with methyl iodide proceeds readily at 110°:

$$GeI_2 + C_2H_5I \rightarrow C_2H_5GeI_3$$

The compound yields the nitride C_2H_5GeN when treated with liquid ammonia, while hydrolysis results in the formation of $(C_2H_5GeO)_2O$.

Trichlorophenylgermane, $C_6H_5GeCl_3$, results when tetraphenylgermane is treated with twice its weight of germanium tetrachloride at 210-220°.[227] Reduction of the trichloride with sodium in xylene gives hexagermanium hexaphenyl, $(GeC_6H_5)_6$, which is readily oxidized.

Phenylgermanium trichloride has been prepared also by heating germanium tetrachloride with mercury diphenyl in dry xylene at 149° in a sealed tube for two days.[266] *p*-Tolyl, *p*-dimethylaminophenyl and benzylgermanium trichlorides have been prepared by this method.

Organogermanium trichlorides have been prepared by heating alkyl or aryl iodides with caesium germanium trichloride:[267]

$$RI + CsGeCl_3 \rightarrow RGeCl_3 + CsI$$

Caesium germanium trichloride is obtained by the reaction of caesium chloride with germanium dichloride.

Hexaethyldigermane, $(C_2H_5)_3GeGe(C_2H_5)_3$, results when triethylgermanium bromide is treated with metallic sodium at 210-270°.[228] The hexaphenyl analog can be obtained similarly from triphenylgermanium bromide.[268] The reaction is carried out in xylene solution. Hexaphenyldigermane apparently does not undergo dissociation to germanium triphenyl.

Octaphenyltrigermane, $(C_6H_5)_3GeGe(C_6H_5)_2Ge(C_6H_5)_3$, results from the reaction of triphenylgermanyl sodium with dichlorodiphenylgermane in benzene solution.[269]

Triphenylgermanyl sodium is formed by the action of sodium in anhydrous ammoniacal solution on tetraphenylgermane:[230]

$$(C_6H_5)_4Ge + 2Na + NH_3 \rightarrow (C_6H_5)_3GeNa + NaNH_2 + C_6H_6$$

Disodiodiphenylgermane, $(C_6H_5)_2GeNa_2$, is formed when a large excess of the metal is used. The monosodio compound is also obtained through the reaction of sodium with bis(triphenylgermanium) oxide

$$(C_6H_5)_3GeOGe(C_6H_5)_3 + 2Na \rightarrow (C_6H_5)_3GeNa + (C_6H_5)_3GeONa$$

The sodio derivatives of tri- and diphenylgermane are highly reactive.

Diphenylgermanium, $Ge(C_6H_5)_2$, has been obtained through the reaction of diphenylgermanium dichloride with sodium in boiling xylene.[229]

Triethylgermane, $(C_2H_5)_3GeH$ has been obtained by the action of ammonium bromide or water on triethylgermanyllithium.[270] Triphenylgermane has been prepared similarly from triphenylgermanylsodium.[271] Diphenylgermane, $(C_6H_5)_2GeH_2$, has been made by reducing diphenylgermanyl dichloride with lithium aluminum hydride.[272]

Triphenylgermanol, $(C_6H_5)_3GeOH$, is obtained by treating a benzene solution of sodium triphenylgermanolate, $(C_6H_5)_3GeONa$, with water.[271] The compound may be purified by crystallization from petroleum ether. *Tricyclohexylgermanol* has been prepared by the reaction of tricyclohexylgermanium bromide with alcoholic silver nitrate solution.[273] Tri-*o*-tolylgermanol has been obtained by a similar reaction.[274]

Bis(triethylgermanium)oxide, $(C_2H_5)_3GeOGe(C_2H_5)_3$, results in 97% yield from the hydrolysis of triethylgermanyl bromide by aqueous potassium hydroxide.[270] Bis(triphenylgermanium)oxide results similarly from triphenylgermanyl bromide. This oxide was obtained in quantitative yield by boiling an alcoholic solution of triphenylgermanyl bromide with silver nitrate.[275] The compound has also been made by the hydrolysis of triphenylgermanylamine.[276] *Bis(tribenzylgermanium)oxide* has been prepared by treating tribenzylgermanium bromide with silver nitrate, or by boiling the bromide with alcoholic potassium hydroxide.[277] *Bis(tri-p-tolylgermanium)-oxide* has been prepared from tri-*p*-tolylgermanium chloride by the action of boiling sodium hydroxide solution.[274]

Diethylgermanium oxide, $(C_2H_5)_2GeO$, has been prepared by hydrolyzing diethylgermanium dibromide.[278] The oxide exists in two polymeric modifications.[279] Treatment of triethylgermanium fluoride with fluorine results in the formation of diethylgermanium difluoride, which gives the oxide on treatment with alkalies. Shaken with concentrated halogen acids, the oxides R_2GeO are converted to the dihalides.

Phenylgermanoic anhydride, $(C_6H_5GeO)_2O$, results when trichlorophenylgermane, $C_6H_5GeCl_3$, is hydrolyzed with dilute ammonia.[280] Treatment of the anhydride with aqueous hydrogen sulfide results in the formation of dithiogermanic anhydride,

$$(C_6H_5GeS)_2S$$

Tetraethoxygermane, $Ge(OC_2H_5)_4$, is formed when a mixture of sodium and ethyl alcohol reacts with germanium tetrachloride.[281]

Organogermanium sulfides, $R_3GeSGeR_3$, have been obtained by the interaction of monobromogermanes R_3GeBr with sodium sulfide.[282] Tricyclohexylgermanium bromide gives the disulfide $(C_6H_{11})_3GeS{\cdot}SGe(C_6H_{11})_3$, by this reaction.

Germanium tetrathiophenolate, $Ge(SC_6H_5)_4$, has been prepared by the reaction of germanium tetrachloride with thiophenol and sodium.[283]

Triethylgermanyl bromide forms an addition compound with ammonia, $(C_2H_5)_3GeBrNH_3$, which may be converted to the imide $(C_2H_5)_3GeNH$.[228]

Triphenylgermanylamine results from the reaction of gaseous ammonia with triphenylgermanium bromide, or other triphenylgermanium halides in organic solvents.[284]

$$2(C_6H_5)_3GeBr + 3NH_3 \rightarrow (C_6H_5)_3GeNHGe(C_6H_5)_3 + 2NH_4Br$$

Deamination sometimes occurs immediately upon precipitation. Conversion to the tertiary amine or nitride, $[(C_6H_5)_3Ge]_3N$ is effected by heating the primary amine above 200° first at atmospheric pressure, then under vacuum.[271]

Aminolysis of a dihalodiphenylgermane with liquid ammonia results in the formation of the imine:[285]

$$(C_6H_5)_2GeCl_2 + 3NH_3 \rightarrow (C_6H_5)_2GeNH + 2NH_4Cl$$

Ethylgermanium nitride, C_2H_5GeN, is formed when trichloroethylgermane is made to react with liquid ammonia. The nitride is converted to the anhydride $(C_2H_5GeO)_2O$ by hydrolysis. Phenylgermanium nitride is formed through the interaction of triiodophenylgermane, $C_6H_5GeI_3$, with ammonia.[286]

Ethylgermanium isocyanates have been prepared through the reaction of ethylgermanium halides with silver isocyanate.[287]

ORGANIC COMPOUNDS OF BISMUTH

Bismuth trialkyls are best obtained through the reaction of bismuth halides with alkyl magnesium halides.[231] They may also be prepared by the interaction of bismuth tribromide with zinc dialkyls:

$$2BiBr_3 + 3Zn(C_2H_5)_2 \rightarrow 2Bi(C_2H_5)_3 + 3ZnBr_2$$

Trimethylbismuth was first prepared from anhydrous bismuth bromide and dimethyltin. The reaction was carried out in ethereal solution, using an excess of dimethyltin.[232] This compound is formed also when aluminum carbide, Al_4C_3, is made to react with bismuth chloride in hydrochloric acid solution.[233]

Triethylbismuth has been prepared by heating diethylmercury with bismuth powder at 100 to 130°.[288] Bismuth trialkyls have been made by the reaction of alkyl iodides with bismuth-alkali metal alloys.[289]

Bismuth trialkyls are colorless liquids which ignite spontaneously in air. They decompose when heated to a temperature in excess of 150°, sometimes with explosive violence. They are decomposed by water only on long boiling. They are soluble in alcohol, ether, ligroin, carbon tetrachloride and benzene; they are practically insoluble in water.

Bismuth trialkyls are not capable of adding halogens, the latter causing cleavage of an alkyl halide and a dialkylbismuth halide. Bismuth triaryls, on the other hand, add halogens to form triarylbismuth dihalides. The reaction is carried out in a suitable solvent, such as ligroin or ether. The halides may be converted to derivatives of other acids.

Bismuth triaryls are generally prepared by heating powdered bismuth-sodium alloy with aryl halides. They are obtained also through the reaction of bismuth bromide or chloride with aryl magnesium halides or mercury diaryls.[234]

Bismuth triaryls result also from the decomposition of aryl diazonium chloride-bismuth chloride complexes with copper, followed by treatment with ammonia.[290]

Triphenylbismuth results in 41% yield on heating bismuth with diphenylmercury at 250°.[291]

Bismuth triaryls are much more stable than bismuth trialkyls. They crystallize well, do not oxidize in air and may be readily obtained in the pure form.

Unsymmetrical organobismuth compounds, R_2BiR' have been prepared by the reaction of the sodio derivatives R_2BiNa with α-iodo compounds IR' in liquid ammonia.[292] Mixed bismuth trialkyls or aryls are also obtained by the reaction of alkyl or aryl bismuth halides with organomagnesium halides:[235]

$$(C_6H_5)_2BiBr + C_{10}H_7MgBr \rightarrow (C_6H_5)_2BiC_{10}H_7 + MgBr_2$$

A bismuth heterocycle has been prepared through the interaction of ethylbismuth dibromide with pentane-1,5-dimagnesium bromide:[239]

$$C_2H_5BiBr_2 + BrMgCH_2(CH_2)_3CH_2MgBr \rightarrow C_2H_5\overline{BiCH_2(CH_2)_3CH_2} + 2MgBr_2$$

Dialkylbismuth chlorides are obtained by the reaction of chlorine with bismuth trialkyls:[293]

$$(CH_3)_3Bi + Cl_2 \rightarrow (CH_3)_2BiCl + CH_3Cl$$

They may be formed also through the reaction of bismuth trialkyls with a half molecular proportion of bismuth trihalide. Diarylbismuth halides result when bismuth triaryls are made to react with anhydrous bismuth trihalides at room temperature in benzene or in ethereal solution.

Diarylbismuth halides react with alkali and alkalineearth metals in anhydrous ammoniacal solution to form compounds of the type $Ar_2BiM\cdot(Ar_2Bi)_2M'$. These are highly reactive bodies.

Monoalkyl bismuth dichlorides or dibromides are obtained by the interaction of bismuth trialkyls with bismuth trichloride or tribromide:

$$(C_2H_5)_3Bi + 2BiBr_3 \rightarrow 3C_2H_5BiBr_2$$

The calculated amount of the anhydrous bismuth trihalide in anhydrous ether is added to an ethereal solution of the tertiary bismuth compound. The reaction proceeds readily and the yields in many instances are almost quantitative.[294]

Compounds of this type are obtained by the reaction of bismuth chloride with alkyl magnesium halides.[295] They are formed also by the action of halogens on bismuth trialkyls, and by the reaction of the latter with silver- or mercury halides.

The diiodides, $RBiI_2$, result when bismuth trialkyls are made to react with alkyl iodides:

$$(CH_3)_3Bi + 2CH_3I \rightarrow CH_3BiI_2 + 2C_2H_6$$

Diphenylbismuth cyanide, $(C_6H_5)_2BiCN$, results from the interaction of bismuth triphenyl and cyanogen iodide,[236] or from the reaction of triphenylbismuth dichloride with potassium cyanide.[237]

Triarylbismuth dichlorides, Ar_3BiCl_2, are formed on passing a stream of dry gaseous chlorine through the ice-cooled solution of the triarylbismuth in chloroform until a permanent yellow color appears indicating the presence of an excess of the gas in the liquid. The compound is recovered by concentrating the solution by evaporation, and precipitating the chloride by the addition of methanol. The chloro compound is obtained in a pure form and in high yield, generally more than 90%. These compounds may be prepared also by passing a stream of dry chlorine over a solution of the tertiary bismuth compound in petroleum ether.

The halogen in tertiary bismuth dihalides is quite reactive, and may be readily exchanged by various groups. The dihydroxides $Ar_3Bi(OH)_2$ are obtained when the halides are treated with moist ammonia or silver oxide.[238] Organic salts of these hydroxy compounds are formed on treating them with organic acids:[296]

$$R_3Bi(OH)_2 + 2RCOOH \rightarrow R_3Bi(OCOR')_2 + 2H_2O$$

These salts may be obtained also by treating the carbonates R_3BiCO_3 with organic acids. This method has been utilized for the preparation of a large number of salts of substituted benzoic acids. Salts of triarylbismuth hydroxides are also formed through the reaction of bismuth triaryls with acyl peroxides:

$$R_3Bi + (C_6H_5CO)_2O_2 \rightarrow R_3Bi(OCOC_6H_5)_2$$

The reaction of carboxylic acids with a triaryl bismuth leads to the formation of a monoarylbismuth salt:

$$(C_6H_5)_3Bi + 2HOCOR \rightarrow C_6H_5Bi(OCOR)_2 + 2C_6H_6$$

With thiophenols monoaryl bismuth diaryl mercaptals are formed:

$$(C_6H_5)_3Bi + 2C_6H_5SH \rightarrow C_6H_5Bi(SC_6H_5)_2 + 2C_6H_6$$

ORGANIC COMPOUNDS OF CHROMIUM

Alkyl chromium compounds are not known.

Aryl chromium compounds are formed through the interaction of chromium trichloride with aryl magnesium halides:[240]

$$3CrCl_3 + 4C_6H_5MgBr \rightarrow (C_6H_5)_4CrCl + 2CrCl_2 + 2MgBr_2 + 2MgCl_2$$

Some $(C_6H_5)_5CrCl$ and $(C_6H_5)_3CrCl$ are also formed.

The chromium dichloride formed reacts further with phenylmagnesium bromide more or less completely according to the following equation:

$$4CrCl_2 + 4C_6H_5MgBr \rightarrow (C_6H_5)_4CrCl + 3CrCl + 2MgCl_2 + 2MgBr_2$$

Pentaphenylchromium hydroxide, $(C_6H_5)_5CrOH$, is prepared by the reaction of pentaphenylchromium chloride in alcoholic solution with potassium hydroxide.[241] The mother liquors from the reaction also contain triphenylchromium hydroxide.[242]

Pentaphenylchromium hydroxide gives salts in the normal manner with only a few acids. Salt formation is usually accompanied by cleavage of a phenyl group and the formation of tetraphenylchromium salts, $(C_6H_5)_4CrX$:

$$(C_6H_5)_5CrOH + KX \rightarrow (C_6H_5)_4CrX + C_6H_5OK + H$$

$$(C_6H_5)_4CrX + H \rightarrow (C_6H_5)_4Cr\begin{matrix}\cdot\cdot\cdot H \\ \diagdown X\end{matrix}$$

The dihydrate of tetraphenylchromium hydroxide may be obtained from tetraphenylchromium chloride. The hydrogen in $(C_6H_5)_4Cr\begin{matrix}\cdot\cdot\cdot H \\ \diagdown X\end{matrix}$ is very loosely bound, and is probably lost when the compound is isolated. The transformation is reversible, however, and the compound $(C_6H_5)_4CrX$ combines with an atom of hydrogen.

The radical $(C_6H_5)_4Cr$ has been prepared through the electrolysis of tetraphenylchromium iodide in liquid ammonia.[243]

Triphenylchromium hydroxide, $(C_6H_5)_3CrOH$, is a stronger base than the tetraphenyl compound and shows a conductivity comparable with that of sodium hydroxide.

ORGANIC IRON COMPOUND – FERROCENE

Cyclopentadiene reacts at 300° under atmospheric pressure with reduced iron to form an orange yellow compound, $C_5H_5FeC_6H_5$, termed Ferrocene.[297] The same compound is obtained when the Grignard compound of cyclopentadiene is treated with ferric chloride.[298] This, the only compound known to date containing only carbon, hydrogen and iron, is a remarkably stable body. It sublimes at 100°, is volatile with steam and alcohol vapor, and resists pyrolysis at 470°.[299]

References

1. Hariot and St. Pierre., *Bull. soc. chim.*, (3) **1**, 774 (1889); (3) **5**, 292 (1891).
2. Krause and Rosen, *J. Am. Chem. Soc.*, **47**, 2739 (1925); Wooster and Ryan, *ibid.*, **54**, 2419 (1932); Jones and Seymour, *ibid.*, **50**, 1150 (1928); Jaeger and Dykstra, *Konink. Akad. Wetensch. Amsterdam*, **27**, 398 (1924).
3. Ziegler and Wallschitt, *Ann.*, **479**, 123 (1930).
4. Ziegler and Thielman, *Ber.*, **56**, 1740 (1923); Connant and Garvey, *J. Am. Chem. Soc.*, **49**, 2599 (1927); Marvel *et al.*, *ibid.*, **50**, 1737, 2840 (1928); **51**, 932 (1929); **52**, 3368 (1930); **53**, 3840, 4057 (1931).
5. Schlenk and Bergmann, *Ann.*, **463**, 1, 98 (1928); Hauk, *Ber.*, **62**, 1771 (1929).
6. Wooster and Smith, *J. Am. Chem. Soc.*, **53**, 179 (1931).
7. Matignon, *Compt. rend.*, **124**, 775 (1897).
8. Ziegler *et al.*, *Ber.*, **61**, 253 (1928); *Ann.*, **473**, 57 (1929); **511**, 13, 45, 64, 101 (1934). *Cf.* Ziegler, *Angew. Chem.*, **49**, 499 (1936).
9. Ziegler, *Angew. Chem.*, **49**, 455 (1936); *French patent*, 736,428.
10. Gilman *et al.*, *J. Am. Chem. Soc.*, **62**, 1514 (1940).
11. Wooster and Mitchell, *ibid.*, **52**, 1042 (1930).
12. Ziegler and Crössmann, *Ber.*, **62**, 1768 (1929); Schlenk and Bergmann, *Ann.*, **463**, 98, 1928).
13. Schorigin, *Ber.*, **56**, 176 (1923); Ziegler and Thielmann, *ibid.*, **56**, 1740 (1923); Ziegler and Schnell, *Ann.*, **437**, 227 (1924).
14. Ziegler and Schnell, *l.c.*
15. Meyer and Fischer, *J. prakt. Chem.*, (2) **82**, 525 (1910).
16. Wanklyn, *Ann.*, **107**, 125 (1858); *Proc. Roy. Soc.* (London), **9**, 341 (1858); Hein *et al.*, *Z. anorg. Chem.*, **141**, 161 (1924); Schlenk and Holtz, *Ber.*, **50**, 262 (1917).
17. Hein *et al.*, *Z. Elektrochem.*, **28**, 469 (1922); *Z. anorg. allgem. Chem.*, **141**, 161 (1924); **158**, 153 (1926); *Z. physik. Chem.* A **151**, 234 (1930).
18. Ziegler *et al.*, *Ber.*, **56**, 1740 (1923); *Ann.*, **437**, 36, 57, 163, 227 (1929); **443**, 161 (1925); *Ber.*, **61**, 253 (1928); **62**, 1768 (1929); **63**, 1847 (1930); **64**, 445, 448 (1931); *Ann.*, **479**, 123, 135, 150 (1930); **485**, 174 (1931); Bergmann *et al.*, *Ber.*, **62**, 893 (1929); **63**, 775, 1617, 2593, 2585 (1930); *Ann.*, **480**, 49, 59, 188 (1930); **483**, 65, 80 (1930).
19. Bried and Hennion, *J. Am. Chem. Soc.*, **60**, 1717 (1938).
20. Lebau and Picon, *Compt. rend.*, **156**, 1077 (1913); Zoss and Hennion, *J. Am. Chem. Soc.*, **63**, 1151 (1941); Picon, *Compt. rend.*, **169**, 32 (1919); Lespieau and Journaud, *Bull. soc. chim.*, (4) **49**, 423 (1931). *Cf.* Nieuwland *et al.*, *J. Org. Chem.*, **2**, 1 (1938).
21. Worall, *J. Am. Chem. Soc.*, **39**, 697 (1917).
22. Gilman *et al.*, *ibid.*, **55**, 1252 (1933); Ziegler and Colonius, *Ann.*, **479**, 135 (1930); Ziegler, *German patent* 512,882.
23. Ziegler *et al.*, *Ann.*, **473**, 1 (1929); **479**, 135, 150 (1930); Spencer and Price, *J. Chem. Soc.*, **97**, 385 (1910); Gilman *et al.*, *J. Am. Chem. Soc.*, **54**, 1957 (1932); **57**, 1061 (1935). *Cf. Rec. trav. chim.*, **54**, 592 (1935).

24. Ziegler and Colonius, *Ann.*, **479**, 135 (1930); Gilman *et al.*, *J. Am. Chem. Soc.*, **54**, 1957 (1932); **55**, 1252 (1933); **57**, 1061 (1935); *Rec. trav. chim.*, **54**, 584 (1935).
25. Haubein, *Iowa State Coll. J. Sci.*, **18**, 48 (1943); Gilman and Haubein, *J. Am. Chem. Soc.*, **66**, 1515 (1944); Ziegler *et al.*, *Ann.*, **473**, 31 (1929).
26. Ziegler and Dersch, *Ber.*, **64**, 448 (1931).
27. Gilman and Jones, *J. Am. Chem. Soc.*, **63**, 1441 (1941).
28. Ziegler *et al.*, *Ann.*, **473**, 1 (1929); **511**, 13 (1934).
29. Wittig and Pockels, *Ber.*, **72**, 89 (1939).
30. Wittig and Witt, *ibid.*, **74**, 1474 (1941).
31. *Cf.* Kharasch and Reynolds, *J. Am. Chem. Soc.*, **63**, 3239 (1941).
32. Gilman *et al.*, *ibid.*, **60**, 2335 (1938); **61**, 109 (1939); Ziegler, *Angew. Chem.*, **49**, 455 (1936).
33. Gilman *et al.*, *J. Am. Chem. Soc.*, **56**, 1415 (1934); **57**, 1121 (1935); **61**, 109 (1939); **67**, 877 (1945); *J. Org. Chem.*, **3**, 108 (1939).
34. Ziegler *et al.*, *Ann.*, **479**, 125 (1930); **485**, 174 (1931); *Ber.*, **63**, 1847 (1930); Rosenthal, *J. prakt. Chem.*, (2) **135**, 267 (1932); Walters and McElvain, *J. Am. Chem. Soc.*, **55**, 4625 (1933); Haskelberg, *Chemistry and Industry*, **54**, 261 (1935).
35. Ziegler and Ohlinger, *Ann.*, **495**, 84 (1932).
36. Ziegler *et al.*, *ibid.*, **504**, 100 (1933).
37. Gilman *et al.*, *J. Am. Chem. Soc.*, **61**, 1170 (1939).
38. Buckton, *Ann.*, **112**, 220 (1859); Schlenk and Holtz, *Ber.*, **50**, 262 (1917); Haeger and Marvel, *J. Am. Chem., Soc.*, **48**, 2689 (1926); Ziegler and Dersch, *Ber.*, **64**, 448 (1931).
39. Schlenk and Holtz, *Ber.*, **50**, 262 (1917).
40. Gilman *et al.*, *J. Am. Chem. Soc.*, **55**, 1965 (1933); *J. Org. Chem.*, **1**, 315 (1936).
41. Ziegler *et al.*, *Ann.*, **511**, 64, 101 (1934); **542**, 90 (1939).
42. Wittig and Leo, *Ber.*, **64**, 2395 (1931).
43. Wittig *et al.*, *ibid.*, **64**, 2395, 2405 (1931); **67**, 667 (1934); **68**, 928 (1935); Leo, *ibid.*, **70**, 1691 (1937).
44. Wittig and Petri, *Ber.*, **68**, 924 (1935).
45. Lüttringhaus, *ibid.*, **67**, 1602 (1934); Koelsch and Rosewald, *J. Am. Chem. Soc.*, **59**, 2166 (1937); Kipping and Wild, *J. Chem. Soc.*, **1940**, 1239; Gilman and Kirby, *J. Am. Chem. Soc.*, **63**, 2046 (1941).
46. Gilman and Breuer, *J. Am. Chem. Soc.*, **55**, 1262 (1933).
47. Gilman and Van Ess, *ibid.*, **55**, 1258 (1933).
48. Gilman *et al ibid.*, **62**, 667 (1940); **66**, 858 (1944).
49. Groll, *ibid.*, **52**, 3000 (1930); Birch, *J. Chem. Soc.*, **1934**, 1132.
50. Gilman *et al.*, *J. Am. Chem. Soc.*, **55**, 1265 (1933); *J. Org. Chem.*, **1**, 315 (1936).
51. Ziegler, *Ann.*, **473**, 21 (1929). *Cf.* Krabbe and Grünwald, *Ber.*, **74**, 1343 (1941).
52. Gilman and Haubein, *J. Am. Chem. Soc.*, **66**, 1515 (1944).
53. Krause and Wendt, *Ber.*, **56**, 2064 (1923); Reich, *Compt. rend.*, **177**, 322 (1923).
54. Pope and Gibson, *J. Chem. Soc.*, **91**, 2061 (1907).
55. Kharasch and Isbell, *J. Am. Chem. Soc.*, **53**, 2701 (1931).
56. Buraway and Gibson, *J. Chem. Soc.*, **1934**, 860.
57. Kharasch and Isbell, *J. Am. Chem. Soc.*, **53**, 3053 (1931).
58. Giuliani, *Gazz. chim. ital.*, **64**, 894 (1934).
59. Gibson and Simonsen, *J. Chem. Soc.*, **1930**, 2531; Kharasch and Isbell, *J. Am. Chem. Soc.*, **53**, 2701 (1931); Pope and Gibson, *J. Chem. Soc.*, **91**, 2061 (1907).
60. Wanklyn, *Ann.*, **140**, 353 (1866).
61. Gilman and Brown, *J. Am. Chem. Soc.*, **52**, 5045 (1930).
62. Fleck, *Ann.*, **276**, 138 (1893).
63. Frankland, *ibid.*, **95**, 36 (1855).
64. Job and Reich, *Bull. soc. chim.*, (4) **33**, 1414 (1923); Lachmann, *Am. Chem. J.*, **24**, 33 (1900); Michael, *ibid.*, **25**, 422 (1901); Bewad, *J. Russ. Phys.-Chem. Soc.*, **39**, 950 (1907).
65. Job and Reich, *Bull. soc. chim.*, (4) **33**, 1414 (1923).
66. Blaise, *ibid.*, (4) **9**, 1-XXVI (1911).
67. Krause and Fromm, *Ber.*, **59**, 931 (1926).
68. Kozeschkow *et al.*, *ibid.*, **63**, 1138 (1934).
69. Noller, *J. Am. Chem. Soc.*, **51**, 594 (1929).
70. Cahours, *Compt. rend.*, **76**, 133, 748, 1383 (1873); Nilson and Petersson, *Ber.*, **17**, 987 (1884); Lavrow, *J. Russ. Phys.-Chem. Soc.*, **16**, 93 (1884); *Bull. soc. chim.*, (2) **41**, 548 (1884).
71. Krause and Wendt, *Ber.*, **56**, 467 (1923); Gilman and Schulze, *J. Chem. Soc.*, **1927**, 2663.
72. Gilman, *J. Am. Chem. Soc.*, **45**, 2693 (1923); Durand, *Compt. rend.*, **182**, 1162 (1926).
73. Gilman and Schulze, *J. Chem. Soc.*, **1927**, 2663; *Rec. trav. chim.*, **48**, 1129 (1929); Schulze, *Iowa State Coll. J. Sci.* **8**, 225 (1933).
74. Krause, *Ber.*, **50**, 1813 (1917); de Mahler, *J. Russ. Phys.-Chem. Soc.*, **48**, 1964 (1916); Gilman and Nelson, *Rec. trav. chim.*, **55**, 518 (1936).
75. Nessmejanow and Makarowa, *J. Russ. Phys.-Chem. Soc.*, **7** (69), 2649 (1937).

76. Frankland, *Ann.*, **111**, 59 (1859); Strecker, *ibid.*, **92**, 76 (1854); Buckton, *ibid.*, **109**, 222 (1859); *J. prakt. Chem.*, (1) **76**, 362 (1859).
77. Sakurai, *J. Chem. Soc.*, **37**, 658 (1880); **39**, 485 (1881); **41**, 360 (1882); Maynard, *J. Am. Chem. Soc.*, **54**, 2108 (1932).
78. Zinin, *Ann.*, **96**, 363 (1855); Linnemann, *ibid. Spl.* **3**, 262 (1865); **140**, 180 (1866); Oppenheim, *Ber.*, **4**, 670 (1871).
79. v. Braun, *Ber.*, **46**, 1792 (1913); **47**, 491 (1914); Hilpert and Grüttner, *ibid.*, **47**, 177, 186 (1914).
80. Kharasch *et al.*, *J. Am. Chem. Soc.*, **47**, 1948 (1925); **48**, 3130 (1926); **54**, 674 (1932).
81. Buckton, *Ann.*, **108**, 105 (1858); Frankland, *ibid.*, **111**, 60 (1859). Frankland and Duppa, *J. Chem. Soc.*, **16**, 415, 422 (1863); *Ann.*, **130**, 114 (1864); Grüttner, *Ber.*, **47**, 1655 (1914); Hilpert and Grüttner, *ibid.*, **47**, 191 (1914).
82. Steinkopf, *Ann.*, **413**, 313 (1917).
83. Hellerman and Newman, *J. Am. Chem. Soc.*, **54**, 2859 (1932).
84. Hilpert and Grüttner, *Ber.*, **46**, 1686 (1913).
85. Marvel and Gould, *J. Am. Chem. Soc.*, **44**, 153 (1922); Calvery, *ibid.*, **45**, 820 (1923); Gilman and Brown, *ibid.*, **52**, 3314 (1930).
86. Kharasch and Marker, *J. Am. Chem. Soc.*, **48**, 3130 (1926).
87. Pope and Gibson, *J. Chem. Soc.*, **101**, 736 (1912); Wolff, *Ber.*, **46**, 65 (1913); Jones and Werner, *J. Am. Chem. Soc.*, **40**, 1266 (1918); Hilpert and Grüttner, *Ber.*, **48**, 907 (1915).
88. Maynard, *J. Am. Chem. Soc.*, **54**, 2118 (1932).
89. Kharasch and Grafflin, *ibid.*, **47**, 1948 (1925).
90. Hein and Wagler, *Ber.*, **58**, 1499 (1925); *German patent* 444,666.
91. Dreher and Otto, *Ber.*, **2**, 542 (1869); Frankland and Dupa, *J. Chem. Soc.*, **16**, 415 (1863); *Ann.*, **130**, 104 (1864); Chapman, *J. Chem. Soc.*, **19**, 150 (1866); Lewis and Chamberlin, *J. Am. Chem. Soc.*, **51**, 291 (1929).
92. Pesci, *Gazz. chim. ital.*, **29 I**, 394 (1899); *Z. anorg. allgem. Chem.*, **15**, 212 (1897); **17**, 282 (1898); *Ber.*, **35**, 2041, 2855 (1902); Prussia, *Gazz. chim. ital.*, **27 I**, 17 (1897); **28 II**, 129 (1898); Kharasch and Piccard, *J. Am. Chem. Soc.*, **42**, 1861 (1920); Whitmore and Middleton, *ibid.*, **43**, 622 (1921); Schoeller *et al.*, *Ber.*, **47**, 1936 (1914); **53**, 642 (1920).
93. Hofmann and Feigel, *Ber.*, **38**, 3654 (1905).
94. Hofmann, *ibid.*, **31**, 1908, 2213, 2783 (1898); **32**, 870 (1899); **33**, 1333 (1900).
95. Hofmann *et al.*, *Ber.*, **32**, 875 (1899); **33**, 1348 (1900).
96. Biilman, *ibid.*, **35**, 2580 (1902); Schoeller and Schrauth, *ibid.*, **41**, 2089 (1906); **42**, 778 (1909).
97. Schrauth and Schoeller, *Ber.*, **42**, 782 (1909).
98. Montignie, *Bull. soc. chim.*, (4) **43**, 1115 (1928).
99. Hofmann and Sand, *Ber.*, **33**, 1344 (1900).
100. Schoeller *et al.*, *ibid.*, **46**, 2864 (1913); Manchot, *ibid.*, **53**, 986 (1920).
101. Manchot, *Ann.*, **420**, 170 (1920); *Ber.*, **53**, 984 (1920). *Cf.* Hofmann *et al.*, *ibid.*, **33**, 1344 (1900); **56**, 123 (1923); Sand, *ibid.*, **34**, 1385 (1901); Adams *et al.*, *J. Am. Chem. Soc.*, 44, 1781 (1922); **45**, 1842 (1923).
102. Hofmann and Kirmreuther, *Ber.*, **41**, 316 (1908); **42**, 4236 (1909).
103. Nieuwland *et al.*, *J. Am. Chem. Soc.*, **55**, 2465, 3728, 4206 (1933).
104. Krause, *Ber.*, **59**, 936 (1926).
105. Schoeller *et al.*, *Biochem. Z.*, **33**, 381 (1911); Forster, *J. Chem. Soc.*, **111**, 1158 (1920).
106. Kotten and Adams, *J. Am. Chem. Soc.*, **46**, 2764 (1924).
107. Hart and Anderson, *ibid.*, **56**, 2752 (1934); **57**, 1059 (1935).
108. Michaelis, *Ber.*, **15**, 2877 (1882).
109. Michaelis and Schent, *ibid.*, **21**, 1501 (1888); *Ann.*, **260**, 6 (1890).
110. Dimroth, *Ber.*, **31**, 2154 (1898); Kharasch *et al.*, *J. Am. Chem. Soc.*, **43**, 1894 (1921); **46**, 1211 (1924); Maschmann, *Ann.*, **450**, 85, 93 (1926).
111. Dimroth, *Ber.*, **35**, 2036 (1902); *Ann.*, **446**, 148 (1925); Jürgens, *Rec. trav. chim.*, **45**, 61 (1926).
112. Desesquelle, *Bull. soc. chim.*, (3) **11**, 266 (1894); Dimroth, *Ber.*, **31**, 2155 (1898); **32**, 761 (1899); **35**, 2033, 2853 (1902); Hofmann, *ibid.*, **38**, 2002 (1905); Kalinowski, *Roczniki Chem.*, **9**, 131 (1929); Cains and Wadia, *J. Indian Chem. Soc.*, **6**, 613 (1929); Amadory, *Atti accad. Lincei*, (6) **13**, 371 (1931); Mameli, *Gazz. chim. ital.*, **52 II**, 18, 23 (1922); Raiziss and Proskouriakoff, *J. Am. Chem. Soc.*, **44**, 787 (1922); Haught *et al.*, *ibid.*, **53**, 2697 (1931); Henry and Sharp, *J. Chem. Soc.*, **1926**, 2432; Whitmore and Middleton, *J. Am. Chem. Soc.*, **45**, 1753 (1923); Krýnsk, *Roczniki Chem.*, **8**, 71 (1928); Sandin, *J. Am. Chem. Soc.*, **51**, 479 (1929); Henry and Sharp, *J. Chem. Soc.*, **1930**, 2279; Neogi and Mukherjee, *J. Indian Chem. Soc.*, **12**, 211 (1935).
113. Dimroth, *Ber.*, **35**, 2856 (1902).
114. Dimroth, *l.c.*, Manchot, *Ann.*, **421**, 333 (1920).
115. Dimroth, *Ber.*, **35**, 2870 (1902); Grignard and Abelmann, *Bull. soc. chim.*, (4) **19**, 19 (1916).
116. Schoeller, *et al.*, *Ber.*, **47**, 1930 (1914); **52**, 1777 (1919); **53**, 634 (1920).

117. Schoeller and Schrauth, *ibid.*, **53**, 636 (1920); Sachs, *ibid.*, **53**, 1740 (1920); Dimroth, *ibid.*, **32**, 765 (1899); **35**, 2872 (1902).
118. Verkade, *Rec. trav. chim.*, **45**, 475 (1926); Dean *et al.*, *J. Am. Chem. Soc.*, **47**, 403 (1925); Rupp and Poggendorf, *Arch. Pharm.*, **269**, 607 (1931); Brennans and Rapilly, *Compt. rend.*, **193**, 55 (1931); Ishihara, *J. Pharm. Soc. Japan*, **49**, 134, 140 (1929); Rodionow and Fedorowa, *Ber. Deutsch. Pharm. Ges.*, **269**, 607 (1931); Whitmore *et al.*, *J. Am. Chem. Soc.*, **51**, 602, 2196, 2785, 3352 (1929); **48**, 784 (1926); Cocchetti and Godi, *Gazz. chim. ital.*, **58**, 764 (1928); Dominikiewitz, *Roczniki Chem.*, **11**, 664 (1931).
119. Vecchiotti, *Gazz. chim. ital.*, **44 II**, 35 (1914).
120. Pesci, *Z. anorg. allgem. Chem.*, **15**, 216 (1897).
121. Whitmore, *J. Am. Chem. Soc.*, **41**, 1841 (1919).
122. Kharasch and Jacobsohn, *ibid.*, **43**, 1894 (1921).
123. Pesci, *Z. anorg. allgem. Chem.*, **15**, 222 (1897); Dimroth, *Ber.*, **35**, 2037 (1902).
124. Scheller *et al.*, *Ber.*, **45**, 2812 (1912); Jacobs and Heidelberger, *J. Biol. Chem.*, **20**, 519 (1915); Vecchiotti, *Gazz. chim. ital.*, **56**, 155 (1926).
125. Pesci, *Gazz. chim. ital.*, **28 II**, 101 (1898); *Z. anorg. allgem. Chem.*, **17**, 276 (1898); Reitzenstein and Stamm, *J. prakt. Chem.*, (2) **81**, 159 (1910).
126. Brieger and Schulemann, *J. prakt. Chem.*, (2) **89**, 141 (1914).
127. Raiziss *et al.*, *J. Biol. Chem.*, **40**, 533 (1919).
128. Fischer and Müller, *Z. physiol. Chem.*, **148**, 155 (1925); Plancher and Rossi, *Gazz. chim. ital.*, **55**, 61 (1925); Sachs and Eberhartinger, *Ber.*, **56**, 2223 (1923); Schrauth and Bauerschmidt, *ibid.*, **47**, 2736 (1914); Ukai, *J. Pharm. Soc. Japan*, **47**, 119 (1927); **48**, 75, 116 (1928); **51**, 73 (1931); Cechetti and Sarti, *Gazz. chim. ital.*, **60**, 189 (1930).
129. Dimroth, *Ber.*, **32**, 759 (1899); Schwalbe, *ibid.*, **38**, 2208 (1905); Steinkopf and Baumeister, *Ann.*, **403**, 62 (1914).
130. Neogi and Chatterji, *J. Indian Chem. Soc.*, **5**, 221 (1928); Mukherjee, *ibid.*, **12**, 211 (1935). *Cf.* Lefèvre and Desgrez, *Compt. rend.*, **200**, 762 (1935).
131. Peters, *Ber.*, **38**, 2567 (1905).
132. Kharasch and Chalkey, *J. Am. Chem. Soc.*, **43**, 611 (1921).
133. Nesmeyanov *et al.*, *Ber.*, **68**, 565 (1935); Gilman and Yale, *J. Am. Chem. Soc.*, **72**, 8 (1950); *German patent* 272,289 (1913); *Chem. Zentr.* **1914 I**, 1469.
134. Kharasch, *J. Am. Chem. Soc.*, **43**, 2238 (1921); Kharasch and Stavely, *ibid.*, **45**, 2961 (1923).
135. Nesmejanow *et al.*, *Ber.*, **62**, 1010, 1018 (1929).
136. Nesmejanow *et al.*, *ibid.*, **67**, 130 (1934); *J. Russ. Phys.-Chem. Soc.*, **66**, 713 (1934).
137. McClure and Lowy, *J. Am. Chem. Soc.*, **53**, 319 (1931).
138. Pfeiffer and Truskier, *Ber.*, **37**, 1127 (1904).
139. Hilpert and Grüttner, *ibid.*, **48**, 3130 (1926).
140. v. Braun, *ibid.*, **46**, 1792 (1913); **47**, 491; Hilpert and Grüttner, *ibid.*, **17**, 177, 186 (1914).
141. Vecchiotti *et al.*, *Ber.*, **63**, 2275 (1930); *Nature*, **126**, 313 (1930); *Gazz. chim. ital.*, **58**, 712 (1928); **60**, 904 (1930).
142. Vecchiotti and Silvestrini, *Gazz. chim. ital.*, **63**, 110 (1933).
143. Pesci, *ibid.*, **23 II**, 526 (1893).
144. Steinkopf and Bauermeister, *Ann.*, **403**, 57 (1914); Steinkopf, *ibid.*, **413**, 328 (1917).
145. Dreher and Otto, *Ber.*, **2**, 543 (1869); *Ann.*, **154**, 97 (1870); Schoeller *et al.*, *Ber.*, **53**, 636 (1920); **47**, 1932 (1914); Sachs, *ibid.*, **53**, 1739 (1920).
146. Schrauth and Bauerschmidt, *Ber.*, **47**, 2740 (1914).
147. Blumenthal and Oppenheim, *Biochem. Z.*, **39**, 51 (1912); Jacobs and Heidelberger, *J. Biol. Chem.*, **20**, 516 (1915).
148. Sachs and Otto, *Ber.*, **59**, 171 (1926); Picon, *Compt. rend.*, **190**, 1430 (1930); Loudon, *J. Chem. Soc.*, **1935**, 535; Sen and Chakravarti, *J. Indian Chem. Soc.*, **6**, 847 (1929); Andrews and Wyman, *J. Biol. Chem.*, **87**, 185, 533 (1932); Nesmejanow and Porsch, *Ber.*, **67**, 971 (1934); Whitmore *et al.*, *J. Am. Chem. Soc.*, **48**, 1013 (1926); **51**, 2782 (1929); Covello, *Rend. Accad. Sci. fis. e. mat. reale Napoli*, (4) **3**, 65 (1933).
149. Buckton and Odling, *Ann. Spl.*, **4**, 109 (1865).
150. Krause and Wendt, *Ber.*, **56**, 466 (1923).
151. Louise and Roux, *Bull. soc. chim.*, (2) **50**, 497 (1888); *Compt. rend.*, **106**, 602 (1888); **170**, 600 (1888); Quincke, *Z. phys. Chem.*, **3**, 164 (1889).
152. Krause and Dittmar, *Ber.*, **63**, 2401 (1930).
153. Krause, *ibid.*, **57**, 216 (1924); Krause and Polack, *ibid.*, **59**, 1428 (1926).
154. Hansen, *Ber.*, **3**, 9 (1870); Hartwig, *ibid.*, **7**, 298 (1874); *Ann.*, **176**, 264 (1875).
155. Meyer and Bertheim, *Ber.*, **37**, 2051 (1904).
156. Krause and v. Grosse, *ibid.*, **58**, 1933 (1925).
157. Melnikoff and Gratschewa, *J. Russ. Phys.-Chem. Soc.*, **67**, 1786 (1935).
158. Groll, *J. Am. Chem. Soc.*, **52**, 2998 (1930); U. S. patent 1,938,179 (1930); Birch, *J. Chem. Soc.*, **1934**, 1132; Rochow and Dennis, *J. Am. Chem. Soc.*, **57**, 486 (1935); Gilman and Jones, *ibid.*, **61**, 1513 (1939); **62**, 2357 (1940).

159. *Cf.* Menzies and Cope, *J. Chem. Soc.*, **1932**, 2862; Birch, *ibid.*, **1934**, 1134; Melnikoff and - Gratschewa, *J. Russ. Phys.-Chem. Soc.*, **6**, (68), 634 (1936).
160. Goddard and Goddard, *J. Chem. Soc.*, **121**, 256, 482 (1922).
161. Krause and Renwanz, *Ber.*, **62**, 1711 (1929).
162. Challenger and Parker, *J. Chem. Soc.*, **1931**, 1462.
163. Kraus and Toonder, *Proc. Nat. Acad. Sci. U. S.*, **19**, 292 (1933); *J. Am. Chem. Soc.*, **55**, 3547 (1933). *Cf.* Renwanz, *Ber.*, **65**, 1308 (1932); Dennis and Patnode, *J. Am. Chem. Soc.*, **54**, 182 (1932); Gilman and Jones, *ibid.*, **62**, 980 (1940); Laubengayer and Gilliam, *ibid.*, **63**, 477 (1941).
164. Dennis and Patnode, *J. Am. Chem. Soc.*, **54**, 182 (1932); Renwanz, *Ber.*, **65**, 1308 (1932); Kraus and Toonder, *l. c.*
165. Kraus and Toonder, *l. c.*, Renwanz, *l. c.*
166. Dennis et al., *J. Am. Chem. Soc.*, **56**, 1047 (1934). *Cf.* Laubengayer and Gilliam, *J. Am. Chem. Soc.*, **63**, 477 (1941); Dennis *et al.*, *ibid.*, **56**, 1047 (1934); Schumb and Crane, *ibid.*, **60**, 306 (1938); Gilman and Jones, *ibid.*, **62**, 2353 (1940).
167. Lowig, *Ann.*, **88**, 318 (1853); Klippel, *Jahresb.*, **1860**, 380; Cahours, *Ann.*, **122**, 67 (1862); Ladenburg, *ibid.*, spl. **8**, 64 (1872); Polis, *Ber.*, **20**, 717, 333 (1887); **21**, 3424 (1888); Gen. Motors Res. Corp., *French patent* 570,135 (1924).
168. Grüttner and Krause, *Ber.*, **49**, 1415 (1916).
169. Krause, *ibid.*, **54**, 2060 (1921).
170. Pfeiffer and Truskier, *ibid.*, **37**, 1126 (1904); Krause *et al.*, *ibid.*, **52**, 2165 (1919); **55**, 888 (1922).
171. Krause and Schmitz, *Ber.*, **52**, 2165 (1919).
172. Krause and Schlöttig, *ibid.*, **63**, 1382 (1930).
173. Krause *et al.*, *ibid.*, **49**, 1420 (1916); **50**, 278 (1917); **62**, 1877 (1929); Pfeiffer and Truskier, *ibid.*, **37**, 1125 (1904).
174. Grüttner and Grüttner, *Ber.*, **51**, 1293 (1918).
175. Austin, *J. Am. Chem. Soc.*, **54**, 3287 (1932).
176. Grüttner, *Ber.*, **51**, 1298 (1918).
177. Grüttner and Krause, *ibid.*, **49**, 1423 (1916).
178. Krause and Pohland, *ibid.*, **55**, 1283 (1922); Midgley *et al.*, *J. Am. Chem. Soc.*, **45**, 1821 (1923); Krause and Pohland, *Ber.*, **55**, 1282 (1922).
179. Krause and Renwanz, *ibid.*, **60**, 1582 (1927); Gilman and Towne, *Rec. trav. chim.*, **51**, 1054 (1932).
180. Grüttner and Krause, *Ber.*, **49**, 2666 (1916).
181. Krause and Reissaus, *ibid.*, **55**, 888 (1922).
182. Grüttner and Krause, *ibid.*, **50**, 204 (1917).
183. Grüttner and Grüttner, *ibid.*, **51**, 1293 (1918); Möller and Pfeiffer, *ibid.*, **49**, 2441 (1916).
184. Krause and Schlöttig, *Ber.*, **58**, 427 (1925); Paneth *et al.*, *ibid.*, **62**, 1335 (1929); *Nature*, **125**, 564 (1930); *Naturwiss.*, **18**, 307 (1930); *Ber.*, **64**, 2702 (1931); *Z. Elektrochem.*, **37**, 577 (1931). *Cf.* Taylor and Jones, *J. Am. Chem. Soc.*, **52**, 1111 (1930); Pearson *et al.*, *Nature*, **129**, 832 (1932).
185. Buckton, *Ann.*, **109**, 225 (1859); Frankland, *ibid.*, **111**, 46 (1859); Pfeiffer and Schurmann, *Ber.*, **37**, 320 (1904); Pope and Peachey, *Proc. Chem. Soc.* No. 273.
186. Austin, *J. Am. Chem. Soc.*, **54**, 3726 (1932).
187. Werner, *Z. anorg. allgem. Chem.*, **17**, 97 (1898).
188. Krause, *Ber.*, **51**, 1456 (1918).
189. Pope and Peachey, *Proc. Chem. Soc.* No. 273. *Cf.* Gilman and Arntzen, *J. Am. Chem. Soc.*, **72**, 3823 (1950); *J. Org. Chem.*, **15**, 994 (1950).
190. Pope and Peachey, *Proc. Chem. Soc.*, **16**, 42, 116 (1900); **19**, 290 (1903); Grüttner and Krause, *Ber.*, **50**, 1804 (1917).
191. Kraus and Session, *J. Am. Chem. Soc.*, **47**, 2361 (1925).
192. Kraus and Neal, *ibid.*, **52**, 695 (1930).
193. Pfeiffer and Heller, *Ber.*, **37**, 4619 (1904).
194. Ladenburg, *Ann.*, *Spl.* **8**, 71 (1869); *Ber.*, **4**, 19 (1871).
195. Kotscheschkow, *Ber.*, **66**, 1661 (1933).
196. Kotscheschkow, *et al.*, *ibid.*, **67**, 1348 (1934).
197. Krause *et al.*, *ibid.*, **51**, 912 (1918); **53**, 176, 182 (1920).
198. Krause and Pohland, *ibid.*, **57**, 533 (1924).
199. Krause, *ibid.*, **51**, 1447 (1918).
200. Grüttner and Krause, *ibid.*, **50**, 1804 (1917).
201. Ladenburg, *Ann. Spl.*, **8**, 75 (1869); Löwig, *Ann.*, **84**, 309, 313 (1852); Cahours, *ibid.*, **114**, 244, 367, 373 (1860).
202. Hilpert *et al.*, *Ber.*, **46**, 3738 (1913).
203. Nesmejanow and Kotscheschkow, *ibid.*, **63**, 2496 (1930); **64**, 628 (1931); *J. Russ. Phys.-Chem. Soc.*, **62**, 1795 (1930).

204. Aronheim, *Ann.*, **194**, 145 (1878); Goddard *et al.*, *J. Chem. Soc.*, **121**, 981 (1922).
205. Kraus and Bullard, *J. Am. Chem. Soc.*, **48**, 2132 (1926).
206. Krause and Becker, *Ber.*, **53**, 173 (1920).
207. Kraus and Greer, *J. Am. Chem. Soc.*, **47**, 2568 (1925).
208. Löwig, *Ann.*, **84**, 320 (1852).
209. Grimm, *ibid.*, **92**, 384, 390 (1854).
210. Cahours, *ibid.*, **114**, 367 (1860).
211. Pfeiffer and Lehnhardt, *Ber.*, **36**, 3030 (1903).
212. Chamber and Scherer, *J. Am. Chem. Soc.*, **48**, 1054 (1926).
213. Pfeiffer and Lehnhard, *Ber.*, **36**, 1057 (1903); Druce, *J. Chem. Soc.*, **113**, 715 (1918); **119**, 758 (1921); **121**, 1859 (1922); *Chem. News*, **127**, 306 (1923).
214. Lesbre and Glotz, *Compt. rend.*, **198**, 1426 (1934).
215. *German Patent*, 431,762 (1923).
216. Kotscheschkow and Nesmejanow, *Ber.*, **64**, 628 (1931); Kotscheschkow, *J. Russ. Phys.-Chem., Soc.* **61**, 1385 (1929); *Ber.*, **62**, 996 (1929).
217. Grüttner and Krause, *Ber.*, **50**, 1549 (1917).
218. Bullard, *J. Am. Chem. Soc.*, **51**, 3065 (1929).
219. Bullard and Holden, *ibid.*, **53**, 3150 (1931).
220. Krause and Weinberg, *Ber.*, **63**, 381 (1930).
221. Bösecken, *Rec. trav. chim.*, **17** (4), 1017 (1923).
222. Dennis *et al.*, *J. Am. Chem. Soc.*, **47**, 2039 (1925).
223. Morgan and Drew, *J. Chem. Soc.*, **127**, 1760 (1925); Kraus and Foster, *J. Am. Chem. Soc.*, **49**, 457 (1927).
224. Kraus and Nutting, *J. Am. Chem. Soc.*, **54**, 1622 (1932).
225. Dennis and Patnode, *ibid.*, **52**, 2779 (1930). *Cf.* Dennis *et al.*, *J. Am. Chem. Soc.*, **49**, 2512 (1927); **51**, 2321 (1929); Kraus and Foster, *ibid.*, **49**, 457 (1927).
226. Kraus and Brown, *ibid.*, **52**, 3690 (1930); Kraus and Foster, *ibid.*, **49**, 457 (1927); Dennis *et al.*, *ibid.*, **49**, 2512 (1927).
227. Schwarz *et al.*, *Ber.*, **64**, 2352 (1932); **69**, 529 (1936).
228. Kraus and Flood, *J. Am. Chem. Soc.*, **54**, 1635 (1932).
229. Kraus and Brown, *ibid.*, **52**, 4031 (1930).
230. Kraus and Foster, *ibid.*, **49**, 457 (1927).
231. Schaefer and Hein, *Z. anorg. allgem. Chem.*, **100**, 297 (1917); Davies *et al.*, *Bull. soc. chim.*, (4) **49**, 187 (1931).
232. Schaefer and Hein, *l. c.*; Marquardt, *Ber.*, **20**, 1517 (1887).
233. Hilpert and Ditmar, *ibid.*, **46**, 3741 (1913).
234. Challenger *et al.*, *J. Chem. Soc.*, **105**, 2210 (1914); **109**, 250, 913 (1916); **121**, 104 (1922); Pfeiffer, *Ber.*, **37**, 4620 (1904); Blicke *et al.*, *J. Am. Chem. Soc.*, **53**, 1025 (1931); Supniewski and Adams, *ibid.*, **48**, 507 (1926); Gilman *et al.*, *ibid.*, **61**, 1170 (1939); Krause and Renwanz, *Ber.*, **62**, 1712 (1929).
235. Challenger *et al.*, *Proc. Chem. Soc.*, **29**, 76 (1913); **30**, 293 (1914) *J. Chem. Soc.*, **105**, 2210 (1914); **109**, 250 (1910); **107**, 16 (1915); **119**, 913 (1921); **117**, 762 (1920); **121**, 104 (1922); Norvick, *Nature*, **135**, 1038 (1935); Gilman and Yablonky, *J. Am. Chem. Soc.*, **63**, 207 (1941).
236. Challenger and Alpress, *J. Chem. Soc.*, **107**, 16 (1915).
237. Challenger and Wilkinson, *ibid.*, **121**, 91 (1921).
238. Challenger and Richards, *ibid.*, **1934**, 405.
239. Grüttner and Wiernik, *Ber.*, **48**, 1473 (1915).
240. Hein *et al.*, *ibid.*, **52**, 195 (1919); **54**, 2708, 2727 (1921); **57**, 8, 899 (1924); **59**, 362, 751 (1926); **60**, 679, 749 (1927); **61**, 730, 2255 (1928); **62**, 1151 (1929); **71**, 1966 (1918); *Z. anorg. allgem. Chem.*, **145**, 95 (1925); *Kolloid-Z.*, **39**, 236 (1926); *J. prakt. Chem.*, (2) **132**, 59 (1931); **153**, 160 (1939); *Angew. Chem.*, **47**, 747 (1933).
241. Hein, *Ber.*, **54**, 1905 (1921).
242. Hein, *ibid.*, **54**, 2727 (1921).
243. Hein and Eissner, *ibid.*, **59**, 362 (1926).
244. Wooster, *Chem. Revs.*, **11**, 1 (1932).
245. Ziegler *et al.*, *Ann.*, **473**, 21 (1929).
246. Gilman and Harris, *J. Am. Chem. Soc.*, **53**, 3541 (1931).
247. Pope and Peachey, *J. Chem. Soc.*, **95**, 571 (1909).
248. Gilman and Lichtenwalter, *J. Am. Chem. Soc.*, **60**, 3085 (1938).
249. Menzies, *J. Chem. Soc.*, **1928**, 565.
250. Gilman and Schulze, *J. Am. Chem. Soc.*, **49**, 2904 (1927).
251. Frankland and Duppa, *J. Chem. Soc.*, **16**, 415 (1863).
252. Dimroth, *Ann.*, **446**, 148 (1925). *Cf.* Holleman, *Rec. trav. chim.*, **42**, 355 (1923); Jurgens, *ibid.*, **45**, 61 (1926).
253. Coffey, *J. Chem. Soc.*, **127**, 1029 (1925); **1926**, 637, 3215; Burton *et al.*, *ibid.*, **1926**, 1802.
254. Vecchiotti *et al.*, *Gazz. chim. ital.*, **44**, 1918 (1914); **48**, 78 (1918); **51**, 208 (1921); **54**, 411

(1924); **55**, 372 (1925); **56**, 147, 216 (1926); **57**, 485 (1927); Rossi and Cecchetti, *ibid.*, **55**, 869 (1925).

255. Menzies *et al.*, *J. Chem. Soc.*, **1928**, 565, 1288. *Cf.* Feigl and Backer, *Monatsh.*, **49**, 401 (1928).
256. Klippel, *J. prakt. Chem.*, (1) **81**, 287 (1860); Polis, *Ber.*, **20**, 716, 3331 (1887); **21**, 3425 (1888); Ghira, *Gazz. chim. ital.*, **24** I, 42 (1894); *Rend. accad. Lincei*, (5) **3**, I, 332 (1894).
257. Buckton, *Proc. Roy. Soc. (London)*, IX, 685 (1895); *Ann.*, **109**, 218 (1859); Frankland and Lawrence, *J. Chem. Soc.*, **35**, 244 (1879).
258. Grütner and Krause, *Ber.*, **49**, 1415 (1910).
259. Gilman and Stuckwisch, *J. Am. Chem. Soc.*, **72**, 4553 (1950).
260. Hoffman and Wölff, *Ber.*, **40**, 2425 (1907); Staehling, *Compt. rend.*, **157**, 1430 (1913); Dillon *et al.*, *Proc. Roy. Soc., Dublin*, XVII, 53 (1922).
261. Kraus and Foster, *J. Am. Chem. Soc.*, **49**, 457 (1927); Morgan and Drew, *J. Chem. Soc.*, **127**, 1760 (1925); Johnson and Harris, *J. Am. Chem. Soc.*, **72**, 5564 (1950).
262. Johnson and Nebergall, *J. Am. Chem. Soc.*, **71**, 1720 (1942); Johnson and Harris, *ibid.*, **72**, 5566 (1950).
263. Rochow, *ibid.*, **69**, 1729 (1947); **70**, 1801 (1950).
264. Rochow, *ibid.*, **69**, 1729 (1947).
265. Schwarz and Reinhardt, *Ber.*, **65**, 1743 (1932).
266. Orndorff *et al.*, *J. Am. Chem. Soc.*, **49**, 2512 (1927).
267. Tchakirian, *Ann. chim.*, (11E) **12**, 415 (1939).
268. Morgan and Drew, *J. Chem. Soc.*, **127**, 1760 (1925). *Cf.* Johnson and Harris, *J. Am. Chem. Soc.*, **72**, 5564, 5566 (1950).
269. Kraus and Brown, *J. Am. Chem. Soc.*, **52**, 3690, 4031 (1930).
270. Kraus and Hood, *ibid.*, **54**, 1635 (1932).
271. Kraus and Foster, *ibid.*, **49**, 457 (1927).
272. Johnson and Harris, *ibid.*, **72**, 5564 (1950).
273. Bauer and Burschkies, *Ber.*, **65**, 956 (1932); Johnson and Nebergall, *J. Am. Chem. Soc.*, **71**, 1720 (1949).
274. Simmons *et al.*, *J. Am. Chem. Soc.*, **55**, 3705 (1933).
275. Morgan and Drew, *J. Chem. Soc.*, **125**, 1261 (1924).
276. Kraus and Wooster, *J. Am. Chem. Soc.*, **52**, 372 (1930).
277. Bauer and Burschkies, *Ber.*, **67**, 1041 (1934).
278. Flood, *J. Am. Chem. Soc.*, **54**, 1663 (1932).
279. *Cf.* Anderson, *ibid.*, **72**, 194 (1950).
280. Orndorff *et al.*, *ibid.*, **49**; 2512 (1927). *Cf.* Bauer and Burschkies, *Ber.*, **65**, 956 1 (1932); Thomas and Southwood, *J. Chem. Soc.*, **1931**, 2083; Flood, *J. Am. Chem. Soc.*, **54**, 1663 (1932).
281. Dennis *et al.*, *J. Am. Chem. Soc.*, **47**, 2039 (1925).
282. Burschkies, *Ber.*, **69**, 1143 (1936). *Cf.* Rochow, *J. Am. Chem. Soc.*, **70**, 1801 (1948).
283. Schwarz and Reinhardt, *Ber.*, **65**, 1743 (1932); Backer and Schenstra, *Rec. trav. chim.*, **52**, 1033 (1933); **54**, 38 (1935).
284. Kraus and Foster, *J. Am. Chem. Soc.*, **49**, 457 (1927); Kraus and Wooster, *ibid.*, **52**, 372 (1930). *Cf.* Kraus and Flood, *ibid.*, **54**, 1635 (1932).
285. Kraus and Brown, *J. Am. Chem. Soc.*, **52**, 3690 (1930).
286. Flood, *ibid.*, **55**, 4935 (1933).
287. Anderson, *ibid.*, **71**, 1799 (1949).
288. Frankland and Duppa, *J. Chem. Soc.*, **17**, 29 (1864).
289. Breed, *Ann.*, **82**, 106 (1852).
290. Gilman and Svigoon, *J. Am. Chem. Soc.*, **61**, 3586 (1939). *Cf.* Gilman and Yablunky, *ibid.*, **63**, 949 (1941).
291. Hilpert and Grüttner, *Ber.*, **46**, 1675 (1913).
292. Gilman and Yablunky, *J. Org. Chem.*, **4**, 162 (1939); *J. Am. Chem. Soc.*, **63**, 212 (1941).
293. Marquardt, *Ber.*, **20**, 1516 (1887); **21**, 2035 (1888).
294. Gilman and Yablunky, *J. Am. Chem. Soc.*, **63**, 207 (1941).
295. Grüttner and Wiernik, *Ber.*, **48**, 1473 (1915).
296. Challenger *et al.*, *J. Chem. Soc.*, **109**, 250 (1916); **117**, 762 (1920); **1927**, 209; Supniewski and Adams, *J. Am. Chem. Soc.*, **48**, 507 (1926); Zhitkowa *et al.*, *J. Gen. Chem. U.S.S.R.* **8**, 1839 (1938); *C.A.*, **33**, 5819 (1939).
297. Miller et al., *J. Chem. Soc.*, **1952**, 632.
298. Kealy and Pauson, *Nature*, **168**, 1039 (1951).
299. *Cf.* Woodward *et al.*, *J. Am. Chem. Soc.*, **74**, 2125 (1952); Kaplan *et al.*, *ibid.*, **74**, 5531 (1952); Cotton and Wilkinson, *ibid.*, **74**, 5764 (1952).
300. Winkler, *J. prakt. Chem.*, (2) **36**, 177 (1887).
301. Calingaert, *Chem. Revs.*, **2**, 43 (1925); Gilman and Bailie, *J. Am. Chem. Soc.*, **61**, 731 (1939). Pfeiffer and Truskier, *Ber.*, **37**, 1125 (1904); Krause and Schmitz, *ibid.*, **52**, 2165 (1919); Krause and Reissaus, *ibid.*, **55**, 88 (1922); Goddard, *J. Chem. Soc.*, **123**,

1161 (1923); Austin, *J. Am. Chem. Soc.*, **54**, 2948 (1933); Calingaert and Soroos, *J. Org. Chem.*, **2**, 535 (1938).

302. Krause and v. Grosse, *Die Chemie der metall-organischen Verbindungen*, p. **372** (1937); Brawn and Whitby, *Discussions Faraday Soc.*, **2**, 228 (1947).
303. Gilman and Jones, *J. Am. Chem. Soc.*, **72**, 1760 (1950); Gilman *et al.*, *J. Org. Chem.*, **17**, 630 (1952).
304. Calingaert and Shapiro, *U. S. patent* 2,535,193 (1950); *C. A.*, **45**, 3865 (1951); Gilman and Jones, *J. Am. Chem. Soc.*, **72**, 1760 (1950).
305. Foster *et al.*, *J. Am. Chem. Soc.* **61**, 1685 (1939); Gilman and Bailie, *ibid.*, **61**, 731 (1939).
306. Gilman *et al.*, *J. Org. Chem.*, **16**, 466 (1951); **18**, 1675 (1953).
307. Gilman *et al.*, *Proc. Iowa Acad. Sci.*, **48**, 273 (1941); *C. A.*, **36**, 1595 (1942); *J. Am. Chem. Soc.*, **74**, 5924 (1952); *J. Org. Chem.* **17**, 630 (1952).

CHAPTER 16

ORGANIC COMPOUNDS OF NON-METALS AND METALLOIDS

ORGANIC COMPOUNDS OF BORON

Boron alkyls have been prepared through the reaction of boron trichloride with zinc alkyls in ethereal solution:[1]

$$2BCl_3 + 3ZnR_2 \rightarrow 2BrR_3 + 3ZnCl_2$$

Esters of boric acid may be used in this reaction instead of the halide.

An excellent method for the preparation of boron alkyls is offered by the reaction of boron trifluoride with Grignard reagents:[2]

$$BF_3 + 3RMgX \rightarrow BR_3 + 3MgFX$$

The mono and dialkyl derivatives may be obtained by this reaction by using the trifluoride in sufficient excess. Mixed boron alkyls have not yet been prepared.

Boron aryls result through the reaction of Grignard reagents with boric esters and subsequent hydrolysis of the reaction product:

$$B(OR)_3 + R'MgX \rightarrow R'B(OR)_2 + XMgOR$$

$$\xrightarrow{H_2O} R'B(OH)_2 + 3ROH + XMgOH$$

$$B(OR)_3 + 2R'MgX \rightarrow R'_2BOR + 2XMgOR$$

$$\xrightarrow{H_2O} R'_2BOH + 3ROH + 2XMgOH$$

Best results are obtained with triisobutyl borate.

It is claimed that the reduction of phenylboron diiodide leads to the formation of phenylborine, $C_6H_5BH_2$, and that the reaction of this compound with phenylboron dichloride results in the formation of borobenzene, $C_6H_5B{:}BC_6H_5$.[3]

Reactions of Organo Boron Compounds

While boron trimethyl ignites when exposed to air, other boron trialkyls and -aryls are gradually oxidized to esters of monoalkyl boric acids, $RB(OR)_2$, when thus exposed.[4] Boron tri-α-naphthyl is more slowly oxidized by air than other boron triaryls. When monoalkyl boric acids are treated with alkylating agents, such as zinc alkyl, etc., esters of dialkyl boric acid, R_2BOR, are obtained. The free acid may be prepared from these esters by hydrolysis with water. Ethylboric diethyl ester, $C_2H_5B(OC_2H_5)_2$, combines with ethyl borate to form ethyl pentaethyldiborate, $C_2H_5B(OC_2H_5)_2 . B(OC_2H_3)_3$.

Mono and diaryl boron halides fume when exposed to air.

Boron alkyls and aryls are not attacked by water or are attacked very slowly. Aryl boron halides are hydrolyzed with water to the corresponding aryl boric acids.

Boron trialkyls combine with alkalies forming compounds the structure of which has not yet been elucidated. Trimethylboron combining with potassium hydroxide gives a compound of the approximate formula $B(CH_3)_3.KOH$.[5]

Ammonia reacts with boron trialkyls to form ammoniates; thus, the compound

$$(CH_3)_3B.NH_3$$

is obtained from trimethylboron. When these ammoniates are rapidly heated to 180°-200° they yield Stock's ring compound, $\overline{\text{HBNHBHNHBHNH}}$.[6] Tricyclohexylboron yields addition compounds with nitrogen bases which are readily attacked by atmospheric oxygen.

Boron triaryls reacting with alkali metals form co-ordination compounds such as $(C_6H_5)_3BNa$, which resemble the alkali metal compounds of triaryl methanes. The alkali metal is bound ionogenically so that solutions of these compounds are capable of conducting the electric current.[7] Boron triphenyl sodium yields its sodium to triphenylmethane. Triphenylboron itself combines with triphenylmethane forming an intensely red crystalline compound.

Boron trialkyls react with borane, $H_3B.BH_3$, to form mono-, di-, tri- and tetraalkylboranes.[8] The individual compounds may be isolated by distillation at a low temperature.

Monoaryl boric acids are weakly acidic, although they dissociate to a greater extent than boric acid. They readily lose water to form anhydrides or aryl boron oxides. Thus, phenylboric acid, kept in a desiccator, loses water and is thereby converted to phenylboron oxide, C_6H_5BO. The oxides exist in the polymeric form.[9]

ORGANIC COMPOUNDS OF SILICON

Alkyl silicons are obtained most readily through the interaction of alkyl magnesium halides with silicon tetrachloride.[10]

A mixture of silicon compounds alkylated to varying degrees is obtained by the reaction. The quantity of the higher alkylated silicon may be increased by increasing the proportion of the Grignard reagent. The final product always contains mono-, di-, tri- and tetraalkyl silicons, and the individual compounds are isolated by fractional distillation. The purification of the various compounds formed becomes more complicated when the halogen in the Grignard compound differs from that in the silicon halide, for then, all the possible combinations of halogen and alkyl groups result. Gaseous silicon tetrafluoride may be used with satisfactory results in this reaction.[11]

While silicon tetrachloride reacts quite vigorously with organo magnesium halides, the last halogen atom in the compound is replaced with difficulty even when an excess of the Grignard reagent is employed. The reaction may be completed by evaporating off the ether and heating the residue at 100° for several hours.

Mixed silicon alkyls may be prepared from carefully purified alkyl silicon halides by reaction with Grignard reagents.

Silicon tetraalkyls may be prepared through the reaction of silicon tetrachloride with other organo metallic compounds, such as zinc alkyls. The reaction takes place slowly, and the entrance of the alkyl groups into the molecule of the silicon halide makes further reaction more difficult. Zinc alkyls may be used to advantage in this reaction in conjunction with metallic sodium.[12] The reaction of silicon tetrachloride with an alkyl halide in the presence of metallic sodium may also be employed for the preparation of silicon tetraalkyls.[13] Silicon tetraaryls may be prepared from silicon tetrachloride by reaction with aryl magnesium halides, or with mercury diaryls, as well as by the reaction of a mixture of silicon tetrachloride and an aryl halide with metallic sodium.[14]

Trialkyl silicon halides as well as di and monoalkyl silicon halides may be prepared from silicon halides and the required amount of an alkyl magnesium halide. The compounds are isolated and purified by fractional distillation. In the preparation of trialkyl silicon halides, the alkyl magnesium halide is added drop by drop to a solution of the calculated quantity of the silicon halide in ether. The bromide is prepared from silicon tetrabromide and alkyl magnesium bromides. Trialkyl silicon monochlorides may also be obtained by the reaction of trialkyl silicon oxides, $(R_3Si)_2O$, with sodium chloride and concentrated sulfuric acid.[15]

Diethylsilicon dichloride has been obtained by the reaction of benzoyl chloride with diethyl disilanol ethyl ether, $(C_2H_5)_2Si(OC_2H_5)_2$.[16] Ethylsilicon trichloride has also been prepared by this method from ethyl trisilanol ethyl ether, $C_2H_5Si(OC_2H_5)_3$.[17]

Triaryl silicon halides may be prepared through the interaction of a triaryl monosilanol alkyl ether, R_3SiOR', and acetyl or benzoyl chloride.[18]

Phenyl- and *p*-tolylsilicon trihalides have been obtained through the interaction of silicon tetrachloride with mercury diphenyl and mercury di-*p*-tolyl.[19] The compounds can also be obtained by the reaction of silicon tetrachloride and the appropriate organomagnesium halides.[20]

Monomethylsilane, CH_3SiH_3, has been prepared from monochlorosilicane and zinc dimethyl.[21] A mixture of this compound with oxygen explodes when shaken over mercury.

Triethylsilane, $(C_2H_5)_3SiH$, forms, among other products, when zinc ethyl is made to react with ethyl orthosilicate in the presence of metallic sodium.[22]

Hexamethyldisilicane, $(CH_3)_3Si.Si(CH_3)_3$, has been obtained through the reaction of disilicon hexachloride and methylmagnesium bromide.[23] Mixed hexaalkyl disilicanes have been obtained by the reaction of sodium with mixed trialkyl silicon halides in boiling toluene.[24]

Hexaphenyldisilicane has been prepared through the action of metallic sodium on triphenylsilicon chloride in boiling xylene solution.[25] The compound may also be obtained through the interaction of triphenylsilicon lithium and triphenylsilicon chloride.[26]

Mixed silicogermanes and -stannanes of the formula, $R_3SiMR'_3$, have been obtained through the reaction of trialkyl silicane bromides with sodio germanium and tin trialkyls.[26]

Polysilicanes

Diaryl silicon dichlorides reduced with sodium in boiling toluene or xylene give a series of silicon compounds, similar to hydrocarbons and having the general formula $[SiAr_2]_n$, $n > 4$.[27] An unsaturated and a saturated series of tetrasilicane derivatives are known. The saturated compounds probably are octaaryl silico tetrasilicanes, $Ar_2SiSi(Ar)_2Si(Ar)_2SiAr_2$, while the unsaturated compounds are thought to have the structure ... $Si(Ar)_2Si(Ar)_2Si(Ar)_2Si(Ar)_2$. ... The latter are capable of adding iodine and yield dichlorides when boiled with tetrachloroethane. They are oxidized by nitrobenzene and are rapidly decomposed under the action of alkalies and piperidine. Their diiodides react with ethylmagnesium halides to form diethyloctaaryl tetrasilicanes.

The reaction of aryl silicon tetrahalides with sodium results principally in the formation of an amorphous gray powder of high molecular weight and a little tetra and triaryl silicanes.[28]

Trialkyl silanols, R_3SiOH, may be obtained from the corresponding chloride by reaction with ammonium hydroxide:

$$(C_2H_5)_3SiCl + NH_4OH \rightarrow (C_2H_5)_2SiOH + NH_4Cl,$$

or by the action of sodium carbonate on trialkyl silicon acetates, $R_3SiOCOCH_3$. The compounds may also be prepared through the reaction of trialkyl silyl ethyl ethers with concentrated sulfuric acid:

$$(C_2H_5)_3SiOC_2H_5 + H_2SO_4 \rightarrow (C_2H_5)_3SiOH + C_2H_5HSO_4$$

Among organic silicane diols, $R_2Si(OH)_2$ only the aromatic and mixed alkyl aromatic members are stable. The alkyl derivatives lose water spontaneously, forming the corresponding oxides, termed silanones. The aromatic and alkyl aromatic derivatives lose water on heating.[29]

Polysilicones

Polymeric silicones result when the elimination of water from dialkyl silanones takes place intermolecularly. In the aliphatic series mixtures of polymers are generally obtained, while in the aromatic series crystalline trimeric and tetrameric diaryl silanones are known.

Trialkyl silyl ethers, R_3SiOR', result through the reaction of a trialkyl silanol and an alcohol by elimination of a molecule of water.

Triethylsilanol ethyl ether, $(C_2H_5)_3SiOC_2H_5$, is obtained as an intermediate in the reaction of zinc ethyl with orthosilicic ester in the presence of metallic sodium.[30]

Triethylsilyl oxide, $(C_2H_5)_2SiOSi(C_2H_5)_3$, has been obtained from triethylmonosilanol by reaction with phosphorus pentoxide,[31] while *triphenylsilyl oxide,* $(C_6H_5)_3SiOSi(C_6H_5)_3$, has been prepared by the treatment of triphenylsilanol with a hot solution of concentrated nitric acid in acetic acid.[32]

Diethylsilanol diethyl ether, $(C_2H_5)_2Si(OC_2H_5)_2$, is obtained by the reaction of ethyl orthosilicate or ethyl orthochlorosilicate, $ClSi(OC_2H_5)_3$, with zinc ethyl and metallic sodium.[33]

Alkyl and aryl silicic acids result from the hydrolysis of the corresponding alkyl and arylsilicon trihalides; they are obtained also by the hydrolysis of the corresponding ortho esters, $RSi(OR')_3$.

Silicon Heterocycles

Cyclopentane ethylene silicon dichloride, $\overline{CH_2(CH_2)_3CH_2}SiCl_2$, results from the reaction of the Grignard reagent derived from 1,5-dibromopentane with silicon tetrachloride in ethereal solution. The compound is transformed to a polymeric solid silanone, $[(CH_2)_5SiO]_x$, on hydrolysis. Dimethyl- and diethylcyclopenta-methylene silicone, $\overline{CH_2(CH_2)_3CH_2}Si(CH_3)_2$ and $\overline{CH_2(CH_2)_3CH_2}Si(C_2H_5)_2$, are obtained through the reaction of dimethyl- and diethylsilicon dichlorides with 1,5-dihalomagnesium pentane. The ethyl compound may be obtained in better yield by the reaction of sodium with a mixture of diethylsilicon dichloride and 1,5-dibromopentane in ethereal solution.[34]

Properties and Reactions of Organo Silicon Compounds

In contrast to most organo metallic compounds, organo silicon compounds are generally quite stable. It is, thus, possible to heat a number of the higher boiling aromatic silicon compounds almost to redness without decomposition. Silicon tetraphenyl may be distilled undecomposed at 530°. Silicon tetramethyl is stable toward concentrated sulfuric acid. It is possible to sulfonate or chlorinate the aromatic ring in aryl silicon compounds, although the yields of nitrated products are low.

The lower *tetraalkyl silicones* are liquids. *Trialkyl silicon halides* are also liquids that fume in air; they are readily decomposed by water. The fluorides are much more stable and can be distilled under atmospheric pressure without decomposition.

Alkyl silicon trihalides fume strongly in air and are decomposed rapidly by water with the formation of alkyl silicic acids.

Trialkyl monosilanols are colorless, very stable liquids which can be distilled without decomposition and show no tendency to dehydration. Phosphorus pentoxide converts these compounds to their oxides. Many possess a characteristic camphor-like odor. Trialkyl silanols readily combine with carbonic and acetic acids to form esters. The acetates may also be obtained through the interaction of acetic anhydride and trialkyl silanol ethers, or of trialkyl silanol halides and silver acetate. The esters are saponified very readily, the propyl compound decomposing on exposure to atmospheric moisture.

Triaryl silanols are solid crystalline compounds soluble in most organic solvents.

Unsymmetrical silicon ethers may exist in optically active forms; thus, two optically active forms have been isolated having the formula

$$[HSO_3\langle\hexagon\rangle CH_2Si(R)C_2H_5]_2O$$

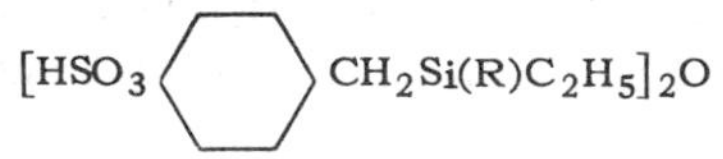

in which $R = n - C_3H_7$, and C_4H_9, by use of *d*-methylhydrindamine and *l*-methylhydrindamine.[35]

The higher members of *monoalkyl silicic acids*, $RSiOOH$, and *monoaryl silicic acids* have been obtained in the form of glasses. The products appear to be mixed polymers.[36] Alkyl silicic acids are weakly acidic; their salts are decomposed by carbon dioxide and are readily hydrolyzed. They do not form esters or chlorides. They yield anhydrides, $(RSiO)_2O$, however, when heated. The anhydrides exist in the polymeric form.

ORGANIC COMPOUNDS OF ARSENIC

Alkyl and Aryl Arsines

Trialkyl arsines, R_3As, may be prepared from arsenic trihalides by reaction with alkyl magnesium halides[37] or with zinc alkyls:[38]

$$AsX_3 + 3RMgX \rightarrow R_3As + 3MgX_2$$

$$2AsX_3 + 3ZnR_2 \rightarrow 2R_3As + 3ZnX_2$$

Trialkyl arsines may be obtained also by this reaction from alkyl dihalo and dialkyl haloarsines. This reaction may serve for the preparation of mixed trialkyl arsines. In the preparation of trimethylarsine from the Grignard compound, ethyl ether is unsuitable, but good results are obtained with *n*-butyl or *n*-amyl ethers. Direct reaction of arsenic trioxide with Grignard reagents also gives alkyl arsines in good yield. Trialkyl arsines are also formed by the reaction of alkyl iodides with sodium arsenide.[39]

Tribenzylarsine, $(C_6H_5CH_2)_3As$, results on boiling a mixture of a solution of benzyl chloride in ether, arsenic trichloride and metallic sodium. The reaction is initiated by the addition of a little acetic ester. Boiling is continued for 6 hours, then more acetic ester is added and the reaction is completed by heating for 14 hours longer.[40] The compound may also be obtained by the Grignard reaction.[41]

Tri-β-chlorovinylarsine, $(ClCH = CH)_3As$, results, together with the primary and secondary chloro arsines, when acetylene is made to react with arsenic trichloride in the presence of aluminum chloride.[42]

Triaryl arsines may be prepared from arsenic trihalides or arsenic trioxide and aryl magnesium halides.[43] They may be obtained also by the reaction of a mixture of an aromatic halo compound and arsenic trichloride in solution in ether or xylene with metallic sodium.[44] Mixed aryl or aralkyl arsines may be prepared by both methods. These compounds may be obtained, further, through the reduction of triaryl arsine oxides with phosphorous acid in alcoholic solution, with hydrogen sulfide or with nascent hydrogen in glacial acetic acid.

Tri-p-dimethylaminephenylarsine, $As[C_6H_4N(CH_3)_2]_3$, results from the interaction of dimethylaniline and arsenic trichloride.[45]

Tri-α-thienylarsine,

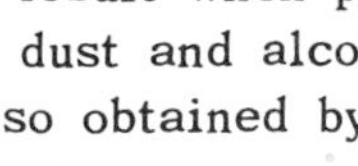

may be prepared by the methods adopted for the preparation of triaryl arsines.[46] Derivatives of *furan* have been obtained by the interaction of furyl mercury compounds with arsenic trihalides.[47]

Monoalkyl arsines, $RAsH_2$, result when primary alkyl arsonic acids are reduced with amalgamated zinc dust and alcoholic hydrochloric acid in the absence of oxygen; they are also obtained by reducing dialkyl arsenic oxides, $(R_2As)_2O$, or dialkyl halo arsines.

Monoaryl arsines may be prepared by reducing aromatic arsonic acids, arsine oxides or arseno compounds with nascent hydrogen in acid solution:

$$RAsO(OH)_2 \rightarrow RAsH_2$$

Diphenylarsine, $(C_6H_5)_2AsH$, the only diaryl arsine known, is obtained by reducing diphenylarsinic acid, $(C_6H_5)_2AsOOH$, with nascent hydrogen.

Tetraalkyl diarsines, $R_2As.AsR_2$, are obtained by the reduction of dialkyl arsine halides with zinc, or from dialkyl arsonic acids by electrolytic reduction,[48] or reduction with phosphorous acid.[49] These compounds are also obtained through the interaction of dialkyl arsines with dialkyl halo arsines.[50]

Tetraaryl diarsines are best prepared by the reduction of diaryl arsenic oxides or diaryl arsonic acids with phosphorous acid or hypophosphorous acid. The compounds separate out as precipitates because of their very slight solubility.

Aryl arseno compounds, RAs = AsR, result when aryl arsonic or aryl arsinic acids are reduced with hypophosphorous acid, or with stannous chloride and hydrochloric acid in the presence of a little potassium iodide. Neutral sodium hyposulfite solution or sodium amalgam and alcohol may also be used as reducing agents. The reduction of arsine oxides proceeds at ordinary or slightly elevated temperature, but arsonic acids are reduced only on prolonged heating. When phosphorous acid is used as the reducing agent, it becomes necessary to heat under pressure, while with sodium hyposulfite reduction is complete on warming at a moderate temperature.

Arseno compounds are formed also through the reaction of monoaryl arsines with aryl arsenic oxides or aryl arsenic halides:

$$RAsH_2 + R'AsO \rightarrow RAs = AsR' + H_2O$$

Simple and mixed arseno compounds may be prepared by this method. Mixed arseno compounds may be prepared by an exchange reaction between simple arseno compounds.

Arsenobenzene results through the reaction of monophenylarsine with triphenylarsine dichloride,[51] or with phenylmercuric chloride, or diphenyllead dichloride.[52]

3,3'-Diamino-4,4'-dihydroxyarsenobenzene, $HOC_6H_3(NH_2)As = AsC_6H_3(NH_2)OH$, is obtained by reducing *m*-nitro-*p*-hydroxyphenylarsonic acid.[53] The dihydrochloride of this compound containing one molecule of methanol of crystallization is the *salvàrsan* or *arsphenamine* of commerce. The sulfoxylate of this compound, known as neosalvarsan, is prepared by reaction with Rongalite, i.e., sodium formaldehyde sulfoxylate, or directly from *m*-nitro-*p*-hydroxyphenylarsonic acid by reduction with an excess of Rongalite.[54]

Sulfarsphenamine, or disodium-3,3'-diamino-4,4'-dihydroxyarsenobenzene-N,N'-dimethylene sulfite, results as a light yellow precipitate when two moles of formaldehyde and two of sodium bisulfite are added to one mole of arsphenamine in alcoholic solution.[55]

Diphenyldiiododiarsine, $C_6H_5As(I)As(I)C_6H_5$, results when phenyldiiodoarsine is reduced with an alcoholic solution of phosphorous acid. It is obtained also through the reaction of diphenylarsine with phenyldiiodoarsine, and through the addition of iodine to arsenobenzene.[56]

Arseno compounds with substituents in the aromatic nuclei oxidize more or less readily on exposure to air.

Arseno compounds decompose on heating to triarylarsines and arsenic. Oxidizing agents convert arsenobenzene to phenylarsenic oxide and phenylarsonic acid.

Alkyl and Aryl Halo Arsines

Dialkyl monohalo arsines, R_2AsX, are best prepared from secondary alkyl arsinic acids, RAsOOH, by reduction with phosphorous acid in the presence of hydrogen chloride:[57]

$$2(CH_3)_2AsOOH + 2H_3PO_2 + 2HCl \rightarrow 2(CH_3)_2AsCl + 2H_3PO_3 + 2H_2O$$

These compounds are formed also through the reaction of alkyl arsinic acids with phosphorus trichloride:

$$3(CH_3)_2AsOOH + 4PCl_3 \rightarrow 3(CH_3)_2AsCl + 3POCl_3 + H_3PO_3$$

They may be prepared, furthermore, by the reaction of a mixture of alkyl halides and arsenic trihalides with sodium:

$$2RX + AsX_3 + 4Na \rightarrow R_2AsX + 4NaX$$

The reaction of dialkyl arsines, R_2AsH, with halogen acids HX also leads to the formation of dialkyl halo arsines.

A general method adaptable to the preparation of simple as well as mixed dialkyl iodo arsines depends on the alkylation of monoalkyl dihalo arsines or monoalkyl arsenic oxides in alkaline solution followed by reduction with sulfur dioxide in aqueous hydriodic acid solution:[58]

$$R'AsX_2 + 2NaOH \rightarrow R'AsO + 2NaX + H_2O$$

$$R'AsO + RX + 2NaOH \rightarrow RR'AsOONa + NaX + H_2O$$

$$RR'AsOONa \xrightarrow{HI + SO_2} RR'AsI$$

Simple and mixed *diaryl halo arsines* may be prepared from monoaryl arsenic oxides by reaction with organo magnesium halides, followed by hydrolysis and conversion of the resulting arsine oxide to the corresponding chloride by treatment with concentrated hydrochloric acid:[59]

$$2RAsO + 2R'MgX \rightarrow 2RR'AsOMgX \xrightarrow{H_2O} (RR'As)_2O$$

$$\xrightarrow{HCl} 2RR'AsCl$$

Diphenylchloroarsine has been made in Germany by this method, the phenylarsenic oxide being obtained from phenylarsinic acid which was in turn prepared from benzene diazonium chloride and sodium arsenite. The compound was prepared commercially in England through the reaction of arsenic trichloride with diphenylamine, or by heating diphenylamine hydrochloride with arsenic at first at 50-60° with stirring, then slowly to 200° until no more water vapor was given off.[60] The compound may also be obtained through the reduction of diphenylarsinic acid, $(C_6H_5)_2AsOOH$, with sulfur dioxide in hydrochloric acid solution.

Diaryl halo arsines result when triaryl arsine dihalides, R_3AsX_2, are heated at 160-200° or are distilled under reduced pressure. They may be obtained also by heating aryl dihalo arsines, $RAsCl_2$, with mercury diaryls; through the interaction of triaryl arsines and arsenic trihalides at high temperatures; by the reaction of aryl magnesium halides with arsenic trihalides; and by the reaction of halogens with tetraaryl diarsines.

Dialkyl cyano arsines, R_2AsCN, result through the reaction of hydrocyanic acid or mercuric cyanide with dialkyl arsine oxides.

Alkyl dichloro arsines, $RAsCl_2$, result when arsonic acids are made to react with phosphorus trichloride;[61] they are formed also through the reaction of a mixture of alkyl halides and an arsenic trihalide with sodium. They are prepared commercially by reducing the sodium salts of alkyl arsonic acids with sulfur dioxide and hydrochloric acid and treating the alkyl arsenic oxide formed with hydrogen chloride:[62]

$$RAsO(ONa)_2 + SO_2 + 2HCl \rightarrow RAsO + H_2SO_4 + 2NaCl$$

$$RAsO + 2HCl \rightarrow RAsCl_2 + H_2O$$

In the preparation of methyldichloroarsine from the oxide and hydrochloric acid, the temperature should not be allowed to rise above $85°$, since otherwise the methyl group may be removed with the formation of arsenic trichloride.

A convenient method of preparation of alkyl dichloro arsines depends on the decomposition of 10-alkyl-5,10-dihydrophenarsazine with hydrogen chloride:[63]

$+ 2HCl \rightarrow RAsCl_2 + (C_6H_5)_2NH$

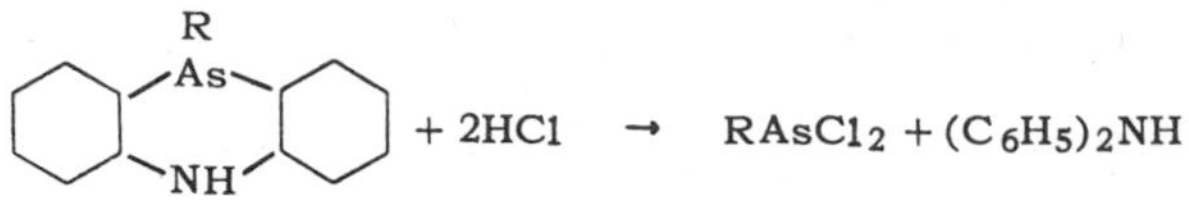

The reaction with 10-*tert*-butyl dihydrophenarsazine should be carried out in liquid hydrogen chloride at $-90°$ to $-85°$ in order to prevent the isomerization of the *tert*-butyl group.[64]

The alkyl phenarsazines required for this method are readily obtained from 10-chloro-5,10-dihydrophenarsazines and alkyl magnesium halides.

Benzyldichloroarsine, $C_6H_5CH_2 \cdot AsCl_2$, is obtained by heating tribenzylarsine with arsenic trichloride at $160-180°$ for 12 hours.[65] This compound is very unstable.

β-Chlorovinyldichloroarsine (Lewisite) is obtained, together with di-*β*-chlorovinylchloro and tri-*β*-chlorovinylarsines, by conducting acetylene into arsenic trichloride containing some aluminum chloride.[66] Fatty acids of the acetylenic series react with arsenic trichloride even in the absence of aluminum chloride to form dichloro arsines.[67] The reaction takes place also with the hydrocarbons of the acetylenic series such as heptyne and octyne. *β*-Chloroethyldichloroarsine, $ClCH_2CH_2AsCl_2$, results through the interaction of ethylene and arsenic trichloride in the presence of aluminum chloride.[68]

Aryl dihalo arsines result through the interaction of arsenic trihalides with mercury diaryls or aryl mercury halides:

$$2AsCl_3 + HgR_2 \rightarrow 2RAsCl_2 + HgCl_2$$

$$AsCl_3 + RHgCl \rightarrow RAsCl_2 + HgCl_2$$

They are formed also by the reaction of arsenic trihalides with triaryl arsines:

$$2AsCl_3 + R_3As \rightarrow 3RAsCl_2$$

They may be further obtained by the interaction of halo acids with monoaryl arsine oxides, $RAsO$; by the reaction of aryl arsonic acids, $RAsO(OH)_2$, and phosphorus trihalides; and finally from arseno compounds $RAs = AsR$ and halogens.

Monoalkyl dicyano arsines result when cyanogen bromide is made to react with dialkyl cyano arsines and the resulting addition compound is heated, preferably in vacuum:

$$(CH_3)_2AsCN + BrCN \rightarrow (CH_3)_2As(CN)_2Br \rightarrow CH_3As(CN)_2 + CH_3Br$$

Trialkyl dihalo arsines, R_3AsX_2, result through the combination of halogens with trialkyl arsines. The reaction proceeds very vigorously and is moderated by use of a solvent and cooling. The compounds are obtained also through the reaction of halo acids with oxides or sulfides of trialkyl arsines:

$$R_3AsO + 2HX \rightarrow R_3AsX_2 + H_2O$$

$$R_3AsS + 2HX \rightarrow R_3AsX_2 + H_2S$$

Triaryl dihalo arsines can also be prepared through the combination of halogens with triaryl arsines. The reaction is best carried out in an anhydrous solvent. Triaryl arsine dihalides are converted to the corresponding dihydroxides by reaction with alkalies or ammonia.

Dialkyl arsenic trihalides, R_2AsX_3, result when dialkyl arsinic acids are treated with phosphorus pentachloride. Dimethyltrichloroarsine is obtained, for example, from cacodylic acid and phosphorus pentachloride; this compound also results when chlorine is led into a solution of cacodyl chloride in carbon disulfide.[69]

Diaryl arsine trihalides are most simply made by treating diaryl monohalo arsines with halogens; they may be obtained also by treating tetraaryl arsines with halogens.

Only a few *monoalkyl arsenic tetrahalides* are brown. Methylarsenic tetrachloride, CH_3AsCl_4, results when chlorine is conducted into a solution of methyl dichloroarsine in carbon disulfide cooled to $-10°$.[70] *Aryl arsenic tetrahalides* may be obtained through the combination of halogens with aryl dihalo arsines. 3-Nitrophenylarsenic tetrachloride, $NO_2C_6H_4AsCl_4$, is obtained by the chlorination of the corresponding arseno compound, $NO_2C_6H_4As = AsC_6H_4NO_2$.

Phenylarsenic oxychloride, $C_6H_5AsOCl_2$, results through the regulated reaction of water with phenylarsenic tetrachloride, or, more conveniently, through the reaction of phenylarsenic oxide with chlorine.

Diaryl dihalo oxides, $(R_2AsX_2)_2O$, result when dry halogens are made to react with diaryl arsine oxides.

Quaternary Arsonium Compounds

Quarternary arsonium iodides are obtained through the combination of tertiary arsines with alkyl iodides:[71]

$$R_3As + RI \rightarrow R_4AsI$$

Mixed quaternary arsonium compounds can also be prepared by this method. Mixed tetraalkyl arsonium compounds of the type $R_2R'_2AsI$ result through the intertion of tetraalkyl diarsines with alkyl iodides:

$$(CH_3)_2As-As(CH_3)_2 + 2C_2H_5I \rightarrow (CH_3)_2(C_2H_5)_2AsI + (CH_3)_2AsI$$

The corresponding hydroxides may be obtained by treating the iodides with moist silver oxide. The bases cannot be freed, however, by use of aqueous alkalies.

Tertiary aromatic arsines readily combine with alkyl halides to form quaternary arsonium halides. The reaction often proceeds at room temperature or at a slightly elevated temperature; occasionally, however, it has been found necessary to heat the reaction mixture in a sealed tube at 100° or higher.

The reaction is applicable to halo fatty acids and halo ketones, triphenylarsine yielding, for example, triphenylcarboxymethylarsonium chloride when heated at 100° with chloracetic acid, and triphenylacetonylarsonium chloride when heated with chloracetone at 120° for several hours. Alkalies convert these chloro compounds to the corresponding hydroxides or inner anhydrides of the latter.

Triphenylarsine combines with methyl iodide but fails to react with ethyl iodide and other alkyl halides.

Triaryl arsines do not combine with aromatic halides, although tetraaryl arsonium compounds may be prepared by indirect methods; they may be obtained, for example, through the reaction of triaryl arsenic oxides with aryl magnesium halides:[72]

$$R_3AsO + RMgX \rightarrow R_3As(R)OMgX \rightarrow R_3As(R)X$$

Quaternary arsonium compounds also result when arseno compounds are heated with alkyl iodides:

$$RAs = AsR + 3R'I \rightarrow RR'_3AsI + RAsI_2$$

Trialkyl arsines are capable of adding cyanogen bromide to form trialkyl arsenic cyanobromides.[73] The latter are readily converted to trialkyl arsenic hydroxybromides when treated with water; they decompose to a dialkyl cyano arsine and an alkylbromide:

$$R_3As(CN)Br \rightarrow R_2AsCN + RBr$$

Mixed tetraalkyl arsonium compounds are quite stable and do not show any tendency to autosymmetrization.

Tetraalkyl arsonium hydroxides deliquesce in air and absorb carbon dioxide from the atmosphere. Their salts with strong acids react neutral. Tetraalkyl arsonium iodides combine with iodine to form triiodides, R_3AsI_3. These are decomposed on heating to alkyl iodides and dialkyl iodo arsines.

Alkyl and Aryl Arsenic Oxides, Acids, Sulfides and Sulfo Acids

There are no generally applicable methods for the preparation of *dialkyl arsenic oxides*, $(R_2As)_2O$. *Cacodyl oxide*, $[(CH_3)_2As]_2O$, is formed as the main product when a mixture of arsenic oxide and potassium acetate is subjected to dry distillation.[74] The compound is also obtained when cacodyl chloride is distilled with alkali in a current of steam.

Diaryl arsine oxides and the corresponding hydroxides, R_2AsOH, result through the interaction of diaryl monohalo arsines with alkalies.

Diaryl arsine sulfides, $(R_2As)_2S$, are prepared from diaryl monohalo arsines or diaryl arsine oxides and hydrogen sulfide. They are also obtained by treating diarylarsinic salts with ammonium sulfide and subsequently treating the resulting thio arsinic salt with an acid:

$$R_2AsOONH_4 + 2(NH_4)_2S \rightarrow R_2AsS.SNH_4 + 2H_2O + 4NH_3$$
$$2R_2AsS.SNH_4 + 2HCl \rightarrow (R_2As)_2S + 2NH_4Cl + H_2S + S_2$$

Monoalkyl arsenic oxides, RAsO , are obtained through the hydrolysis of monoalkyl arsenic dihalides with potassium carbonate or potassium hydroxide.[75] They are prepared on the technical scale by reducing alkyl arsinic acids with sulfur dioxide.[76]

Aryl arsenic oxides are also readily obtained by treating aryl arsenic dihalides with alkali hydroxides or carbonates. Substituted aryl arsenic oxides may be prepared more conveniently by reducing the corresponding aryl arsonic acids with sulfurous acid in the presence of a little hydriodic acid, or with phosphorus trichloride in an indifferent solvent such as ether or ethyl acetate. The presence of an amino or substituted amino group in aryl arsenic oxides enhances their reactivity to such an extent that their isolation in the pure form becomes difficult. If the aromatic group contains a nuclear nitro or carboxyl group, the reaction product is a dihydroxy arsine.

Alkyl phenylarsenites, $C_6H_5As(OR)_2$, are readily formed by the reaction of phenylarsine dichloride with sodium alcoholate.[77]

Aryl arsenic oxides decompose to a triaryl arsine and arsenic trioxide when heated above their melting point.

Aryl arsenic sulfides, RAsS, are obtained from the corresponding oxides or dihalides and hydrogen sulfide, the reaction proceeding well in alcoholic solution:

$$RAsO + H_2S \rightarrow RAsS + H_2O$$
$$RAsCl_2 + H_2S \rightarrow RAsS + 2HCl$$

Nuclearly substituted arsine sulfides may also be obtained by the action of hydrogen sulfide on the corresponding arsonic acids.

Triaryl arsine oxides, R_3AsO, may be obtained by dehydrating the corresponding dihydroxides, or by decomposing the addition product of triaryl arsines and sulfur monochloride, $R_3As(Cl)SSCl$, with water.

Triphenylarsenic dihydroxide, $(C_6H_5)_3As(OH)_2$, results when the corresponding chloride is treated with ammonia.[78] The compound loses a molecule of water when heated under vacuum at 105-110°, and gives the oxide $(C_6H_5)_3AsO$.

Trialkyl arsine sulfides, R_3AsS, are obtained by conducting hydrogen sulfide through a solution of the compound $R_3As(Cl)S.SCl$ in carbon disulfide, and subsequently distilling off the solvent. The chloro disulfochlorides are the addition compound of trialkyl arsines and sulfur monochloride and are obtained by heating sulfur monochloride with a solution of the trialkyl arsine in carbon disulfide.[79]

Triaryl arsenic sulfides are formed directly from triaryl arsines and sulfur by melting the mixture of the ingredients, or by heating the arsine with sulfur in carbon disulfide for a prolonged period.[80] They are formed also when the arsine is heated with an alcoholic solution of yellow ammonium sulfide.

Dialkyl arsinic acids, R_2AsOOH, result when dialkyl arsenic oxides or halides are oxidized in the presence of water, the reaction proceeding quite vigorously. They are also obtained through the interaction of alkyl arsenic oxides with alkyl iodides in the presence of sodium hydroxide: [81]

$$RAsO + R'I + 2NaOH \rightarrow RR'AsOONa + NaI + H_2O$$

Dialkyl arsinic acids are further obtained through the reaction of alkyl halides with sodium alkyl arsenites. In this reaction the reactivity of the halogen of the alkyl halides determines the rate of reaction between the halide and the arsenite. Benzyl chloride, alkyl bromides and ethylene chlorohydrin react five to ten times more rapidly than ethyl or isopropyl bromide. High molecular alkyl halides react much more slowly, while aryl halides fail to react altogether. These compounds may also be obtained through the reduction of dialkyl arsonic acids with sulfur dioxide in the presence of hydrochloric acid, the reaction first resulting in the formation of alkyl dichloro arsines, which are converted to disodium alkyl arsenites by treatment with four molal proportions of sodium hydroxide. The alkyl arsenites are finally converted to dialkyl arsinates by treatment with alkyl halides. The acids may be readily isolated by concentrating the solution of the sodium salt, filtering off the inorganic salts which separate, and acidifying the filtrate, whereupon the dialkyl arsinic acid precipitates out.

Dialkyl arsinic acids are very stable and crystallize well.

Dimethylarsinic acid, (cacodylic acid) may be prepared by the oxidation of cacodyl oxide, $(CH_3)_2AsO$, with mercuric oxide.

Dibenzylarsinic acid results through the interaction of metallic sodium with benzyl chloride and arsenic trichloride in absolute ethereal solution in the presence of a little acetic ester. Dibenzyl arsenic trichloride is first formed and is converted to the sodium salt of the acid by hydrolysis with aqueous sodium hydroxide. [82]

Diaryl arsinic acids result when diaryl arsenic trihalides are hydrolyzed. These compounds may be prepared also through the interaction of potassium aryl arsenites with aromatic diazo or isodiazo compounds (*Bart's reaction*):

$$RN = NX + R_1As(OK)_2 \rightarrow RR_1AsOOK + KX + N_2$$

Diphenylarsinic acid, $(C_6H_5)_2AsOOH$, is obtained in the form of the sodium salt by the reaction of phenylarsenic oxide with benzenediazonium chloride in the presence of sodium hydroxide:

$$C_6H_5As(ONa)_2 + C_6H_5N_2Cl \rightarrow (C_6H_5)_2AsOONa + NaCl + N_2$$

Alkyl arsonic acids, $RAsO(ONa)_2$, result when alkyl halides are made to react with sodium arsenite: [83]

$$As(ONa)_3 + RX \rightarrow RAsO(ONa)_2 + NaX$$

It is possible that an addition compound is first formed from which the alkyl arsonic acid results by cleavage of sodium halide. Alkyl iodides are generally used in the reaction; they are added in solution in aqueous alcohol in order to bring the reaction components into solution. The reaction proceeds at ordinary temperature in some instances, and in other cases it is necessary to heat the mixture in a sealed tube. In most cases the reaction is almost complete within one hour. It is of advantage to employ the potassium salt of the acid, since much less alcohol is then required to bring the components into solution, and the yields are practically doubled. The reaction proceeds less rapidly with alkyl bromides. The reaction proceeds more slowly with the higher alkyl iodides.

In preparing ethylarsonic acid by this method, by use of ethyl iodide, half the amount of the latter is converted to ethyl ether by reaction with ethyl alcohol. The formation of ether may be avoided by carrying out the reaction in aqueous medium without the addition of alcohol.

When an attempt is made to precipitate the free alkyl arsonic acids by acidifying the final reaction mixture, the acid is rapidly reduced by the metallic iodide present. This situation does not hold, however, when alkyl bromides or chlorides are employed in the preparation of the alkylarsonic acid.

Alkyl arsonic acids result also through the hydrolysis of alkyl arsenic tetrahalides or alkyl arsenious oxyhalides, by the oxidation of alkyl arsines by atmospheric oxygen, and through the oxidation of alkyl arsenic dihalides with moist silver oxide or with hydrogen peroxide.

Heated at 130°, *methyl arsonic* acid loses the elements of water, and is thereby transformed to dimethylpyroarsinic acid,

$$\begin{array}{c} CH_3\underset{\displaystyle OH}{\underset{|}{As}}O.\underset{\displaystyle OH}{\underset{|}{As}}OCH_3 \end{array}$$

which is readily hydrolyzed with water to methylarsonic acid. The acid decomposes to methanol and arsenic trioxide.

Phenylarsonic acid has been prepared from arsanilic acid through the elimination of the amino group by diazotizing, and subsequently decomposing the diazo compound by adding it to a solution of sodium hypophosphite in hydrochloric acid solution maintained at 2° or lower, the mixture being then kept at 2-5° for 18 hours. The acid may be purified by conversion, successively to the barium, zinc and finally the sodium salt.[19]

Benzylarsonic acid is exceptionally unstable and is readily decomposed by mineral acids.

Bart's Reaction

Aryl arsonic acids are formed by the interaction of an alkali arsenite with an aromatic diazo, or preferably isodiazo compound, at room temperature in neutral solution in the presence of catalysts such as copper, copper salts or certain other metals or metallic salts:[84]

$$RN = NX + As(OK)_3 \rightarrow RAsO(OK)_2 + KX + N_2$$

Various arsenated and arsenic-free compounds are also formed in the reaction as byproducts.[85]

In the preparation of phenylarsonic acids by this method, the yields obtained with normal diazobenzene are quite small, while potassium benzene isodiazo oxide gives more satisfactory results. Diazo compounds with nuclearly substituted aromatic groups react readily. A neutral or slightly acid medium is most suitable for carrying out the reaction of normal diazo compounds with potassium arsenite without the assistance of a catalyst.

In the *Mounerat's modification* of Bart's reaction, the normal diazo compounds are made to react with arsenious acid in a cold or warm aqueous or dilute alcoholic solution in the presence of special catalysts, which consist of a copper salt and a reducing agent. The reaction may be carried out in acid, neutral or alkaline medium. If an acid medium is employed, an acid reducing agent such as hypophosphorous acid is used; in neutral medium, sodium hyposulfite or sodium formaldehydesulfoxolate may be employed. In alkaline medium, these same reducing agents, or an excess of alkaline arsenite give satisfactory results.

Bart's reaction is of wide applicability. Aryl diarsonic acids may be obtained by its use from amino aryl arsonic acids. Arsonic acids may be prepared also by this reaction from heterocyclic amino compounds.

Thus, pyridylarsonic acids have been made from amino pyridines,[86] quinoline arsonic acids from amino quinolines.[87] Arsonic acids of 1,4-benzisoxazine have also been prepared by Bart's method,[88] and α-methylcarbazole-3-arsonic acid has been obtained from the corresponding amino compound.[89]

Bechamp's Reaction

Primary aromatic amines can be converted to amino aryl arsonic acids by direct reaction with arsenic acid at an elevated temperature:[90]

$$C_6H_5NH_2 + H_3AsO_4 \rightarrow C_6H_5NH_2.H_3AsO_4 \rightarrow (HO)_2AsOC_6H_4NH_2 + H_2O$$

The arsonic group enters the ring at the *para* position with respect to the amino group, and if this position is not available, it enters the ortho position. The reaction is applicable also to phenols.

Direct arsonation of methylindole and α-naphthindole is also possible, both compounds giving 3-arsonic acids.[91]

Esters of aryl arsonic acids may be prepared from aryl arsine oxychlorides by reaction with sodium alkoxides:

$$C_6H_5AsOCl_2 + 2RONa \rightarrow C_6H_5AsO(OR)_2 + 2NaCl$$

They may be prepared also through the reaction of alkyl iodides with silver aryl arsonates:

$$RAsO(OAg)_2 + 2R'I \rightarrow RAsO(OR')_2 + 2AgI$$

The reaction proceeds in the cold in dry ether, but is completed by heating under reflux. The calculated quantity of alkyl iodide must be employed, since the use of an excess results in the formation of aryl alkyl arsenites with separation of iodine.

Alkyl arsine disulfides, $RAsS_2$, result through the reaction of hydrogen sulfide with alkyl arsonic acids in aqueous solution.

Aryl trithio arsonic acids, $RAsS(SH)_2$, are obtained in the form of their ammonium salts by passing hydrogen sulfide through an ammoniacal solution of aryl arsonic acids. The free acids are unstable and decompose to arsine disulfides, $RAsS_2$, or to the anhydrides of the acids, $(RAsS)_2S$.

Arsenic Heterocycles

Cyclopentamethylenephenylarsine, $\overline{CH_2(CH_2)_3CH_2As}C_6H_5$, is obtained through the reaction of phenyldichloroarsine with pentane-1,5-dimagnesium bromide. *Cyclotetramethylenephenylarsine*, $\overline{CH_2(CH_2)_2CH_2As}C_6H_5$, is obtained similarly from phenyldichloroarsine and butane-1,4-dimagnesium bromide.[92]

Phenylthiarsan, $\overline{CH_2CH_2SCH_2CH_2As}C_6H_5$, is obtained through the reaction of phenylarsinedimagnesium chloride, $C_6H_5As(MgCl)_2$, with $\beta.\beta$-dichlorodiethyl sulfide.[93]

2,5-Diaryl derivatives of tetrahydro-1,4,2,5-dioxadiarsine are obtained through the condensation of monoaryl arsines with aliphatic aldehydes:[94]

$$2ArAsH_2 + 4RCHO \rightarrow Ar\overline{AsCH(R)OAs(Ar)CH(R).O} + 2RCH_2OH$$

Bis-α-hydroxytertiaryarsines, $ArAs[CH(R)OH]_2$, are formed at first and condense to the tetrahydrodioxarsazines.

The procedure followed in carrying out the reaction is to cool the arsine with ice under an indifferent atmosphere, and to pass dry hydrogen chloride through it while adding the aldehyde drop by drop. The mixture is allowed to stand for several days and the volatile constituents are removed by distillation under vacuum, the dioxarsine remaining as a residue. The yield varies between 50 and 90%. These compounds are oxidized in air but are stable toward water, dilute hydrochloric acid and caustic.

Bis-α-hydroxy arsines are obtained when an excess of the aldehyde is used, and the reaction is carried out at a low temperature in the presence of a little concentrated hydrochloric acid.

Arseno compounds may be obtained when equimolecular quantities of arsine and aldehyde are employed, and the reaction is carried out at a higher temperature, or the reaction mixture is allowed to stand for a long period at room temperature:

$$2RAsH_2 + 2R'CHO \rightarrow RAs = AsR + 2R'CH_2OH$$

γ-Phenylpropylmethylhaloarsines in carbon disulfide solution subjected to the action of aluminum chloride condense to methyltetrahydroarsenoline:[95]

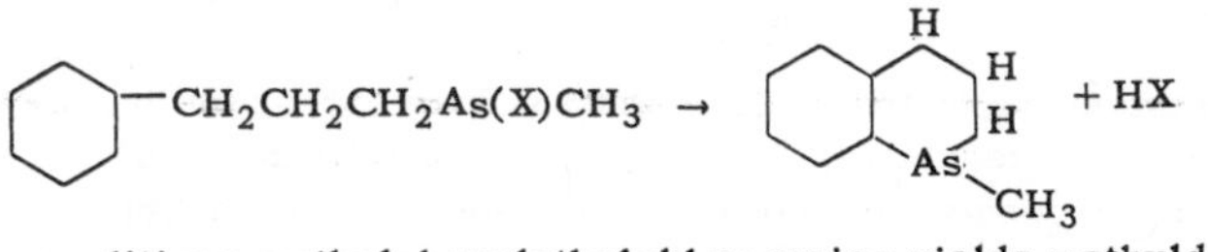

Under similar conditions methylphenylethylchloroarsine yields methyldihydroarsindole:

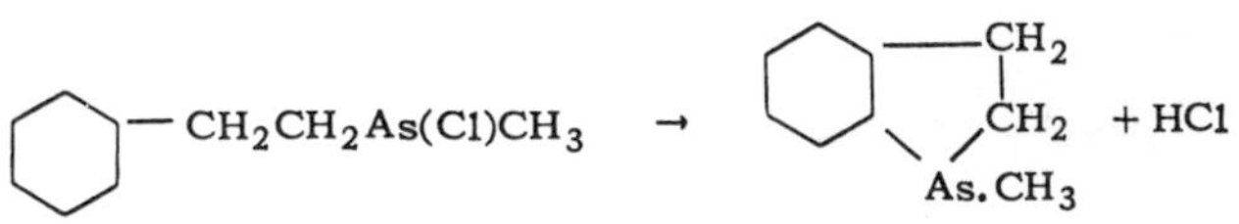

o,o'-Diphenylenearsinic acid is obtained through the condensation of diphenylene-*o*-arsonic acid with concentrated sulfuric acid:

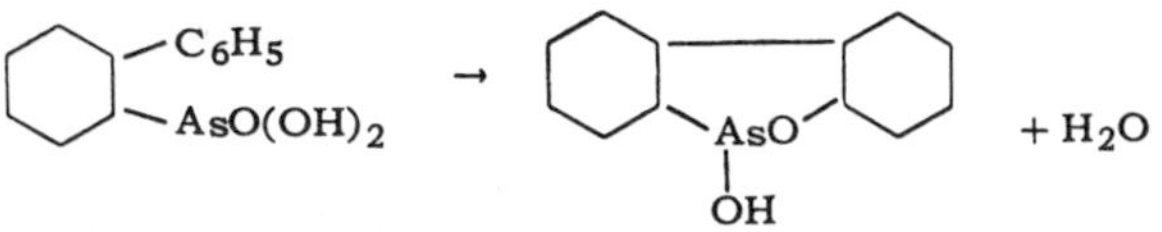

Reduction of the compound results in the formation of *o,o'*-diphenylenearsine. Acridarsinic acid results similarly from *o*-benzylphenylarsinic acid:[96]

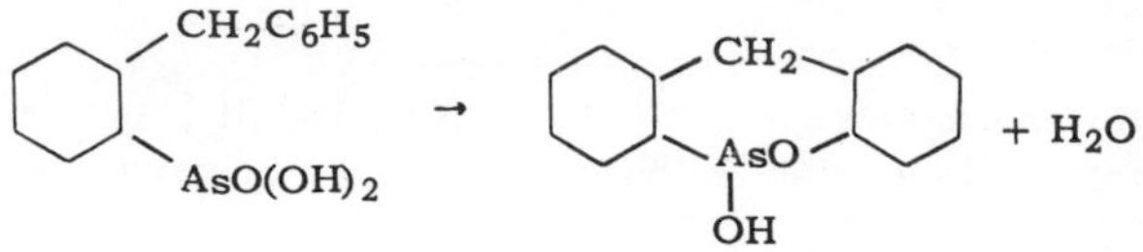

The reduction of phenylarsinophenyl-*o*-arsinic acid with sulfur dioxide in solution in concentrated hydrochloric acid in the presence of a little potassium iodide results in the formation of arsanthrene chloride, which is converted to arsanthrene oxide on treatment with sodium carbonate: [97]

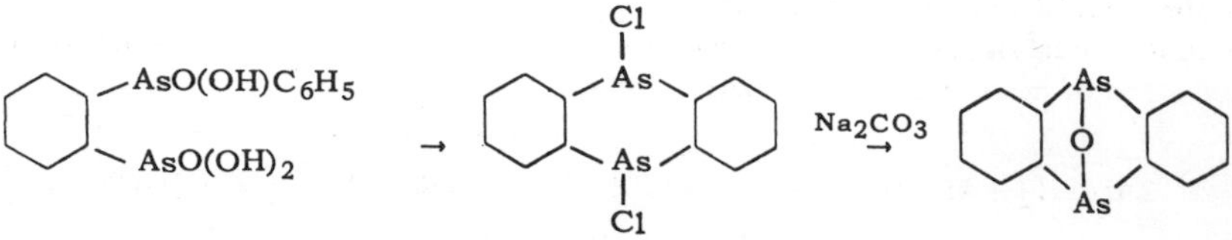

Warm nitric acid converts the chloride to arsanthronic acid,

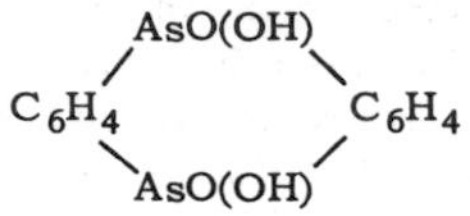

while zinc and alcoholic hydrochloric acid convert it to arsanthrene. Phenylarsinophenyl-*o*-arsinic acid is obtained through the interaction of hydroxy-*o*-diazoarsanilic acid,

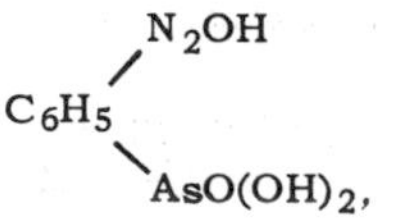

and phenylarsinic oxide, C_6H_5AsO.

Triphenylenediarsine,

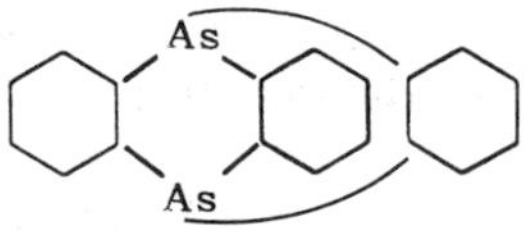

results when arsanthrene oxide is distilled under reduced pressure in a current of carbon dioxide. [98] This compound reacts with bromine to form a tetrabromide.

5-Chlorophenoxarsine results through the condensation of diphenyl ether with arsenic trichloride in the presence of aluminum chloride. [99]

$$C_6H_5OC_6H_5 + AsCl_3 \xrightarrow{AlCl_3} \text{(structure)} + 2HCl$$

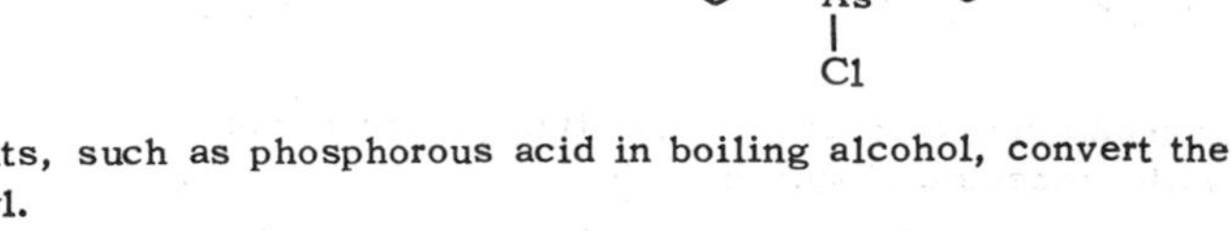

Reducing agents, such as phosphorous acid in boiling alcohol, convert the compound to phenoxycacodyl.

10-Chloro-5,10-dihydrophenarsazine (Adamsite) results through the condensation of diphenylamine with arsenic trichloride:

$$C_6H_5NCH_6H_5 + AsCl_3 \rightarrow \text{(structure)} + 2HCl$$

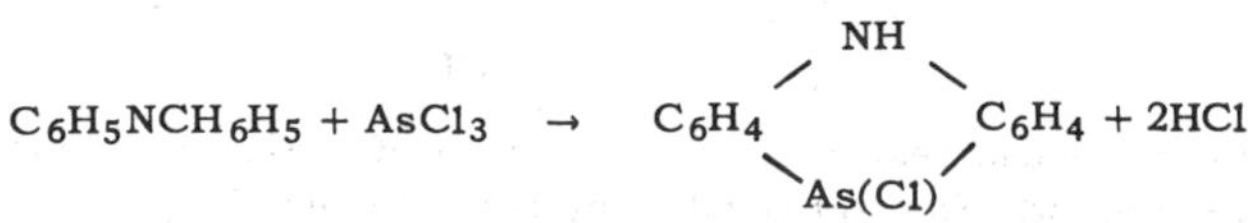

14-Chloro-7,14-dihydroxy-di-*n*-benzophenarsazine may be similarly obtained from di-β-naphthylamine.

Phenarsazine chloride heated two hours in anhydrous pyridine is converted to triphenarsazine chloride,

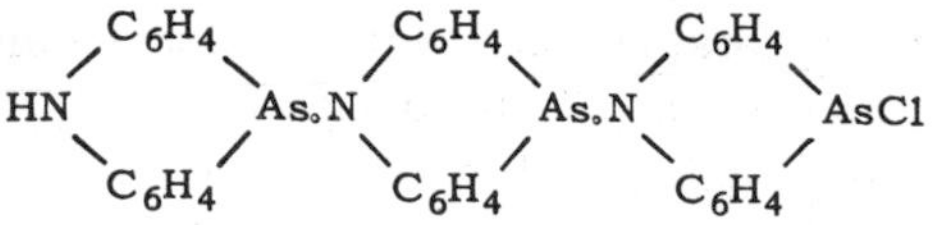

[100]

When 10-chlorodihydro and benzodihydrophenarsazines are heated with formic acid, colored *half-radicals* (Rasuwajew's radicals) are obtained:[101]

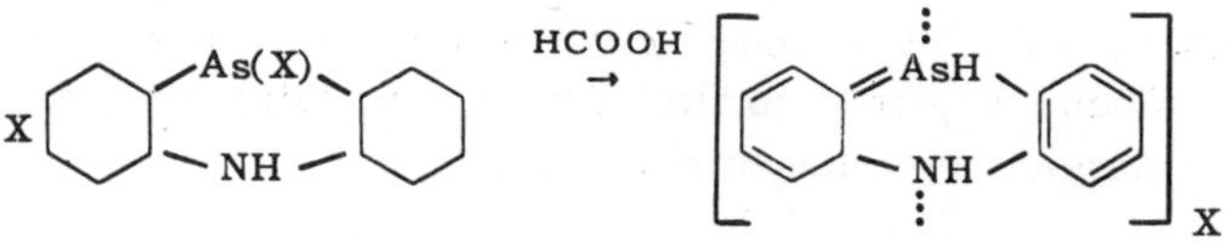
X
As(X)
NH
HCOOH
→
AsH
NH
X

These compounds are also formed when chloro and benzophenarsazines are reduced catalytically in the presence of platinum black, or with stannous chloride or zinc and acetic acid. The radical salts show a high degree of electrolytic conductivity. The color of these radicals is discharged with iodine, oxygen or sulfur.

Properties and Reactions of Organo Arsenic Compounds

Tertiary alkyl arsines are colorless liquids with a characteristic odor. They are miscible with organic solvents. They oxidize rapidly in air, though less readily than antimony alkyls. The reactivity of alkyl arsines with oxygen increases with increase in the number of alkyl groups attached to arsenic. Tertiary alkyl arsines are stable when protected from the action of atmospheric oxygen. Mixed alkyl arsines do not show any tendency toward symmetrization. They are of a weakly basic character and combine with halogen acids to form unstable salts which are decomposed by water. Tertiary alkyl arsines combine readily with sulfur and selenium to form trialkyl arsenic sulfides and selenides. Sulfides result also through the interaction of trialkyl arsenic oxides with hydrogen sulfide.

Triaryl arsines are mostly solid compounds, much more stable than tertiary aliphatic arsines. Thus, triphenylarsine may be distilled in an indifferent atmosphere without decomposition. These compounds are not readily oxidized by atmospheric oxygen when in the crystalline state. They do not show a basic character. Mixed triaryl arsines do not show any tendency toward rearrangement to symmetrical compounds.

Dialkyl arsines are very reactive and are attacked by atmospheric oxygen; dimethylarsine ignites spontaneously in air even at -10° although it is not affected by sunlight, and may be heated at 242° in the absence of air for several hours without undergoing change. Decomposition begins at 335° with the formation of polymeric compounds, hydrocarbons and water. Dimethylarsine acts as a reducing agent toward oxidizing agents, the arsine being oxidized and transformed in the process to cacodyl, cacodyl oxide or chloride and finally cacodylic acid, depending on the quantity and character of the oxidizing agent. The hydrogen in dimethylarsine may be exchanged for a halogen by reaction with chlorocarbonic ester or dibromosuccinic acid. Dimethylarsine combines with acids to form unstable salts.

Primary alkyl arsines are oxidized when exposed to atmospheric oxygen, although not as energetically as secondary and tertiary alkyl arsines, which ignite spontaneously in contact with ari. Primary alkyl arsines are almost devoid of basic properties, and form very unstable salts. Reacting with an excess of alcoholic iodine, methylarsine gives methyldiiodoarsine, CH_3AsI_2. If the arsine is in excess, it reacts with the arsine iodide to form a brown mass.

Aromatic arsines are viscous oils or solids with a characteristic odor. They are oxidized when exposed to air; they do not possess basic properties, and are vigorous skin poisons. Phenylarsine reacts with ethylmagnesium bromide to give phenylarsenic dimagnesium bromide, $C_6H_5As(MgBr)_2$.

Tetraalkyl diarsines are liquids with a repugnant odor; they are so readily oxidized that they ignite spontaneously when exposed to air.

Tetraaryl diarsines are only slightly soluble in organic solvents. They are in the monomolecular form in solution, in contrast to tetraalkyl diarsines, which are largely associated. These compounds are readily oxidized in air to diaryl arsine oxides. When subjected to dry distillation, tetraphenyldiarsine decomposes to triphenylarsine and elemental arsenic.

Diaryl arsenic monohalides are liquids, the vapors of which attack the eyes producing tears. They have a very unpleasant odor and are highly toxic. They are soluble in organic solvents, but insoluble in water; they are not acted on by water, but alkalies convert them to the corresponding oxides, the reaction proceeding especially vigorously with nuclearly substituted members.[102]

Phenyldichloroarsine causes slow healing burns on coming in contact with the skin. It is not attacked by water even on heating, but reacts with ammonia to form phenylarsenimide, $C_6H_5As = NH$. Primary and secondary amines react with phenyldichloroarsine replacing only one chlorine to form compounds of the type $C_6H_5As(Cl)NHR$ and $C_6H_5As(Cl)NR_2$. Tertiary amines give addition compounds $C_6H_5AsCl_2.NR_3$.

Monoaryl arsenic tetrahalides decompose on heating to arsenic trihalide and an aromatic halide or to aryl arsenic dihalides and halogen, depending on the conditions. Phenylarsenic tetrachloride is rapidly decomposed by water.

Aryl arsonic acids are quite stable as a rule. The presence of a hydroxyl group in the *para* position with respect to arsenic appears to weaken the carbon-to-arsenic bond. The carbon-to-arsenic linkage in amino aryl arsonic acids is ruptured on treatment with halogens in aqueous or in mineral acid solution. This decomposition does not take place if halogenation is carried out in an anhydrous solvent, such as methanol or glacial acetic acid. Decomposition may be avoided also by use of nascent halogen derived from sodium hypochlorite, sodium hypobromite, or a mixture of potassium iodate and iodide by reaction with sulfuric acid.

Estimation of Arsenic Acids

Pentavalent arsenic in the form of arsenic acid may be estimated by iodometric titration.[103] Since derivatives of trivalent arsenic can be oxidized quantitatively to the corresponding arsenic acids with hydrogen peroxide, trivalent arsenic derivatives can also be estimated by this method.

ORGANIC COMPOUNDS OF ANTIMONY

Alkyl and Aryl Stibines

Trialkyl stibines, R_3Sb, result from the reaction of alkyl halides with antimony-potassium alloys:

$$K_3Sb + 3RX \rightarrow R_3Sb + 3KX$$

Owing to the violence of the reaction and the inflammability of alkylstibines, it is necessary to mix the alloy with sand and to work in an inert atmosphere with small quantities. Although alkyl chlorides or bromides may be used, it is preferable to employ the iodides. The alloy is always used in excess.

Trialkyl stibines are obtained also through the interaction of antimony trichloride with zinc or mercury alkyls,[104] or, preferably, with alkyl magnesium halides:[105]

$$2SbCl_3 + 3ZnR_2 \rightarrow 2SbR_3 + 3ZnCl_2$$

$$SbCl_3 + 3RMgX \rightarrow SbR_3 + 3MgXCl$$

If an excess of antimony trihalide is used in the reaction, a complex mixture containing little or no trialkyl stibine is obtained.

The lower members may be separated from their ethereal solution by the addition of bromine, whereby trialkyl antimony dibromides, R_3SbBr_2, precipitate out. The filtered dibromide may be reconverted to the trialkyl stibine by distillation with zinc dust.[106]

Triaryl stibines are formed when aromatic bromides are boiled for a long period with antimony-sodium alloys. The compounds are also obtained through the interaction of antimony trichloride with mercury aryls and aryl magnesium halides.[107] The higher molecular compounds may be prepared through the reaction of a mixture of antimony trichloride and aryl bromides with an excess of sodium suspended in benzene or xylene.[108] Antimony triphenyl has been prepared successfully by this method, and antimony tri-*p*-biphenyl has been obtained similarly from *p*-chlorobiphenyl and antimony trichloride.[109] Triaryl stibines are formed also when aryl antimony oxides are heated:[110]

$$3(Ar_2Sb)_2O \rightarrow 4SbAr_3 + Sb_2O_3$$

$$3C_6H_5SbO \rightarrow Sb(C_6H_5)_3 + Sb_2O_3$$

Tri-α-thienylstibine, $(C_4H_3S)_3Sb$, is obtained through the reaction of α-thienylmagnesium bromide with antimony trichloride.[111]

Tetraphenyldistibine, $(C_6H_5)_2Sb.Sb(C_6H_5)_2$, results when diphenylstibine oxide is oxidized with hypophosphorous acid.[112] The compound rapidly absorbs oxygen to form the peroxide, $(C_6H_5)_2SbO.OSb(C_6H_5)_2$. Iodine gives diphenylstibine iodide.

Aromatic stibonium compounds, RSb = SbR, which are analogs of salvarsan, are obtained through the reduction of aryl stibinic acids with sodium hyposulfite, $Na_2S_2O_4$. Aryl stibinic oxides, RSbO, may be reduced to stibino compounds with sodium hypophosphite. The correct experimental conditions must be strictly observed, since otherwise cleavage of the antimony-carbon bond occurs.

Arsenostibino compounds, RSb = AsR′, may be obtained through the reduction of mixtures of aryl arsenic and aryl stibinic acids with sodium hyposulfite, or through the interaction of a primary aryl arsine with an aryl stibine oxide or halide in methanolic solution:

$$RSbO + R'AsH_2 \rightarrow RSb = AsR' + H_2O$$

m,m′-Diamino-*p*-hydroxy-*p′*-chloroarsenostibinobenzene and the salvarsan analog, *m,m'*-diamino-*p-p'*-dihydroxyarsenostibinobenzene, have been prepared by this method.[113]

Reduction of the hydrochloride of *m*-amino-*p*-hydroxyphenylstibine dichloride with sodium hypophosphite results in the formation of the antimony analog of salvarsan.[114]

Dialkyl antimony halides, R_2SbX, result when trialkyl antimony dihalides are heated in a carbon dioxide atmosphere:

$$(CH_3)_3SbCl_2 \rightarrow (CH_3)_2SbCl + CH_3Cl$$

Dialkyl antimony cyanides are formed when trialkyl cyano antimony bromides are heated similarly:[115]

$$(CH_3)_3SbBrCN \rightarrow (CH_3)_2SbCN + CH_3Br$$

Methylphenylstibine cyanide, $CH_3(C_6H_5)SnCN$, results on heating dimethylphenylstibine bromocyanide.[116]

Monoalkyl antimony halides result through the decomposition of dialkyl antimony trihalides with the cleavage of an alkyl halide. Decomposition takes place with the chlorides on melting, while the iodides decompose even at -15°.

Aryl antimony halides of the type R_2SbX and $RSbX_2$ may be obtained by replacement of aryl groups in antimony triaryls with halogens; by decomposition of triaryl antimony dihalides, or through the reduction of the corresponding pentavalent antimony compounds.

The reaction of antimony triaryls with antimony trichloride, which is carried out by heating in sealed tubes, leads to the formation of diaryl and monoaryl antimony chlorides.[117] The products can only be isolated in a partially pure form by fractional distillation. Triarylstibines heated with alcoholic hydrochloric acid give diaryl stibine chlorides:[118]

$$Sb(C_6H_5)_3 + HCl \rightarrow (C_6H_5)_2SbCl + C_6H_6$$

This reaction proceeds at different temperatures depending on the type of aryl stibine, the tri-*p*-acetylaminophenyl compound reacting with evolution of heat at ordinary temperature and requiring cooling with ice for successful control of the reaction.

Diaryl antimony monohalides, treated with caustic, are converted to diaryl antimony oxides:

$$2(C_6H_5)_2SbCl + 2NaOH \rightarrow 2NaCl + 2(C_6H_5)_2SbOH \rightarrow$$
$$[(C_6H_5)_2Sb]_2O + H_2O$$

These compounds are partially dearylated and are converted to monoaryl stibine diacetate when boiled with glacial acetic acid:

$$[(C_6H_5)_2Sb]_2O + 4CH_3COOH \rightarrow 2C_6H_6 + 2C_6H_5Sb(OCOCH_3)_2 + H_2O$$

Treatment of the diacetate with hydrochloric acid results in the formation of the corresponding dichloride. Formation of the monoaryl diformate is observed at room temperature on treatment with formic acid.

Aryl chloro stibinic acids, $HArSbCl_5$, result when monoaryl stibinic tetrachlorides are dissolved in hydrochloric acid. Monoaryl stibinic tetrachlorides, in turn, are obtained from aryl stibinic acids, $RAsO(OH)_2$, by reaction with hydrochloric acid.[119]

Tetramethylstibinium iodide, $(CH_3)_4SbI$, results readily through the interaction of trimethylstibine with methyl iodide, reaction proceeding vigorously with generation of heat. Combination of triethylstibine with ethyl iodide proceeds slowly in the cold, but rapidly at 100°; the reaction between triethylstibine and methyl iodide takes place more readily. Triisoamylstibine and amyl iodide do not combine at 100°.

Tetraalkyl stibonium hydroxides may be prepared readily from the corresponding chlorides by reaction with silver oxide. The hydroxides are soluble in water; they absorb carbon dioxide from the air, liberate ammonia from solutions of salts of ammonia, and are capable of saponifying fats.

Tetraaryl stibonium compounds are not known, although mixed aralkyl stibines with only one aromatic group combine with alkyl iodides to form quaternary stibonium iodides.[120]

Triaryl stibinic sulfides are obtained in 80% yield through the reaction of hydrogen sulfide with triaryl stibinic dichlorides. The use of an excess of hydrogen sulfide should be avoided in order to prevent the formation of complexes which cannot be reconverted to the sulfide.[121]

Bart Type Reaction

Aromatic stibinic acids are obtained through the reaction of aromatic diazo compounds with sodium antimonite:[122]

$$RN_2OH + NaHSbO_3 \rightarrow RSbO_3Na + H_2O + N_2$$

The reaction generally proceeds at room temperature without the use of a catalyst. Copper accelerates the reaction. It would appear that an addition compound, $RN_2SbOONaH$, is first formed which subsequently breaks down into nitrogen and the substituted stibinic acid. Side reactions also take place, giving rise to coloring matters and reduction products. The formation of the latter may be largely prevented by controlling the alkalinity of the reaction medium. If a nitro group is present in the diazo compound, the reaction is carried out in neutral or weakly acid solution.

Sodium antimonite is obtained by treating freshly precipitated antimony trioxide with aqueous sodium hydroxide.

The reaction can also be carried out by use of antimony trichloride, which combines with the diazo compound to form an insoluble complex, the latter giving the stibinic acid on treatment with caustic.[123]

Diaryl stibinic acids result when aromatic diazo compounds are made to react with an aryl stibine oxide in the presence of an alkali:[124]

$$RN_2X + R'SbO + 2KOH \rightarrow RR'SbO_2K + N_2 + KX + H_2O$$

This appears to be the best method of preparation of diaryl stibinic acids.

o-Nitrophenylstibinic acid may be reduced to the corresponding amino compound by treatment with a mixture of freshly precipitated ferrous hydroxide and aqueous caustic, or with a methyl alcohol solution of titanium trichloride.[125]

Antimony Heterocycles

Phenylcyclopentamethylenestibine, $\overline{CH_2(CH_2)_3CH_2}SbC_6H_5$, results through the interaction of pentane-1,5-dimagnesium bromide with phenyldichlorostibine.[126] Phenylcyclo-

tetramethylenestibine, $\overline{CH_2(CH_2)_2CH_2}SbC_6H_5$, is obtained similarly from butane-1,4-dimagnesium bromide and phenyldichlorostibine.[127] Pyridine, pyrrolidine and acridine type of antimony heterocycles have been prepared similarly.[128]

Antimony carbazole may be prepared from o-phenylphenylstibinic acid, which is first converted for the purpose to the corresponding chloride by reduction in the presence of hydrogen chloride.[129]

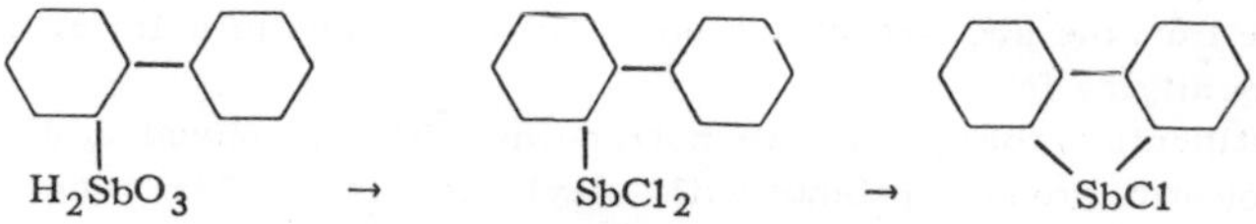

Stibacridic acid,

$$
\begin{array}{c}
CH_2 \\
C_6H_4 \diagup \quad \diagdown C_6H_4 \\
\diagdown SbO(OH) \diagup
\end{array}
$$

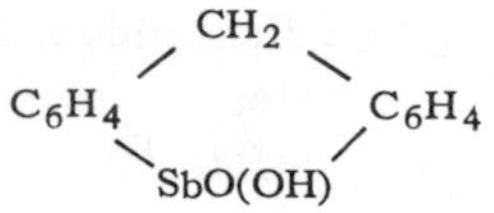

results on heating diphenylmethane-2-stibic acid.[130]

Properties and Reactions of Organoantimony Compounds

Antimony trialkyls are colorless compounds insoluble in water but soluble in organic solvents. They are stable toward water and many can be distilled under vacuum without decomposition. They combine with oxygen of the air, the methyl and ethyl compounds igniting spontaneously on exposure to air. The tendency to oxidation decreases with increase in molecular weight. They are oxidized also by mercuric oxide. Halogens react vigorously with antimony trialkyls to form trialkyl antimony dihalides. Sulfur and selenium also react readily with these compounds; antimony trialkyls differ in this respect from antimony triaryls. The tendency toward combination with chlorine is so strong that these compounds react with hydrogen chloride forming trialkyl antimony dichlorides with liberation of hydrogen.

Antimony alkyls are generally quite stable, although the antimony-carbon bond is not so strong as the arsenic-carbon bond.

Alkyl antimony halides of the type $RSbX_2$ and R_2SbX are dangerous skin poisons and cause painful burns; they penetrate under the nails, causing an annoying irritation of the flesh. They are absorbed by rubber.

Antimony *triaryls* are crystalline compounds with sharp melting points. In contrast to antimony trialkyls, they are entirely stable in air, and do not give addition compounds with alkyl halides. The antimony-carbon bond in antimony triaryls is sufficiently strong to allow the nitration of the aromatic groups and the reduction of nitro groups attached to the aromatic nucleus; even sulfonation is possible in some instances. When triaryl stibines are subjected to the action of nitric acid at $40°$, the dinitrate, $R_3Sb(NO_3)_2$, is formed, and at the same time nitration of the aromatic groups proceeds, the nitro groups entering the *para* position with respect to antimony. The nitro groups may be successfully reduced by zinc dust and glacial acetic acid, with tin and alcoholic hydrogen chloride or with zinc and alcoholic ammonium chloride,[131] although rupture of the antimony-carbon bond takes place to some extent during reduction. Tri-p-anisylstibine reacting with cupric chloride gives tri-p-anisylstibine dichloride; the latter is decomposed by chlorine.

Aromatic stibino compounds, RSb = SbR, are amorphous, dark brown powders, insoluble in water unless the aromatic nucleus carries salt forming groups. They are readily oxidized in air, oxidation occasionally proceeding so vigorously as to cause automatic ignition. Hydrochloric acid decomposes these compounds to dark colored products.

Aromatic stibinic acids are amorphous, colorless powders that cannot be melted without decomposition. They are insoluble in water, but dissolve in concentrated hydrochloric acid, aqueous caustic, and even in solutions of alkali carbonates and ammonia. Their behavior toward alkalies indicates that they are not derivatives of *ortho*-antimonic acid, but rather consist of a complex formed by association.[123] Secondary stibinic acids also appear to form complex molecules by association. The properties of these complexes vary according to the quantity of water with which they are combined, and their method of preparation.[132]

ORGANIC COMPOUNDS OF SELENIUM AND TELLURIUM

Selenium dialkyls or selenoethers, SeR_2, as well as *diseleno dialkyls*, Se_2R_2, and alkyl selenium hydroxides or *selenols*, RSeH, may be prepared by the methods employed for the preparation of their sulfur analogs. They may be obtained, for example, by the reaction of metallic selenides or hydroselenides with sulfuric esters:

$$SeM_2 + 2ROSO_2OM \rightarrow SeR_2 + 2M_2SO_4$$

$$MSeSeM + 2ROSO_2OM \rightarrow RSeSeR + 2M_2SO_4$$

$$MSeH + ROSO_3M \rightarrow RSeH + M_2SO_4$$

Selenium dialkyls are also obtained through the reaction of selenium dichloride with Grignard reagents.

Selenols result through the reaction of selenium with alkyl or aryl magnesium halides, the latter reacting especially well:

$$RMgX + Se \rightarrow RSeMgX$$

Decomposition of the halomagnesium compound with a mixture of hydrochloric acid and ice, followed by treatment with caustic, yields the selenol in the form of its sodium compound.

Organo selenium monohalides are obtained by treating selenocyanides with halogens:

$$C_6H_5SeCN + Br_2 \rightarrow C_6H_5SeBr + BrCN$$

Aromatic seleno cyanides are obtained through the reaction of potassium selenocyanide with aromatic diazonium compounds:

$$RN_2X + KSeCN \rightarrow RSeCN + KX + N_2$$

Addition of halogens to the monohalide results in the formation of the *trihalides*, $RSeX_3$.

Trialkyl seleno halides, R_3SeX, result through the combination of alkyl halides with selenium dialkyls. The free hydroxides, R_3SeOH, are strong bases and give neutral salts with acids.

Dialkyl or diaryl selenides are converted to the monoxides, R_2SeO, on oxidation with potassium dichromate; oxidation with potassium permanganate solution results in the formation of the dioxides, R_2SeO_2.

Selenonic acids, $RSeO_2OH$, are obtained through the reaction of selenic acid with aromatic compounds in a sealed tube at elevated temperatures. *Phenylseleninic acid,* C_6H_5SeOOH, is obtained as the nitrate through the oxidation of dephenyldiselenide with nitric acid. Seleninic acids react sufficiently basic to form salt-like compounds with strong mineral acids.

Tellurium dialkyls may be prepared through the reaction of tellurium dihalides with alkyl magnesium halides. They are obtained also through the reduction of dialkyl tellurium dihalides, R_2TeX_2, with sulfurous acid or other suitable reagent.

Tellurium diaryls are best prepared through the reaction of tellurium iodide or bromide with aryl magnesium bromides. The yields may be as high as 75% of the theoretical in this reaction. These compounds may also be obtained in good yield by heating elemental tellurium with mercury diaryls in a sealed tube.[133] Elemental tellurium also reacts with phenylmagnesium bromide to form tellurium diphenyl, diphenylditelluride, and probably tellurophenol, C_6H_5TeH.[134]

Tellurium di-α-thienyl, $(C_4H_4S)_2Te$, is the only heterocyclic tellurium compound of its type known; it combines with methyl iodide to form a tertiary telluronium iodide.[135]

Diaryl tellurium dihalides result through the reaction of tellurium tetrahalides with phenyl ethers, monoaryl tellurium trihalides being the intermediate products of the reaction.

Trialkyl telluronium halides, R_3TeX, result through the combination of tellurium dialkyls with alkyl halides; they are formed also by the alkylation of tellurium tetrachloride. Triaryl telluronium halides can also be prepared by the latter method, or from diaryl tellurium halides by reaction with aryl magnesium halides.[136]

Isomerism was believed to exist in tetravalent dialkyl tellurium compounds, and two types designated as the α- and β-isomers were identified.[137] Later work showed, however, that no real isomerism existed, and that the α-compounds were the normal bodies, while the β-compounds were, in reality, complexes of the same empirical composition possessing a salt-like character. The β-bases are, at present, considered to be anhydrides having a structure of the type $(CH_3)_2TeO.TeO.CH_3$.[138] The β-iodide of the methyl derivative has, in fact, been prepared through the combination of trimethyltellurium iodide, $(CH_3)_3TeI$, with methyltellurium triiodide, CH_3TeI_3, and may be considered to have the structure $[(CH_3)_3Te]^{+}[CH_3TeI_4]^{-}$ The α-compound is apparently changed to the β-compound by a pinacol-pinacoline type transformation:

$$2(CH_3)_2Te(OH)_2 \rightarrow H_2O + HOTe(CH_3)_2O.Te(CH_3)_2OH \rightarrow$$
$$(CH_3)_2Te.O.Te(CH_3)_2O \rightarrow (CH_3)_3TeO.TeO.CH_3$$

Tellurium diaryls react with alkyl iodides to form *diaryl alkyl tellurium iodides,* often in quantitative yield.[139] The iodides are converted to the corresponding hydroxides by treatment with moist silver oxide. The aqueous solutions of the hydroxides have an alkaline reaction, although they form unstable carbonates. Telluretin compounds, $Ar_2Te(X)C(R_2)COOR'$, are obtained without difficulty from tellurium diaryls and esters of bromo and iodoacetic acids and other α-halo esters. The free acids also undergo the reaction. [140]

Telluroketones, $R_2C = Te$, result when ketones, R_2CO, are made to react with hydrogen telluride in cooled concentrated hydrochloric acid solution. [141]

Tellurium tetrachloride reacts with ketones forming *diketo telluro dichlorides:* [142]

$$2CH_3COCH_3 + TeCl_4 \rightarrow (CH_3COCH_2)_2TeCl_2 + 2HCl$$

In a few instances monoketo telluro trichlorides have also been isolated.

Tellurium Heterocycles

The reaction of β-diketones with tellurium tetrachloride leads to the formation of cyclic tellurium compounds:

$$CH_2(COCH_3)_2 + TeCl_4 \rightarrow \overline{CH_2COCH_2Te(Cl_2)CH_2CO} + 2HCl$$

Open-chain compounds also form simultaneously. The dihalo compounds may be converted to the telluro compound by reduction with sulfurous acid, potassium metabisulfite, zinc dust, etc. [143]

Cyclopentamethylenetellurium is obtained through the reaction of 1,5-dibromopentane with aluminum telluride:

$$Al_2Te_3 + 3BrCH_2(CH_2)_3CH_2Br \rightarrow 3\overline{CH_2(CH_2)_3CH_2Te} + 2AlBr_3$$

The compound reacts with an excess of dibromopentane, forming the compounds

$$\overline{CH_2(CH_2)_3CH_2Te(Br)}CH_2(CH_2)_3CH_2Br$$

and

$$\overline{CH_2(CH_2)_3CH_2Te(Br)}CH_2(CH_2)_3CH_2Te(Br)CH_2(CH_2)_3\overline{CH_2}$$

The reaction of tellurium tetrachloride with diphenyl oxide leads to the formation of p-phenoxyphenyltellurium trichloride, $C_6H_5OC_6H_4TeCl_3$; heated at 200°, this compound is converted to 10,10-dichlorophenoxtellurine,

$$\begin{array}{c} TeCl_2 \\ \diagup \quad \diagdown \\ C_6H_4 \qquad C_6H_4 \\ \diagdown \quad \diagup \\ O \end{array}$$

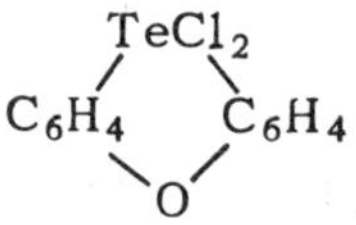

which on reduction with potassium metabisulfite gives phenoxtellurine,

$$\begin{array}{c} Te \\ \diagup \quad \diagdown \\ C_6H_4 \qquad C_6H_4 \qquad \text{[144]} \\ \diagdown \quad \diagup \\ O \end{array}$$

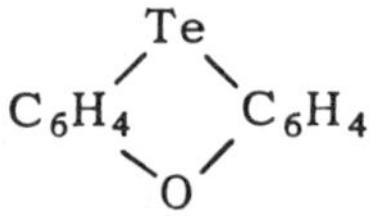

ORGANIC COMPOUNDS OF PHOSPHORUS

Phosphorus forms two series of compounds, one in which this element is trivalent, and another in which it is pentavalent. Compounds in which organic groups are attached directly to phosphorus are represented by the various phosphines, $R_1R_2R_3P$, R_1R_2PH, RPH_2, the phosphinous, phosphonous and phosphonic acids and their derivatives, etc. The subject of phosphorous and phosphoric esters and their thio and amino derivatives, while strictly coming under the heading of inorganic esters dealt with in the chapter on alcohols, is taken up under the present section because of its importance as much as because of the variety of special methods employed in the preparation of these compounds.

Esters by Replacement of Halogen in Phosphorus Compounds

Compounds of the type $ROPCl_2$ are obtained by the addition of the appropriate alcohol or phenol to a moderate excess of phosphorus trichloride:

$$PCl_3 + ROH \rightarrow ROPCl_2 + HCl$$

The mixture of the reagents is subjected to vacuum distillation after the evolution of hydrogen chloride ceases.[145] It should be noted that the dichlorophosphite obtained with benzyl alcohol invariably *explodes* on attempted distillation.

This reaction is applicable to thiols.

Compounds of the general type $(RO)_2PCl$ are obtained in rather unsatisfactory yield by the above reaction, by use of two equivalents of the hydroxy compound. The use of still larger quantities of phenols leads to the formation of triaryl phosphates in satisfactory yield, but aliphatic alcohols give dialkyl phosphites:[229]

$$3AlkOH + PCl_3 \rightarrow (AlkO)_2POH + AlkCl + 2HCl$$

This reaction offers the most convenient method for the preparation of dialkyl phosphites. The temperature of the reaction mixture should be held below 10-15° in preparing the methyl and isopropyl derivatives. Other esters may be prepared at somewhat higher temperatures.

Phenols, especially when used in excess, readily yield triaryl phosphites on refluxing with phosphorus trichloride. Compounds of high molecular weight react satisfactorily in the presence of catalytic amounts of magnesium chloride.[146]

Trithiophosphites are obtained by this method when the indicated proportions of a thiol are used in the reaction, and the mixture is heated. Yields are quite satisfactory with aliphatic thiols, and aromatic thiols react in a fairly satisfactory manner:[147]

The reaction of phosphorus trihalides with hydroxy compounds in the presence of a tertiary base offers the most satisfactory method for the preparation of trialkyl phosphites:

$$PCl_3 + 3ROH + 3C_6H_5N(C_2H_5)_2 \rightarrow (RO)_3P + 3C_6H_5N(C_2H_5)_2.HCl$$

The reaction is carried out by adding the trihalide to the solution of the alcohol in an inert solvent, such as ether, petroleum ether or benzene, containing the required quantity of a tertiary base.[148] Pyridine or diethyl aniline are satisfactory for the purpose. Reaction proceeds satisfactorily at 10-15°. After completion of the reaction, the amine hydrochloride is removed by filtration, and the product is isolated by distillation under reduced pressure.

Somewhat less satisfactory results are obtained with sodium alkoxides, since the separation of the finely divided sodium halide is troublesome, and side reactions caused by free alkali and alkoxides tend to give byproducts.

The method is applicable also to thiols.

Triaryl methyl carbinols react with phosphorus trichloride to give triarylmethane phosphonyl dichlorides:

$$Ar_3COH + PCl_3 \rightarrow Ar_3C\,POCl_2 + HCl$$

The neutral esters of phosphinous, phosphonous and phosphonic acids are formed through the reaction of the corresponding halides with an alcohol in the presence of a tertiary base:

$$RPX_2 + 2R'OH + 2C_6H_5N(C_2H_5)_2 \rightarrow RP(OR')_2 + 2C_6H_5N(C_2H_5)_2.HX$$

$$R_2PX + R'OH + C_6H_5N(C_2H_5)_2 \rightarrow R_2POR' + C_6H_5N(C_2H_5)_2.HX$$

$$RPOX_2 + 2R'OH + 2C_6H_5N(C_2H_5)_2 \rightarrow RPO(OR')_2 + 2C_6H_5N(C_2H_5)_2.HX$$

The reaction of a dichlorophosphite with one molecular equivalent of an alcohol in the presence of a base is the best available method for the preparation of dialkyl chlorophosphites:

$$ROPCl_2 + ROH + C_6H_5N(C_2H_5)_2 \rightarrow (RO)_2PCl + C_6H_5N(C_2H_5)_2.HCl$$

When an excess of phenol is heated with phosphorus oxychloride, generally satisfactory yields of triaryl phosphates are obtained. The reaction is facilitated by magnesium chloride, ultraviolet radiation, or traces of iodine.

Three equivalents of a hydroxy compound reacting with one of phosphorus oxychloride in the presence of three molecular equivalents of a tertiary base give a tertiary phosphate:

$$POCl_3 + 3ROH + 3C_6H_5N(C_2H_5)_2 \rightarrow (RO)_3PO + 3C_6H_5N(C_2H_5)_2.HCl$$

The reaction, which may be conveniently carried out in an inert solvent at or below room temperature, offers the best method for the preparation of these compounds.[149] A few halophosphates and halothiophosphates have also been prepared by using the calculated quantity of the base.

Aromatic tertiary phosphates may be obtained in satisfactory yield from phosphorus oxychloride by the Schotten-Baumann method using 10% sodium hydroxide in excess.[150]

Dihalophosphates are prepared by the reaction of alcohols or phenols with phosphorus oxyhalides:[151]

$$POCl_3 + ROH \rightarrow ROPOCl_2 + HCl$$

The reaction proceeds satisfactorily at room temperature with phosphorus oxychloride and primary aliphatic alcohols. Secondary and tertiary alcohols generally do not react smoothly. Reaction with phenols requires heating, often at reflux temperature.[152]

Thiophosphoryl chloride reacts well with phenols in the presence of aqueous sodium hydroxide to yield mixtures of primary and secondary halothiophosphates:[153]

$$PSCl_3 + RONa \rightarrow ROPSCl_2 + NaCl$$

$$PSCl_3 + 2RONa \rightarrow (RO)_2PSCl + 2NaCl$$

Best yields of the halothiophosphates are usually obtained in the cold, when 2 moles of the phosphorus compound are allowed to react with 3 moles of the phenol in an excess of 10% sodium hydroxide with shaking.

Monoaryl dichlorothionophosphates do not react beyond the disubstituted stage even with 25-30% alkali, either in the cold or on heating.

Secondary halothiophosphates react slowly with sodium phenate even on long refluxing.

Thiophosphoryl chloride reacts unsatisfactorily with free phenols; however, the addition of a catalytic amount of phosphorus trichloride brings about the formation of triaryl thiophosphates in essentially quantitative yields in a short time.

Amido halo thiophosphates are very unreactive, and their esters may be obtained only in poor yield through the reaction of the sodium derivative of a hydroxy compound with the halides at high temperatures for a prolonged period of time.

Pyrophosphates may be prepared through the reaction of metal salts of secondary phosphoric esters with the chlorides of the acid esters:[216]

$$(RO)_2POOM + ClPO(OR')_2 \rightarrow (RO)_2PO.O.PO(OR')_2 + NaCl$$

Amides of pyrophosphoric acid may be prepared in a similar manner:[154]

$$(R_2N)_2POOM + ClPO(NR_2)_2 \rightarrow (R_2N)_2PO.OPO(NR'_2)_2 + MCl$$

Tetraalkyl pyrophosphites may be prepared from the metal salt of secondary phosphites with the chlorides of the same:

$$(RO)_2PONa + ClP(OR')_2 \rightarrow (RO)_2POP(OR')_2 + NaCl$$

Pyrophosphates have been prepared in good yield by heating trialkyl phosphates at 80° with a half molecular equivalent of thionyl chloride:[219]

$$2(C_2H_5O)_3PO + SOCl_2 \rightarrow (C_2H_5O)_2POOPO(OC_2H_5)_2 + SO_2 + 2C_2H_5Cl$$

Replacement of Halogens with Oxygen

The chlorine in dichlorophosphoric esters may be replaced with oxygen by heating these compounds to 75 to 85° with an equimolecular quantity of oxalic acid:[155]

$$ROPOCl_2 + (COOH)_2 \rightarrow ROPO_2 + COCl_2 + HCOOH$$

Phosphoryl halides are obtained through the partial replacement of halogens in phosphine tri- or tetrahalides by gently warming with an organic acid:[156]

$$RPCl_4 + CH_3COOH \rightarrow RPOCl_2 + CH_3COCl + HCl$$

Replacement of the halogen with oxygen may also be effected by treatment with sulfur dioxide:[157]

$$RPX_4 + SO_2 \rightarrow RPOX_2 + SOX_2$$
$$R_2PX_3 + SO_2 \rightarrow R_2POX + SOX_2$$

The reaction may be carried out in an inert solvent, SO_2 being bubbled through the solution until conversion is complete. This reaction is also applicable to aminophosphohalides:

$$R_2NPCl_4 + SO_2 \rightarrow R_2NPOCl_2 + SOCl_2$$

Phosphoryl halides have been obtained through the interaction of organophosphoric tetrahalides with phosphorus pentoxide.[230] Thiophosphoryl halides are formed through the reaction of organophosphoric tetrahalides with phosphorus pentasulfide.

Phosphonyl chlorides react smoothly with the corresponding phosphonic acids on heating, preferably in benzene solution, to form metaphosphonates:[158]

$$RPOCl_2 + RPO(OH)_2 \rightarrow 2RPO_2 + 2HCl$$

Phosphonyl and phosphinyl chlorides may be prepared from the corresponding acids by heating with phosphorus pentachloride:[159]

$$RPO(OH)_2 + 2PCl_5 \rightarrow RPOCl_2 + 2POCl_3 + 2HCl$$
$$R_2POOH + PCl_5 \rightarrow R_2POCl + POCl_3 + HCl$$

Usually the pentachloride is added gradually to the acid, and the mixture is warmed gently until the evolution of hydrogen chloride ceases. Thionyl chloride may be used successfully in place of phosphorus pentachloride, especially for the preparation of secondary phosphonic halides.[160]

Replacement of Halogens and Sulfur by use of Grignard Reagents

The halogen atoms in phosphorus oxyhalides may be replaced with organic residues by reaction with organomagnesium halides;[161] thus, tertiary phosphine oxides are obtained when an excess of the Grignard reagent is employed:

$$POX_3 + 3RMgX \rightarrow R_3PO_3 + MgX_2$$

The reaction is applicable to thiophosphoryl halides, although thiophosphoryl chloride yields a secondary compound when treated with an excess of the Grignard reagent.[162]

The reaction of esters of the type $ROPOCl_2$ with Grignard reagents results in the formation of tertiary phosphine oxides:[163]

$$C_6H_5OPOCl_2 + 3RMgCl \rightarrow R_3PO + 2MgCl_2 + C_6H_5OMgCl$$

One chlorine atom in phosphorus oxychloride may be eliminated by reaction with a secondary amine; the resulting monoamino dichloride, reacting with an excess of the organomagnesium halide, gives a secondary phosphine amide oxide; decomposition of the latter with hydrochloric acid gives the secondary phosphinic acid:[164]

$$R_2NPOCl_2 + 2R'MgCl \rightarrow 2MgCl_2 + R_2NPOR'_2 \rightarrow R'_2POOH$$

Sulfur in phosphorus sulfides may be replaced with organic radicals by reaction with organomagnesium halides.[165] Thus, the secondary and tertiary phosphines R_2PH and R_3P are obtained as the final products, after hydrolysis of the intermediate complexes formed, from the reaction of P_2S_3 with organomagnesium halides RMgX.

The procedure is to add the ethereal solution of the Grignard reagent to the phosphorus sulfide. This results, as a rule, in an initial exothermic reaction. The mixture is then heated under reflux for ten to twelve hours. The phosphines are recovered from the organic layer after the decomposition of the excess Grignard reagent with water. The yield may be as high as 22% of aliphatic phosphines and 40% of aromatic phosphines when 8.5 to 16 molecular proportions of the organomagnesium halide are employed.

Preparation of Phosphines and Related Compounds

Phosphines by the Wurtz Reaction

Tertiary aromatic phosphines have been prepared by the Wurtz reaction from phosphorus trihalides and aromatic halides:[166]

$$PX_3 + 3RX + 6Na \rightarrow R_3P + 6NaX$$

The reaction is carried out by heating a solution of the halides in an inert solvent with the metallic sodium under reflux for several hours until the sodium disappears completely. Occasionally it may be necessary to heat for 24 hours. Yields are generally higher than 50%. The method is applicable to aliphatic halides. The reaction with high molecular halides may be carried out in higher boiling solvents, such as benzene. These halides may be activated by the addition of antimony trichloride.[167]

A number of aromatic phosphonamides have been prepared from aryl halides and chloroamidophosphates by the Wurtz reaction:

$$R_2NPOCl_2 + 2ArX + 4Na \rightarrow R_2NPOAr_2 + 2NaCl + 2NaX$$

The metallic sodium is added in lumps to the mixture of the reagents in an inert solvent, usually ether, and the mixture is warmed gently until the reaction subsides.[168]

A very satisfactory method of preparation of phosphines is through the reaction of phosphorus trihalides and halophosphines with organomagnesium compounds:

$$PX_3 + 3RMgX \rightarrow R_3P + 3MgX_2$$

$$RPX_2 + R'MgX \rightarrow RR'PX + MgX_2$$

The reaction is usually carried out in ether; the mixture of the halide with the ethereal solution of the Grignard reagent is heated under reflux until the reaction is complete. The aryl derivatives are obtained in yields up to 70 to 80%, but aliphatic derivatives are obtained in extremely variable yields. Best results are obtained with primary halides; alkyl halides with branched chains, and in particular, secondary halides give poor yields or fail to react.[169]

Phosphines from Metallic Phosphides

Metal phosphides and metallic derivatives of primary and secondary phosphines react readily with alkyl halides to give alkyl phosphines in good yields:

$$Na_3P + 3RX \rightarrow R_3P + 3NaX$$

$$NaPH_2 + RX \rightarrow RPH_2 + NaX$$

The procedure is to add the halide to a suspension of the metal derivative in an inert organic solvent, and to warm to complete the reaction.[170] Yields are generally higher than 50% of the theoretical when the reaction is carried out with care.

The metal derivatives may be prepared through the reaction of the phosphine with sodium or potassium in liquid ammonia or with sodium or potassium triphenyl methyl in ethereal solution.

Phosphines by Reaction of Phosphorus Trichloride with Organic Mercury Compounds

A number of aromatic and aliphatic dichlorophosphines have been prepared by heating phosphorus trichloride with a dialkyl or diaryl mercury in a sealed tube at 180-230° for several hours:[171]

$$PCl_3 + R_2Hg \rightarrow RPCl_2 + RHgCl$$

The reaction usually yields some monochlorophosphine resulting from the continued action of the organo mercury compound on the dichlorophosphine formed. Cadmium dialkyls have been used instead of mercury dialkyls with excellent results.[227]

Halogen Exchange

Chlorophosphines may be converted to bromophosphines by passage of dry hydrogen bromide into the heated chlorophosphine:

$$RPCl_2 + 2HBr \rightarrow RPBr_2 + 2HCl$$

The reaction may be carried out in phosphorus tribromide solution.

Phosphines by Friedel-Crafts Reaction

Aromatic phosphine halides may be prepared from phosphorus trichloride by reaction with aromatic hydrocarbons in the presence of aluminum chloride:[172]

$$RH + PCl_3 \xrightarrow{AlCl_3} RPCl_2 + HCl$$

The reaction is carried out by heating a mixture of the aromatic compound, phosphorus trichloride and anhydrous aluminum chloride under a reflux condenser. The cooled reaction mixture is treated under agitation with an amount of water equivalent to three moles per mole of aluminum chloride used in the reaction; benzene or petroleum ether is then added with good shaking, the organic layer is removed, and the phosphine isolated from this by fractional distillation. Alternatively, the aluminum chloride may be removed by the addition of one equivalent of phosphorus oxychloride, heating shortly and diluting with petroleum ether; the complex $AlCl_3POCl_3$ precipitates out and may be removed by filtration. The yield is good (70-80%) with most aromatic compounds.

The method is not applicable to stilbene, iodobenzene, benzonitrile, ethyl benzoate, trichlorobenzene and bromotoluene. The successful application of the reaction to anisole and phenetole requires the use of partially hydrated aluminum chloride.

The reaction of an aromatic dialkylamine with phosphorus oxychloride proceeds in the absence of a catalyst when the mixture of the two compounds is heated at 130-140°.[173]

$$6R_2NC_6H_5 + POCl_3 \rightarrow (R_2NC_6H_4)_3PO + 3R_2NC_6H_5.HCl$$

Yields of the *tert*-phosphine oxide are good when an excess of the aromatic amine is employed. A similar reaction has been observed with phosphorus pentachloride.[174]

The reaction of phosphorus trichloride with diphenylamine results in the formation of a cyclic phosphine monochloride, which may be oxidized, after hydrolysis, to the corresponding phosphinic acid:

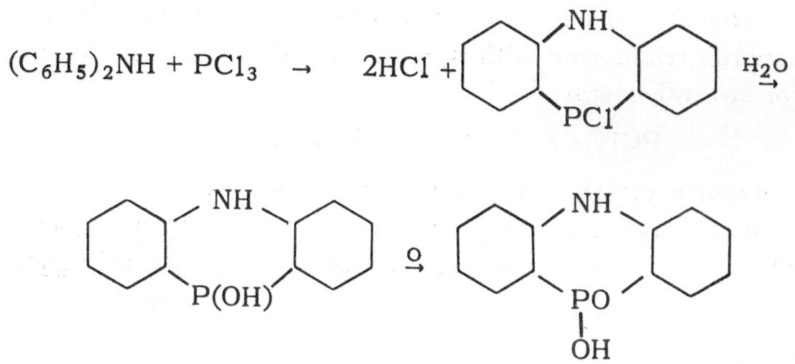

Phosphines and their Derivatives by the Addition of Phosphorus Halides to Unsaturated Compounds

Phosphorus trichloride reacts additively with aliphatic olefins of the type $RCH = CH_2$ under the action of ultraviolet radiation to form halogenated phosphine dihalides:[175]

$$RCH = CH_2 + PCl_3 \rightarrow RCHClCH_2PCl_2$$

A 1,2-addition has been observed with α-β-unsaturated ketones; the resulting compounds are transformed to phosphonates on hydrolysis:

$$C_6H_5CH = CHCOC_6H_5 + PCl_3 \xrightarrow[H_2O]{CH_3COOH} C_6H_5CH(PO_3H_2)CH_2COC_6H_5$$

Phosphorus pentachloride also adds readily to certain olefins to form compounds of the type $RPCl_4$.[176] The reaction has been employed for the preparation of phosphonic acids resulting from the hydrolysis of the halo compounds.

The procedure is to add the olefin to a suspension of the pentachloride in an inert liquid miscible with the olefin, and to agitate for several hours, whereupon the adduct precipitates out and is removed by filtration.

As a rule, only 1,2-olefins react. *Ortho* substituents in any aromatic nuclei attached to the 2-carbon atom exert a steric hindrance. Indene reacts probably because of the "exposed" position of the double bond. The reaction is applicable also to acetylenic compounds:

$$RC \equiv CH + PCl_5 \rightarrow RCCl = CHPCl_4$$

Treatment of the adducts with olefins with water results in the formation of *unsaturated* phosphoric acids. Unsubstituted 1,2-olefins and 1,2-olefins with a methyl or aryl group in 2-position give 2-haloolefin phosphonic acids. Adducts with acetylenic compounds yield 2-halo olefinic phosphonic acids on hydrolysis.[228] Phosphonic esters are obtained when the adducts are treated with alcohols.

Michaelis - Arbuzov Reaction

Phosphinous or thiophosphinous esters are capable of isomerization to phosphine oxides or sulfides.[177] The reaction generally takes place when an attempt is made to bring about an ester exchange with an organic halide:

$$R_2POR' + R''X \rightarrow R_2R''PO + R'X$$

$$R_2PSR' + R''X \rightarrow R_2R''PS + R'X$$

This is a special case of a general rearrangement characteristic of esters of trivalent phosphorus known as the *Michaelis - Arbuzov rearrangement.*

The reaction is carried out by mixing the reactants and warming the mixture to the required temperature, usually about 150°. The more reactive compounds begin to react at room temperature.[178] If the groups OR are aliphatic, the intermediate complex breaks down spontaneously, and it is only necessary to distill the mixture to obtain the final product. On the other hand, phenols usually form rather stable intermediates which can be broken down by treatment with aqueous alkalies, or by heating. The reaction proceeds best with primary aliphatic halides.

The Michaelis – Arbuzov reaction takes place with any derivative of trivalent phosphorus carrying an ester group OR, and with a great variety of organic halides R′X. In its most general form it may be formulated as follows:

$$>POR + R'X \rightarrow >PR(OR)X' \rightarrow >P(O)R' + RX$$

It is generally applied to tertiary phosphites $(RO)_3P$, to obtain esters of primary phosphonic acids, although it can be used with success for the preparation of esters of phosphonic acids R_2POOR' from those of phosphonous acids $RP(OR)_2$, and of phosphine oxides from esters of phosphinous acids R_2POR.

Tertiary trithiophosphites do not undergo the reaction, but di-S-alkyl benzenedithiophosphites, such as $C_6H_5P(SR)_2$, react normally to a large extent.

The reaction proceeds satisfactorily with primary aliphatic halides, but secondary and tertiary halides do not react or react to form olefins. Isopropyl iodide, ethyl-α-bromopropionate and triarylmethyl halides form exceptions and react satisfactorily. Compounds with aromatically bound halogen fail to react; 9-chloroacridine forms an exception, however, and reacts readily.

Primary alkyl halides with other functional groups may be used successfully in the reaction; primary alkyl halides with aromatic groups, such as compounds of the type $ArCH_2Cl$, also undergo the reaction. α-Bromonitro compounds do not give the expected nitroalkane phosphonates. Allylic rearrangement apparently occurs occasionally when unsaturated halides are subjected to the reaction.

Primary dihalides yield haloalkane phosphonates, or alkanediphosphonates, according to the proportion of phosphite to halide employed in the reaction.[210]

Carbon tetrachloride reacts readily with trialkyl phosphites to form esters of trichloromethanephosphonic acid.[211] Chloroform fails to react at reflux temperature.

Acid halides react readily with trialkyl phosphites to form α-ketophosphonic esters.[212] These compounds cannot be hydrolyzed to the free acids without decomposition.

Phosphorous esters of 2-chloroethanol undergo molecular rearrangement to phosphonates when heated:

$$P(OCH_2CH_2Cl)_3 \rightarrow ClCH_2CH_2PO(OCH_2CH_2Cl)_2$$

$$ClCH_2CH_2OP(OC_2H_5)_2 \rightarrow ClCH_2CH_2PO(OC_2H_5)_2$$

An ethanediphosphonic ester is formed when the phosphite contains two aryloxy residues:[213]

$$2(ArO)_2POCH_2CH_2Cl \rightarrow (ArO)_2P(O)CH_2CH_2PO(OAr)_2 + ClCH_2CH_2Cl$$

The reaction of sodium diethyl phosphite with allyl chloride results in the formation of a bisphosphonate in the following manner:[220]

$$CH_2 = CHCH_2Cl + 2NaOP(OC_2H_5)_2 + H_2O$$

$$\rightarrow (C_2H_5O)_2P(O)CH(CH_3)CH_2PO(OC_2H_5)_2 + NaCl + NaOH$$

Diethyl (3-methoxypropylphenyl)phosphine is converted to 1-ethyl-1,2,3,4- tetrahydrophospholine in 78% yield when a stream of hydrogen bromide is passed for 3 hours through its solution in acetic acid, the product isolated as the picrate and distilled at 350-370° under 30 mm pressure:[221]

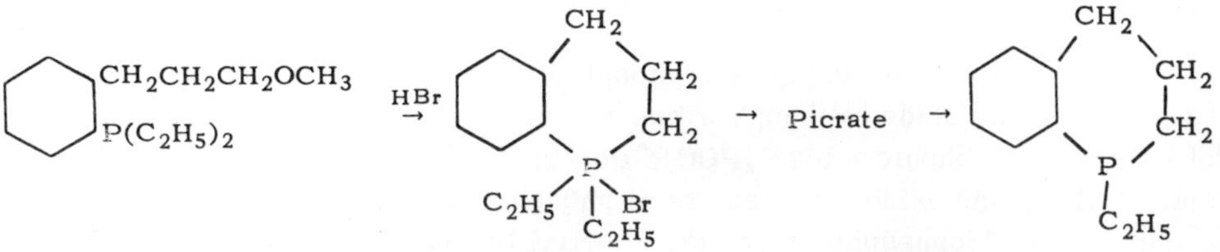

Metal salts of secondary phosphinous esters undergo the Michaelis-Arbuzov reaction:[214]

$$(RO)_2POM + R'X \rightarrow (RO)_2POR' + MX$$

The reaction is preferably carried out with the sodium and potassium salts and the metal halide is removed from the reaction product by filtration prior to distillation.

The ethyl ester of α-halo acids undergo this reaction in satisfactory manner, while higher esters of such acids fail to give phosphonic esters, but react to form compounds resulting from the coupling of two ester residues.

The Michaelis-Arbuzov rearrangement is observed also in the reaction of secondary phosphites with primary or secondary amines in the presence of aliphatic polyhalogen compounds:[180]

$$(RO)_2POH + CCl_4 + 2R'NH_2 \rightarrow (RO)_2PONHR' + HCCl_3 + R'NH_2.HCl$$

Halogens react additively with tertiary or secondary phosphites to form halophosphates with elimination of hydrogen halide or an aromatic halide:[179]

$$(RO)_3P + X_2 \rightarrow (RO)_3PX_2 \rightarrow (RO)_2POX + RX$$

$$(RO)_2POH + X_2 \rightarrow (RO)_2POX + HX$$

Reaction proceeds in the cold.

Alkali metal salts of dialkyl phosphites react with alkyl thiocyanates to form thiophosphoric esters:[181]

$$(RO)_2PONa + CNSR \rightarrow (RO)_2POSR + NaCN$$

Addition of Compounds of the Type of RX to Phosphines

Tertiary phosphines have the ability to combine additively with oxygen, forming phosphine oxides:

$$R_3P + O \rightarrow R_3PO$$

Trialkyl phosphines are oxidized simply by exposure to air; phosphines with at least one benzyl group are also readily oxidized, but purely aromatic phosphines are usually less subject to attack by oxygen.

Oxidation may be effected with 40% fuming nitric acid; nitrous oxide and aqueous potassium permanganate are also effective.[182] Oxidation may be carried out at room temperature by use of hydrogen peroxide, mercuric oxide or ferric chloride.

Alkyl phosphinic acids result through the oxidation of primary and secondary alkyl phosphines with nitric acid:

$$RPH_2 \rightarrow RPO(OH)_2$$

$$R_2PH \rightarrow R_2POOH$$

Primary phosphines cannot be converted to alkyl phosphinous acids, $RP(OH)_2$, by partial oxidation, but the latter may be obtained by the hydrolysis of alkyl dichlorophosphines.[222]

Monoalkyl phosphonic acids, $RPO(OH)_2$, are colorless, crystalline, very stable compounds, soluble in water and alcohol. They may be partially distilled without decomposition. Phosphorus pentachloride converts them to their chlorides.

Tertiary phosphines combine additively with sulfur and selenium to give phosphine sulfides and selenides:

$$R_3P + S \rightarrow R_3PS$$

$$R_3P + Se \rightarrow R_3PSe$$

The reaction is carried out in ether or benzene by moderate warming.[184] Triethylphosphine sulfide, $(C_2H_5)_3PS$, is best prepared by gradually adding sulfur to a dilute ethereal solution of triethylphosphine.[223]

Dialkyl phosphines react with sulfur to form crystalline compounds. Diethylphosphine gives $(C_2H_5)_2PSSSPS(C_2H_5)_2$, which reacts with ammonium sulfide to form $(C_2H_5)_2PSSNH_4$.[224]

Sulfur also adds readily to esters of phosphonous and phosphinous acids and their thio analogs on heating a mixture of the ester with sulfur:[183]

$$RP(OR')_2 + S \rightarrow RPS(OR')_2$$

$$RP(SR')_2 + S \rightarrow RPS(SR')_2$$

$$R_2PSR' + S \rightarrow R_2PS.SR'$$

Alkyl dichlorophosphines heated with sulfur at 120° give alkyl sulfochlorophosphines, $RPSCl_2$.[225] These compounds may be distilled under reduced pressure, are stable toward water, and yield esters $RPS(OR')_2$ with sodium alcoholates NaOR'.

Alkyl phosphines are capable of reacting with carbon disulfide to give well defined crystalline addition compounds insoluble in water. Triethylphosphine, for example, gives the compound $(C_2H_5)_3\overline{PCSS}$. The reaction between tertiary phosphines and carbon disulfide proceeds very vigorously. It can be moderated by use of diluents, such as alcohol or ether. The triethyl compound treated in in alcoholic solution with silver oxide is converted to triethylphosphine sulfide.

Addition of Halogens to Phosphines and Related Compounds

Phosphines react additively with halogens:[185]

$$R_3P + X_2 \rightarrow R_3PX_2$$

Addition of halogens to halophosphines results in the formation of phosphine tri- or tetrahalides:[186]

$$R_2PX + X_2 \rightarrow R_2PX_3$$

$$RPX_2 + X_2 \rightarrow RPX_4$$

Disubstituted monohalophosphines show a greater tendency toward addition reactions than substituted dihalophosphines.[187]

Halophosphines are best treated with the halogen in a suitable solvent, such as carbon tetrachloride or tetrachlorethane, with cooling and agitation. The reaction with tertiary phosphines must be carried out with good cooling. The reaction generally proceeds well only with triaryl phosphines.

Halophosphines may be obtained also by the action of phosphorus pentachloride on tertiary phosphine oxides:[188]

$$R_3PO + PCl_5 \rightarrow R_3PCl_2 + POCl_3$$

The reaction is most suitable for the preparation of tertiary aliphatic phosphine dichlorides. It is carried out by mixing the reagents and gently warming for a short time; the phosphorus oxychloride formed is then removed by distillation under reduced pressure. Thionyl chloride may be used instead of phosphorus pentachloride, although the yields obtained with this reagent are somewhat lower.

Tertiary phosphine dihalides, R_3PX_2, may be readily converted to the corresponding oxides by hydrolysis. The halogen, usually bromine, is added to the phosphine in solution in an inert solvent and the resulting product is hydrolyzed by warming with water or with aqueous sodium hydroxide. Alcohol may be employed in the reaction in place of water.[189] Tertiary phosphine dichlorides may be converted to monochlorophosphines R_2PCl, in 40 to 70% yield by heating at 150-220°.[215]

Alkyl halides react additively with tertiary phosphines to form *quaternary phosphonium compounds:*

$$R_3P + RX \rightarrow R_4PX$$

The reaction is carried out simply by mixing and heating the reactants. The lower alkyl halides react spontaneously, but the additive power of the halide decreases with increase in size of the alkyl group. Solvents of polar type such as nitromethane, favor the reaction.

Addition to Carbonyl Compounds

Aldehydes and ketones react additively with phosphorous acid to form a partial ester of phosphorous acid:

$$(HO)_2POH + OCHR \rightarrow \rightarrow (HO)_2POCH(OH)R$$

The reaction is carried out by heating a mixture of the reactants on a water bath for a prolonged period, frequently for several days. The reaction is applicable to hypophosphorous acid and to phosphonous acids:

$$HOPHOH + OCHR \rightarrow HOPHOCH(OH)R$$

$$HOPR'OH + OCHR \rightarrow HOPR'O.CH(OH)R$$

Phosphorus trichloride also reacts additively with aldehydes, combining with three molecular equivalents of the carbonyl compound, and giving, upon hydrolysis of the original reaction product, a hydroxy phosphonic acid:[190]

$$PCl_3 + 3RCHO \rightarrow PCl_3 3RCHO \xrightarrow{H_2O} RCH(OH)PO(OH)_2$$

Combination takes place on mixing the trihalide with the aldehyde at room temperature, or on gentle heating. With paraldehyde under pressure, the compound $ClCH_2POCl_2$ is obtained. Ketones of the type of benzophenone require heating to a higher temperature. Hydrolysis is effected by adding water gradually,[191] or by adding a considerable excess of acetic acid, and allowing the mixture to stand for two or three hours.

Diphenylchlorophosphine adds carbonyl compounds in the presence of glacial acetic acid to give tertiary phosphine oxides:[192]

$$RCHO + (C_6H_5)_2PCl + CH_3COOH \rightarrow (C_6H_5)_2POCH(OH)R + CH_3COCl$$

Ketones in which a double bond conjugated with the carbonyl group is present undergo a 1,2-addition when subjected to the conditions of this reaction:

$$(C_6H_5)_2PCl + RCOCH = CHR' + CH_3COOH$$
$$\rightarrow \quad (C_6H_5)_2POCHR'CH_2COR + CH_3COCl$$

The reaction is carried out by mixing the reactants at substantially room temperature, adding the acetic acid and allowing the mixture to stand for several hours. The product is isolated following treatment with water and dilute ammonia. If it should become necessary to heat the reaction mixture above 35°, benzoic acid must be used instead of acetic acid, since the latter reacts vigorously with phosphorous trichloride at temperatures in excess of 35°.

Aldehydes react satisfactorily in this reaction, but ketones tend to yield mixtures containing appreciable amounts of unsaturated phosphonic acids. Considerable difficulty is experienced, for this reason, in the purification of the products of the reaction. The crude products can be converted to unsaturated derivatives by passage through a tube heated to 190-220°, or by heating at 150° with acetic anhydride. The reaction of phosphorus trichloride or phosphine chlorides with benzophenone must be carried out at 150° in the presence of benzoic acid; benzil and anthraquinone fail to react even at this temperature.

A smooth reaction takes place when an aldehyde in ethereal solution is heated with a mixture of hydrogen chloride and phosphine, and results in the formation of a quaternary phosphonium chloride:[193]

$$4RCHO + PH_3 + HCl \quad \rightarrow \quad [RCHOH]_4PCl$$

This is a special case of a general reaction involving the combination of carbonyl compounds with acids of phosphorus containing a hydrogen atom directly bound to phosphorus:[209]

$$RCHO + HPO(OH)_2 \quad \rightarrow \quad RCH(OH)PO(OH)_2$$

The procedure in carrying out the reaction is to heat a mixture of an excess of the carbonyl compound with the acid of phosphorus for the required period. The reaction velocity varies according to the carbonyl compound employed, and the time required for the completion of the reaction must be determined for each individual case. The crude reaction product can be readily isolated by evaporating off the excess of carbonyl compound, and may be purified by crystallization. The lead salt of the acid may be used to advantage for this purpose. The purified lead salt may be reconverted to the original acid with hydrogen sulfide. A preliminary separation of the α-hydroxyphosphonous acids from the phosphinic acids may be effected by taking advantage of the lower solubility of the latter.

The reaction mixture usually contains appreciable amounts of phosphonic acids, presumably as a result of atmospheric oxidation of the primary products of the reaction. Two molecules of the carbonyl compound may react with the phosphorus acid, an excess of the carbonyl compound and prolonged reaction favoring disubstitution.

Since phosphine is generated during the reaction, due precautions should be observed to eliminate hazards due to this compound.

Triethylphosphine combines readily with diphenylketene to form the very unstable compound

$$(C_2H_5)_3P \overset{O}{\overbrace{}} C = C(C_6H_5)_2 \quad [226]$$

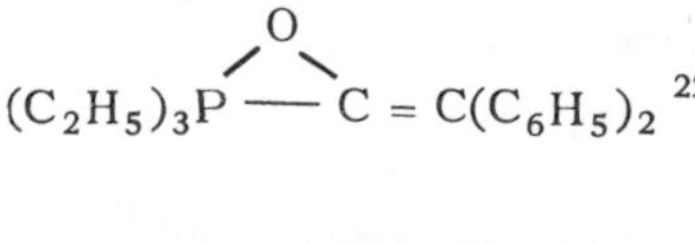

Phosphines combine with diazoalkanes to form coordination compounds:[194]

$$R_3P + N_2CR_2 \rightarrow R_3P \rightarrow N_2CR_2$$

When these compounds are heated, they decompose to a phosphomethylene and nitrogen:

$$2R_3P \rightarrow N_2CR_2 \rightarrow 2R_3P = CR_2 + N_2$$

This reaction takes place somewhat more readily with quaternary phosphonium halides in which at least one hydrogen atom is combined with a carbon atom attached to the phosphorus.[195]

Addition compounds have been obtained through the interaction of aromatic phosphines with aromatic azides; these undergo decomposition with liberation of nitrogen to form phosphine amides:[217]

$$ArN = N \equiv N + PAr_3 \rightarrow ArN = N - N = PAr_3 \rightarrow ArN = PAr_3 + N_2$$

Sulfonimides of the same type have been obtained through the reaction of sodio N-chloro-*p*-toluenesulfonamide with various phosphines:[218]

$$R_3P + C_7H_7SO_2NClNa \rightarrow R_3PNSO_2C_7H_7 + NaCl$$

Replacement of Halogens in Phosphorus Compounds with Amino Groups. Phosphorus Amides

The halogen in phosphorus trihalides and primary and secondary halophosphines may be replaced with amino groups by reaction with amines, to form phosphorus amides:[196]

$$PX_3 + 2RNH_2 \rightarrow RNHPX_2 + RNH_2.HX, \text{ etc.}$$

$$R_2PX + 2RNH_2 \rightarrow R_2PNR + RNH_2.HX$$

$$RPX_2 + 4R_2NH \rightarrow R'P(NR_2)_2 + 2R_2NH.HX$$

The reaction is carried out in an inert solvent, such as ether or ligroin, at a low or moderate temperature, and the products are isolated by evaporating off the solvent after filtration of the amine halide crystals which separate out.

The reactions with primary amines deviate from the expected course. It is possible to control the reaction with secondary amines by using the hydrochloride of the amine:[197]

$$PCl_3 + R_2NH.HCl \rightarrow R_2NPCl_2 + 2HCl$$

Prolonged heating of primary amine hydrochlorides with an excess of phosphorus trichloride results in the formation of N-arylimido chlorophosphites:[198]

$$PCl_3 + RNH_2.HCl \rightarrow RN = PCl + 3HCl$$

The products react with amines and form the corresponding amido derivatives RN:PNHR. The preparation may be carried out in a single step:[199]

$$PCl_3 + 5RNH_2 \rightarrow RN = PNHR + 3RNH_2.HCl$$

Usually the trichloride is added to the amine, dissolved in warm, dry toluene, and the reaction is completed by refluxing for about two hours. The amine hydrochloride formed may be removed by filtration or by careful washing with cold water or alcohol.

Products of the amido imido phosphite structure are very reactive, and recrystallization from organic solvents often changes the structure of the original material.

Primary and secondary amines react smoothly with phosphorus oxyhalides, halophosphates and haloamidophosphates to form the corresponding amides:

$$POCl_3 + 2RNH_2 \rightarrow RNHPOCl_2 + RNH_2.HCl, \text{ etc.}$$

$$R'OPOCl_2 + 4RNH_2 \rightarrow R'OPO(NHR)_2 + 2RNH_2.HCl, \text{ etc.}$$

Somewhat more elevated temperatures are usually required to complete the formation of phosphoric triamides.[200]

Satisfactory yields of N-arylamidodichlorophosphates $RNH.POCl_2$, have been obtained by the slow addition of two molecular equivalents of the amine to phosphorus oxychloride dissolved in benzene. Amidodihalophosphates and diamidohalophosphates should not be subjected to unduely high temperatures, as otherwise these compounds change to imides.

Mono- and diamino compounds are obtained through the reaction of phosphorus oxychloride with the amine hydrochlorides:[197]

$$POCl_3 + RNH_2.HCl \rightarrow RNHPOCl_2 + 2HCl$$

$$POCl_3 + 2RNH_2.HCl \rightarrow (RNH)_2POCl + 4HCl$$

The reaction is carried out at a moderate temperature under reflux, disappearance of the amine hydrochloride indicating the end of the reaction. A small amount of high boiling solvent, such as xylene, is usually added to the reaction mixture to preserve fluidity and to avoid local overheating.

When an excess of a primary amine is heated with phosphorus pentachloride, the final product of the reaction is a tetraamidophosphorus chloride:[201]

$$PCl_5 + 8ArNH_2 \rightarrow (ArNH)_4PCl + 4ArNH_2.HCl$$

The reaction requires fairly high temperatures for completion, although initially it is quite vigorous.

Thiophosphoryl halides, PSX_3, are also capable of reacting with amines. Mono and diamido derivatives may be obtained from thiophosphoryl chloride, $PSCl_3$, by reaction with hydrochlorides of amines.[202] N-Alkyl or N-dialkylamidodihalothiamidophosphates, and the primary and secondary halothiophosphates, $(RO)_2PSX$ and $ROPSX_2$, also react with amines to form the corresponding amido derivatives.

Use of Schotten – Baumann Reaction

The reaction of halophosphorus compounds with amines proceeds at or somewhat below room temperature in the presence of an excess of caustic. As a rule, diamido derivatives are formed in the presence of 10% sodium hydroxide solution, while a solution of a concentration in excess of 25% favors the formation of triamides:[203]

$$POCl_3 + 3ArNH_2 + 3NaOH \rightarrow (ArNH)_3PO + 3NaCl + 3H_2O$$

Thiophosphoryl chloride yields thionotriamides and salts of diamidothiophosphates.

Chlorophosphates in general can be used in this reaction, but better results are obtained with aryl esters since these are less readily hydrolyzed by alkalies than the alkyl esters.

Reaction of Salts of Hypophosphorous Acid with Aromatic Hydrazines

Salts of hypophosphorous acid, reacting with aromatic hydrazines in the presence of copper salts, give salts of phosphinous acids:[204]

$$H_2POONa + C_6H_5NHNH_2 \rightarrow H_2\overset{\overset{ONa}{|}}{P}ONH(C_6H_5)NH_2$$

$$\rightarrow NaOH + C_6H_5NHNHPH_2O \xrightarrow{Cu} C_6H_5PHO.ONa$$

The procedure is to add a given amount of the hydrazine to a solution of the sodium hypophosphite, filter the liquid, decolorize with charcoal and evaporate off the water.

Reaction of Hydroxy Compounds with Phosphorus Pentoxide and Phosphorus Pentasulfide

The reaction of alcohols or other hydroxy compounds with phosphorus pentoxide yields a mixture of primary and secondary phosphates:[205]

$$3ROH + P_2O_5 \rightarrow RO(HO)_2PO + (RO)_2(HO)PO$$

The reaction may be carried out with an ethereal suspension of the pentoxide. On the commercial scale the pentoxide is mixed directly with the alcohol. The temperature of the mixture should not be allowed to rise much above 100°. The reaction mixture is quenched with water to hydrolyze any pyrophosphate residue, and the individual primary and secondary esters are separated by fractional crystallization of their barium salts. This procedure of purification fails with the esters of the higher molecular hydroxy compounds, and separation then becomes extremely laborious if pure products are desired.

The reaction of hydroxy compounds with phosphorus pentasulfide proceeds in a similar manner. A secondary dithiophosphate is the principal product of the reaction when four molecular equivalents of the hydroxy compound are used to one of the pentasulfide:[206]

$$P_2S_5 + 4ROH \rightarrow 2(RO)_2PSSH + H_2S$$

The free acid esters, subjected to the action of the aqueous reagent in the presence of air, undergo simultaneous hydrolysis and oxidation fairly readily. The metal salts of the ester are much more stable. The reaction mixture should not be warmed much above 100°.

The reaction of thiols with phosphorus pentasulfide has been reported to yield tertiary tetrathiophosphates.

Reaction of Amines, etc., with Phosphorus Pentasulfide

Thiophosphoric amides result through the reaction of amines with phosphorus pentasulfide. Four moles of the amine reacting with one of sulfide at room temperature give a diaminodithiophosphate:

$$P_2S_5 + 4RNH_2 \rightarrow 2(RNH)_2PSSH + H_2S$$

A mixture of six molar equivalents of a primary amine with one of phosphorus pentasulfide, heated for several hours at 180°, gives thionophosphoric amides in generally satisfactory yield:[207]

$$6RNH_2 + P_2S_5 \rightarrow 2(RNH)_3PS + 3H_2S$$

Aliphatic primary amines must be heated in sealed vessels. Yields are in the neighborhood of 50%. Secondary amines usually give untractable oils.

Warm aqueous solutions of these products should not be exposed to air in order to avoid oxidation.

Alkyl trithiometaphosphates are formed on heating trialkyl tetrathiophosphates with a molecular equivalent of phosphorus pentasulfide in xylene:[208]

$$(RS)_3PS + P_2S_5 \rightarrow 3RSPS_2$$

References

1. Frankland and Dupa, *Ann.*, **115**, 319 (1860); **124**, 129 (1862), *Cf.* Stock and Zeidler, *Ber.*, **54**, 531 (1921).
2. Krause and Nitsche, *Ber.*, **54**, 2784 (1921).
3. Pace, *Atti accad. Lincei*, (6) **10**, 193 (1929).
4. Khotinsky and Melamed, *Ber.*, **42**, 3090 (1909).
5. Frankland and Dupa, *Ann.*, **124**, 129 (1862).
6. Stock and Kuss, *Ber.*, **56**, 807 (1923); **59**, 2216 (1926).
7. Krause and Polack, *ibid.*, **61**, 271 (1928); Bent and Dorfman, *J. Am. Chem. Soc.*, **57**, 1924 (1935).
8. Schlesinger *et al.*, *J. Am. Chem. Soc.*, **57**, 621 (1935); **58**, 407 (1936).
9. Kinney and Pontz, *ibid.*, **58**, 197 (1936).
10. Kipping, *Proc. Chem. Soc.*, **20**, 15 (1904); Dilthey, *Ber.*, **37**, 319 Note 1 (1904).
11. Jaeger and Dykstra, *Konink, Akad. Wetenschap., Amsterdam*, **27**, 398 (1924).
12. Friedel and Crafts, *Ann.*, **136**, 203 (1865); Ladenburg, *ibid.*, **164**, 302 (1872); **173**, 151 (1874).
13. Kipping and Lloyd, *J. Chem. Soc.*, **79**, 449 (1901); *Cf.* Taurke, *Ber.*, **38**, 1663 (1905).
14. Polis, *Ber.*, **18**, 1540 (1885); **19**, 1017 (1886).
15. Flood, *J. Am. Chem. Soc.*, **55**, 1735 (1933).
16. Ladenburg, *Ann.*, **164**, 310 (1872).
17. Ladenburg, *ibid.*, **164**, 306 (1872).
18. Ladenburg, *ibid.*, **164**, 314 (1872).
19. Ladenburg, *ibid.*, **173**, 151, 165 (1874).
20. Bygdén, *Ber.*, **44**, 2646 (1911); Melzer, *ibid.*, **41**, 3390 (1908); Kipping, *J. Chem. Soc.*, **91**, 214 (1907).
21. Stock and Somieski, *Ber.*, **52**, 706 (1919).
22. Ladenburg, *Ann.*, **164**, 302, 327 (1872).
23. Bygdén, *Ber.*, **45**, 707 (1912); *Z. phys. Chem.*, **90**, 246 (1915).
24. Kipping, *J. Chem. Soc.*, **117**, 647 (1921).
25. Schlenk and Renning, *Ber.*, **44**, 1178 (1911), *Cf.* Kipping, *Proc. Chem. Soc.*, **27**, 143 (1911).
26. Kraus and Eatough, *J. Am. Chem. Soc.*, **55**, 5008 (1933); Kraus and Nelson, *ibid.*, **56**, 195 (1934).
27. Kipping *et al.*, *J. Chem. Soc.*, **119**, 830, 848 (1921); **123**, 2590, 2598 (1923); **1928**, 1431; **1929**, 1176, 2545.
28. Kipping *et al.*, *ibid.*, **1929**, 1180; **1930**, 1029; **1931**, 1290.
29. Friedel and Crafts, *Ann. chim.*, (4) **19**, 358 (1870); Ladenburg, *Ann.*, **164**, 312 (1872); Dilthey and Eduardoff, *Ber.*, **37**, 1139 (1904); **38**, 4132 (1905); Martin, *ibid.*, **45**, 403 (1912); Kipping *et al.*, *J. Chem. Soc.*, **79**, 455 (1901); **91**, 218 (1907); **93**, 442, 452 (1908); **95**, 313 (1909); **99**, 138 (1911); **101**, 2108 (1912); **105**, 40 (1914).
30. Ladenburg, *Ann.*, **164**, 313 (1872).
31. Ladenburg, *ibid.*, **164**, 325 (1872).

32. Kipping *et al.*, *J. Chem. Soc.*, **79**, 449 (1901); **1929**, 305.
33. Friedel and Ladenburg, *Ann.*, **159**, 264 (1871); Ladenburg, *ibid.*, **164**, 301, 307 (1872).
34. Gruttner and Wiernik, *Ber.*, **48**, 1474 (1915) note.
35. Kipping *et al.*, *Proc. Chem. Soc.*, **23**, 9 (1907); **24**, 47, 224, 236 (1908); *J. Chem. Soc.*, **91**, 224 (1907); **93**, 200, 460 (1908); **97**, 773 (1910); Bygdén, *J. prakt. Chem.*, (2) **96**, 93 (1917).
36. Kipping and Meads, *J. Chem. Soc.*, **105**, 679 (1914); **107**, 459 (1915).
37. Hibbert and Müller, *Ber.*, **54**, 844 (1921).
38. Hofman, *Jahresb.*, **1855**, 538; *Ann.*, **103**, 357 (1857); Mannheim, *ibid.*, **341**, 182 (1905); Renshaw and Hohn, *J. Am. Chem. Soc.*, **42**, 1470 (1920).
39. Landolt, *Ann.*, **89**, 321 (1854); **92**, 370 (1854).
40. Michaelis and Paetow, *Ber.*, **18**, 42 (1885).
41. Challenger and Peters, *J. Chem. Soc.*, **1929**, 2610.
42. Green and Price, *ibid.*, **119**, 448 (1921).
43. Pfeiffer, *Ber.*, **37**, 4621 (1904); Sachs and Kantorowicz, *ibid.*, **41**, 2767 (1908); Jones *et al.*, *J. Chem. Soc.*, **1932**, 2284.
44. Michaelis and Reese, *Ann.*, **321**, 160 (1902); Michaelis and Loesner, *Ber.*, **27**, 264 (1894).
45. Michaelis and Rabinerson, *Ann.*, **270**, 145 (1892); Zuckerkandl and Sinai, *Ber.*, **54**, 2485 (1921).
46. Finzi, *Gazz. chim. ital.*, **55**, 824 (1925); Steinkopf, *Ann.*, **413**, 310 (1917).
47. Lowe and Hamilton, *J. Am. Chem. Soc.*, **57**, 1081 (1935).
48. Fichter and Elkind, *Ber.*, **49**, 246 (1916).
49. Auger, *Compt. rend.*, **142**, 1153 (1906).
50. Dehn, *J. Am. Chem. Soc.*, **40**, 123 (1908).
51. Blicke and Powers, *ibid.*, **55**, 1161 (1933).
52. Nesmejanow and Freidlina, *Ber.*, **67**, 735 (1934).
53. *German patent* 271,894.
54. *German patents* 263,460; 264,014; 271,893.
55. Voegtlin and Johnson, *J. Am. Chem. Soc.*, **44**, 2573 (1922).
56. Blicke and Powers, *ibid.*, **52**, 2937 (1930); **54**, 3353 (1932).
57. Auger, *Compt. rend.*, **142**, 1152 (1906).
58. Wilgren, *J. prakt. Chem.*, (2) **126**, 223 (1930).
59. Blicke and Smith, *J. Am. Chem. Soc.*, **51**, 3479 (1929).
60. Contardi, *Giorn. chim. ind. applicata*, **1**, 11 (1920).
61. Auger, *Compt. rend.*, **142**, 1152 (1906); Steinkopf and Mieg, *Ber.*, **53**, 1015 (1920).
62. Uhlinger and Cook, *Ind. Eng. Chem.*, **11**, 105 (1919); Norris, *ibid.*, **11**, 826 (1919).
63. Seide and Garski, *Ber.*, **62**, 2186 (1929).
64. Govaert, *Compt. rend.*, **200**, 1603 (1935).
65. Michaelis and Paetow, *Ann.*, **233**, 91 (1886).
66. Green and Price, *J. Chem. Soc.*, **119**, 448 (1921); Lewis and Stiegler, *J. Am. Chem. Soc.*, **47**, 2546 (1925); *Ind. Eng. Chem.*, **15**, 290 (1923); Mann and Pope, *J. Chem. Soc.*, **121**, 1754 (1922).
67. Fischer, *Ann.*, **403**, 109 (1914).
68. Renshaw and Ware, *J. Am. Chem. Soc.*, **47**, 2991 (1925); Gough and King, *J. Chem. Soc.*, **1928**, 2426; Nekrassow and Nekrassow, *Ber.*, **61**, 1816 (1928); Scherlin and Epstein, *ibid.*, **61**, 1821 (1928).
69. Baeyer, *Ann.*, **107**, 263 (1858).
70. Baeyer, *ibid.*, **107**, 274 (1858).
71. *Cf.* Davies and Lewis, *J. Chem. Soc.*, **1934**, 1599.
72. Blicke and Marzano, *J. Am. Chem. Soc.*, **55**, 3056 (1933).
73. Steinkopf and Müller, *Ber.*, **54**, 847 (1921).
74. Bunsen, *Ann.*, **24**, 271 (1837); **31**, 175 (1839); **37**, 1 (1841); **42**, 14 (1842); **46**, 1 (1843); Dumas, *ibid.*, **27**, 148 (1838); v. Baeyer, *ibid.*, **107**, 282 (1858).
75. v. Bayer, *Ann.*, **107**, 281 (1858); Auger, *Compt. rend.*, **142**, 1152 (1906).
76. Auger, *Compt. rend.*, **137**, 926 (1903); Uhlinger and Cook, *Ind. Eng. Chem.*, **11**, 105 (1919).
77. Michaelis, *Ann.*, **320**, 286 (1902).
78. Coste and Michaelis, *ibid.*, **201**, 243 (1880); *Ber.*, **11**, 1888 (1878); Michaelis, *Ann.*, **321**, 164 (1902); Philips, *Ber.*, **19**, 1032 (1886); Zuckerkandl and Sinai, *ibid.*, **54**, 2484 (1921).
79. Zuckerkandl and Sinai, *Ber.*, **54**, 2485 (1921).
80. La Coste and Michaelis, *Ann.*, **201**, 244 (1880).
81. Auger, *Compt. rend.*, **137**, 925 (1903).
82. Michaelis and Paetow, *Ber.*, **18**, 42 (1885); *Ann.*, **233**, 61 (1886).
83. Meyer, *Ber.*, **16**, 1440 (1883); Klinger and Kreutz, *Ann.*, **249**, 147 (1889); Dehn, *Am. Chem. J.*, **33**, 131 (1905); Valeur and Delaby, *Bull. soc. chim.*, **27**, 366 (1920); Quick and Adams, *J. Am. Chem. Soc.*, **44**, 805 (1922).
84. Bart, *German patents*, 250,264; 254,092; 268,172; 264,924; Mouneyrat, *British patent* 142,947 (1919); *Cf.* Schmidt, *Ann.*, **421**, 159 (1920).
85. Schmidt, *Ann.*, **421**, 159 (1920).

86. Binz *et al.*, *Biochem. Zeit.*, **223,** 176 (1930); **241,** 256 (1931); *Z. angew. Chem.*, **44,** 835 (1931); **46,** 349 (1933); Plazek, *Rocznicki Chemji*, **10,** 751 (1930).
87. Berlingozzi, *Ann. chim. applicata*, **18,** 31, 333 (1928); Slater, *J. Chem. Soc.*, **1931,** 107, 1938; Fourneau *et al.*, *Ann. Inst. Pasteur*, **44,** 719 (1930); Barnett *et al.*, *J. Chem. Soc.*, **1934,** 433.
88. Newbery *et al.*, *J. Chem. Soc.*, **1928,** 305.
89. Burton and Gibson, *ibid.*, **1927,** 2386.
90. Béchamp, *Compt. rend.*, **56,** 1172 (1863); Ehrlich and Bertheim, *Ber.*, **40,** 3292 (1907).
91. Boehringer and Söhne, *German patent* 240,793; Funakuto, *J. Chem. Soc. Japan*, **48,** 526 (1927).
92. Grüttner and Krause, *Ber.*, **49,** 437 (1916).
93. Job *et al.*, *Bull. soc. chim.*, (4) **35,** 1404 (1924).
94. Adams and Palmer, *J. Am. Chem. Soc.*, **42,** 2375 (1920); **44,** 1356 (1922).
95. Burrows and Turner, *J. Chem. Soc.*, **119,** 430 (1921).
96. Gump and Stoltzenberg, *J. Am. Chem. Soc.*, **53,** 1428 (1921).
97. Kalb, *Ann.*, **423,** 39 (1921); Wieland and Reinheimer, *ibid.*, **423,** 1 (1921).
98. McCleland and Whitwortt, *J. Chem. Soc.*, **1927,** 2753.
99. Lewis *et al.*, *J. Am. Chem. Soc.*, **43,** 890 (1921).
100. Wieland and Rheinheimer, *l.c.*
101. Rasuwajew, *Ber.*, **62,** 605, 1208, 2675 (1929).
102. *Cf.* Blicke and Oakdale, *J. Am. Chem. Soc.*, **54,** 2993 (1932).
103. Das Gupta, *J. Indian Chem. Soc.*, **9,** 95, 203 (1932).
104. Hofmann, *Ann.*, **103,** 357 (1857); Buckton, *Jahresb.* **1860,** 371; **1861,** 469; *J. Chem. Soc.*, **13,** 116 (1861); **16,** 22 (1866).
105. Auger and Billy, *Compt. rend.*, **39,** 599 (1904); Hibbert, *Ber.*, **39,** 160 (1906); Dyke *et al.*, *J. Chem. Soc.*, **1930,** 463.
106. Morgan and Tarsley, *J. Chem. Soc.*, **127,** 184 (1925).
107. Hasebäumer, *Ber.*, **31,** 2910 (1898); Pfeiffer and Heller, *ibid.*, **37,** 4620 (1904).
108. Michaelis *et al.*, *Ber.*, **15,** 2877 (1882); **17,** 924 (1884); **20,** 52 (1887); *Ann.*, **233,** 39 (1886); Goddard, *J. Chem. Soc.*, **124,** 2315 (1923); Löloff, *Ber.*, **30,** 2835 (1897).
109. Werrall, *J. Am. Chem. Soc.*, **52,** 2046 (1930).
110. Schmidt, *Ann.*, **429,** 132 (1922).
111. Krause and Renwanz, *Ber.*, **65,** 777 (1932).
112. Schmidt, *Ann.*, **421,** 235 (1920); Blicke *et al.*, *J. Am. Chem. Soc.*, **53,** 1025 (1931); **55,** 1198 (1933).
113. Schmidt, *Ann.*, **421,** 232 (1920); *U.S. patent* 1,422,294.
114. Schmidt, *Ann.*, **429,** 151 (1922); *German patent* 268,451.
115. Morgan and Davies, *Proc. Roy. Soc.*, **A, 110,** 523 (1926); *Nature*, **116,** 499 (1925).
116. Steinkopf *et al.*, *Ber.*, **65,** 409 (1932).
117. Michaelis and Reese, *Ber.*, **15,** 2877 (1882).
118. Schmidt, *Ann.*, **429,** 123 (1922).
119. Weinland and Schmidt, *Z. anorg. Chem.*, **44,** 43 (1905).
120. Grüttner and Wiernik, *Ber.*, **48,** 1759 (1915).
121. Kaufmann, *ibid.*, **41,** 2762 (1908).
122. Schmidt, *Ann.*, **421,** 174 (1920).
123. Schmidt, *ibid.*, **421,** 177 (1920).
124. Schmidt, *ibid.*, **421,** 233 (1920).
125. Macallum, *J. Soc. Chem. Ind.*, **42,** 468T (1923).
126. Grüttner and Wiernik, *Ber.*, **48,** 1484 (1915).
127. Grüttner and Krause, *ibid.*, **49,** 442 (1916).
128. Lecoq, *Bull. soc. chim. Belg.*, **42,** 199 (1933).
129. Morgan and Davies, *Proc. Roy. Soc. (London)*, **A, 127,** 1 (1930); **143,** 38 (1933).
130. Morgan and Davies, *ibid.*, **A, 143,** 38 (1933).
131. May, *J. Chem. Soc.*, **97,** 1958 (1910).
132. Michaelis and Reese, *Ann.*, **233,** 39 (1886); Michaelis and Günther, *Ber.*, **44,** 2319 (1911); Morgan and Micklethwait, *J. Chem. Soc.*, **99,** 2296 (1911); Schmidt, *Ann.*, **421,** 241 (1920).
133. Kraft and Lyons, *Ber.*, **27,** 1768 (1894).
134. Gina and Cherchi, *Gazz. chim. ital.*, **50,** 362 (1920).
135. Krause and Renwanz, *Ber.*, **65,** 782 (1932).
136. Lederer, *Compt. rend.*, **151,** 611 (1910).
137. Vernon *et al.*, *J. Chem. Soc.*, **117,** 86, 889 (1920); **119,** 105, 687 (1921).
138. Drews, *ibid.*, **1929,** 560.
139. Lederer, *Ann.*, **399,** 260 (1913).
140. Lederer, *Ber.*, **46,** 1810 (1913); **48,** 1944 (1915).
141. Lyons and Scudder, *ibid.*, **64,** 530 (1931).
142. Rust, *ibid.*, **30,** 2828 (1897); Morgan and Elvins, *J. Chem. Soc.*, **127,** 2625 (1925); Rohrbach, *Ann.*, **315,** 9 (1901).

143. Morgan *et al.*, *Biochem. J.*, **17**, 30 (1923); **18**, 190 (1924); *J. Soc. Chem. Ind.*, **431**, 304 (1924); **451**, 106 (1920), *Cf.* Tourneau, *Compt. rend. VI, Conf. Internat. Chim. Bucarest*, **1925**, 72.
144. Drew *et al.*, *J. Chem. Soc.*, **1926**, 223, 3054.
145. Menshutkin, *Ann.*, **139**, 343 (1866); Knauer, *Ber.*, **27**, 2569 (1894); Michaelis, *Ann.*, **293**, 265 (1896).
146. Moyle, *U.S. patent* 2,220,845 (1940).
147. Lippert and Reid, *J. Am. Chem. Soc.*, **60**, 2370 (1938).
148. Ford-Moore and Williams, *J. Chem. Soc.*, **1947**, 1465; Rogers *et al.*, *U.S. patent* 2,175,509 (1939); Craig and Hester, *U.S. patent* 2,492,158 (1950).
149. Bergel *et al.*, *J. Chem. Soc.*, **1943**, 286; Euler *et al.*, *Ber.*, **62**, 2451 (1929); Fischer *et al.*, *J. Am. Chem. Soc.*, **70**, 3943 (1948); Mastin *et al.*, *ibid.*, **67**, 1662 (1945).
150. Autenrieth, *Ber.*, **30**, 2369 (1897).
151. Balorew, *Z. anorg. Chem.*, **99**, 187 (1917); Gerard, *J. Chem. Soc.*, **1940**, 1464; Saunders *et al.*, *ibid.*, **1948**, 699; Schiff, *Ann.*, **102**, 334 (1857); Wichelhaus, *ibid.*, Suppl., **6**, 257 (1868). Gardner and Kilby, *J. Chem. Soc.*, **1950**, 1769.
152. Ephraim, *Ber.*, **44**, 633 (1911); Hoeflake, *Rec. trav. chim.*, **36**, 24 (1916); Jacobsen, *Ber.*, **8**, 1521 (1875); Michaelis, *Ann.*, **326**, 129 (1903); Rapp., *ibid.*, **224**, 156 (1884); Rosenmund and Vogt, *Arch. Pharm.*, **281**, 317 (1943).
153. Autenrieth *et al.*, *Ber.*, **31**, 1094 (1898); **58**, 840 (1925); Anschütz and Emery, *Ann.*, **253**, 105 (1889).
154. *BIOS Final Rep.* 714, 1095.
155. Anschütz *et al.*, *Ann.*, **228**, 308 (1885); **346**, 286, 300 (1906); **415**, 51 (1918); Couper, *Compt. rend.*, **46**, 1108 (1858).
156. Michaelis, *Ber.*, **6**, 816 (1873).
157. Guichard, *ibid.*, **32**, 1572 (1899); Michaelis, *ibid.*, **6**, 816 (1873); **13**, 2174 (1880); *Ann.*, **181**, 265 (1876); **293**, 193 (1896); **294**, 1 (1896); Michaelis and Kammerer, *Ber.*, **8**, 1306 (1875).
158. Guichard, *Ber.*, **32**, 1572 (1899); Michaelis *et al.*, *ibid.*, **25**, 1747 (1892); **34**, 1291 (1901); *Ann.*, **293**, 193 (1896); **294**, 1 (1896); **315**, 43 (1901).
159. Hofmann, *Ber.*, **6**, 303 (1873); Michaelis, *Ann.*, **181**, 265 (1876).
160. Gibson and Johnson, *J. Chem. Soc.*, **1928**, 92; Hamilton, *U.S. patents*, 2,365,466 (1944); 2,382,309 (1945).
161. Challenger and Wilkinson, *J. Chem. Soc.*, **125**, 2675 (1924); Davies and Jones, *ibid.*, **107**, 367 (1915); Hofmann, *Ber.*, **6**, 292, 301, 303 (1873); Pickard and Kenyon, *J. Chem. Soc.*, **89**, 262 (1906); Sauvage, *Compt. rend.*, **139**, 674 (1904); Kosolapoff, *J. Am. Chem. Soc.*, **72**, 5508 (1950).
162. Strecker and Grossmann, *Ber.*, **49**, 63 (1916).
163. Michaelis and Wegner, *ibid.*, **48**, 316 (1915); Kosolapoff, *J. Am. Chem. Soc.*, **64**, 2982 (1942).
164. Kosolapoff, *J. Am. Chem. Soc.*, **71**, 369 (1949); Malatesta and Pizzotti, *Gazz. chim. ital.*, **76**, 167, 182 (1946); Michaelis and Wegner, *Ber.*, **48**, 316 (1915).
165. Malatesta, *Gazz. chim. ital.*, **77**, 509, 518 (1947).
166. Michaelis *et al.*, *Ann.*, **315**, 43 (1901); *Ber.*, **10**, 807 (1877); **15**, 1610 (1882).
167. Worall, *J. Am. Chem. Soc.*, **52**, 2933 (1930); **62**, 2514 (1940).
168. Guichard, *Ber.*, **32**, 1576 (1899); Jackson *et al.*, *J. Chem. Soc.*, **1931**, 2109.
169. Hibbert, *Ber.*, **39**, 160 (1906); Davies and Jones, *J. Chem. Soc.*, **1929**, 33; Davies *et al.*, *ibid.*, **1929**, 1262.
170. Albers and Schuler, *Ber.*, **76**, 23 (1943); Johannis, *Compt. rend.*, **119**, 557 (1894); *Ann. chim. phys.*, (8) **7**, 105 (1906); Walling, *U.S. patent* 2,437,795 (1948).
171. Guichard, *Ber.*, **32**, 1572 (1899); Michaelis, *Ann.*, **293**, 193 (1896); **294**, 1 (1896).
172. Michaelis, *Ann.*, **293**, 193 (1896); **294**, 1 (1896); **315**, 43 (1901). *Cf.* Dye, *J. Am. Chem. Soc.*, **70**, 2595 (1948); Kosolapoff and Huber, *ibid.*, **68**, 2020 (1947); Bucher and Lockhardt, *Organic Syntheses*, **31**, 88 (1951); *J. Am. Chem. Soc.*, **73**, 755 (1951).
173. Dye, *J. Am. Chem. Soc.*, **70**, 2595 (1948); Kosolapoff and Huber, *ibid.*, **69**, 2020 (1947); Lindner *et al.*, *Monatsh.*, **70**, 1 (1937); Davies, *J. Chem. Soc.*, **1935**, 462; Kamai, *J. Gen. Chem. U.S.S.R.*, **4**, 192 (1934); *J. Russ. Phys.-Chem. Soc.*, **64**, 524 (1932); Davies and Morris, *J. Chem. Soc.*, **1932**, 2880; Michaelis *et al.*, *Ber.*, **21**, 1497 (1888); *Ann.*, **260**, 1 (1890); **212**, 203 (1882); *Ber.*, **12**, 1009 (1879).
174. Bourneuf, *Bull. soc. chim.*, (4) **33**, 1808 (1923); Raudnitz, *Ber.*, **60**, 743 (1927); Lemoult, *Compt. rend.*, **140**, 249 (1905).
175. Kharasch *et al.*, *J. Am. Chem. Soc.*, **67**, 1864 (1945); **68**, 154 (1946); Ladd and Little, *U.S. patent* 2,510,699.
176. Bachmann and Hatton, *J. Am. Chem. Soc.*, **66**, 1513 (1944); Bergmann and Bondi, *Ber.*, **63**, 1158 (1930); **64**, 1455 (1931); **66**, 278, 286 (1933); Harnist, *ibid.*, **63**, 2307 (1930); Kosolapoff and Huber, *J. Am. Chem. Soc.*, **68**, 2540 (1946); Marsh *et al.*, *J. Chem. Soc.*, **59**, 648 (1891); Toy, *U.S. patent* 2,425,766 (1947).
177. Kosolapoff and Huber, *J. Am. Chem. Soc.*, **68**, 2540 (1946); Kosolapoff, *U.S. patent* 2,389,576; C.A. **40**, 1536 (1946); Bergman and Bondi, *Ber.*, **63**, 1158 (1930); **64**, 1455 (1931); Thiele,

Chem. Ztg., **36**, 657 (1912); Arbuzov, *J. Russ. Phys.-Chem. Soc.*, **42**, 395,-549 (1910); Michaelis and La Coste, *Ber.*, **18**, 2109 (1885).
178. Arbuzov, *et al.*, *J. Russ. Phys.-Chem. Soc.*, **38**, 687 (1906); **42**, 549 (1910); **61**, 1599, 1905 (1929); *J. Gen. Chem. U.S.S.R.*, **4**, 898 (1934); **15**, 766 (1945); *Bull. acad. sci., U.R.S.S. Classe sci. chim.*, **1945**, 167; Ford-Moore and Williams, *J. Chem. Soc.*, **1947**, 1465; Staronka, *Roczniki chem.*, **7**, 42 (1927).
179. Gerrard, *J. Chem. Soc.*, **1940**, 1464; McCombie *et al.*, *ibid.*, **1945**, 380, 873; Saunders and Stacey, *ibid.*, **1948**, 695.
180. Atherton *et al.*, *J. Chem. Soc.*, **1945**, 660; **1947**, 674.
181. Schrader, *Germ. application* p. 41994 D. Class 120, 23/05.
182. Arbuzov, *J. prakt. Chem.*, (2) **131**, 357 (1938); Davis and Jones, *J. Chem. Soc.*, **1929**, 33; Hoffman, *J. Am. Chem. Soc.*, **43**, 1684 (1921); **52**, 2995 (1930); Staudinger *et al.*, *Helv. Chim. Acta*, **4**, 861, 897 (1921); Gilman and Brown, *J. Am. Chem. Soc.*, **67**, 824 (1945); Michaelis, *Ann.*, **293**, 193 (1896); **315**, 43 (1901).
183. Arbuzov and Kamar, *J. Russ. Phys.-Chem. Soc.*, **61**, 2037 (1929).
184. Cahours and Hoffmann, *Ann.*, **104**, 1 (1857); Michaelis *et al.*, *ibid.*, **181**, 265 (1876); **229**, 295 (1885); **260**, 1 (1890); **315**, 43 (1901); *Ber.*, **17**, 921 (1884); Page, *J. Chem. Soc.*, **101**, 423 (1912); Renshaw and Bell, *J. Am. Chem. Soc.*, **43**, 916 (1921).
185. Guichard, *Ber.*, **32**, 1572 (1899); Michaelis *et al.*, *ibid.*, **6**, 816 (1873); **8**, 1306 (1875); **9**, 519, 1053 (1876); **10**, 627 (1877); **13**, 2174 (1880); *Ann.*, **181**, 265 (1876); **212**, 203 (1882); **229**, 295 (1885); **293**, 193 (1896); **294**, 1 (1896).
186. Connant *et al.*, *J. Am. Chem. Soc.*, **39**, 2679 (1917); **42**, 830, 2337 (1920); **43**, 1677, 1928 (1921); **46**, 1003 (1924); Drake and Marvel, *J. Org. Chem.*, **2**, 387 (1937); Bernton, *Ber.*, **58**, 661 (1925); Guichard, *Ber.*, **32**, 1572 (1899); Meisenheimer, *Ann.*, **397**, 273 (1913); Michaelis *et al.*, *Ber.*, **6**, 601, 816 (1873); **7**, 1688 (1874); *Ann.*, **181**, 265 (1876); **293**, 193 (1896); **294**, 1 (1896).
187. Michaelis, *Ann.*, **315**, 42 (1901).
188. Collie and Reynolds, *J. Chem. Soc.*, **107**, 367 (1915); Grignard and Savard, *Compt. rend.*, **192**, 592 (1931); Crafts and Silva, *J. Chem. Soc.*, **24**, 629 (1871).
189. Collie and Reynolds, *J. Chem. Soc.*, **107**, 367 (1915); Dörken, *Ber.*, **21**, 1505 (1888); Fleissner, *ibid.*, **13**, 1665 (1880); Michaelis, *Ann.*, **315**, 43 (1901); Steinkopf *et al.*, *Ber.*, **54**, 1024 (1921); Worrall, *J. Am. Chem. Soc.*, **52**, 2933 (1930); Arbuzov, *J. prakt. Chem.*, (2) **31**, 357 (1938); Crafts and Silva, *J. Chem. Soc.*, **24**, 629 (1971); *Jabresb*, **1871**, 764; Masson and Kirkland, *J. Chem. Soc.*, **55**, 126, 135 (1889); Michaelis and Gleichmann, *Ber.*, **15**, 801 (1882).
190. Fossek, *Monatsh.*, **5**, 121 (1884); **7**, 20 (1886); Page, *J. Chem. Soc.*, **101**, 423 (1912); Conant *et al.*, *J. Am. Chem. Soc.*, **43**, 1928 (1921).
191. Conant, *J. Am. Chem. Soc.*, **39**, 2679 (1917).
192. Conant *et al.*, *ibid.*, **45**, 165 (1923).
193. Girard, *Ann. chim.*, (6) **2**, 11 (1884); Messinger and Engels, *Ber.*, **21**, 326, 2919 (1888).
194. Staudinger and Meyer, *Helv. Chim. Acta*, **2**, 612, 619, 635 (1919).
195. Coffman and Marvel, *J. Am. Chem. Soc.*, **51**, 3496 (1929); Staudinger and Lüscher, *Helv. Chim. Acta*, **5**, 75 (1922).
196. Michaelis, *Ber.*, **31**, 1037 (1898); *Ann.*, **326**, 129 (1903); **407**, 290 (1915); Michaelis and Luxemburg, *Ber.*, **28**, 2205 (1895); Autenrieth *et al.*, *ibid.*, **31**, 1094 (1898); **58 B**, 848, 2144 (1925). *Cf.* Strecker and Heuser, *ibid.*, **57 B**, 1364 (1924).
197. Michaelis, *Ann.*, **326**, 129 (1903).
198. Michaelis and Schroeber, *Ber.*, **27**, 490 (1894).
199. Grimmel *et al.*, *J. Am. Chem. Soc.*, **68**, 539 (1946).
200. Audrieth and Toy, *ibid.*, **64**, 1337 (1942); Caven, *J. Chem. Soc.*, **81**, 1362 (1902); Michaelis, *Ann.*, **326**, 129 (1903).
201. Anschütz *et al.*, *Ann.*, **346**, 300, 335 (1906); Arbuzov and Arbuzov, *J. prakt. Chem.*, (2) **130**, 103 (1931); *Ber.*, **63**, 195 (1932).
202. Michaelis, *Ann.*, **326**, 129 (1903); **407**, 290 (1915).
203. Autenrieth, *Ber.*, **30**, 2369 (1897); Autenrieth and Rudolph, *ibid.*, **33**, 2099, 2112 (1900).
204. Pleta, *J. Gen. Chem. (U.S.S.R.)* **7**, No. 1, 84, 90 (1937).
205. Adler and Gottlieb, *U.S. patent* 1,983,588 (1934); Adler and Woodstock, *Chem. Industries*, **51**, 516 (1942); Balarew, *J. prakt. Chem.*, **104**, 368 (1922); *Z. anorg. Chem.*, **158**, 105 (1926); Biehringer, *Ber.*, **38**, 3974 (1905); Carius, *Ann.*, **137**, 121 (1866); Cavalier, *Compt. rend.*, **122**, 69 (1895); **124**, 91 (1897); *Bull soc. chim.*, (3) **19**, 883 (1898); *Ann. chim. phys.*, (7) **18**, 449 (1899); Cherbuliez and Weniger, *Helv. Chim. Acta*, **28**, 1584 (1945); Harlay, *J. pharm. chim.*, **20**, 160 (1934); Hochwalt *et al.*, *Ind. Eng. Chem.*, **34**, 20 (1942); Lossen and Kohler, *Ann.*, **262**, 209 (1891); Rakuzin and Arsenev, *J. Russ. Phys.-Chem. Soc.*, **53**, 376 (1921); *Ann.*, **69**, 180 (1849); *Chem. Ztg.*, **47**, 178 (1923).
206. Cambi, *Chimica et industrie*, **26**, 97 (1944); Malatesta and Pizzotti, *ibid.*, **27**, 6 (1945); Pishchimuka, *J. Russ. Phys.-Chem. Soc.*, **44**, 1406 (1912); Salzberg and Werutz, *U.S.*

patent 2,063,629 (1936); Wagner-Jauregg *et al.*, *Ber.*, **74**, 1513 (1941); **75**, 178 (1942); Japp and Raschen, *J. Chem. Soc.*, **49**, 478 (1886).
207. Buck *et al.*, *J. Am. Chem. Soc.*, **70**, 744 (1948); Hammelmeyer, *Monatsh.*, **26**, 765 (1905).
208. Rosnati, *Gazz. chim. ital.*, **76**, 272 (1946).
209. Sergeev and Kudryashov, *J. Gen. Chem., (U.S.S.R.)*, **8**, 266 (1938); *C.A.*, **32**, 5403 (1938).
210. Ford-Moore and Williams, *J. Chem. Soc.*, **1947**, 1465; Arbuzov and Kushkova, *J. Gen. Chem., (U.S.S.R.)*, **6**, 283 (1936); *C.A.*, **30**, 4813 (1936).
211. Kosolapoff, *J. Am. Chem. Soc.*, **69**, 1002 (1947); Kamai and Egorova *J. Gen. Chem. (U.S.S.R.)*, **16**, 1521 (1946); *C.A.* **41**, 5439 (1947).
212. Kabachnik and Rossiiskaya, *Bull. acad. sci. U.R.S.S., classe sci. chim.*, **1945**, 364; *C.A.* **40**, 4688 (1946).
213. Kabachnik and Rossiiskaya, *Bull. acad. sci. U.R.S.S., classe sci. chim.*, **1947**, 631; *C.A.* **42**, 5845 (1948).
214. Michaelis, *Ann.*, **326**, 129 (1903); Michaelis and Becker, *Ber.*, **30**, 1003 (1897); Kosolapoff, *J. Am. Chem. Soc.*, **67**, 1180 (1945); Chavane, *Compt. rend.*, **224**, 406 (1947).
215. Michaelis, *Ann.*, **293**, 193 (1896); **294**, 1 (1897); *Ber.*, **31**, 1037 (1898); Pope and Gibson, *J. Chem. Soc.*, **101**, 735 (1912).
216. U.S. patents 2,567,154 (1951); 2,514,150; 2,523,252; 2,479,938. *Cf.* Toy, *J. Am. Chem. Soc.*, **70**, 3882 (1948); **72**, 2065 (1950); **73**, 4670 (1951); Schrader and Mühlmann, *Germ. patent* 848,812 (1952); Kosolapoff, *U.S. patents* 2,479,939; 2,502,966; 2,594,455; 2,634,226; 2,634,227; Bell, *U.S. patent* 2,495,220; Bell and Hagemeyer, *U.S. patent* 2,566,194 (1951); Dye, *U.S. patent* 2,610,139; Tolkmith, *U.S. patents* 2,620,355; 2,668,836; 2,668,837.
217. Staudinger and Meyer, *Helv. Chim. Acta*, **2**, 635 (1919).
218. Chaplin and Mann, *J. Chem. Soc.*, **1937**, 527; *Nature*, **135**, 686 (1934).
219. Bell, *U.S. patent* 2,495,220 (1950). *Cf. U.S. patent* 2,486, 658.
220. Schwarzenbach *et al.*, *Helv. Chim. Acta*, **34**, 455 (1951); Rueggeberg *et al.*, *J. Am. Chem. Soc.*, **72**, 5336 (1950).
221. Beeby and Mann, *J. Chem. Soc.*, **1951**, 411.
222. Guichard, *Ber.*, **32**, 1574 (1899).
223. Hofmann and Cahours, *Ann.*, **104**, 23 (1857).
224. Hofmann and Hahta, *Ber.*, **25**, 2436 (1892).
225. Guichard, *Ber.*, **32**, 1574 (1899).
226. Staudinger and Meyer, *Helv. Chim. Acta*, **2**, 612 (1919).
227. Fox, *J. Am. Chem. Soc.*, **72**, 4147 (1950).
228. *U.S. patent* 2,471,412.
229. Cook *et al.*, *J. Chem. Soc.*, **1949**, 2921; Anderson *et al.*, *J. Am. Chem. Soc.*, **74**, 5304 (1954).
230. Woodstock, *U.S. patent* 2,471,472; Toy, *U.S. patent* 2,482,810.